CHEMISTRY
The Study of Matter

Second Edition

Henry Dorin

formerly

Assistant Professor
Chemistry Department, New York University

Chairman, Physical Science Department
Boys High School, New York City

CEBCO · ALLYN AND BACON, INC.
Newton, Massachusetts

This book is dedicated
to Jeremy, Ryan, Matthew, Joshua,
and their generation.
May they inherit a world that will banish
war, disease, and pollution
in their lifetime.

Other Books by the Author

In addition to this book, Henry Dorin is the author of the following:

Vitalized Chemistry
Modern Principles of Chemistry
Unified Chemistry
Practice Book for College Entrance Tests in Science
    (with coauthor Samuel Langholz)

Staff Credits

Editorial Development	**Edward M. Steele**
Preparation Services	**Martha E. Ballantine**
Design Coordination	**Richard Dalton**
Book Manufacturing	**Annie Puciloski**
Art Direction	**L. Christopher Valente**

Outside Credits

Editorial Services	**Mary C. Hicks**
Illustrations	**Lee Ames & Zak, Ltd.**
Photo Research	**Susan Van Etten**

Cover Design

Ligature, Incorporated/Chicago

A Message to the Student from the Author

I was originally drawn to the study of chemistry by observing chemical reactions that produced color changes, precipitates, and, I must admit, sparks and explosions. I was also fascinated by chemistry in the darkroom where I watched photographic papers in the developing solution turn from white to the vivid images that make up the finished prints. Perhaps most important in pointing me toward a career in chemistry was my high school chemistry teacher. He was able to explain difficult concepts clearly, and his sense of humor and his love of chemistry inspired me.

Textbooks cannot replace teachers but they can be a great learning aid. Reading about a topic in your text before it is discussed in class can lay a foundation of understanding that makes a classroom discussion more meaningful. Reading about the topic after it is discussed in class can supply important insights that you may not have fully understood during class. Because science concepts are not always easy to understand, you will find yourself reading some topics several times before the meaning sinks in. A second reading may shed considerable light on a topic that at first seemed hopelessly beyond your powers of understanding. If you stick with it, you will increase your capacity to learn and will develop greater confidence in your ability to extract meaning from the written word. These new powers will enhance your chances of success as you face the greater challenges that await you after high school. With learning, as with many other things, patience is the key. Be patient with yourself (and persevering), and you will succeed.

A number of features in this textbook will help you learn chemistry. Chemical terms are highlighted in **boldface** the first time they appear, and a listing of terms is printed at the end of every chapter. Questions are interspersed throughout the chapters instead of appearing only at the ends of chapters. It is important that you read these interspersed questions after you've read the sections to which they apply. If necessary, review the sections before you go on to the section immediately following the interspersed questions. Some of the interspersed questions are marked with an asterisk (*). Answers to these questions are given in the back of the book (in Appendix I). Work through the problem completely before looking up the answer. If your answer doesn't agree with the given answer, go back over your work (and the reading, if necessary). When you take a closer look at your work, you will often be able to see where you went wrong. It is quite natural to make mistakes while you are learning; correcting errors and mistaken impressions is all part of the learning process.

Two of the special features that appear in this text are "Chemistry in Action" and "Careers." These features will give you an idea of the wide-ranging applications of chemistry to our world today and the many types of employment open to people with training in chemistry. The page numbers of the special features are listed on page xiii.

The editors of this text and I worked very hard to make this book an effective learning aid. However, the text cannot always give you a direct answer to a question that may be puzzling you. If there is something you do not understand, take advantage of your teacher's help. A good teacher is the greatest learning aid of all. What puzzles you will often be puzzling to others. Your teacher's answer to your question will usually be helpful to your classmates, too. If you think that what bothers you is not of general interest, you can still get help from your teacher or some other qualified person out of class.

Here's to an enjoyable and satisfying study of chemistry!

Henry Dorin

Acknowledgements

Many people contributed their ideas and services in the preparation of the second edition of this book. In addition to those cited on the copyright page, the following writers and editors deserve special mention: **Bertram Coren,** the former Editor-in-Chief of Cebco, **Antonia Goodspeed,** and **Mary Ellen Brehm Raposa.**

Many chemistry teachers read parts of the manuscript and suggested changes that were incorporated into the first edition. A number of other chemistry teachers, most of whom have had one or more years of experience teaching from the first edition, gave helpful suggestions for improving the text in the second edition. A combined list of their names appears below.

Patricia L. Barker, Minisink Valley H.S., Slate Hill, New York

Donald P. Beard, Cypress H.S., Cypress, California

Dean E. Bladel, Lake Park H.S., Roselle, Illinois

Ernest Bosco, Spring Valley H.S., Spring Valley, New York

David C. Brooks, Bradford H.S., Starke, Florida

Joseph D. Brungard, Hornell Sr. H.S., Hornell, New York

Lydia B. Campbell, Lane Tech. H.S., Chicago, Illinois

Carol Boyce Collins, Jefferson Comp. H.S., Tampa, Florida

Herb Copenhaver, Shenandoah Valley Academy, New Market, Virginia

Anne Dacey, Moore Catholic H.S., Staten Island, New York

Julie C. Danielson, Southwestern Cen. H.S., Jamestown, New York

Mary Ann Davis, Gaither H.S., Tampa, Florida

Diana Doepken, Canfield H.S., Canfield, Ohio

Brother Thomas Dominic, FSC, St. Patrick H.S., Chicago, Illinois

John P. Farnsworth, Midlakes H.S., Clifton Springs, New York

Alan Friend, Beach Channel H.S., Rockaway Park, New York

James Fucini, New Britain H.S., New Britain, Connecticut

Patrick E. Funk, Sheridan H.S., Thornville, Ohio

Thomas L. Gath, Cortland Jr./Sr. H.S., Cortland, New York

Paul J. Giangrave, Bulkeley H.S., Hartford, Connecticut

Stanley E. Hamann, Leland H.S., San Jose, California

Luise Hanold, Riverside H.S., Painesville, Ohio

Father John A. Hanrahan, SJ, Bishop Connolly H.S., Fall River, Massachusetts

Janet A. Harris, Cy-Fair H.S., Houston, Texas

Thomas R. Hoesman, Bay H.S., Bay Village, Ohio

H. Hossack, Burnaby North Sen. Sec. School, Burnaby, B.C., Canada

Robert P. Houle, Lewis S. Mills H.S., Burlington, Connecticut

Robert Iverson, Irondale H.S., New Brighton, Minnesota

Sister Agnes Joseph, Marian H.S., Birmingham, Michigan

Mary Leistner, Sidney H.S., Sidney, Ohio

Cecilia Anne Lerner, Dixie County H.S., Cross City, Florida

Sister Mary Lewellin, SND, Notre Dame Academy, Toledo, Ohio

David Paul Licata, Ocean View H.S., Huntington Beach, California

David R. Lichtenheld, Community Unit Sch. Dist. 200, Woodstock, Illinois

Estelle R. Lussier, George J. Penney H.S., East Hartford, Connecticut

Sister Marielle, SND, Regina H.S., South Euclid, Ohio

G. Keith McAuley, Lake Howell H.S., Maitland, Florida

Patricia D. McCollom, Canyon H.S., Anaheim, California

Patrick G. McGuire, East Jefferson H.S., Metairie, Louisiana

Floyd A. Mittleman, Glenbrook H.S., Northbrook, Illinois

Harry L. Moore, Osceola H.S., Kissimmee, Florida

Marjorie Peabody, Yuma H.S., Yuma, Arizona

Thomas A. Pierce, Xavier H.S., Middletown, Connecticut

Harold Pratt, Jefferson County School System, Denver, Colorado

Mike D. Reynolds, D.U. Fletcher H.S., Neptune Beach, Florida

Janet O. Richards, Minisink Valley H.S., Slate Hill, New York

Michael Roadruck, Coshocton H.S., Coshocton, Ohio

Anne Roy, Fayetteville Manlius H.S., Manlius, New York

Barbara H. Shafer, Westerly H.S., Westerly, Rhode Island

Frederick A. Smith, Zanesville City Schools, Zanesville, Ohio

Phyllis A. Snyder, Lake Placid H.S., Lake Placid, Florida

Leonard B. Soloff, Kennedy H.S., Granada Hills, California

Don Suderman, Churchill School, Winnipeg, Manitoba. Canada

David Tanis, Holland Christian H.S., Holland, Michigan

Gerald P. Theisen, Ossining H.S., Ossining, New York

Natalie Foote Tiernan, Warren Township H.S., Gurnee, Illinois

Jo Ann Tunt, Washington Community H.S., Washington, Illinois

Liliana Turco, Lincoln H.S., Yonkers, New York

Kathryn Voehl, Luther H.S., Orlando, Florida

Maxine Wagner, St. John the Baptist D.H.S., West Islip, New York

Clair G. Wood, Cony H.S., Augusta, Maine

Timothy Watters, Bishop Connolly H.S., Fall River, Massachusetts

Max Zakon, Ft. Hamilton H.S., Brooklyn, New York

Roger W. Zuerlein, San Diego Academy, National City, California

CONTENTS

UNIT 1   MATTER AND ENERGY

UNIT 2   PHASES OF MATTER

UNIT 3   FORMULAS AND EQUATIONS

Chapter

14 Chemical Bonding—I 272

Chapter

15 Chemical Bonding—II 290

Chapter

16 Periodic Table 306

UNIT 5 SOLUTIONS

Chapter

17 Solutions 332

Chapter

18 The Colligative Properties of Solutions ==========357

UNIT 6   KINETICS AND EQUILIBRIUM

Chapter

19 Chemical Kinetics ==========372

Chapter

20 Enthalpy and Entropy ==========388

Chapter

21 Chemical Equilibrium ==========409

Chapter
22 The Solubility Product Expression ━━━━━━ 430

UNIT 7 ACIDS, BASES, AND SALTS

Chapter
23 Acids, Bases, and Salts—I ━━━━━━ 442

Chapter
24 Acids, Bases, and Salts—II ━━━━━━ 471

Chapter
25 Acid-Base Titration ━━━━━━ 486

UNIT 8 REDOX AND ELECTROCHEMISTRY

UNIT 9 ORGANIC CHEMISTRY

Chapter 30 Organic Chemistry—II —————————————————————————604

UNIT 10   NUCLEAR CHEMISTRY

Chapter 31 Nuclear Chemistry—————————————————————————————630

Special Features

CHEMISTRY IN ACTION

This is a series of essays and photos that describe some of the wide-ranging applications of chemical knowledge to the modern world. (Page numbers follow the titles.)

CAN YOU EXPLAIN THIS?

This is a series of demonstrations illustrating chemical phenomena that can be explained by an application of chemical principles. (Page numbers follow the titles.)

PEOPLE IN CHEMISTRY

This is a series of brief biographies of people —from the past and in the present—whose work in chemistry has been outstanding. (Page numbers follow the names.)

CAREERS

This is a series of essays that describe some of the careers that require training in chemistry. (Page numbers follow the titles.)

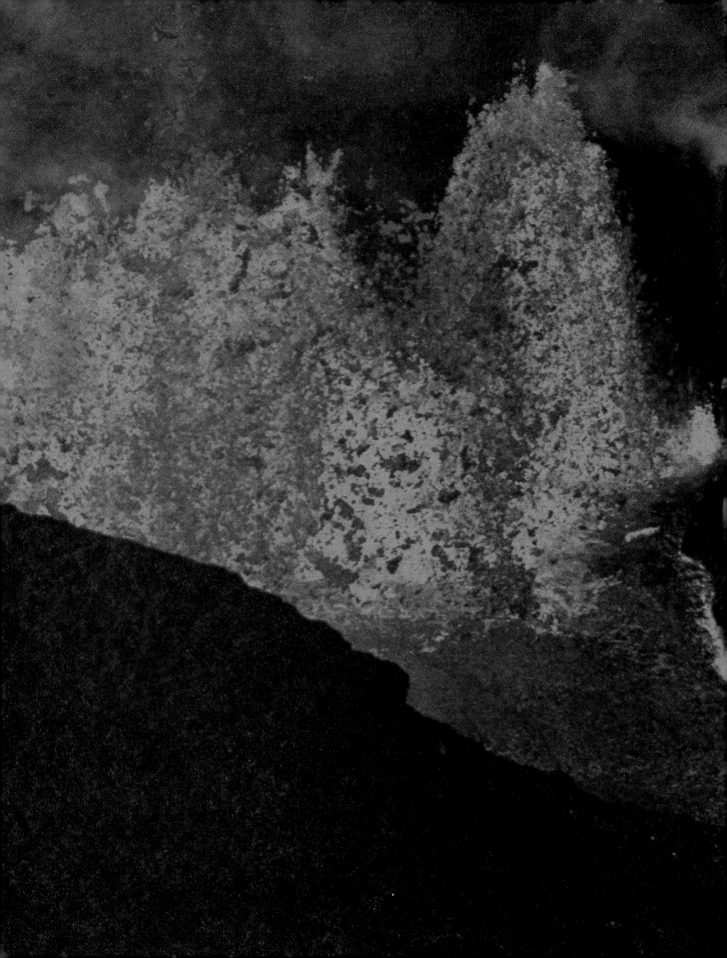

UNIT 1

Matter and Energy

A volcanic eruption attracts our attention precisely because it is exceptional. However, it is only magnitude that sets apart an active volcano from the everyday world whose peace it shatters. On a grand scale, the eruption displays the unceasing interplay of the two fundamental realities of the universe—matter and energy. Forcibly expelled from the volcano is matter in all three of its basic forms—*liquid* lava, *solid* ash, and hot *gases*. Associated with this matter is a huge amount of energy in the form of heat, light, and the energy of motion (kinetic energy).

In this first unit of the text we will describe the major properties of matter and energy and examine the processes by which each is transformed from one form to another. The notion of physical and chemical change, and how such change accounts for the activity and shape of the world, will be introduced. In this way we will enter the arena in which the scientific discipline known as chemistry provides a description of our world.

CHAPTER 1
Introduction to Chemistry

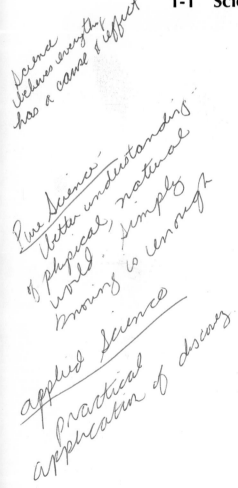

Objectives

After you have completed this chapter, you will be able to:
- Distinguish between pure science and applied science or technology.
- List some helpful and harmful results of science.
- Explain the scientific method, and compare the scientific law, hypothesis, and theory.

1-1 Science

Scientists search for facts about the world around us. They try to find logical explanations for what they observe. Scientists believe in the principle of cause and effect. According to this principle, everything that happens is related in a definite way to something that preceded it. Iron rusts because damp air has come into contact with the iron. There is a cause-effect relationship between damp air and the formation of iron rust. By discovering what causes certain changes to take place, scientists enable us to understand past events and to predict and control future events.

For some scientists, discovery and explanation are ends in themselves. The work of these scientists is called pure science. **Pure science** is the search for a better understanding of our physical and natural world for its own sake. Pure scientists are not concerned about finding uses for their discoveries. Pure scientists get satisfaction from simply knowing why things are as they are and why they happen as they do. Most of us have some of this type of curiosity. The study of science can give you the satisfaction that comes with understanding.

Science also has a practical side, called applied science. **Applied science** or **technology,** is the practical application of scientific discoveries. Applied scientists put scientific discoveries to work. The technology produced by applied scientists has made possible the present state of our civilization. As a result of technology, people today have easier lives and live longer. But technology has also led to the development of terrible weapons of war and to harmful disturbances of the natural environment. Most of these environmental disturbances, such as air and water pollution, have arisen as side effects of otherwise beneficial technology. The goal of most scientists is to achieve only beneficial results from their work. Therefore, much time, energy, and money is being spent in finding ways to decrease or even eliminate the

Figure 1-1

This painting, an oil on wood done in 1661 by Adriaen van Ostade, shows the laboratory of an alchemist.

Figures 1-2 and 1-3

Chemical laboratories today are a far cry from those of the alchemists. Various kinds of glassware are among the most common types of apparatus found in modern laboratories.

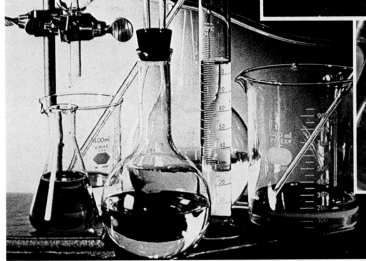

Cost/Benefit
Technology vs.
its side effects
(pollution, weapons of
war)

harmful side effects without lowering the high standard of living that technology has made possible.

1-2 The Scientific Method

The way in which a scientist goes about solving a problem is called the **scientific method.** Although the scientific method may vary in some details from one branch of science to another, there are certain steps that are common to all science.

These steps are:
1. Stating a problem
2. Collecting observations
3. Searching for scientific laws
4. Forming hypotheses
5. Forming theories
6. Modifying theories

Chapter 1   Introduction to Chemistry   **3**

These six steps are discussed in some detail below.

1. *Stating a problem.* In any scientific investigation, it is necessary to know just what we are trying to find out. Often, the problem can be stated in the form of a question. One of the important problems that many scientists worked on in past years was: What are the properties of gases?

2. *Collecting observations.* We start the investigation of a scientific problem by setting up **experiments.** Experiments are carefully devised plans and procedures that enable scientists to make observations and gather facts that shed light on a problem. In an experiment, we set up a situation in which we can control certain factors. We vary these factors, usually one at a time, and note the results. The results are our observations, or **data.** Scientific data are thus the results obtained from an experiment. Here, for example, is a simple experiment that you could do:

Blow up a balloon. Tie the balloon closed tightly so that no air can escape. Put the balloon into the freezing compartment of the refrigerator for 15 minutes. Take the balloon out. Note that the balloon has become smaller, showing that the gas is taking up less space when cold. As the gas-filled balloon sits outside the refrigerator for a while,

Figure 1-4

The chemical laboratory is the "proving ground" where chemical theories must be tested.

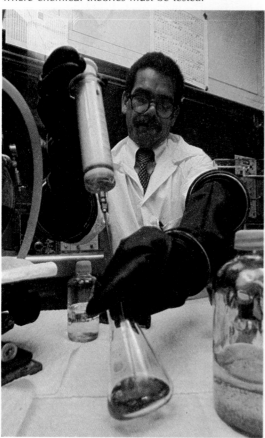

Figure 1-5

Chemists had to perform many experiments to develop the fiber shown in this photograph. The fiber, known commercially as "Nomex," is used in fire-resistant protective clothing because it can resist high temperatures. The colored spheres in the top part of the photo show how the atoms in Nomex are arranged.

the gas will expand the balloon again. It appears that changing the temperature of a gas causes a change in the volume of a gas.

The chief trouble with this experiment is that the results are not very useful. The observations would have much more meaning if we arranged to *measure* the volumes and temperatures accurately. Also, by making measurements we could collect data for many different quantities of gas and many different temperatures. We could do the same experiments with different gases and compare the results. The making of accurate measurements is an essential part of most scientific investigations.

Figure 1-6

Measuring instruments enable scientists to state observations in a precise manner.

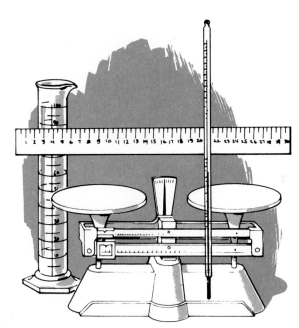

3. *Searching for scientific laws.* During the 17th and 18th centuries, many scientists carried out experiments with gases. They collected much data about the behavior of gases when various conditions were changed. Jacques Charles was one of these investigators. He collected data about the effect of temperature on the volume of a gas. By studying this data, Charles was able to state a scientific law. A **scientific law** states a relationship between observed facts. It often takes a mathematical form. The relationship that Charles discovered between the temperatures and volumes of gases is called Charles's law. It is discussed in more detail in Chapter 6.

Scientific laws describe natural events but do not explain them. Charles's law describes what happens to the volume of a gas when its temperature is changed. But Charles's law does not explain *why* a change in temperature causes the volume of a gas to change.

4. *Forming hypotheses.* A scientist tries to find out why things obey an observed law. Often, the scientist will make a guess about the reasons for the law. For example, the scientist may guess that heat is an invisible fluid. When a gas is heated, the heat fluid enters the gas,

③ Stating scientific law: really stating what you observed in experiments

④ Hypothesis: Guess why thing happened the way they did.

Figure 1-7

Antoine Lavoisier and his wife are depicted in this 1788 oil painting by J.L. David. Lavoisier, known as "the father of modern chemistry," was one of the first chemists to stress the importance of laboratory work for gaining chemical knowledge.

(5) Theories unite many like observations like a jigsaw puzzle.

thus causing it to take up more space. Such a guess, based on observed facts, is called a **hypothesis.** It may seem to be a good explanation of the facts, but it must be tested by new and different experiments. If the results of these experiments agree with the hypothesis, belief in the hypothesis becomes stronger. But if the results of the new experiments don't agree with the hypothesis, it will usually be given up as wrong. The fluid hypothesis of heat was accepted by scientists for a long time. But in the end it had to be given up because it did not agree with later experiments.

5. *Forming theories.* Scientific observations and laws are like the pieces in a jigsaw puzzle. When enough pieces have fallen into place, a meaningful pattern emerges. This pattern is a **theory.** A theory pro-

vides a general explanation for the observations made by many scientists working in different areas of research over a long period of time. A theory shows a relationship between observations that at first seemed totally unrelated. A theory, therefore, unifies many pieces of information to produce a grand design.

One of the great theories of science is called the kinetic theory of gases. This theory has been highly successful in explaining and predicting the behavior of all kinds of gases under all sorts of conditions. You will learn more about this theory in Chapter 6.

6. *Modifying theories.* A theory can never be established beyond all doubt. There is always the chance that someone will make a new observation or discover a new law that the theory should be able to explain, but cannot. When this happens, it may be possible to modify the theory to fit the new facts. For example, the molecular theory of gases, in its original form, did not accurately predict the behavior of gases under great pressure or at very low temperatures. As you will see, it was possible to modify the theory to make it agree with these new observations.

While scientific laws describe behavior in nature, theories explain observed behavior.

Figure 1-8

Two theories of burning.

Phlogiston theory of burning. (A) When an object burns, it gives off a substance called phlogiston. (B) When the space surrounding the burning object is filled with phlogiston, the object will no longer be able to burn.

Modern theory of burning. (C) When an object burns, it uses up a substance (oxygen) in the surrounding space. (D) When the space surrounding the burning object has too little oxygen in it, the object will no longer be able to burn.

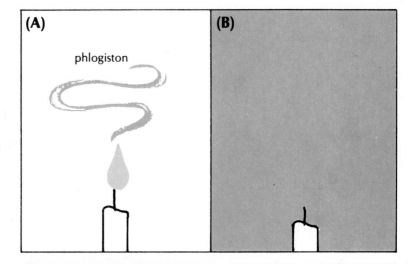

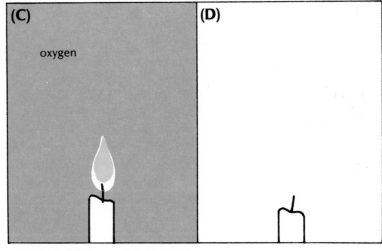

Chemical Warfare — Bug Style

The insect shown in the photo is a bombardier beetle caught in the act of spraying its foe with a foul-smelling fluid. (In this case, the beetle's foe is a person holding the beetle's foot with a forceps.)

Another animal with a chemical defense is a fish found in the Red Sea called the Moses sole. The Moses sole releases a chemical that has a strongly repellent effect on sharks. Chemists have analyzed this chemical, hoping that they will be able to make a substance with similar properties that can be put into suntan lotion, thus providing protection against sharks for swimmers and oceanographic researchers.

A thoroughly tested theory seldom has to be thrown out completely. But sometimes a theory may be widely accepted for a time and later disproved. The phlogiston (flō-JIS-tun) theory of burning is an example of one such theory. It stated that all materials that burn contain a substance called phlogiston. According to the theory, when substances burned, they gave off phlogiston. When the air became filled with phlogiston, a substance could no longer burn in that air. The phlogiston theory seemed to explain why a candle will burn for only a short time in a closed container. The theory was even used to explain why substances burn more vigorously in oxygen than in ordinary air. Oxygen was supposed to be a kind of air that had less phlogiston in it than ordinary air. But in 1778, the French chemist Antoine Lavoisier demonstrated that a burning substance, rather than giving off something to the air (giving off phlogiston), actually removed something from it (removed oxygen). Lavoisier's work became the basis of our modern theory of burning. The phlogiston theory was gradually discarded. See Figure 1-8, page 7.

1-3 The Science of Chemistry

There are many branches of science. The branch this book is concerned with is **chemistry,** which is the study of matter, its structure, properties and composition, and the changes that matter undergoes. The work of chemists is all about us. The toothpaste we use in the morning is the work of chemists. Chemists had much to do with the clothing we wear. They may have made the fiber or created the dye that gives it color. From the test tubes of chemists have come modern medicines and many kinds of vitamins. It is the chemist we must thank for many of the materials we find in our homes, at school, and in the car, bus, plane, and train.

CHAPTER SUMMARY

1. Scientists believe in the principle of cause and effect, which states that everything that happens is related in a definite way to something that preceded it.
2. Pure scientists try to develop a better understanding of the natural world, but are not concerned if immediate uses for their discoveries cannot be found. Applied scientists put scientific discoveries to work.
3. The way in which a scientist goes about solving a problem is called the scientific method. Important steps in the scientific method are stating the problem, collecting observations, searching for scientific laws, forming hypotheses and theories, and modifying theories.
4. Theories are modified or discarded if they are contradicted by new observations.
5. Chemistry is the study of matter, its structure, properties, and composition, and the changes that matter undergoes.

TERMS YOU SHOULD KNOW

pure science— *just studying to know why*   experiment— *holding variables*   hypothesis —*educated guess*

technology— *bettering world*   data   theory— *series of proven hypothesis forming puzzle*

applied science— *using ——— science to help*   scientific law — *states relationship between observed facts*   chemistry *study of matter & changes in it.*

scientific method— *form of experimenting*

side effects

REVIEW QUESTIONS

Section 1-1

1. Scientists believe that everything that happens is related to something that happened earlier. What is this principle called? *Cause - Effect*

2. Briefly describe how the role of the pure scientist differs from that of the applied scientist. *— Collecting vs. Using*

1-2 **3.** What is the purpose of an experiment in science? *to observe what happens when factors are present*

4. A balloon is blown up and the end tied so that no air can escape. What will happen to the size of the balloon if it is placed in a refrigerator?

5. What happens to a theory when a new observation is made that the theory should be able to explain but cannot?

gas **6.** According to the phlogiston theory, (a) what supposedly happened to the space surrounding a burning candle? (b) what property was phlogiston supposed to have?

7. What is meant by a "controlled" experiment? Why are controls necessary?

8. A hypothesis is often described as being an "educated guess." Explain why you agree or disagree with this description.

9. In the first three steps of the scientific method, activities are directed toward finding out what happens in certain situations. Toward what end are the activities in the next two steps of the scientific method directed?

First 3 steps observe
Next 2 Testing theories

FOR FURTHER THOUGHT

1-1 **1.** Objects seen though red glass appear red. State whether each of the following is a cause or an effect: (a) the color of the glass *CAUSE* (b) the apparent color of the object as seen through the glass. Explain your answers. *EFFECT*

2. Listed below are several products of scientific research and technology that have influenced our lives and affected our standard of living. Briefly describe the benefits and any undesirable effects that have been realized from each of these products: (a) internal combustion (automobile) engines (b) pesticides and fungicides (c) air conditioners (d) chemical fertilizers (e) nuclear reactors. *Safe plants, poison comfort waste energy* *car pollutes* *beautiful grass poison*

1-2 **3.** As the head chef for a company that sells baked goods, you have baked a cake according to a recipe, but you don't like the texture of the cake. You decide to try again, using less flour and one more egg than the recipe calls for. The result this time is a little better, but you would like to improve the cake still further. Can you tell, from this experience, what to do next time? Explain.

more flour
Less flour
Same Eggs.

4. Suppose you were asked to conduct a controlled experiment to determine the effect of storage temperature on the rate at which milk spoils. What equipment would you need? What would be your plan for the experiment?

Refrigerator that can change temps
Clock, Something to determine spoilage.

Chapter 1   Introduction to Chemistry   **9**

CHAPTER 2

Measurement

Objectives

After you have completed this chapter, you will be able to:
- Use metric units to make measurements.
- Derive conversion factors and use factor-labels in problems.
- Apply the rules of significant figures and scientific notation.

2-1 The Importance of Measurement

Modern science relies heavily on the use of measurements. Measurements make observations more meaningful. To say that a person is tall tells less about the person than to say that the person's height is 6 feet 6 inches or 198 centimeters. Almost all the laws and theories of science are derived from measurements. As you study chemistry, you will see that measurements play a large role in the development of chemical theory.

2-2 Units of Measurement

Every measurement is actually a comparison between the quantity being measured and a certain standard quantity called a *unit* of measurement. For example, suppose we measure a fence and find that it is 29.4 meters long. This means that the length of the fence is 29.4 times as great as a standard unit of length called one meter.

We need units of measurement for every quantity we wish to measure. We are completely free to make these units any size we wish. We may also give them any names we choose. However, if we want our measurements to mean something to other people, we must all agree on the units we are going to use. By international agreement, a set of units called the International System of Units has been defined for scientific work. These units are also called metric units or SI units. SI is an abbreviation based on the French "Système International d'Unités."

The SI, or metric, system has several advantages over the so-called "English" system, the system commonly used in the United States.

[handwritten margin notes: In order for measurements to be meaningful, they must have meaning to others]

[handwritten margin note: INTERNATIONAL SYSTEM OF UNITS (SI) or (METRIC SYSTEM)]

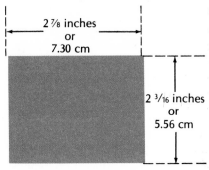

Figure 2-1

An exercise in metric calculations. Calculate the area of the rectangle in two ways. First, find its area in square inches by multiplying its length in inches by its width in inches. Second, find its area in square centimeters by multiplying its length in centimeters by its width in centimeters. To make these calculations, use either paper and pencil or a calculator. Which was easier, calculating in inches, or calculating in centimeters?

[handwritten notes:]

ENGLISH SYSTEM

Kilogram – 1000
Gram – 1

LENGTH – METER
MASS – quantity in a body
STD. UNIT – Kilogram
Basic Unit – gram
Time – seconds, minute, hour, day

Common units in the English system are inches, feet, yards, miles, ounces, pounds, pints, quarts, and gallons. Scientists find that the metric system enables them to measure and calculate more easily. Calculations are easier in the metric system because measurements that are not exact whole-number units are expressed as decimal numbers rather than fractions. To illustrate this point, try the exercise in Figure 2-1.

A second advantage of the metric system is that changing from one unit to another is much easier than in the English system. For example, suppose that the distance between two points, as measured in the English system, is 146 000 inches. How many miles is this? To find out, you first have to divide 146 000 by 12 (the number of inches per foot). Next, you divide your answer by 5280 (the number of feet per mile). The answer is 2.30 miles.

In metric units, the distance between the same two points is 371 000 centimeters. How many kilometers is this? No arithmetic is needed to find out. The answer is 3.71 kilometers. To arrive at this answer you only need to know how many places to shift the decimal point.

Units of length. The basic unit of length in the metric system is the **meter.** A *standard* meter bar made of a special alloy (platinum-iridium) is kept at the International Bureau of Standards in Sèvres, France, a suburb of Paris. Many nations have duplicates of this standard meter in their capital cities. In 1983, the meter was defined more precisely as the distance traveled in 1/299 792 458 of a second by plane electromagnetic waves in a vacuum.

Units of mass. The term *mass* refers to the quantity of matter in a body. The standard unit of mass is the *kilogram*. This is the mass of a platinum-iridium cylinder that is also kept at Sèvres. The basic unit of mass is the **gram,** which is 1/1000 of the mass of the standard kilogram.

Units of time. The basic unit of time in the metric system is the *second.* Less often used units are the *minute, hour,* and *day.*

Units of volume. Volume is a quantity whose units are derived from measurements of length. Volume can be expressed in cubic units of length, such as cubic meters (abbreviated m³) or cubic centimeters (abbreviated cm³). A cube 10 cm on a side (a cubic decimeter) has a volume of 1000 cm³. There is also a special unit of volume in the metric system called the **liter.** One liter is defined as being equal to 1000 cm³. One milliliter (1 mL) is equal to one cubic centimeter (1 cm³).

The symbol for the liter is the letter l. In most typewriter and printing types, the letter l and the number 1 are alike. To avoid confusion between the two, the capital letter L is often used as the symbol for the liter. This is the symbol used in this book. The cubic centimeter was at one time abbreviated cc, and laboratory equipment for measuring volumes was often marked in cc. This abbreviation is now out of favor, and either cm³ or mL should be used. The abbreviation mL (sometimes written ml with a small letter l) seems to be most common on apparatus made in recent years.

Spelling of meter and liter. In the International System, *metre* and *litre* (*-re* rather than *-er* at the end of the word) are the preferred spellings of these unit names. Most organizations in the United States, however, including the National Bureau of Standards, still use the more familiar spellings, *meter* and *liter*. Either spelling may be found in your reading or on package labels. Both are considered correct. This book uses the *-er* spelling.

Relationships of metric units. The units of length, mass, and volume in the metric system are related through the properties of water. The mass of 1 liter of water is almost exactly 1 kilogram. Since 1 liter equals 1000 cubic centimeters, the mass of 1 cubic centimeter of water is almost exactly 1 gram. The equivalents of these units in the so-called English units are also given.

Symbols of units. To save time and space when expressing quantities, units of measurement are represented by symbols, which are usually abbreviations of the unit names. The most common symbols in the metric system are shown in Figure 2-2.

Figure 2-2

Common metric units and their symbols.

Quantity	Name of Unit	Symbol
LENGTH	meter	m
	centimeter	cm
	millimeter	mm
	kilometer	km
MASS	gram	g
	kilogram	kg
	milligram	mg
VOLUME	liter	L
	milliliter	mL
	cubic centimeter	cm^3
TIME	second	s
	minute	min
	hour	h

Writing large numbers. The common practice in the United States when writing large numbers is to separate groups of 3 digits with commas, as in 79,288 and 14,202,000. The recommended practice in the International System of Units is to use a space rather than a comma. These numbers would then be written 79 288 and 14 202 000. This recommended style is used in this book, except for 4-digit numbers, such as 2750, which are printed without a space.

Changing from one metric unit to another. The most common metric prefixes encountered by the chemist are *kilo-, centi-,* and *milli-*.

Kilo- means 1000. Therefore, a kilometer is 1000 times the length of a meter. A kilogram is 1000 times the mass of a gram.

Centi- means 1/100th. A centimeter is 1/100th of a meter.

Milli- means 1/1000th. A millimeter is 1/1000th of a meter. A milligram is 1/1000th of a gram.

Figure 2-3 gives a listing of metric prefixes.

Because the metric system is a decimal system, changing from one unit to another is simple. You simply shift the decimal place. For example, to change 1250 meters to kilometers, you shift the decimal point 3 places to the left: 1250 meters = 1.250 kilometers. While you are becoming familiar with the system, you may find it helpful to use conversion factors, as discussed in the next section.

Figure 2-3

Metric prefixes. Prefixes commonly used in chemistry are printed on a yellow background.

Prefix	Symbol	MEANING	
		Multiply root word by*	
tera-	T	trillion	1 000 000 000 000
giga-	G	billion	1 000 000 000
mega-	M	million	1 000 000
kilo-	k	thousand	1 000
hecto-	h	hundred	100
deka-	da	ten	10
deci-	d	tenth	0.1
centi-	c	hundredth	0.01
milli-	m	thousandth	0.001
micro-	μ	millionth	0.000 001
nano-	n	billionth	0.000 000 001
pico-	p	trillionth	0.000 000 000 001
femto-	f	quadrillionth	0.000 000 000 000 001
atto-	a	quintillionth	0.000 000 000 000 000 001

*Example: In the word *kilometer*, the root word is *meter*, and the prefix is *kilo-*. Kilo- means multiply the root word by 1000. Therefore, a kilometer is 1000 meters.

Questions for Sections 2-1 and 2-2

1. Why is it necessary to have a *standard* set of units of measurement?
2. Why are calculations using metric units easier than those using "English" system units?
3. What is the only thing you have to know in order to change from one unit to another in the metric system?
4. Name the standard metric unit of measure for each of the following: length, mass, volume.
5. Give the names and meanings of the three most commonly used metric prefixes.
6. Write the symbols for each of the following metric units: centimeter, liter, kilogram, millimeter, and minute.
7. Write the name of the metric unit represented by each of the following symbols: cm^3, mL, kg, h, and km
8. How does the method of writing large numbers in the SI system differ from the method we are most familiar with?
9. What is the unit of mass that is 1000 times the mass of a gram?
10. What is the unit of volume that is 1000 times the volume of a milliliter?
11. What is the unit of length that is 1/100 the length of a meter?

2-3   Problem Solving—Factor-Label Method

Conversion factors are numbers that are used to convert from one unit to another. Conversion factors are formed from equalities that state a relationship between two units. For example, take the equality that states the relationship between kilometers and meters:

$$1 \text{ kilometer} = 1000 \text{ meters}$$

Two conversion factors can be formed from this equality. They are:

Conversion factor 1: $\dfrac{1 \text{ kilometer}}{1000 \text{ meters}}$

Conversion factor 2: $\dfrac{1000 \text{ meters}}{1 \text{ kilometer}}$

Multiplying a length in meters by conversion factor 1 will convert the length from meters to kilometers. Multiplying a length in kilometers by conversion factor 2 will convert the length from kilometers to meters.

As an example of the use of conversion factors, let us ask ourselves the question, "How many kilometers are equal to 250 meters?" This question can be written briefly:

$$? \text{ kilometers} = 250 \text{ meters}$$

To find the answer to this question, we must convert the length from meters to kilometers. Therefore, we multiply 250 meters by the first conversion factor:

$$? \text{ kilometers} = 250 \text{ meters} \times \frac{1 \text{ kilometer}}{1000 \text{ meters}}$$

$$= \frac{250 \text{ meters-kilometer}}{1000 \text{ meters}}$$

$$= 0.250 \text{ kilometer}$$

When conversion factors are used properly, all units will cancel out *except* the unit being converted to. In the above example, *meters* in the numerator and in the denominator cancel each other, leaving only kilometers. Checking to see that all units cancel but the unit being converted to provides a convenient way of checking the accuracy of our conversion.

To illustrate this point, we repeat the question asked earlier: How many kilometers are equal to 250 meters?

$$? \text{ kilometers} = 250 \text{ meters}$$

Now suppose that we had multiplied by the second conversion factor instead of the first:

$$? \text{ kilometers} = 250 \text{ meters} \times \frac{1000 \text{ meters}}{1 \text{ kilometer}}$$

$$= 250 \times 1000 \frac{\text{meters-meters}}{\text{kilometers}}$$

$$= 250\ 000\ \frac{\text{meters}^2}{\text{kilometers}}$$

But the unit should be kilometers, not meters²/kilometers. The incorrect unit tells us that we have done something wrong.

When calculating in science, you will find it helpful always to label numbers with their proper units, and to use these units as a check on the accuracy of your work. The use of conversion factors and unit-labelled numbers to solve problems is called the factor-label method of problem solving.

SAMPLE PROBLEM 1

How many meters are equal to 14.50 kilometers?

Solution   The equality used to form the conversion factor is:

$$1 \text{ kilometer} = 1000 \text{ meters}$$

The conversion factors that can be formed from this equality are:

$$\frac{1 \text{ kilometer}}{1000 \text{ meters}} \quad \text{and} \quad \frac{1000 \text{ meters}}{1 \text{ kilometer}}$$

The problem can be stated briefly:

$$? \text{ meters} = 14.50 \text{ kilometers}$$

Next, we multiply 14.50 kilometers by the appropriate conversion factor:

$$? \text{ meters} = 14.50 \text{ kilometers} \times \frac{1000 \text{ meters}}{1 \text{ kilometer}} \qquad \textbf{(SETUP)}$$

The above expression is called the *setup* for the problem. The setup shows what numbers are to be combined and how they are to be combined to arrive at the answer. By combining the numbers given in the setup, we arrive at the answer:

$$? \text{ meters} = 14.50 \text{ kilometers} \times \frac{1000 \text{ meters}}{1 \text{ kilometer}}$$

$$= 14\ 500 \text{ meters} \qquad \textbf{(ANSWER)}$$

SAMPLE PROBLEM 2

How many milligrams are equal to 3.54 grams?

Solution   The equality used to form the conversion factor is 1 gram = 1000 milligrams.

$$? \text{ milligrams} = 3.54 \text{ grams}$$

$$= 3.54 \text{ grams} \times \frac{1000 \text{ milligrams}}{1 \text{ gram}} \qquad \textbf{(SETUP)}$$

$$= 3.54 \times 1000 \frac{\text{grams-milligrams}}{\text{gram}}$$

$$= 3540 \text{ milligrams} \qquad \textbf{(ANSWER)}$$

SAMPLE PROBLEM 3

How many meters are equal to 125 centimeters?

Solution   The equality used to form the conversion factor is
1 m = 100 cm.

$$? \text{ meters } = 125 \text{ cm}$$

$$= 125 \text{ cm} \times \frac{1 \text{ m}}{100 \text{ cm}} \qquad \textbf{(SETUP)}$$

$$= \frac{125 \text{ cm-m}}{100 \text{ cm}}$$

$$= 1.25 \text{ m} \qquad \textbf{(ANSWER)}$$

SAMPLE PROBLEM 4

How many milligrams are equal to 0.5420 kilograms?

Solution   Two equalities (and, hence, two conversion factors) are
used in solving this problem:

$$1 \text{ kilogram } = 1000 \text{ grams}$$

$$1 \text{ gram } = 1000 \text{ milligrams}$$

Solving the problem:

$$? \text{ mg } = 0.5420 \text{ kg}$$

$$= 0.5420 \text{ kg} \times \frac{1000 \text{ g}}{1 \text{ kg}} \times \frac{1000 \text{ mg}}{1 \text{ g}} \qquad \textbf{(SETUP)}$$

$$= 0.5420 \times 1000 \times 1000 \frac{\text{kg-g-mg}}{\text{kg-g}}$$

$$= 542 \ 000 \text{ mg} \qquad \textbf{(ANSWER)}$$

*12. How many millimeters are equal to 5.43 meters?   (a) What equality is the basis for solving this problem?   (b) What conversion factors can be formed from the equality in (a)?   (c) Write the setup for the problem.   (d) What is the numerical answer?

13. How many liters is 0.642 milliliters?   (a) Write the equality that is the basis for solving this problem.   (b) What conversion factors can be formed from the equality in (a)?   (c) Write the setup for the problem.   (d) Find a numerical answer.

14. How many milligrams is 0.0462 kilograms?   (a) What equalities are the basis for solving this problem?   (b) Write the conversion factors that can be formed from the equalities in (a).   (c) Write the setup. (d) Find the numerical answer.

15. How many kilometers are 86 000 cm?   (a) What equalities are the basis for solving this problem?   (b) Write the conversion factors that can be formed from the equalities in (a).   (c) What is the setup for this problem?   (d) Find the numerical answer.

2-4   Scientific Notation

In science, very large or very small numbers often appear. For example, there are about 1 700 000 000 000 000 000 000 oxygen atoms in one drop of water. The distance between the centers of the two atoms in a chlorine molecule is 0.000 000 1 cm. These very large and very small numbers can be written more easily in scientific notation. In **scientific notation,** a number is expressed as the product of two factors. The first factor is a number falling between 1 and 10. The second factor is a power of ten. Here are some examples:

Number	Number expressed in scientific notation
20	2.0×10
200	2.00×10^2
501	5.01×10^2
2000	2.000×10^3
0.3	3×10^{-1}
0.21	2.1×10^{-1}
0.06	6×10^{-2}
0.002	2×10^{-3}
0.0002	2×10^{-4}
0.000 314	3.14×10^{-4}

Scientific notation simplifies and standardizes the writing of very large and very small numbers.

*The answers to questions marked with an asterisk are given in the back of the book.

Calculating with numbers written in scientific notation. The rules for calculating with numbers in scientific notation are the same as those for calculating with simple algebraic expressions such as $4a$, $5a$, and $3a^2$. In these expressions, the letter a and its exponent correspond to the second factor (the 10 and its exponent) in scientific notation. The numbers preceding the letter *a* correspond to the first factor in scientific notation.

Rules for calculating in scientific notation are illustrated in Appendix A.

Questions for Section 2-4

16. What are the two factors in a number expressed in scientific notation?
*17. Express the following in scientific notation.
    (a) 40   (c) 0.4   (e) 4004   (g) 0.004
    (b) 400   (d) 404   (f) 4400   (h) 0.0404
*18. Express the following as whole numbers or decimals.
    (a) 6.1×10^2 (c) 6.0×10^{-2} (e) 6.01×10^{-4}
    (b) 6.01×10^3 (d) 6.6×10^1 (f) 6.01×10^4
19. Express the following in scientific notation.
    (a) 420   (c) 0.03
    (b) 48 000   (d) 0.000 78
20. Express the following as whole numbers or decimals.
    (a) 2.4×10^3 (c) 3.01×10^{-1} (e) 5.43×10^{-5}
    (b) 6.23×10^5 (d) 8.2×10^{-3} (f) 3.6×10^{-4}
21. Perform the following calculations, expressing your answer in scientific notation.
    *(a) $(6.0 \times 10^4)(2.0 \times 10^5)$ (b) $(6.0 \times 10^{-3})(3.0 \times 10^5)$
    *(c) $(4.0 \times 10^4)(2.0 \times 10^{-6})$ (d) $(6.0 \times 10^6) \div (2.0 \times 10^4)$
     (e) $(8.0 \times 10^3) \div (2.0 \times 10^6)$ *(f) $(3.0 \times 10^4) \div (6.0 \times 10^{-2})$
     (g) $(2.0 \times 10^{-3}) \div (4.0 \times 10^{-8})$

2-5 Uncertainty in Measurement

No measurement of a physical quantity will be absolutely certain. Or, stated another way, all measurements contain a certain degree of uncertainty. The two main causes of uncertainty are (1) the skill and carefulness of the person making the measurement, and (2) the limitations of the measuring instrument. The first cause is obvious. The more skill people have in using the instrument and the greater care they exercise, the less chance there will be for human error to affect the measurement. The second cause of uncertainty is illustrated by the following example.

To measure the length and width of a sheet of paper, a metric ruler is an adequate measuring instrument. The amount of uncertainty in a measurement obtained by a person skilled in the use of this instrument would be quite small. However, measurement of the *thickness* of the sheet of paper is beyond the limitations of the metric ruler. Regardless of the skill of the investigator, the amount of uncertainty in any such "measurement" would make it worthless. Obviously, an instrument designed for the purpose must be used to make such a measurement.

Precision and accuracy. Assuming that the proper instrument is used by a skilled, careful investigator, the degree of certainty (or uncertainty) of a measurement depends on two factors—precision and accuracy. **Precision** indicates the reliability or reproducibility of a measurement. **Accuracy** indicates how close a measurement is to its known or accepted value.

For example, suppose a skilled investigator makes several temperature measurements of a sample of boiling water in an open container at sea level. Using the same thermometer each time, the investigator obtains the following readings: 96.9°C, 97.0°C, 97.0°C, and 96.9°C. The consistency of these readings show high reproducibility, and thus they are *precise*. But, the values differ considerably from the accepted value for the temperature of boiling water at sea level, which is 100°C. Thus, these values are clearly *inaccurate*. In this case, the inaccuracy can probably be traced to a faulty thermometer.

2-6   Significant Figures

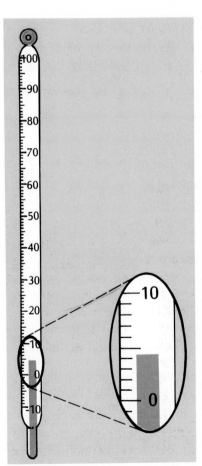

Suppose we want to measure the temperature reading on the thermometer in Figure 2-4. From a quick glance we can see that the temperature is greater than 4° but less than 5°. We cannot be sure exactly how far above 4° the reading is. But we can make an approximate guess, or *estimate*. We can see that the liquid is more than 1/10 the distance between the 4° and 5° marks, but less than 5/10 (half) the distance. We can be fairly sure the reading is between 4.2 and 4.4. We therefore report the temperature as 4.3°C, feeling confident that this reading is not off by more than 0.1°C.

Now let us look at the number 4.3. We are certain that the first digit, the 4, is correct. We are not completely certain that the second digit, the 3, is correct. It may actually be 2 or 4. We also know that 4.3 is more accurate than rounding the reading off to one digit and calling the measurement simply 4. In other words, by including the 3 in the measurement, we are giving a measurement that is more accurate than the measurement obtained by rounding off to the one-digit number 4. The two digits in the measurement 4.3°C are called significant figures. **Significant figures** in a measurement are the digits we are certain of plus one digit which we are not completely certain of. The measurement 4.3°C is a measurement with two significant figures.

Let us illustrate this idea further with a measurement of length. Suppose that we want to determine as accurately as possible the length of a strip of magnesium metal. These strips are called magnesium rib-

Figure 2-4

The liquid in the thermometer has risen to less than halfway between the 4-degree and 5-degree marks.

Figure 2-5

Measuring the length of a strip of magnesium ribbon with a metric ruler.

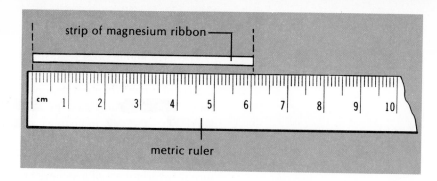

strip of magnesium ribbon

metric ruler

bon. To begin, we line up one end of the magnesium ribbon with the mark for the 0 on the ruler. See Figure 2-5. Notice that the right end of the ribbon falls between the marks for 6.0 and 6.1. The right end appears to fall halfway or perhaps slightly more than halfway between these two marks. The reading could be 6.05, 6.06, 6.07, or even 6.08. We can report the reading as 6.06 or 6.07. For sake of argument, let us choose 6.07. We are certain of the first two digits, 6.0. There is some uncertainty in the third digit, the 7. All three digits, the two we are certain of and the one in which there is some uncertainty, are significant figures. The length of the strip to three significant figures is 6.07 cm.

		EXAMPLES	
Rule		**Measurement**	**Number of Significant Figures in the Measurement**
1. All digits other than zero are significant.		25 g 246.31 g	2 5
2. Zeros between non-zero digits are significant.		409 cm 20.06 cm	3 4
3. Final zeros to the right of a decimal point are significant.		29.200 L 1.050 L	5 (The two final 0s are significant.) 4 (Both 0s are significant.)
4. In numbers smaller than one, zeros directly to the left or directly to the right of the decimal are not significant.		0.12 mL 0.030 mL	2 (The 0 merely calls attention to the decimal point.) 2 (The first 0 calls attention to the decimal point. The second 0 is a place holder. The final zero is significant.)

5. Depending upon the degree of accuracy of the measuring instrument, final zeros in whole numbers may or may not be significant. Consider the measurement *200 meters*. Are both the zeros significant, is only one zero significant, or is neither zero significant? In some books, a dash is printed over the last zero that is significant. Thus, in the measurement *7̄0̄0 cm*, there are 2 significant figures, the 7 and the 0 that follows it. In the measurement *70̄0̄ cm*, there are 3 significant figures.

In this book, you should understand that when measurements are printed, all final zeros in whole numbers are considered significant. Thus, *as written in this book* the measurement *200 meters* has 3 significant figures, the measurement *30 grams* has 2 significant figures, and the measurement *4000 milliliters* has 4 significant figures. Where final zeros in whole numbers are not significant, the measurement in this book is written in scientific notation to show the correct number of zeros. For example, this text shows that the measurement *4000 milliliters* contains 3 significant figures by writing it as *4.00 × 10³ milliliters*. The measurement *50,000 grams* is shown to have 2 significant figures by writing it as *5.0 × 10⁴ grams*.

2-7 Calculating with Measurements

We must be careful how we report the answers we get when we calculate with measurements. To illustrate this point, suppose that we want to calculate the area of a rectangle. To make this calculation, we need to make two measurements—the length and the width of the rectangle. Suppose we measure the rectangle's length and find it to be 4.26 cm. For the width, we get 3.14 cm. Using a calculator or paper and pencil, we get for the area: 4.26 cm × 3.14 cm = 13.3764 cm².

Recall that the rectangle was measured to be 4.26 cm long by 3.14 cm wide. These three-digit numbers are measurements. If the measurements were reported correctly, then all three digits in each number are significant figures. This means that there is some uncertainty in the last digit in each measurement. There is some uncertainty, for example, in the 6 in the measurement 4.26 cm. The true value for this measurement might be 4.26 cm, but if the length can be read with the same degree of accuracy as the magnesium strip in Figure 2-7, then the reading might also be as small as about 4.24 cm and as large as about 4.28 cm. The same is true of the 4 in the measurement of the rectangle's width, 3.14 cm. The true width may be 3.14 cm, but it could also be as small as about 3.12 cm and as large as about 3.16 cm. Let us take the smaller of distances for both the length and width. If we multiply these, we will get the smallest possible value for the rectangle's area: 4.24 cm (smallest length) × 3.12 cm (smallest width) = **13.2288 sq cm (smallest possible area).**

If we multiply the largest possible length and width, we get the largest possible area: 4.28 cm (largest length) × 3.16 (largest width) = **13.5248 sq cm (largest possible area).**

In other words, all we can really say about the area of the rectangle is that it is somewhere between 13.2288 cm² and 13.5248 cm². Note that only the first two digits, 13, in these two areas agree. Even the third digit is in doubt since the digit is a 2 for the smallest and a 5 for the largest area. The third digit could therefore be either of these two digits or one of the two digits in between, giving four possibilities: 2, 3, 4, and 5. In our first calculation of the area, 13.2288 cm², the last three digits have no meaning whatever. To report 13.2288 cm² as the area is misleading. It suggests that we know the area to a far greater degree of exactness than is really the case. To avoid a misunderstanding, we should drop the three meaningless digits and choose for the third digit one of the four possibilities—2, 3, 4, or 5—referred to above. We pick one of the numbers nearest to the middle of the sequence (the 3 or 4), and report the area as 13.3 cm³ or 13.4 cm².

2-8   Rules for Determining Significant Figures

There are some simple rules that tell with fair accuracy how many significant figures a calculated result has. See Appendix B.

Questions for Sections 2-5 through 2-8

22. What are the two main causes of uncertainty in measurement?
23. What is meant by   (a) the precision of a measurement?   (b) the accuracy of a measurement?
24. Explain how it is possible to make precise measurements with a faulty measuring instrument.
25. What are significant figures in a measurement?
26. What is the smallest division marked on   (a) the thermometer shown in Figure 2-4?   (b) the ruler shown in Figure 2-5?
27. Suppose you measured one side of a square and found it to be 6.45 cm in length.   (a) How many significant figures does this measurement contain?   (b) Which digit is uncertain?
28. Three students are asked to calculate the area of the square in question 27, and each arrives at a different answer. The three answers given are: 41.6025 cm²; 41.60 cm²; and 41.6 cm². Which answer is reported to the correct number of significant figures? Explain.

2-9   Percent Error

Measurements are often made during laboratory work. Sometimes these measurements have meaning in themselves. For example, you may want to know the temperature at which a liquid boils. On other

Figure 2-6

When you measure the temperature of freezing water in the laboratory, the measurement you obtain is an observed value. The true value for the freezing temperature of water is the value based on generally accepted references. As described in the text, the observed value and the true value are used to calculate the percent error in your measurement.

occasions, two or more measurements must be combined to produce a number that has meaning. The density of a substance is an example of this kind of number. To determine the density of a substance, both the mass of a sample of a substance and its volume must be measured. The density (discussed in detail later) is then calculated by dividing the mass by the volume.

When working in the laboratory, a distinction must be made between an observed value and a true value. An **observed value** is the value based on a scientist's laboratory measurements. It may be a value obtained from a simple measurement or a value obtained by combining two or more measurements. A **true value** is the most probable value based on generally accepted references. The difference between the observed value and the true value is called the **absolute error.**

For example, putting a thermometer in a beaker of boiling methyl alcohol, you may read 66.0°C as the temperature of the boiling methyl alcohol at normal pressure. The true value—that is, the value derived from the careful work of many experienced experimenters—is 65.0°C at normal pressure. The absolute error is 66.0°C − 65.0°C = 1.0°C.

For some of the experiments you do, you may want to calculate your **percent error**. This is actually a relative error.

$$\text{Percent error} = \frac{\text{observed value} - \text{true value}}{\text{true value}} \times 100\%$$

If your laboratory measurement for the temperature of boiling methyl alcohol at normal pressure is 66.0°C, then your percent error is:

$$\text{Percent error} = \frac{66.0°C - 65.0°C}{65.0°C} \times 100\%$$

$$= 1.5\%$$

Calculating a percent error helps you determine the accuracy of experimental work.

Questions for Section 2-9

*29. A block of wood has the dimensions 50.00 cm x 10.00 cm x 5.00 cm. A student determined its volume to be 2490 cm³ by measuring the volume of water displaced by the block when it was immersed in water. What is the percent error in the student's determination of the volume?

30. The mass of a certain chemical was determined by a very accurate balance to be 1.4200 g. The same mass of chemical was measured on a less accurate balance and found to be 1.43 g. What is the percent error?

1. Measurements make scientific observations more meaningful and play a large role in the development of chemical theory.
2. It is easy to measure and calculate using metric units.
3. In science, very large and very small numbers are usually written in scientific notation.
4. When measuring and calculating with measurements, it is important to write numbers to the correct number of significant figures.
5. Some simple rules can be used to determine the correct number of significant figures in a calculation.
6. The percent error is obtained by dividing the absolute error by the true value and converting the fraction to percentage units.

TERMS YOU SHOULD KNOW

meter	milli-	significant figures
gram	scientific notation	observed value
liter	precision	true value
kilo-	accuracy	absolute error
centi-		percent error

REVIEW QUESTIONS

Section

2-2
1. Scientists worldwide use a set of units called the International System of Units. By what other names are these units known?
2. Why are units of volume called derived units?
3. Explain how the metric units of mass, length, and volume are related through the properties of water.
4. The metric system is described as being a decimal system. What is a decimal system?
5. Rewrite the following numbers in the form recommended by the International System of Units.

    (a) 245703   (c) 8627   (e) 500.000005
    (b) 1000000   (d) 10000.00001   (f) 7500.001

2-3
6. Express the following in scientific notation.

    (a) 600   (c) 0.125   (e) 250 000
    (b) 7770   (d) 000.125   (f) 0.000 025

7. Express the following as a whole number or a decimal

    (a) 2.5×10^{-3} (c) 5.05×10^{2} (e) 1.0×10^{-5}
    (b) 6.25×10^{-6} (d) 2.0×10 (f) 8.1×10^{4}

2-4
8. Perform the following calculation, expressing your answer in scientific notation.

$$\frac{(2.0 \times 10^{-6})\,(4.0 \times 10^{18})}{(6.0 \times 10^{2})\,(8.0 \times 10^{-21})}$$

9. Using thermometers with Celsius scales marked at one-degree intervals, three students each made three different temperature mea-

surements of a sample of water. After their observations were recorded, the students learned that the actual temperature of the water had remained constant at exactly 90°C throughout the exercise. The measurements recorded by the three students were:

Student A	Student B	Student C
85.6°C	92.4°C	89.9°C
85.7°C	87.9°C	90.1°C
85.6°C	93.4°C	90.0°C

Describe the results obtained by each of the students in terms of precision and accuracy.

2-6 **10.** How many uncertain digits are present in a precise measurement?

2-7 **11.** One side of a cube measures 2.76 cm. Find the volume of the cube and express your answer in the correct number of significant digits.

2-9 **12.** In problem #28 in this chapter, the area of the square was correctly calculated by a student to be 41.6 cm². Another student found it to be 41.5 cm². What is this student's percent error?

FOR FURTHER THOUGHT

2-1 **1.** Describe some object in your classroom as completely as possible without referring to any measurements.

2. Describe the object you chose for Question 1, this time allowing measurements to be part of your description.

3. Using your descriptions from Questions 1 and 2 as an example, explain what is meant by the statement: "Measurements make observations more meaningful."

2-4 **4.** A student was asked to determine the area of a room to three significant figures. She obtained the following data:

Length of one wall: 7.28 m
Length of other wall: 4.12 m

She then calculated the area as follows: 7.28 m × 4.12 m = 30.0 m²
Assuming the measurements were accurate, is the result correct? (What unstated assumption was made?)

2-5 **5.** A student was given a laboratory assignment to find the boiling point of an unknown liquid. He placed some of the liquid in a beaker and suspended a laboratory thermometer in it. He heated the beaker with a burner. After the liquid had been boiling for two minutes, he used an insulated glove to remove the thermometer. He then carried the thermometer to a wall where another thermometer was reading the air temperature in the laboratory. The student compared the two thermometers and recorded the reading on each. If you were given this assignment, what changes, if any, would you make in this procedure? Why?

2-6 **6.** Which of the following measurements is or are probably beyond the measuring limitations of an ordinary metric ruler? (a) circumference of a basketball (b) diameter of a dime (c) length of a pencil (d) height of a table (e) thickness of a piece of transparent tape (f) width of a piece of movie film

CHAPTER 3

Matter

Objectives

After you have completed this chapter, you will be able to:
- Explain the meaning of density.
- Give examples of chemical and physical changes.
- State the law of conservation of matter.
- Distinguish among elements, compounds, and mixtures.

3-1 Mass

Matter is usually defined as anything that has mass and occupies space.

There are different ways of describing the quantity of matter. Volumes are often used for this purpose. You commonly buy milk, soda pop, and other liquids by volume. Weight is another way of describing the quantity of matter. You buy meats, for example, by weight. However, volumes and weights are not always reliable for describing the quantity of matter because they change under different circumstances. The volume of a sample of matter, for example, may change with its temperature. (This property of matter is put to good use in thermometers.) Weights change with location. The weight of a body is slightly less at the top of a mountain than at sea level. Its weight is much less on the moon than on earth.

For specifying the amount of a particular sample of matter, we need a property of matter that is constant. Such a property is the **mass** of a body. Mass is a measure of the quantity of matter. The mass of a body is not affected by temperature, location, or any other factors that are known to make other measures of quantity unreliable.

A balance is usually used to measure masses. A common type of balance has two pans (or platforms). On one platform the object of unknown mass is placed. On the other platform objects of known mass are placed until the two platforms balance each other. The mass of the unknown is equal to the sum of all the known masses. In chemistry it is common to measure masses in grams.

Figure 3-1

The Harvard Trip Balance is one kind of balance for measuring masses.

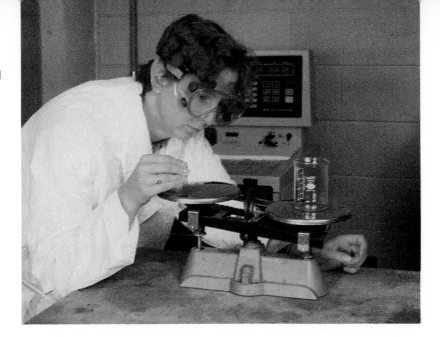

3-2   Varieties of Matter

As we look about us, we see many different kinds of matter. Each kind has its own particular characteristics. For example, some materials have colors and textures that help identify them. Some are heavier or stronger than others. Some can be bent or stretched. Some are liquids, some are solids, and some are gases under ordinary conditions. By experience, we learn to recognize various types of matter by these characteristics. We learn, too, that materials can change in characteristic ways. Ice melts, paper burns, iron rusts, and milk spoils.

Chemistry is the study of matter—its composition, properties, and changes. Chemists attempt to discover and describe all the kinds of matter that can exist. They also try to learn why each kind of matter has its special characteristics and why it can change in certain ways. This understanding may lead to the production of new materials with desirable properties, such as plastics, synthetic fibers, alloys, fertilizers, and drugs. Through chemical theory we also attempt to control problems such as that of pollution, which is to a great extent a problem in the control of chemical changes.

Homogeneous and heterogeneous matter. The term matter refers to all the materials found in nature. As we have just seen, these materials exist in a seemingly endless variety of shapes, forms, and colors. However, all matter can be classified into two groups. Some materials seem to be uniform throughout. That is, all parts are exactly the same. Matter that has uniform characteristics throughout is said to be **homogeneous.** Homogeneous materials include elements, compounds, and solutions. These categories of matter are described later in this chapter.

Other materials consist of parts that are not all the same. A sample taken from one part of such a material will differ in some way from a

Figure 3-2

Chemists have been making plastics since 1869, when John W. Hyatt made celluloid. Over the past 40 years many new kinds of plastics have been made to serve a variety of purposes, some of which are shown above.

sample taken from another part of the same material. How the parts differ may or may not be readily apparent. Matter that has parts with different characteristics is said to be **heterogeneous.** Most mixtures are heterogeneous materials.

3-3   Substances

A **substance** is a variety of matter, all samples of which have the same properties, or characteristics. For example, if two samples of matter are both to be called water, they must have the same set of properties. These properties will correctly describe water wherever it is found. In fact, they may be considered to be a definition of water. For example, here are three of the properties of water. It freezes at 0°C. It boils at 100°C when under standard pressure. (The meaning of the term "standard pressure" will be made clear later.) One milliliter of water has a mass of 1 gram at 4°C. Other substances may have some of these properties, but water is the only substance that has all of them.

3-4   Properties

The **properties** of a substance are the definite set of characteristics by which the substance is recognized. Properties are a description of (a) what can be observed by examining the substance and (b) the manner in which it behaves when it is brought into contact with other substances or exposed to sources of energy. We can observe quite simply the color, taste*, odor of a substance, and whether the substance is ordinarily a gas, liquid, or solid. A flame may be applied to see whether it will burn. How dense the substance is can be determined from measurements of the mass and volume of a sample. A thermometer can be used to measure the temperature at which it melts or boils. It can be brought into contact with chemicals, such as acids, and the results observed. Such properties can be used to describe and recognize substances.

Questions for Sections 3-1 through 3-4

1. What property of matter is most reliable for specifying a quantity of a sample of matter?
2. What three categories of matter consist of homogeneous materials?
3. Describe three properties that can be used to identify a sample of matter as being water.
4. Name some properties of a substance that can be easily observed by the senses only.
5. What properties of a substance can be measured with a thermometer?

*Never taste a chemical unless instructed to do so by your teacher. Many chemicals are poisonous.

3-5   Extensive and Intensive Properties

Properties of substances can be either extensive properties or intensive properties. **Extensive properties** depend upon how much of a particular sample is on hand. Volume, weight, and mass are all extensive properties. A large sample of a particular substance will have a larger volume, a larger weight, and a larger mass than a small sample of the same substance.

Intensive properties of a substance are properties that do not depend on the size of the sample. The melting point of a substance is an intensive property. Ice melts at 0°C regardless of the size of the piece of ice. The boiling point of a substance is another intensive property since all samples of pure water, large or small, boil at 100°C when the air pressure is normal.

Figure 3-3

Pure water boils at 100°C when the air pressure is normal. The normal boiling point of a substance is an intensive property that can help identify a substance.

Intensive properties are used to identify substances. If a solid substance melts at 0°C, we suspect that the substance is ice. A close look at other properties of the substance will tell us if we are right. Extensive properties are not useful in identifying substances. A sample of matter whose mass, for example, is 20 grams can be almost any substance.

3-6   Physical and Chemical Properties

Physical properties of a substance are those characteristics that can be observed without the production of new substances. Examples are color, odor, taste, hardness, density, melting and boiling points, and electrical conductivity. Most metals have a set of physical properties that are very different from the properties of nonmetallic substances. Metals are *ductile* (they can be drawn into wires) and *malleable* (they can be hammered into sheets). Also, they have metallic *luster* (they shine in a way typical of metals), and they are good conductors of electricity.

Figure 3-4

Two ways of viewing density.
(A) For equal volumes of different substances, the sample with the greater mass will have the greater density. (B) For equal masses, the sample with the larger volume will have the smaller density.

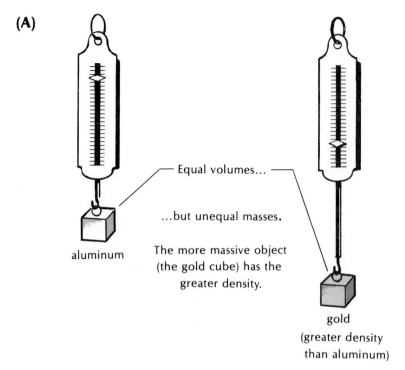

(A)

Equal volumes...

...but unequal masses.

The more massive object (the gold cube) has the greater density.

aluminum

gold
(greater density than aluminum)

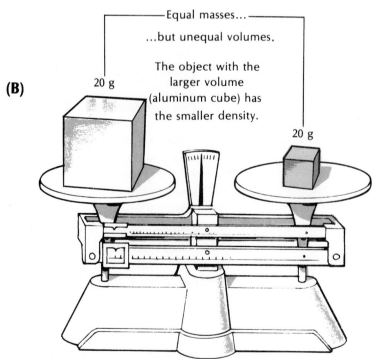

Equal masses...

...but unequal volumes.

The object with the larger volume (aluminum cube) has the smaller density.

(B)

20 g

20 g

Chemical properties of a substance are those characteristics that describe how the substance interacts (or fails to interact) with other substances to produce new substances. That iron interacts with moist air to form rust is a chemical property of iron. That nitrogen gas under most conditions does not interact with other substances is a chemical property of nitrogen.

3-7 Density

Density is an intensive physical property often used to identify substances. **Density** is the quantity of matter in a given unit of volume. Since mass is a measure of the quantity of matter, this definition can be expressed mathematically:

$$\text{density} = \frac{\text{mass}}{\text{volume}}$$

For example, if a block of wood has a mass of 11 grams and its volume is 10 cm³, then its density

$$= \frac{11 \text{ grams}}{10 \text{ cm}^3} = 1.1 \text{ grams/cm}^3$$

To understand the meaning of density, consider the "trick" question, "Which is heavier, a kilogram of aluminum or a kilogram of lead?" The answer is, of course, that they have the *same* weight. Yet we commonly say that lead is "heavier" than aluminum. To be correct, we should say that lead is *denser* (or has a greater *density)* than aluminum. Density describes the relationship between the mass and the volume of a sample of a substance. There is much less mass in 1 cm³ of aluminum than in 1 cm³ of gold. Put another way, 1 gram of aluminum has a much larger volume than an equal mass of gold. See Figure 3-4. The density of aluminum is only 2.7 g/cm³, while the density of gold is 19.3 g/cm³. Figure 3-5 gives the densities of some common substances.

Figure 3-5

Densities of some common substances at 20°C. All densities are expressed in grams per cubic centimeter.

GASES (under normal atmospheric pressure)		LIQUIDS		SOLIDS	
hydrogen	0.000 083 7	ethyl alcohol	0.79	aluminum	2.70
helium	0.000 166 3	water	1.00	iron	7.87
nitrogen	0.001 165	chloroform	1.49	copper	8.96
air	0.001 205	mercury	13.55	silver	10.50
oxygen	0.001 331			lead	11.35
				gold	19.32

The density of a liquid or solid will change slightly with changes in temperature and pressure. When liquids and solids warm up, they expand, making their volumes greater while their masses remain the same. This causes the density to decrease. Changes in pressure affect the volumes of liquids and solids, too. Normally the change in density for ordinary changes of pressure is too small to be noticeable. While changes in temperature and pressure have little effect on the densities of liquids and solids, the effect of these changes on the densities of gases can be large. Chapter 6 describes these changes in some detail.

This picture was taken less than a minute after the cube was removed from an oven set at 1260°C (2300°F). The corners of the cube cooled enough to allow the person to hold the cube by the corners with his bare fingers. At the same time, the rest of the cube was hot enough to glow red. Made of high-purity silica fiber, this super-insulating material is used on the space shuttle (see facing page) to prevent the craft from burning up from frictional heat as it re-enters the earth's atmosphere.

Chemists have often played important parts in the development of materials with unusual properties needed for special purposes.

SAMPLE PROBLEM 1

A piece of lead has a mass of 22.7 g. It occupies a volume of 2.00 cm³. What is the density of the lead?

Solution

The density of a substance is the mass of one unit of volume of the substance. The problem states that 2 units of volume (the unit here is cm³) have a mass of 22.7 g. One unit of volume would have a mass ½ as great, or ½ × 22.7 g = 11.4 g. The density of the lead is, therefore, 11.4 g/cm³.

The problem can also be solved using a formula.

$$\text{density} = \frac{\text{mass}}{\text{volume}}$$

$$= \frac{22.7 \text{ g}}{2.00 \text{ cm}^3}$$

$$= 11.4 \text{ g/cm}^3$$

Note: All samples of a pure substance at the same temperature and pressure have the same density, regardless of how large or small they are. Density is an intensive property.

SAMPLE PROBLEM 2

A piece of lead occupies a volume of 4.00 cm³. What is the mass of this piece of lead?

Solution

From Sample Problem 1, the density of lead was found to be 11.4 g/cm³. Its density could also be found listed in tables giving the densities of substances. (See the table in Figure 3-5, page 31.)

If

$$\text{density} = \frac{\text{mass}}{\text{volume}}$$

then

$$\text{mass} = \text{density} \times \text{volume}$$

$$= 11.4 \text{ g/cm}^3 \times 4.00 \text{ cm}^3$$

$$= 45.6 \text{ g}$$

A piece of lead whose volume is 4.00 cm³ has a mass of 45.6 g.

The Space Shuttle

SAMPLE PROBLEM 3

A piece of lead (density of lead = 11.4 g/cm³) has a mass of 22.8 g. What volume does it occupy?

Solution

If

$$\text{density} = \frac{\text{mass}}{\text{volume}}$$

then

$$\text{volume} = \frac{\text{mass}}{\text{density}}$$

$$= \frac{22.8 \text{ g}}{11.4 \text{ g/cm}^3}$$

$$= 2.00 \text{ cm}^3$$

A piece of lead whose mass is 22.8 g will occupy a volume of 2.00 cm³.

Questions for Sections 3-5 through 3-7

6. Is density an intensive or extensive property? Explain.
7. State whether each of the following describes a chemical property or a physical property: (a) water is a liquid at room temperature (b) copper can be hammered into thin sheets (c) a tarnish forms on silver when silver interacts with air (d) gold can be cut with a knife (e) helium gas will not burn (react with oxygen)
8. A sample of lead and a sample of aluminum have equal volumes. How does the mass of the lead sample compare with that of the aluminum sample? (See the table of densities in Figure 3-5, p. 31.)
*9. A sample of gold occupying a volume of 3.00 cm³ has a mass of 57.9 g. What is the density of gold?
10. The density of silver is 10.5 g/cm³. What will be the volume of a piece of silver having a mass of 31.5 g?
11. A sample of iron occupies a volume of 10 cm³. If the density of iron is 7.9 g/cm³, what is the mass of the sample?

3-8 Changes of Phase

Matter exists in three phases—solid, liquid, and gaseous. Water, a liquid, can freeze to form ice, a solid. Water can boil to form steam, a gas. We say that ice is "water in the solid phase," and that steam is "water in the gaseous phase." When a substance changes from one phase into another, there is no change in the composition of the substance. For example, water, ice, and steam all consist of hydrogen

Chapter 3   Matter   **33**

Figure 3-6

Samples of matter in three phases. On the left, sealed in a glass tube, is a gas having a brown color, nitrogen dioxide. In the middle, the liquid lying in the watch glass is mercury. On the right are three samples of a common solid, an alloy of copper metal.

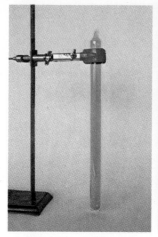

atoms and oxygen atoms. All are made up of 89% oxygen and 11% hydrogen by mass.

In a sense, ice, liquid water, and steam *are* different substances, since some of their properties are different. However, the differences are entirely physical. Chemically, they are alike. Besides, ice and steam can be changed to liquid water by simple physical means. It is therefore customary to consider water in its three phases to be the same substance. The same applies to any other substance that can exist in more than one phase.

3-9   Physical Change

When one or more physical properties of a substance are changed, but without any change in its chemical properties or composition, the substance has undergone a **physical change.** In a physical change, no new substance is formed. Any change of phase is a physical change. Other examples of physical change are a change of color (with no change in composition), the grinding of a substance to a powder, and the magnetizing of iron.

Figure 3-7

Grinding a solid into a powder is a physical change.

Figure 3-8

The caldron shown here is filled with iron whose temperature was raised enough to make the iron melt. When melted iron, commonly called molten iron, is formed from solid iron, a physical change occurs.

3-10   Chemical Change

A **chemical change** is any change that results in the production of one or more substances that differ in chemical properties and composition from the original substances. The rusting of iron, the souring of milk, and the burning of paper are examples of chemical changes.

Figure 3-9

When something burns, a chemical change takes place. This kind of chemical change is called combustion.

3-11   Changes in Energy

Why does one feel cool when emerging from a swimming pool?

Every change in a substance, whether physical or chemical, involves an energy change. The energy changes that accompany physical changes are generally not as noticeable as those that accompany chemical changes. This is especially true of changes that give off energy. Dramatic chemical changes, such as explosions and burning, cannot be matched by physical changes, such as crystallization and freezing, which also release energy.

Some physical and chemical changes occur with the *absorption* of energy. Examples of physical changes that absorb energy are the melting of ice and the evaporation of water. An example of a chemical change that absorbs energy is the formation of hydrogen gas and oxygen gas when an electric current is passed through water. The concept of energy will be treated in more detail in Chapter 4.

3-12   Conservation of Matter

At the time that Lavoisier was investigating the process of burning, it was known that when certain metals were heated in air, they formed a new substance called a calx. It was also known that the calx weighed more than the original metal. To the scientists of the time this seemed to show that a change in weight (or mass) could occur during a chemical change. Lavoisier believed, moreover, that the increase in weight was the result of the metal combining with a substance from the air. In a famous experiment, Lavoisier heated tin and air in a sealed container. Lavoisier found that the weight of the container and its contents did not change as the metal changed to a calx. However, when the container was opened, air rushed in to replace the gas that had combined with the tin. The container now showed an increase in weight. See Figure 3-10. Experiments of this kind led Lavoisier to conclude that matter cannot be created or destroyed by a chemical change. This principle became known as the **law of conservation of matter.***

CAUTION: It is extremely dangerous to heat any container, either empty or with something in it, when it is closed.

*For all practical purposes, this law is true for all ordinary chemical changes. No measurable change in mass takes place during ordinary chemical reactions. However, it is possible for a measurable amount of mass to be converted to energy by changes in the nuclei of atoms. The energy given off by the sun is the result of such a process. The same is true of energy generated in nuclear power plants. We will consider nuclear changes, and the changes in mass that accompany them, in Chapter 31.

Figure 3-10

An investigation of the process of burning similar to that done by Lavoisier. (A) A strip of magnesium metal. (B) The white powder that is formed when the magnesium metal is burned. The white powder weighs more than the strip of metal. (C) A device for burning magnesium metal inside a sealed container (a dangerous procedure that should be done only under supervision). When the ends of the wire are connected to a battery, the nichrome wire will get red hot. (D) If magnesium metal is wrapped around the nichrome wire, and the battery is then connected to the ends of the wire, the magnesium metal will burn, forming the white powder shown in (E). This time there is no weight change before and after the burning. Flask and contents in (D) weigh the same as flask and contents in (E).

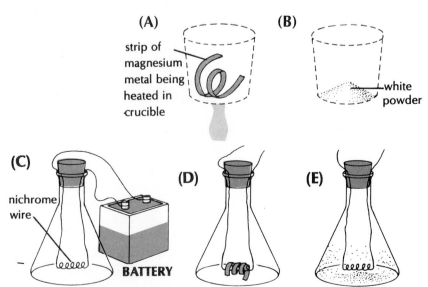

12. What do we call ice in its liquid phase?
13. Classify each of the following as a physical change or a chemical change: (a) the burning of coal (b) the melting of glass (c) the grinding of coal to a powder (d) the rusting of iron (e) the boiling of water
14. Give an example of a chemical change that releases energy.
15. Give an example of a physical change that absorbs energy. *melt*
16. How did Lavoisier explain the fact that the substance formed by heating a metal has a mass greater than that of the metal before heating?
17. Lavoisier's famous experiment led to the formulation of what scientific law?

3-13   Elements

Early experimenters discovered that some substances could be changed into others. For example, hydrogen gas and oxygen gas could be changed into water. Often, one substance could be broken down into two or more others. It was also discovered that the same substance could often be obtained from several different starting materials. For example, copper could be obtained from a number of different kinds of rocks. However, copper itself could not be broken down any further. These observations led to the idea of simple substances, called *elements,* and composite substances, called *compounds*. A third class of materials, mixtures, was also recognized. See Figure 3-11.

Elements are pure substances that cannot be broken down into other substances by means of an ordinary chemical change*. Oxygen, mer-

*One element may be changed to another by means of a change known as a *nuclear change*. This is described in Chapter 13.

Figure 3-11

Elements, compounds, and mixtures.
The element hydrogen (A) consists entirely of atoms of the same kind. The compound water (B) consists of hydrogen and oxygen atoms chemically combined in a fixed ratio of two atoms of hydrogen to one atom of oxygen. In a mixture of hydrogen and oxygen, the hydrogen and oxygen atoms may be present in any proportions. In (C), there is more oxygen than hydrogen. In (D), there is more hydrogen than oxygen.

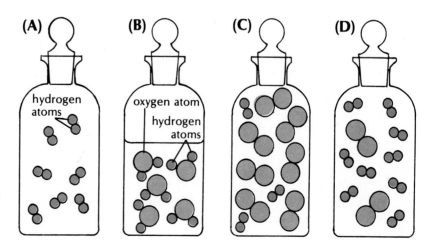

(A) hydrogen atoms

(B) oxygen atom / hydrogen atoms

(C)

(D)

cury, copper, and carbon are a few of the more familiar elements. At present, 109 elements are known to exist. Ninety-one have been found in nature. The others have been created by scientists in the laboratory, most of these in very small quantities.

3-14 Occurrence of Elements

When elements exist alone, uncombined with other elements, they are said to be in a **free state** or in an **elemental state.** Elements that are combined with other elements as part of a compound are said to be in chemical combination or in a **combined state.** Most of the elements occur in nature only in chemical combination. A few elements occur in the free state as well as in compounds. Examples of such elements are copper, silver, sulfur, oxygen, and nitrogen. A few other elements are so inactive chemically that they are found almost entirely in the free state.

As shown in Figure 3-12, oxygen is the most common element in the earth. Combined with other elements, it makes up almost half of the mass of the earth's solid crust. Combined with hydrogen, oxygen makes up almost 90% of the mass of the earth's waters. And as the free element, oxygen makes up about 23% of the mass of the air. The second most common element is silicon. About ¼ of the earth's crust is silicon in the form of compounds. Six other elements make up nearly all the rest of the crust. The rest of the elements in the crust make up less than 2% of its mass.

Figure 3-12

Distribution of elements in the earth's crust. The figures are percentages by weight of the solid crust. If water and the atmosphere are included, the percentage of oxygen increases to 49.5%, and the other percentages become slightly less.

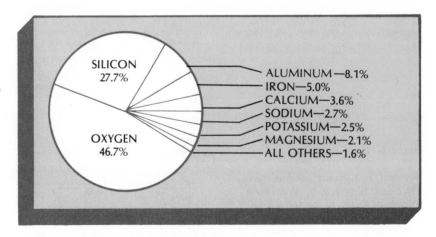

The relative abundance of the elements, however, is not an accurate guide to their importance. Carbon, hydrogen, and nitrogen, while relatively scarce in the earth's crust, are important ingredients of the bodies of all living things. Copper, chlorine, zinc, and tin are examples of relatively scarce elements that are used in great amounts by industry.

The elements are not found uniformly throughout the crust. Certain rocks, called **ores**, contain a high percentage of useful metals. Sulfur is found in large beds in almost pure form. Coal deposits are a rich source of carbon.

3-15   Symbols of the Elements

The chemist uses abbreviations for the names of the elements. These abbreviations are called **chemical symbols.** The symbol may be either a single letter, such as O (used to represent oxygen), or two letters, such as Al (used to represent aluminum). A single-letter symbol is always a capital letter. In a two-letter symbol, only the first letter is capitalized.

The symbols are based on the names of the elements. In some cases, the Latin name of the element is used. For example, Fe, the symbol for iron, comes from its Latin name, *ferrum.* Symbols for Latin names are used chiefly for those elements that have been known since the early days of chemistry. During that period, Latin was the language used for all scholarly work. A number of important elements and their symbols are listed in Figure 3-13. Where the Latin name is the basis for the symbol, it is also included (in *italics).*

Figure 3-13

The names of some of the elements and their symbols. The Latin names of some of the elements are given in parentheses.

Symbol	Element	Symbol	Element	Symbol	Element
✓Al	aluminum	Au	gold (*aurum*)	✓K	potassium (*kalium*)
Ar	argon	✓He	helium	Ra	radium
As	arsenic	✓H	hydrogen	Rn	radon
✓Ba	barium	I	iodine	Rb	rubidium
Be	beryllium	Fe	iron (*ferrum*)	Se	selenium
B	boron	Kr	krypton	Si	silicon
Br	bromine	Pb	lead (*plumbum*)	Ag	silver (*argentum*)
Cd	cadmium	Li	lithium	✓Na	sodium (*natrium*)
✓Ca	calcium	✓Mg	magnesium	Sr	strontium
✓C	carbon	Mn	manganese	✓S	sulfur
Cs	cesium	Hg	mercury (*hydrargyrum*)	Te	tellurium
✓Cl	chlorine	Ne	neon	Th	thorium
Cr	chromium	Ni	nickel	Sn	tin (*stannum*)
Co	cobalt	✓N	nitrogen	W	tungsten
Cu	copper (*cuprum*)	✓O	oxygen	U	uranium
✓F	fluorine	P	phosphorus	Xe	xenon
Fr	francium	Pt	platinum	Zn	zinc

Questions for Sections 3-13 through 3-15

18. What is an element? Name several.
19. What do the elements carbon, hydrogen, and nitrogen have in common?
20. What makes a rock an ore?
21. Coal contains a high percentage of a certain element. What is that element?

22. What is true about those elements that are represented by chemical symbols based on their Latin names?
23. Write the chemical symbols that represent the following elements: (a) sodium (b) lead (c) silicon (d) helium (e) nitrogen
24. Write the names of the elements represented by the following symbols: (a) S (b) C (c) Ca (d) Cu (e) Au

3-16 Compounds

A **compound** is a homogeneous substance made up of two or more elements chemically combined. As described on page 27, a homogeneous material is one that has the same properties throughout. Any part of a homogeneous material is exactly like any other part.

Unlike elements, compounds can be broken down (decomposed) into simpler substances by a chemical change. Water and table salt are examples of compounds. By passing an electric current through melted salt, the salt can be broken down into a very soft metal, sodium, and a greenish-yellow gas, chlorine. Water can be broken down by an electric current into two gases, hydrogen and oxygen.

The important characteristics of a compound are:

1. The elements making up a compound (its *constituents)* are combined in a definite proportion (ratio) by mass. This proportion is the same in all samples of the compound.

2. The chemical and physical properties of a compound are different from those of its constituents.

3. Compounds can be made from simpler substances by chemical change and can be decomposed into simpler substances by chemical change. When decomposed, some compounds break down into elements. Others may break down into elements and simpler compounds.

3-17 Mixtures

Some materials consist of parts that have different properties. In most rocks, for example, particles of different substances are clearly visible to the naked eye. Milk that is not homogenized will separate into two layers when allowed to stand. Salt water shows properties of both salt and water, and can be separated into these substances by evaporation of the water. Air is composed of several gases, one of which is oxygen. Unlike the oxygen present in water (a compound), the oxygen in air has all the characteristic properties of the free element. For example, it can support combustion and respiration.

Rocks, milk, salt water, and air are called mixtures. A **mixture** consists of two or more substances, each of which retains its individual properties.

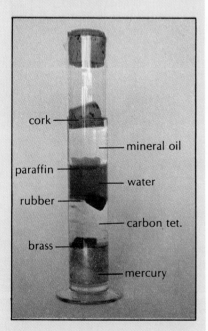

cork
mineral oil
paraffin
water
rubber
carbon tet.
brass
mercury

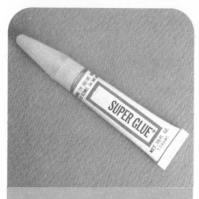

Super-Strong Glues

One of the recent "miracles" that chemists have produced is modern glues that have vastly superior powers of adhesion. These glues are so strong that they are being used to replace metal rivets in aircraft construction, making the aircraft lighter and more fuel-efficient. The insulating tiles on the space shuttle (see page 32) are held in place by one of these "space age" adhesives.

A mixture may be any of the following combinations:

—one element mixed with one or more other elements
—one compound mixed with one or more other compounds
—one or more elements mixed with one or more compounds

A mixture can be distinguished from a compound by these characteristics:

1. A mixture can be prepared or separated into its components by physical change. A compound can be formed or decomposed only by chemical change.

2. The substances making up a mixture have essentially the same properties they had when separate. The properties of a compound are different from those of the elements of which it is composed.

3. The substances making up a mixture may be present in any proportions. For example, varying amounts of salt may be dissolved in the same amount of water in preparing salt water. Sugar and sand may be mixed in any proportion to make a sugar-sand mixture. In a compound, the elements making up the compound are always present in the same proportion by mass.

4. Mixtures may be either homogeneous or heterogeneous. In a homogeneous mixture, the substances making up the mixture are evenly spread throughout the mixture. Ordinary solutions, such as salt water, and mixtures of gases, such as air, are homogeneous. The substances in a heterogeneous mixture are not uniformly distributed. Most rocks are heterogeneous mixtures. But in either case, the composition of the mixture may vary. That is, salt solutions can be concentrated or dilute. One granite rock may vary in its composition from another.

3-18   Some Applications of the Term Substance

As defined in the early part of this chapter, a substance is a variety of matter all samples of which have the same properties. An element may be referred to as a substance. A compound may also be referred to as a substance. But a mixture is never referred to as a substance. The more general word "material" is used to refer to a mixture.

Questions for Sections 3-16 through 3-18

25. What is the major difference between an element and a compound?
26. The ratio, by mass, of hydrogen to oxygen in a 1-gram sample of water is 1 to 8. What will the ratio of these two elements be in a 10-gram sample of water?
27. What happens to the properties of a substance when that substance becomes part of a mixture?
28. What type of change, physical or chemical, is involved in separating a mixture into its component substances?
29. Why aren't mixtures considered to be substances?

CHAPTER SUMMARY

1. Matter is defined as anything that has mass and occupies space.
2. A substance is a variety of matter, all samples of which have the same characteristics, or properties.
3. Density is a physical property that describes the relationship between the quantity of matter in a sample of a substance and the amount of space that the sample occupies. Density is defined as mass per unit of volume.
4. A physical change is a change in one or more physical properties.
5. A chemical change results in the production of one or more substances that differ in chemical properties and composition from the original substances.
6. Every change in a substance involves an energy change.
7. The law of conservation of matter states that matter cannot be created or destroyed by a chemical change.
8. Elements are pure substances that cannot be broken down into other substances by means of ordinary chemical change.
9. A compound is a homogeneous substance made up of two or more elements chemically combined in definite proportions by mass.
10. A mixture consists of two or more substances physically combined.

TERMS YOU SHOULD KNOW

✓ matter	extensive property	chemical change	combined state
✓ mass	intensive property	law of conservation of	ore
homogeneous matter	physical property	matter	chemical symbol
heterogeneous matter	chemical property	element	compound
substance	density	free state	mixture
property	physical change	elemental state	

REVIEW QUESTIONS

Section 3-1
1. How is matter usually defined?
2. Explain why weight and volume are not always reliable measurements for describing quantities of matter.
3. What units are commonly used to measure mass in chemistry?

3-2
4. Describe some of the different characteristics that various kinds of matter exhibit.
5. Differentiate between homogeneous and heterogeneous materials.

3-3
6. What is a substance?

3-4
7. What do the properties of a substance describe?

3-6
8. What are chemical properties?
9. What is meant by the physical properties of a substance? Give several examples of physical properties.

3-7
10. Define density. How is density expressed?

3-8
11. Why is a change of phase considered to be a physical change?

3-9
12. Differentiate between physical change and chemical change.

3-10
13. Classify the following as physical or chemical changes: (a) the burning of paper (b) the melting of ice (c) the breaking of glass (d) the tearing of paper (e) the tarnishing of silver

3-11	**14.** In general, how do energy changes that accompany physical changes compare with those that accompany chemical changes?
3-12	**15.** Briefly describe the experiment that led Lavoisier to discover the principle behind the law of conservation of matter.
3-13	**16.** How many elements are known to exist? How many of these have been found in nature?
3-14	**17.** How do elements in the free state differ from those in the combined state? In which state are most elements found in nature?
3-15	**18.** Write the symbols that represent the following elements: (a) iron (b) hydrogen (c) carbon (d) nitrogen (e) sulfur
	19. Write the names of the elements represented by the following symbols: (a) O (b) Na (c) Ne (d) Hg (e) Si
3-16	**20.** What is a compound? What characteristic do compounds and elements have in common?
	21. Briefly describe the important characteristics of a compound.
3-17	**22.** What is a mixture?
	23. Describe the characteristics that distinguish a mixture from a compound.

REVIEW PROBLEMS

3-7	**1.** A sample of copper having a mass of 44.5 g occupies a volume of 5.00 cm³. What is the density of copper?
	2. Iron has a density of 7.86 g/cm³. A sample of iron having a mass of 393 g will occupy what volume?
	3. A piece of lead occupies a volume of 40.0 cm³. The density of lead is 11.35 g/cm³. What is the mass of this piece of lead?
	4. Suppose you have samples of two substances, A and B. The mass of substance A is 20 g; that of substance B is 60 g. The density of substance A is 10 g/cm³; that of substance B is 4.0 g/cm³. Which sample occupies the larger volume, and by how much?

FOR FURTHER THOUGHT

3-5	**1.** A student was trying to determine the boiling point of a mixture of water and alcohol. He suspended a thermometer in the liquid and heated it until it began to boil. He continued to boil the liquid for 5 minutes, and then he recorded the reading of the thermometer. It was 92.2°C. He allowed the mixture to cool and repeated the procedure. The observed boiling point this time was 92.8°C. When he ran a third trial, the reading was 93.0°C. What is a likely explanation for these results?
3-7	**2.** You can find the density of a substance if you know the mass and volume of a sample of the substance. The mass of a sample can usually be found by weighing it. The volume can be found by dropping it into a graduated cylinder containing water and observing the change in volume. What would you do if: (a) the substance floats in water? (b) the substance dissolves in water? (c) the substance is a liquid?
3-13	**3.** The idea that all material things are made up of one or more simple substances, called elements, is a very old one. According to one ancient theory, there were four elements: earth, air, fire, and water. In what way or ways would fire probably differ from the other three elements in this scheme? That is, what properties did fire *not* share with earth, air, and water?

Energy

4-1 The Concept of Energy

The concept of energy plays an important role in the sciences, especially in physics and chemistry. As stated in Chapter 3, all the physical and chemical changes that we will be studying are accompanied by energy changes. An understanding of energy is essential for understanding chemistry.

Figure 4-1

Burning is one type of chemical reaction that is accompanied by the release of heat energy.

Reprinted by permission. © 1981, Factory Mutual Engineering Corp.

Figure 4-2

A wound watch spring has potential energy. This energy, slowly released, keeps the gears of the watch turning.

Energy is defined as the capacity to do work. Work is done whenever a force is applied over a distance. Therefore, anything that can force matter to move (or force moving matter to change speed or direction) has energy. The following example may help you understand this definition of energy. When you wind a watch, you bend a steel spring into a position of strain. The bent spring then exerts a force on the gears in the watch. This force causes the gears to turn. Therefore, as the spring unwinds, it does work on the gears. After a time, the watch stops because the spring is unwound. When the spring is unwound, it no longer exerts a force on the gears. In its wound-up condition, the spring had the capacity to do work. In other words, it contained energy. In its unwound condition, it no longer has that capacity.

4-2 Classes of Energy

All energy can be grouped into two classes—stored energy and energy of motion. In the previous section we used a wound-up watch spring as an example of something that has energy—the capacity to do work. However, unless the spring is allowed to unwind, no work is done by the energy it contains. We think of this energy as being *stored* in the wound-up spring, ready to do work under certain conditions. Such stored energy is called **potential energy.**

Once the watch spring starts to unwind, its motion enables it to do work—to move the gears of the watch. The stored-up energy is "released" as moving energy, or energy of motion. Such energy is called **kinetic** (ki-NET-ik) **energy.** All matter in motion has kinetic energy.

4-3 Forms of Energy

We generally give special names to energy depending on the conditions under which it appears. Energy associated with chemical change is called *chemical energy.* When energy is used to exert a force and produce motion, as in a watch, the energy of the moving parts is called *mechanical energy.* An electric current carries energy and can do work. It can turn an electric motor, for example. The energy in electric currents is called *electrical energy.*

Energy is observed in various other phenomena. For example, light waves carry *electromagnetic* (or *radiant*) *energy.* Sound waves carry *sound energy. Magnetic energy* can be stored in the space around a magnet. This space is called the magnet's magnetic field. Finally, there is a very common form of energy called *heat.* Heat is a very important form of energy, especially in chemistry. The subject of heat will be treated in detail later in this chapter.

4-4   Measurement of Energy

The basic SI unit of energy is the **joule** (JOWL or JOOL). This unit is named in honor of James P. Joule, a British scientist who devoted much of his life investigating energy in all its forms. Joule was especially interested in the relationship between work accomplished and the amount of heat produced by that work. He determined that work (or energy) could be measured in terms of the heat it could produce. The heat equivalent of a joule is discussed later in this chapter, Sec. 4-9.

Questions for Sections 4-1 through 4-4

1. What is energy?
2. In the sense in which scientists use the term *work,* what must happen in order for work to be done?
3. Why is work being done as the gears of a watch turn?
4. What is another name for stored energy?
5. What kind of energy does a wound-up watch spring have?
6. What is kinetic energy?
7. Name five forms of energy.
8. What is the basic SI unit of energy?

4-5   Energy and Chemical Reactions

Figure 4-3

Supplying an automobile with chemical potential energy. When gasoline combines chemically with oxygen (when it burns), the chemical potential energy of the fuel is released. As a result, work is done as the car is moved along.

Earlier it was stated that every change in a substance is accompanied by an energy change. The energy changes that accompany chemical changes generally are more noticeable than are those that accompany physical changes. As mentioned above, energy associated with chemical change is called chemical energy. Many substances contain potential energy that can be released through a chemical change. A common example is the energy stored in fuels, such as coal or gasoline. When these fuels are burned, a chemical reaction called **combustion** takes place. The energy released during combustion can do useful work, such as operate a steam or gasoline engine.

Burning is an example of a chemical reaction that *releases* energy. Reactions that release energy are called **exothermic** (EK-so-THER-mik). There are also chemical reactions that *absorb* energy. That is, energy must be supplied continuously to the reacting substances while the reaction is going on. Such reactions are called **endothermic** (EN-do-THER-mik).

Even though a reaction is exothermic (releases energy), it may still require an initial input of energy to get it started. This minimum starting energy is called the **activation energy** of the reaction. When you strike a match, you produce frictional heat. This heat provides the

Figure 4-4

Burning is an exothermic reaction, in this case producing enough heat to melt the metal framework of the windows.

Figure 4-5

Activation energy of a match. The head of a match (A) contains potential chemical energy. In order for that energy to be released, the match head must be heated. When you strike a match (B), you are producing frictional heat. The amount of heat necessary to cause the match head to burst into flame (C) is the activation energy required for the burning of the match head. Once started, the exothermic reaction (burning) supplies its own activation energy and burning continues (D).

(A)   **(B)**   **(C)**   **(D)**

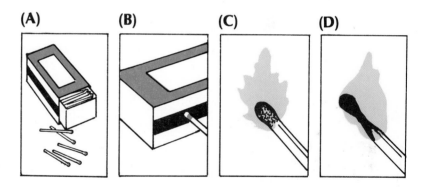

activation energy that must be supplied before the match can begin to burn. Once the match begins to burn, the reaction (combustion) is exothermic. The heat given off is sufficient to keep the reaction going. The relation of energy to chemical change is treated in some detail in later chapters.

4-6 Conversion of Energy

Energy is often changed, or converted, from one form into another. For example, within our bodies the chemical energy of food substances is changed to mechanical energy of muscle contractions. Light energy enters our eyes and becomes electrical energy in our nerves. In the industrial world, coal is burned, changing chemical energy to heat. The heat is used to change water to steam. Some of the heat becomes

Figure 4-6

A number of energy conversions take place in an automobile, two of which are shown here. (A) When the gasoline is ignited by the spark plug, a chemical reaction takes place that releases heat. Thus, chemical energy is converted to heat energy. (B) The heat energy in the cylinder causes the gases in the cylinder to expand. As they do so, they make the piston move, giving it mechanical energy (energy of motion). Thus, heat energy is converted to mechanical energy.

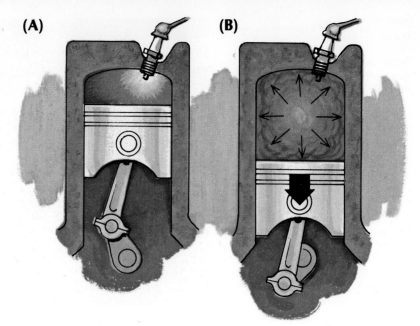

(A)   **(B)**

potential energy in the steam. The potential energy of the steam may then be changed to mechanical energy in a steam engine, or electrical energy in a generator. Electrical energy can be carried by wires to homes and factories. There it may be turned into mechanical energy by an electric motor, into heat energy by a toaster, into light energy by an incandescent lamp, or into chemical energy by a storage battery.

4-7   Conservation of Energy

We have been considering a number of types of energy changes. Each type of energy can be measured in terms of the amount of work it can do or the amount of heat it can be changed to. Scientists have found that, whatever changes occur from one type of energy to another, the total amount of energy remains the same during all energy changes. That is, no energy can be created or destroyed as a result of these changes. This basic principle is called the **law of conservation of energy.**

Equivalence of mass and energy. One of the outcomes of Albert Einstein's Theory of Relativity was the conclusion that mass and energy are related. According to this theory, whenever a body or system gives off energy, the body or system decreases in mass. Likewise, when a body or system absorbs energy, it increases in mass. However, changes in mass that accompany common energy changes are so small that the change in mass cannot be detected. There are types of reactions in which measurable changes in mass do occur. These reactions involve changes in the nuclei of atoms. Changes of this kind occur in a nuclear reactor or an atomic bomb. These reactions are sometimes

Figure 4-7

When an object gives off energy, it
loses mass, although the loss is
ordinarily too small to measure.

considered to be exceptions to the principle of conservation of energy,
since energy appears to be created by the loss of mass. The conservation principle nevertheless remains true in these cases if mass is recognized as one of the forms in which energy may appear.

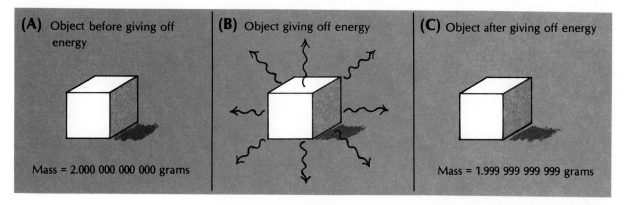

(A) Object before giving off energy

Mass = 2.000 000 000 000 grams

(B) Object giving off energy

(C) Object after giving off energy

Mass = 1.999 999 999 999 grams

Questions for Sections 4-5 through 4-7

9. What is the difference between an exothermic reaction and an endothermic reaction?
10. What is the minimum starting energy of a reaction called? *activation*
11. Give specific examples of the following energy conversions: *energy*
    (a) chemical to heat *coal burned*
    (b) electrical to heat *toaster*
    (c) electrical to light *incandescent lamp*
12. State the law of conservation of energy.

4-8 Heat Energy and Temperature

We have said that heat is one of the forms in which energy appears.
It is, in fact, a very important form of energy. No understanding of the
concept of energy is possible without understanding what is meant by
heat and how it is measured. The following sections are concerned with
this subject.

The concept of temperature is based upon human sensations of
"hotness" and "coldness." We can judge whether one object is hotter

Figure 4-8

Carefully feeling the side of the
flask gives an approximate idea of
how hot the water is. Scientists
often want to measure temperature
by more accurate means.

CHEMISTRY IN ACTION

or colder than another by touching them. A hotter object is said to be at a higher temperature. There is only a limited range of temperatures that we can safely test by our sense of touch. Furthermore, we cannot assign numerical values to temperatures judged this way. To measure temperatures, rather than just compare them, we use thermometers. Various types of thermometers have enabled us to measure temperatures over a wide range.

The most common types of thermometer make use of the expansion of substances when their temperature increases. A very familiar example is the mercury thermometer. This instrument consists of a thin-walled bulb attached to a long, narrow glass tube. The bulb is filled with the liquid mercury (other liquids may also be used). Some of the liquid extends into the narrow tube. If the temperature of the bulb increases, the volume of the mercury inside the bulb will increase. More of the mercury will therefore be forced into the tube. On the other hand, if the temperature decreases, the mercury contracts. Some of the contracting liquid flows back into the bulb. Since the tube is very narrow, a small change in the total volume of the mercury results in a relatively large change in the length of the column of mercury in the tube. The actual temperature is indicated by a scale marked on the glass tube or fixed alongside it.

A temperature scale for a thermometer of this type is made by first marking two fixed points. One point is the temperature at which ice melts or water freezes. The other is the temperature at which water boils (under normal atmospheric pressure). The thermometer is brought to each of these temperatures in turn. A mark for each is placed on the glass tube. The scale is then subdivided into equal units (degrees) between these markings. Using the same units, the scale is extended beyond the two fixed points in either direction. See Figure 4-9.

Figure 4-9

Making a Celsius thermometer. (A) A mark is made showing the height of the liquid when the thermometer is immersed in melting ice. (B) Another mark is made when the thermometer is immersed in boiling water. (C) Space between the two marks is divided equally into 100 spaces and marked. A rise of the liquid from one mark to the next shows a 1° rise in temperature. (D) Spaces of the same size are marked below the 0° mark and above the 100° mark for measuring temperatures below 0°C and above 100°C.

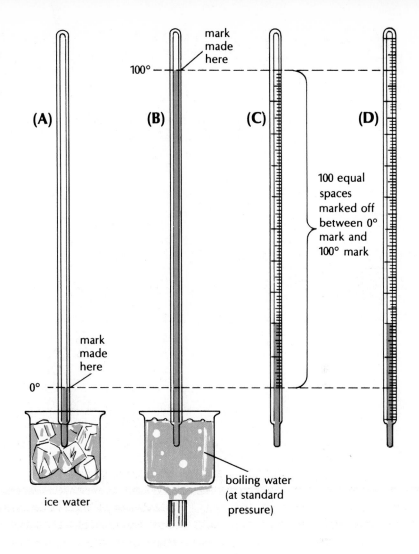

mark made here

100°

(A)   (B)   (C)   (D)

100 equal spaces marked off between 0° mark and 100° mark

mark made here

0°

ice water

boiling water (at standard pressure)

Celsius scale is the revised name for the *centigrade scale.*

The Celsius scale. The temperature scale most commonly used for scientific work is the **Celsius** (SEL-see-us) **scale.** It was devised by a Swedish astronomer, Anders Celsius, in 1742. It was at first named the centigrade scale, meaning a scale divided into a hundred steps or degrees. On this scale, the freezing point of water was indicated as 0°C, and the boiling point, 100°C. The interval between these fixed points was divided into 100 equal parts. Divisions below 0°C became negative quantities. These were used to measure temperatures below the freezing temperature of water. Those above 100°C measured temperatures higher than the temperature of boiling water.

The Kelvin scale. There is a temperature that is theoretically the lowest possible temperature. It has been given the name **absolute zero.** A temperature of absolute zero has never actually been reached, but scientists in laboratories have reached temperatures within about a thousandth of a degree above absolute zero. Lord William Kelvin, an English physicist, proposed a temperature scale on which the zero point would be absolute zero, although the size of the degree would be the same as the Celsius degree. This scale is called the **Kelvin scale.** Temperatures on the Kelvin scale are designated by the letter K. Through experiment and theory, it has been estimated that the temperature of absolute zero is −273.15°C, that is 273.15 degrees below zero (the freezing point of water) on the Celsius scale. Thus, on the Kelvin scale, the freezing point of water is 273.15 K, and the boiling point is 373.15 K. For practical purposes, these values are rounded to 273 and 373. See Figure 4-10.

Figure 4-10

Three temperature scales and how they compare.

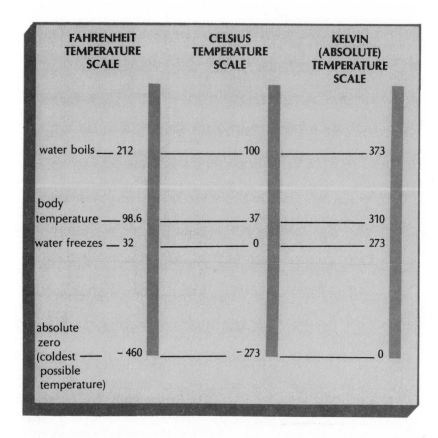

To convert temperatures from one scale to the other, add 273 to the Celsius reading or subtract it from the Kelvin reading:

$$K = °C + 273$$
$$°C = K − 273$$

Questions for Section 4-8

13. What concept is based on the sensations of "hotness" and "coldness"?
14. What are the individual units of a temperature scale called?
15. What are the two fixed points on which the Celsius temperature scale is based?
16. On the Celsius scale, what is the freezing point of water?

17. How are temperatures below the freezing point of water indicated on the Celsius scale?
18. What is the boiling point of water on the Kelvin scale?
19. How do you convert Celsius temperatures to Kelvin temperatures?
*20. Convert the following to Kelvin temperatures: (a) 10°C (b) −20°C
*21. Convert the following to Celsius temperatures: (a) 25 K (b) 300 K

4-9 Heat and Its Measurement

Suppose we heat a brick in an oven. Then we place the brick in a large container of water that is at room temperature. We then observe the temperatures of the brick and the water. We find that the temperature of the brick falls. That of the water rises. This continues until both are at the same temperature. This temperature will be somewhere between the original temperatures of the brick and the water.

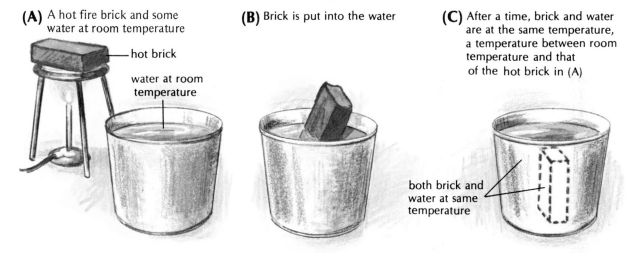

(A) A hot fire brick and some water at room temperature
— hot brick
water at room temperature

(B) Brick is put into the water

(C) After a time, brick and water are at the same temperature, a temperature between room temperature and that of the hot brick in (A)

both brick and water at same temperature

Figure 4-11

When a hot brick is placed in water at room temperature, the brick gives heat to the water. In doing so, the brick cools off while the water heats up, until both are at the same temperature.

To explain these observations, we say that something called *heat* left the brick and entered the water. When heat leaves a material, the material usually gets cooler. That is, its temperature drops. When heat enters a material, its temperature usually rises. When two bodies of matter at different temperatures are near each other, heat will always flow from the hotter one to the cooler one. This flow of heat will continue until both have reached the same temperature.

Quantity of heat can be measured by the temperature change it produces in a substance. For this purpose, water has been selected as the substance to be used. The unit of heat quantity is the **calorie.** A calorie is defined as the quantity of heat that will increase the temperature of 1 gram of water by 1°C. This is a rather small unit for the quantities of heat that are involved in most chemical processes. Therefore, the **kilocalorie** is more often used. The kilocalorie is equal to 1000 calories. It is the quantity of heat that will increase the temperature of 1 kilogram of water by 1°C.

*The answers to questions marked with an asterisk are given in the back of the book.

Research Chemist

Research is being conducted in all the branches of chemistry. If you enjoy the challenge of searching for the answers to questions, you should consider becoming a research chemist. Research is conducted in the colleges and universities by teachers and their graduate students, and by chemists in industry and government. Some research chemists roll up their sleeves and get involved in the laboratory work that is carried out to test ideas. Others act principally as directors who supervise a staff of laboratory workers.

Research chemists are good in science and math, most have advanced degrees, and all must have the staying power to go "back to the drawing board" when experiments prove their ideas to be wrong. For the research chemist, the satisfaction of finally reaching success is great enough to justify the false starts that are always a part of research.

The calorie as a unit of energy. Under suitable conditions, any form of energy can be entirely converted to heat. This often happens during chemical changes. For that reason, chemists often measure the energy of chemical reactions in calories (or kilocalories) rather than in joules. As a unit of energy, 1 calorie* is approximately 4.18 joules.

The difference between heat and temperature. The difference between heat and temperature can be illustrated by the following problem. Suppose that a drinking glass and a bathtub are both filled with water at room temperature (20°C). To raise the temperature of the water in both containers requires the addition of heat. Which would require more heat, raising the temperature of the water in the drinking glass by 80°C (raising its temperature to its boiling point), or raising the temperature of the water in the tub by 0.5°C?

A typical drinking glass holds about 250 mL of water, while a typical bathtub holds about 400 000 mL of water. To raise the temperature of 250 mL of water by 80°C requires 250 mL × 80°C = 20 000 calories of heat. To raise the temperature of 400 000 mL of water by 0.5°C requires 400 000 mL × 0.5°C = 200 000 calories of heat. Therefore, to raise the temperature of the bath water by 0.5°C requires ten times as much heat as to raise the temperature of the drinking water by 80°C! A large temperature rise does not necessarily mean that a large quantity of heat is being absorbed by an object. Nor does a small temperature rise necessarily mean that a small quantity of heat is being absorbed.

Calorimetry. The measurement of the amount of heat released during a chemical reaction is called **calorimetry** (kal-u-RIM-u-tree). It is usually done with the aid of a device called a **calorimeter** (kal-uh-RIM-uh-ter). In a calorimeter, the reaction to be measured occurs inside a reaction chamber surrounded by a known mass of water. Heat released by the reaction enters the water and raises its temperature. The temperature change is measured with a thermometer. The outside of the calorimeter is well insulated to prevent any significant loss of heat. See Figure 4-12.

The quantity of heat transferred to the water in the calorimeter can be calculated by multiplying three factors: (1) the mass of the water in the calorimeter (in grams), (2) the change in the water's temperature (in degrees Celsius), and (3) a constant called the specific heat of water. The **specific heat of water** is the amount of heat energy required to raise the temperature of 1 gram of water by 1° Celsius. As we have already seen, this amount of heat is 1 calorie or 4.18 joules. Therefore, for determining reaction heats in calories, the value of the specific heat is 1 calorie per gram per degree Celsius, or 1 cal/g-°C. For determining reaction heats in joules, the value of the specific heat of water is 4.18 joules per gram per degree Celsius, or 4.18 J/g-°C.

---

*The "calorie" used for measuring the energy value of foods is actually 1000 calories or 1 kilocalorie. The food calorie is sometimes called the *large calorie,* and spelled or abbreviated with a capital letter C, to avoid confusion with the calorie as defined here.

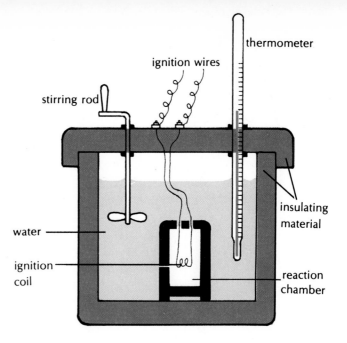

Figure 4-12

A calorimeter. The substances in the reaction chamber are ignited by a spark. The heat of the reaction is transmitted to the water, whose mass is known and whose temperature change is measured.

SAMPLE PROBLEM 1

A 2000-gram mass of water in a calorimeter has its temperature raised by 3.0°C while an exothermic chemical reaction is taking place. How much heat is transferred to the water by the heat of the reaction?

Solution. The heat transferred to the water is the product of three factors, as given in the following formula:

$$\text{Heat} = \left(\begin{array}{c}\text{mass}\\\text{of}\\\text{water}\end{array}\right) \times \left(\begin{array}{c}\text{change in}\\\text{temperature}\\\text{of the water}\end{array}\right) \times \left(\begin{array}{c}\text{specific}\\\text{heat}\\\text{of water}\end{array}\right)$$

$$= 2000 \text{ g} \times 3.0°C \times 1.0 \frac{\text{cal}}{\text{g-}°C}$$

$$= 6000 \text{ calories}$$

To the correct number of significant figures (Section 2-6), this answer is 6.0×10^3 calories.

To calculate the heat energy in joules, we use the value

$$4.18 \frac{J}{\text{g-}°C}$$

for the specific heat of water:

$$\text{Heat} = 2000 \text{ g} \times 3.0°C \times 4.18 \frac{J}{\text{g-}°C}$$

$$= 25\,080 \text{ J} \quad \text{or} \quad 25\,080 \text{ joules}$$

To the correct number of significant figures, this answer is 2.5×10^4 joules.

SAMPLE PROBLEM 2

A 1000-gram mass of water whose temperature was 50°C lost 8000 calories of heat over a 5-minute period. What was the temperature of the water at the end of the 5-minute period?

Solution

$$\text{Heat} = \left(\begin{array}{c} \text{mass} \\ \text{of} \\ \text{water} \end{array} \right) \times \left(\begin{array}{c} \text{change in} \\ \text{temperature} \\ \text{of the water} \end{array} \right) \times \left(\begin{array}{c} \text{specific} \\ \text{heat} \\ \text{of water} \end{array} \right)$$

$$8000 \text{ cal} = 1000 \text{ g} \times \Delta t \times 1.0 \frac{\text{cal}}{\text{g--}°\text{C}}$$

(Note: Δt is the symbol for "change in temperature.")

$$\Delta t = \frac{8000 \text{ cal}}{1000 \text{ g} \times 1.0 \frac{\text{cal}}{\text{g--}°\text{C}}}$$

$$\Delta t = 8.0°\text{C}$$

If the temperature of the water changed (dropped) by 8°C, its final temperature must have been 42°C if it started the 5-minute period at 50°C.

The temperature of the water at the end of the 5-minute period was 42°C.

Questions for Section 4-9

22. What usually happens to the temperature of a material when heat enters the material?
23. Describe what happens when two bodies of matter at different temperatures are brought together.
24. What is the SI unit for measuring energy?
25. What unit do chemists often use for measuring the energy of chemical reactions?
26. What is calorimetry?
*27. How many calories of heat were added to 5000 grams of water to change its temperature from 20°C to 80°C? (a) What is the mathematical relationship that is the basis for solving this problem? (b) Use the relationship to find a numerical answer.
28. What is the energy equivalent, in joules, of the heat added to the water in question 27?
29. How many calories of heat were absorbed by 2000 grams water whose temperature rose from 20°C to 50°C? (a) What is the mathematical relationship that is the basis for solving this problem? (b) Use the relationship to find a numerical answer.
30. If 500 grams of water at 25°C loses 2500 calories of heat, what will the final temperature of the water be? (a) What is the mathematical relation that is the basis for solving this problem? (b) Use the relationship to find a numerical answer.

4-10   The Kinetic Theory of Heat and Temperature

The modern view of matter is that every sample of matter consists of very small particles. The nature of these particles will be discussed in later chapters. The important idea for our purposes here is that these particles of matter are in continuous motion. That is, even though an object, such as a block of wood, is at rest, the particles making up the object are in constant motion. The faster one of these particles moves, the greater its kinetic energy. The temperature of a body of matter is a measure of the average kinetic energy of the random motions of its particles. At absolute zero, this average kinetic energy would be zero. That is, particles would no longer have any random motions. At higher and higher temperatures, the average kinetic energy of random motion becomes greater and greater. The relationship between the temperature of a body and the average kinetic energy of its particles is the same for all kinds of matter. For all bodies at the same temperature, the average kinetic energy of their particles is the same.

This theory of temperature explains the relationship between heat and temperature. Heat is a form of energy. When heat enters a body, the energy may be used to increase the kinetic energy of the particles of the body. Therefore, its temperature will increase. When a body cools, its particles lose kinetic energy, and this energy may be given off as heat.

We will see, in the next chapter, that heat can enter or leave a body without causing a change in temperature. In such cases, the average kinetic energy of the particles of the body remains the same. However, some other energy change takes place in the body. For example, as ice melts, forming water, heat enters the melting ice, but the temperature of the ice and water mixture does not change while the melting is going on. The energy going into the ice is being used to rearrange the particles of the substance. During melting, the particles are rearranged into positions of greater potential energy, while their kinetic energy remains unchanged. As the melting proceeds, energy is stored in the water produced by the melting.

Questions for Section 4-10

31. What do we call the theoretical temperature at which particles of matter have no kinetic energy?
32. What does the temperature of a body of matter actually measure?
33. Give an example of an instance where heat can enter a body without causing a change in the temperature of the body.

4-11   Positive and Negative Electric Charge

The concept of electric charge is important in understanding the structure and properties of substances. The principle of electric charge is based on certain simple experiments that anyone can do. A typical experiment is the rubbing of a piece of hard rubber with fur. After the rubbing, the hard rubber will at first attract small bits of paper, hair, or other light objects. After coming in contact with the rubber, these light objects are then repelled by the rubber. They also repel one another. These effects are the result of the bodies having acquired an *electric charge*.

Many experiments have led to the conclusion that there are two kinds of charge, which are called *positive* and *negative*. Every object normally has both kinds of charge in equal amounts. Objects with an equal amount of positive and negative charge are said to be electrically neutral. When certain neutral materials are rubbed or pressed together

Figure 4-13

Positive and negative charge. (A) When a plastic ruler is rubbed vigorously with a piece of cloth, the ruler acquires a positive charge while the cloth acquires a negative charge. (Some kinds of cloth work better than others.) (B) If the charged ruler is held near small pieces of paper, the pieces will be attracted to the ruler by an electrostatic force.

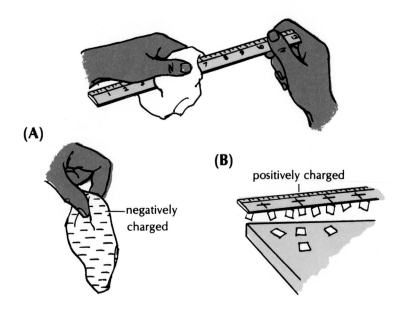

and then separated, electric charge is transferred from one material to the other. One of the materials acquires an excess negative charge, and the other acquires an excess positive charge. For example, when hard rubber is rubbed with fur, the rubber acquires an excess negative charge, while the fur acquires an excess positive charge.

4-12 Forces Between Charges

Two bodies with a charge of the same sign repel each other. Two bodies with charges of opposite sign attract each other. The force of attraction or repulsion is called an **electrostatic** (uh-lek-truh-STAT-ik) **force.** The electrostatic force becomes greater when the excess charge on either object becomes greater. The force becomes smaller when the distance separating the charged objects becomes greater.

Conservation of charge. When two charges of equal amount but opposite sign are brought together, their electrostatic forces cancel each other. However, no net charge has ever been created or destroyed in any experiment. Whenever a charge seems to appear or disappear, an equal amount of charge of opposite sign also appears or disappears at the same time.

Figure 4-14

Like charges repel. (A) This can be demonstrated by sticking two pieces of transparent tape to the same surface. When the pieces of tape are pulled off the surface, they each acquire the same charge. (B) The force of repulsion between the like charges can be seen when one piece of tape is brought close to the other.

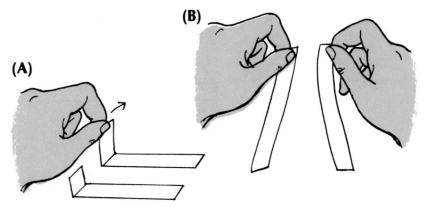

Figure 4-15

Unlike charges attract. (A) The glass test tube and the silk cloth are uncharged. (B) Rubbing the test tube with the cloth will cause the two objects to become oppositely charged. (C) The cloth and test tube now attract each other.

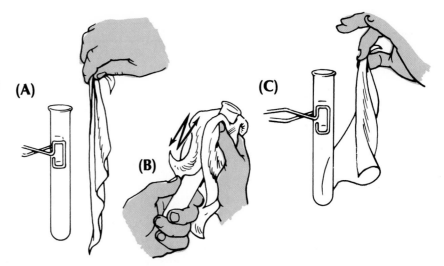

4-13   Electrical Energy

Bodies with charges of like sign repel each other. In order to move these two charged bodies closer together, a force must be exerted to overcome the force of electrostatic repulsion. When forces are exerted over a distance, work is done (Section 4-1). Therefore, work must be done to move a charged body toward another body with a charge of like sign. Likewise, work must be done to move two bodies apart having unlike charges. Energy is needed to do work. The energy used to move charged bodies against an electrostatic force is converted to potential energy. This kind of potential energy is called electrical energy.

Figure 4-16

(A) Work must be done to force two like charges (both positive or both negative) together against the electrostatic force of repulsion. (B) Work must be done to force two unlike charges apart against the electrostatic force of attraction.

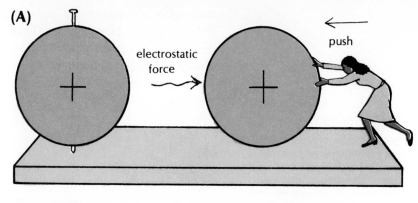

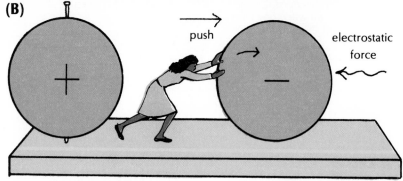

Figure 4-17

Positive and negative charges. (A) Two objects have equal but opposite electric charges. (B) When the two objects are connected by a wire conductor, negative charges flow from the negatively charged object through the wire to the positively charged object until the net charge on each object is zero. A flow of charge is called an electric current. (For reasons that will become apparent later, the negative charges move while the positive charges remain in place.)

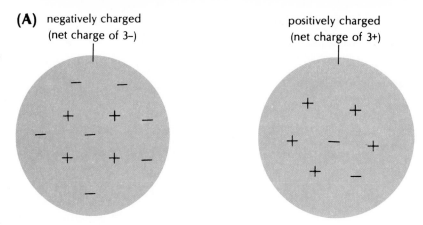

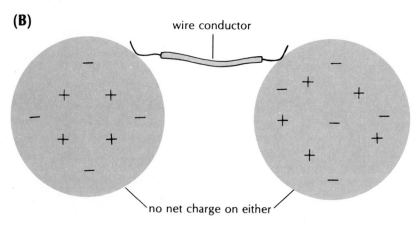

Electric current. If two metal objects with equal and opposite charges are connected by a piece of wire, charge will flow through the wire until both metal objects have no net charge. This flow of charge is called an **electric current.** Substances through which electric charge flows readily are called **electrical conductors.** All metals are conductors, although some are better conductors than others. Many solutions are conductors. Other substances (including gases) are ordinarily poor conductors. However, when the difference in charge between two bodies becomes great enough, a nonconductor between them, such as air, may ''break down'' and permit the flow of current. A lightning flash is a flow of current through the air between a highly charged cloud and the earth's surface, or between two clouds with opposite charges.

Questions for Sections 4-11 through 4-13

34. After passing a comb through your hair, your hair will sometimes be attracted to the comb. What accounts for this phenomenon?
35. Why is matter normally electrically neutral?
36. What is the force between two electrically charged bodies called?
37. What happens to energy used to overcome an electrostatic force?
38. What is an electric current?

CHAPTER SUMMARY

1. Energy is the capacity to do work. Anything that can cause matter to move or to change direction has energy.
2. All energy can be grouped into two classes—potential energy and kinetic energy. Potential energy can be described as stored energy. Kinetic energy is energy of motion.
3. There are many different forms of energy. Some forms of energy are chemical energy, mechanical energy, radiant energy, sound energy, magnetic energy, and heat energy. The basic unit of energy in the International System is the joule.
4. Chemical reactions that release energy are called exothermic reactions. Those that absorb energy are called endothermic. The activation energy of a reaction is the minimum amount of energy necessary to get the reaction started.
5. Energy can be changed, or converted, from one form to another. However, the law of conservation of energy states that energy can be neither created nor destroyed as a result of these changes. According to Einstein's theory of relativity, mass and energy are closely related. Einstein considered mass to be a form of energy that could be converted to other forms of energy.
6. The concept of temperature is based on the sensations of ''hotness'' and ''coldness.'' A thermometer measures temperature. All temperature scales are subdivided into units called degrees. On the Celsius temperature scale, the freezing point of water is 0° and the boiling point is 100°.
7. Heat is a form of energy. The basic unit of heat is the calorie—the amount of heat required to raise the temperature of 1 gram of water by 1°C. The energy

equivalent of 1 calorie is 4.18 joules.

8. Matter is believed to consist of tiny particles in constant motion. The faster a particle moves, the greater the amount of kinetic energy the particle has. As heat is added to a body of matter, the particles of that body speed up. The temperature of a body of matter is a measure of the average kinetic energy of its particles.

9. There are two kinds of electric charge—positive and negative. Normally, every sample of matter has both kinds of charge and is electrically neutral. Objects that acquire an excess of one kind of charge or the other are said to be electrically charged. An electrostatic force always exists between two electrically charged bodies. The energy used to move charged bodies against an electrostatic force is converted to electrical energy.

10. A flow of charge through a conductor is called an electric current.

TERMS YOU SHOULD KNOW

energy	law of conservation of	temperature
potential energy	energy	calorimetry
kinetic energy	Celsius scale	calorimeter
joule	Kelvin scale	specific heat of water
combustion	absolute zero	electrostatic force
exothermic reaction	calorie	electric current
endothermic reaction	heat	electrical conductor
activation energy	kilocalorie	

REVIEW QUESTIONS

Section 4-2   **1.** Name the two classes of energy and briefly describe each class.

4-3   **2.** Name several different forms of energy.

4-4   **3.** What is the basic unit of energy in the international system?

4-5   **4.** Identify the class of energy (potential or kinetic) represented in each of the following examples: (a) water behind a dam (b) gunpowder in a rifle cartridge (c) a stretched rubber band (d) a speeding bullet (e) gasoline in the tank of an automobile (f) kerosene in the wick of a burning lamp.

4-6   **5.** Give a specific example of each of the following energy conversions:
(a) chemical to heat   (d) electrical to heat and light
(b) heat to mechanical   (e) electrical to mechanical
(c) mechanical to electrical (f) chemical to electrical

6. Many energy conversions take place in an automobile. For example, mechanical energy in an alternator is changed to electrical energy which is stored in the battery. Describe as many other energy conversions in an automobile as you can think of.

4-8   **7.** How does the size of one degree on the Kelvin scale compare with that of a degree on the Celsius scale?

4-9   **8.** Suppose you have two containers, A and B, each holding 100 mL of water. The water in container A is at 80°C; that in container B is at 40°C. If you were to pour the water from these two containers into a single container, C: (a) What would happen to the temperature of the water from container A? (b) What would happen to the temperature of the water from container B? (c) How would the temperature of the 200 mL of water in container C compare with that of the water in container A? In container B? (d) What would you expect the final temperature of the water in container C to be? Explain.

9. Name and define the basic unit chemists use to measure the quantity of heat. What is its equivalent in joules?

10. What are the three factors used in calculating heat transfer in a calorimeter?

4-10 11. What is the relationship between the temperature of an object and the average kinetic energy of its particles?

12. Explain the relationship between heat and temperature.

4-12 13. What happens when (a) two bodies with like electrical charge are brought together? (b) two bodies with opposite charge are brought together?

REVIEW PROBLEMS

Section 4-9 1. How much heat is required to raise the temperature of 250 g of water from 50°C to 75°C? (a) Set up the problem. (b) Find the numerical answer.

2. What is the energy requirement, in joules, of the heat required in example 1?

3. If 700 g of water at 90°C loses 3500 calories of heat, what will its final temperature be? (a) Set up the problem. (b) Find the numerical answer.

4. A quantity of water is heated from 10°C to 50°C. During the process, 12 000 calories of heat is added to the water. How many grams of water is heated? (a) Set up the problem (b) Find the numerical answer.

FOR FURTHER THOUGHT

4-5 1. Assume that plants absorb energy from sunlight and store it in the wood and other materials they make. If so, are these processes exothermic or endothermic? Explain your answer.

4-9 2. You are a nutritionist using a calorimeter to measure the energy content of a certain food. You measure out 10 grams of the food and place it in the reaction chamber. You also measure out 200 mL of water and pour it into the calorimeter. You seal everything properly, make the necessary temperature observations, and carry out the other steps of the investigation. After recording all your data, you realize you had neglected to weigh the water to determine its mass.

Is it necessary to start over and repeat the procedure? Explain.

UNIT 2

Phases of Matter

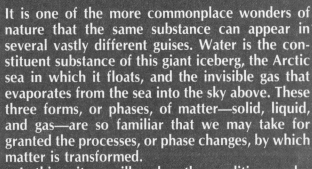

It is one of the more commonplace wonders of nature that the same substance can appear in several vastly different guises. Water is the constituent substance of this giant iceberg, the Arctic sea in which it floats, and the invisible gas that evaporates from the sea into the sky above. These three forms, or phases, of matter—solid, liquid, and gas—are so familiar that we may take for granted the processes, or phase changes, by which matter is transformed.

In this unit we will explore the conditions under which phase changes occur and we will examine the characteristics that distinguish each phase. Our investigations will provide some insight into the very nature of matter itself.

Phases of Matter—Gases

5-1   The Physical Phases

Substances may exist in the form of a solid, a liquid, or a gas. These forms of matter are called **physical phases**. (The term *state* is also used to refer to these forms of matter, but *phase* is the preferred term.)

In the **solid** phase, a sample of a substance is relatively rigid and has a definite volume and shape.

In the **liquid** phase, a substance has a definite volume, but it is able to change its shape by flowing. Under the action of gravity, a liquid will take the shape of a container and will come to rest with its upper surface horizontal.

In the **gaseous** phase, a substance has no definite volume or shape, and it shows very little response to gravity. If unconfined, it spreads out indefinitely. If confined in a closed container, it fills the container, but it will escape through any opening. (The force of gravity does have some effect on gases. The earth's atmosphere, which is a mixture of gases, is prevented from escaping to outer space by the earth's gravity. The pressure exerted by the atmosphere is the result of the weight of the gases and the kinetic energy of the gaseous particles.)

Questions for Section 5-1

1. In which physical phase does a substance have
   (a) no definite volume or shape?
   (b) a definite volume and shape?
   (c) a definite volume but no definite shape?
2. What causes atmospheric pressure?

Figure 5-1

The three phases (states) of matter.

When a solid has its position changed,
its volume and shape remain unchanged

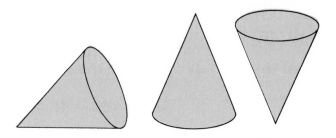

Same shape, same volume. Only position has changed.

A liquid can be poured from container to container,
changing its shape but not its volume.

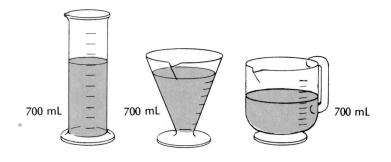

700 mL   700 mL   700 mL

Different shape, same volume.

A gas fills its container. A change in container can,
therefore, change both its shape and volume.

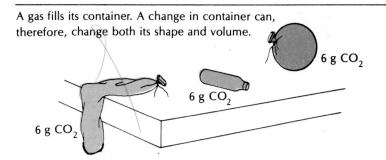

6 g CO_2

6 g CO_2

6 g CO_2

Different shape, different volume.

$$P = \frac{F}{A}$$

5-2   The Meaning of Pressure

Pressure is defined as force per unit of area. For example, suppose a
book with a weight of 20 newtons* and a back cover area of 500 cm² is
resting on a table. The force of 20 newtons is spread evenly over the

*1 pound equals 4.45 newtons   Chapter 5   Phases of Matter—Gases   **67**

Figure 5-2

(A) The 20-newton book when resting on its back exerts a pressure on the table of 20 newtons/500 cm² = 0.040 newton/cm². (B) Raised on its end, the book exerts a pressure of 20 newtons/100 cm² = 0.20 newton/cm². The pressure is greater when the book stands on end because the same force is exerted on a smaller area.

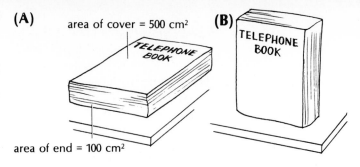

(A) area of cover = 500 cm² (B)

area of end = 100 cm²

area of 500 cm². The pressure exerted by the book on the table is

$$\text{pressure} = \frac{\text{force}}{\text{area}}$$

$$\text{pressure} = \frac{20 \text{ newtons}}{500 \text{ cm}^2} = 0.040 \text{ newton/cm}^2$$

This pressure is 0.040 newtons/cm², which means that 0.040 newtons is pushing down on each square centimeter of the table's surface lying under the book. If the same book is standing on end, and the area of the end is 100 cm², the pressure will be

$$\frac{20 \text{ newtons}}{100 \text{ cm}^2} = 0.20 \text{ newton/cm}^2$$

Thus we see that the same force applied to a smaller area results in a greater pressure.

5-3 Atmospheric Pressure

In the example in the last section, the weight of a book produced a pressure on a surface (the table top). A liquid in a container also produces pressure on the container because of the weight of the liquid. Pressure in a liquid increases with depth because of the increasing weight of the liquid above the point of pressure. Liquid pressure is exerted not only downward against the bottom of a container, but also against the sides. In fact, at any given depth in a liquid, pressure is exerted equally in all directions. Swimmers under water feel the increasing pressure of the water as they go deeper (Figs. 5-3, 5-4).

The atmosphere, which is a mixture of gases, also exerts pressure as a result of its weight. We may think of ourselves as living at the bottom of an "ocean" of air and subject to its pressure. This pressure is called **atmospheric pressure, air pressure,** or **barometric pressure.** Air pressure at sea level is approximately equal to the weight of a kilogram mass on every square centimeter of surface exposed to it. This weight is about 10 newtons. We are not conscious of air pressure because it is exerted in all directions, both inside and outside our body. However, the presence of this pressure can be shown in a simple way. If the air is pumped out of a thin-walled metal container, such as a gasoline can, the can will be crushed by the unbalanced pressure of the air outside. See Figure 5-6. To get some idea of the amount of force involved,

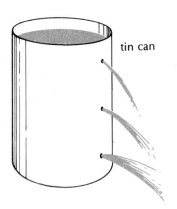

tin can

Figure 5-3

The pressure in a fluid (liquid or gas) is greater at greater depth, as shown in the drawing where the water spurts out of the bottom hole with the greatest pressure.

assume that one side of the can measures 30 cm × 15 cm. Its area is 450 cm². As previously stated, the air pressure is equivalent to a weight of 10 newtons on each square centimeter. Removing the air from inside the can therefore has the same effect as exerting a force of 4500 newtons on the side of the can. We would not expect the can to withstand such a load—and it doesn't.

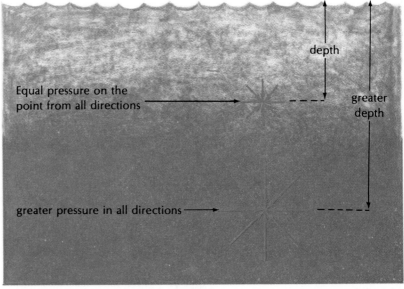

Figure 5-4

At a given point within a liquid, pressure is exerted equally in all directions. The pressure is greater at a greater depth.

depth

Equal pressure on the point from all directions

greater depth

greater pressure in all directions

Figure 5-5

Air pressure exerts a total force of about 4500 newtons on the side of a can whose surface area is 450 square centimeters. (Six average-sized men weigh about 4500 newtons.) This force is normally balanced by an equal force exerted by the air pressure inside the can.

Figure 5-5

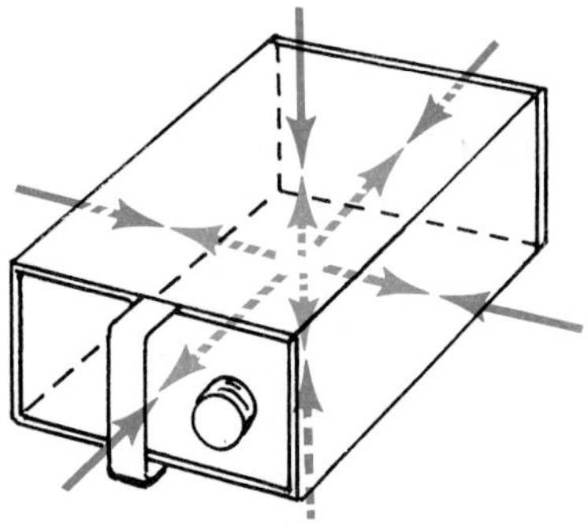

atmospheric pressure pushes inward in all directions

air pressure in the can pushes outward in all directions

Figure 5-6

If the air is pumped out of the can, it is easily crushed by the tremendous force of the unbalanced atmospheric pressure.

Figure 5-6

4500 newtons total unbalanced force on top of can alone

to vacuum pump

5-4   Measuring Air Pressure

The instrument most often used for accurate measurements of air pressure is the **mercury barometer.** See Figure 5-7. This instrument

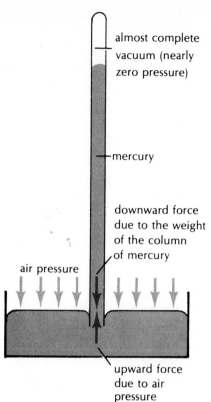

almost complete vacuum (nearly zero pressure)

mercury

downward force due to the weight of the column of mercury

air pressure

upward force due to air pressure

Figure 5-7

Principle of the mercury barometer. The height of the column of mercury depends only on the air pressure and is therefore a measure of the air pressure.

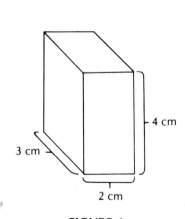

4 cm

3 cm

2 cm

FIGURE A
(for Question 3)

consists of a glass tube that is sealed at one end, and that contains a column of mercury. The open end of the tube is immersed in a container of mercury. The space in the tube above the column of mercury is nearly a perfect vacuum. It contains a very small amount of mercury vapor, but no air. There is therefore almost no pressure in the space above the mercury column. You might expect the mercury to fall out of the tube into the container of mercury. It does not fall because it is held up by the pressure of the atmosphere on the surface of the mercury in the container. When this air pressure becomes greater, more mercury is pushed up into the tube, and the column of mercury becomes longer. When the air pressure becomes smaller, some of the mercury in the tube falls out of the tube into the container, making the column of mercury shorter. Mercury stops flowing out of the column when a balance is achieved again, that is, when the air pressure and the pressure exerted by the column of mercury are once again the same. The height of the mercury can thus be used as a measure of the atmospheric pressure.

The pressure of the atmosphere varies with altitude. It decreases at higher altitudes, since the weight of the overlying atmosphere is less. Air pressure also varies somewhat with weather conditions. Shortly before it rains or snows there is usually a drop in atmospheric pressure. On the average, however, the air pressure at sea level can support a column of mercury 760 mm in height. This average, sea-level air pressure is called **normal atmospheric pressure** or normal air pressure. Thus, normal atmospheric pressure is the pressure that will support a column of mercury 760 mm long. A pressure of 760 mm of mercury (abbreviated 760 mm Hg) is also called **one atmosphere.** Twice as great a pressure would be two atmospheres, etc. Normal atmospheric pressure has been adopted as **standard pressure.** The purpose of establishing a standard pressure will become clear as we go on.

Technically, the unit of pressure in the metric system is the **pascal,** which is defined as a pressure of 1 newton per square meter. (The newton is a unit of force that equals about one-tenth the weight of a kilogram.) Since one pascal is a very small pressure, the unit used most often is the *kilopascal* (abbreviated *kPa*), equal to 1000 pascals. Standard atmospheric pressure is about 100 kPa. However, because of the convenience of measuring gas pressures directly in millimeters of mercury, this is the unit that is still most often used. A pressure of 1 mm of mercury is also called one **torr.**

Questions for Sections 5-2 through 5-4

*3. Figure A shows a block of wood, whose weight is 18 newtons, resting on a table top. How much pressure is the block of wood exerting on the surface of the table directly beneath it?
4. What is the relationship between depth in a liquid and pressure exerted by the liquid?
5. What is the scientific definition of pressure?

5-5   Gas Pressure

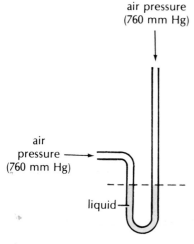

air pressure
(760 mm Hg)

air pressure → (760 mm Hg)

liquid

Figure 5-8

With both sides of the U-tube open to the air, the height of the liquid in both arms is the same.

Figure 5-9

U-tube manometer connected to a container of gas. The mercury will go down on the left if the pressure exerted by the gas in the container is greater than atmospheric pressure. The gas in the container is exerting a pressure of 760 mm Hg + 40 mm Hg = 800 mm Hg.

Figure 5-10

The mercury will go down on the right if the atmospheric pressure is greater than the pressure exerted by the gas in the container. The gas in the container is exerting a pressure of 760 mm Hg − 40 mm Hg = 720 mm Hg.

Any gas confined in a container is found to exert pressure on the walls of the container. The amount of this pressure can be measured with a device called a **manometer.** A manometer is basically a U-tube containing mercury, or some other liquid. When both ends of the U-tube are open to the air, the levels of the liquid on both sides of the U will be the same. See Figure 5-8. This happens because the same pressure is pushing down on both sides of the U. This pressure is simply the pressure exerted by the air (atmospheric pressure). Now suppose that one end of the tube is connected to a container of gas, and the valve is opened. The liquid level will go down on the left (and up on the right) if the pressure exerted by the gas in the container is *greater* than atmospheric pressure. See Figure 5-9. The liquid will rise on the right until the difference in height of the two levels corresponds to the difference in pressure. If the liquid is mercury, the difference in pressure can be measured directly in millimeters of mercury. The actual gas pressure can be found by adding the atmospheric pressure to the pressure difference. Therefore, the pressure exerted by the gas in Figure 5-9 is 760 mm Hg + 40 mm Hg = 800 mm Hg.

Next, suppose that the atmospheric pressure is greater than the pressure of the gas in the container. Then the liquid will go down on the right (and up on the left). See Figure 5-10. If the liquid is mercury, it

Figure 5-9   **Figure 5-10**

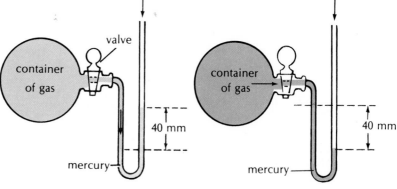

air pressure = 760 mm Hg

air pressure = 760 mm Hg

valve

container of gas

40 mm

mercury

container of gas

40 mm

mercury

stops moving when the difference in heights of the levels of mercury in the two arms of the U-tube is equal to the difference in pressure between atmospheric pressure and the pressure of the gas in the container. The actual gas pressure can be found by subtracting the pressure difference from the atmospheric pressure (as read from a barometer). The gas in Figure 5-10 is exerting a pressure of 760 mm Hg − 40 mm Hg = 720 mm Hg.

The pressure of a confined gas depends upon many factors and can vary greatly. In the early period of modern science, many investigators studied the changes in gas pressure brought about by different conditions. These investigations provide good examples of the importance of measurement in arriving at useful observations. The combined results of these investigations led to the modern theory of the nature and properties of gases. The experimental results of these investigations is the subject of our next chapter.

Questions for Section 5-5

*11. An open-end manometer, shown in Figure B, is attached to a container of gas which is exerting a pressure of 785 mm Hg. The atmospheric pressure (as read on a barometer) is 750 mm Hg. (a) When the valve is opened, will the mercury in the open-end arm of the U-tube move up or down? (b) After the mercury in the U-tube stops moving, what will be the difference in height of the mercury levels in the two arms of the tube?

12. A container of gas is hooked up to an open-end manometer, as shown in Figure C. What pressure is the gas in the container exerting?

13. A container of gas is hooked up to an open-end manometer, as shown in Figure D. What pressure is the gas in the container exerting?

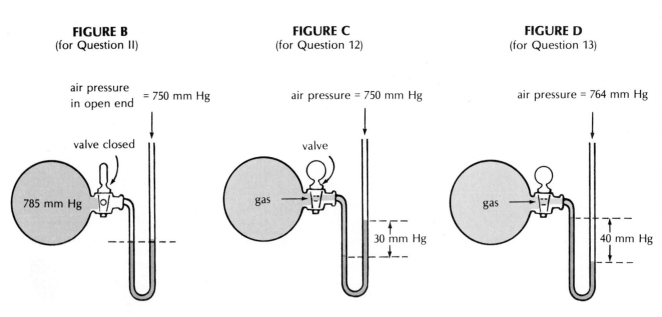

FIGURE B
(for Question II)

air pressure in open end = 750 mm Hg

valve closed

785 mm Hg

FIGURE C
(for Question 12)

air pressure = 750 mm Hg

valve

gas

30 mm Hg

FIGURE D
(for Question 13)

air pressure = 764 mm Hg

gas

40 mm Hg

5-6 Boiling and Melting

You may have been told that water boils at 100°C or 212°F. Perhaps you know that this statement is not complete. Water can boil at other temperatures, too, depending upon the pressure. High in the mountains, where the air pressure is less than at sea level, water boils at a lower temperature. In a pressure cooker, water boils at a higher temperature. Pressure affects the boiling points of all liquids, not just water. It also has a very slight effect on the melting points of substances. However, at a particular pressure, there is only one temperature at which a given substance will boil and only one temperature at which it will melt. The **boiling point** is defined as the temperature at which a substance changes phase between liquid and gas at a particular pressure. To be precise we must be careful to tell the air pressure when we state the melting or boiling point of a substance. For example, we should say that the boiling point of water is 101°C at *788 mm.* In other words, when the air pressure is 788 mm of mercury, water will boil at 101°C. The boiling point of a substance at normal air pressure is called the **normal boiling point.** (Recall that normal air pressure, 760 mm Hg, is also called standard pressure.) The normal boiling point of water is 100°C.

When a substance melts, it passes from the solid phase to the liquid phase. When it freezes, the reverse takes place. The substance passes from liquid to solid. Both these changes take place at the same temperature. Therefore, the **melting point** and **freezing point** of a substance are the same temperature. These points are defined as the temperature at which a substance makes a phase change (in either direction) between the liquid and solid phases. The **normal melting point** is the temperature at which a substance melts at normal air pressure. The normal melting point of water is 0°C.

When the "boiling point" or "melting point" of a substance is re-

Water boils at about 90°C at an altitude of 3000 meters above sea level.

Figure 5-11

Sugar gradually turns brown when it is slowly heated (left photo), rather than melting at one particular temperature. With continued heating, the sugar turns into pure carbon as water vapor escapes from the tube (right photo). In this case, applying heat causes a chemical change (decomposition of the sugar) rather than a physical change.

Figure 5-12

As glass is heated, it at first gets soft. When hot enough it can be pulled into a thin "thread." Because there is no temperature at which it turns into a liquid, it is not considered a true solid.

ferred to, we understand this to mean the *normal* boiling point or *normal* melting point unless a pressure is stated at the same time.

There are a few substances that have no melting point or boiling point. Instead of melting or boiling, these substances change into other substances when heated. The heat causes a chemical reaction that makes the substances break down and decompose. Sugar, for example, cannot be melted. When heated, it turns into water and carbon.

In order for a substance to be classified as a solid, it must have a precise temperature at which it melts. By this test, there are a few "solid" substances that are not true solids. Glass is one such substance. As the temperature of glass is raised, glass becomes softer and softer. During this softening period, there is no temperature at which glass melts and becomes a liquid. Glass is therefore considered to be a liquid with a very high **viscosity** (vis-KAHS-uh-tee) (resistance to flow) at room temperature. A more precise definition of the solid phase in relation to crystal structure will be developed in Chapter 7.

Questions for Section 5-6

14. Someone makes the statement: "Water boils at 96°C." What is wrong with this statement?
15. What is the normal boiling point of water?
16. What do we call the temperature at which a substance changes phase from   (a) a solid to a liquid?   (b) a liquid to a solid?
17. What property must a substance have in order to be classified as a true solid?
18. What does the phrase "slow as cold molasses" indicate about this sugary substance?

5-7   Theory of Physical Phase

It is well known that different substances may be in different phases under the same conditions. At room temperature, sodium chloride (common salt) is a solid, water is a liquid, and oxygen is a gas. These substances also change phase at widely different temperatures. The reasons for these different properties are related to the forces that exist between the particles of the substances.

As stated in Chapter 4, the particles of every substance at a given temperature have the same average kinetic energy of random motion. As the particles move, they tend to collide and rebound. As they rebound from the collisions, forces of attraction between the particles tend to slow them down and pull them back again. In a solid, these forces are relatively large. The particles never get very far away from their average position in the material. They merely vibrate around these fixed locations.

In liquids, the forces of attraction are relatively weaker. The particles are able to leave their original positions and move to other locations in the material. But most of them remain within the limits of the material. Some near the surface, with the highest energies, do escape through the surface and enter the gaseous phase. The air always contains some water in the gaseous phase. This gaseous water is called **water vapor.** The amount of water vapor in the air determines the humidity. Steam is water vapor that is at or above the boiling point of water. The process by which liquid water enters the gaseous phase is called **evaporation.**

In gases, the attractive forces between particles are too weak to keep the particles within a definite space. After each collision, the particles tend to rebound and separate indefinitely. That is why a gas always fills its container.

We can now understand to some extent why substances change phase when their temperature changes. For example, as a solid is heated, the particles acquire greater average kinetic energy. They vibrate farther and farther from their central positions. Finally they have enough energy on the average to break out of the fixed pattern of the solid phase and enter the liquid phase. The reverse takes place as a liquid is cooled.

The situation with regard to changes between the liquid and gaseous phase is more complicated. As explained earlier, some particles of a liquid escape to the gaseous phase through the liquid surface at any temperature. However, there is a temperature at which the particles

Figure 5-13

Particles of matter in the three phases. (A) In solids, the particles vibrate around fixed positions. (B) In liquids, the particles move quite freely throughout the material. Some particles near the surface escape and enter the gaseous phase. (C) In gases, the particles move about freely. The container must be closed to prevent the particles from escaping.

(A) **(B)** **(C)**

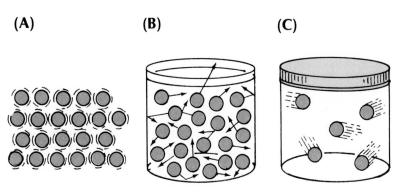

acquire enough energy to form bubbles of gas inside the liquid. This temperature is the boiling point of the liquid. The reverse process takes place as a gas is cooled from above the boiling point. When the temperature drops to the liquid's boiling point, the gas changes directly to droplets of liquid. This process is called **condensation.** Like evaporation, condensation can also occur at temperatures below the boiling point.

5-8   Temperature and Phase Change

In Section 4-10 we noted that when a sample of matter is heated, its temperature usually increases. We explained this observation in terms

Modern Instruments
of Analysis

The photo shows a gas chromatograph. Instruments of this type were used at the 1984 Olympic Games in Los Angeles, California, to analyze urine samples of the athletes. The purpose of these analyses was to determine if any of the athletes were taking illegal drugs.

Urine is an extremely complex mixture of many substances. Before the substances in the urine can be identified, they must be separated from one another. The gas chromatograph provides a fast, economical way to separate such mixtures into their component parts. Once the mixture has been separated, another instrument, the mass spectrometer, is used to identify the substances. Now analyses can be performed in only a small fraction of the time that was necessary before these modern instruments existed. As time has passed, chemists have been making greater and greater use of sophisticated analytical instruments.

of the kinetic energy of the particles of the body. As heat energy enters a body, the kinetic energy of its particles increases. This corresponds to an increase in its temperature. However, we also stated that at certain times a body may gain or lose heat energy *without* changing temperature.

Let us look at an example of this phenomenon. We have a container with 600 grams of ice in it. The temperature of the ice when we start is $-20°C$. The container sits on a hotplate that provides heat at an even rate. We read the temperature of the ice every minute. We observe that its temperature is increasing by about 10°C each minute. See Figure 5-14 (A). We can use the formula discussed in Section 4-9 to calculate the heat being absorbed by the ice each minute. It takes about 0.5 calories of heat to increase the temperature of 1 gram of ice by 1°C. (Recall that for water it takes 1 calorie.) Therefore, the constant in the formula is 0.5 cal/g-°C. This constant is, of course, the specific heat of ice.

$$\begin{array}{l}\text{heat absorbed by ice} \\ \text{each minute}\end{array} = (\text{mass of ice}) \times \left(\begin{array}{c}\text{temp.} \\ \text{change}\end{array}\right) \times \left(\begin{array}{c}\text{specific} \\ \text{heat of ice}\end{array}\right)$$

$$= 600 \text{ grams} \times 10°C \times 0.5 \; \frac{\text{calories}}{\text{gram-}°C}$$

$$= 3000 \text{ calories}$$

Rounding the answer to one significant figure, the answer is 3×10^3 calories. The ice is absorbing heat at the rate of 3×10^3 calories per minute.

When the temperature of the ice reaches 0°C, the temperature stops rising even though the heat is still turned on! We notice that the container no longer has only ice in it. It now contains ice with a small amount of water. We continue to take temperature readings every minute for about a quarter of an hour longer. All this time the heater is turned on. We assume that it is still supplying 3×10^3 calories of heat to the beaker each minute. We notice that while the ice continues to melt, the temperature remains constant at 0°C. See Figure 5-14 (B).

If the temperature remains constant, then none of the heat being supplied to the beaker is being used to increase the speed of the randomly moving particles in the ice-water mixture. What is happening to this heat? It cannot simply disappear. We conclude that heat is needed to change ice at 0°C to water at that same temperature. The heat is causing the particles in the ice to rearrange themselves into the positions they have in the liquid phase. Here we have an instance where heat is not causing an increase in temperature. Instead, the heat is being converted into another form of energy. The arrangement of liquid water particles at 0°C is one of greater potential energy than the arrangement of these same particles in ice at the same temperature. The heat energy supplied by the hot plate is being converted into potential energy. The water from the melting ice is storing energy. We will see later that this stored energy can be gotten back.

Figure 5-14

Heating ice on a hot plate. (A) After 2 minutes of heating, the temperature of the ice goes from −20°C to 0°C. (B) Once the ice starts to melt, the temperature no longer rises even though the hot plate continues to supply heat. (C) Once all the ice has melted, the temperature again rises as the water heats up. (D) The temperature of the water stops rising once the water starts to boil even though the hot plate continues to supply heat at a constant rate. Curves such as that shown here are called heating curves.

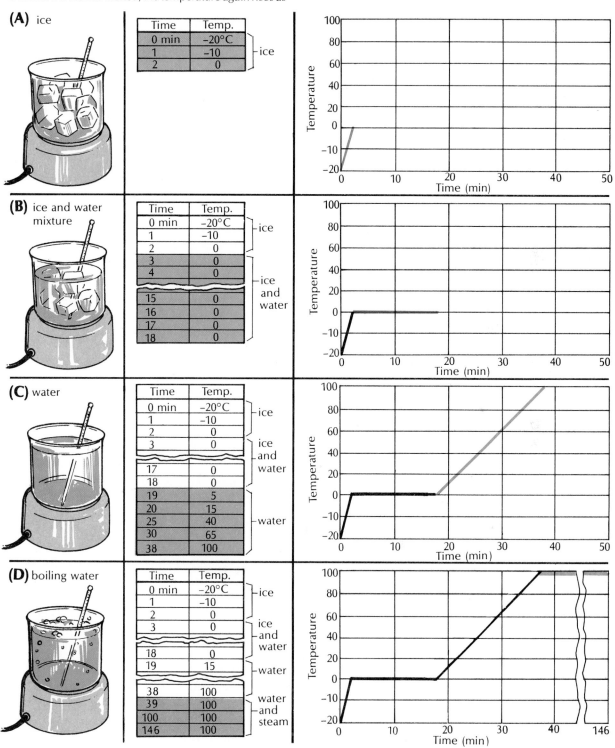

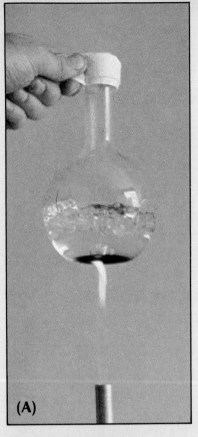

(A)

(B)

After all the ice is melted, the temperature begins to rise again. See Figure 5-14 (C). This rise in temperature continues until the water reaches 100°C. At this temperature the water begins to boil. With the hotplate still supplying 3 x 10³ calories per minute, the water will finally all boil away. Throughout the entire time that the water is boiling, the temperature remains constant at 100°C. See Figure 5-14 (D). The boiling of water evidently is another instance when supplying heat does not cause an increase in temperature. We conclude that heat is needed to change liquid water at 100°C into gaseous water (steam) at that same temperature. The heat is causing the particles to break up their arrangement in the liquid water and become the freely moving particles of the gaseous phase. The particles in steam at 100°C have greater potential energy than they have in the liquid phase at the same temperature. During boiling, heat energy is converted into potential energy. The steam is storing energy. This stored energy can be gotten back from the steam. If we allow the steam to condense back to liquid water, we find that it gives off a very large amount of heat while doing so. While it gives off this heat, its temperature again remains constant at 100°C. The large amount of heat given off by steam when it condenses explains why a steam burn can be much more serious than one caused by hot water at the same temperature.

The potential energy stored in water can also be recovered. As water hardens into ice, it gives off heat to its surroundings. In the freezing compartment of a refrigerator, the cooling coils carry off this heat.

When other substances are melted or boiled, they behave the same way that water does. While melting or boiling, they absorb heat with no change in temperature. The absorbed heat is converted into potential energy as the particles of the substance rearrange themselves. A temperature-time graph that describes this behavior, such as that shown in Figure 5-14, page 77, is called a heating curve.

Questions for Sections 5-7 and 5-8

19. How does the average kinetic energy of the particles of a solid compare with the average kinetic energy of the particles of a liquid at the same temperature?

CAN YOU EXPLAIN THIS?

Photo A shows a flask of boiling water. The flask was removed from the heat, and the boiling stopped. A rubber stopper was placed into the neck of the flask to form an airtight seal. In Photo B, the flask has been turned upside down, and ice water is being poured over the flask. This action caused the water to boil again.

1. As ice water is poured over the flask, what happens to the temperature of the water inside the flask?
2. Why does the water inside the flask boil when ice water is poured over it?

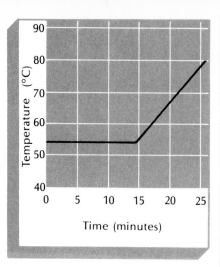

FIGURE E

20. How does the force of attraction between particles of a solid compare with that between particles of a liquid at the same temperature?
21. What do we call the process by which (a) a liquid changes to a gas? (b) a gas changes to a liquid?
22. What effect does adding heat to ice at its melting point have on the temperature of the ice?
23. What effect does adding heat to water at 100°C have on the water?
24. A student finds a beaker containing paradichlorobenzene. Some of the paradichlorobenzene is in the solid phase and the rest of it is in the liquid phase. The student heats the beaker on a hotplate and makes a graph showing the temperature of the paradichlorobenzene over a period of time. Use this graph, shown in Figure E, to answer the following questions. (a) Can you tell from the graph what is the melting point of paradichlorobenzene? If so, what is it? (b) Can you tell from the graph what is the boiling point of paradichloro-benzene? If so, what is it? (c) After 20 minutes of heating, in what phase or phases is the paradichlorobenzene?

CHAPTER SUMMARY

1. The physical phases in which matter may exist are solid, liquid, and gas.
2. Pressure is defined as force per unit area. Atmospheric pressure is caused by the weight of the earth's atmosphere.
3. Any gas confined in a container will exert pressure on the walls of the container. This pressure can be measured by an instrument called a manometer.
4. The boiling point of a substance is the temperature at which the substance changes phase between liquid and gas at a particular pressure.
5. The melting (or freezing) point is the temperature at which a substance changes phase between liquid and solid at a particular pressure. Normal boiling and melting points are the temperatures at which the indicated phase changes occur at a pressure of one atmosphere.
6. Evaporation is the process by which a liquid enters the gaseous phase. Condensation is the process by which a gas enters the liquid phase.
7. The temperature of a substance undergoing a phase change remains constant until the change is complete, even though the substance is absorbing or releasing heat at a constant rate.
8. Phase changes involve a rearrangement of particles into positions of greater (or smaller) potential energy. During these rearrangements, heat energy is converted to potential energy, or vice versa.

TERMS YOU SHOULD KNOW

phase	mercury barometer	boiling point
solid	normal atmospheric	normal boiling point
liquid	pressure	melting point
gas	one atmosphere	freezing point
pressure	standard pressure	normal melting point
atmospheric pressure	pascal	viscosity
air pressure	torr	water vapor
barometric pressure	manometer	evaporation
		condensation

Chapter 5   Phases of Matter—Gases   **79**

Section   5-1   **1.** Describe the characteristics of a substance in each of the three physical phases.

            2. What prevents the gases of the earth's atmosphere from escaping into outer space?

      5-2   **3.** Define pressure.

      5-4   **4.** What instrument is commonly used to measure atmospheric pressure? Describe how this instrument works.

            5. What is the relationship between atmospheric pressure and altitude?

            6. (a) What is meant by standard pressure? (b) Express standard pressure in units of (1) millimeters of mercury (2) kilopascals (3) torr

      5-5   **7.** An open-end manometer is connected to a container of gas. When the valve is opened, the mercury rises in the open-end arm of the U-tube and goes down in the arm connected to the container of gas. When the mercury stops moving, the difference in the mercury levels is 25 mm. The barometer shows that atmospheric pressure is 755 mm Hg. How much pressure does the confined gas exert?

      5-6   **8.** (a) What is the relationship between pressure and the temperature at which a substance will boil? (b) Define normal boiling point.

            9. What is the melting point of sugar?

           10. Explain why glass is not considered to be a true solid.

      5-7   **11.** Describe the motion of the particles of a substance in the solid phase.

           12. How do the forces of attraction between particles of a liquid compare with those forces between particles of a gas?

           13. Define evaporation.

           14. Describe the process by which a substance changes from the solid phase to the liquid phase. What is this process called?

           15. What is the relationship of steam to water vapor?

      5-8   **16.** Describe what happens when heat is added to a substance in the solid phase when the temperature of the substance is (a) below its melting point (b) at its melting point

           17. Explain why steam at 100°C can produce a more severe burn than an equal mass of water at the same temperature.

FOR FURTHER THOUGHT

      5-1   **1.** In discussing liquids and gases, the term *bubble* occurs often. You probably have a clear idea of what a bubble is. Or do you? Write a description or definition of a bubble.

      5-7   **2.** A can of cold soda is poured into a glass. After a short time, droplets of water are observed running down the outside of the glass.

              (a) What is wrong with the above statement?

              (b) Which of the following are likely to be related to the observed effect? State reasons for your answers.

                 (1) the temperature of the soda   (4) the thickness of the glass

                 (2) the kind of soda   (5) the air temperature

                 (3) the color of the glass   (6) the humidity of the air

The Gas Laws and Kinetic Theory

Objectives

After you have completed this chapter, you will be able to:
- Solve problems that involve the gas laws.
- Show how the absolute temperature scale is derived.
- Use the kinetic theory to provide a logical basis for the gas laws.
- Explain the origin of the concept of the mole.

6-1 Introduction

Scientists who studied gases in the 1600's, 1700's, and 1800's were each able to describe a limited amount of their subject. The description provided by each scientist was a statement of fact based on experimental observations. These facts did not at first seem related. After many observations were on record, some scientists began to realize that all these observations could be explained if certain assumptions were made about the nature of gases. These assumptions formed the basis of a unifying theory.

In this chapter we discuss the work of Boyle, Charles, Dalton, and Graham. Each of these scientists experimented with gases, and each described a different aspect of the behavior of gases. The unifying theory that ties together the work of these scientists and that explains why gases behave as they do is called the kinetic theory of gases. These topics are the subject of this chapter.

Figure 6-1

Robert Boyle (1627-1691) discovered the relationship that exists between the pressure exerted by a gas and the volume occupied by the gas.

6-2 The Relationship Between Pressure and Volume of a Gas

If a fixed mass of a gas is confined in a container, and its volume is changed, its pressure also changes. You may have tried squeezing a balloon that has air tied in it. When you do this, you can feel the resistance of the air to being squeezed into a smaller volume. This means that the pressure of the air inside the balloon increases as its volume is made smaller.

Figure 6-2

The harder you push in on a balloon, the harder it pushes back. As you decrease the volume of a confined gas, its pressure increases.

Figure 6-3 shows an apparatus that can be used to investigate the relationship between the pressure and volume of a gas. The apparatus consists of a cylinder with a piston that forms a tight seal with the walls of the cylinder, so that none of the gas trapped in the cylinder can escape around the piston. At the bottom of the cylinder is an outlet tube with a stopcock. The stopcock can be turned to a closed position, so that no more gas can then enter or leave the cylinder. Gas can be introduced into the cylinder by hooking up the gas storage bottle, which holds gas under pressure. When the stopcock is open, a small sample of gas can be introduced into the cylinder by momentarily opening the control valve on the storage bottle. As gas enters the cylinder, the piston rises to make room for it. When the stopcock is turned to the closed position, the cylinder then has a sample of gas trapped in it.

When the volume of a gas remains constant, then the pressure the gas exerts on its container is the same as the pressure the container exerts on the gas.

Figure 6-3 shows the apparatus when there is 1.0 atmosphere of pressure pushing down on the gas in the cylinder. (The gas, of course, pushes back with the same pressure.) In this example, when the pressure is 1 atmosphere, the volume occupied by the gas is 2.0 liters. Figure 6-4 shows what happens to the volume of the gas sample when the downward pressure is doubled to 2.0 atmospheres. The volume becomes smaller. To be more precise, the volume becomes half as much (provided the temperature has remained constant throughout).

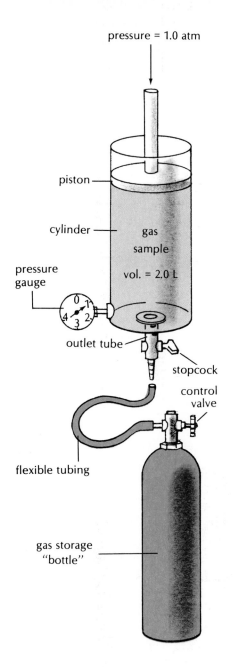

pressure = 1.0 atm

piston

cylinder

gas sample

vol. = 2.0 L

pressure gauge

outlet tube

stopcock

control valve

flexible tubing

gas storage "bottle"

Figure 6-3

Gas was introduced into the cylinder by connecting the flexible tubing to the outlet tube and momentarily opening the control valve on the gas storage bottle.

Figure 6-4

The same apparatus as shown in the previous illustration. When the pressure pushing down on the gas is increased, the volume occupied by the gas becomes smaller.

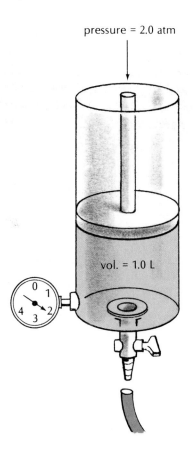

pressure = 2.0 atm

vol. = 1.0 L

To develop a good understanding of the relationship between the pressure and volume of a gas at constant temperature, a number of different pressures can be applied to the gas. Figure 6-5 gives the data obtained from an experiment of this sort. When scientists have obtained data from an experiment, they look carefully to see if the figures show any regularity or pattern. Can you see any pattern to the numbers in Figure 6-5?

Figure 6-5

Applying different pressures to a sample of gas at constant temperature.

Trial	Pressure	Volume
1	1.0 atm	2.0 liters
2	2.0	1.0
3	3.0	.67
4	4.0	.50

Look at Trials 1 and 2. When the pressure doubles (goes from 1.0 atm to 2.0 atm), the volume halves (goes from 2.0 liters to 1.0 liter). The same kind of change is shown by the data from Trials 2 and 4. When the pressure doubles (goes from 2.0 atm to 4.0 atm), the volume halves (goes from 1.0 liter to 0.50 liter). Trials 1 and 3 show that tripling the pressure (from 1.0 atm to 3.0 atm) causes the volume to become ⅓ as much (goes from 2.0 liters to 0.67 liter). Trials 1 and 4 show that quadrupling the pressure (from 1.0 atm to 4.0 atm) causes the volume to become ¼ as much (goes from 2.0 liters to 0.50 liter). We summarize these changes below:

Pressure Change	Volume Change
Increase by a factor of $\frac{2}{1}$	Decrease by a factor of $\frac{1}{2}$
Increase by a factor of $\frac{3}{1}$	Decrease by a factor of $\frac{1}{3}$
Increase by a factor of $\frac{4}{1}$	Decrease by a factor of $\frac{1}{4}$

A relationship of the kind described above is called an inverse relationship. ($\frac{1}{2}$ is the inverse of $\frac{2}{1}$; $\frac{1}{3}$ is the inverse of $\frac{3}{1}$; and $\frac{1}{4}$ is the inverse of $\frac{4}{1}$.) We say that the pressure and volume of a gas are inversely proportional or indirectly proportional (when the temperature remains constant).

You may have noticed another pattern or regularity in the data of Figure 6-5. When the pressure and volume for a particular experiment are multiplied together, the same product is obtained for all four trials. In other words, the product of pressure and volume is constant. See Figure 6-6.

Figure 6-6

The pressure for a particular experiment multiplied by the volume for that same experiment gives a product that is the same for all experiments.

Trial	Pressure	Volume	Pressure x Volume
1	1.0 atm	2.0 liters	2.0 atm-liters
2	2.0	1.0	2.0
3	3.0	0.67	2.0
4	4.0	0.50	2.0

We can sum up the last column of Figure 6-6 by writing:

$$P_1V_1 = P_2V_2 = P_3V_3 = P_4V_4 = 2.0 \text{ atm-liters}$$

where P_1V_1 refers to the pressure and volume for Trial 1, P_2V_2 refers to those for Trial 2, etc.

We can also write that:

$$PV = K \qquad \textbf{(Eq. 1)}$$

(at constant temperature)

Equation 1 says that the product of the pressure and volume of a sample of gas at constant temperature is a constant. The value of the constant is 2.0 atm-liters for the sample of gas yielding the experimental measurements in Figure 6-6.

A constant (often represented by the symbol K or k) is a number that does not change when other quantities in a formula change. In the formula $PV = K$, K is a constant only for a particular mass of a particular gas at a particular temperature. The value of K will change if a larger or smaller mass of gas is used for the sample, or if the temperature is changed to a new value, or if another kind of gas is used for the sample.

Questions for Section 6-2

1. Suppose that two quantities, A and B, are related to each other by inverse proportion. If the value of A becomes five times as great, what will happen to the value of B?
2. What regularity exists between two variables that are inversely proportional to each other?
3. Give the inverse of (a) 7 (b) $\frac{1}{3}$ (c) 0.28
4. Two quantities, A and B, are inversely proportional to each other. Write an equation describing their relationship.
5. The pressure exerted by a sample of gas is 2.0 atmospheres while its volume is 100 mL. Write the equation expressing the relationship between the pressure and the volume of this sample when the temperature is held constant.
6. In the equation

$$PV = K$$

under what circumstances will the value of the constant, K, change?

6-3 Boyle's Law

Robert Boyle, an Irish scientist, is credited with being the first scientist to understand the relationship between the pressure and the volume of a gas. In 1662, based on data from his experiments on gases, Boyle reported the relationship now called Boyle's law. **Boyle's law** states that the volume of a sample of gas is inversely proportional to the pressure, if the temperature is kept constant. This inverse relationship is expressed by the equation

$$PV = K \qquad \text{(Eq. 2)}$$

(at constant temperature)

A useful equation can be derived from Equation 2. Suppose we let P_1 and V_1 represent the pressure and volume of a sample of gas at one particular time. Now, suppose that the pressure is changed to a new pressure, P_2, causing the volume to change to a new volume, V_2. Then, Equation 2 can be applied to both pairs of pressure and volume:

$$P_1 V_1 = K \qquad \text{(Eq. 3)}$$

$$P_2 V_2 = K \qquad \text{(Eq. 4)}$$

Since the K in Equations 3 and 4 is the same number, the left-hand sides of Equations 3 and 4 can be set equal to each other:

$$P_1 V_1 = P_2 V_2 \qquad \text{(Eq. 5)}$$

Equation 5 enables us to find any one of the four quantities (P_1, V_1, P_2, V_2) if we know the other three. It is not necessary to know the value of K. For example, Equation 5 can be solved for the new volume, V_2:

$$V_2 = V_1 \times \frac{P_1}{P_2} \qquad \text{(Eq. 6)}$$

(at constant temp.)

Equation 6 allows us to calculate the new volume (V_2) when we know the old volume (V_1) and the new and old pressures (P_2 and P_1).

Similarly, we can solve Equation 5 for the new pressure if we know the new and old volumes and the old pressure:

$$P_2 = P_1 \times \frac{V_1}{V_2} \qquad \text{(Eq. 7)}$$

(at constant temp.)

SAMPLE PROBLEM

A sample of gas under a pressure of 720 mm Hg has a volume of 300 mL. The pressure is increased to 800 mm Hg. What volume will the gas then occupy, assuming that the temperature is constant throughout?

Solution 1

Step 1. Write the mathematical relationship that applies to this problem. The problem is concerned with gas pressures and gas volumes. The relationship between gas pressures and gas volumes is given by Boyle's law:

$$P_1V_1 = P_2V_2$$

Step 2. Write the known values of P and V and indicate which one of the four quantities is unknown:

$P_1 = 720$ mm Hg $V_1 = 300$ mL $P_2 = 800$ mm Hg $V_2 = ?$ mL

Step 3. Substitute the numbers into the formula and solve for the unknown:

$$P_1V_1 = P_2V_2$$

$$(720 \text{ mm Hg}) (300 \text{ mL}) = (800 \text{ mm Hg}) \ V_2$$

$$V_2 = \frac{(720 \text{ mm Hg})(300 \text{ mL})}{(800 \text{ mm Hg})}$$

The above expression for V_2 shows what numbers must be used in making the calculation. The expression also tells what must be done to those numbers (add, subtract, multiply, divide) in order to arrive at the answer. Writing such an expression is called "setting up" a problem. (Setting up problems was discussed briefly in Section 2-3.) Setting up a chemical problem correctly requires a good understanding of the chemical principles that apply to the problem. Once a problem has been

CHEMISTRY IN ACTION

Weed and Insect Killers

The photo shows a field worker testing the water in a stream that had become overrun with aquatic weeds before the stream was treated with a weed-killing chemical. Weed killers are important chemicals for keeping canals and irrigation ditches free of plant growth that can impede the flow of water.

Herbicides and insecticides must be carefully tested before they are used on a large scale, for these chemicals are a two-edged sword. The dual nature of these chemicals was dramatized in the late 1950's and early 1960's when it was learned that the insecticide DDT was being absorbed into the body tissues of people who ate animals and plants that had come into contact with DDT. Since 1972, very little DDT has been used in the United States.

correctly set up, anyone who can do arithmetic or use a calculator can find the correct answer to the problem even though the person making the calculation knows nothing about chemistry. In setting up problems, it is a good idea to write all numbers with their proper units. Check to see that the answer will come out in the right units. If it doesn't, there is something wrong with the way the problem is set up.

To go back to our problem, the correct setup for the problem is

$$V_2 = \frac{(720 \text{ mm Hg}) (300 \text{ mL})}{(800 \text{ mm Hg})}$$

Note that the units "mm Hg" will cancel out, leaving only mL, which is the right unit for a volume. The correct answer is 270 mL:

$$V_2 = \frac{(720 \text{ mm Hg}) (300 \text{ mL})}{(800 \text{ mm Hg})} = 270 \text{ mL}$$

As a final check, we see if our answer is reasonable. When the pressure increases from 720 mm Hg to 800 mm Hg, we expect that the increased pressure will compress the gas. That is, we expect the volume to decrease. Since the change from 720 mm Hg to 800 mm Hg is relatively small, we expect the decrease to be relatively small. Our answer, 270 mL, does show a relatively small decrease from the starting volume of 300 mL.

Solution 2

Another way to solve gas law problems is to understand that the unknown quantity in such problems can usually be found by multiplying the known quantity of the same kind by a fraction made from the other given quantities. In this case, the unknown is the new volume. It will therefore be equal to the old volume multiplied by a "pressure fraction" or "pressure factor:"

$$V_2 = V_1 \times (\underbrace{\frac{\qquad}{\qquad}}_{\text{pressure fraction}})$$

$$V_2 = 300 \text{ mL} \times (\frac{\qquad}{\qquad})$$

The pressure fraction is composed of one of the given pressures divided by the other. For the above problem, the fraction would be either:

$$\frac{720 \text{ mm Hg}}{800 \text{ mm Hg}} \qquad \text{or} \qquad \frac{800 \text{ mm Hg}}{720 \text{ mm Hg}}$$

To decide which is the correct fraction, we must ask ourselves what an increase in pressure (from 720 mm Hg to 800 mm Hg, in the case of the above problem) will do to the volume. Increases in pressure cause *decreases* in volume (at constant temperature). Therefore, we need the pressure fraction that will make the volume smaller. In this case it is 720 mm Hg/800 mm Hg.

$$V_2 = 300 \text{ mL} \times \frac{720 \text{ mm Hg}}{800 \text{ mm Hg}}$$

In arriving at the above expression, we have set up the problem. The answer is 270 mL. If the unknown is a pressure rather than a volume, the same method can be applied. In this case, the given pressure must be multiplied by an appropriate volume fraction.

Questions for Section 6-3

*7. With temperature constant, the pressure exerted by a confined gas will increase if the volume of the container is   (a) increased   (b) decreased   (c) kept constant.

*8. A quantity of gas under a pressure of 200 mm Hg has a volume of 600 mL. The pressure is increased to 400 mm Hg. (Temperature remains constant.)   (a) Will the volume of the gas increase, decrease, or remain the same?   (b) Without actually making a written calculation, which of the following do you think is the most probable value for the new volume: 300 mL; 450 mL; 900 mL; 1200 mL.   (c) Set up the problem.   (d) From your setup, find the numerical answer.

9. A quantity of gas has a volume of 400 mL when confined under a pressure of 600 mm Hg. What will be the new volume of the gas if the pressure is reduced to 200 mm Hg at constant temperature? Show the setup for the problem and find a numerical answer.

10. Under a pressure of 800 mm Hg, a confined gas has a volume of 750 mL. At constant temperature, the pressure is increased until the gas has a volume of 600 mL. What is the new pressure? Show the setup for the problem and find a numerical answer.

6-4   The Relationship Between Temperature and Volume of a Gas

Figure 6-7 shows a quantity of gas confined in a cylinder with a weighted piston. The piston exerts a downward pressure. The downward pressure is caused by three factors. These factors are the weight of the piston, the weight of the masses on the piston, and the force exerted by air pressure. Since the piston is not moving, the upward pressure of the gas must be just equal to the total downward pressure.

If the temperature of the gas is now increased by heating it, we will notice that the gas will expand (increase in volume), forcing the piston upward to a new position. See Figure 6-7b. Keep in mind that the downward pressure will remain unchanged because no change will occur in the weight of the piston, the weight of the masses, or the force caused by air pressure. Thus, any changes in volume of the gas must be related to changes in temperature.

Figure 6-7

(A)   **(B)**

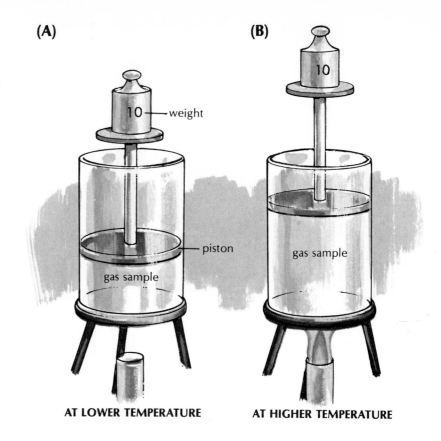

AT LOWER TEMPERATURE   AT HIGHER TEMPERATURE

If more trials are made, we will find that each time the temperature of the gas is changed, the volume of the gas changes. Figure 6-8 gives typical data for an experiment of this kind.

Figure 6-8

When the temperature of a sample of gas is changed, its volume will change if the pressure remains constant.

Trial	Temperature	Volume
A	10.0°C	100 mL
B	50.0	114
C	100.0	132
D	200.0	167

We now ask ourselves the same question that we asked about the pressure-volume data given in Figure 6-5. Can we find a pattern or regularity in the data?

It is clear that increasing the temperature causes the volume to increase. Looking at the data for Trials B and C, we see that the Celsius temperature appears to double (goes from 50.0°C to 100.0°C), but the volume only increases slightly (goes from 114 mL to 132 mL). Whatever regularity exists, it seems that it is not as simple as the relationship between pressure and volume.

When analyzing experimental data, scientists often find it helpful to graph the data. A graph tends to reveal an over-all pattern better than numbers do and can show at a glance what it is often difficult to see when looking at numbers. A graph provides the "picture that is worth a thousand words."

The two measurements for Trial A (10°C and 100 mL) determine one point on a graph having two axes that intersect at right angles. In the relationship between temperature and volume, volume is the dependent variable. That is, the volume of a gas sample depends upon the temperature when pressure is held constant. On our graph, we put a volume scale on the vertical axis because it is customary to put the dependent variable on this axis. Temperature, of course, will then go on the horizontal axis. See Figure 6-9.

When we locate the three other points—those for Trials B, C, and D—we get the graph shown in Figure 6-10. The four plotted points fall on a straight line. When the graph for two variables is a straight line, the relationship between the variables is called a linear (LIN-ee-ur) relationship.

What will happen to the volume of the gas if the temperature is cooled below 0°C? Based on our observations, we would expect the volume to decrease. Rather than express temperatures in negative values, the graph of temperatures cersus volume can be simplified if the temperatures are expressed in kelvins rather than in degrees Celsius. (The Kelvin scale was discussed in Section 4-8.) Adding 273° to each of the temperatures in Figure 6-8 converts these temperatures to

Figure 6-9

For Trial A of Figure 6-8, the temperature of the sample of gas was 10°C when the volume of the sample was 100 mL. These two numbers determine one point on the graph of temperature versus volume. The volume of a sample of gas depends upon the temperature. Volume is, therefore, the dependent variable. Dependent variables are customarily put on the vertical axis. The independent variable, temperature, is put on the horizontal axis.

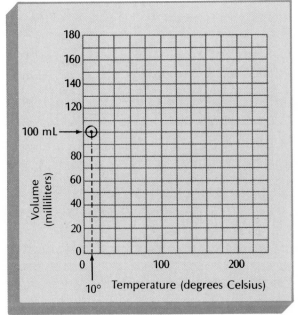

Figure 6-10

The data for the four trials listed in Figure 6-8 determine four points on the graph. For this experiment, the four plotted points fall on a straight line.

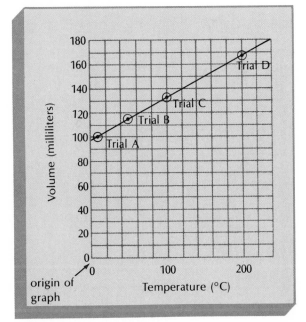

Figure 6-11

Trial	Temperature, T	Volume, V
A	283 K	100 mL
B	323	114
C	373	132
D	473	167

Kelvin temperatures. Figure 6-11 gives the experimental data of Figure 6-8 with the temperatures expressed in kelvins rather than degrees Celsius.

The graph of the data in Figure 6-11 is shown in Figure 6-12. Using the Kelvin scale, the origin has been shifted to the left so that it occupies the lower left corner of the dashed area of Figure 6-12. Plotting temperatures in kelvins has made the graphed line go through the origin (zero-zero point). When the graph of two variables is a straight line that goes through the origin, the two variables are *directly* proportional to each other. Therefore, the graph of Figure 6-12 shows that the volume of a sample of gas is directly proportional to its *Kelvin* temperature when pressure remains constant. In symbols, this statement is written

$$V \propto T$$

(at constant pressure)

where the symbol "$\propto$" is read "is directly proportional to."

Figure 6-12

The data of Figure 6-11 with the horizontal axis now plotted in kelvins. When the line is extended to the left to cover temperatures below 0°C, it intersects the origin, the point for 0 mL and 0 K.

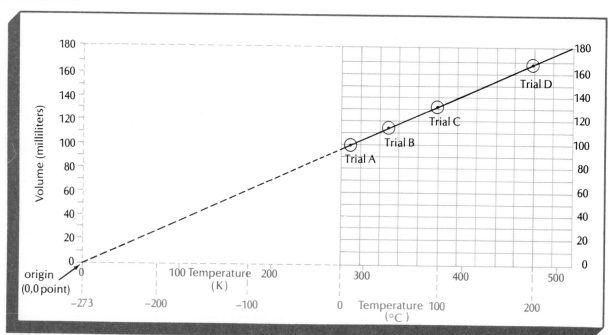

Whenever two variables, y and x, are related by direct proportion, the equation that describes their relationship has the general form

$$y = Kx \qquad \textbf{(Eq. 8)}$$

where K is a constant called the *proportionality constant*.

In the case of the volume and Kelvin temperature of a sample of gas, the y in Equation 8 is replaced by V, and the x is replaced by T:

$$V = KT \qquad \textbf{(Eq. 9)}$$

(at constant pressure)

Equation 9 can be rearranged to give the following form to the equation:

$$\frac{V}{T} = K \qquad \textbf{(Eq. 10)}$$

(at constant pressure)

Equation 10 indicates that the volume of a sample of gas divided by its Kelvin temperature will produce the same constant number if the pressure remains constant. The constancy of the $\frac{V}{T}$ ratio can be illustrated by the data of Figure 6-11. The constant ratio is shown in Figure 6-13.

Figure 6-13

The ratio of the volume of a sample of gas to its Kelvin temperature $\frac{V}{T}$ is a constant if the pressure remains constant.

Experiment	Temperature T	Volume V	Ratio: $\frac{V}{T}$
1	283 K	100 mL	$\frac{100 \text{ mL}}{283 \text{ K}} = 0.35$ mL/K
2	323	114	$\frac{114}{323} = 0.35$
3	373	132	$\frac{132}{373} = 0.35$
4	473	167	$\frac{167}{473} = 0.35$ ← constant

The ratio

$$\frac{V}{T} = K$$

is constant only for a particular sample of gas at a particular pressure. The value of the constant will change if any of the following changes:

Chapter 6   Gas Laws and Kinetic Theory   93

Guadalupe Fortuño
(1955-   )

Guadalupe Fortuño was born in Santurce, Puerto Rico. She attended the University of Puerto Rico and completed her masters and received her Ph.D. in physics from Harvard University.

At the Harvard-Smithsonian Center for Astrophysics, Guadalupe Fortuño carried out research on the reaction rates of certain radicals with oxygen, ozone, and nitrogen dioxide. These reactions are important in the study of the chemistry of the atmosphere.

Now a physicist with IBM, Dr. Fortuño analyzes the emission spectra of the gases that are used to etch circuit patterns on silicon computer chips.

Aside from her work in the laboratory, Dr. Fortuño writes articles and gives lectures about her research.

—the mass of the sample
—the kind of gas making up the sample
—the pressure exerted by the gas

The data given in Figure 6-13 were obtained using a 0.189-gram sample of carbon dioxide at a pressure of 760 mm Hg. For a carbon dioxide sample of that mass and at that pressure, the value of the constant is 0.35 mL/K, as shown in the column on the right in the table.

Equation 10,

$$\frac{V}{T} = K, \qquad \text{(at constant pressure)}$$

can be used to derive another useful equation. Suppose that V_1 and T_1 represent the volume and Kelvin temperature of a sample of gas at a particular time. Now, suppose that the temperature is changed to a new temperature, T_2, causing the volume to change to a new volume V_2. Equation 10 can be applied to both pairs of volume and temperature:

$$\frac{V_1}{T_1} = K \qquad \textbf{(Eq. 11)}$$

$$\frac{V_2}{T_2} = K \qquad \textbf{(Eq. 12)}$$

Since K in Equations 11 and 12 has the same value, the left-hand sides of Equations 11 and 12 can be set equal to each other:

$$\frac{V_1}{T_1} = \frac{V_2}{T_2} \qquad \textbf{(Eq. 13)}$$

Equation 13 enables us to find any one of the four quantities (V_1, T_1, V_2, T_2) if we know the other three. It is not necessary to know the value of K. For example, Equation 13 can be solved for the new volume, V_2:

$$V_2 = \frac{V_1}{T_1} \times T_2 \qquad \textbf{(Eq. 14)}$$

(at constant pressure)

Equation 14 allows us to calculate the new volume (V_2) when we know the old volume (V_1) and the new and old temperatures (T_2 and T_1).

Similarly, we can solve Equation 13 for the new temperature, T_2, if we know the old temperature and the new and old volumes:

$$T_2 = T_1 \times \frac{V_2}{V_1} \qquad \textbf{(Eq. 15)}$$

(at constant pressure)

The graph in Figure 6-12 makes it appear that the volume of any gas would be zero at 0 K (or −273°C). Of course, this is assumed to be impossible. The smallest volume the gas could have would be the total volume of all its molecules with no spaces between them. However, we cannot put this conclusion to a test. All gases change to the liquid phase at temperatures above −273°C. The above observations apply only to gases. Nevertheless, it can be shown that −273°C (or more precisely, −273.15°C) is the lowest possible temperature. No heat energy can be taken from a body or system at this temperature. Since the temperature of a body can be lowered only by removing heat from it, and heat cannot be removed from a body at −273°C, it follows that this is the lowest possible temperature. That is why it is called absolute zero.

Temperatures only a few thousandths of a degree above absolute zero have been reached in the laboratory. But absolute zero itself can never be reached because there would have to be something colder to which the remaining heat in a body could be transferred.

Let us sum up what we have learned so far about the relationship between the temperature of a sample of gas and its volume:

——If we graph Celsius temperatures against volume, we obtain a straight line that cuts through the vertical axis (volume axis) at some point above the origin. This is shown in Figure 6-10.

——The ratio of volume of gas sample to Celsius temperature, V/T, does *not* produce a constant. See the data in Figure 6-8.

——When Kelvin temperatures are graphed against gas volumes, a straight line is obtained that goes through the origin. Furthermore, the ratio of volume of gas sample to its Kelvin temperature, V/T, is a constant. This is shown in the last column of Figure 6-13:

$$\frac{V}{T} = K$$

where T is a temperature on the Kelvin scale and where the relationship holds true only under conditions of constant pressure.

——When two variables are so related that their graph (on Cartesian coordinates) is a straight line going through the origin, the variables are directly proportional to each other.

——One way to test experimental data to determine the relationship between two variables is to graph the data. A straight line going through the origin means that the relationship is a direct proportion.

——Another way to test the data is to divide a value of one variable by the corresponding value of the other. If the result is a constant for all pairs of data, then the two variables are related by direct proportion.

——Variables are related by direct proportion if doubling the value of one variable causes the other variable to double, too; or if halving one variable causes the other to halve, too, etc.

——The general equation for a direct proportion is

$$y = Kx$$

where y and x are variables and K is a constant. The constant, K, is called the proportionality constant.

Questions for Section 6-4

11. What factors cause a weighted piston to produce a downward pressure?
12. If a sample of gas is heated at constant pressure, what will happen to the volume of the sample?
13. If the temperature of the sample of gas shown in Figure 6-7 (page 90) is raised, why will the pressure exerted by the gas after heating be the same as it was before heating?
14. The temperature and volume of a sample of gas are recorded. Then the volume is recorded for several different temperatures while the pressure remains constant. A graph is made of the data. (a) Which of the lines in Figure A would the graph look like if the horizontal axis was calibrated in degrees Celsius? (b) Which of the lines in Figure A would the graph look like if the horizontal axis was calibrated in degrees Kelvin?
15. Give the general equation relating the two variables x and y if they are directly proportional to each other.
16. What is the name given to the relationship that exists between the volume and Kelvin temperature of a sample of gas under constant pressure?
17. Two quantities, A and B, are directly proportional to each other. The value of A becomes ⅓ as much. What will happen to the value of B?
*18. Two quantities, A and B, are directly proportional to each other. When A has a value of 10 liters, B has a value of 100 K. (a) What is the equation that describes the relationship between A and B? (b) If the value of A changes to 14 liters, what will B change to?
19. Given the experimental data in Figure B. (a) On a separate piece of paper draw a grid like that shown in Figure C and graph the data of Figure B. (b) What is the proportionality constant relating V and T? (c) What is the equation of the graphed line?

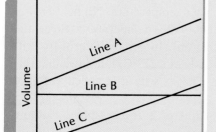

Figure A
(for Question 14)

THE TEMPERATURE AND VOLUME OF A SAMPLE OF GAS AT CONSTANT PRESSURE	
Temperature (K)	Volume (mL)
250	200
300	240
400	320
500	400

Figure B
(for Question 19)

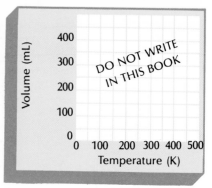

Figure C
(for Question 19)

20. Under what circumstances will the value of the constant, K, change in the expression $\frac{V}{T} = K$?
21. Why has the volume of a sample of gas never been measured at a temperature of 0 K?

6-5 Charles's Law

The relationship between the temperature of a sample of gas and its volume was discovered by the French scientist Jacques Charles in the late 1700's. The relationship is known by his name. Charles's law states that at constant pressure, the volume of a gas is directly proportional to its Kelvin temperature.

The formula for Charles's law is

$$\frac{V}{T} = K \qquad \textbf{(Eq. 16)}$$

(at constant pressure)

Equation 16 states that the volume of a sample of gas divided by the temperature of the gas is a constant when the pressure remains constant.

Charles's law is also given by the formula

$$\frac{V_1}{T_1} = \frac{V_2}{T_2} \qquad \textbf{(Eq. 17)}$$

(at constant pressure)

In Equation 17, V_1 and T_1 represent the volume and pressure at one particular time. If the pressure remains constant and the temperature changes to a new temperature, represented by T_2, then the volume will change to a new volume, V_2.

SAMPLE PROBLEM

A sample of gas has a volume of 150 mL when its temperature is 17°C. If its temperature is increased to 32°C, what will its volume become, assuming the pressure remains constant throughout?

Solution 1

Step 1. Write the mathematical relationship that applies. This problem is concerned with the relationship between gas temperatures and gas volumes. It is, therefore, a Charles's law problem:

$$\frac{V_1}{T_1} = \frac{V_2}{T_2} \qquad \text{(at constant pressure)}$$

Step 2. Charles's law applies to Kelvin temperatures. Therefore, change all temperatures to Kelvin temperatures:

$$T_1 = 17°C + 273 = 290 \text{ K}$$

$$T_2 = 32°C + 273 = 305 \text{ K}$$

Step 3. Assign the known values to the letter symbols:

$$V_1 = 150 \text{ mL} \qquad T_1 = 290 \text{ K} \qquad T_2 = 305 \text{ K} \qquad V_2 = ?$$

Step 4. Substitute the known values into the equation for the relationship, and solve for the unknown:

$$\frac{150 \text{ mL}}{290 \text{ K}} = \frac{V_2}{305 \text{ K}}$$

$$V_2 = 150 \text{ mL} \times \frac{305 \text{ K}}{290 \text{ K}}$$

$$= 158 \text{ mL}$$

Finally, check to see if the answer is reasonable. When the temperature of a gas increases at constant pressure (from 17°C to 32°C, in this case), we expect its volume to increase. Our answer, 158 mL, is an increase over the starting volume of 150 mL. Note that although a change from 17°C to 32°C seems large, it is small when the temperatures are changed to Kelvin temperatures.

Solution 2
Another way to solve this problem is to understand that the unknown quantity can be found by multiplying the known quantity of the same kind by a fraction made from the other quantities. In this case, the unknown is a new volume. It will, therefore, be equal to the old volume multiplied by a "temperature fraction:"

temp. fraction

$$V_2 = V_1 \times \left(\underline{\qquad} \right)$$

$$V_2 = 150 \text{ mL} \times \left(\underline{\qquad} \right)$$

The temperature fraction is composed of one of the known temperatures divided by the other. For the above problem, it is either

$$\frac{290 \text{ K}}{305 \text{ K}} \qquad \text{or} \qquad \frac{305 \text{ K}}{290 \text{ K}}$$

To decide which is the correct fraction, we must ask ourselves what an increase in temperature (from 290 K to 305 K) will do to the volume. Increases in temperature cause increases in volume. Therefore, we need the fraction that will make the volume larger. The fraction is $\frac{305 \text{ K}}{290 \text{ K}}$.

$$V_2 = 150 \text{ mL} \times \frac{305 \text{ K}}{290 \text{ K}} \qquad \text{(SETUP)}$$

$$= 158 \text{ mL} \qquad \text{(ANSWER)}$$

If the unknown in a Charles's law problem is a temperature rather than a volume, the setup for the problem takes the form:

$$T_2 = T_1 \times \frac{V_2}{V_1}$$

volume fraction

Questions for Section 6-5

*22. At constant pressure, as the temperature of a confined gas increases, the volume of the gas will (a) increase (b) decrease (c) remain unchanged.

23. As temperature decreases (at constant pressure), at what point will a gas cease to behave according to Charles's law?

*24. A quantity of a gas has a volume of 100 mL at a temperature of 200 K. The temperature of the gas is raised to 400 K, while pressure remains constant. (a) Will the volume of the gas increase, decrease, or remain unchanged? (b) Without actually calculating an answer, which of the following do you think is the most likely value for the volume at the new temperature? 50 mL; 100 mL; 200 mL; 400 mL? (c) Show the correct setup for the problem.

25. A quantity of gas has a volume of 200 mL at a temperature of $-3°C$. If the temperature of the gas is raised to $27°C$ at constant pressure, what volume (V_2) will the gas occupy? Set up the problem and find a numerical answer. (Remember: Change temperatures to Kelvin temperatures.)

26. What volume will a quantity of gas occupy at $-23°C$ if its volume is 500 mL at $52°C$? Set up the problem and find the numerical answer.

27. A quantity of gas occupies a volume of 800 mL at a temperature of $127°C$. If pressure remains constant, at what temperature will volume of the gas be 600 mL? Set up the problem and find the numerical answer.

6-6 The Relationship Between Temperature and Pressure at Constant Volume

If a gas is heated, its molecules move more rapidly. The gas pressure, caused by the number of molecular impacts per unit of time, is thus increased. Keeping the volume of the gas constant, experimental data can be obtained showing gas pressures at different Kelvin temperatures. When the data is graphed, the graph is found to be a straight line going through the origin, similar to the temperature-volume curve in Figure 6-12. We can conclude, therefore, that the pressure exerted by a gas varies directly with the Kelvin temperature when the volume of the gas is kept constant. That is,

$$P = KT$$

or,

$$\frac{P_1}{P_2} = \frac{T_1}{T_2}$$

(Eq. 18)

(at constant volume)

In Equation 18, P_1 and T_1 are the initial pressure and temperature, and P_2 and T_2 are the final pressure and temperature.

Questions for Section 6-6

*28. If a gas confined in a rigid container is heated, what will happen to the pressure exerted by that gas?

*29. At a temperature of $-33°C$, a quantity of a confined gas exerts a pressure of 400 mm Hg. If volume remains constant, at what temperature will the pressure reach 1000 mm Hg? Set up the problem and find a numerical answer.

30. A gas confined in a rigid container exerts a pressure of 250 mm Hg at a temperature of 17°C. What pressure will the gas exert at a temperature of $-23°C$?

6-7   Standard Temperature and Pressure (STP)

In chemical investigations, it is usually important to know the masses of the substances involved. Masses of solids and liquids can be measured fairly easily. Solids can be placed directly on a balance. The masses of liquids in their containers can be determined, and the mass of the container can then be subtracted. In the case of gases, determining their masses is not very practical. They have to be kept in sealed containers. The mass of a gas is usually so much less than the mass of its container that we could not measure very accurately the difference in mass between a container with gas in it and the same container without gas in it.

We can measure the *volume* of gases fairly easily and accurately. But does the volume of a gas tell us anything about its mass? If two containers of exactly the same volume are filled with the same gas, do they contain the same mass of gas? Usually not. We can put almost any mass of gas into the same volume, simply by changing the pressure or temperature. See Figure 6-14.

Still, we would like to be able to use volume as a measure of the quantity of a gas. We could do this if we always measured the volume at the same temperature and pressure. Even this is not necessary. We could measure the volume at a known temperature and pressure, and then use the gas laws to find out what the volume would be at some generally accepted "standard" temperature and pressure. The condi-

Figure 6-14

The two containers both contain 1 liter of oxygen at a temperature of 20°C. Although the volumes and temperatures of the two samples are the same, their masses must be different because each sample is exerting a different pressure. The mass of Sample B must be greater since the molecules must be pushed closer together in order to be exerting the greater pressure.

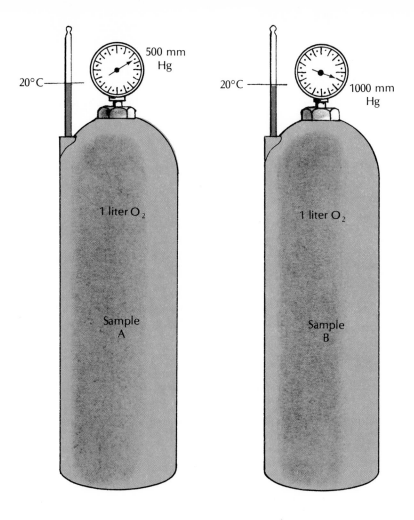

tions of temperature and pressure that have been agreed upon for this purpose are 0°C and 760 mm of mercury. These are called **standard conditions of temperature and pressure,** or **STP.** Whenever the volume of a gas is given without stating its temperature and pressure, it is understood that conditions of STP are meant.

To see why STP enables us to use volume to measure the mass of a gas, we have to understand that a given volume of the same gas at STP always has the same mass. For example, 1000 mL of oxygen at 0°C and 760 mm Hg is a certain definite mass of oxygen. The mass of 500 mL of oxygen at those conditions is half as much, and of 2000 mL is twice as much.

Now suppose we measure the volume of a quantity of oxygen at 20°C and 740 mm Hg. This information by itself does not tell us the mass. But by using the gas laws we can "correct" the volume to 0°C and 760 mm Hg. That is, we can calculate what the volume of this quantity of oxygen would be at STP. Then, if we know the mass of 1000 mL of oxygen at STP, we can calculate the mass of this corrected volume of oxygen. Later in this chapter, you will see a sample problem that shows how this type of calculation is done.

31. What are the standard conditions of temperature and pressure? Why are they called "standard conditions"?
32. What is the abbreviation used to indicate standard conditions?

6-8   The Combined Gas Laws

Boyle's law tells us how the volume of a gas changes when its pressure changes at constant temperature. Charles's law tells us how the volume changes when the temperature changes at constant pressure. But in most real experiments, we need to know what happens to the volume of a gas when we change both the pressure and the temperature. For example, we may measure a gas volume at room temperature and the existing air pressure. We need to know what the volume would have been at STP. To make this volume "correction," we can use a formula that combines Boyle's and Charles's laws. The formula is:

$$\text{new volume} = \text{old volume} \times \frac{\text{old pressure}}{\text{new pressure}} \times \frac{\text{new temperature}}{\text{old temperature}}$$

$$V_2 = V_1 \times \frac{P_1}{P_2} \times \frac{T_2}{T_1} \qquad \textbf{(Eq. 19)}$$

This formula can be changed to:

$$\frac{P_1 V_1}{T_1} = \frac{P_2 V_2}{T_2} \qquad \textbf{(Eq. 20)}$$

or

$$\frac{P\,V}{T} = K \qquad \textbf{(Eq. 21)}$$

Equation 21 means that if the pressure and the volume of a given sample of gas are multiplied, and the resulting product is divided by the Kelvin temperature, then the result will be a constant for all combinations of pressure, volume, and temperature. The constant applies to a particular mass of a particular gas. If the mass of the sample is made larger or smaller, or if a different gas is used, then a different constant will apply to the new sample.

Referring to Equation 20, when temperature remains constant, then $T_1 = T_2$, and T_1 and T_2 cancel out, leaving the equation for Boyle's law: $P_1 V_1 = P_2 V_2$. When pressure remains constant, then $P_1 = P_2$, and P_1 and P_2 cancel out, leaving the equation for Charles's law:

$$\frac{V_1}{T_1} = \frac{V_2}{T_2}$$

SAMPLE PROBLEM

A sample of gas has a volume of 200 liters when its temperature is 20°C and its pressure is 300 mm Hg. (a) What volume will the gas occupy at STP (0°C and 760 mm Hg)? (b) If the density of oxygen at STP is 1.43 g/L, what is the mass of the sample?

Solution 1

Step 1. Determine the relationship that applies to the problem. The problem concerns gas volumes, pressures, and temperatures. It is, therefore, a combined gas law problem:

$$\frac{P_1 V_1}{T_1} = \frac{P_2 V_2}{T_2} \qquad \textbf{(Eq. 20)}$$

Step 2. Assign numbers to the letter symbols:

$P_1 = 300$ mm Hg $V_1 = 200$ L $T_1 = 20°C + 273 = 293$ K

$P_2 = 760$ mm Hg $V_2 = ?$ $T_2 = 0°C + 273 = 273$ K

Step 3. Substitute the numbers into Equation 20 and solve for the unknown:

$$\frac{(300 \text{ mm Hg}) (200 \text{ L})}{293 \text{ K}} = \frac{(760 \text{ mm Hg}) V_2}{273 \text{ K}}$$

$$V_2 = 200 \text{ L} \times \frac{300 \text{ mm Hg}}{760 \text{ mm Hg}} \times \frac{273 \text{ K}}{293 \text{ K}}$$

$$= 73.6 \text{ L}$$

As a check on this answer, note that the pressure factor, $\frac{300 \text{ mm}}{760 \text{ mm}}$, is a number less than one. (It equals 0.395.) This factor, multiplying the original volume of 200 liters, will cause the volume to decrease. This is what we expect, since increasing the pressure (from 300 mm to 760 mm) should cause a decrease in the volume. The temperature factor, $\frac{273 \text{ K}}{293 \text{ K}}$, is also a number less than one. When it multiplies the original volume, this factor will also cause the volume to decrease. A decrease in volume is what we expect when the temperature is decreased as it was in this problem.

To answer part (b) of this problem, if density = mass/volume, then

$$\text{mass} = \left(\begin{array}{c} \text{density} \\ \text{at STP} \end{array} \right) \times \left(\begin{array}{c} \text{volume} \\ \text{at STP} \end{array} \right)$$

$$= 1.43 \text{ g/L} \times 73.6 \text{ L}$$

$$= 105 \text{ g}$$

The mass of the sample of gas is 105 grams.

Solution 2

We can also solve part (a) of the problem by setting the unknown volume equal to the known volume multiplied by appropriate pressure and temperature factors:

$$V_1 = V_2 \times (\underline{\quad\quad}) \times (\underline{\quad\quad})$$

pressure ↑   ↑ temperature
factor ⌐———⌐ factor

$$= 200 \text{ L} \times \frac{300 \text{ mm Hg}}{760 \text{ mm Hg}} \times \frac{273 \text{ K}}{293 \text{ K}}$$

$$= 73.6 \text{ L}$$

Questions for Section 6-8

33. Why is it convenient to have a formula which combines the gas laws of Boyle and Charles?
*34. A quantity of gas has a volume of 850 mL when its temperature is 27°C and its pressure is 730 mm Hg. The conditions are changed to those of STP. (a) Based on the temperature change only, should the new volume be greater or less than 850 mL? (b) Based on the pressure change only, should the new volume be greater or less than 850 mL? (c) Show how the problem is to be set up. (d) What is the numerical value for the answer? (e) If the density of the gas at STP is 1.50 g/L, what is the mass of the sample of gas?
35. The volume of a quantity of gas at STP is 500 liters. What volume will this gas sample occupy at 37°C and 740 mm Hg pressure? (a) Set up the problem. (b) Find a numerical value for the answer. (c) Find the mass of the gas if its density at STP is 1.20 g/L.

6-9   Dalton's Law of Partial Pressures

The English chemist John Dalton investigated pressures in mixtures of gases. In 1802, he announced the following conclusion:

In a mixture of gases, the total pressure of the mixture is equal to the sum of the pressures that each gas would exert by itself in the same volume. (It is assumed that the gases do not chemically interact under the conditions present in the experiment.) For example, suppose that we have one liter of oxygen at a pressure of one atmosphere, and one liter of nitrogen also at one atmosphere. We now transfer one of the gases into the container occupied by the other. We will find that the total pressure is now two atmospheres. Each gas is occupying the same volume of one liter (although they are mixed). Each gas is therefore exerting its original pressure of one atmosphere. Within the single volume of one liter, the two pressures combine to produce a total of two atmospheres.

Figure 6-15

Dalton's law of partial pressures. (A) The gases in both cylinders are at the same pressure and have the same volume. (B) When the stopcock is opened and the piston is pushed down, all the gas in the cylinder on the left is forced into the cylinder on the right. The pressure exerted by the mixture of gases is the sum of the pressures exerted by each gas separately.

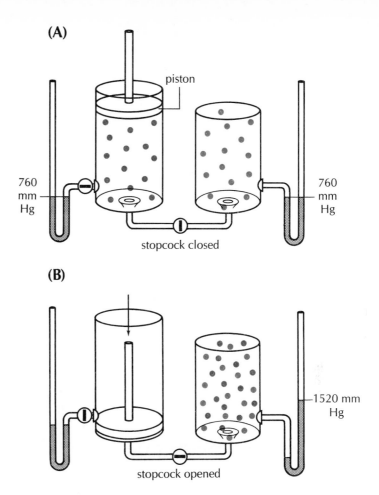

The pressure exerted by each of the separate gases in a mixture is called the **partial pressure** of that gas. Therefore, Dalton's law is called the **law of partial pressures.** See Figure 6-15.

6-10 Graham's Law of Diffusion

As noted before, a gas tends to expand and occupy any volume available to it. This spreading of a substance is called **diffusion.** The presence of another gas is no obstacle to diffusion. Different gases can intermingle very easily. Diffusion can be demonstrated by removing the lid from a bottle of perfume. Molecules of the perfume that escape from the bottle will diffuse through the air surrounding the bottle. Even if the room has no air currents in it and you are sitting at some distance from the bottle, you would finally be able to smell the perfume if a large enough concentration of perfume molecules diffused to the area where you were sitting. Thomas Graham (1805-1869), an English chemist, studied the rates of diffusion of different gases. He found that gases having low densities diffused faster than gases with large densities. He was able to describe quantitatively the relationship between the density of a gas and its rate of diffusion. In 1829, he announced what is known as **Graham's law:**

Under the same conditions of temperature and pressure, gases diffuse at a rate inversely proportional to the square roots of their densities.

That is, a denser gas diffuses more slowly than a less dense gas.

Graham's law may also be stated in terms of molecular masses:

Under the same conditions of temperature and pressure, gases diffuse at a rate inversely proportional to the square roots of their molecular masses.

The formula for Graham's law may be written:

$$\frac{v_1}{v_2} = \sqrt{\frac{d_2}{d_1}} \qquad \text{or} \qquad \frac{v_1}{v_2} = \sqrt{\frac{m_2}{m_1}}$$

where v represents the rate of diffusion, d represents the density of the gas, and m represents the molecular mass of the gas.

Questions for Sections 6-9 and 6-10

*36. Suppose you have one liter of oxygen gas at a pressure of one atmosphere, one liter of nitrogen gas at a pressure of two atmospheres, and one liter of hydrogen gas at a pressure of three atmospheres. All three samples are at room temperature. If you transfer the oxygen and nitrogen to the container occupied by the hydrogen, the pressure exerted by the oxygen in the final mixture will be
(a) 1 atm (b) 2 atm (c) 3 atm (d) 6 atm

37. In question 36 the pressure exerted by the mixture of gases will be
(a) 1 atm (b) 2 atm (c) 3 atm (d) 6 atm

38. What is the relationship between the density of a gas and the rate at which it spreads throughout its container (diffuses)?

6-11   The Kinetic Theory of Gases

The discoveries of Boyle, Charles, Graham, and Dalton at first seemed unrelated. Later it occurred to scientists that a single conceptual scheme could explain the various laws describing the behavior of gases. This scheme was based on the assumption that gases are made of separate, individual particles (called *molecules)* in continuous motion. The **molecule** may be defined as the smallest particle of a substance that possesses the chemical properties of that substance. With these assumptions as a foundation, the combined efforts of many scientists produced what is called the **kinetic theory of gases.** The word "kinetic" comes from the Greek word *kinetikos,* meaning "motion." This theory, like all theories, is a *model.* By the term "model" we mean a picture, mathematical expression, or some other device that can be useful in explaining and interpreting observed behavior. The kinetic theory was proposed to account for observed facts. Like all models, it is only as good as its ability to predict what actually happens in new situations. No model is ever perfect. However, the kinetic theory has proved to be of great value in explaining the behavior of gases under most conditions.

The main assumptions of the kinetic theory are:

1. Gases are composed of separate, tiny (invisible) particles called molecules. These molecules are so far apart, on the average, that the total volume of the molecules is extremely small compared to the total volume of the gas. Therefore, under ordinary conditions, the gas consists chiefly of empty space. This assumption explains why gases are so easily compressed and why they can mix so readily.

2. Gas molecules are in constant, rapid, straight-line motion and, therefore, possess kinetic energy. This motion is constantly interrupted by collisions with other molecules or with the walls of a container. The pressure of a gas is the effect of these molecular impacts.

3. The collisions between molecules are completely elastic. This means that no kinetic energy is changed to heat or other form of energy as a result of the collisions. The total kinetic energy of the molecules remains the same as long as the temperature and volume do not change. Therefore, the pressure of an enclosed gas remains the same if its temperature and volume do not change.

4. The molecules of a gas display *usually* no attraction or repulsion for one another.

5. At any particular moment, the molecules in a gas have different velocities. The mathematical formula for kinetic energy is K.E. $= \frac{1}{2}mv^2$, where m is mass and v is velocity. Since the molecules have different velocities, they have different kinetic energies. However, it is assumed that the *average* kinetic energy of the molecules is directly proportional to the absolute (Kelvin) temperature of the gas. An example of the distribution of kinetic energy among the particles of a gas at two temperatures is shown graphically in Figure 6-16.

Figure 6-16

Distribution curves for a sample of a gas at two different temperatures, where T_2 is a higher temperature than T_1. The curve shifts to the right as the temperature is increased from T_1 to T_2, indicating that the average kinetic energy of the molecules has increased.

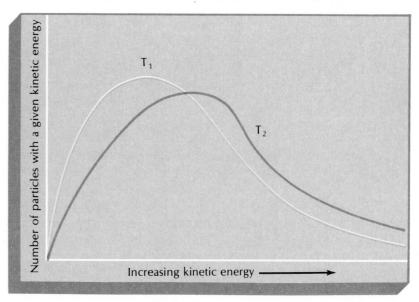

A gas whose behavior would exactly conform to the assumptions of the kinetic theory is called a **perfect** or **ideal** gas. The behavior of real gases often closely resembles the behavior of an ideal gas. However, under certain conditions, the behavior of real gases deviates from what would be expected of an ideal gas. These deviations will be discussed later in the chapter.

6-12   The Kinetic Theory and the Gas Laws

One test of a theory is how well it accounts for observed laws or phenomena. The kinetic theory is successful in explaining the gas laws that have been discussed in this chapter. To do this in an exact fashion we would have to use the mathematical equations of Newton's laws of force and motion. Since you may not have yet studied Newton's laws (a topic of high school physics), we will show how the kinetic theory agrees with the observed laws only in general terms.

Boyle's law and the kinetic theory. According to the kinetic theory, the pressure a gas exerts is caused by the impact of its molecules as they strike a surface. Figure 6-17 shows a cylinder and piston device for observing the relation between pressure and volume of a confined gas at constant temperature. In (B), the gas has been compressed to half the volume it had in (A). We can see that twice as many molecules are now present in any given volume. Therefore there will be twice as many impacts per second on the piston and on the walls of the cylinder. The kinetic theory assumes that the average energy of the molecules is the same if the temperature is the same. Therefore, the average force of each impact will be the same. But since there are twice as many impacts in a given time, their combined force on the piston and the cylinder's walls must be twice as great. Since the area of the piston is the same, and pressure is force per unit area, the pressure is twice as great as before. This theoretical conclusion agrees with the observations of Boyle. (The reasoning would be the same for any change in volume—not just a halving of the volume.)

Charles's law and the kinetic theory. According to the kinetic theory, the absolute temperature of a gas is directly proportional to the average kinetic energy of its molecules. Thus, doubling the absolute temperature would double the kinetic energy. It can be shown mathematically, using Newton's laws of force and motion, that this doubling of the kinetic energy of the molecules of a gas also doubles its pressure. To reduce the pressure to its original value, the volume would have to be doubled (Boyle's law). Thus we arrive at Charles's law that the volume of a gas, at constant pressure, is proportional to its absolute temperature.

Dalton's law and the kinetic theory. When we mix two or more gases at the same temperature, we are bringing together different molecules having the same average kinetic energies. Because of the large spaces

Figure 6-17

(A) The sample of gas is at 1 atmosphere pressure. (B) The piston has been pushed down, crowding the molecules into half the volume they were occupying. With twice as many molecules in each unit of volume, there will be twice as many molecular impacts per unit of time and therefore twice the pressure.

(A)

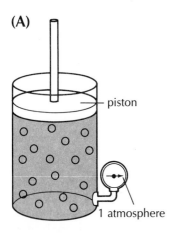

piston

1 atmosphere

(B)

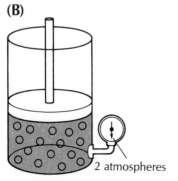

2 atmospheres

between the molecules, the number and intensity of molecular impacts of each gas do not change. Each gas, therefore, exerts the same pressure as it would if no other gas were present. However, the total pressure of the mixture is equal to the sum of the partial pressures of the component gases. These are the chief ideas in Dalton's law.

Graham's law and the kinetic theory. The rapid motion of gas molecules and the relatively large spaces between them explain why gases diffuse easily. If, at a given temperature, all gas molecules had the same average velocity, we would expect gases to diffuse at the same rate. However, the molecules of different gases at the same temperature have the same average *kinetic energy,* not the same velocity. Since kinetic energy is equal to $\frac{1}{2}mv^2$, less massive gas molecules must move at a greater average velocity to have the same average kinetic energy as more massive molecules. It is this greater speed that enables molecules with smaller mass to diffuse more rapidly than molecules with larger mass.

Questions for Sections 6-11 and 6-12

39. What is a molecule?
40. What is a model?
41. What two basic assumptions form the foundation of the kinetic theory of gases?
42. What fact explains why gases are so easily compressed?
43. What property of a gas is directly related to the impacts of gas molecules with the walls of its container?
44. Using the kinetic theory of gases, explain why
    (a) decreasing the volume of a gas (at constant temperature) increases the pressure exerted by the gas.
    (b) increasing the temperature of a gas (at constant pressure) increases the volume occupied by the gas.
    (c) gases diffuse at different rates.

6-13 The Ideal or Perfect Gas

Deviations from the gas laws occur because the model is not perfect. A gas that would conform strictly to the model is a hypothetical one. Its molecules would be points without any volume and these molecules would have absolutely no attraction for one another. Such a gas is called an **ideal** or **perfect** gas. No real gas behaves like an ideal gas under all conditions of temperature and pressure. The ideal gas is an imaginary standard to which the behavior of a known gas is related. At ordinary conditions, most gases obey the gas laws fairly well and their behavior resembles that of an ideal gas. However, at *high* pressures and *low* temperatures, there are marked deviations from the ideal behavior expressed by the gas laws.

6-14   Deviations from Ideal Behavior

As the pressure on a sample of gas is increased greatly at constant temperature, the volume of the gas becomes much smaller. At some point the volume of the molecules is no longer negligible compared with the free space between the molecules. Because the molecular volume is now appreciable, further compression is resisted more strongly than if the molecules were true points. Therefore, at high pressures, volumes tend to be greater than those predicted by Boyle's law.

On the other hand, the forces of attraction that exist between molecules tend to have the opposite effect. Under ordinary conditions, gas molecules spend most of the time at relatively great distances from one another. They come together only very briefly at moments of collision. The forces of attraction therefore act for such a small fraction of the time that they have almost no noticeable effect. However, these forces of attraction do become noticeable when the molecules spend more time close together. This happens when high pressure greatly reduces the volume of the gas. The attractive forces are also more effective at very low temperatures, when the molecules are moving relatively slowly. Thus at high pressure and low temperature, these effects tend to make a gas volume smaller than that predicted by the gas laws.

The actual behavior of gases at high pressure and low temperature can be predicted by a mathematical equation (van der Waals's equation) that modifies Boyle's and Charles's laws. Some gases, such as ammonia and carbon dioxide, show greater deviations than other gases, such as oxygen and hydrogen. By assigning to each gas one correction factor for

Figure 6-18

Deviations from ideal gas behavior for real gases. The graph shows the value of the PV product for the ideal gas and for two real gases, nitrogen and carbon dioxide *at high pressure.* (Note that laboratory pressures, usually around 1 atmosphere, are on the extreme left of the horizontal scale.) As pressure increases, the PV product for nitrogen and carbon dioxide are at first less than that of an ideal gas because molecular attractions cause their volumes to be less than that of an ideal gas. At still higher pressures, the PV products for the real gases are greater than the product for the ideal gas because the molecules are so close to each other that the space they occupy is a significant part of the volume of the container, making the volumes occupied by the gases greater than that of an ideal gas.

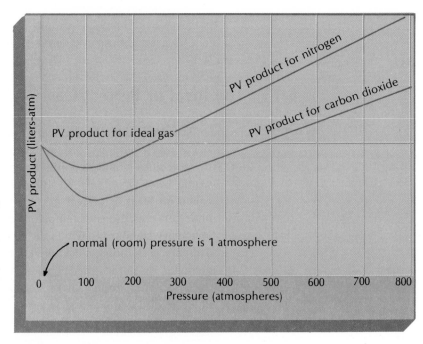

the attractive force of its molecules and another factor for the volume of the molecules, the equation accounts for volume changes of real gases with changes in temperature and pressure. This extension of the kinetic theory illustrates how theories may be modified rather than discarded when new observations make a new explanation necessary.

The graphs in Figure 6-18 show how nitrogen and carbon dioxide deviate from the ideal gas laws. The observations were made at constant temperature for each gas. PV is plotted against P. According to Boyle's law, the PV values should be constant. This is indicated on the graph. Where the effect of the attractive force of the molecules predominates, the volume of the gas is decreased, and the PV values are less than that of the ideal gas. Where the effect of the molecular volume predominates, the PV values of the real gas are greater than that of the ideal gas.

Questions for Sections 6-13 and 6-14

45. What is meant by an ideal gas?
46. What conditions cause real gases to deviate from ideal gas behavior?
47. In Figure 6-18, what factor causes the PV values of the two gases to be less than that of an ideal gas?
48. In Figure 6-18, what factor is responsible for the PV values of the two gases being *greater* than that of an ideal gas?

6-15   Avogadro's Hypothesis

The discussion of kinetic theory would not be complete without referring to an Italian chemist, Amedeo Avogadro. In 1811, Avogadro made a far-reaching scientific assumption (hypothesis) that bears his name. He stated that *equal volumes of different gases, at the same temperature and pressure, contain the same number of molecules*. The statement was called **Avogadro's hypothesis.** It tells us that, under the same conditions, the number of molecules in 1 liter of hydrogen is the same as the number of molecules in 1 liter of oxygen or in 1 liter of carbon dioxide, although the individual molecules of these substances have different masses and sizes. For about 50 years, most scientists found the hypothesis hard to believe. However, the slow accumulation of facts that were easily explained by the hypothesis made its acceptance inevitable. At the present time it is supported by much data. For that reason many scientists refer to it as **Avogadro's law.** It is a very important chemical principle.

6-16   The Mole

The theory of chemical reactions is concerned mainly with combinations and recombinations of individual particles. It is not so much the mass or volume of substances that is important as the numbers of atoms or molecules involved in a chemical process. Avogadro's

Figure 6-19

The word "mole" refers to a particular number of anything in the same sense that the word "dozen" refers to a particular number. While "dozen" means exactly 12, the exact number represented by "mole" cannot be determined. Its approximate value is 6.02×10^{23}.

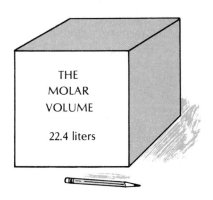

Figure 6-20

The molar volume. One mole of gas molecules occupies the molar volume at STP. The molar volume is 22.4 liters.

hypothesis allows us to calculate the relative numbers of particles involved in a reaction between gases. If equal volumes of two gases react, we know that equal numbers of molecules are reacting.

For reasons that will become clear in later chapters, the number of molecules in 22.4 liters of any gas at STP has been chosen as a standard unit called one **mole.** The mole is a unit used to measure the number of particles of any kind. One mole is equal to approximately 6.02×10^{23} particles. This number is called **Avogadro's number.** The capital letter N is used to represent Avogadro's number. One mole of a substance consists of N particles of that substance. One mole of oxygen gas, for example, consists of N molecules of oxygen. Since there is 1 mole of molecules in 22.4 liters of any gas at STP, 22.4 liters is called the **molar volume** of gases.

6-17 The Ideal Gas Law

As was stated in Section 6-8, we can express the combined gas law in the form

$$\frac{PV}{T} = K \qquad \text{(Eq. 21)}$$

where P, V, and T are the pressure, volume, and Kelvin temperature of a sample of a gas, and K is a constant. Recall that Equation 21 is limited in its use to a particular sample of a particular gas. It applies, for example, to a 20-gram sample of hydrogen, for which K will have a certain value. But the value of K will change if the mass of the sample of hydrogen is changed, or if the sample consists of a gas other than hydrogen.

An equation that is related to Equation 21 has the form

$$\frac{PV}{nT} = R \qquad \text{or} \qquad PV = nRT \qquad \text{(Eq. 22)}$$

In Equation 22, P, V, and T have the same meaning as in Equation 21. The letter n represents the number of moles of gas molecules in the sample, and R is a constant. Equation 22 is called the *ideal gas law*. As its name suggests, the **ideal gas law** describes the behavior of an ideal gas (discussed in Section 6-13). However, under ordinary conditions of temperature and pressure, real gases resemble an ideal gas closely enough that Equation 22 describes their behavior fairly accurately. Equation 22 also applies to any size sample of any gas and is thus free from the limitations that apply to Equation 21.

Because we know that 1 mole of an ideal gas occupies a volume of 22.4 liters at 0°C (273 K) and 760 mm Hg, we can obtain a numerical value of R by substituting those numbers into Equation 22:

$$PV = nRT \qquad \textbf{(Eq. 22)}$$

or

$$R = \frac{PV}{nT}$$

$$R = \frac{760 \text{ mm Hg} \times 22.4 \text{ L}}{1.00 \text{ mole} \times 273 \text{ K}}$$

$$R = 62.4 \frac{\text{mm Hg-L}}{\text{mole-K}}$$

Questions for Sections 6-15 through 6-17

49. State Avogadro's law or hypothesis.
50. According to Avogadro's law, how will the number of molecules in 2 liters of hydrogen gas compare with the number of molecules in 1 liter of oxygen gas at the same temperature and pressure?
51. Why is 22.4 liters called the molar volume of a gas?
52. Under what conditions will 22.4 liters of oxygen gas contain 1 mole of oxygen molecules?
53. At STP, 22.4 liters of nitrogen gas contain how many molecules?
54. At STP, how many molecules are present in 3 molar volumes of a gas?
55. A gas whose behavior closely resembles that of an ideal gas has a volume of 31.2 liters at a temperature of 27°C and a pressure of 600 mm Hg.   (a) How many moles of molecules are in the sample?   (b) How many molecules are in the sample?

CHAPTER SUMMARY

1. Of the three physical phases of matter, only gases respond dramatically to changes in temperature and pressure.
2. For a fixed mass of any gas at constant temperature, volume is inversely proportional to pressure (Boyle's law): $PV = K$.
3. For a fixed mass of any gas at constant pressure, volume is directly proportional to absolute (Kelvin) temperature (Charles's law): $V = KT$.
4. For a fixed mass of any gas at constant volume, pressure is directly proportional to absolute temperature: $P = KT$.

5. The volume of a given mass of any gas depends on its temperature and its pressure. Thus, these conditions must always be expressed whenever the volume of a gas is given.

6. Standard conditions of temperature and pressure, abbreviated STP, are 0°C (273 K) and 760 mm of mercury (1 atm).

7. When two or more gases that do not react with one another are mixed together in the same container, each gas exerts the same pressure it would exert if it were alone. The total pressure exerted by the mixture of gases is equal to the sum of the pressures exerted by each individual gas (Dalton's law of partial pressures).

8. Gases tend to spread out, or diffuse, and occupy any volume available. Under the same conditions of temperature and pressure, gases diffuse at a rate inversely proportional to the square roots of either their densities or molecular masses (Graham's law). Thus, the denser a gas is, the more slowly it diffuses.

9. According to the kinetic theory of gases, gases are composed of tiny, separate, widely spaced particles called molecules. These molecules are in constant, rapid, straight-line motion, and thus possess kinetic energy. Collisions between gas molecules or with container walls are completely elastic. That is, no kinetic energy is changed to heat or any other form of energy. Under ordinary conditions of temperature and pressure, gas molecules display no attraction or repulsion for one another.

10. A gas whose behavior would conform exactly to the kinetic theory model is called an ideal gas, or a perfect gas. The molecules of such a gas would be points without volume and would have absolutely no attraction for one another under any conditions. Because molecules of real gases do have volume and mutual attraction, real gases tend to deviate from ideal behavior, especially under conditions of high pressure and low temperature.

11. At the same temperature and pressure, equal volumes of different gases contain the same number of molecules (Avogadro's law).

12. A mole is a standard unit used to measure the number of particles of any kind. One mole is equal to approximately 6.02×10^{23} particles. This number is called Avogadro's number.

13. At STP, 22.4 liters of any gas contains Avogadro's number of molecules. This volume (22.4 liters) is called the molar volume of gases.

14. For any sample of an ideal gas, the value of the product of the pressure and the volume divided by the product of the number of moles of gas molecules and the Kelvin temperature is a constant: $\frac{PV}{nT} = R$, or $PV = nRT$.

TERMS YOU SHOULD KNOW

Boyle's law	Dalton's law of partial pressures	perfect (or ideal) gas
Charles's law		Avogadro's hypothesis (or law)
standard temperature and pressure	diffusion	
STP	Graham's law of diffusion	mole
combined gas laws	molecule	Avogadro's number
partial pressure	kinetic theory of gases	molar volume of gases
		ideal gas law

Section

6-1   1. What is the name of the unifying theory that explains the observed behavior of gases?

6-2   2. When considering the relationship between volume and pressure of a gas, what condition must be kept constant?

6-5   3. When considering the relationship between temperature and volume of a fixed mass of a gas, what condition must be kept constant?

4. At constant pressure, by what fraction of its volume will a quantity of gas change if the temperature changes from 0°C to 50°C?

5. At constant pressure, what effect will raising the temperature of a quantity of gas from 0°C to 273°C have on the volume of the gas?

6. Why is a temperature of 0 K (absolute zero) impossible to attain?

6-6   7. Why is it dangerous to heat a tightly stoppered flask?

8. What is the relationship between temperature and pressure of a gas kept at a constant volume?

6-7   9. What difficulties are encountered when conducting investigations involving gases that are not encountered in investigations involving solids and/or liquids?

10. Suppose you are told that a quantity of a gas has a volume of 800 liters. Why is this information incomplete?

6-9   11. Suppose you have a one-liter container of oxygen gas at two atmospheres pressure and a two-liter container of nitrogen gas at one atmosphere pressure. If you transfer the oxygen to the container holding the nitrogen, (a) what pressure would the oxygen exert? (b) what would be the total pressure exerted by the mixture?

6-10   12. What property of a gas determines the rate at which it diffuses? According to Graham's law, what is the relationship between this property and the diffusion rate of a gas?

6-11   13. According to the kinetic theory of gases: (a) How large is the average distance between the molecules of a gas compared to the diameters of the molecules? (b) What accounts for the pressure exerted by a confined gas? (c) How does the fact that molecular collisions are perfectly elastic affect the average kinetic energy of the molecules of a gas?

14. What determines the average kinetic energy of the molecules of a gas?

6-12   15. Using the kinetic theory, explain the following: (a) At constant temperature, the pressure exerted by a given quantity of a gas decreases by half if the volume of its container is expanded to twice its original size. (b) At constant pressure, doubling the absolute temperature of a gas confined in an expandable container will double the volume of the gas. (c) If the Kelvin temperature of a gas confined in a rigid container is doubled, the pressure exerted by the gas is also doubled. (d) If different gases that do not react with one another are placed in a single container, each gas will exert the same pressure as it would if no other gases were present. (e) At any given temperature, gas molecules of small mass will have the same average kinetic energy as gas molecules of larger mass.

6-13   16. Describe the characteristics of an ideal gas.

6-16   17. Define the term *mole*. How many particles of any kind does one mole represent?

Chapter 6   Gas Laws and Kinetic Theory   **115**

Section 6-3

1. A quantity of gas under a pressure of 800 mm Hg has a volume of 380 liters. What is its volume at standard pressure (temperature constant)?

6-3

2. A quantity of gas has a volume of 120 liters when confined under a pressure of 700 mm Hg at a temperature of 20°C. At what pressure will its volume be 30 liters at 20°C?

6-5

3. At constant pressure, the volume of a gas is increased from 150 liters to 300 liters by heating it. If the original temperature of the gas was 20°C, what will its final temperature be?

4. A quantity of gas exerts a pressure of 740 mm Hg at a temperature of 22°C. If the volume remains unchanged, what pressure will it exert at −8°C?

6-8

5. A quantity of oxygen gas has a volume of 850 mL when measured at 27°C and 730 mm Hg of pressure. Determine its volume at STP.

6. When measured at STP, a quantity of gas has a volume of 500 liters. What volume will it occupy at 0°C and 700 mm Hg of pressure?

7. A quantity of gas has a volume of 200 liters at 17°C and 800 mm Hg of pressure. To what temperature must the gas be cooled for its volume to be reduced to 150 liters at a pressure of 740 mm Hg?

6-17

8. A gas whose behavior closely resembles that of an ideal gas has a volume of 2.00 liters at a temperature of 27°C and a pressure of 900 mm Hg. (a) How many moles of molecules are in the sample? (b) How many molecules are in the sample?

6-5

1. A student devised a simple apparatus consisting of a balloon and a thermometer enclosed in a glass vessel. He filled the balloon with a sample of gas, sealed it, and placed it in the vessel. He then heated the vessel and observed the diameter of the balloon at various temperatures.

    The student corrected the temperatures to Kelvin degrees and used the formula for the volume of a sphere to find the volume of gas for each data point. According to Charles's law, the volume should increase in direct proportion to the Kelvin temperature. However, the observed volumes were all smaller than predicted by the law.

    How can you account for the disagreement?

6-6

2. A person had a barometer on the wall of her living room. One cold morning, she read the barometer and found that the air pressure was considerably below normal. She turned up the thermostat to start the heating system and warm the house. An hour later, she read the barometer again. Since the air in the room was now much warmer than before, and its volume was the same, she expected the pressure to be greater. Actually, the pressure was even lower. How do you explain this apparent contradiction of the gas laws?

Phases of Matter—Liquids and Solids

> ## Objectives
>
> After you have completed this chapter, you will be able to:
> - Use the kinetic theory to explain the properties of liquids and solids.
> - Compare properties of liquids and solids.
> - Describe equilibrium in mixtures of phases at the melting point of a substance.

7-1 The Kinetic Theory Applied to Liquids

The rapidly moving molecules in gases fly apart after colliding with one another. Suppose the molecules are slowed down by a decrease in temperature, and, in addition, are brought closer together by an increase in pressure. Then the intermolecular attraction may overcome the tendency of the molecules to fly apart. Under such conditions, the gas will change to a liquid. In the liquid phase, the molecules are held together by mutual attraction, but still have some freedom of motion. The attractive forces hold the molecules close to one another. The small spaces between liquid molecules allow liquids to be only *slightly* compressed by an increase in pressure. The molecular motion keeps liquids from having a fixed shape. This motion makes them flow freely and assume the shape of a container. Molecular motion also accounts for the ability of molecules to diffuse past one another within the body of the liquid. Because of greater intermolecular attractions, diffusion in liquids is much less rapid than diffusion in gases.

7-2 Evaporation

The kinetic theory gives us this picture of a liquid. Like a gas, a liquid is made up of molecules that move past each other in random fashion. However, the molecules of a liquid have a more restricted motion than the molecules of a gas. Attractive forces between the molecules of a liquid stop them from spreading far apart, as in gases.

Figure 7-1

The molecules making up a liquid can diffuse past each other. Those near the surface with enough kinetic energy, such as *A*, will escape from the liquid phase and will enter the gaseous phase. Others, such as *B*, will have too little kinetic energy for escape.

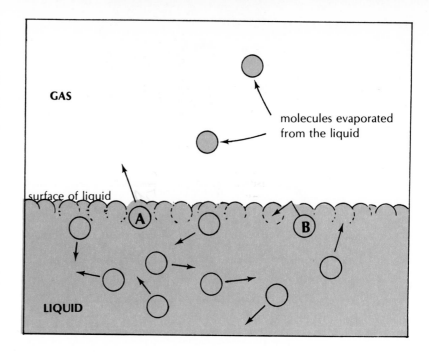

GAS

molecules evaporated from the liquid

surface of liquid

A   B

LIQUID

As is true for matter in all phases, the *average* kinetic energy of the molecules in a liquid depends on the temperature. However, at any temperature, some of the molecules are moving slower than average. Others are moving faster. Some faster moving molecules at the surface of the liquid will have enough kinetic energy to overcome the attraction of nearby molecules. These molecules will leave the liquid and enter the gaseous phase. In an open container, molecules may continue to escape until all the liquid has changed to a gas. The process in which a liquid changes to a gas is called **evaporation.** See Figure 7-1.

There is an important difference between evaporation and boiling. Evaporation is a change to the gaseous phase that takes place at the *surface* of a liquid (or a solid) at a temperature *below* the boiling point. Boiling occurs *throughout* a liquid *at* its boiling point temperature. When a substance exists as a liquid or solid under ordinary conditions, its gaseous phase is called a **vapor.** The gas formed by the evaporation of water is called **water vapor.** There is always some water vapor present in the open air at any temperature.

In evaporation, the more rapidly moving molecules leave first. These are the molecules with the largest kinetic energies. The molecules remaining in the liquid will possess a lower average kinetic energy. Therefore, the temperature of the liquid tends to fall during the process. Our skin is cooled by the evaporation of sweat. As some of the sweat is evaporated, the remaining sweat falls below skin temperature. Heat is then transferred from warm skin to cool sweat. The skin continues to be cooled as more sweat is produced and evaporated.

The rate of evaporation is increased by any factor that will help molecules to escape. An increase in temperature aids evaporation by increasing the average kinetic energy of the molecules. More

Figure 7-2

The evaporation of perspiration helps to keep a person cool.

Figure 7-3

Three ways to increase the rate of evaporation of a liquid. (A) Raise the temperature of the liquid. This will increase the average kinetic energy of the molecules, increasing the likelihood that those near the surface will escape. (B) Because evaporation takes place at the surface of a liquid, increasing the surface area will cause a given amount of liquid to evaporate faster. The water evaporates faster in a puddle than in a beaker. (C) Air currents over the surface of a liquid will make it evaporate faster by preventing evaporated molecules from returning to the liquid.

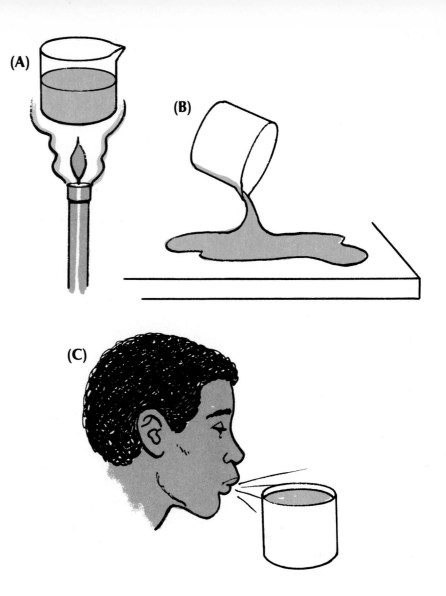

molecules then have enough energy to escape. Evaporation rate can also be increased by increasing the area of the liquid surface exposed to the air. Finally, the rate of evaporation is increased by the presence of air currents. These remove molecules of vapor from the space above the liquid, preventing them from returning to the liquid. See Figure 7-3.

7-3 Condensation

The process in which a vapor or gas changes to a liquid is called **condensation.** Condensation is the reverse of evaporation. Condensation takes place whenever the space over the surface of a liquid contains molecules of its vapor. Molecules of vapor that strike the liquid surface may be captured if they are moving slowly enough. They thus become part of the liquid. Molecules moving at high speeds will rebound from the molecules of the liquid surface and remain in the gaseous phase. Thus we see that in condensation, it is the higher-energy molecules that remain in the vapor phase as the lower-energy molecules condense to a liquid. Condensation thus tends to raise the temperature of the vapor. (Recall that evaporation has the opposite effect. It tends to *lower* the temperature of the liquid.)

Questions for Sections 7-1 through 7-3

1. What holds the molecules together in the liquid phase?
2. Compare the motion of the molecules of a liquid with that of the molecules of a gas.
3. When is a substance in the gaseous phase called a vapor?
4. Why does the average kinetic energy of the molecules of a liquid decrease when evaporation occurs at the liquid's surface?
5. What effect does an increase in temperature have on evaporation rate?
6. What happens to the temperature of a vapor when condensation occurs?

7-4   Vapor-liquid Equilibrium

If a liquid is placed in a closed container, evaporation will take place and vapor will collect in the space above the liquid surface. As soon as this happens, condensation of the vapor will also begin. At first, the rate of evaporation will be much faster than the rate of condensation. But as the concentration of vapor increases, its rate of condensation will also increase. A condition will finally be reached in which the rate at which molecules are evaporating from the liquid is equal to the rate at which molecules are condensing back into it. Such a balance in the rates of opposing changes is called an *equilibrium*. See Figure 7-4.

Evaporation and condensation are physical changes. Their occurrence at equal rates in the same vessel is referred to as a *physical equilibrium*. When equilibrium is reached in the container, the space above the liquid holds as much vapor as it can at the given conditions. It is said to be *saturated* with vapor.

Figure 7-4

(A) Shortly after the jar is closed, few molecules of the liquid will have had time to escape into the air above the liquid. More molecules will be evaporating (1, 2, and 3) than will be condensing (4). (B) A while later many more molecules will have escaped into the space above the liquid. A time will be reached when the rate at which molecules (1, 2, 3) evaporate will be equal to the rate at molecules (4, 5, 6) condense. When this condition exists, the vapor phase and the liquid phase are said to be in equilibrium.

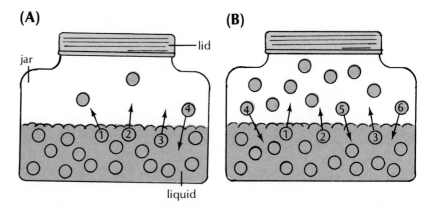

Figure 7-5

Measuring the vapor pressure of a liquid. (A) With both arms of the manometer exposed to the atmosphere, the mercury in both arms is at the same level. (B) After the manometer and the flask are connected, a few drops of the liquid are squeezed into the flask. As the liquid evaporates, the pressure of its vapor is added to the atmospheric pressure inside the flask, causing the mercury to go down on the left and up on the right. When the liquid and its vapor reach equilibrium, the difference in height of the mercury column, 120 mm Hg, measures the vapor pressure of the liquid.

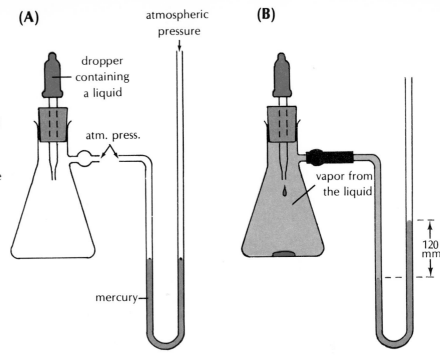

Vapor pressure. The kinetic theory states that molecules in the gaseous or vapor phase exert pressure. The pressure of a vapor in equilibrium with its liquid is called the **equilibrium vapor pressure,** or simply, the **vapor pressure** of that liquid. See Figure 7-5. At any given temperature, vapor pressure has a definite value. For example, the vapor pressure of water at 20°C is 17.5 mm of mercury. Figure 7-6 shows values of the vapor pressure of water at various temperatures. When gases are

Figure 7-6

The vapor pressure of water at various temperatures.

°C	torr (mm Hg)	°C	torr (mm Hg)
0	4.6	26	25.2
5	6.5	27	26.7
10	9.2	28	28.3
15	12.8	29	30.0
16	13.6	30	31.8
17	14.5	40	55.3
18	15.5	50	92.5
19	16.5	60	149.4
20	17.5	70	233.7
21	18.7	80	355.1
22	19.8	90	525.8
23	21.1	100	760.0
24	22.4	105	906.1
25	23.8	110	1074.6

prepared in the laboratory, they are often "collected over water," as shown in Figure 7-7. Since water evaporates into the space above its surface, the collected gas becomes saturated with water vapor. To calculate the mass of the gas collected, we need to know its pressure and its volume. We can measure the total pressure of the gas-water vapor mixture, but we need to know the pressure due to the gas alone (its partial pressure). To find this pressure, we must subtract the vapor pressure of the water from the total pressure. For example, assume that the total pressure of the gas-water vapor mixture is 755.0 mm of mercury at 20°C. From Figure 7-6, the partial pressure of the water vapor at that temperature is 17.5 mm of mercury. The partial pressure of the gas is therefore:

$$755.0 \text{ mm Hg} - 17.5 \text{ mm Hg} = 737.5 \text{ mm Hg}$$

This calculation is illustrated in Figure 7-7.

Figure 7-7

Vapor pressure correction. When the water level inside and outside the bottle is the same, the total pressure inside the bottle is the same as the external atmospheric pressure. The partial pressure of the water vapor must be subtracted from the total pressure inside the bottle to arrive at the pressure exerted by the hydrogen molecules alone.

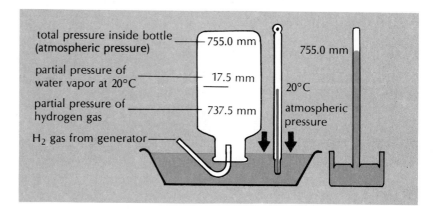

total pressure inside bottle (atmospheric pressure) — 755.0 mm

partial pressure of water vapor at 20°C — 17.5 mm

partial pressure of hydrogen gas — 737.5 mm

H_2 gas from generator

755.0 mm

20°C

atmospheric pressure

7-5 Boiling

We have seen that in a sealed container the partial pressure of the vapor over a liquid cannot be greater than its equilibrium pressure for the existing temperature. Imagine that a bubble of vapor has formed inside a liquid. This bubble would be like a sealed container. The vapor pressure inside such a bubble would be the equilibrium pressure. On the other hand, the pressure exerted on the bubble by the surrounding liquid would be equal to the atmospheric pressure (plus any additional pressure resulting from the depth in the liquid). If the vapor pressure is less than one atmosphere, the bubble clearly cannot exist. It would collapse under the excess pressure of the liquid.

As the temperature of the liquid is increased, its vapor pressure also increases. At some temperature the vapor pressure becomes equal to the atmospheric pressure. The vapor pressure is now great enough to form a bubble inside the liquid. At this temperature (or slightly above it) we can expect to see bubbles of vapor forming below the surface of the liquid. This is the condition called *boiling*. The temperature at which boiling takes place is called the *boiling point* of the liquid. In other words, the boiling point of a liquid is that temperature at which its vapor pressure is equal to the pressure on the surface of the liquid.

Once a liquid is brought to its boiling point at a given pressure, its temperature cannot be forced any higher. Heating the liquid more strongly at the boiling point causes it to vaporize more rapidly, but does not raise its temperature.

Comparison of boiling points. The vapor pressure curves in Figure 7-8 compare the vapor pressures of water, ethyl alcohol, and chloroform at various temperatures. These curves show that at any given temperature, the vapor pressure of chloroform is greater than that of alcohol, and the vapor pressure of alcohol is greater than that of water. As the temperature is raised, the vapor pressures increase. As the vapor pressure of each liquid reaches atmospheric pressure, the liquid begins to boil. We can see that chloroform will boil at the lowest temperature. Water will boil at the highest temperature. Alcohol will boil at a temperature in between.

Figure 7-8

Vapor pressure curves for three substances. A heated liquid will finally reach a temperature at which the vapor pressure of the liquid equals atmospheric pressure. That temperature is the boiling point of the liquid.

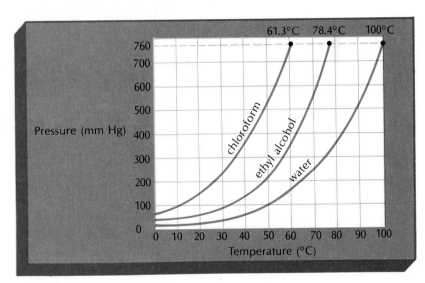

Ordinarily, boiling points are stated for standard atmospheric pressure, 760 mm. This is called the *normal boiling point* of the liquid. The normal boiling point of water is 100°C, of alcohol, 78.4°C, and of chloroform, 61.3°C.

Boiling points change with changes in pressure. A liquid will boil at any temperature at which its vapor pressure equals the pressure on the surface of the liquid. This can be shown by putting an open vessel of water at room temperature in a sealed container. By removing most of the air from the container, the water can be made to boil. This boiling takes place because the pressure on the surface of the liquid has been greatly reduced. For example, Figure 7-6 shows that the vapor pressure of water at 20°C (room temperature) is 17.5 mm. If the pressure inside the container is reduced to 17.5 mm, the water will begin to boil.

Chapter 7   Phases of Matter—Liquids and Solids   **123**

A pressure cooker operates on the principle of *increasing* the pressure on the surface of a liquid. Remember that the temperature of a boiling liquid cannot rise above its boiling point. At a pressure of one atmosphere, the temperature of the boiling water remains at 100°C, no matter how hot the flame heating it. When the pressure is increased, the liquid must be raised to a temperature *higher* than its normal boiling point before it will boil. Foods cook faster at the higher water temperatures that are made possible in a pressure cooker. See Figure 7-9.

Figure 7-9

Principle of the pressure cooker. In an open container, vapor from heated water escapes into the air. Therefore, the gas pressure above the water remains at atmospheric pressure. In a closed container, such as a pressure cooker, vapor from the water cannot escape. As a result, gas pressure above the water reaches a level above atmospheric pressure. Only when the vapor pressure within the water reaches this elevated pressure can boiling occur. To achieve this elevated pressure, the water must be heated to a temperature above its normal boiling point.

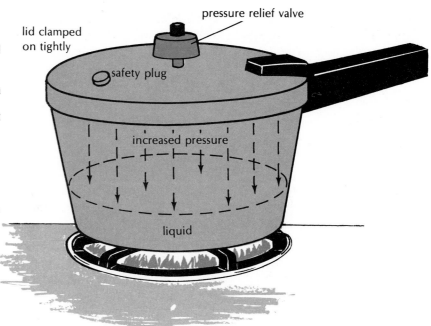

pressure relief valve

lid clamped on tightly

safety plug

increased pressure

liquid

Questions for Sections 7-4 and 7-5

7. Why is a condition of equilibrium between evaporation and condensation known as a physical equilibrium?
8. Describe the relationship between temperature and vapor pressure of water.
*9. A jar half-filled with water has its lid screwed on tightly. Above the water is hydrogen gas mixed with water vapor that is in equilibrium with its liquid phase. The mixture of hydrogen gas and water vapor is exerting a combined pressure of 780.2 mm Hg. If the temperature of the water and the gases is 22°C, how much pressure is the hydrogen alone exerting? That is, what is the partial pressure of the hydrogen? (Refer to Figure 7-6.)
10. Why don't vapor bubbles form in water at room temperature and standard pressure?
11. What happens to a liquid in an open container when its vapor pressure is equal to atmospheric pressure?
12. What happens to the boiling point of a liquid if the pressure exerted on its surface is reduced?

7-6 Liquefaction of Gases

In order for a gas to condense to a liquid, the attraction between its molecules must be strong enough to hold them together in the liquid phase. The smaller the distance between molecules, the greater the attraction between them. Increasing the pressure on a gas causes its molecules to crowd together. If enough pressure is exerted on the gas, the attractive forces may then be strong enough to cause the gas to liquefy. Moreover, as the temperature is lowered, the molecules move less rapidly. At slower speeds, they are less able to overcome the attractive forces. Therefore, a combination of *increased pressure* and *lowered temperature* favors *liquefaction*. **Liquefaction** is the process in which a substance enters the liquid phase.

Most gases will liquefy if the temperature is lowered enough. Some gases, whose molecular attractions are very low, require extremely low temperatures before they will condense. This is true of oxygen and nitrogen, the chief components of air. The temperature of oxygen gas, for example, must be lowered to −183°C in order to liquefy it. It can be liquefied at higher temperatures if it is placed under greater pressures. For example, at 20 atmospheres pressure, oxygen liquefies at −140°C.

For each gas there is a maximum temperature at which it is possible to liquefy it by increasing the pressure. Above that temperature, no amount of pressure will cause the gas to change to a liquid. This maximum temperature is called the **critical temperature** of the substance. The pressure required to liquefy a gas at its critical temperature is called its **critical pressure.** For example, the critical temperature of carbon dioxide is 31.1°C, and its critical pressure is 73.0 atmospheres. It is thus possible to have a tank of liquid carbon dioxide at room temperature (20°C), although it would have to be under great pressure. However, it is *not* possible to have a tank of liquid *oxygen* at room temperature. Its critical temperature is −119°C.

7-7 Heat of Vaporization

An evaporating liquid absorbs energy. This energy is used to do the work of overcoming the attractive forces between the molecules of the liquid, so that they can enter the vapor phase. Although this absorption of energy increases the potential energy of the molecules, it does not change their average kinetic energy. Therefore, the temperature of the vapor does not change. The energy absorbed during evaporation may be taken from the immediate surroundings of the liquid. This lowers the temperature of the surroundings. The energy may also come directly from the kinetic energy of the molecules of the liquid, thus lowering the temperature of the liquid. In either case, evaporation of a liquid has a cooling effect. This effect is quite noticeable when alcohol, for example, evaporates from the skin or when one steps out of water after bathing.

Figure 7-10

The quantity of energy needed to vaporize a unit mass of liquid at constant temperature is called its **heat of vaporization.** The heat of vaporization of any particular liquid varies with the temperature. It usually decreases as the temperature increases. The reason for this is that at higher temperatures the molecules have a greater average kinetic energy and are farther apart on the average. It therefore takes less energy to bring about a complete separation into the vapor phase than it does at a lower temperature. As an example, the heat of vaporization of water at 70°C is 557 calories per gram, while at 100°C it is 539 calories per gram.

Heats of vaporization are usually given for the normal boiling point temperature of the liquid. The value for alcohol is 204 calories per gram. This is much less than that for water. We can therefore conclude that the intermolecular forces of attraction in alcohol are smaller than those in water. The value for chloroform is lower still—59 calories per gram.

When a vapor condenses to a liquid at the boiling point, the process of vaporization is reversed, and energy is *released*. This energy is called the **heat of condensation.** The amount of energy given up is equal to the heat of vaporization. When steam condenses, it gives up 539 calories per gram without changing temperature. Therefore, a burn caused by steam at 100°C is worse than that caused by an equal mass of liquid water at the same temperature.

SAMPLE PROBLEM 1

At standard pressure, 760 mm Hg, and at 100°C, a 250-gram sample of a liquid is boiled over a 10-minute period. As the liquid boils, the temperature remains constant as 5.40×10^4 calories of heat are absorbed by the liquid. At the end of the 10-minute period, only 150 grams of the liquid remain. What is the heat of vaporization of the liquid?

Solution. The heat of vaporization is the heat needed to evaporate a unit mass of a substance. While the liquid boiled, a total of 250 g − 150 g = 100 g of the liquid was evaporated. Therefore,

$$\text{heat of vaporization of a substance} = \dfrac{\left(\begin{array}{c}\text{heat to vaporize}\\ \text{the substance}\end{array}\right)}{\left(\begin{array}{c}\text{mass of the}\\ \text{substance vaporized}\end{array}\right)} \quad \textbf{(FORMULA A)}$$

$$= \dfrac{5.40 \times 10^4 \text{ cal}}{100 \text{ g}} \quad \textbf{(SETUP)}$$

$$= 5.40 \times 10^2 \text{ cal/g}$$

or

$$540 \text{ cal/g} \quad \textbf{(ANSWER)}$$

Allowing for experimental error, the substance is probably water, since its heat of vaporization at 760 mm Hg and 100°C is 539 cal/g. The answer in joules is 540 cal/g $\times$ 4.18 J/cal = 2.26 $\times$ 10^3 J/g.

SAMPLE PROBLEM 2

The heat of vaporization of water is 539 cal/g at 760 mm Hg and 100°C. How much heat must be supplied to evaporate 50 g of water at 100°C and 760 mm pressure?

Solution. If it takes 539 cal to evaporate 1 gram of water at 760 mm and 100°C, then it takes 50 times as much heat to evaporate 50 grams:

$$50 \times 539 \text{ cal} = 26\ 950 \text{ cal}$$

We can arrive at the same result by using a rearranged form of Formula A, given in Sample Problem 1:

$$\begin{array}{c}\text{heat to vaporize}\\ \text{a substance}\end{array} = \left(\begin{array}{c}\text{heat of vaporization}\\ \text{of the substance}\end{array}\right) \times \left(\begin{array}{c}\text{mass}\\ \text{of the substance}\end{array}\right)$$

$$= \dfrac{539 \text{ cal}}{\text{g}} \times 50 \text{ g} \quad \textbf{(SETUP)}$$

$$= 26\ 950 \text{ cal} \quad \textbf{(ANSWER)}$$

To the correct number of significant figures, this answer is 2.7 $\times$ 10^4 calories. In joules, the answer is 2.7 $\times$ 10^4 cal $\times$ 4.18 joules/cal = 1.1 $\times$ 10^5 joules.

7-8   Distillation

Water and other liquids often contain impurities. Some impurities are not objectionable, and no attempt is made to remove them. Drinking water commonly has a number of impurities of this type. However, many impurities, although present in small amounts, render a liquid unsuitable for an intended use. Impurities may be dissolved solids, dissolved liquids, or dissolved gases, or they may be small particles of suspended matter. Some of these impurities can be removed from water or other liquids by **distillation.** See Figure 7-11.

Figure 7-11

A distillation apparatus. The condenser has two parts. One part is a long hollow tube. The other part is a glass jacket that surrounds the long tube. The hollow tube and the jacket are not connected. Therefore, gases and liquids passing through the tube cannot enter the jacket. Cold water from the water faucet enters the bottom of the jacket, surrounds the hollow tube, and passes to the outlet at the top of the jacket. The cold water in the jacket absorbs heat from the gases passing through the tube, thus causing gases from the distillation flask to condense into a liquid before dripping out of the condenser into the receiving flask.

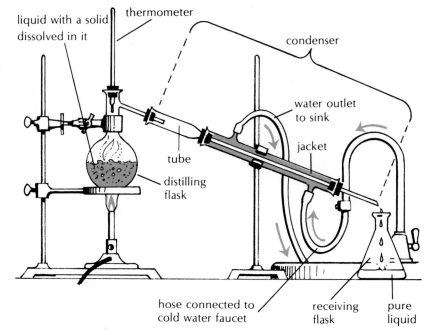

Distillation is a process in which a liquid is evaporated from one container, and the vapor then condensed into another container. Dissolved solids and suspended matter are not vaporized at the temperature of distillation. Therefore, these types of impurities will remain behind in the distilling flask. Although rather costly, distillation has been used at times to prepare drinking water from sea water or from polluted sources. However, now there are other less expensive methods for this purpose. Distillation is used widely in the laboratory and in industry to purify many chemicals.

Questions for Sections 7-6 through 7-8

13. Why does increasing the pressure on a gas favor liquefaction?
14. In addition to increasing pressure, what other change favors liquefaction?
15. What is true about any gas at a temperature above its critical temperature?
16. What happens to the heat of vaporization of most liquids as the temperature of the liquid increases?
17. Describe the relationship between heat of vaporization and intermolecular attraction.
*18. How much heat is required to vaporize 250 g of water at 100°C and one atmosphere pressure? (a) Set up the problem. (b) Calculate the answer.

19. A quantity of water vapor at 100°C and 1 atmosphere pressure is condensed to liquid water at the same temperature and pressure. In the process, 43 120 calories of heat is released. What quantity of water is condensed? (a) Set up the problem. (b) Calculate the quantity.
20. Describe the process of distillation.

7-9 Solids and the Kinetic Theory

As a liquid is cooled, the molecules move more slowly. Finally, a temperature is reached at which the molecules take fixed positions in a regular geometric pattern. There they retain only vibratory motion. At this point, the liquid is said to freeze. That is, it changes from a liquid to a solid. The particles in a solid remain in fixed positions close to one another. They are held in these positions by relatively strong inter-molecular forces. Solids are, therefore, rigid and even less compressible than liquids. They have definite shapes and volumes. However, the molecules of solids do show a slight tendency to diffuse and do possess some vapor pressure.

7-10 Melting and Freezing Points

As mentioned in the previous section, when a liquid substance cools by losing heat to its surroundings, it will finally reach a temperature at which it changes to the solid phase. The temperature at which this takes place is called the *freezing point* of the substance. In the reverse process of adding heat to the solid, a temperature is reached at which the solid changes to the liquid phase. This temperature is the *melting point* of the substance. For pure substances, the freezing point and melting point temperatures are the same. When measured at one atmosphere pressure, the temperature is called the normal freezing or melting point.

When the solid and liquid phases of a substance are in contact at the melting (freezing) point, and no energy is being added to or removed from them, they remain in equilibrium. Any melting of the solid is balanced by freezing of the liquid at the same rate. As a result, there is no change in the amounts of solid and liquid present.

Heat of fusion. As a solid is being melted, the mixture of solid and liquid undergoes no temperature change until all of the solid is changed to liquid. The quantity of heat needed to change a unit mass of solid to a liquid at a constant temperature is called the **heat of fusion** at that temperature. The heat of fusion at the normal melting point of the solid is most commonly used as reference. For ice, the heat of fusion at 0°C is 80 calories per gram. Exactly the same amount of heat is given up when one gram of water is changed to ice. This heat is called the **heat of crystallization.** It is defined as the quantity of heat given up at a con-

Figure 7-12

It takes 80 calories of heat to cause each gram of ice at 0°C to change to water at the same temperature. This heat is called the heat of fusion of ice.

stant temperature, when one gram of liquid is changed to a solid. For any given substance, the heat of crystallization is equal to the heat of fusion.

SAMPLE PROBLEM 1

The heat of fusion of ice at 0°C is 80 cal/g. How much heat is needed to change 75 grams of ice at 0°C to liquid water at the same temperature?

Solution. If it takes 80 calories to melt 1 gram of ice at 0°C, then it takes 75 times as much heat to melt 75 grams:

$$75 \times 80 \text{ cal} = 6000 \text{ cal}$$

The same result can be arrived at by using a formula:

$$
\begin{array}{ccc}
\begin{matrix}\text{heat to fuse}\\ \text{(melt) a substance}\end{matrix} & = \left(\begin{matrix}\text{heat of fusion}\\ \text{of the substance}\end{matrix}\right) & \times \left(\begin{matrix}\text{mass}\\ \text{of the substance}\end{matrix}\right)\\
& = \qquad 80 \text{ cal/g} & \times \qquad 75 \text{ g}\\
& = \qquad 6000 \text{ cal} &
\end{array}
$$

To the correct number of significant figures, this answer is 6.0×10^3 cal. In joules, the answer is $6.0 \times 10^3 \text{ cal} \times 4.18 \text{ joules/cal} = 2.5 \times 10^4$ joules.

SAMPLE PROBLEM 2

The heat of crystallization of water at 0°C is 80 cal/g. How much heat is released when 250 g of water at 0°C changes to ice at the same temperature?

Solution

$$
\begin{array}{ccc}
\begin{matrix}\text{heat to crystallize}\\ \text{a substance}\end{matrix} & = \left(\begin{matrix}\text{heat of crystallization}\\ \text{of the substance}\end{matrix}\right) & \times \left(\begin{matrix}\text{mass}\\ \text{of the substance}\end{matrix}\right)\\
& = \qquad 80 \text{ cal/g} & \times \qquad 250 \text{ g}\\
& = \qquad 20\ 000 \text{ cal} &\\
& = \qquad 2.0 \times 10^4 \text{ cal} &
\end{array}
$$

In joules, the answer is:

$$2.0 \times 10^4 \text{ cal} \times 4.18 \text{ joules/cal} = 8.4 \times 10^4 \text{ joules.}$$

SAMPLE PROBLEM 3

What quantity of ice at 0°C can be melted by 6800 calories of heat?

$$\begin{pmatrix} \text{heat to fuse} \\ \text{(melt) a substance} \end{pmatrix} = \begin{pmatrix} \text{heat of fusion} \\ \text{of the substance} \end{pmatrix} \times \begin{pmatrix} \text{mass} \\ \text{of the substance} \end{pmatrix}$$

$$6800 \text{ cal} = 80 \text{ cal/g} \times ?$$

$$? = \frac{6800 \text{ cal}}{80 \text{ cal/g}}$$

$$= 85 \text{ g}$$

Questions for Sections 7-9 and 7-10

21. Describe the arrangement and motion of the molecules of a substance in the solid phase.
22. How does the melting point of a pure substance compare with the freezing point of the same substance.
23. Describe the processes involved in maintaining the equilibrium that exists between the solid and liquid phases of a substance in contact with one another at the melting/freezing point of the substance.
24. What do we call the heat required to melt a unit mass of a solid?
25. At constant pressure, how does the quantity of heat absorbed by one gram of ice as it melts compare with the amount of heat released when one gram of liquid water freezes?
*26. How much heat is released when 440 grams of liquid water at 0°C freezes to form ice at the same temperature? (a) Set up the problem. (b) Calculate the answer.
27. What quantity of ice at 0°C will be melted by 2.80×10^3 calories of heat? (a) Set up the problem. (b) Calculate the answer.

7-11 Sublimation

Figure 7-13
Carbon dioxide below −78.5°C exists as a solid. As the solid warms, it passes directly into the gaseous phase without first becoming a liquid. Its coldness and its failure to become a liquid has earned solid carbon dioxide the common name "dry ice." The white clouds are condensed water vapor that forms when the temperature of the surrounding air is cooled.

We stated earlier that solids evaporate and produce a vapor pressure in the space around them. As in the case of liquids, the vapor pressure of solids increases with temperature. Although most solids have extremely low vapor pressures at any temperature, a few solids vaporize to a significant extent at ordinary temperatures. For example, naphthalene, a compound used in moth balls, will slowly evaporate in air at room temperature.

The element iodine is another example of a solid with high vapor pressures. If gently heated, iodine produces a noticeable amount of vapor. The iodine vapor will condense directly to the solid phase when it strikes a cool surface. This process by which a solid changes directly to a vapor without passing through a liquid phase, is called **sublimation.** The substance itself is said to **sublime.** The process is reversible.

Solid carbon dioxide ("dry ice") is another solid that sublimes. The vapor pressure of solid carbon dioxide is 1 atmosphere at −78.5°C. A piece of solid carbon dioxide exposed to the air will therefore remain at a temperature of −78.5°C while it changes directly to the gaseous phase. Just as a boiling liquid remains at the boiling point until it has

Chapter 7   Phases of Matter—Liquids and Solids   **131**

On a cold, dry winter day, snow and ice often disappear by subliming.

completely changed to vapor, solid carbon dioxide remains at −78.5°C until it has all changed to vapor. Because of these properties, solid carbon dioxide is sometimes used as a portable refrigerant. It remains colder than ice, and it does not melt.

Because of the high vapor pressure of its solid phase, carbon dioxide cannot be liquefied at normal atmospheric pressure. The gas changes directly to the solid phase when it is cooled. Carbon dioxide can exist as a liquid only under high pressure.

7-12 Crystals

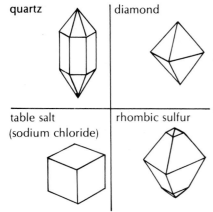

quartz   diamond

table salt (sodium chloride)   rhombic sulfur

Figure 7-14

Some common crystal shapes.

All *true* solids* form characteristic, geometric figures in which the atoms or molecules are arranged in a regular repeating pattern. These geometric forms have plane surfaces that are at definite angles to one another. Such geometric forms are called **crystals.** See Figure 7-14. The pattern of the atoms or molecules in a crystal is called the **crystal lattice.** Although the particles in solids are always vibrating, they do not change their relative positions in the crystal lattice. There are a number of different crystal shapes. Whether a solid has one shape or another is determined chiefly by two factors. One factor is the relative sizes of the particles. The other is the nature of the forces holding the particles together. Where the bonding forces are strong, the crystals have relatively high melting points and boiling points.

Some solids form large crystals rather easily. Their crystalline nature can be easily seen. Examples of such substances are salts (Chapter 23) such as copper sulfate, calcite (calcium carbonate), and ordinary table salt (sodium chloride). Other solids do not appear to be crystalline to the naked eye. However, microscopic or X-ray examination shows that they do have a crystalline nature. This point is illustrated with diamonds and graphite, two forms of the element carbon. Diamonds clearly are crystalline. A microscope is needed to see graphite crystals.

Crystal formation. When the water is evaporated from a salt solution, the salt will precipitate (become a solid) in the form of crystals.

*As previously stated (Section 5-6), certain materials, such as glass and some plastics, are often considered to be solids, but are technically highly viscous liquids.

Figure 7-15

Quartz crystals.

Small crystals form if the evaporation is rapid. Larger crystals form if the evaporation is slow. Slow evaporation allows atoms to attach themselves to previously formed crystals, building them up instead of forming their own centers of crystallization. Crystals large enough to be seen by the naked eye may be formed in other ways. Iodine vapor changes directly to crystals by sublimation. Diamond and graphite crystals form under conditions of high temperature and great pressure in the earth's crust. Sulfur crystals form when melted sulfur cools.

Questions for Sections 7-11 and 7-12

28. Define sublimation.
29. What property of a substance in the solid phase enables it to sublime?
30. What do we call the pattern, or arrangement, of molecules in a crystal?
31. What two factors determine the shape of a true solid?
32. When the water evaporates from a salt water solution, what effect does the rate of evaporation have on the size of the salt crystals that form?

7-13   Water of Hydration

When a sample of water is completely evaporated, the crystals of any solid substance that was dissolved in the water are left behind. These crystals may be of three types. (1) The crystals may be a pure solid. (2) The crystals may contain water mechanically enclosed within the crystal. The amount of water thus enclosed can vary. (3) The crystals may be made up of the solid substance combined chemically with water in a definite ratio. The third type is called a **hydrate.** The water with which it is combined is called **water of hydration.** Although hydrates contain significant amounts of water, they are perfectly dry to the touch. The blue copper sulfate crystal is a hydrate. In the formation of a unit molecule of this hydrate, five molecules of water became chemically united with one formula unit of copper sulfate. The formula of this hydrate is written by the chemist as $CuSO_4 \cdot 5H_2O$. (The meaning of formulas like this one is discussed in detail in the next chapter.) If the blue crystals are heated, water is driven off as steam. Then the substance changes its crystalline form and becomes a grayish-white powder. See Figure 7-16.

Figure 7-16

(A) The blue copper sulfate crystals, even though dry to the touch, contain 36 grams of water molecules for every 100 grams of the crystals. (B) Heating the blue copper sulfate drives off the water of hydration, leaving white anhydrous crystals.

Crystals without water in their composition are said to be **anhydrous.** Anhydrous means without water. If water is added to anhydrous copper sulfate, crystals of the hydrate are formed again, and the blue color returns.

When crystals of the second type are heated, tiny explosions occur as the mechanically enclosed water changes to steam and blows the crystals apart. This action is known as **decrepitation.** When true hydrates (the third type) are heated, they lose their water quietly.

Efflorescence. Sometimes the water of hydration is held so loosely that the hydrated substance doesn't even have to be heated for the water of hydration to be driven off. That is, the water of hydration will be driven off while the hydrated substance simply sits at room temperature. The spontaneous loss of water of hydration from a substance at room temperature is called **efflorescence.** Washing soda, $Na_2CO_3 \cdot 10H_2O$, is efflorescent. As the water of hydration leaves the crystals, they change to a dry, white substance. This substance is *anhydrous* sodium carbonate.

7-14   Hygroscopic and Deliquescent Substances

Certain substances absorb moisture from the air. These substances are said to be **hygroscopic.** Some solid hygroscopic substances simply get damp. Others absorb so much water from the air that they actually dissolve in it. A puddle of solution forms where the crystals of the hygroscopic substance had been sitting. Solid substances that absorb enough moisture from the air to dissolve themselves in it are called **deliquescent.** The process itself is called **deliquescence.** See Figure 7-17.

Calcium chloride and magnesium chloride are examples of deliquescent substances. All such substances are very soluble in water. Magnesium chloride is often found as an impurity in salt (sodium chloride) obtained from sea water. It causes the salt to cake or form lumpy masses in humid air. Calcium chloride is often spread on dirt roads and clay tennis courts. There it absorbs enough moisture to keep the dust down. It is also used in closets and basements to absorb moisture and thus reduce the humidity.

7-15   Densities of the Solid and Liquid Phases

In almost all solids, the molecules are held in fixed positions and are packed tightly together. When a solid is heated, the vibratory motion of the molecules increases. This increased motion usually results in a slight increase in the volume of the solid. When the solid melts, the molecular motion speeds up and the distance between molecules increases considerably. The liquid phase, therefore, has a larger volume (and lower density) than does the solid phase. As the temperature of the liquid rises above the melting point, its volume usually continues to

Figure 7-17

(A) Anhydrous calcium chloride crystals, CaCl$_2$, just after they were taken from a tightly sealed reagent bottle. (B) After one day, the crystals have absorbed enough moisture from the air to almost completely dissolve the crystals.

increase. The increase in volume is accompanied by a decrease in density.

With few exceptions, then, we can say that the density of the solid phase of a substance is greater than that of the liquid phase of the same substance. Thus, when a sample of a substance in the solid phase is placed in a sample of the same substance in the liquid phase, the solid will sink. For example, if a piece of pure lead is placed in a container of molten lead, the solid lead will sink to the bottom of the container.

The unusual behavior of water. When heat is added to ice below its melting point temperature, the ice behaves in a "normal" fashion. That is, its temperature rises and its volume increases slightly. When melting begins, however, the behavior of ice is quite different from that exhibited by other solids. Instead of continuing to expand, the ice *contracts* as it melts. Its volume decreases. Even after all the ice has melted and the temperature of the liquid water starts to rise, the volume of the water continues to decrease until the temperature reaches 4°C. At that point water behaves in a "normal" fashion, expanding as the temperature increases above 4°C.

The unusual behavior of water near its melting point temperature is due to the arrangement of water molecules in the crystal lattice. In the solid phase, water molecules are arranged in a relatively open pattern. (See Figure 7-18.) When ice starts to melt, the open structure collapses, allowing some of the molecules in the liquid phase to fill in

Figure 7-18

Three phases of water. Because the open structure of the solid collapses when ice melts, liquid water is denser than ice. In the gaseous state, the molecules are actually much further apart on the average than the diagram suggests.

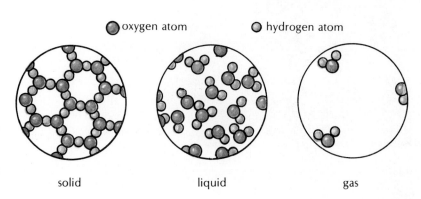

oxygen atom   hydrogen atom

solid   liquid   gas

some of the open spaces. The open structure is not completely broken down until the temperature of the liquid water reaches a temperature of 4°C. At this temperature, water is at its maximum density. Because of the unusual behavior of water, the liquid phase of this substance is denser than the solid phase. Thus, the solid phase (ice) floats in the liquid phase.

Questions for Sections 7-13 through 7-15

33. What is a hydrate?
34. Differentiate between efflorescence and deliquescence.
35. For most substances, how does the density of the liquid phase compare with the density of the solid phase?
36. Describe briefly the changes that take place as a sample of ice is slowly heated over a temperature range from −10°C to +10°C.

(A)

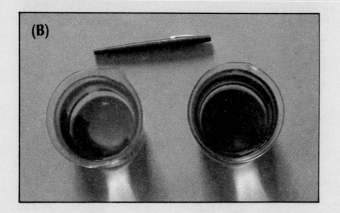

(B)

CAN YOU EXPLAIN THIS?

Potassium permanganate, KMnO₄, dissolves in water to produce a colored solution. One crystal of KMnO₄ was dropped into a beaker of cold water at the same time that another crystal of the same size was dropped into a beaker of hot water. Photograph A was taken 10 minutes after the crystals had been dropped into the beakers. The cold water is in the beaker on the left. Photograph B was taken just after Photograph A, but it shows what the contents of the beakers looked like when viewed from above.

How do you account for the difference in appearance of the two beakers?

1. Molecules of a substance in the liquid phase have some freedom of motion, but are held together by forces of mutual attraction. Liquids are only slightly compressible.

2. Evaporation occurs when molecules at the surface of a liquid attain enough kinetic energy to overcome the attractive forces of nearby molecules and thereby enter the gaseous phase.

3. Evaporation is a cooling process. When the more energetic molecules leave the surface of a liquid, the average kinetic energy of the remaining molecules is lowered. Thus, the temperature of the liquid tends to fall.

4. The rate of evaporation can be increased by an increase in temperature, by an increase in the surface area of the liquid, and by the presence of air currents in the space above the surface of the liquid.

5. Condensation is the reverse of evaporation. In this process, when slow-moving molecules of vapor strike the surface of a liquid, they are captured and become part of the liquid. Condensation raises the temperature of the vapor.

6. If a liquid is placed in a closed container, eventually a condition of physical equilibrium will be reached between evaporation and condensation.

7. The pressure exerted by a vapor in equilibrium with its liquid is called the equilibrium vapor pressure (or vapor pressure) of that liquid. The higher the vapor pressure of a liquid, the greater its rate of evaporation and the lower its boiling point.

8. The boiling point of a liquid is the temperature at which its vapor pressure is equal to the air pressure on the surface of the liquid. Normal boiling points are the boiling points at standard air pressure.

9. A combination of increased pressure and decreased temperature favors the liquefaction of gases. The critical temperature of a gas is the maximum temperature at which the gas can be liquified. No gas can be liquefied at a temperature above its critical temperature regardless of how much pressure is applied. Critical pressure is the pressure required to liquefy a gas at its critical temperature.

10. The heat of vaporization of a liquid is the quantity of energy (heat) required to vaporize a unit mass of that liquid at constant temperature.

11. The energy released when a gas condenses is called the heat of condensation. The heat of condensation is equal to the heat of vaporization at the same temperature.

12. The heat of fusion of a substance is the quantity of heat required to liquefy (melt) a unit mass of a solid at a constant temperature. The heat of crystallization is the quantity of heat released by a unit mass of a liquid when it crystallizes (freezes) at a constant temperature. The heats of fusion and crystallization are the same for any given substance at the same temperature.

13. Solids generally have very low vapor pressures. Some, however, have vapor pressures high enough to enable them to vaporize. The process by which a solid changes directly to a vapor (and vice versa) without passing through the liquid phase is called sublimation.

14. All true solids form geometric figures called crystals. The pattern, or arrangement, of molecules in a crystal is called the crystal lattice. Crystals consisting of a solid substance combined chemically with water in a definite ratio are called hydrates.

15. In some hydrates, the water of hydration is so weakly held that it will evaporate from the crystal at room temperature, a process called efflorescence.

16. Hygroscopic substances absorb moisture from the air. In some cases, hygroscopic substances absorb enough moisture to dissolve themselves. This process is called deliquescence.

17. For most substances, the solid phase is denser than the liquid phase. Thus, when placed in its own liquid, the solid phase will sink. Water, however, is denser than the liquid phase. Thus solid water (ice) floats in the liquid.

TERMS YOU SHOULD KNOW

evaporation	critical pressure	crystal lattice
vapor	heat of vaporization	hydrate
water vapor	heat of condensation	water of hydration
condensation	distillation	anhydrous
equilibrium vapor	heat of fusion	decrepitation
pressure	heat of crystallization	efflorescence
vapor pressure	sublimation	hygroscopic
liquefaction	sublime	deliquescence
critical temperature	crystal	

REVIEW QUESTIONS

Section

7-1   **1.** Why are gases more readily compressed than liquids?

7-2   **2.** Under normal conditions, why isn't oxygen gas considered to be a vapor?

      3. What effect does evaporation from the surface of a liquid have on the average kinetic energy of the molecules remaining in the liquid phase?

      4. How does evaporation differ from boiling?

      5. Describe three factors that affect evaporation rate.

7-3   **6.** What effect does condensation of vapor molecules have on the temperature of the vapor?

7-4   **7.** What condition exists when the space above a liquid in a closed container is saturated with water vapor?

      8. A pressure of 755.0 mm Hg is exerted by a mixture of nitrogen gas and water vapor in equilibrium with liquid water at 18°C. What is the partial pressure exerted by the gas? (Refer to Figure 7-6, page 121, for vapor pressure values for water.)

7-5   **9.** How can you make water boil without heating it?

    10. Explain the principle behind a pressure cooker.

7-6   **11.** Why does decreasing the temperature of a gas favor liquefaction?

    12. The critical temperature of carbon dioxide gas is 31.1°C and the critical pressure is 73.0 atm. What pressure will liquefy this gas at a temperature of 62.2°C?

7-7   13. How does the heat of vaporization of water at 70°C compare with the heat of condensation of water at the same temperature?

7-8   14. What happens to any dissolved solid impurities present in a liquid during the process of distillation?

7-10   15. How does the heat of fusion of a substance compare to the heat of crystallization of the same substance?

7-11   16. What properties of solid carbon dioxide make it useful as a portable refrigerant?

   17. At room temperature, what happens to solids that have high vapor pressures?

7-12   18. Differentiate between the terms crystal and crystal lattice.

7-13   19. Describe the three types of crystals that may form from dissolved solids left behind by evaporation of a solution.

7-14   20. Rewrite the following statement in simple, non-technical terms: Some hygroscopic substances undergo deliquescence.

REVIEW PROBLEMS

Section

7-7   1. What quantity of heat, in joules, is required to vaporize 600 g of water at 100°C and 1 atm pressure? (a) Set up the problem. (b) Calculate the answer in calories. (c) Convert to joules.

   2. A quantity of water vapor at 100°C is condensed to liquid water at 100°C and 1 atm. In the process, 1.62×10^4 calories of heat is released. What quantity of water is involved? (a) Set up the problem. (b) Calculate the answer.

7-10   3. How much heat is released when 75 g of liquid water freezes to form ice at 0°C? (a) Set up the problem. (b) Calculate the answer.

   4. What quantity of ice at 0°C will be melted by 6.8×10^4 calories of heat? (a) Set up the problem. (b) Calculate the answer.

FOR FURTHER THOUGHT

7-3   1. Evaporation of water from the body's surface has a cooling effect on the body. Would this cooling effect be greater at high altitudes, where air pressure is lower? Explain.

7-4   2. The force of gravity on the moon is about one-sixth as much as that on the earth. Since air pressure is a result of gravity, how would the reduced gravity on the moon affect the vapor pressure of water on the moon?

7-5   3. The moon has no atmosphere and therefore zero atmospheric pressure. (a) How would this condition affect the vapor pressure of water on the moon? (b) Suppose a container of water were opened on the moon. Describe what would be observed. (c) Give reasons for your answers.

7-15   4. (a) In a pond during a long subfreezing cold spell, where is the densest water? Where is the coldest water? (b) Use your answer to help explain why a pond freezes from the top down.

Cumulative Review

Section

1-2   **1.** Briefly state what is meant by a scientific theory. How does a theory differ from a scientific law?

2-3   **2.** For each of the following conversions, first write the setup for the problem and then find the numerical answer. (a) How many millimeters is 2.512 meters? (b) How many grams is 0.0524 kilograms? (c) How many kilometers is 7500 centimeters?

2-4   **3.** Perform the following calculation and express your answer in scientific notation:

$$\frac{(3.0 \times 10^{-2})(2.0 \times 10^{3})}{(4.0 \times 10^{-5})(6.0 \times 10^{-7})}$$

3-1   **4.** (a) How may a sample of matter, without having anything added to it, undergo a change in weight? (b) During the weight change, what quantity of the sample does not change?

3-7   **5.** The density of aluminum is 2.70 g/cm³. What will be the volume occupied by 135 g of aluminum?

       6. A sample of magnesium has a mass of 52.1 g and occupies a volume of 30.0 mL. What is the density of magnesiuim?

3-8   **7.** (a) State the changes in volume and phase that occur when a sample of ice is melted and the liquid is changed to steam at the boiling point. (b) Why are these changes considered to be physical changes?

3-17   **8.** (a) What is the difference between an element and a compound? (b) Why are elements and compounds, but not mixtures, referred to as substances?

4-5   **9.** When hydrogen and oxygen are mixed together at room temperature, no chemical reaction occurs until a flame or spark is applied to the mixture. Then an explosion occurs. (a) Describe the role of the flame or spark. (b) Is the reaction endothermic or exothermic? Explain.

4-9   **10.** If a 900-gram sample of water at 40°C loses 3600 calories of heat, what will its final temperature be? (a) Set up the problem. (b) Find the numerical answer.

4-10   **11.** According to the kinetic theory, what is the difference between heat and temperature? Use the kinetic theory to explain why the temperature of water will rise when the water is heated in a test tube.

5-5   **12.** An open-ended manometer is connected to a container of gas. The level of the mercury in the open end is 16 millimeters lower than the level of the mercury in the closed end. If the atmospheric pressure is 750 mm Hg, what is the pressure exerted by the gas in the container?

5-7   **13.** In terms of the kinetic energy of its particles, what happens when a solid melts?

5-8   **14.** While water is being heated at its boiling point, its temperature does not change. Explain why.

6-3   **15.** The volume of a sample of gas is 5.00 liters at 5.00 atmospheres. At constant temperature, what will be the volume of the sample at (a) 1.00 atmosphere? (b) 0.500 atmosphere?

6-5   **16.** At 37°C, a quantity of gas occupies a volume of 30.0L. What volume will it occupy at 47°C if pressure remains constant?

Cumulative Review

Section

6-6   **17.** A gas confined in a rigid container exerts a pressure of 2.0 atmospheres at a temperature of 27°C. What pressure will it exert if the temperature is lowered to 273 K?

6-9   **18.** Two liters of nitrogen at one atmosphere pressure are transferred to a one-liter container of oxygen at two atmospheres pressure and at the same temperature. (a) What is the pressure of the nitrogen in the mixture? (b) What is the total pressure of the mixture?

6-12   **19.** Using the kinetic theory, explain the following: (a) At constant temperature, decreasing the volume of a mass of oxygen gas from 50 mL to 25 mL will double its pressure. (b) At constant pressure, changing the temperature from 0°C to 273°C will double its volume. (c) Placing 1 liter of helium and 1 liter of hydrogen, both at 1 atm pressure, into a 1-liter container produces a mixture at 2 atm pressure while each gas retains its original pressure. (d) If the temperature of a confined mass of carbon dioxide gas at 0°C and 1.00 atm pressure is raised to 273°C, the pressure is increased to 2.00 atm.

6-16   **20.** In 10 liters of hydrogen at STP, (a) how many molecules of gas are present, and (b) how many moles of gas are present?

7-2   **21.** Explain why liquids diffuse less rapidly than gases do.

       22. Why do you feel cool when emerging from a swimming pool?

7-3   **23.** During the process of condensation, the temperature of the vapor increases. Explain why this occurs.

7-4   **24.** The vapor pressure of water at 23°C is 21.1 mm Hg. A student collects hydrogen over water at this temperature when the atmospheric pressure is 755 mm Hg. What is the pressure of the dry hydrogen?

7-6   **25.** The critical temperature of water is 374°C. What does this mean?

7-7   **26.** What is the relationship between a liquid's heat of vaporization and the attractive forces between the molecules of the liquid?

       27. How much heat, in joules, is needed to vaporize 400 g of water at 100°C and standard pressure? (a) Set up the problem. (b) Find the answer.

7-10   **28.** What quantity of ice at 0°C can be melted by 4000 calories of heat? (a) Set up the problem. (b) Calculate the answer.

7-11   **29.** Solid carbon dioxide is a substance that undergoes sublimation. Describe what happens during this process and explain why it occurs.

7-12   **30.** What are two characteristics of all true solids?

7-13   **31.** When grayish-white copper sulfate powder is moistened with water, a blue substance is obtained. Explain.

7-14   **32.** Anhydrous calcium chloride is spread on some roads and tennis courts. Explain the purpose of this procedure and how it works.

7-15   **33.** How does the crystal structure of ice account for the fact that ice is less dense than liquid water?

UNIT 3

Formulas and Equations

Pyrotechnics, from the Greek words *pyr*, meaning fire, and *technē*, meaning art, is another word for fireworks. Chemistry, the parent science of pyrotechnics, has a different way of expressing the same concept. Some of the chemical reactions that produce fireworks are expressed in these equations:

$$S + O_2 \rightarrow SO_2 \qquad C + O_2 \rightarrow CO_2$$

This "shorthand" would be understood by a chemist to represent the burning of sulfur and carbon. Chemists use symbols, formulas, and equations to describe substances and chemical reactions of all kinds. This unit explains how to read and write the language of chemistry.

Chemical Formulas

Objectives

After you have completed this chapter, you will be able to:
- Interpret the information conveyed by chemical formulas.
- Derive the formulas for various compounds.
- Apply the rules for determining the names of compounds.

8-1 Introduction

When atoms of one element combine with atoms of another element, a compound is formed. Compounds have names and they have chemical formulas. A **chemical formula** is a statement in chemical symbols that represents the composition of a substance. We have already mentioned the names of a number of compounds. For example, we have spoken of water, sodium chloride, and carbon dioxide. The formulas for these three compounds are:

Name of Compound	Formula
water	H_2O
sodium chloride	$NaCl$
carbon dioxide	CO_2

A chemical formula tells several things about a compound. First of all, it tells what elements make up the compound. For example, in the formula for water, H_2O, we see the symbols for the elements hydrogen (H) and oxygen (O). The formula thus tells us that water is made up of the elements hydrogen and oxygen. In a similar fashion, the formula for sodium chloride tells us that it is made up of sodium (Na) and chlorine (Cl). Carbon dioxide is made up of carbon (C) and oxygen (O).

The formulas of compounds also contain numbers, such as the number 2 in H_2O. These numbers are called subscripts. A subscript applies to the symbol that precedes it in the formula. The subscript 2 in H_2O refers to the H, the symbol for hydrogen. By convention, the subscript 1 is not written in formulas. When a symbol is not followed by a subscript, the subscript 1 is understood. In the formula H_2O, the subscript 1 is understood for the symbol *O*. In the formula NaCl, the subscript 1 is understood for both *Na* and *Cl*.

The *subscripts* in a formula show the ratios of the atoms of the elements that combine to form the compound. For example, the formula H_2O tells us that there are 2 atoms of hydrogen for each atom of oxygen in the compound water. The formula NaCl tells us that there is 1 atom of sodium for each atom of chlorine in sodium chloride. In CO_2, there are 2 atoms of oxygen for each atom of carbon.

8-2   Empirical Formulas

When a new substance is discovered, chemists set out to identify the substance. A *qualitative* (KWAL-uh-tay-tiv) *analysis* is done to find out what elements make up the substance. A *quantitative* (KWAN-tuh-tay-tiv) analysis will tell the chemist how much of each element is in the compound. For example, suppose that a qualitative analysis shows a new substance to be made up of carbon and hydrogen. This information by itself is only a start in identifying the substance. There are many compounds made up of carbon and hydrogen.

Next, suppose that a quantitative analysis shows that every 13-gram sample of the compound is made up of 1 gram hydrogen and 12 grams carbon. This information can be used to determine the relative number of atoms of each element in the compound. The methods used to make this determination are discussed in Chapter 9.

As you will learn in Chapter 9, the compound just described must be made up of an equal number of carbon atoms and hydrogen atoms. That is, in any sample of the compound, there is one carbon atom for every hydrogen atom. This information can be used to write what is called an empirical (em-PIR-ih-kul) formula. An **empirical formula** represents the simplest ratio in which the atoms combine to form a compound. This means that the subscripts in an empirical formula express the simplest whole-number relationship between the number of atoms of each element in the compound. For example, the empirical formula for the compound having one carbon atom for each hydrogen atom is CH. Had the quantitative analysis of the compound shown 2 carbon atoms for every 3 hydrogen atoms, the empirical formula would have been C_2H_3.

Note that the formula C_2H_2 could not be an empirical formula. The formula C_2H_2, like the formula CH, tells that there is an equal number of carbon and hydrogen atoms in the compound. However, the subscripts (2 and 2) are not in the simplest whole-number relationship to one another. The 2-to-2 relationship can be reduced to the simpler 1-to-1 relationship by dividing both subscripts by 2.

8-3   Molecular Formulas

The last section referred to a substance made up of an equal number of carbon and hydrogen atoms. The empirical formula for such a substance is CH. Our identification of the substance is still not complete, because there is more than one compound made up of an equal number

Figure 8-1

The clear, colorless, flammable liquid in the upper photo is benzene. Acetylene is a gas that burns in oxygen to produce the hot temperatures (about 3000°C) of the oxyacetylene torch used to cut and weld metals. Both benzene and acetylene have the same empirical formula, CH, because in any sample of either substance the number of hydrogen atoms is equal to the number of carbon atoms. However, their different molecular structures make their properties different. Note: Benzene is a suspected carcinogen and should be handled only under close supervision.

of carbon and hydrogen atoms. For example, benzene (ben-zeen) and acetylene (uh-SET-uh-leen) are both carbon-hydrogen compounds in which there are 12 grams of carbon for every 1 gram of hydrogen. Both substances are made up of an equal number of carbon atoms and hydrogen atoms. Thus, both substances have the same empirical formula, CH. Yet, the set of properties that describes benzene is quite different from the set that describes acetylene. Benzene, for example, is a liquid at room temperature, whereas acetylene is a gas. See Figure 8-1.

Benzene and acetylene have different properties because of differences in the ways in which the carbon and hydrogen atoms are joined to one another to form molecules. By methods to be discussed in Chapter 9, it has been shown that a benzene molecule has 6 carbon atoms and 6 hydrogen atoms. An acetylene molecule has 2 carbon atoms and 2 hydrogen atoms.

The above information can be used to write *molecular* formulas for these two substances. A **molecular formula** tells the total number of atoms of each element in one molecule of a substance. The molecular formula for benzene is C_6H_6. The molecular formula for acetylene is C_2H_2.

To repeat, both substances, benzene and acetylene, are made up of carbon and hydrogen atoms in equal numbers. Both, therefore, have the same empirical formula, CH. But each substance has molecules of a different size and structure. These differences give each substance a different set of properties. Figure 8-2 gives the *structural* formulas for both substances. A **structural formula** shows the way in which atoms are joined together in a molecule.

Questions for Sections 8-1 through 8-3

1. (a) State the definition of a chemical formula. (b) What does it tell about a compound? (c) What information is conveyed by the formula H_2SO_4?
2. (a) How does the information obtained from a qualitative analysis differ from that obtained from a quantitative analysis? (b) Which one gives more information about the formula of a substance? Explain.
3. (a) What is an empirical formula? (b) What is the empirical formula of hydrogen peroxide, H_2O_2?
4. One molecule of a certain compound is made up of 4 carbon atoms and 10 hydrogen atoms. (a) What is the molecular formula of the compound? (b) What is the empirical formula of the compound?
5. What information about the qualitative composition of sucrose can be obtained from its formula, $C_{12}H_{22}O_{11}$?
6. (a) In a 10-gram sample of carbon dioxide, CO_2, how many carbon atoms are there compared to the number of oxygen atoms? (b) In a 7-gram sample of the same compound, how many carbon atoms are there compared to the number of oxygen atoms?

Figure 8-2

Structural formulas for benzene, whose molecular formula is C_6H_6, and for acetylene, whose molecular formula is C_2H_2. Both substances have the same empirical formula, CH, indicating that in one molecule of either substance the number of carbon atoms is equal to the number of hydrogen atoms.

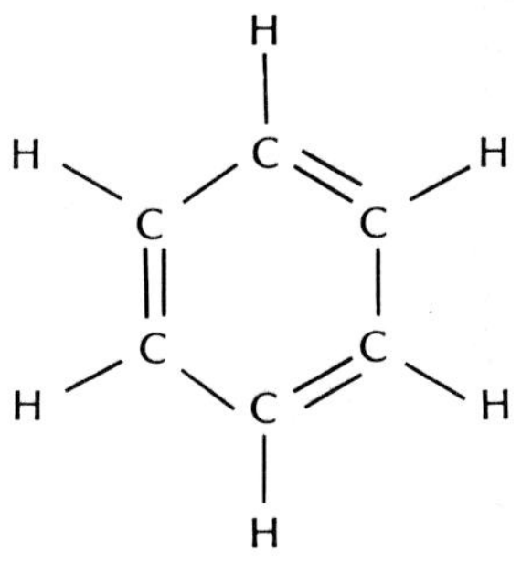

benzene, C_6H_6

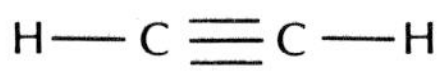

acetylene, C_2H_2

8-4 Ionic Substances

Atoms of elements are made up of smaller particles, some of which carry electric charges. These particles are the positively charged **protons** and negatively charged **electrons.** An atom of an element in the uncombined state contains equal numbers of protons and electrons. This makes an uncombined atom electrically neutral. That is, an uncombined atom has a net charge that is zero. For example, an uncombined atom of sodium contains 11 protons and 11 electrons:

Atom	**Charges**	
sodium, Na	11 protons having a charge of.	11+
	11 electrons having a charge of. . . .	11−
	net charge of. . . .	0

For another example, consider an uncombined atom of chlorine. With 17 protons and 17 electrons, it, too, has a net charge that is zero:

Atom	**Charges**	
chlorine, Cl	17 protons having a charge of.	17+
	17 electrons having a charge of. . . .	17−
	net charge of. . . .	0

Sodium is an example of a group of elements know as **metals,** and chlorine is among the group of elements known as **nonmetals.** As you will learn in Chapter 16, the properties that distinguish metals from nonmetals are determined by their atomic structures.

When some elements combine chemically with other elements to form compounds, one or more electrons may be transferred from each atom of the one element to the atoms of the other element. When this happens, the atoms of both elements will no longer have a net charge of zero. The atoms that lose electrons will contain more protons than electrons. The atoms that gain electrons will contain more electrons than protons. That is, the atoms of both elements will become charged. These electrically charged atoms are called **ions**.

As an illustration, let us consider the chemical change, or *reaction*, that takes place between the elements sodium and chlorine to produce the compound sodium chloride. During this reaction, each sodium atom loses one electron, producing a sodium ion with 11 protons and 10 electrons.. This gives the sodium ion a net charge of 1+:

Ion	**Charges**	
sodium, Na^+	11 protons having a charge of.	11+
	10 electrons having a charge of. . . .	10−
	net charge of. . . .	1+

Each chlorine atom gains one electron, producing a chlorine ion (more commonly called a *chloride ion*) with 17 protons and 18 electrons. This gives the chloride ion a net charge of $1-$:

Ion	Charges
chloride, Cl^-	17 protons having a charge of. . . . . .17+
	18 electrons having a charge of. . . . .18−
	net charge of. . . . . 1−

Compounds of a metal and a nonmetal, such as sodium chloride, that are made up of ions are called **ionic compounds.** In a later chapter you will learn more about ionic compounds.

Since ionic compounds consist of ions, not molecules, they cannot be represented by molecular formulas. Empirical formulas are used instead. The formula for sodium chloride, $NaCl$, is an empirical formula. It merely indicates that sodium chloride is made up of an equal number of sodium and chlorine atoms (actually ions). Magnesium chloride, another ionic compound, has the formula $MgCl_2$. This formula, an empirical formula, indicates that magnesium chloride is made up of twice as many chloride ions as magnesium ions.

The symbols used to represent ions consist of the symbol of the element followed by a superscript that tells the charge. The plus sign, written as a superscript, that appears in the symbol for the sodium ion, Na^+, tells us that a sodium ion contains one more proton than it does electrons. The superscript $2+$ in the symbol for the magnesium ion, Mg^{2+}, tells us that a magnesium ion contains two more protons than electrons. The superscript $2-$ in the symbol for the sulfide ion, S^{2-}, tells us that a sulfide ion contains two more electrons than protons.

8-5 Predicting Formulas of Ionic Compounds

Positive ions, such as Mg^{2+} and Na^+, are called **cations** (KAT-i-uns). Negative ions, such as F^- and S^{2-}, are called **anions** (AN-i-uns). Ionic compounds always consist of cations and anions in a fixed ratio. In MgF_2, the ratio is 1 magnesium ion to 2 fluoride ions. One magnesium ion has a charge of $2+$:

Ion	Charge
Mg^{2+}	(1 ion) × 2+ = 2+

Two fluoride ions have a total charge of $2-$:

Ion	Charge
F^{1-}	(2 ions) × 1− = 2−

In any sample of magnesium fluoride, there are 2 fluoride ions to every 1 magnesium ion. Therefore, the total positive charge in any sample

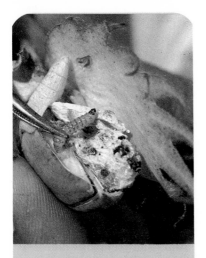

*Mass Confusion
Among the Bollworm Population*

The photo shows a pink bollworm being pulled from a cotton plant. These insects, if unchecked, can destroy a large amount of the cotton crop. They are among the worst insect pests in the United States.

One way to keep these pests under control is to spray the fields with an insecticide. A better approach is to spray the fields with the chemical that the female bollworm emits to attract males. (This chemical can be made by the chemical industry.) When the fields are saturated with the attractant, the males don't know where to look for a mate. As a result, few females lay fertilized eggs, and the size of the bollworm population is drastically reduced.

Chemicals that act as sex attractants are called phero-mones (FUR-uh-mones). The pheromone emitted by the female bollworm is called glossy-plure. Spraying with glossy-plure reduces only the population of the bollworm, whereas insecticides can foul the environment and reduce the populations of beneficial insects as well as harmful ones.

will always equal the total negative charge, making the sample electrically neutral. In the formula for any ionic compound, this same equality of positive and negative charges must be present. Therefore, to write the formula of an ionic compound, we must use subscripts for the ions that make the total positive and negative charge balance (be equal). If the positive and negative ions have the same charge, the charges of the two ions will balance when the ions are present in equal numbers. The ratio will be 1:1. The formula will then consist of the two symbols with no written subscripts (the subscript 1 will be understood for each element). A familiar example is the formula for sodium chloride:

$$NaCl$$

The charge of the sodium ion is $1+$; the charge of the chlorine ion is $1-$. The charges are equal, making both subscripts 1 (understood). This can be shown by writing the formula with the ionic charges indicated:

$$Na^{1+}Cl^{1-} \quad \text{or} \quad Na^{+}Cl^{-}$$

Another example is the formula for magnesium sulfide: MgS. The charge on the magnesium ion is $2+$. The charge on the sulfide ion is $2-$. The charges are equal, making both subscripts 1 (understood). This can be shown by writing the formula with the ionic charges indicated:

$$Mg^{2+}S^{2-}$$

Suppose one ion has twice the charge of the other. We have seen this situation in magnesium fluoride. It means that the formula must have twice as many ions with the smaller charge as ions with the larger charge. Thus the formula of magnesium fluoride is MgF_2. The balance of charge can be seen if the formula is written with the ionic charges indicated:

$$Mg^{2+}_{(1)} \; F^{1-}_{2}$$

Charge per ion:	2+	1-
Number of ions:	× 1	× 2
Total charge:	2+	2- (Positive and negative charge balance)

To take another substance, what is the formula of sodium sulfide if the ionic charge of sodium is $1+$ and that of sulfur is $2-$? Now it is the positive ion that must exist in the compound in greater number. The formula is Na_2S. With charges indicated, the formula is:

$$Na^{1+}_{2} \; S^{2-}_{(1)}$$

Charge per ion:	1+	2-
Number of ions:	× 2	× 1
Total charge:	2+	2- (Positive and negative charge balance)

Now let us consider the case where one ion has a charge of 2 and the other a charge of 3. An example is the compound aluminum sulfide.

Chapter 8   Chemical Formulas   **149**

The aluminum ion has a charge of 3+; the sulfur ion, a charge of 2−. The balance can be obtained by combining 2 Al^{3+} ions with 3 S^{2-} ions:

$$Al_2^{3+}S_3^{2-}$$

Charge per ion   3+   2−
Number of ions   x 2   x 3
_____

Total charge   6+   6−   (Positive and negative charge balance)

The formula for aluminum sulfide without showing the charges is:

$$Al_2S_3$$

A simple rule can be obtained from these examples. Write the symbols with their ionic charges indicated. Then use the charge of each ion as the subscript for the other. If the subscripts are the same, omit them. (In an empirical formula, we show the simplest ratio). If a subscript is 1, omit it. Figure 8-3 gives some examples of these rules.

Figure 8-3

Examples of the "criss-cross" method of determining the subscripts of ionic compounds.

Symbols with charges:	$Mg^{2+}N^{3-}$	$Na^{1+}O^{2-}$	$Al^{3+}Cl^{1-}$	$K^{1+}Br^{1-}$	$Ca^{2+}S^{2-}$
Formulas:	Mg_3N_2	Na_2O_1	Al_1Cl_3	K_1Br_1	Ca_2S_2
Final Formulas*:	Mg_3N_2	Na_2O	$AlCl_3$	KBr	CaS

*Subscripts of 1 are always removed in writing final formulas. Also, where subscripts have a common whole-number divisor, they are reduced, as was done for CaS.

The formula-writing method described above, with one additional step, can be used for writing formulas containing ions made up of two or more elements. Such ions are called **polyatomic ions.** When using subscripts with polyatomic ions, the formula of the ion is placed in parentheses. The subscript is placed outside the parentheses. For example, in aluminum sulfate, there are two aluminum ions (Al^{3+}) for every three sulfate ions (SO_4^{2-}). The formula for aluminum sulfate is:

$$Al_2(SO_4)_3$$

2 aluminum
ions for every 3 sulfate ions

Figure 8-4 gives some examples of the "criss-cross" method of writing formulas when it is applied to substances containing polyatomic ions.

Figure 8-4

Examples of the "criss-cross" method of determining subscripts of ionic compounds containing polyatomic ions.

Symbols with charges:	$Na^{1+}NO_3^{1-}$	$H^{1+}CO_3^{2-}$	$Ca^{2+}OH^{1-}$	$Al^{3+}SO_4^{2-}$	$Al^{3+}PO_4^{3-}$
Formulas:	$Na_1(NO_3)_1$	$H_2(CO_3)_1$	$Ca_1(OH)_2$	$Al_2(SO_4)_3$	$Al_3(PO_4)_3$
Final Formulas*:	$NaNO_3$	H_2CO_3	$Ca(OH)_2$	$Al_2(SO_4)_3$	$AlPO_4$

*Subscripts of 1 are always removed in writing final formulas. Also, where subscripts have a common whole-number divisor, they are reduced, as was done for $AlPO_4$.

Questions for Sections 8-4 and 8-5

7. Why are ionic compounds represented by empirical formulas?

8. When calcium combines with chlorine, each Ca atom loses two electrons and each Cl atom gains one electron. (a) What is the charge on a Ca ion? (b) What is the charge on a Cl ion? (c) Write the formula for calcium chloride.

9. Define (a) anion (b) cation.

*10. How many magnesium atoms (that is, magnesium ions) are represented by one formula unit of each of the following ionic compounds? *(a) $MgCl_2$ (b) $MgSO_4$ (c) $Mg_3(PO_4)_2$

*11. If a magnesium ion has a charge of 2+ (Mg^{2+}), what is the total positive charge represented by one formula unit of each of the compounds listed in question 10? *(a) $MgCl_2$ (b) $MgSO_4$ (c) $Mg_3(PO_4)_2$

12. How many nitrate ions, NO_3^-, are represented by one formula unit of each of the following ionic compounds? *(a) $Mg(NO_3)_2$ (b) $NaNO_3$ (c) $Al(NO_3)_3$

*13. If the nitrate ion has a charge of 1− (NO_3^-), what is the total negative charge represented by one formula unit of each of the compounds listed in question 12? *(a) $Mg(NO_3)_2$ (b) $NaNO_3$ (c) $Al(NO_3)_3$

*14. (a) How are the total positive and negative charges related in the formula of an ionic compound? (b) What is the total positive charge expressed by one formula unit of aluminum oxide, Al_2O_3, a compound made up of aluminum ions, Al^{3+}, and oxide ions, O^{2-}? (c) What is the total negative charge?

15. Show how the "criss-cross" method is used to derive the formula of (a) aluminum nitrate, a compound made up of Al^{3+} and NO_3^- ions. (b) calcium phosphate, a compound made up of Ca^{2+} and PO_4^{3-} ions.

*16. Write the correct ionic formulas for the compounds made up of the following ions: *(a) Ba^{2+} and Cl^- *(b) Li^+ and S^{2-} *(c) Sr^{2+} and PO_4^{3-} (d) K^+ and Br^- (e) NH_4^+ and S^{2-} (f) Al^{3+} and CO_3^{2-}.

*The answers to questions marked with an asterisk are given in the back of the book.

8-6 Elements that Form More than One Kind of Ion

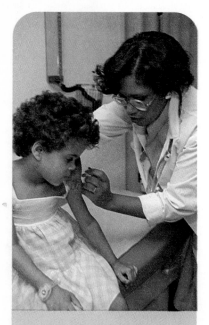

Physician

So far we have considered elements that form one kind of ion during ionic bonding. However, some elements form two kinds of ions. Copper is such an element. For reasons that are discussed in Chapter 14, we expect the copper atom to lose one electron during ionic bonding to form an ion whose charge is 1+. This does happen in some of the reactions of copper. The ion thus formed has the symbol Cu^{1+} or simply Cu^+. The ion is called the cuprous ion.

In some copper reactions, a transfer takes place of more than just a single electron. When two electrons are transferred, the copper ion that is formed has a charge of 2+. Its symbol is written Cu^{2+}. This ion is called the cupric ion.

The **Stock system** is a relatively new system for naming the ions of metals that form two kinds of ions. With the Stock system, the name of the ion is simply the name of the metal followed by a Roman numeral in parentheses. The Roman numeral tells the charge on the ion. For example, the cuprous ion, Cu^{1+}, is called the copper(I) ion (pronounced "copper one ion"). The cupric ion, Cu^{2+}, is called the copper(II) ion (pronounced "copper two ion"). Iron also forms two ions: the ferrous ion, Fe^{2+}, and the ferric ion, Fe^{3+}. In the Stock stystem, the ferrous ion is called the iron(II) ion. The ferric ion is called the iron(III) ion. Lead forms the plumbous or lead(II) ion, Pb^{2+}, and the plumbic or lead(IV) ion, Pb^{4+}. Similarly, tin forms the stannous or tin(II) ion, Sn^{2+}, and the stannic, or tin(IV) ion, Sn^{4+}.

Another element that forms ions with two different charges is mercury. In most of its compounds the mercury ion has a charge of 2+. However, mercury is also able to form a diatomic ion in which two mercury atoms are joined, and each atom seems to have a charge of 1+. The ion may be represented as $(Hg\text{-}Hg)^{2+}$ but is usually written as Hg_2^{2+}. The compound of mercury and chlorine containing this ion has an empirical formula of HgCl. Because the chloride ion has a charge of 1−, the formula HgCl makes it appear as though the mercury ion in the compound has a charge of 1+. However, there is no Hg^+ ion. The compound consists of Hg_2^{2+} ions and Cl^- ions in the ratio of 1 Hg_2^{2+} ion to 2 Cl^- ions. For this reason the formula of the compound is written Hg_2Cl_2. In forming the ion, each atom of mercury loses only one electron. The ion is called the mercurous ion. The compound is called mercurous chloride. The more normal ion, Hg^{2+}, is called the mercuric ion. It can also combine with chlorine to produce mercuric chloride, $HgCl_2$.

The Stock and old systems for naming ions are illustrated in Figure 8-5. Figure 8-6 gives a listing of the names and charges of all the ions mentioned so far along with some other common ions. This list includes some ions that are polyatomic. Writing formulas and equations will be easier for you if you learn the names of these ions and their formulas.

Figure 8-5

The old system and the Stock system for naming certain ions.

Element		Ion		
Symbol	Name	Symbol	Name Old System	Stock System
Cu	copper	Cu^{1+} Cu^{2+}	cuprous cupric	copper (I) copper (II)
Fe	iron	Fe^{2+} Fe^{3+}	ferrous ferric	iron (II) iron (III)
Hg	mercury	Hg_2^{2+} Hg^{2+}	mercurous mercuric	mercury (I) mercury (II)
Pb	lead	Pb^{2+} Pb^{4+}	plumbous plumbic	lead (II) lead (IV)
Sn	tin	Sn^{2+} Sn^{4+}	stannous stannic	tin (II) tin (IV)

Figure 8-6

The names and charges of some common ions.

1+
ammonium, NH_4^+
cesium, Cs^+
copper (I), Cu^+
potassium, K^+
silver, Ag^+
sodium, Na^+

2+
barium, Ba^{2+}
beryllium, Be^{2+}
cadmium, Cd^{2+}
calcium, Ca^{2+}
cobalt (II), Co^{2+}
copper (II), Cu^{2+}
iron (II), Fe^{2+}
lead (II), Pb^{2+}
magnesium, Mg^{2+}
mercury (I), Hg_2^{2+}
mercury (II), Hg^{2+}
nickel, Ni^{2+}
strontium, Sr^{2+}
zinc, Zn^{2+}

3+
aluminum, Al^{3+}
chromium (III), Cr^{3+}
iron (III), Fe^{3+}

1-
acetate, $C_2H_3O_2^-$
bromide, Br^-
chlorate, ClO_3^-
chlorite, ClO_2^-
chloride, Cl^-
cyanide, CN^-
fluoride, F^-
hydrogen carbonate,
  or bicarbonate, HCO_3^-
hydrogen sulfate, HSO_4^-
hydroxide, OH^-
iodide, I^-
nitrate, NO_3^-
nitrite, NO_2^-

2-
carbonate, CO_3^{2-}
chromate, CrO_4^{2-}
dichromate, $Cr_2O_7^{2-}$
oxide, O^{2-}
oxalate, $C_2O_4^{2-}$
peroxide, O_2^{2-}*
sulfate, SO_4^{2-}
sulfide, S^{2-}
sulfite, SO_3^{2-}
tartrate, $C_4H_4O_6^{2-}$

3-
phosphate, PO_4^{3-}

*Note: Like the mercurous ion discussed earlier, the peroxide ion is also diatomic. It consists of two oxygen atoms sharing one pair of electrons in a single bond,.plus two electrons gained during reaction with another element.

*17. Below are listed the correct formulas of some ionic compounds. Use the information given in Figure 8-6 to determine the name and symbol of each of the ions present in each compound. *(a) NaCl *(b) $BaBr_2$ *(c) $CaSO_4$ (d) KCl (e) $CdCO_3$ (f) $CuCl_2$

18. There are two iron chloride compounds, $FeCl_2$ and $FeCl_3$. Give the names of both compounds, using both the old system and the Stock system.

19. Name each of the following compounds using both the old system and the Stock system: (a) Cu_2O (b) $Hg_2(NO_3)_2$

*20. Referring to Figure 8-6, write the formulas of *(a) ammonium carbonate (b) barium sulfate (c) sodium phosphate (d) aluminum bromide (e) sodium peroxide.

8-7 Formulas of Molecular Compounds

Many compounds are made up of molecules rather than ions. Compounds made up of molecules are called *molecular compounds*. Molecular formulas are used to write the formulas of molecular compounds. In many cases, however, the molecular formula of a compound is also an empirical formula. For example, carbon dioxide is a molecular compound. Its molecular formula, CO_2, is also an empirical formula.

As you have learned in this chapter, writing formulas for ionic compounds is a relatively simple task. Because the formation of ionic compounds involves the *transfer* of electrons, charged atoms (ions) are produced. Writing proper formulas for ionic compounds simply means making the total positive and negative charges equal. Where necessary, subscripts are used to equalize the charges. Unfortunately, there is no such "simple" method for predicting and writing formulas for molecular compounds.

Writing the formulas of molelcular compounds is more complicated because the very same elements may form a number of different compounds. Different compounds, of course, have different formulas. An example is the five compounds formed from nitrogen and oxygen that are shown in Figure 8-7.

The names of the nitrogen-oxygen compounds listed in Figure 8-7 tell us how to write correct formulas if we understand the system for naming the compounds. In naming a molecular compound, the prefixes **mon(o)-, di-, tri-, tetr(a)-,** and **pent(a)-** are often used to tell how many atoms of each element are in a molecule of the compound. See Figure 8-8. You should apply the information given in Figure 8-8 to the names given in Figure 8-7 to see if you understand how the prefixes are used.

The Stock system is also used to name molecular compounds, but for molecular compounds the Roman numerals refer to the *oxidation number* of each element. The oxidation number of an element is

Figure 8-7

Formula	Name of Compound
N_2O	dinitrogen monoxide
NO	nitrogen monoxide
N_2O_3	dinitrogen trioxide
NO_2	nitrogen dioxide
N_2O_5	dinitrogen pentoxide

Figure 8-8

*The prefixes commonly used to
name molecular compounds.*

Prefix	Meaning	Example
mon(o)–	1	lead _mon_oxide, PbO
di–	2	lead _di_oxide, PbO_2
tri–	3	phosphorus _tri_chloride, PCl_3
tetr(a)–	4	carbon _tetra_chloride, CCl_4
pent(a)–	5	phosphorus _penta_chloride, PCl_5

discussed in some detail in Chapter 26. Here it should only be noted that the oxidation number is the *apparent* charge on one atom of an element. The word *apparent* is emphasized because in molecular compounds there are no ions. None of the reacting atoms gains or loses electrons during the formation of a molecular compound. In molecular compounds, electrons are *shared,* as will be explained in Chapter 14. However, within the molecules in a molecular compound, the atoms of some elements attract shared electrons more strongly than do the atoms of other elements. Those elements that have a relatively stronger attraction for electrons are said to be more *electronegative* than those that have a relatively weaker attraction for electrons. In a given molecular compound, the more electronegative element acquires a partial negative charge, giving the less electronegative element a partial positive charge. Because oxygen is more electronegative than nitrogen, oxygen has a partial negative charge in all five of the nitrogen-oxygen compounds shown in Figure 8-7, giving the nitrogen atom a partial positive charge in these compounds. Oxygen is considered to have an apparent charge of 2− in almost all of its compounds, including the five compounds of interest here. The apparent positive charge of each nitrogen atom can be determined by observing the rule that the total apparent positive charge must be equal to the total apparent negative charge. Let us see how this applies to the compound N_2O where the letter x is used to represent the apparent charge of a nitrogen atom.

$$N_2O$$

Apparent charge on one atom of
each element in the molecule: $\quad x \quad 2-$

Total apparent charge on all atoms
of that element in the molecule: $\quad 2x \quad 2-$

Formula	Stock System Name
N_2O	nitrogen (I) oxide
NO	nitrogen (II) oxide
N_2O_3	nitrogen (III) oxide
NO_2	nitrogen (IV) oxide
N_2O_5	nitrogen (V) oxide

Figure 8-9

The Stock system names for the compounds of nitrogen and oxygen.

Note that the total apparent positive charge contributed by the nitrogen atoms is $2x$ because there are 2 atoms of nitrogen in the molecule. If the total apparent negative charge is $2-$, then the total apparent positive charge must be $2+$.

$$2x = 2+$$

$$x = 1+$$

The number $1+$ for x is the apparent positive charge on each nitrogen atom in the compound N_2O. Put another way, $1+$ is the oxidation number of nitrogen in the compound N_2O. Using the Stock system, the compound N_2O is called nitrogen (I) oxide. By similar reasoning, it can be shown that the other nitrogen-oxygen compounds have the Stock system names given in Figure 8-9.

Questions for Section 8-7

21. Without consulting Figure 8-7, name the following compounds using the prefixes mon(o)-, di-, tri-, etc. (a) N_2O (b) NO (c) N_2O_3 (d) NO_2 (e) N_2O_5. Check the correctness of your answers by consulting Figure 8-7.
22. If an atom of oxygen has an apparent charge (an oxidation number) of $2-$ in the compound P_4O_{10}, what is the apparent charge of a phosphorus atom?
23. The oxygen atoms in carbon monoxide, CO, and in carbon dioxide, CO_2, each have an apparent charge or oxidation number of $2-$. (a) What is the apparent charge of the carbon atom in each of these two compounds? (b) What is the name of each compound according to the Stock system?

8-8   Binary Compounds

The chemical name of a compound generally indicates the chemical composition of the substance. The simplest types of compounds consist of only two elements. Such compounds are called **binary compounds.** The nitrogen-oxygen compounds discussed in the last section are all binary compounds. Binary compounds are named by giving the names of the elements in the order in which their symbols appear in the formula of the compound. In most cases the less electronegative element is named first.

Binary compounds composed of a metal and a nonmetal are generally ionic compounds. These compounds are named by simply naming the ions of which they are composed. Several ionic compounds were named in Section 8-5. Binary compounds composed of two nonmetallic elements are generally molecular. In naming these compounds, the less electronegative element is named first, and the name of the second element ends in -*ide*. Examples of binary compounds whose names end in -*ide* are given in Figure 8-10.

Figure 8-10

Ionic Compounds		Molecular Compounds	
Formula	Name	Formula	Name
Na_2S	sodium sulfide	CO	carbon monoxide
MgO	magnesium oxide	NO_2	nitrogen dioxide
$NaCl$	sodium chloride	SO_2	sulfur dioxide
CaI_2	calcium iodide	N_2O_3	dinitrogen trioxide
Na_2O_2	sodium peroxide	CCl_4	carbon
NaH	sodium hydride		tetrachloride

The typical properties of acids are shown by the solution, not by the undissolved compound.

Binary acids. *Acids* are water solutions of certain hydrogen compounds. These solutions have certain characteristics that are described in detail in Chapter 23. As the name suggests, **binary acids** are water solutions of binary hydrogen compounds. Three of these compounds and the names of the acids they form are listed in Figure 8-11.

Figure 8-11

Some common binary acids.

Formula of Compound	Name of Dry (Undissolved) Compound	Name of Water Solution
HCl	hydrogen chloride	hydrochloric acid
HBr	hydrogen bromide	hydrobromic acid
H_2S	hydrogen sulfide	hydrosulfuric acid

All three of the compounds listed in Figure 8-11 are gases under normal conditions when they are undissolved. The acids are prepared by bubbling the gases through water. The names of the water solutions have several features in common. The prefix *hydro-* indicates that the acid consists of a binary hydrogen compound—that is, hydrogen and only one other element. The prefix is followed by the name of that other element. The ending of the name is modified by the suffix *-ic*. The word acid is included as part of the name.

8-9   Ternary Compounds

Compounds made up of three elements are called **ternary compounds.** Many ternary compounds are ionic compounds in which the cation is a metal and the anion is polyatomic. Examples include sodium sulfate, Na_2SO_4, and calcium nitrate, $Ca(NO_3)_2$. The only common polyatomic ion having a positive charge is the ammonium ion, NH_4^+. Some ternary compounds containing this ion are ammonium chloride, NH_4Cl, ammonium sulfide, $(NH_4)_2S$, and ammonium nitrate, NH_4NO_3. The names of all these ionic compounds are derived from the names of the ions. Note that the names of some of these ternary compounds end in -ide. Thus, although all binary compounds end in -ide, not all compounds with this ending are binary.

Ternary acids. Some ternary compounds of hydrogen dissolve in water to produce acid solutions. These compounds are called **ternary acids.** The dry (undissolved) compounds consist of molecules. When these compounds are placed in water, their molecules interact with water molecules to produce cations and anions. The cations are H^+ ions. The anions are polyatomic, and usually contain oxygen. These polyatomic anions are named by adding a suffix, either -ate or ite, to the name of the element that is combined with the oxygen. In general, the anion ending in -ate contains one more oxygen atom than does the related -ite anion. For example, the formula of the chlorate ion is ClO_3^-, while that of the chlorite ion is ClO_2^-.

The names given to ternary acids are related to the names of the anions. If the name of the anion ends in -ate, the name of the acid ends in -ic. If the name of the anion ends in -ite, the name of the acid ends in -ous. Figure 8-12 lists some ternary compounds.

Figure 8-12

Some ternary acids and the anions they are related to.

Anion	Related Acid
NO_3^-, nitrate	HNO_3, nitric acid
NO_2^-, nitrite	HNO_2, nitrous acid
SO_4^{2-}, sulfate	H_2SO_4, sulfuric acid
SO_3^{2-}, sulfite	H_2SO_3, sulfurous acid

8-10 Prefixes Hypo- and Per-

Chlorine and oxygen form four different ions with a charge of $1-$. These ions are ClO^-, ClO_2^-, ClO_3^-, and ClO_4^-. Note that these anions all contain *one* chlorine atom. They differ *only* in the number of oxygen atoms present. Hydrogen compounds of all these anions form acids. The names of these anions and the names and formulas of the related acids are given in Figure 8-13.

Figure 8-13

Acids composed of hydrogen, chlorine, and oxygen.

Anions Composed of Chlorine and Oxygen	Related Ternary Acids	Oxidation Number of Chlorine
hypochlorite ion, ClO^-	hypochlorous acid, $HClO$	1+
chlorite ion, ClO_2^-	chlorous acid, $HClO_2$	3+
chlorate ion, ClO_3^-	chloric acid, $HClO_3$	5+
perchlorate ion, ClO_4^-	perchloric acid, $HClO_4$	7+

We are already familiar with anions ending in *-ite* and *-ate*, and their related acids, which end in *-ous* and *-ic* respectively. In this series of compounds, we have the chlorite ion and the chlorate ion. But, we also have two additional ions. These are named by adding prefixes—*hypo-* to the *-ite* ion and *per-* to the *-ate* ion. **Hypo-** is a Latin prefix meaning "less than." **Per-** is an abbreviated form of *hyper-*, a Latin prefix meaning "greater than." In a series of acid formulas like those in Figure 8-13, these prefixes refer to the oxidation numbers (or apparent charges) of the chlorine atoms.

In hypochlorous acid, the oxidation number of chlorine is less than it is in chlorous acid. In perchloric acid, the oxidation number of chlorine is greater than it is in chloric acid. In Chapter 26, you will see how the oxidation numbers of chlorine are determined for these acids.

Questions for Sections 8-8 through 8-10

24. (a) What is a binary compound? (b) Write the names and formulas of two ionic and two molecular binary compounds.
25. For the following acid formulas, state the name of the pure substance and of its water solution: (a) HF (b) H_2S (c) HCl
26. (a) What is a ternary compound? (b) State the name and formula of a ternary chloride and a ternary nitrate.
27. Name the following acids: (a) H_2CO_3 (b) H_2SO_3 (c) H_3PO_4 (d) $HC_2H_3O_2$.
28. (a) Write the formulas for hypochlorous, chlorous, and chloric acids. (b) For each, state the apparent charge on the chlorine atom.
29. (a) Write the formulas of the chlorate and perchlorate ions. (b) What does the prefix *per-* signify in the *perchlorate* name?
30. What does the prefix *hypo-* indicate in the name *hypochlorite*?

CHAPTER SUMMARY

1. A chemical formula is a representation of the composition of a compound using chemical symbols and subscripts. It indicates the elements in the compound and the ratio of their atoms.
2. The qualitative analysis of a substance shows what elements it contains. The quantitative analysis states the percentage by mass, or the mass ratio, of the elements in the substance.
3. The empirical formula represents the simplest ratio of atoms in the compound.
4. A molecular formula indicates the number of atoms of each element in one molecule of a compound. A structural formula shows the way in which atoms are bonded together in a molecule.
5. Ionic compounds are formed when electrons are transferred from metallic elements to nonmetallic elements.
6. The units in an ionic compound are ions. The formula of an ionic compound is an empirical one.
7. The formula of an ionic substance shows that the total charge on the positive ions balances the total charge on the negative ions.
8. A convenient method of obtaining the formula of an ionic compound is to bring down the integers of the ionic charges, in reverse order, as subscripts.

When possible, reduce the whole number ratio of the subscripts to simpler terms.

9. The *-ous* and *-ic* endings can be used in naming compounds of metallic elements that form two ions, each having a different positive charge. The *-ous* ending indicates the ion with the lower positive charge.

10. The units in molecular compounds are molecules in which the atoms are held together by sharing electrons.

11. The same elements may form a number of different molecular compounds. The names of these compounds reveal the differences in their formulas. The prefixes *mono-, di-, tri-*, etc. are used to indicate the number of atoms of some element in the formula. The Stock system may also be used to name such compounds.

12. The total apparent positive charge (oxidation number) in molecular formulas should equal the total apparent negative charge.

13. In naming binary compounds, the less electronegative element is named first. The name of the second element ends in *-ide*.

14. A binary compound consists of two elements; a ternary compound has three.

15. Binary compounds that are composed of a metal and nonmetal are usually ionic. Those composed of two nonmetallic elements are generally molecular.

16. Binary acids are water solutions of certain binary hydrogen compounds. Their names are preceded by the prefix *hydro-* and end with the suffix *-ic*.

17. Certain ternary compounds of hydrogen and a polyatomic ion form acids in water solution. The pure, undissolved compounds consist of neutral molecules. If the name of the polyatomic ion ends in *-ate,* the acid name ends in *-ic*. If the name of this ion ends in *-ite,* the acid name ends in *-ous*.

18. The *-ate* and *-ite* endings of the names of polyatomic ions are related to the apparent positive charge (oxidation number) of the element in the ion that is combined with oxygen. Because this charge is higher in the *-ate* ion, this ion has more oxygen atoms in it than the *-ite* ion. The *hypo-* and *per-* prefixes are also related to oxidation numbers.

TERMS YOU SHOULD KNOW

chemical formula	cation	binary compound
empirical formula	anion	binary acid
molecular formula	polyatomic ion	ternary compound
structural formula	Stock system	ternary acid
ion	prefixes *mon(o)-, di-,*	prefixes *hypo-*
ionic compound	*tri-, tetra-, penta-*	and *per-*

REVIEW QUESTIONS

Section   8-1   **1.** Ammonium dichromate is an ionic compound with the formula $(NH_4)_2Cr_2O_7$. What information can be gained from the formula?

8-2   **2.** (a) Distinguish between molecular and empirical formula. (b) Label each of the following as molecular or empirical and explain your answer: (1) C_4H_{10} (2) CO_2 (3) CH_3COOH.

8-4   **3.** Why is $CaCl_2$ not considered to be a molecular formula?

8-5   **4.** (a) Write the symbol for an ion of each of the following: sodium, sulfur, aluminum, oxygen, magnesium, chlorine. (b) Write the formulas of sodium sulfide, aluminum oxide, and magnesium chloride. For each formula, mention the total positive and negative charge.

8-6   **5.** Write the formulas of (a) sodium sulfate (b) magnesium carbonate (c) calcium phosphate (d) barium nitrate (e) ammonium nitrite.

6. Using the Stock system and the older one, supply two chemical names for each of the following: (a) HgO (b) $SnCl_4$ (c) Cu_2O (d) $FeCl_2$.

7. Write the formulas of (a) stannous chloride (b) cupric sulfide (c) mercury (II) bromide (d) iron (III) oxide.

8-7   **8.** Write the Stock system names for the five (5) oxides of nitrogen.

9. Using prefixes *mon(o)-*, *di-*, *tri-*, etc., name the following compounds: (a) Sb_2S_3 (b) SnO_2 (c) $SiCl_4$ (d) CO.

10. What is the apparent charge on one atom of Sn as it occurs in the compound SnO_2 if the apparent charge of oxygen in SnO_2 is 2−?

8-8   **11.** Write the names and formulas of two binary ionic compounds.

12. Write the names and formulas of two binary molecular compounds.

13. For the following, state the chemical name of the pure compound and, also, the name of the solution of the compound: (a) H_2S (b) HF (c) HBr.

8-9   **14.** (a) What is a ternary compound? (b) Write the name and formula of one ternary compound.

15. Write the formulas of (a) calcium acetate (b) magnesium hydroxide (c) sodium carbonate (d) silver nitrate (e) ammonium phosphate.

16. Write the chemical names of the following substances when undissolved and, also, when in solution: (a) HCN (b) H_2CrO_4 (c) $H_2C_2O_4$ (d) H_2SO_3.

17. If the formula of phosphoric acid is H_3PO_4, what is the formula of phosphorous acid?

8-10   **18.** Write the names and formulas of four (4) ternary acids containing the element chlorine.

19. Explain the significance of the prefix *hypo-* in the name hypochlorous acid.

20. Explain the significance of the prefix *per-* in perchloric acid.

FOR FURTHER THOUGHT

8-3   **1.** Give reasons for your answers to the following questions:
(a) How many different empirical formulas can a single substance have?
(b) How many different molecular formulas can a single substance have?
(c) Can two different substances have the same empirical formula?
(d) Can two different substances have the same molecular formula?

8-5   **2.** Assume that chlorine always forms the same ion in other compounds as it does in sodium chloride. Which of the following could be formulas of ionic compounds? (R, X, and Z are any three different elements.)
(a) R_2Cl_3 (b) XCl   (c) Z_2Cl

8-7   **3.** Which comes first, the chemical name or the chemical formula of a compound? Explain.

Chapter 8   Chemical Formulas   **161**

CHAPTER 9

The Mathematics of Chemical Formulas

Objectives

After you have completed this chapter, you will be able to:
- Derive quantitative information about the elements of a compound from its formula.
- Calculate the number of moles in a given mass of a substance.
- Determine the percentage composition of a substance from its formula.

9-1   Introduction

In this chapter, you will explore the mathematical relationships that have to do with chemical formulas. To understand these relationships, you must understand what the subscripts in a chemical formula mean. Based on the information provided by both the symbols and the subscripts in a chemical formula, you will be able to calculate how many grams of each element are present in any particular mass of a compound. You will be able, for example, to calculate how many grams of hydrogen and how many grams of oxygen are present in a 100-gram sample of water, H_2O.

This chapter also explains how to do the reverse—that is, how to determine the empirical formula of a compound from the known masses of all the elements in a sample of the compound. For example, if you know that a sample of a compound consists of 12 grams of carbon and 32 grams of oxygen, you will be able to determine that its empirical formula must be CO_2.

Other chemical calculations are based on the equations for chemical changes or reactions. Chemical equations and their mathematics are discussed in Chapters 10 and 11. **Stoichiometry** (stoy-kee-OM-uh-tree) is the name given to the study of the quantitative relationships that can be derived from formulas and equations.

9-2 Information Provided by Formulas

The information provided by formulas is important for solving certain kinds of chemical problems. As already stated in Sections 8-1 to 8-3, *all formulas tell . . .*

1. *. . . the elements present in a compound.* The formula for sodium chloride, NaCl, tells us that it is made up of the elements sodium (Na) and chlorine (Cl).

2. *. . . the relative number of atoms of each element in a compound.* The subscripts in the formula Na_2S show that for every 2 sodium atoms there is 1 sulfur atom.

If a formula is a molecular formula, *it also tells . . .*

3. *. . . the number of atoms of each element present in 1 molecule of the substance.* The formula for hydrogen peroxide, H_2O_2, shows that 1 molecule of hydrogen peroxide contains 2 atoms of hydrogen and 2 atoms of oxygen.

Questions for Sections 9-1 and 9-2

1. What is the meaning of the term *stoichiometry?*
2. What information provided by formulas is useful in solving chemical problems?
*3. An *ionic* compound has the formula Li_3N. What information does this formula give about the compound?
4. A molecular compound has the formula CO_2. What information does this formula give about the compound?

9-3 Atomic Mass and Formula Mass

The atoms of different elements have different masses. The mass of an atom of a particular element is called the atomic mass of that element. For your work with problems having to do with chemical formulas, you will need to know the atomic masses of a variety of elements. These can be found in the table titled "The Chemical Elements" that has been placed at the end of the book. If you look there now, you will find, for example, that the atomic mass of oxygen is 16.0 atomic mass units, or 16.0 u, and that the atomic mass of sulfur is 32.1 u. (Sulfur atoms have about twice the mass of oxygen atoms.) For the purposes of this chapter, we leave you with this simplified explanation of atomic masses. A complete discussion is given in Chapter 12.

The **formula mass** of a substance is the sum of all the atomic masses in the formula of the substance. For example, the formula for hydrogen gas is H_2. This formula represents two hydrogen atoms. Since the atomic mass of hydrogen is 1.00 u (or 1.008 u, to four significant figures), the formula mass of the two atoms represented by the formula is 2.00 u.

*The answers to questions marked with an asterisk are given in the back of the book.

Figure 9-1

**The compound calcium hydroxide,
Ca(OH)₂.** What is the formula mass
of calcium hydroxide?

We determine the formula mass of H_2O by first noting that the formula represents two hydrogen atoms and one oxygen atom. Then:

Element	Atomic mass		Number of atoms per formula		Product
H	1 u	×	2	=	2 u
O	16 u	×	1	=	16 u
					18 u.

The formula mass of H_2O, to two significant figures, is 18 u.

SAMPLE PROBLEM

What is the formula mass of calcium hydroxide, $Ca(OH)_2$?

Solution. Note that the formula represents one calcium atom, two oxygen atoms (one in each of the two hydroxide ions), and two hydrogen atoms (also one in each of the two hydroxide ions). Then:

Element	Atomic mass		Number of atoms per formula		Product
Ca	40 u	×	1	=	40 u
O	16 u	×	2	=	32 u
H	1 u	×	2	=	2 u
					74 u

The formula mass of $Ca(OH)_2$ is 74 u.

If the formula is that of a molecular substance, the formula mass may also be called the molecular mass. Therefore, the **molecular mass** is the sum of all the atomic masses indicated by the formula of a molecular substance. It is correct to say that the formula mass or the molecular mass of H_2 is 2 u, or that the formula mass or molecular mass of H_2O is 18 u. Since $Ca(OH)_2$ is an ionic substance, only *formula mass* is correct in referring to the sum of the atomic masses in its formula. However, this distinction is often overlooked. Chemists themselves have been known to refer to the "molecular mass of sodium chloride," even though sodium chloride is not a molecular substance.

In reading other chemistry texts, you may find the term atomic weight used in place of atomic mass, the term formula weight used in the place of formula mass, and the term molecular weight used in the place of molecular mass.

5. (a) Define formula mass. (b) When is the formula mass considered to be the same as the molecular mass? (c) Which of the two terms above should be applied to CO_2? Explain. (d) Which of the two terms should be applied to KCl? Explain.

*6. For the substance magnesium nitrate, $Mg(NO_3)_2$, make a table that shows how you can arrive at the formula mass of the substance. Your table should have the headings Element, Atomic mass, Number of atoms per formula, and Product—similar to the tables shown in this section of the text. Using your table, what value do you get for the formula mass of $Mg(NO_3)_2$?

7. Make a table showing how you can arrive at the formula mass of ammonium sulfate, $(NH_4)_2SO_4$? What value do you get?

9-4   Gram Atomic Mass

There are several quantities that chemists use to make their calculations easier. One of these is the gram atomic mass. A **gram atomic mass** of an element is that quantity of the element which has a mass in grams numerically equal to its atomic mass. For example, the atomic mass of oxygen is 16 u. Therefore, 16 grams of oxygen is 1 gram atomic mass of oxygen. One gram of hydrogen is one gram atomic mass of hydrogen. The term can be applied either to the naturally-occurring mixture of isotopes or to any particular isotope. For example, 35.5 grams of natural chlorine is one gram atomic mass of natural chlorine; 35 grams of chlorine-35 is one gram atomic mass of chlorine-35. A gram atomic mass is also called a gram-atom, which is a shorter and more convenient term.

Can you see that a gram atomic mass, or gram-atom, of one element must have the same number of atoms as a gram-atom of any other element? To understand why this is true, imagine a sample of oxygen and a sample of hydrogen with the same number of atoms. Since the oxygen atoms have 16 times as much mass as the hydrogen atoms, the mass of the oxygen will be 16 times as much as the mass of the hydrogen. Equal numbers of oxygen and hydrogen atoms will always have a mass ratio of 16 to 1. Looking at this fact another way, we can say that whenever two quantities of oxygen and hydrogen have a mass ratio of 16 to 1, they must have equal numbers of atoms. Therefore, 16 grams of oxygen (one gram-atom of oxygen) must have the same number of atoms as 1 gram of hydrogen (one gram-atom of hydrogen). In fact, one gram-atom of oxygen has the same number of atoms as one gram-atom of *any* other element.

Earlier in the book (Section 6-16) we introduced Avogadro's number, 6.02×10^{23}. This quantity is called one mole. We can now explain how Avogadro's number was chosen. It is the number of atoms in a gram-atom of an element. Since this number is also one mole, we see that one mole of atoms of any element is the same as one gram-atom of that element. The mass in grams of a mole of atoms is numerically equal to the atomic mass of the atoms. Thus, the mass of one mole of oxygen atoms is 16 grams. The mass of one mole of hydrogen atoms is 1 gram.

SAMPLE PROBLEM

What is the mass in grams of one mole of sulfur atoms?

Solution. The mass in grams of 1 mole of atoms of an element is numerically the same as the atomic mass of the element. The table at the back of the text, gives the atomic mass of sulfur as 32. Therefore, the mass of one mole of sulfur atoms is 32 g.

Figure 9-2

The element sulfur. What is the mass in grams of one mole of sulfur atoms?

9-5   Gram Formula Mass and the Mole

Another useful chemical quantity is the gram formula mass. The **gram formula mass** is the quantity of a substance that has a mass in grams numerically equal to its formula mass. For example, 18 grams of water is a gram formula mass of water, since the formula mass of water is 18 u. In a molecular compound like water, a gram formula mass of the compound will contain a mole of molecules. We can check this statement as follows:

One mole of H_2O molecules contains 2 moles of H atoms and 1 mole of O atoms. The mass of 1 mole of H atoms is 1 g and the mass of 1 mole of O atoms is 16 g. Therefore,

$$2 \text{ moles H atoms} \times \frac{1 \text{ g H}}{\text{mole H atoms}} = 2 \text{ g H}$$

$$1 \text{ mole O atoms} \times \frac{16 \text{ g O}}{\text{mole O atoms}} = 16 \text{ g O}$$

mass of 1 mole of H_2O molecules = 18 g

See Figure 9-3.

Figure 9-3

A water molecule is made up of 3 atoms—2 hydrogen atoms and 1 oxygen atom. A mole of water molecules therefore contains 3 moles of atoms—2 moles of hydrogen atoms and 1 mole of oxygen atoms.

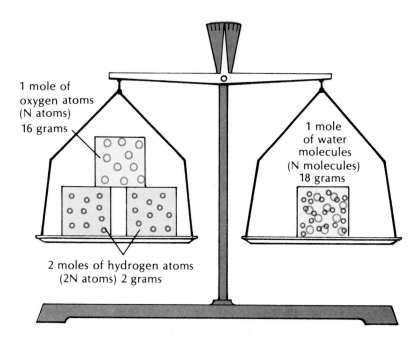

1 mole of oxygen atoms (N atoms) 16 grams

1 mole of water molecules (N molecules) 18 grams

2 moles of hydrogen atoms (2N atoms) 2 grams

A gram formula mass of an ionic compound does not contain a mole of molecules, since there are no molecules in an ionic compound. However, it does contain a mole of formula units.

SAMPLE PROBLEM

What is the mass of one mole of calcium hydroxide, $Ca(OH)_2$?

Solution. From Section 9-3, the formula mass of $Ca(OH)_2$ is 74 u. Therefore, the mass of one mole of $Ca(OH)_2$ is 74 g.

9-6 Extended Meaning of the Mole

The term *mole* refers to Avogadro's number, 6.02×10^{23}. This is the number of atoms of an element that has a mass in grams equal numerically to the atomic mass of the element. However, this number can be used to count identical units of any kind. We can therefore refer to a mole of molecules, a mole of formula units, or a mole of ions. We can also talk about a mole of electrons or protons. In every case, a mole is simply a certain number of objects.

Confusion can occur when the term *mole* is applied to the gaseous elements. When we talk about a mole of water, it is understood that we mean a mole of water molecules. However, if we refer to a mole of oxygen, the meaning is not so clear. It could mean a mole of oxygen atoms (6.02×10^{23} oxygen atoms). It could also mean a mole of oxygen molecules. Since each oxygen molecule consists of two atoms, a mole of oxygen molecules has twice as many atoms as a mole of oxygen atoms.

Figure 9-4

Gram atomic and gram formula masses.

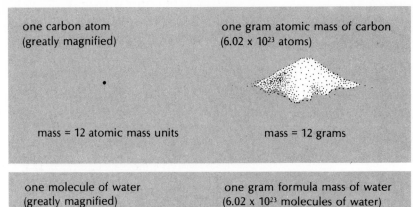

one carbon atom
(greatly magnified)

one gram atomic mass of carbon
(6.02 x 10²³ atoms)

mass = 12 atomic mass units

mass = 12 grams

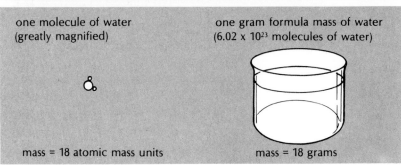

one molecule of water
(greatly magnified)

one gram formula mass of water
(6.02 x 10²³ molecules of water)

mass = 18 atomic mass units

mass = 18 grams

To avoid this kind of confusion, it would be better to state the intended quantity as "1 mole of oxygen atoms" or "1 mole of oxygen molecules." Or, it would be better to give the formula of the particles being referred to. "One mole of O_2" clearly refers to oxygen molecules, while "1 mole of O" clearly refers to atoms. "One mole of $CaCO_3$" refers to one mole of formula units of $CaCO_3$.

SAMPLE PROBLEM 1

How many moles of calcite, $CaCO_3$, are there in a 350-g sample of calcite?

Solution.

Step 1. Calculate the mass of one mole of $CaCO_3$.
One mole of formula units consists of:

$$1 \text{ mole Ca atoms} \times 40 \text{ g Ca/mole Ca atoms} = 40 \text{ g Ca}$$
$$1 \text{ mole C atoms} \times 12 \text{ g C/mole C atoms} = 12 \text{ g C}$$
$$3 \text{ moles of O atoms} \times 16 \text{ g O/mole O atoms} = 48 \text{ g O}$$

The mass of 1 mole of $CaCO_3$ is = 100 g

Step 2. Calculate the number of moles in 350 g of $CaCO_3$.

$$\frac{350 \text{ g CaCO}_3}{100 \text{ g CaCO}_3/\text{mole}} = 3.5 \text{ moles}$$

Figure 9-5

Calcium carbonate occurs in nature in several forms, including marble, chunks of which are called marble chips. Another form of calcium carbonate is calcite, characterized by its hexagonal crystals.

SAMPLE PROBLEM 2

How many grams of glucose are there in a 5-mole sample of glucose? The formula of glucose is $C_6H_{12}O_6$.

Solution.

Step 1. Calculate the mass of one mole of $C_6H_{12}O_6$.
One mole of $C_6H_{12}O_6$ consists of:

$$6 \text{ moles C atoms} \times 12 \text{ g C/mole C atoms} = 72 \text{ g C}$$

$$12 \text{ moles H atoms} \times 1 \text{ g H/mole H atoms} = 12 \text{ g H}$$

$$6 \text{ moles O atoms} \times 16 \text{ g O/mole O atoms} = \underline{96 \text{ g O}}$$

$$\text{The mass of one mole of } C_6H_{12}O_6 = 180 \text{ g}$$

Step 2. Calculate the number of grams in 5 moles of $C_6H_{12}O_6$.

$$5 \text{ moles glucose} \times \frac{180 \text{ g glucose}}{\text{mole}} = 900 \text{ g glucose}$$

Figure 9-6

The white solid in this photo is glucose, one of a number of sweet-tasting substances that are chemically related and are called sugars. Grapes are a rich source of glucose, which is also known as grape sugar. (The sugar commonly used to sweeten foods at the table is sucrose.)

Questions for Sections 9-4 through 9-6

8. (a) What is the meaning of *gram atomic mass* (gram-atom)? (b) What are the gram atomic masses of hydrogen, oxygen, and chlorine?
9. Why is it logical to assume that the gram-atoms of magnesium and carbon have the same number of atoms?
10. (a) What is Avogadro's number? (b) How is the mole related to the gram-atom of an element?
11. (a) What is the mass in grams of a mole of oxygen atoms? (b) How many atoms are present in two moles of oxygen atoms? (c) What is the mass in grams of a mole of oxygen molecules? (d) How many atoms are present in a mole of ordinary oxygen gas?
*12. (a) What is the mass of a mole of Al_2S_3? (b) How many moles are there in 15 g of Al_2S_3?
*13. What is the mass in grams of 3 moles of NaOH?
14. (a) What is the mass of a mole of Fe_2O_3? (b) How many moles of Fe_2O_3 are there in 32 g of Fe_2O_3? (c) What is the mass of 5 moles of Fe_2O_3?

9-7   Mole Relationships

Figure 9-7

The quantity of peas in a bag can be described by . . .
. . . the mass of the peas.
. . . the volume the peas occupy.
. . . the total number of peas.

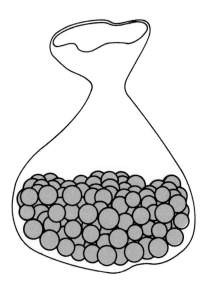

The mole has an important place in the mathematics of chemistry because it plays a central role in the relationship between a number of chemical quantities. Before we talk about chemical quantities, let's take a look at something we are all more familiar with. Suppose that we have a bag filled with peas. There are three ways that we can describe the amount of peas in the bag. We can tell (1) the mass of the peas, (2) the number of peas, and (3) the volume occupied by the peas.

In some respects, samples of chemical substances (samples of elements or compounds) are like peas. Suppose that a flask with a tight-fitting stopper contains a sample of a certain gas. We can describe the amount of gas in the flask using the same three quantities: (1) the mass of the sample of gas, (2) the number of molecules in the sample, and (3) the volume the sample occupies.

A bag of peas and a sample of a chemical substance are different in an important respect. If you had a bag of peas and someone wanted to know the amount of peas in the bag using all three quantities, we'd have to (1) measure their mass, (2) count them, and then (3) measure their volume. For chemical substances, we need to make only one measurement because all three quantities are related through the mole. If we understand the relationship, then we can find by calculation two of the quantities if we are told or know the third quantity.

The mole relationship allows us to solve the three kinds of problems listed below:

	Mass	Number of atoms or molecules	Volume
Problem 1:	given	find	find
Problem 2:	find	given	find
Problem 3:	find	find	given

The method of solving these problems is illustrated in the sample problem, but first we describe the general solution. All three problems can be solved in two steps. In Step 1, the given quantity is divided by a conversion factor that converts the given quantity to the equivalent number of moles. In Step 2, the number of moles found in Step 1 is multiplied by a conversion factor that converts the number of moles to the quantity to be found.

The conversion factors used to solve these problems are quantities you are already familiar with. They are:

Conversion Factor	Use
(1) The gram atomic mass (if the substance is an element) or the gram formula mass (if the substance is a compound).	To convert a given mass to moles and to make the reverse calculation (to convert moles to mass).

(2) The molar volume, 22.4 liters per mole for gases at STP.

To convert a given volume of a gas at STP to moles and to make the reverse calculation (to convert moles to gaseous volume at STP).

(3) Avogadro's number, 6.02×10^{23} molecules (or atoms) per mole.

To convert a given number of molecules (or atoms) to moles and to make the reverse calculation (number of moles to number of molecules or atoms).

In solving problems of the kind discussed here, you may find it helpful to use a mole diagram. See Figure 9-8.

Figure 9-8

A mole diagram. The diagram shows how to find how many moles there are in a given mass, in a given volume of a gas at STP, and in a given number of atoms or molecules of a sample of an element or compound. In each case, the given quantity must be divided by a conversion factor. Each reverse conversion (for example, converting from moles to a mass) requires multiplying by the conversion factor rather than dividing by it.

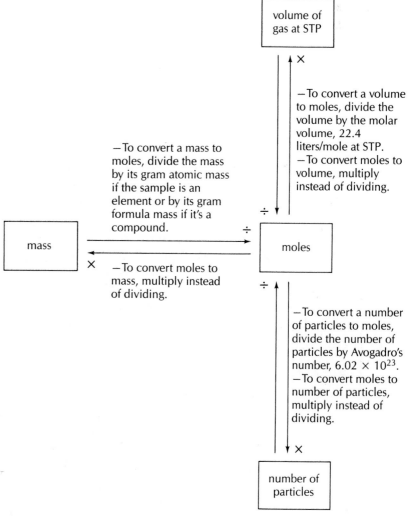

volume of gas at STP

×

—To convert a volume to moles, divide the volume by the molar volume, 22.4 liters/mole at STP.
—To convert moles to volume, multiply instead of dividing.

—To convert a mass to moles, divide the mass by its gram atomic mass if the sample is an element or by its gram formula mass if it's a compound.

mass

moles

×

—To convert moles to mass, multiply instead of dividing.

—To convert a number of particles to moles, divide the number of particles by Avogadro's number, 6.02×10^{23}.
—To convert moles to number of particles, multiply instead of dividing.

×

number of particles

Figure 9-9

The mole diagram for the sample problem. In Step 1, 64.0 grams of O_2, the given quantity, must be divided by the gram formula mass of O_2 to find the number of moles of O_2 making up the sample. In Step 2, the number of moles of O_2 found in Step 1 must be multiplied by Avogadro's number to find the number of molecules in the sample.

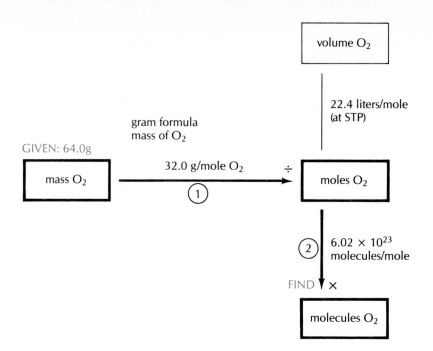

SAMPLE PROBLEM

A sample of oxygen gas (O_2) has a mass of 64.0 grams. Find the number of molecules in the sample.

Solution. Figure 9-9 is the mole diagram for this problem. Notice that over the box marked *mass O_2* we've written *GIVEN,* since the mass of oxygen is given in the statement of the problem. Over the box marked *number of molecules O_2* we've written *FIND,* since this is the quantity we are to find. Step 1 in the solution, converting the given mass of O_2 to the number of moles of O_2, is marked with the number 1 enclosed in a circle. Step 2, converting from the number of moles of O_2 to the number of molecules of O_2, is marked with the number 2 enclosed in a circle.

Step 1. Figure 9-9 shows that we must divide the given mass of O_2 by its gram formula mass. The formula mass of O_2 is 32.0 u since the atomic mass of oxygen is 16.0 u and there are 2 atoms of oxygen in the formula. The gram formula mass of O_2 is, therefore, 32.0 g.

$$64.0 \text{ grams } O_2 \div \frac{32 \text{ grams } O_2}{1 \text{ mole } O_2} =$$

Inverting and multiplying gives:

$$64.0 \text{ grams } O_2 \times \frac{1 \text{ mole } O_2}{32.0 \text{ grams } O_2} = 2.00 \text{ moles } O_2$$

Step 2. Figure 9-9 shows that to convert from moles to molecules, we must multiply the number of moles by Avogadro's number.

$$2.00 \text{ moles O}_2 \times \frac{6.02 \times 10^{23} \text{ molecules O}_2}{1 \text{ mole O}_2} =$$

$$1.204 \times 10^{24} \text{ molecules O}_2$$

To three significant figures, 1.20×10^{24} molecules of O_2 are the number of molecules in a sample of oxygen whose mass is 64.0 grams.

Questions for Section 9-7

*15. A sample of CO_2 has a mass of 22.0 grams. What volume will the sample occupy at STP? As part of your solution to the problem, you may find it helpful to draw a mole diagram.

*16. A sample of N_2 is composed of 3.01×10^{23} molecules. What is the mass of the sample? Draw a mole diagram if you find this helpful in solving the problem.

17. A sample of methane, a gas whose formula is CH_4, has a volume of 67.2 liters at STP. What is the mass of the sample? Draw a mole diagram if you find this helpful in solving the problem.

9-8 Percentage Composition

Compounds are made up of two or more elements. As you will learn in Chapter 12, the proportion, by mass, of the elements in a given compound is always the same. For example, all samples of water are 11% hydrogen and 89% oxygen by mass. We say that the *percentage composition* of water is 11% hydrogen and 89% oxygen. The **percentage composition** of a compound is the percentage by mass of each of the elements in the compound.

Knowing the percentage composition is useful to chemists. It enables them, for example, to calculate how much of a compound needs to be decomposed into its elements to obtain a given amount of a particular element.

Percentage composition can be determined by experiment. It can also be determined by making use of information supplied by the formula of the compound, if the formula is known. To determine percentage composition experimentally, a known mass of the compound is decomposed into its elements. The mass of each of the elements thus obtained is measured. The mass of one of the elements is divided by the mass of the compound. The quotient obtained by this division tells what fraction of the compound is made up of that particular element. **Multiplying the quotient by 100% converts it to a percent. The same calculation is made for each of the other elements in the compound.**

SAMPLE PROBLEM 1

A sample of a compound containing carbon and oxygen had a mass of 88 g. Experimental procedures showed that 24 g of this sample was carbon, and the remaining 64 g was oxygen. What is the percentage composition of this compound?

Solution. The percentage of carbon in the compound is:

$$\% \text{ carbon} = \frac{\text{mass of carbon in sample}}{\text{mass of sample}} \times 100\%$$

$$= \frac{24 \text{ g}}{88 \text{ g}} \times 100\%$$

$$= 27\%$$

The percentage of oxygen in the compound is:

$$\% \text{ oxygen} = \frac{\text{mass of oxygen in sample}}{\text{mass of sample}} \times 100\%$$

$$= \frac{64 \text{ g}}{88 \text{ g}} \times 100\%$$

$$= 73\%$$

Check: 73% + 27% = 100%

The percentage composition of the compound is 27% carbon and 73% oxygen.

Using carbon dioxide, CO_2, we now illustrate how percentage composition is determined from the formula of a compound. Assume that we have a 1-mole sample of CO_2 molecules. One mole of CO_2 molecules consists of 1 mole of carbon atoms and 2 moles of oxygen atoms.

$$\text{The mass of 1 mole of carbon atoms} = 1 \text{ mole} \times 12 \text{ g/mole} = 12 \text{ g C}$$

$$\text{The mass of 2 moles of oxygen atoms} = 2 \text{ moles} \times 16 \text{ g/mole} = \underline{32 \text{ g O}}$$

$$\text{Total} = 44 \text{ g}$$

The computation tells us that a 44-gram sample of carbon dioxide is made up of 12 grams of carbon and 32 grams of oxygen. The percentage composition of carbon dioxide is determined by dividing the mass of each element in the 44-gram sample by the mass of the sample itself. By multiplying by 100%, this quotient is converted to a percentage:

$$\% \text{ carbon in CO}_2 = \frac{12 \text{ g}}{44 \text{ g}} \times 100\% = 27\%$$

$$\% \text{ oxygen in CO}_2 = \frac{32 \text{ g}}{44 \text{ g}} \times 100\% = 73\%$$

SAMPLE PROBLEM 2

Ammonia has the formula NH_3. Use the formula to determine the percentage composition of ammonia.

Solution. Assume that you have a 1-mole sample of ammonia. One mole of NH_3 molecules consists of 1 mole of nitrogen atoms and 3 moles of hydrogen atoms. Their masses are as follows:

$$\text{Mass of nitrogen} = 1 \text{ mole N} \times 14 \text{ g N/mole N} = 14 \text{ g N}$$

$$\text{Mass of hydrogen} = 3 \text{ moles H} \times 1 \text{ g H/mole H} = \underline{3 \text{ g H}}$$

$$\text{Mass of sample} = 17 \text{ g}$$

$$\% \text{ nitrogen} = \frac{\text{mass of nitrogen in sample}}{\text{mass of sample}} \times 100\%$$

$$= \frac{14 \text{ g}}{17 \text{ g}} \times 100\%$$

$$= 82\%$$

$$\% \text{ hydrogen} = \frac{\text{mass of hydrogen in sample}}{\text{mass of sample}} \times 100\%$$

$$= \frac{3 \text{ g}}{17 \text{ g}} \times 100\%$$

$$= 18\%$$

Figure 9-10

Household ammonia, used for cleaning purposes, is a solution of ammonia gas, NH_3, dissolved in water. The formula of the gas can be used to determine the percentage composition of the gas, as illustrated in the sample problem.

Questions for Section 9-8

18. (a) What is meant by the *percentage composition* of a compound? (b) What two ways can be used to determine the percentage composition of a compound?
19. What is the percentage composition of an iron oxide sample that consists of 28 g of iron and 12 g of oxygen? Show how you arrive at your answer.
*20. What is the percentage composition of ferric oxide, Fe_2O_3? Show how you arrive at your answer.
21. What is the percentage composition of a compound that contains 53 g of sodium and 37 g of oxygen in a 90-g sample? Show how you get your answer.
22. What is the percentage composition of sodium peroxide, Na_2O_2? Show how you get your answer.

9-9 Determining the Formula of a Compound

Chemists know when they have discovered or made a new compound because its set of properties will not match those of any known substance. In order to identify a new compound, chemists must run a number of laboratory tests on samples of the compound. Some of these tests will provide the information needed to determine the formula of the compound. You will learn more about these tests later in the course, and may run some of them in a class lab. Some types of lab tests tell what elements are in a compound. Others reveal how many grams of each element are present in a measured mass of the compound. These masses can be used to determine the percentage composition of a compound, as was discussed in Section 9-8. We can determine the empirical formula of a compound if we know either (1) the masses of each element in a sample of the compound or (2) the percentage composition of the compound. We illustrate these ideas below.

SAMPLE PROBLEM 1

Laboratory procedures show that a 9.2-gram sample of a compound is 2.8 g nitrogen and 6.4 g oxygen. The percentage composition of the compound is 30.4% nitrogen and 69.6% oxygen. (Using the given gram masses, you can verify the percentages by following the method outlined in Section 9-8.) Find the empirical formula of the nitrogen-oxygen compound (1) by making use of the given gram masses, and (2) by making use of the given percentage composition.

Solution 1. Determining empirical formulas from gram masses.

Step 1. Convert gram masses to moles. From the table of atomic masses, back of book, 1 mole of nitrogen atoms has a mass of 14 g, and 1 mole of oxygen atoms has a mass of 16 g.

Number of moles of nitrogen atoms:

$$\frac{2.8 \text{ g nitrogen}}{14 \text{ g nitrogen/mole nitrogen atoms}} = 0.20 \text{ mole nitrogen atoms}$$

Number of moles of oxygen atoms:

$$\frac{6.4 \text{ g oxygen}}{16 \text{ g oxygen/mole oxygen atoms}} = 0.40 \text{ mole oxygen atoms}$$

Step 2. Using the numbers of moles from Step 1, determine the smallest whole-number ratio of the number of atoms of each element in the compound. (Divide the larger number by the smaller.)

$$\frac{\text{Number of moles of oxygen atoms}}{\text{Number of moles of nitrogen atoms}} = \frac{0.40}{0.20} = \frac{2}{1}$$

(This is another way of saying that there are twice as many oxygen atoms in 0.40 moles of oxygen as there are nitrogen atoms in 0.20 moles of nitrogen.)

Step 3. Use the whole-number ratio determined in Step 2 to write the empirical formula.

$$N_1O_2 \quad \text{or} \quad NO_2$$

Solution 2. Determining the empirical formula from percentage composition.

Step 1. Assume that you have a 100-gram sample of the compound. (Any other size will do, but the arithmetic is easier with a 100-gram sample.) Use the percentage composition to determine the number of grams of each element in the sample.

$$30.4\% \text{ of } 100 \text{ g} = 30.4 \text{ g nitrogen}$$

$$69.6\% \text{ of } 100 \text{ g} = 69.6 \text{ g oxygen}$$

These figures tell us that in every 100 grams of the compound there are 30.4 grams nitrogen and 69.6 grams oxygen.

Step 2. We now have gram masses, and can follow the procedure outlined above for "Determining the empirical formula from gram masses."

You should now follow these steps and verify that you get the same result for the empirical formula, namely, NO_2.

Some compounds are molecular. For these, chemists are not satisfied knowing only empirical formulas. Chemists also want to know the molecular formulas of these compounds. In addition to percentage composition, one more piece of information allows the chemist to determine the molecular formula of a compound. That piece of information is the molecular mass of the compound.

As an illustration, the nitrogen-oxygen compound we just considered, whose empirical formula is NO_2, is a molecular compound. Suppose that laboratory work has revealed that its molecular mass is 46 u. (A method for determining molecular masses is discussed later in Chapter 11.) We wish to take our problem one step farther by finding the molecular formula of the compound.

If the empirical formula of the compound is NO_2, then possible molecular formulas are NO_2, N_2O_4, N_3O_6, N_4O_8, etc. We can determine which of these is the correct molecular formula by seeing which one has a molecular mass that matches the experimentally determined molecular mass.

Possible molecular formula	Molecular mass
NO_2	$14 \text{ u} + 2(16 \text{ u}) = 46 \text{ u}$
N_2O_4	$2(14 \text{ u}) + 4(16 \text{ u}) = 92 \text{ u}$
N_3O_6	$3(14 \text{ u}) + 6(16 \text{ u}) = 138 \text{ u}$

Figure 9-11

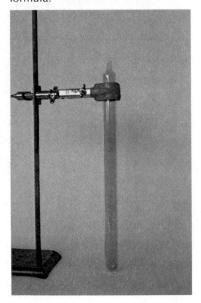

Nitrogen dioxide, a gas with a brownish color. Knowing that its molecular mass is 46 and that it contains twice as many oxygen as nitrogen atoms is enough information for determining its molecular formula.

The molecular mass of 46 u for the first formula matches the experimentally determined value given earlier. The molecular formula of the compound must be NO_2. See figure 9-11.

Recall (Section 8-3) that the empirical formula is the formula in which the subscripts are in the smallest whole number ratio. For the compound of nitrogen and oxygen we just considered, the smallest whole-number ratio is 1:2. The empirical formula is NO_2. In this case, the empirical and molecular formulas are the same.

SAMPLE PROBLEM 2

What is the empirical formula of the compound whose percentage composition is 65.2% arsenic (As) and 34.8% oxygen by mass?

Solution. Assume that we have a 100-gram sample of the compound. In that sample, there would be

$$65.2\% \text{ of } 100 \text{ g} = 65.2 \text{ g arsenic}$$

$$34.8\% \text{ of } 100 \text{ g} = 34.8 \text{ g oxygen}$$

The number of moles of arsenic atoms and moles of oxygen atoms in the above masses are

$$\frac{65.2 \text{ g As}}{74.9 \text{ g As/mole As atoms}} = 0.870 \text{ mole As atoms}$$

$$\frac{34.8 \text{ g O}}{16.0 \text{ g O/mole O atoms}} = 2.18 \text{ moles O}$$

The ratio of oxygen atoms to arsenic atoms is 2.18 to 0.870. This ratio simplifies to 2.18/0.870 = 2.51/1. However, the ratio 2.51/1 needs to be simplified further since 2.51 is not a whole number. Note that 2.51 is very close to 2.5 or 2½. The third digit, 1, in 2.51 is the result of rounding off numbers to three digits. The original percentages, 65.2% and 34.8%, for example, are rounded to three digits. Therefore, we take the ratio 2.51/1 to be the simpler ratio 2.5/1. This last ratio can be simplified by multiplying numerator and denominator by 2:

$$\frac{2.5}{1} \times \frac{2}{2} = \frac{5}{2}$$

The empirical formula of the compound is As_2O_5. Its name is arsenic pentoxide.

SAMPLE PROBLEM 3

What is the molecular formula of a compound whose percentage composition is 65.2% arsenic (As) and 34.8% oxygen by mass and whose molecular mass is 230 u?

Solution. If the molecular mass of the compound is 230 u, the mass of one mole would be 230 g. Assume that we have a 1-mole (230-g) sample of the compound. The masses of the 230-gram sample that are arsenic and oxygen are:

$$65.2\% \times 230 \text{ g} = 150 \text{ g As}$$

$$34.8\% \times 230 \text{ g} = 80.0 \text{ g O}$$

Making use of the table of atomic masses in the back of the book, the number of moles of atoms of each element would be:

$$\frac{150 \text{ g As}}{74.9 \text{ g As/mole As atoms}} = 2.00 \text{ moles As atoms}$$

$$\frac{80.0 \text{ g O}}{16.0 \text{ g O/mole O atoms}} = 5.00 \text{ moles O atoms}$$

The molecular formula of the compound is As_2O_5.
(Note that the empirical formula, as determined in Sample Problem 2, is the same as the molecular formula for this particular substance.)

Another approach to solving this problem would have been to determine the empirical formula, as outlined in Sample Problem 1. From the empirical formula, write possible molecular formulas. Determine which molecular formula has a molecular mass equal to the one given.

Possible molecular formula	Molecular mass
As_2O_5	$2(74.9 \text{ u}) + 5(16 \text{ u}) = 230 \text{ u}$
As_4O_{10}	$4(74.9 \text{ u}) + 10(16 \text{ u}) = 460 \text{ u}$
As_6O_{15}	$6(74.9 \text{ u}) + 15(16 \text{ u}) = 690 \text{ u}$

The first formula, As_2O_5, has the mass, 230 u, given in the problem.

Questions for Section 9-9

23. (a) What information about a compound's composition can be used to determine its empirical formula? (b) What else must be known in order to determine its molecular formula?
*24. A 39-g sample of a gas contains 18 g carbon and 21 g nitrogen. What is its empirical formula?
*25. What is the empirical formula of a compound that contains 46.2% carbon and 53.8% nitrogen?
*26. The compound in question 25 has a molecular mass of 52 u. What is its molecular formula?
27. (a) What is the empirical formula of a hydrocarbon that consists of 80.0% carbon and 20.0% hydrogen? (b) If its molecular mass is 30.0 u, what is its molecular formula?
28. What is the molecular formula of a compound that contains 28.2% potassium, 25.6% chlorine, and 46.2% oxygen? Its formula mass is 138.5 u.

1. The formula mass is the sum of all atomic masses in a formula. Either formula mass or molecular mass may be used to describe the sum of atomic masses in molecular substances. Only the term formula mass should be used for ionic substances since they are not molecular.
2. The gram atomic mass is the quantity of an element that has a mass in grams equal to the atomic mass.
3. The gram formula mass of a substance has a mass in grams equal to its formula mass. In a molecular substance, a gram formula mass contains a mole of molecules.
4. A mole of a substance contains Avogadro's number (6.02×10^{23}) of units of that substance. Depending on the substance, a mole of the substance may have a mass equal to a gram atomic mass, gram formula mass, or gram molecular mass.
5. The percentage composition of a compound is the percentage by mass of each of the elements in the compound.
6. The empirical formula of a compound can be determined from its percentage composition or from the masses of each element in a sample of the compound. In order to determine the molecular formula, the molecular mass must be known.

TERMS YOU SHOULD KNOW

stoichiometry	molecular mass	gram formula mass
formula mass	gram atomic mass	percentage composition

REVIEW QUESTIONS

Section

9-2   **1.** What information is provided in the formula of glucose, $C_6H_{12}O_6$?

9-3   **2.** The formula mass of potassium dichromate, $K_2Cr_2O_7$, is 294 u. Explain how this is obtained from the formula.

3. (a) What two chemical terms can be used to describe 18 g of H_2O? (b) Which of these terms describes 111 g of $CaCl_2$ more appropriately?

9-4   **4.** State the interrelationships of the mole, gram-atom, and Avogadro's number.

5. Explain why a sample of oxygen and one of hydrogen, which have a mass ratio of 16 to 1, respectively, have an equal number of atoms.

9-5   **6.** (a) Relate the gram formula mass to the mole. (b) Describe 58.5 g of NaCl in terms of moles of formula units and moles of atoms.

9-6   **7.** Distinguish between a mole of chlorine atoms and a mole of chlorine gas molecules.

9-8   **8.** (a) Why do all samples of a given compound always show the same percentage composition? (b) Why is a knowledge of the percentage of a metal in an ore useful in mining operations?

9. What information must chemists have about a compound if they are to determine its empirical formula?

10. (a) Distinguish between empirical formula and molecular formula. (b) State an example of a formula that is both empirical and molecular. (c) State the empirical and molecular formulas of a compound where such formulas differ.

REVIEW PROBLEMS

In solving the problems below, use the following atomic masses:

aluminum, Al	27.0 u	mercury, Hg	200
carbon, C	12.0	nitrogen, N	14.0
calcium, Ca	40.0	oxygen, O	16.0
chlorine, Cl	35.5	potassium, K	39.0
copper, Cu	63.5	sulfur, S	32.0
hydrogen, H	1.01		

9-6   **1.** How many grams of sulfur are there in a 3-mole sample of $Al_2(SO_4)_3$?

9-8   **2.** What is the percentage composition of mercuric chloride, $HgCl_2$?

3. What is the percentage of water in blue vitriol, $CuSO_4 \cdot 5H_2O$?

9-9   **4.** A compound consists of 10.05% carbon, 0.84% hydrogen, and 89.11% chlorine. What is its empirical formula?

5. A compound has a molecular mass of 80 u and is composed of 50% calcium, 15% carbon, and 35% nitrogen. What is its molecular formula?

FOR FURTHER THOUGHT

9-5   **1.** You are given one gram formula mass of a compound, but the compound is not identified. (a) What would you do to find the formula mass of the compound? (b) What would you do to find the number of moles you have?

9-6   **2.** You are given a sample of an element and are told it contains 6 gram atomic masses. You have a table of atomic masses, but no measuring instruments. Which of the quantities listed below can you determine (a) if you do not know which element it is? (b) if you do know which element it is? Explain your answers.
(1) The number of moles in the sample.
(2) The number of atoms in the sample.
(3) The total mass of the sample.
(4) The density of the sample.

9-9   **3.** You are told the mass of a sample of a compound and its percentage composition. You have a table of atomic masses. Which of the following can you determine from this information? Explain your answers. (a) The empirical formula of the compound. (b) The molecular formula. (c) The formula mass. (d) The number of moles in the sample.

CHAPTER 10

Chemical Equations

Objectives

After you have completed this chapter, you will be able to:

- Interpret the information in chemical equations.
- Balance chemical equations and relate this process to the law of conservation of matter.
- Classify many reactions as belonging to one of four categories.

10-1 Introduction

Chemists learn a great deal about matter by studying the changes it undergoes. Whenever a substance undergoes a chemical change, a *chemical reaction* takes place. To describe what actually takes place in a chemical reaction, chemists write chemical equations. A **chemical equation** is a condensed statement of facts about a chemical reaction. In this chapter you will learn how to write, balance, and interpret chemical equations.

10-2 Information Given by an Equation

The following is a description of a particular chemical reaction: Hydrogen gas reacts with oxygen gas to produce water.

Another way to describe this chemical change is to write a word equation:

WORD EQUATION

$$\text{hydrogen gas} + \text{oxygen gas} \longrightarrow \text{water} \qquad \textbf{(Eq. 1)}$$

The arrow in Equation 1 is read "produce" or "yield." The + sign is read "plus." In words, the word equation is read: "Hydrogen gas plus oxygen gas produce water." All substances to the left of the arrow are called reactants. **Reactants** are the substances that exist before a chemical reaction takes place. All substances to the right of the arrow are called products. **Products** are the substances that come into existence as a result of a chemical reaction. In the reaction above, hydrogen gas and oxygen gas are the reactants, and water is the product. Chemical reactions can have one or more reactants and one or more products.

hydrogen gas + oxygen gas $\longrightarrow$ water

REACTANTS   **PRODUCT**

In writing equations, chemists prefer to use formulas for the reactants and products instead of their names. The *symbol* for the element hydrogen is H. However, the *formula* for hydrogen gas is H_2, because hydrogen gas consists of **diatomic** (two-atom) **molecules.** Oxygen gas is also diatomic. Its formula is O_2. The formula for water is H_2O. When we replace the words in the word equation with these formulas, we get an unbalanced formula equation:

UNBALANCED FORMULA EQUATION

$$H_2 + O_2 \longrightarrow H_2O \qquad \textbf{(Eq. 2)}$$

The unbalanced formula equation needs more work on it to make it complete. To see what it lacks, we repeat the equation using structural formulas:

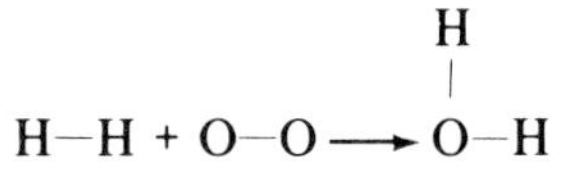

$$H-H + O-O \longrightarrow \overset{\displaystyle H}{\underset{}{\overset{|}{O}}}-H \qquad \textbf{(Eq. 3)}$$
(unbalanced)

During chemical reactions, chemical bonds are broken and new bonds are formed. Atoms are rearranged to form new substances, but atoms do not disappear. In chemical reactions, atoms are never created or destroyed. If we look closely at Equation 3, we see 2 atoms of hydrogen to the left of the arrow and 2 atoms of hydrogen to the right of the arrow. However, while there are 2 atoms of oxygen on the left, there is only 1 atom on the right. An oxygen atom is missing on the right. By adding another water molecule to the right, we will be supplying the right side with another oxygen atom:

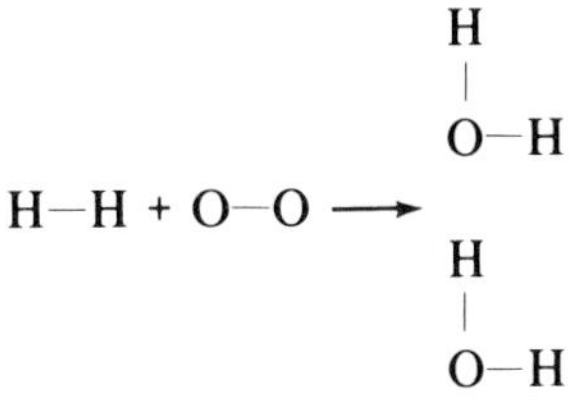

$$H-H + O-O \longrightarrow \begin{array}{c} H \\ | \\ O-H \\ \\ H \\ | \\ O-H \end{array} \qquad \textbf{(Eq. 4)}$$
(unbalanced)

Stated in words, Equation 4 reads: 1 molecule of hydrogen reacts with 1 molecule of oxygen to produce 2 molecules of water. By adding a second molecule of water, we balanced the number of oxygen atoms. That is, we made the number of oxygen atoms on the right equal to the number on the left.

Let us see if adding the second water molecule threw the hydrogen out of balance. Equation 4 shows 2 atoms of hydrogen on the left, but 4

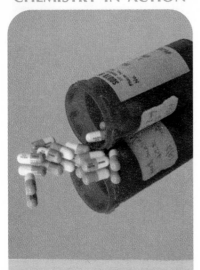
on the right. There is now too little hydrogen on the left. To increase it, we add a second molecule of hydrogen:

$$
\begin{array}{ccc}
\text{H—H} & & \text{O—H} \\
& + \text{O—O} \longrightarrow & \\
\text{H—H} & & \text{O—H}
\end{array}
\qquad
\begin{array}{l}
\textbf{(Eq. 5)} \\
\text{(balanced)}
\end{array}
$$

Equation 5 shows 4 atoms of hydrogen and 2 atoms of oxygen on both sides. It is a balanced equation. Equation 5 can also be written:

FORMULA EQUATION (balanced)

$$2H_2 + O_2 \longrightarrow 2H_2O \qquad \textbf{(Eq. 6)}$$

In words, Equation 6 reads: 2 molecules of hydrogen plus 1 molecule of oxygen yield 2 molecules of water.

Coefficients. The numbers written in front of formulas to balance a chemical equation are called **coefficients.** Like the subscript 1 in formulas, the coefficient 1 is understood but not written. In a balanced formula equation, coefficients indicate the smallest number of molecules of a substance that may take part in the reaction. "$2H_2O$" means "2 molecules of water." "H_2O" means "1 molecule of water." Equation 6, the balanced equation, says that 2 molecules of hydrogen react with 1 molecule of oxygen to produce 2 molecules of water. Notice that a coefficient multiplies *all* the atoms in a formula. Since 1 molecule of H_2O has 2 atoms of hydrogen and 1 atom of oxygen, 2 molecules have 4 atoms of hydrogen and 2 atoms of oxygen.

A word of caution: When balancing equations, beginning students sometimes make the mistake of adjusting subscripts rather than coefficients. For example, the *unbalanced* formula equation for the reaction between hydrogen and oxygen to produce water is

$$H_2 + O_2 \longrightarrow H_2O$$

Seeing that there are too few oxygen atoms on the right, the beginning student is tempted to add a subscript of 2 following the oxygen in H_2O:

$$H_2 + O_2 \longrightarrow H_2O_2$$

This is wrong because H_2O_2 is not the correct formula for water. The correct formula for water is H_2O. There *is* a substance having the formula H_2O_2, but H_2O_2 is an entirely different substance from H_2O.

A chemical formula represents the chemical composition of a substance. Thus, once a correct formula is written, the subscripts in the formula should be left alone. You change only coefficients when balancing equations.

1. What is a chemical equation?
2. Differentiate between the reactants and the products of a chemical reaction.
3. What is a balanced equation?
4. Why must a chemical equation be balanced to properly represent a chemical reaction?
5. What is the difference between the symbol for the element oxygen and the formula for oxygen gas?
6. What is the difference between 2CO and CO_2?
*7. Sodium reacts with chlorine gas to produce sodium chloride. The unbalanced equation for this reaction is $Na + Cl_2 \rightarrow NaCl$. Which of the following is the *properly* balanced equation for this reaction? (a) $Na + Cl \rightarrow NaCl$ (b) $Na + Cl_2 \rightarrow NaCl_2$ (c) $2Na + Cl_2 \rightarrow 2NaCl$ (d) $2Na + 2Cl \rightarrow 2NaCl$

10-3   Steps in Writing a Balanced Equation

In the last section, we started with a word description of a chemical change. We developed this description, step by step, into a balanced formula equation. We now set down the rules we followed during the development. These rules serve as a general guide for writing balanced equations for many chemical reactions.

Step 1—*Know what the reactants and products are, and write a word equation for the reaction.* As a beginner in chemistry, there is no way for you to know if two substances react unless you actually observe a reaction taking place. Even if you see a reaction taking place, you cannot be sure what the product or products are without running tests to identify them. For the time being you will be told what the reactants and products of a reaction are before being asked to write a balanced equation.

Step 2—*Write the correct formulas for all reactants and products.* It is important to remember that the following elements, which are gases under normal conditions, exist as diatomic molecules:

hydrogen	H_2	
oxygen	O_2	**GASES UNDER NORMAL**
nitrogen	N_2	**CONDITIONS**
chlorine	Cl_2	
fluorine	F_2	

When these substances are either reactants or products of a reaction, the subscript 2 must appear after the symbol, as shown above.

Bromine, a liquid under normal conditions, and iodine, a solid, also exist as diatomic molecules.

bromine	Br_2	**LIQUID**	**UNDER NORMAL**
iodine	I_2	**SOLID**	**CONDITIONS**

As you will learn in Chapter 16, bromine and iodine are chemically related to fluorine and chlorine. All the members of this group—fluorine, chlorine, bromine, and iodine—have atoms that easily form diatomic molecules. This happens regardless of the phase of the element. (Section 14-6 describes in detail how diatomic molecules are formed by the sharing of electrons.)

Step 3—*Balance the equation.* That is, supply coefficients that will make the number of atoms of each element the same on both sides of the arrow.

SAMPLE PROBLEM 1

Write a balanced equation for the reaction between chlorine and sodium bromide to produce bromine and sodium chloride.

Solution

Step 1—We have been told what the reactants and products are. The word equation is:

$$\text{chlorine} + \text{sodium bromide} \longrightarrow \text{bromine} + \text{sodium chloride}$$

Step 2—*Write the correct formulas.* Chlorine and bromine have been mentioned as elements that are diatomic. The symbols of these elements (back of the book) are Cl and Br. Their formulas are Cl_2 and Br_2. Replacing the names of these substances with their formulas, we have:

$$Cl_2 + \text{sodium bromide} \longrightarrow Br_2 + \text{sodium chloride}$$

Now we determine the formulas for sodium bromide and sodium chloride by the method explained in Chapter 8, Section 8-5. The correct formulas are NaBr and NaCl. Putting these into the word equation gives the unbalanced formula equation:

$$Cl_2 + NaBr \longrightarrow Br_2 + NaCl \qquad \textbf{(Eq. 7)}$$
$$\text{(unbalanced)}$$

Step 3—*Adjust the coefficients to make the equation balance.* Starting with the first element, chlorine, notice that there are 2 atoms of chloride by the method explained in Chapter 8, Section 8-5. The correct the right. By supplying a coefficient of 2 to the NaCl, we equalize the number of chlorine atoms:

$$Cl_2 + NaBr \longrightarrow Br_2 + 2NaCl \qquad \textbf{(Eq. 8)}$$
$$\text{(unbalanced)}$$

Checking the number of the next element, sodium, there is 1 atom on the left but 2 on the right. By supplying a coefficient of 2 to the NaBr, we can bring the sodium into balance:

$$Cl_2 + 2NaBr \longrightarrow Br_2 + 2NaCl \qquad \textbf{(Eq. 9)}$$

Checking the number of atoms of the next element, bromine, there are 2 atoms on each side of Equation 9. Bromine is balanced. Now atoms of all three elements are in balance. Equation 9 is the complete, balanced equation.

SAMPLE PROBLEM 2

Write the balanced equation for the reaction between aluminum sulfate and calcium chloride to produce aluminum chloride and a white precipitate of calcium sulfate. See Figure 10-1.

Solution

Step 1. *Write the word equation.*

$$\begin{array}{ccccc} \text{aluminum} & & \text{calcium} & & \text{aluminum} & & \text{calcium} \\ \text{sulfate} & + & \text{chloride} & \rightarrow & \text{chloride} & + & \text{sulfate} \\ & & & & & & \text{(a white} \\ & & & & & & \text{precipitate)} \end{array}$$

Step 2. *Replace the words in the word equation with the correct formulas.*

$$Al_2(SO_4)_3 + CaCl_2 \rightarrow AlCl_3 + CaSO_4 \qquad \textbf{(Eq. 10)}$$

Step 3. *Adjust the coefficients to make the equation balance.*

First element in the equation, aluminum: There are 2 atoms of aluminum on the left but only 1 on the right. Increase the number on the right to 2 by putting a coefficient of 2 in front of $AlCl_3$:

$$Al_2(SO_4)_3 + CaCl_2 \rightarrow 2AlCl_3 + CaSO_4 \qquad \textbf{(Eq. 11)}$$

Figure 10-1

The photo on the left shows white crystals of aluminum sulfate, $Al_2(SO_4)_3$ (watch glass on the left), and white crystals of calcium chloride, $CaCl_2$ (watch glass on the right). Also shown are the solutions that are formed when these solids are dissolved in water. The photo on the right shows the white solid formed when one solution is poured into the other.

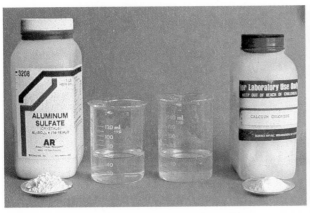 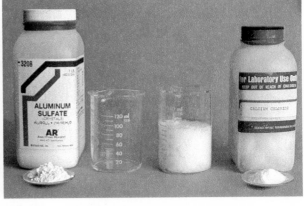

George Washington Carver
(1859?-1943)

Carver was an agricultural chemist and experimenter of international fame and is regarded as a benefactor of the southern states. He was born a slave in Missouri, but was determined to get a formal education. His studies at Simpson College in Iowa were financed by his working as a janitor and cook, and by taking in laundry. He went on to Iowa State Agricultural College, graduating in 1894 and getting a master's degree in 1896. That year, he was made head of the Department of Agriculture at Tuskegee Institute in Alabama. He spent the rest of his life there, devoting his time to agricultural research.

Using as raw materials sweet potatoes, soybeans, peanuts, and pecans, he was extremely successful in developing hundreds of useful products. He convinced southern farmers to grow these crops instead of cotton, which opened up new sources of income. Carver was rewarded for his work by many honors. He was elected a fellow of the Royal Society and received the Spingarn Medal. By the time of his death, 18 schools had been named after him. Congress honored him by designating January 5 as George Washington Carver day.

Second element in the equation, sulfur: There are 3 atoms of sulfur on the left (1 atom in each of the 3 sulfate ions), but only 1 atom on the right. Increase the number on the right to 3 by putting a 3 in front of $CaSO_4$:

$$Al_2(SO_4)_3 + CaCl_2 \rightarrow 2AlCl_3 + 3CaSO_4 \qquad \textbf{(Eq. 12)}$$

Third element in the equation, oxygen:

IN THE REACTANTS OF EQUATION 12

In $1Al_2(SO_4)_3$, there are

$1 \times 4 \times 3 = 12$ atoms of oxygen

IN THE PRODUCTS OF EQUATION 12

In $3CaSO_4$, there are

$3 \times 4 = 12$ atoms of oxygen

The oxygen balances without any change in the coefficients of Equation 12.

Fourth element in the equation, calcium: There is 1 calcium atom in $CaCl_2$ on the left, but 3 calcium atoms in $3CaSO_4$ on the right. By supplying $CaCl_2$ with a coefficient of 3, there will be 3 calcium atoms on both sides:

$$Al_2(SO_4)_3 + 3CaCl_2 \rightarrow 2AlCl_3 + 3CaSO_4 \qquad \textbf{(Eq. 13)}$$

Fifth element in the equation, chlorine: In $3CaCl_2$, there are $3 \times 2 = 6$ chlorine atoms. In $2AlCl_3$, there are $2 \times 3 = 6$ chlorine atoms. Therefore, Equation 13 is already balanced with respect to chlorine. Since Equation 13 is also balanced with respect to all the other elements, it is the correctly balanced equation.

8. Briefly (one sentence each) state the steps in writing a balanced chemical equation.

*9. Study each of the formula equations shown below. Indicate whether the equation is balanced or unbalanced and use coefficients to balance those equations that are not in balance.
  (a) $Na + O_2 \rightarrow Na_2O$
  (b) $Cu + S \rightarrow Cu_2S$
  (c) $CuO + H_2 \rightarrow Cu + H_2O$
  (d) $AgNO_3 + H_2SO_4 \rightarrow Ag_2SO_4 + HNO_3$
  (e) $Ba(OH)_2 + CO_2 \rightarrow BaCO_3 + H_2O$

*10. The chemical reaction between iron and oxygen gas produces iron (III) oxide.
  (a) Write the word equation for this reaction.
  (b) Write the unbalanced formula equation for the reaction.
  (c) Balance the equation.

11. Repeat the steps in question 10 for the reaction in which sodium and water react to produce sodium hydroxide and hydrogen gas.

12. Repeat the same steps for the reaction between copper and sulfuric acid (hydrogen sulfate) which yields copper (II) sulfate, water, and sulfur dioxide.

10-4 Showing Phases in Chemical Equations

We have seen that chemical equations show what substances take part in reactions. They also show the relative number of atoms of each element.

If they wish to, chemists can give additional information in an equation. They can indicate the phases of the substances, telling whether the substance is in the liquid phase (l), the gaseous phase (g), or the solid phase (s). Since many solid substances will not react to any appreciable extent unless they are dissolved in water, the notation (aq) is used to indicate that the substance exists in a water solution (aqueous solution). Information concerning phase is given in parentheses following the formula for each substance. Several illustrations of this notation are given below and in Figure 10-3.

Figure 10-2

When writing equations, chemists always write the formulas of the reactants and products. Chemists sometimes indicate phase and tell if substances are dissolved in water.

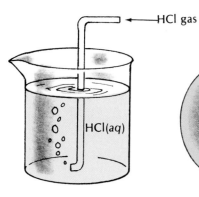

(aq) means that the HCl is dissolved in water to form an aqueous solution.

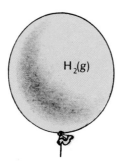

(g) means that hydrogen is in the gaseous phase.

(l) means that the water is in the liquid phase.

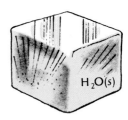

(s) means that the water is in the solid phase.

FORMULA WITH PHASE NOTATION	MEANING
$Cl_2(g)$	chlorine gas
$H_2O(l)$	water as a liquid (as opposed to being ice or steam)
$NaCl(s)$	sodium chloride as a solid
$NaCl(aq)$	sodium chloride dissolved in water

Following is an example of phase notation in an equation:

$$2HCl(aq) + Zn(s) \longrightarrow ZnCl_2(aq) + H_2(g) \qquad \textbf{(Eq. 14)}$$

In words, Equation 14 says: Hydrogen chloride dissolved in water (this solution is called hydrochloric acid) reacts with solid zinc to produce zinc chloride dissolved in water plus hydrogen gas. See Figure 10-4.

Figure 10-4

The reaction of zinc metal and hydrochloric acid to produce zinc chloride and hydrogen gas.

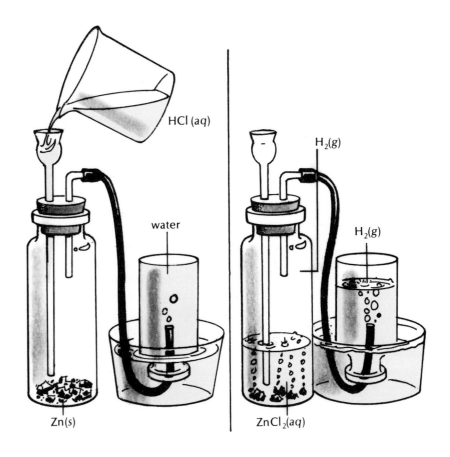

HCl (aq)

$H_2(g)$

water

$H_2(g)$

Zn(s)

$ZnCl_2(aq)$

10-5 Showing Energy Changes in Equations

A reaction is either an endothermic reaction or an exothermic reaction. Chemists can show in an equation what kind of reaction is taking

place. In endothermic reactions, the energy term is written on the le̶f̶t̶
(with the reactants):

ENDOTHERMIC REACTION

$$2H_2O(l) + \text{energy} \longrightarrow 2H_2(g) + O_2(g) \qquad \textbf{(Eq. 15)}$$

This tells us that energy is absorbed or used by the reaction as it proceeds.

In exothermic reactions, the term for energy is written on the right (with the products):

EXOTHERMIC REACTION

$$2H_2(g) + O_2(g) \longrightarrow 2H_2O(l) + \text{energy} \qquad \textbf{(Eq. 16)}$$

The energy term on the right tells us that energy is given off as the reaction proceeds.

10-6   Ionic Equations

Earlier in the chapter we balanced this equation:

$$Cl_2(aq) + 2NaBr(aq) \longrightarrow Br_2(aq) + 2NaCl(aq) \qquad \textbf{(Eq. 17)}$$

We will consider now in some detail what is going on in this reaction. We begin by taking a look at the reactants. Sodium bromide, NaBr, is a white crystalline solid. It looks like table salt. Solid sodium bromide will not react with chlorine to any noticeable extent. The reaction described by Equation 17 occurs only when the ionic solid has been dissolved in water. The same is true of most reactions involving ionic compounds. When sodium bromide is placed in water, the water molecules pull the sodium and bromide ions into solution. The solution of sodium bromide consists of sodium ions and bromide ions surrounded by water molecules. The solution is transparent and looks like plain water.

To get the reaction going, chlorine gas is bubbled into the solution. We see evidence that a change is taking place because the solution develops a brownish color. See Figure 10-5. This color is from the bromine, Br_2, that is being produced by the reaction. If enough bromine is formed, the water will be unable to hold all of it in solution. Some of the bromine will collect as a dense brown liquid at the bottom of the beaker.

Although we cannot see it, something new besides the bromine is formed. The new "something" is chloride ions, Cl^-. After reaction, the water contains fewer bromide ions, Br^-, because some have been turned into bromine molecules. A pair of negative chloride ions takes the place of every pair of negative bromide ions that are changed to a neutral Br_2 molecule. Because negative chloride ions are formed in the solution while negative bromide ions are removed from it, the amount

The reaction of chlorine gas with sodium bromide solution to produce bromine and sodium chloride.

(A) Solid NaBr

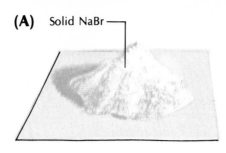

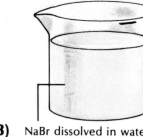

(B) NaBr dissolved in water to form a NaBr solution consisting of aqueous Na^+ and Br^- ions

(C) Chlorine gas being bubbled into the NaBr solution

$Cl_2(g)$

(D) After the reaction is complete

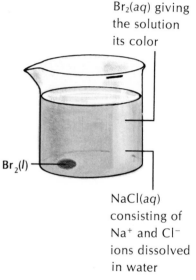

$Br_2(aq)$ giving the solution its color

$Br_2(l)$

NaCl(aq) consisting of Na^+ and Cl^- ions dissolved in water

of negative charge remains constant while the reaction proceeds.

What happened to the sodium ions that were dissolved in the water before the chlorine gas was bubbled into the solution? The answer is *nothing*. They are still dissolved in the water after the reaction is over. The sodium ions did not take part in the reaction. The number of sodium ions before reaction is the same as the number after the reaction.

We summarize the changes that did take place during the reaction:

——Cl_2 molecules were changed
     to chloride ions, Cl^-: $Cl_2(g) \longrightarrow Cl^-(aq)$

——Bromide ions, Br^-, were
     changed to bromine
     molecules, Br_2: $Br^-(aq) \longrightarrow Br_2(l)$

We combine these two statements into an equation by adding the substances at the left of each arrow and also those at the right of the arrows:

$$Cl_2(g) + Br^-(aq) \longrightarrow Cl^-(aq) + Br_2(l) \qquad \textbf{(Eq. 18)}$$
(unbalanced)

To balance Equation 18, we need coefficients of 2 before both Br⁻(aq) and Cl⁻(aq):

$$Cl_2(g) + 2Br^-(aq) \longrightarrow 2Cl^-(aq) + Br_2(l)$$

(Eq. 19)
(balanced)

Equation 19 is called an ionic equation. **Ionic equations** stress the reaction and production of ions. The chlorine changes to chloride ions, while the bromide ions change to bromine. Equations 17 and 19 give the same information, but the emphasis is different. The ionic equation, Equation 19, omits the sodium ions because they do not react. Ions, such as the sodium ions, that do not react are called "spectator ions."

When ionic equations are balanced correctly, not only will there be conservation of atoms, but there will also be conservation of charge. Equation 19 shows that on the left side there are two excess negative charges (one on each of the two bromide ions). Equation 19 also shows that on the right side there are two excess negative charges (one on each of the two chloride ions). Hence, the charge balances.

Does this mean that the solution has a negative charge? No. For every negative bromide ion as reactant, there is a positive sodium ion. These positive and negative charges balance, making the solution as a whole neutral. Sodium ions also balance the negative charge of the chloride ions that are formed during the reaction.

When writing ionic equations, chemists check to see that the numbers of atoms balance. They also make sure that charge balances. If it does not, they know that an error has been made in writing the equation.

10-7 Another Meaning for Coefficients

Earlier in the chapter it was stated that $3H_2O$ means 3 molecules of water. Coefficients can also have a second meaning. The expression $3H_2O$ can also mean 3 *moles* of H_2O molecules.

Recall that 1 mole of molecules is 6.02×10^{23} molecules. Therefore, 3 moles of molecules are $3 \times 6.02 \times 10^{23}$, or 18.06×10^{23} molecules. Equations such as

$$2H_2 + O_2 \rightarrow 2H_2O$$

can now be given two meanings.

(1) 2 molecules of hydrogen + 1 molecule of oxygen yield 2 molecules of water.
(2) 2 moles of hydrogen molecules + 1 mole of oxygen molecules yield 2 moles of water molecules.

As you will learn in Chapter 11, the second meaning is useful in solving certain chemical problems

13. Why is it important to be able to indicate that a substance involved in a chemical reaction is dissolved in water?
14. Tell what each of the following means: (a) HBr(aq) (b) $CO_2(s)$ (c) $CO_2(g)$ (d) $H_2O(l)$
15. What is the difference between NaCl(aq) and NaCl(l)?
16. How do you indicate that heat is released by a reaction? Is such a reaction endothermic or exothermic?
17. Express the following balanced formula equation as a word equation: $2Na(s) + 2H_2O(l) \rightarrow 2NaOH(aq) + H_2(g) + energy$
18. What is a spectator ion?
19. What is an ionic equation?
*20. Study this balanced formula equation:
$$2HCl(aq) + Zn(s) \rightarrow ZnCl_2(aq) + H_2(g)$$
(a) What ions are present as reactants? (b) What ions are present as products? (c) Name the spectator ion.
21. Rewrite the following formula equation as a balanced ionic equation showing only the changes that take place during the reaction. (Omit spectator ions, if any are present.)
$$Cu(s) + 2AgNO_3(aq) \rightarrow Cu(NO_3)_2(aq) + 2Ag(s)$$
*22. How many molecules are present in (a) 2 moles of NO? (b) in 2 moles of N_2O_5? How many nitrogen atoms are present in (c) 2 moles NO? (d) 2 moles N_2O_5?

10-8   Classifying Chemical Reactions

There are a number of ways of classifying chemical reactions. We present here one such scheme. This scheme has four categories. Not all chemical reactions can be put into one of these four categories, but many can.

1. **Direct combination,** also called **synthesis.**

element   element
or   +   or   ⟶ compound
compound compound

2. **Decomposition** or **analysis.**

compound→two or more elements or compounds

3. **Single replacement.**

element + compound→element + compound

4. **Exchange of ions,** also called **double replacement.**

compound + compound→compound + compound

In the following sections, the scheme is illustrated with some examples.

*The answers to questions marked with an asterisk are given in the back of the book.

194   Chapter 10   Chemical Equations

10-9   Direct Combination or Synthesis Reactions

In this type of reaction, two or more substances combine to produce a single, more complex substance. The combining substances may be elements, compounds, or both. The following are examples of some familiar synthesis reactions.

a. *The burning of hydrogen to form water.*

$$2H_2 + O_2 \rightarrow 2H_2O$$

b. *The burning of carbon to form carbon dioxide.*

$$C + O_2 \rightarrow CO_2$$

c. *The burning of carbon monoxide to form carbon dioxide.*

$$2CO + O_2 \rightarrow 2CO_2$$

d. *The reaction of calcium oxide and water to form calcium hydroxide, Ca(OH)$_2$.*

$$CaO + H_2O \rightarrow Ca(OH)_2$$

Check the above reactions to confirm that they all have the general form *element or compound + element or compound produces a compound.*

10-10   Decomposition or Analysis

Figure 10-6

The decomposition of mercury (II) oxide, HgO.

BEFORE REACTION

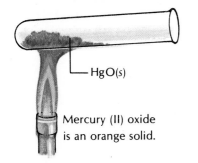

— HgO(s)

Mercury (II) oxide is an orange solid.

AFTER REACTION

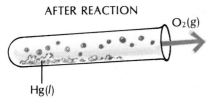

O$_2$(g)

Hg(l)

Mercury remains. Almost all the oxygen escapes as the reaction proceeds.

In this type of reaction, a single substance is broken down into two or more simpler substances. These simpler substances may be either elements or compounds. Most decomposition reactions are endothermic. Some, however, such as the breakdown of unstable compounds, are exothermic. The energy for the endothermic reactions is usually supplied as heat or electricity. The following are examples of endothermic decompositions.

a. *Decomposition of water by an electric current, a reaction also called the electrolysis (uh-lek-TRAHL-uh-sis) of water.* A small amount of dilute sulfuric acid is usually added as a catalyst. A **catalyst** is a substance that speeds up a chemical reaction without itself being permanently altered. (Chapter 27 discusses electrolysis in detail.)

$$2H_2O \rightarrow 2H_2 + O_2$$

b. *Mercury (II) oxide decomposed by heat.* The symbol delta, $\triangle$, over the arrow shows that the reactant is heated.

$$2HgO \overset{\triangle}{\rightarrow} 2Hg + O_2$$

c. *The decomposition of melted ionic solids by electrolysis.* Ionic solids are for the most part very stable, but many can be decomposed by melting them, and then electrolyzing the liquid. Very active metals, such as Na, K, Ca, Al, and Mg, are obtained by the electrolysis of melted compounds of these metals. Here are two examples.

$$2NaCl \xrightarrow{\text{elec.}} 2Na + Cl_2$$

$$2Al_2O_3 \xrightarrow{\text{elec.}} 4Al + 3O_2$$

You should check the decomposition reactions listed in this section to confirm that they all have the general form *compound yields two or more elements or compounds*.

Questions for Sections 10-8 through 10-10

23. Name four categories of chemical reactions.
24. Name the category of chemical reaction represented by each of the following:
    (a) element + compound→element + compound
    (b) element + compound→compound
    (c) compound→element + element
    (d) compound + compound→compound + compound
    (e) compound + compound→compound
*25. Complete and balance the following incomplete equations for synthesis reactions:
    (a) $H_2 + ? \rightarrow 2H_2O$
    (b) $Na + Cl_2 \rightarrow ?$
    (c) $N_2 + ? \rightarrow NO_2$
    (d) $NH_3 + ? \rightarrow NH_4Cl$
    (e) $? + O_2 \rightarrow Al_2O_3$
26. What is another name for a decomposition reaction?
27. What is a catalyst?
28. Complete and balance the following incomplete equations for decomposition reactions:
    (a) $CO \rightarrow ? + O_2$ (d) $NH_4OH \rightarrow NH_3 + ?$
    (b) $? \rightarrow Al + 3Cl_2$ (e) $P_4O_{10} \rightarrow P + ?$
    (c) $CCl_4 \rightarrow C + ?$
29. What phase notation is used to show a precipitate?

10-11 Single Replacement

A single replacement reaction is one in which a free element replaces a less active element in a compound, setting this less active element free. An example of this type of reaction is the replacement of hydrogen in an acid with an active metal, such as zinc. The equation for this reaction may be written in molecular or ionic form.

MOLECULAR EQUATION

$$Zn(s) + H_2SO_4(aq) \rightarrow ZnSO_4(aq) + H_2(g)$$

IONIC EQUATION

$$Zn(s) + 2H^+(aq) + SO_4^{2-}(aq) \rightarrow Zn^{2+}(aq) + SO_4^{2-}(aq) + H_2(g)$$

The Chemist in Agriculture

The photo shows a worker studying the effect of a growth modification chemical whose purpose is to enhance plant growth.

Agriculture has come a long way from the days when horse and pig manure were the "chemicals" that farmers applied to their crops, and progress in agriculture and in chemistry have gone hand in hand.

Chemists who work in agriculture may be employed by industry, by the government, or by schools of agriculture. Four or more years of education at the university level are a must. In addition to extensive training in chemistry, the chemist in agriculture usually has a good background in biology.

Notice that in the ionic equation, sulfate ions appear as both reactants and products. In other words, the sulfate ions are not undergoing any change. They are spectator ions. Sometimes spectator ions are omitted from ionic equations:

$$Zn(s) + 2H^+(aq) + SO_4^{2-}(aq) \rightarrow Zn^{2+}(aq) + SO_4^{2-}(aq) + H_2(g)$$

$$Zn(s) + 2H^+(aq) \rightarrow Zn^{2+}(aq) + H_2(g)$$

In omitting the spectator ions, attention is being drawn to the fact that a number of substances can be the source of the hydrogen ions. There are other substances, besides sulfuric acid, that can provide them. They can come, for example, from hydrochloric acid. The molecular equations for the reaction of zinc with sulfuric acid and zinc with hydrochloric acid will be different:

$$Zn(s) + H_2SO_4(aq) \rightarrow ZnSO_4(aq) + H_2(g)$$

$$Zn(s) + 2HCl(aq) \rightarrow ZnCl_2(aq) + H_2(g)$$

But their ionic equations, omitting spectator ions, will be the same:

$$Zn(s) + 2H^+(aq) + SO_4^{2-}(aq) \rightarrow Zn^{2+}(aq) + SO_4^{2-}(aq) + H_2(g)$$

$$Zn(s) + 2H^+(aq) + 2Cl^-(aq) \rightarrow Zn^{2+}(aq) + 2Cl^-(aq) + H_2(g)$$

IONIC EQUATION OMITTING SPECTATOR IONS

$$Zn(s) + 2H^+(aq) \rightarrow Zn^{2+}(aq) + H_2(g)$$

Let us take a closer look at the reaction of zinc with sulfuric acid. The hydrogen that is formed by the reaction will bubble out of solution. The zinc ions and the spectator sulfate ions are both in solution at the end of the reaction. If this solution is boiled, the water will evaporate, and solid crystals of zinc sulfate will form. Thus, the sulfate ions that started out in a sulfuric acid solution end up in crystals of zinc sulfate. In effect, the zinc replaces the hydrogen in the sulfuric acid.

Another example of a single replacement reaction is the replacement of bromide ions in a compound by the element chlorine. This reaction was referred to in some detail in Section 10-6.

$$Cl_2(aq) + 2NaBr(aq) \rightarrow Br_2(aq) + 2NaCl(aq)$$

In this reaction, sodium ions are spectator ions. Rather than using NaBr, other bromides, such as KBr, may be used as a source of bromide ions in this reaction. Either way, the ionic equation, omitting spectator ions, is:

$$Cl_2(aq) + 2Br^-(aq) \rightarrow Br_2(aq) + 2Cl^-(aq)$$

You should check the single replacement reactions listed in this section to confirm that they all have the general form *element + compound yields element + compound.*

Chapter 10 Chemical Equations **197**

(A) water solution   water solution   (B)

K$_2$CrO$_4$ Pb (NO$_3$)$_2$

10-12   Exchange of Ions or Double Replacement

Figure 10-7

The photo on the left shows solid crystals of potassium chromate, K$_2$CrO$_4$, and lead nitrate, Pb(NO$_3$)$_2$. Also shown are the solutions that are formed when these solids are dissolved in water. The photo on the right shows the yellow precipitate that is formed when the one solution is poured into the other. What is the formula of the precipitate?

Precipitation in a physical change can be demonstrated by dissolving as much sugar as possible in some hot water and then cooling the solution.

In this type of reaction, a solution of an ionic compound is added to a solution of another ionic compound. Then the anions of one compound react with the cations of the other compound to form a precipitate (see below), a gas, or water.

The formation of a precipitate (prih-SIP-uh-tate) in ion-exchange reactions is quite common. A **precipitate** is a solid substance formed by a physical or chemical change in a liquid (or even gaseous) medium. In ion-exchange reactions, the cation of one of the reactants combines with the anion of the other reactant and forms a solid that is insoluble in the liquid medium of the reaction. This solid is more dense than the liquid medium. It therefore separates from the liquid medium by settling to the bottom of the container.

Because both solutions are transparent before they are mixed, the formation of a precipitate is dramatic. See Figure 10-7. When writing the equation, the letter s in parentheses is written after the formula of the precipitate to indicate that it is a solid. The formation and settling of insoluble solids is called precipitation. An example of this type of reaction is the precipitation of silver chloride (AgCl) when sodium chloride and silver nitrate solutions are mixed.

MOLECULAR EQUATION

$$\text{NaCl}(aq) + \text{AgNO}_3(aq) \rightarrow \text{NaNO}_3(aq) + \text{AgCl}(s)$$

IONIC EQUATION

$$\text{Na}^+(aq) + \text{Cl}^-(aq) + \text{Ag}^+(aq) + \text{NO}_3^-(aq) \rightarrow \text{Na}^+(aq) + \text{NO}_3^-(aq) + \text{AgCl}(s)$$

Notice from the ionic equation that sodium ions are in solution in equal numbers both before and after the reaction. The same is true of the nitrate ions. These ions are not really taking part in the reaction. They

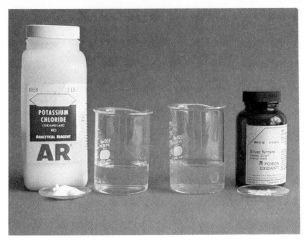
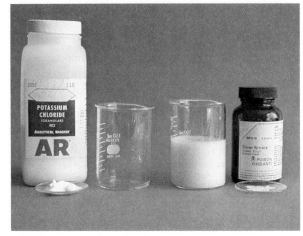

Figure 10-8

The left photo shows white crystals of potassium chloride, KCl (left watch glass), and silver nitrate, $AgNO_3$ (right watch glass). Also shown are their aqueous solutions. The right photo shows the white precipitate that is formed when the solutions are mixed. What is the formula of the white precipitate?

are spectator ions. Here is the ionic equation after the spectator ions have been eliminated.

$$Na^+(aq) + Cl^-(aq) + Ag^+(aq) + NO_3^-(aq) \rightarrow Na^+(aq) + NO_3^-(aq) + AgCl(s)$$

$$Cl^-(aq) + Ag^+(aq) \qquad\qquad \rightarrow \qquad\qquad AgCl(s)$$

This kind of equation emphasizes that chloride ions and silver ions form the insoluble substance silver chloride. It calls attention to the fact that the chloride ions may have a number of sources. They don't have to come from NaCl. They can come from other soluble chloride compounds such as KCl (Figure 10-8) and LiCl. Different sources of chloride ions will have different molecular equations, but will have the same ionic equation, as illustrated below.

$$KCl(aq) + AgNO_3(aq) \rightarrow KNO_3(aq) + AgCl(s)$$

$$LiCl(aq) + AgNO_3(aq) \rightarrow LiNO_3(aq) + AgCl(s)$$

IONIC EQUATION, SPECTATOR IONS OMITTED, FOR BOTH THE MOLECULAR EQUATIONS ABOVE

$$Cl^-(aq) + Ag^+(aq) \rightarrow AgCl(s)$$

Let us take another look at the reaction between NaCl and $AgNO_3$ to form the insoluble substance AgCl. As the solid AgCl settles to the bottom of the reaction container, the spectator ions, Na^+ and NO_3^-, remain in solution. After a while, all the solid AgCl will have settled to the bottom. The solution above, containing the spectator ions, can be carefully poured off. If the solution is boiled, the water will evaporate, leaving behind crystals of $NaNO_3$. This $NaNO_3$ is a substance that was not present before reaction took place. The final result of the reaction between the solutions of NaCl and $AgNO_3$ will be for the cations of these substances to have changed places. (Or, to look at it another way, the anions will have changed places.)

Chapter 10   Chemical Equations

$$NaCl(aq) + AgNO_3(aq) \rightarrow NaNO_3(aq) + AgCl(s)$$

This is why reactions of this kind are called exchange of ions.

You should check the double replacement reactions listed in this section to confirm that they have the general form *compound + compound yields compound + compound*.

10-13   Reversible Reactions

Many chemical reactions are reversible. A **reversible reaction** is one in which the products can themselves react with each other to re-form the reactants. For example, suppose that substance *A* and substance *B* are substances that react to form *C* and *D*, but that *C* and *D* can react to form *A* and *B* under the same conditions.

$$A + B \rightarrow C + D \qquad\qquad \textbf{(Eq. 20)}$$

$$C + D \rightarrow A + B \qquad\qquad \textbf{(Eq. 21)}$$

The changes described by Equations 20 and 21 can also be written:

$$A + B \rightleftharpoons C + D \qquad\qquad \textbf{(Eq. 22)}$$

The double arrow in Equation 22 shows that the reaction can run in both directions at the same time, in the forward direction (from left to right) and in the reverse direction (from right to left).

In reversible reactions, the reaction vessel always contains both the reactants and the products as long as none of these substances is allowed to escape.

Now suppose that the substance represented by *D* in Equation 22 is a medicine, and that pharmaceutical chemists want to produce *D* from the reactants *A* and *B*. The chemists will try to remove *D* from the reaction vessel as fast as it is formed. With no *D* present, *C* and *D* can no longer react with each other to form *A* and *B*. Then, only *A* and *B* will react until one or the other is completely used up. Chemists have various ways of separating and removing one substance in a reaction mixture from the other substances.

Sometimes nature itself removes a product from a reaction vessel. This can happen, for example, when one of the products of a reaction is a gas that rises out of the test tube or flask. Then, only the reaction between the reactants will take place until one or more of the reactants is completely used up. Chemists say that the reaction has run to completion.

Nature also removes a product of a reaction when two substances that are dissolved in water or some other solvent react to produce two or more products, one of which is insoluble in (cannot remain dissolved in) the solvent. The insoluble, solid precipitate sinks to the bottom of the solution. This removes the solid product, to a large extent, from contact with the other product(s). Moreover, and what is more important, the elements in the insoluble substance are held together by strong attractive forces. They will not separate and react with the other product(s). Therefore, reactions of this sort also run to completion.

30. What is the general form for a single replacement reaction?
31. What is another name for a double replacement reaction?
32. What is a precipitate?

The following equations are for answering questions 33-35:

(a) $2Na(s) + 2H_2O(l) \rightarrow 2NaOH(aq) + H_2(g)$
(b) $Ca(s) + MgSO_4(aq) \rightarrow CaSO_4(aq) + Mg(s)$
(c) $BaCl_2(aq) + K_2SO_4(aq) \rightarrow BaSO_4(s) + 2KCl(aq)$
(d) $Na_2CO_3(aq) + Ca(OH)_2(aq) \rightarrow 2NaOH(aq) + CaCO_3(s)$
(e) $2AgNO_3(aq) + Zn(s) \rightarrow Zn(NO_3)_2(aq) + 2Ag(s)$
(f) $Al_2(SO_4)_3(aq) + 3BaCl_2(aq) \rightarrow 2AlCl_3(aq) + 3BaSO_4(s)$

33. Identify each reaction as single replacement or ion exchange.
*34. Rewrite each as a balanced ionic equation.
35. Identify the spectator ions (if any) in each equation.
36. What is a reversible reaction?
37. How are some reversible reactions indicated in a chemical equation?

CHAPTER SUMMARY

1. A chemical equation is a condensed statement of facts about a chemical reaction.
2. Chemical equations consist of reactants and products. Reactants are substances that exist before a reaction takes place. Products are the substances that come into existence as a result of the reaction.
3. Coefficients are numbers in a chemical equation that indicate the smallest number of formula units of a substance that may take part in the reaction. Coefficients may also indicate the number of moles of each substance in the reaction.
4. The steps in writing a balanced chemical equation are:
   • Write a word equation.
   • Write an unbalanced formula equation.
   • Write coefficients to balance the formula equation.
5. Chemical equations can include additional information, such as phase notations, energy changes, and the formation of precipitates and gases.
6. In an ionic reaction, those ions that remain unchanged are called spectator ions.
7. Ionic equations stress the reaction and production of ions. Spectator ions are often omitted from ionic reactions.

8. Four categories of chemical reactions are:
   - Direct combination or synthesis
   - Decomposition or analysis
   - Single replacement
   - Exchange of ions or double replacement
9. A catalyst is a substance that changes the rate of a reaction without itself being permanently altered.
10. Precipitation is the formation of an insoluble solid that settles, or precipitates, out of solution.
11. A reversible reaction is one in which the products can react with each other to re-form the reactants.

TERMS YOU SHOULD KNOW

chemical equation	direct combination	single replacement	catalyst
reactants	reaction	reaction	precipitate
products	synthesis reaction	exchange of ion reaction	reversible reaction
coefficient	decomposition reaction	double replacement	
ionic equation	analysis reaction	reaction	

REVIEW QUESTIONS

Section

10-1   **1.** What changes are involved in chemical reactions?

10-2   **2.** What is an unbalanced chemical equation?

3. What scientific law makes it necessary to have a balanced chemical equation?

4. Why is it incorrect to change formula subscripts to achieve a balanced equation?

5. What is the difference between H_2O_2 and $2H_2O$?

10-3   **6.** Explain why iodine, which is a solid under normal conditions, is represented as a diatomic molecule.

10-4   **7.** What change is represented by the "equation" $H_2O(l) \rightarrow H_2O(s)$?

10-5   **8.** Referring to the "equation" in question 7, on which side of the arrow would you write the word *energy?* State the reasoning behind your answer.

10-6   **9.** Why is it necessary to conserve charges in a balanced ionic equation?

10-7   **10.** How many oxygen *atoms* are there in one mole of CO_2 molecules?

10-8   **11.** Give the names and general forms of four categories of chemical reactions.

10-10   **12.** Why isn't it necessary to include the formula of a catalyst when it is used to speed up the rate of a chemical reaction?

10-3 ***1.** Balance each of the following equations:

*(a) $Al(OH)_3 \rightarrow Al_2O_3 + H_2O$

*(b) $Ti + N_2 \rightarrow Ti_3N_4$

*(c) $Al + ZnCl_2 \rightarrow AlCl_3 + Zn$

(d) $Bi + H_2O \rightarrow Bi_2O_3 + H_2$

(e) $BaCO_3 + C + H_2O \rightarrow CO + Ba(OH)_2$

(f) $Cu + H_2SO_4 \rightarrow CuSO_4 + H_2O + SO_2$

(g) $KMnO_4 + HCl \rightarrow KCl + MnCl_2 + H_2O + Cl_2$

(h) $Cu + HNO_3 \rightarrow Cu(NO_3)_2 + NO + H_2O$

10-8 ***2.** Identify the category of the reaction and write balanced formula equations for the following:

*(a) calcium carbonate→calcium oxide + carbon dioxide

*(b) potassium bromide + chlorine→potassium chloride + bromine

(c) tin + oxygen→tin(IV) oxide

(d) zinc nitrate + hydrogen sulfide→zinc sulfide + nitric acid

10-11 ***3.** Write balanced ionic equations for each of the following:

*(a) $CaBr_2(aq) + Na_2CO_3(aq) \rightarrow CaCO_3(s) + 2NaBr(aq)$

*(b) $AgNO_3(aq) + NaCl(aq) \rightarrow AgCl(s) + NaNO_3(aq)$

(c) $Zn(s) + AgNO_3(aq) \rightarrow Zn(NO_3)_2(aq) + Ag(s)$

(d) $BaCl_2(aq) + H_2SO_4(aq) \rightarrow BaSO_4(s) + HCl(aq)$

4. Name the spectator ions in the four equations in problem 3.

FOR FURTHER THOUGHT

10-2 **1.** Which of the following are uses of chemical equations?

(a) To predict reactions.

(b) To determine the masses of reactants and products.

(c) To determine the properties of new substances.

(d) To test the laws of chemistry.

(e) To prove the conservation of mass.

10-3 **2.** (a) Why is it not permitted to balance an equation by changing the subscripts in formulas? (b) Why is it permitted to balance an equation by changing coefficients?

10-7 **3.** Which of the following are the same on both sides of all balanced equations?

(a) The number of molecules.

(b) The number of atoms.

(c) The total atomic mass.

(d) The number of different phases.

(e) The number of moles.

(f) The number of ions.

The Mathematics of Chemical Equations

Objectives

After you have completed this chapter, you will be able to:

- From a chemical equation, derive quantitative information about the reacting substances.
- Calculate molecular masses and determine formulas from molar volumes and experimental data.
- Solve problems based upon mass-mass, volume-volume, and volume-mass relationships in equations.

11-1   The Importance of Mathematics in Chemistry

In the early days of chemistry, chemists did not pay much attention to measurement. They mixed and heated various substances, and they observed the changes that occurred. But they did not make careful measurements of quantities used or produced. The phlogiston theory of burning, discussed in Section 1-2, was accepted because it was not tested by quantitative experiments. Antoine Lavoisier (1743-1794) was one of the first chemists to measure the masses of reactants and products in combustion reactions. As you saw in Chapter 1, it was the result of these experiments that overthrew the phlogiston theory and explained the true nature of burning.

Calculations made from measurements enable us to see relationships in chemical reactions and to understand chemical changes. The mathematics of chemistry gives the chemist control over chemical reactions in industry. Using the principles to be described in this chapter, the chemist can calculate the exact quantities of the substances that take part in a reaction.

11-2   Mass-Mass Problems

In a common type of chemical problem, the mass of one substance taking part in a chemical reaction is to be found when the mass of another substance taking part in the reaction is stated. Problems of this

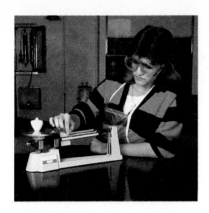

Figure 11-1

Progress in chemistry became much more rapid after chemists began to make accurate measurements.

kind are called mass-mass problems. We can illustrate mass-mass problems with the general reaction

$$A + B \rightarrow C + D$$

In one type of mass-mass problem, you may be asked to find the number of grams of C that is produced when a certain number of grams of A reacts with an excess of B. In another kind of mass-mass problem you may be asked to find the number of grams of B that will react with a certain number of grams of A. In still another kind of mass-mass problem, you may be asked to find the number of grams of D that are produced when a certain number of grams of C are produced. In mass-mass problems, masses are usually expressed in grams, but can, of course, be expressed in any other unit of mass. In discussing how to solve this type of problem, the following terms will be used:

—"Given mass" refers to the mass given in the statement of the problem.

—"Unknown mass" refers to the mass that is to be found.

The key to solving mass-mass problems is a correctly balanced equation. The coefficients in the equation state the relative amounts of each substance taking part in the reaction. They express these relative amounts in terms of moles. For the reaction $A + 3B \rightarrow 2C$, we see that 1 mole of A reacts with 3 moles of B to produce 2 moles of C. However, there is no way of measuring amounts of substances directly in moles. In a practical situation in the laboratory or in industry, we usually find the amount of a substance by weighing it, and we express the result in units of mass, such as grams or kilograms. We can find the equivalent number of moles only by calculating it from the known mass. Therefore, to solve a mass-mass problem, we must first convert given masses to the corresponding number of moles. Then, the balanced equation can be used to determine the number of moles of the substance of unknown mass. This number of moles can then be converted to a corresponding mass in grams or kilograms. The sample problem illustrates the process.

SAMPLE PROBLEM

How many grams of NaCl must be decomposed to yield 355 grams of Cl_2? (Sodium, Na, is the other product of the reaction.)

Solution. Always begin by writing the balanced equation for the reaction:

$$2NaCl \rightarrow 2Na + Cl_2 \qquad \textbf{(Eq. 1)}$$

This equation tells us that 2 moles of NaCl yield 2 moles of Na and 1 mole of Cl_2. These mole ratios must hold, regardless of the amounts of substances involved. It is also helpful to write the given mass and unknown mass:

Given: 355 g Cl_2 Unknown: ? g NaCl

The solution of the problem requires three steps.

Chapter 11   The Mathematics of Chemical Equations   **205**

Step 1. *Convert the given mass to moles.* The given mass is 355 g Cl_2. From the molecular formula and the known atomic mass of Cl, we calculate that the mass of 1 mole of Cl_2 is 71 g. To convert 355 g Cl_2 to moles, we must multiply 355 g Cl_2 by a conversion factor that will change *g* Cl_2 to *moles* Cl_2. We have to decide whether the conversion factor is

$$\textbf{(A)} \quad \frac{71 \text{ g } Cl_2}{1 \text{ mole } Cl_2} \qquad or \qquad \textbf{(B)} \quad \frac{1 \text{ mole } Cl_2}{71 \text{ g } Cl_2}$$

We can see that factor (B) will cancel *g* Cl_2 and leave *moles* Cl_2:

$$355 \text{ g } Cl_2 \times \frac{1 \text{ mole } Cl_2}{71 \text{ g } Cl_2} = 5.0 \text{ moles } Cl_2$$

Step 2. *From the mole ratios of the balanced equation, find the number of moles of the "unknown" that are equivalent to the number of moles of the given substance.* The equation tells us that 2 moles of NaCl must be decomposed to produce 1 mole of Cl_2. Again, we have a choice of factors for converting 5.0 *moles* Cl_2 to equivalent *moles NaCl:*

$$\textbf{(C)} \quad \frac{2 \text{ moles NaCl}}{1 \text{ mole } Cl_2} \qquad or \qquad \textbf{(D)} \quad \frac{1 \text{ mole } Cl_2}{2 \text{ moles NaCl}}$$

We see that factor (C) will cancel moles Cl_2 and leave moles NaCl:

$$5.0 \text{ moles } Cl_2 \times \frac{2 \text{ moles NaCl}}{1 \text{ mole } Cl_2} = 10 \text{ moles NaCl}$$

Step 3. *Convert moles of unknown to mass of unknown.* The mass of 1 mole of NaCl is 58.5 g. As in previous steps, we find the factor that will convert moles NaCl to g NaCl. It is

$$\frac{58.5 \text{ g NaCl}}{1 \text{ mole NaCl}}$$

$$10 \text{ moles NaCl} \times \frac{58.5 \text{ g NaCl}}{1 \text{ mole NaCl}} = 585 \text{ g NaCl}$$

Although we have carried out each conversion step separately to make the process clearer, it is not necessary to do this. The entire process can be expressed as a series of multiplication by three factors: (1) the factor that converts grams of "given" to moles of "given"; (2) the factor that converts moles of "given" to equivalent moles of "unknown"; and (3) the factor that converts moles of "unknown" to grams of unknown. The solution can be expressed as follows:

$$? \text{ g NaCl} = 355 \text{ g } Cl_2 \times \frac{1 \text{ mole } Cl_2}{71 \text{ g } Cl_2} \times \frac{2 \text{ moles NaCl}}{1 \text{ mole } Cl_2} \times \frac{58.5 \text{ g NaCl}}{1 \text{ mole NaCl}}$$

$$= \frac{355 \times 1 \times 2 \times 58.5 \text{ g NaCl}}{71 \times 1 \times 1} = 585 \text{ g NaCl}$$

Note how all the factor labels except the desired one (g NaCl) cancel out.

We now repeat the expression given above, showing the various parts that make it up:

Figure 11-2

When platinum electrodes are immersed in molten sodium chloride, the sodium chloride decomposes into chlorine gas and sodium metal according to the equation $2NaCl \rightarrow 2Na + Cl_2$. Using electricity to bring about a chemical reaction is called electrolysis.

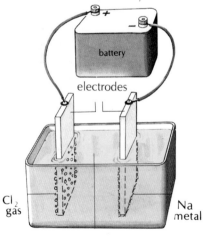

molten NaCl

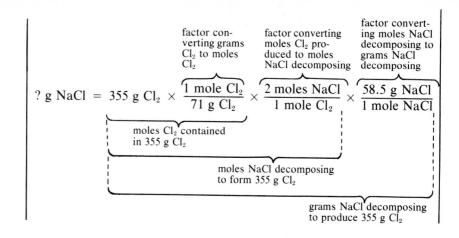

$$? \text{ g NaCl} = 355 \text{ g Cl}_2 \times \frac{1 \text{ mole Cl}_2}{71 \text{ g Cl}_2} \times \frac{2 \text{ moles NaCl}}{1 \text{ mole Cl}_2} \times \frac{58.5 \text{ g NaCl}}{1 \text{ mole NaCl}}$$

factor converting grams Cl_2 to moles Cl_2

factor converting moles Cl_2 produced to moles NaCl decomposing

factor converting moles NaCl decomposing to grams NaCl decomposing

moles Cl_2 contained in 355 g Cl_2

moles NaCl decomposing to form 355 g Cl_2

grams NaCl decomposing to produce 355 g Cl_2

The relationships upon which mass-mass problems are based can be shown pictorially by what is known as an expanded mole diagram. An expanded mole diagram is a conceptual scheme that summarizes a great deal of information about stoichiometry. The diagram is helpful not only in solving mass-mass problems but also in solving the kinds of problems that appear in some of the later sections of this chapter.

You may wonder what connection there is between the mole diagram described in Chapter 9 and the expanded mole diagram referred to here. An expanded mole diagram is simply two mole diagrams in one drawing, one of which is a mirror image of the other. See Figure 11-3 on page 208.

The boxes on the left side of Figure 11-3 represent quantities of one of the substances taking part in a chemical reaction. In the diagram, the letter A is used to represent that substance. The boxes on the right side of the diagram represent quantities of one of the other substances taking part in the reaction. In the diagram, the letter B is used to represent that substance.

In Figure 11-3, you'll notice that there is a line connecting the left side of the diagram with the right. It runs between the box for *moles A* on the left and the box for *moles B* on the right. The conversion factor that connects these two boxes is a fraction formed from the coefficients of substances A and B in the balanced equation for the reaction in which A and B are either reactants or products.

Figure 11-4 on page 209 is an expanded mole diagram for the sample problem given earlier in this section.

In the sample problem, we are given an amount of Cl_2 and asked to find how much NaCl must be decomposed to produce the given amount. The problem, then, involves the substances Cl_2 and NaCl. It doesn't matter which substance goes on which side of the expanded mole diagram. That is, in Figure 11-4, we put the NaCl into the boxes on the left side, but we could have put it into the boxes on the right side just as well. Since we are given the mass of the Cl_2, notice that the box for "mass Cl_2" is marked *GIVEN*. Since we are asked to find the mass of NaCl obtainable from the Cl_2, the box for "mass NaCl" is marked *FIND*.

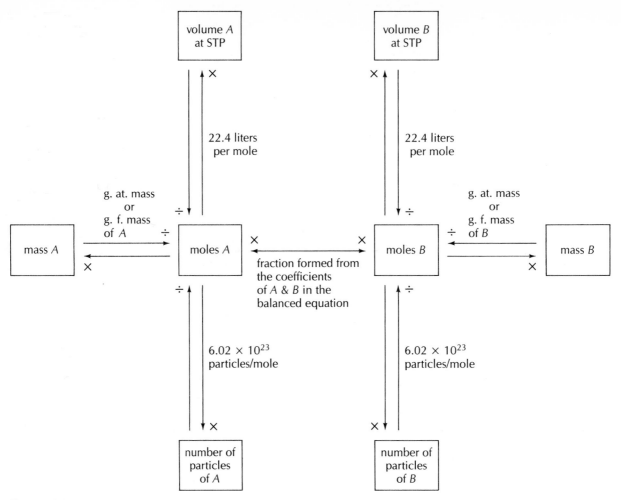

Figure 11-3

An expanded mole diagram. The left half of an expanded mole diagram consists of the mole diagram discussed in Chapter 9. The right half is a mirror image of the left. The letter *A* shown in the boxes on the left side of the diagram represents one of the substances taking part in a chemical reaction. The letter *B* shown on the right side represents one of the other substances in the same reaction. The two sides of the diagram are related to each other by a conversion factor that is a fraction formed from the coefficients of *A* and *B* in the balanced equation for the reaction. The sample problem explains how the fraction is formed.

The three steps in the solution to the problem are shown in Figure 11-4 by the numbers 1, 2, and 3 enclosed in circles. The diagram shows that in Step 1, the given mass of Cl_2 is divided by the gram formula mass of Cl_2 in order to convert from the mass of Cl_2 to the number of moles of Cl_2. Step 2 in the diagram shows that to convert from moles of Cl_2 produced (found in Step 1) to moles of NaCl reacting, the number of moles of Cl_2 must be multiplied by a fraction formed from the coefficients of the substances in the balanced equation. Step 3 in the diagram shows that to convert from the number of moles of NaCl reacting (found in Step 2) to the number of grams of NaCl reacting, the number of moles of NaCl must be multiplied by the gram formula mass of NaCl.*

*The expanded mole diagrams in this chapter (Figures 11-3 and 11-4) and the mole diagrams in Chapter 9 (Figures 9-8 and 9-9) are adapted from Dorothy Gabel's *Solving Chemistry Problems: A Student's Illustrated Guide to Applying the Mole Concept,* 1983, Allyn and Bacon, Inc.

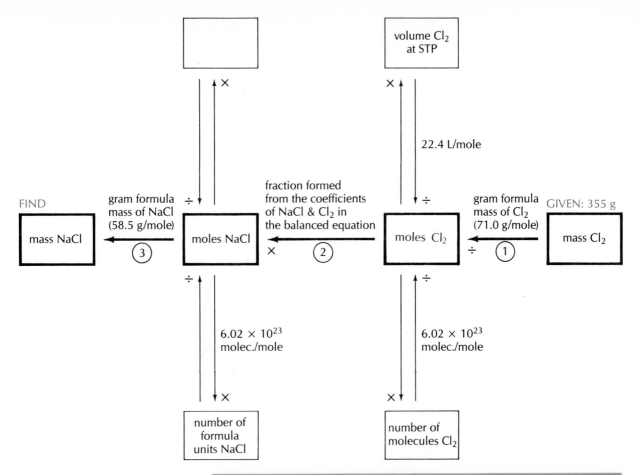

Figure 11-4

An expanded mole diagram for this sample problem. In Step 1, the given mass of Cl_2 is divided by the gram formula mass of Cl_2 to find the number of moles of Cl_2 in the given mass. In Step 2, the number of moles of Cl_2 found in Step 1 is multiplied by a fraction formed from the coefficients of NaCl and Cl_2 in the balanced equation for the reaction. In Step 3, the number of moles of NaCl found in Step 2 is multiplied by the gram formula mass of NaCl to find the mass in grams of NaCl that must react to produce the given quantity of Cl_2.

Questions for Sections 11-1 and 11-2

1. What information is given by the coefficients in a balanced equation?
2. Sodium metal, Na, reacts with water to produce hydrogen gas, H_2, according to the equation

$$2Na + 2H_2O \rightarrow 2NaOH + H_2$$

   (a) Suppose that 23 grams of sodium react. How many moles is this? (b) How many moles of H_2 will be produced from the number of moles of Na that you found for your answer to (a)? (c) How many grams of H_2 is this?

*3. For the reaction $Ca(OH)_2 + H_2SO_4 \rightarrow CaSO_4 + 2H_2O$, how many grams $Ca(OH)_2$ will react with 29.4 g H_2SO_4? Show what conversion factors must multiply 29.4 g H_2SO_4 in order to produce the correct number of grams of $Ca(OH)_2$.

*4. When a solution of sodium chloride is added to a solution of silver nitrate, a solid precipitate of silver chloride is formed. (Throughout the reaction the sodium and nitrate ions remain in solution as spectator ions.) What is the mass of silver chloride that is precipitated when 8.50 g of silver nitrate react? (Show all work, being careful to label all numbers with their proper units. If it is helpful to you, draw an expanded mole diagram for the problem.)

11-3   The Mole Concept and Volume Relationships

In 1811, Avogadro advanced the hypothesis that equal volumes of all gases at the same temperature and pressure contain the same number of molecules. (Avogadro's hypothesis was discussed in Section 6-15.) At first, this hypothesis was generally disregarded. Later, experiments proved that it was true. It is now known as Avogadro's law.

Avogadro's law suggests a way of determining the molecular masses of gases. Let us consider one-mole samples of various gases. These one-mole samples all contain the same number of molecules, namely 6.02×10^{23} molecules. By Avogadro's law, these one-mole samples should all occupy the same volume at the same temperature and pressure. When the gas samples are measured at STP, that volume is 22.4 liters. The volume, 22.4 liters, occupied by one mole of any gas at STP is called the molar volume. See Figure 11-5.

> The mass in grams of 22.4 liters of a gas at standard conditions is equal to the gram formula mass.

Figure 11-5

The molar volumes of gases.
Avogadro's law states that equal volumes of all gases at the same temperature and pressure contain equal numbers of molecules. Thus, equal volumes of gases are in the same mass ratio as single molecules of gases. The volume occupied by 1 mole of a gas at STP is called the molar volume. The molar volume is the same for all gases: 22.4 liters.

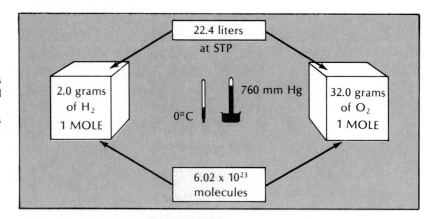

Here is how the molar volume enables us to determine experimentally the molecular mass of a gas. We obtain a sample of the gas that occupies 22.4 liters at STP. That sample will contain one mole of molecules. We determine the mass of the sample. The mass in grams of 1 mole of molecules is numerically equal to the molecular mass. For example, if at STP the mass of the 22.4-liter sample is 40 grams, then the molecular mass of the gas is 40 u.

To determine the molecular mass of a gas, a 22.4-liter sample of the gas is convenient (mathematically) but not necessary. A larger or smaller sample can be used. For these samples, we divide the mass of the sample by its volume in liters at STP. The result is the density of the gas at STP. The density of a gas at STP is called its standard density. If we know the mass of 1 liter of a gas at STP (that is, if we know its standard density), we need only multiply this density by 22.4 liters to arrive at the mass of one mole of the gas. This mass is numerically equal to the molecular mass.

SAMPLE PROBLEM 1

The standard density of a gas is 1.35 grams/liter. What is the molecular mass of the gas?

Solution. If 1 liter of a gas has a mass of 1.35 grams/liter, then 22.4 liters of the gas has a mass 22.4 times as great. This mass is, of course, the mass of 1 mole of the gas, since 22.4 liters is the volume occupied by 1 mole of any gas at STP.

$$? \quad \frac{grams}{liter} \quad = \quad 1.35 \quad \frac{grams}{liter} \quad \times \quad 22.4 \quad \frac{liters}{mole}$$

$$= \quad 30.2 \quad \frac{grams}{mole}$$

If the mass of 1 mole is 30.2 grams, then the molecular mass is 30.2 atomic mass units, or 30.2 u.

The figure for the molar volume, 22.4 liters, is not exact. The volume at STP of one mole of a gas may vary slightly from 22.4 liters. Differences of this sort are due to differences in the force of intermolecular attraction among gases. (Intermolecular attractions were discussed in Section 6-14.)

Even though the volume occupied by one mole of a gas at STP may not be exactly 22.4 liters at STP, the number is still useful. It is especially helpful in determining the molecular formulas of gaseous substances when only their empirical formulas are known. The following problem illustrates this idea.

SAMPLE PROBLEM 2

At STP a sample of a gas has a mass of 6.5 grams and a volume of 5.4 liters. Laboratory work reveals that 6.0 grams of the sample is carbon and the remaining 0.5 gram is hydrogen. What is the molecular formula of this gas?

Solution. If 6.5 grams of gas occupies a volume of 5.4 liters, then the standard density of the gas is obtained by dividing 6.5 grams by 5.4 liters. (Recall that density is mass divided by volume.) Multiplying the standard density by 22.4 liters will give the mass of 1 mole:

$$? \quad \frac{grams}{mole} \quad = \quad \frac{6.5 \ grams}{5.4 \ liters} \quad \times \quad 22.4 \quad \frac{liters}{mole}$$

$$= \quad 27 \quad \frac{grams}{mole}$$

The calculation shows that the mass of 1 mole is 27 grams. Therefore, the molecular mass is 27 atomic mass units, or 27 u.

Next, we determine the number of moles of carbon atoms and moles of hydrogen atoms in the sample:

$$\text{moles C} = \frac{6.0 \text{ grams C}}{12 \text{ grams C/mole C atoms}} = 0.5 \text{ mole C atoms}$$

$$\text{moles H} = \frac{0.5 \text{ gram H}}{1.0 \text{ gram H/mole H atoms}} = 0.5 \text{ mole H atoms}$$

The 0.5 mole of carbon atoms contain the same number of atoms as the 0.5 mole of hydrogen atoms. For every one atom of carbon there is one atom of hydrogen. The empirical formula of the compound is C_1H_1, or simply CH.

Possible molecular formulas are CH, C_2H_2, C_3H_3, etc. The molecular masses of these compounds are:

Possible molecular formula	Molecular mass
CH	12 u + 1 u = 13 u
C_2H_2	2(12 u) + 2(1 u) = 26 u
C_3H_3	3(12 u) + 3(1 u) = 39 u

Based on information given at the beginning of the problem, the experimentally determined value for the molecular mass was 27 u, a value close to 26 u, the molecular mass of C_2H_2. Even though the 27 u doesn't exactly match the true value of 26, it is close enough to eliminate easily the other possibilities. The molecular formula of the gas is C_2H_2.

11-4   Volume Relationships in Equations

It can be stated, as an outgrowth of Avogadro's law, that samples of different gases with the same number of molecules will occupy the same volume when at the same temperature and pressure. Since the coefficients of gases in a balanced equation tell the relative number of molecules, they also tell the relative volumes. Thus, the equation

$$N_2(g) + 3H_2(g) \rightarrow 2NH_3(g)$$

can be read "one volume of nitrogen gas combines with three volumes of hydrogen gas to produce two volumes of ammonia (NH_3) gas (all volumes measured at the same temperature and pressure). See Figure 11-6.

This interpretation of the coefficients enables us to calculate the quantities of reactants and products of reactions in terms of their volumes. Problems of this kind are called volume-volume problems. The sample problem shows how these problems are solved.

Figure 11-6

In gaseous reactions, the coefficients in the balanced equation can be interpreted as relative volumes, if pressure and temperature are constant.

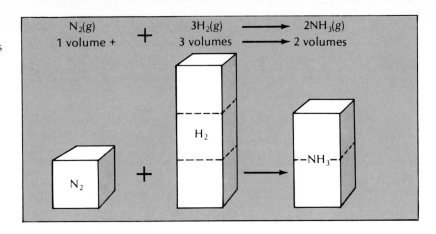

SAMPLE PROBLEM

What volume of hydrogen, H_2, reacts with excess nitrogen, N_2, to produce 100 liters of ammonia gas, NH_3 (assuming that all gas volumes are measured at the same temperature and pressure)?

Solution. As for mass-mass problems, start by writing the balanced equation for the reaction:

$$N_2(g) + 3H_2(g) \rightarrow 2NH_3(g) \qquad \textbf{(Eq. 2)}$$

It is also helpful to write the given volume and the unknown volume:

Given: 100 liters NH_3 Unknown: ? liters H_2

The problem can be solved in one step. The balanced equation shows that 1 mole N_2 reacts with 3 moles H_2 to produce 2 moles NH_3. But 1 mole of any gas occupies the same volume as 1 mole of any other gas (providing that the volumes are measured at the same temperature and pressure). Therefore, for those substances that are gases, the coefficients in the balanced equation state relative volumes of reactants and products as well as relative numbers of moles. These relative volumes can be expressed in liters or any other unit of volume. The equation, therefore, shows that 3 liters of H_2 (reacting with 1 liter of N_2) will produce 2 liters of NH_3. From these relative volumes, a factor can be composed for converting *liters H_2 reacting* to *liters NH_3 produced*. We must decide which factor is the correct one:

$$\textbf{(A)} \ \frac{3 \text{ liters } H_2}{2 \text{ liters } NH_3} \qquad \text{or} \qquad \textbf{(B)} \ \frac{2 \text{ liters } NH_3}{3 \text{ liters } H_2}$$

We see that factor (A) will cancel liters NH_3 and leave liters H_2:

$$100 \text{ liters } NH_3 \ \times \ \frac{3 \text{ liters } H_2}{2 \text{ liters } NH_3} \ = \ 150 \text{ liters } H_2$$

The result   tells us that 150 liters of H_2 (the answer) must react with excess N_2 in order to produce 100 liters NH_3. The answer assumes that all volumes are measured under the same conditions of temperature and pressure.

5. (a) Explain what is meant by the *molar volume* of a gas. (b) What is its value at standard conditions? (c) How can it be used to determine the molecular mass of a gas if the mass of a given volume, at STP, is known?

* 6. The density of a gas is 1.26 g/L at STP. What is its molecular mass?

* 7. At STP, 1.12 L of a gaseous compound consisting of carbon and hydrogen has a mass of 1.50 g. Of this mass, 0.300 g is hydrogen. What is the molecular formula of the gas?

8. At STP, 1.60 g of a gas sample has a volume of 0.56 L. Half of this mass is due to sulfur and the other half, to oxygen. What is the molecular formula of the gas?

9. (a) Explain why the coefficients of gases in an equation represent the relative volumes of the gases as well as their relative number of molecules. (b) Using the balanced equation for the electrolysis of water, $2H_2O \rightarrow 2H_2 + O_2$, state the relative volumes of the products.

*10. In the reaction $2C_2H_6 + 7O_2 \rightarrow 4CO_2 + 6H_2O$, how many liters of oxygen are required for the complete combustion of 15.6 liters of ethane?

11. How many liters of air are needed to burn 450 L of acetylene in the reaction $2C_2H_2 + 5O_2 \rightarrow 4CO_2 + 2H_2O$? Assume that the air contains 20.0% oxygen.

11-5 Mixed Mass-Volume Relationships in Equations

The problems of Section 11-2 were concerned with the masses of reactants and products. Those of Section 11-4 were concerned with volumes. However, for some reactions, a *mass* of a reactant or product is given, and from that information we want to calculate the *volume* of another reactant or product. Or, a *volume* may be given, and we want to calculate a *mass*. Problems of this sort are called mass-volume problems.

As for the problems in earlier sections, the coefficients in the balanced equation provide the information needed to solve mass-volume problems. These coefficients tell the relative number of particles taking part in a reaction. Relative numbers of particles are expressed in terms of moles. To solve a mass-volume problem, we must first determine how many moles of molecules there are in a given volume of gas or how many moles of molecules there are in a given mass of a substance. The coefficients in the balanced equation relate moles of one substance to moles of another. Once we have determined our answer in terms of moles of particles, we convert from moles to a unit of mass or volume.

SAMPLE PROBLEM

Calcium carbonate, $CaCO_3$, a solid, reacts with dilute hydrochloric acid, HCl, to produce carbon dioxide, CO_2, calcium chloride, $CaCl_2$, and water. What volume of CO_2, measured at STP, will be produced when 80 g $CaCO_3$ react?

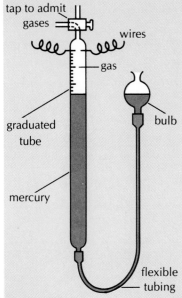

Figure 11-17

A eudiometer. Reactions involving the combustion of measured quantities of gases can be carried out in graduated glassware called eudiometers. Connected to a source of electrical voltage, the wires sealed into the top of the eudiometer can cause a spark that will ignite a flammable gas mixture. This apparatus can be used, for example, to determine what volume of hydrogen will exactly use up a measured volume of oxygen when the two elements react to form water. The pressure exerted by the gases inside the graduated tube can be adjusted to atmospheric pressure by moving the bulb up or down until the level of the mercury in the bulb is the same as its level in the graduated tube.

Solution. As for mass-mass and volume-volume problems, we start mass-volume problems by writing the correctly balanced equation.

$$CaCO_3(aq) + 2HCl(aq) \rightarrow CO_2(g) + CaCl_2(aq) + H_2O(l) \quad \textbf{(Eq. 3)}$$

We also write either the given mass or given volume (whichever appears in the statement of the problem) and the unknown mass or volume:

Given: 80 g $CaCO_3$ **Unknown:** ? liters CO_2
(at STP)

Step 1. *Convert the given mass or given volume to moles.* For $CaCO_3$, 1 mole has a mass of 100 g, and these numbers are used in the conversion factor:

$$\frac{1 \text{ mole } CaCO_3}{100 \text{ grams } CaCO_3}$$

The factor will convert 80 g $CaCO_3$ to the corresponding number of moles:

$$80 \text{ g } CaCO_3 \times \frac{1 \text{ mole } CaCO_3}{100 \text{ g } CaCO_3} = 0.80 \text{ mole } CaCO_3$$

Step 2. *From the mole ratios of the balanced equation, find the number of moles of the "unknown" equivalent to the number of moles of the given substance.* The equation tells us that 1 mole of CO_2 is produced for every 1 mole of $CaCO_3$ reacting. To convert *moles $CaCO_3$ reacting* to *moles CO_2 produced,* the factor is *1 mole CO_2 divided by 1 mole $CaCO_3$*:

$$0.80 \text{ mole } CaCO_3 \times \frac{1 \text{ mole } CO_2}{1 \text{ mole } CaCO_3} = 0.80 \text{ mole } CO_2$$

Step 3. *Convert the number of moles of the unknown to a mass or a volume (whichever is called for).* The problem asks for the *volume* of CO_2 formed at STP. One mole of any gas occupies 22.4 liters at STP, and those are the numbers that form the conversion factor. To convert *moles CO_2* to *liters CO_2* (at STP), the factor is *22.4 liters CO_2 divided by 1 mole CO_2*:

$$0.80 \text{ mole } CO_2 \times \frac{22.4 \text{ liters } CO_2}{1 \text{ mole } CO_2} = 18 \text{ liters}$$

(ANSWER)

If you should encounter a mass-volume problem in which stated volumes are not at STP, Boyle's law and Charles's law can be used to obtain the volumes at STP.

Although we have carried out each conversion step separately to make the process clearer, it is not necessary to do this. The entire process can be expressed as a series of multiplications by the three factors used in Steps 1, 2, and 3. The solution can be expressed as:

$$? \text{ liters } CO_2 = 80 \text{ g } CaCO_3 \times \frac{1 \text{ mole } CaCO_3}{100 \text{ g } CaCO_3} \times \frac{1 \text{ mole } CO_2}{1 \text{ mole } CaCO_3} \times \frac{22.4 \text{ liters } CO_2}{1 \text{ mole } CO_2}$$

$$= \frac{80 \times 1 \times 1 \times 22.4 \text{ liters } CO_2}{100 \times 1 \times 1} = 18 \text{ liters } CO_2$$

Note that all the factor labels except the desired one (liters CO_2) cancel out when the factors are formed properly.

We now repeat the expression above, showing the various parts that make it up:

$$? \text{ liters } CO_2 = 80 \text{ g } CaCO_3 \times \underbrace{\frac{1 \text{ mole } CaCO_3}{100 \text{ g } CaCO_3}}_{\substack{\text{factor converting} \\ \text{grams } CaCO_3 \text{ to} \\ \text{moles } CaCO_3}} \times \underbrace{\frac{1 \text{ mole } CO_2}{1 \text{ mole } CaCO_3}}_{\substack{\text{factor converting} \\ \text{moles } CaCO_3 \text{ to} \\ \text{moles } CO_2}} \times \underbrace{\frac{22.4 \text{ liters } CO_2}{1 \text{ mole } CO_2}}_{\substack{\text{factor converting} \\ \text{moles } CO_2 \text{ to} \\ \text{liters } CO_2}}$$

moles $CaCO_3$ in 80 grams $CaCO_3$

moles CO_2 produced when 80 grams $CaCO_3$ react

liters CO_2 produced when 80 grams $CaCO_3$ react

Questions for Section 11-5

12. The volume of a gas was measured when the gas was at room temperature and at atmospheric pressure. To solve a mass-volume problem making use of this volume, what must be done to the volume as part of the solution to the problem?

*13. Ammonium chloride reacts with $Ca(OH)_2$ (slaked lime) as follows:

$$2NH_4Cl + Ca(OH)_2 \rightarrow CaCl_2 + 2NH_3 + 2H_2O$$

What mass of ammonium chloride must be used to obtain 2.80 liters of ammonia, NH_3, at STP? (Use an expanded mole diagram to help solve the problem if you find it helpful.)

14. In the reaction $Zn + 2HCl \rightarrow ZnCl_2 + H_2$, what volume of hydrogen is produced, at STP, when 3.27 g of zinc are reacted with excess hydrochloric acid.

15. What is the maximum volume of oxygen that can be obtained at STP from 98.0 g of $KClO_3$ in the reaction $2KClO_3 \rightarrow 2KCl + 3O_2$? (Use an expanded mole diagram to help solve the problem if you find it helpful.)

CHAPTER SUMMARY

1. Calculations made from measurements enable the chemist to see relationships in chemical reactions and to understand chemical changes.
2. The coefficients in a balanced equation tell the relative number of moles of reactants and products. If the mass of one of these substances is known, the masses of the others can be calculated.
3. Avogadro's law leads to the conclusion that all one-mole samples of gases occupy the same volume at the same conditions. This volume, 22.4 liters at STP, is called the molar volume.
4. In a balanced equation, the coefficients of gases state their relative volumes. This information can be used to calculate volumes of gaseous reactants and products.

Section

11-1   1. State two reasons why the mathematics of chemistry is important to the chemist.

11-2   2. What two meanings are conveyed by the coefficients in the equation $2HgO \rightarrow 2Hg + O_2$?

11-3   3. How does Avogadro's law lead to the idea of a molar volume?

   4. How is the standard density of a gas used to measure its gram molecular mass?

11-4   5. (a) What relationship is there between the volumes of samples of two different gases if the samples are at the same temperature and pressure and are made up of an equal number of molecules? (b) Use this fact to explain how the coefficients of gases in equations can be used to describe their relative volumes.

11-5   6. In mass-volume problems, what possibilities exist with regard to the nature of the quantity given and of the quantity to be found?

REVIEW PROBLEMS

In solving the problems below, use the table of atomic masses at the back of this book.

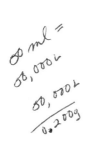

11-2   1. A tin ore contains 3.5% SnO_2. How much tin is produced by reducing 2.0 kilograms of the ore with carbon? ($SnO_2 + C \rightarrow Sn + CO_2$)

11-3   2. At STP, 50.0 mL of a gaseous compound has a mass of 0.200 g. What is the gram molecular mass of the compound?

11-4   3. What volume of oxygen is used to convert 750 L of SO_2 to SO_3 in the contact process reaction, $2SO_2 + O_2 \rightarrow 2SO_3$?

11-5   4. Using the reaction $Cu + 4HNO_3 \rightarrow Cu(NO_3)_2 + 2NO_2 + 2H_2O$, calculate what volume of nitrogen dioxide is produced at STP when 9.6 g of copper are reacted with excess acid.

   5. In the reaction $FeS(s) + 2HCl(aq) \rightarrow FeCl_2(aq) + H_2S(g)$, how much FeS will react with excess acid to produce 100 mL of H_2S at STP?

FOR FURTHER THOUGHT

For the following questions, assume you have a table of atomic masses.

11-2   1. You are given the balanced equation for a reaction. You wish to determine the ratio between the mass of one reactant and the mass of one product. Which of the following pieces of information will you need? (a) The mass in grams of the reactant. (b) The formula mass of either the reactant or the product. (c) The formula mass of both the reactant and the product. (d) Avogadro's number. (e) Moles of either another reactant or another product.

11-3   2. We have been accepting H_2O as the molecular formula of water. Yet quantitative analysis of water gives us only its empirical formula. The molecular formula could be H_4O_2, H_6O_3, etc. We could use Avogadro's law and the molar volume of gases to determine the formula, but water is a liquid. Can you suggest a solution to this problem?

Chapter 11   The Mathematics of Chemical Equations   **217**

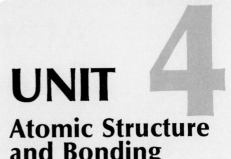

UNIT 4

Atomic Structure and Bonding

This photo may look like a painting in a modern art gallery; however, it is actually a thin section of an ammonium acetate crystal illuminated by polarized light and enlarged about 10,000 times. To a chemist, the surface pattern of a crystal is more than beautiful; it reflects the underlying structure of the substance. The shape of a crystal is a direct expression of the kind of atoms that make it up, and how they fit together.

The basic design of matter is a subject of great concern to chemists. How do atoms and molecules arrange themselves and bond together to create the unlimited diversity of materials we observe? This question is the topic of this unit.

Atomic Structure—I

12-1   Historical Background

More than 2000 years ago, the Greek philosophers Democritus and Leucippus suggested that all matter was made up of tiny invisible particles. These particles were supposed to be so small and indestructible that they could not be divided into anything smaller. The particles were called *atomos,* after the Greek word for indivisible. The English word *atom* comes from this Greek word. The early concept of atoms was not based upon experimental evidence. It was simply a result of careful thinking and reasoning on the part of the philosophers. However, many people of the time did not believe in atoms. Many differing views were held. One differing view was known as the continuous theory of matter. It stated that a solid body could be divided and subdivided into smaller and smaller pieces without limit. The Greeks had no way of testing these ideas. It was not until the eighteenth century that experimental evidence in favor of the atomic hypothesis began to accumulate. Let us see what some of this evidence was.

The law of conservation of matter. Antoine Lavoisier, a French chemist, was the first to explain correctly the nature of ordinary burning. He based his conclusions on careful measurements obtained from experiments he did in the 1770's. He is also credited with providing the first experimental evidence for the **law of conservation of matter.** The law of conservation of matter states that matter can be neither created nor destroyed. Applied to chemical change, this law means that the mass of the materials before a chemical reaction takes place is exactly equal to the mass of the materials after the reaction. In one experiment, Lavoisier heated tin in air to form tin oxide, a compound of tin and oxygen. Using precise methods of measurement, he proved that the mass of the tin oxide was exactly equal to the mass of the tin plus the mass of the oxygen taken from the air.

The law of definite proportions. Many chemists of the eighteenth century worked on the problem of determining the composition of compounds. Beginning in 1799, the French chemist Joseph Proust showed that the proportion by mass of the elements in a given compound is always the same. This general observation, called the **law of definite proportions** (or definite composition), applies to all pure compounds. For example, water can be broken down into two gaseous elements, hydrogen and oxygen. If the masses of the hydrogen and oxygen are carefully measured, it is found that the mass of oxygen is always 8 times the mass of the hydrogen. That is, in every 9 grams of water there are 8 grams of oxygen and 1 gram of hydrogen. Thus, the ratio of mass of oxygen to mass of hydrogen is always 8:1. This ratio is the same for all natural samples of pure water regardless of the source of the water. Figure 12-1 shows how the mass ratio of oxygen to hydrogen in water may be determined experimentally.

The law of multiple proportions. Hydrogen and oxygen are the only elements in water. There is another compound, called hydrogen

Figure 12-1

Determining the composition of water by experiment.

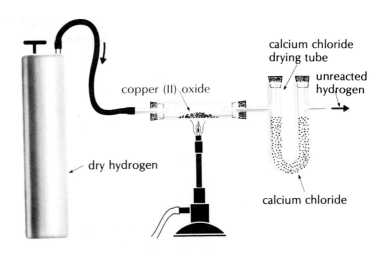

Measurements

Step 1. Before setting up the apparatus, determine the mass of the copper oxide (Mass CuO Before). Also determine the mass of the drying tube and its contents (Mass D.T. Before).

Step 2. After the experiment, repeat the measurements of Step 1.

Calculations

The measurements in Steps 1 and 2 above will give the following results:

(Mass CuO Before) — (Mass CuO After) = Mass of oxygen forming water (M_o)

(Mass D.T. After) — (Mass D.T. Before) = Mass of water formed (M_w)

M_w — M_o = Mass of hydrogen forming water

CAUTION: DO NOT TRY THIS EXPERIMENT, IT IS DANGEROUS!

peroxide, that is also composed of only hydrogen and oxygen. Analysis of hydrogen peroxide shows that the mass ratio of oxygen to hydrogen in this compound is 16:1. That is, in every 17 grams of hydrogen peroxide, there are 16 grams of oxygen and 1 gram of hydrogen. In water, the ratio is only 8:1.

There are many other pairs of elements that form two or more compounds. In all cases, the masses of one element that combine with a *fixed* mass of the other element form simple, whole-number ratios. This is called the **law of multiple proportions.** For example, in hydrogen peroxide and water, the masses of oxygen that combine with 1 gram of hydrogen are 16 grams and 8 grams, respectively. The ratio is 16:8, or 2:1.

As another illustration, consider the two oxides of sulfur, sulfur dioxide and sulfur trioxide. In sulfur dioxide, there are *2* grams of oxygen for each 2 grams of sulfur. In sulfur trioxide, there are *3* grams of oxygen for each 2 grams of sulfur. Thus, the ratio of the masses of oxygen that combined with a fixed mass (2 grams) of sulfur is *2:3*. Or, if the mass of oxygen is held constant, the ratio of the masses of sulfur that combine with the oxygen will be *3:2*. See Figure 12-2.

Figure 12-2

The law of multiple proportions, illustrated with two sulfur-oxygen compounds, sulfur dioxide and sulfur trioxide.

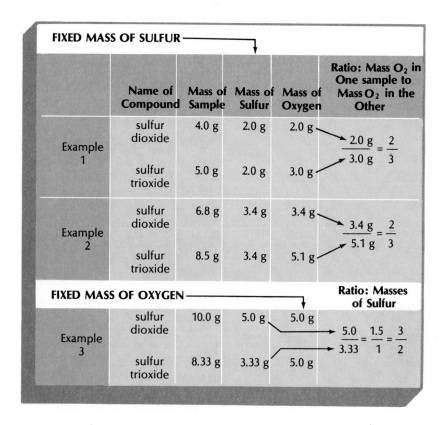

12-2 Dalton's Atomic Theory

John Dalton, an English chemist, first stated the law of multiple proportions in 1803. He had observed this law at work in compounds of

John Dalton (1766-1844)

Born in Cumberland, England, John Dalton began a teaching career in 1788. In 1793, he became a teacher of mathematics and natural philosophy at New College, Manchester. Dalton's studies in meteorology led to a better understanding of the Aurora Borealis, the trade winds, and the cause of rain.

While Dalton's work in meteorology was important, he is remembered primarily for his contributions to chemistry. In 1802, he formulated the law of partial pressures and soon after proposed an atomic theory of matter that became one of the foundations of chemistry. Applying the theory, Dalton determined the chemical formulas of a number of substances. He produced the first table of atomic weights (what is now usually called a table of atomic masses). Although many of the masses were inaccurate, the table was nevertheless a notable contribution. Dalton was honored by being elected a fellow of the Royal Society and a foreign associate member of the French Academy of Sciences.

carbon and hydrogen, and in the oxides of nitrogen (compounds of nitrogen and oxygen). Dalton saw that this law, together with conservation of mass and the law of definite proportions, gave strong support to the idea of atoms. As a result, in 1803 Dalton proposed an atomic theory of matter based on these observed laws. A few years later, he developed his theory in greater detail.

The basic ideas of Dalton's atomic theory are:

1. All elements are composed of atoms, which are indivisible and indestructible particles.

2. All atoms of the same element are exactly alike; in particular, they all have the same mass.

3. Atoms of different elements are different; in particular, they have different masses.

4. Compounds are formed by the joining of atoms of two or more elements. In any compound, the atoms of the different elements in the compound are joined in a definite whole-number ratio, such as 1 to 1, 2 to 1, 3 to 2, etc.

It is easy to see that Dalton's theory accounted very well for the three laws that we have mentioned.

Law of conservation of mass. If atoms have definite masses and cannot be divided or destroyed, then a chemical change is simply a rearrangement of atoms. Their total mass should be the same before and after the chemical reaction.

Law of definite proportions. If atoms of different elements combine in a definite ratio whenever they form a certain compound, the ratio of the masses in the compound should also be fixed. It will depend only on the masses of the different atoms and the ratio in which they combine.

Law of multiple proportions. According to Dalton's theory, atoms of different elements always combine in whole number ratios. For example, in one compound of elements A and B, the ratio of A atoms to B atoms may be 2:1. In another compound, the ratio may be 3:1. In the first compound, there will be 2000 A atoms combined with 1000 B atoms. In the second compound, there will be 3000 A atoms combined with 1000 B atoms. The ratio of A atoms that combine with a fixed number of B atoms in these two compounds is therefore 2:3. Since all A atoms have the same mass, the ratio of *masses* of A that combine with a fixed *mass* of B will also be 2:3. Thus the theory accounts for the law of multiple proportions.

12-3   The Modern Atomic Theory

Since Dalton's time we have gained much detailed information about the structure of matter. We no longer think of atoms as solid, unchanging particles. We know they have many parts and a complex organization, which we will examine later in this chapter and in the next.

However, the essential ideas of Dalton's theory are still useful today. Elements *are* made of atoms. Compounds *do* form by the combination of atoms in fixed, whole-number ratios. And atoms are *not* permanently changed by chemical reactions, but only rearranged into different combinations.

The chief differences between the modern atomic theory and Dalton's theory are:

1. In the modern theory, atoms have a detailed structure, which is altered temporarily during chemical change. Atoms can be changed from one element to another, but not by chemical reactions.

2. Atoms of the same element are not necessarily exactly alike. They are alike in those characteristics that determine the chemical properties of an element. However, atoms of the same element can and do have different masses.

You may wonder how the laws of definite proportions and multiple proportions can hold true if the atoms of an element can have different masses. Wouldn't the mass ratios in a compound vary, depending on which atoms entered into the combination? The answer lies in the fact that in every natural sample of an element, the atoms of various masses are always present in the same proportions. As a result, the atoms of the element have a certain *average* mass, which is always the same for that element. In terms of mass ratios in compounds, each element seems to consist of atoms that all have the same mass—the average mass for that element. We will refer again to this fact when we come to discuss the subject of atomic mass later in this chapter.

Questions for Sections 12-1 through 12-3

1. Explain why the atomic nature of matter as suggested by the early Greek philosophers is not considered to be a scientific concept.
2. What three scientific laws provided basic evidence for Dalton's atomic theory?
3. Which of the scientific laws referred to in question 2 is based on work done by Dalton himself?
4. Briefly describe the four basic ideas of Dalton's atomic theory.
5. What modifications of Dalton's atomic theory are found in the modern atomic theory?

12-4 Electrons

Dalton postulated that the atom was the smallest possible particle of matter. The discovery that the atom was actually made up of yet smaller particles was not made until almost 100 years after Dalton announced his theory. In 1897 the first of these **subatomic particles,** the electron, was discovered.

The first evidence for the existence of electrons came from studies of electric currents in gases at very low pressures. The apparatus for these studies was a discharge tube and a vacuum pump. A **discharge tube** is a glass tube in which two metallic electrodes are sealed. Most of the air was removed from such a tube. A high-voltage current was made to flow through the tube. During this electrical discharge, a glow appeared at the end of the tube opposite the cathode, which is the negatively charged electrode. It was believed that the glow was caused by some kind of either invisible radiation or invisible particles that came from the cathode and passed away from it. Since the radiation or particles came from the cathode, they were called **cathode rays.** See Figure 12-3.

Figure 12-3

A simple discharge tube. Most of the air has been removed from the tube. When connected to a high voltage source, a stream of either invisible radiation or invisible particles passes from the cathode to the anode, causing the end of the tube opposite to the cathode to glow. These emanations from the cathode were named cathode rays.

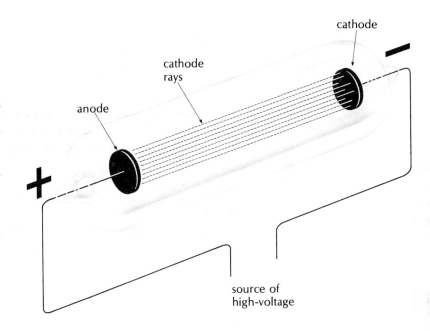

Figure 12-4

When a magnet is held alongside the discharge tube of Figure 12-3, the cathode rays are deflected from their straight-line path.

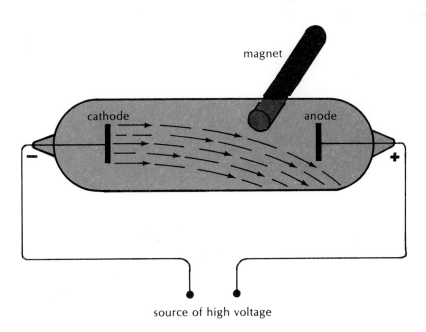

*Gas Station
Powered by the Sun*

The photo shows a gasoline station in West Chicago, Illinois, with an array of solar cells mounted on its roof. These cells convert sunlight directly into electricity that is used to pump gas, provide lighting, and power other electrical devices within the station.

The photovoltaic (FO-to-vahl-TAY-ik) cells (solar cells) on the roof are made up almost entirely of the element silicon. Silicon is the second most abundant element. (See Figure 3-12 on page 38.) Recent advances in the manufacture of silicon for solar cells have sharply reduced their cost. If more advances of this kind are made, electricity from solar cells, now more costly than that purchased from electric power companies, may be supplying some of the electricity that we now use in the home, school, and place of business.

In the 1870's, an English physicist, William Crookes, worked with cathode rays. He showed that these "rays" could be deflected from their straight-line course by a magnet. See Figure 12-4. Crookes believed that the rays consist of electrically charged particles. Some 20 years later, another English scientist, J.J. Thomson, proved that Crookes was right. Working with discharge tubes, Thomson showed that cathode rays are deflected by an electric field as well as by a magnetic field. With this evidence, scientists realized that cathode rays are actually charged particles in motion. Thomson went on to prove that cathode-ray particles are always deflected the same way, regardless of what kind of material the cathode is made of or what kind of gas is present in the tube. Cathode-ray particles are what we now know as *electrons*.

Charge and mass of the electron. Experiments have shown that all **electrons** appear to be exactly alike. They are extremely small particles with very little mass and with a fixed amount of negative charge. Using data from his experiments, Thomson tried to obtain values for the electric charge (e) and mass (m) of an electron. Although he was unable to obtain a value for either e or m, he was able to calculate the *ratio* of the charge of an electron to its mass (e/m). This ratio is known as the **charge/mass ratio** of the electron. The value found for e/m is 1.76×10^8 coulombs per gram.

In 1911, in a famous experiment called the oil-drop experiment, the American physicist Robert Millikan measured the charge on an electron. Its charge is 1.60×10^{-19} coulomb. This amount of charge seems to be a fundamental and indivisible unit of charge. No fraction of this charge has ever been observed. All electric charges are carried and transferred in units no smaller than this size.

Once Millikan knew the charge of the electron, he could use the e/m ratio of Thomson to calculate the mass of an electron:

THOMSON'S e/m RATIO

$$\frac{e}{m} = 1.76 \times 10^8 \text{ coulombs/gram}$$

Solving the above expression for m:

$$m = \frac{e}{1.76 \times 10^8 \text{ coulombs/gram}}$$

Substituting 1.60×10^{-19} coulomb for e:

$$m = \frac{1.60 \times 10^{-19} \text{ coulomb}}{1.76 \times 10^8 \text{ coulombs/gram}}$$

$$= 9.1 \times 10^{-28} \text{ gram}$$

The mass of the electron, 9.1×10^{-28} grams, is only a very small fraction of the mass of even the least massive atom, that of hydrogen.

12-5　Nucleons

Atomic research in the first quarter of this century led to the nuclear concept of the atom. According to this concept, an atom consists of a small, dense, central portion, called the **nucleus,** and one or more electrons found at relatively large distances from the nucleus. The space occupied by the electrons makes up most of the volume of the atom. Because the mass of the electron is so small, practically all of the mass of an atom is concentrated in the nucleus.

The particles that make up the nucleus of an atom are called **nucleons.** The two most important nucleons are *protons* and *neutrons.* (Neutrons are discussed in Section 12-11.) These are the particles that give atoms almost all of their mass.

Protons. Investigations have shown that the simplest atoms are those of hydrogen. The most common kind of hydrogen atom consists of a single nucleon and a single electron. Since the hydrogen atom is electrically neutral, its one nucleon must carry a positive electrical charge that is equal in magnitude to the charge on the electron. This positively charged particle is called a **proton.** Although the positive charge on the proton is the same size as the negative charge on the electron, the mass of the proton is about 1800 times as large as that of the electron. The mass of the proton is about 1.67×10^{-24} gram.

Atomic number. The number of protons in the nucleus of an atom is called its **atomic number.** All atoms of the same element have the same number of protons and thus the same atomic number. Atoms of different elements have a different number of protons in their nuclei. Therefore, each element has a unique atomic number that identifies the element. The atomic number also tells the number of electrons that are normally present in an atom. In its normal state an atom is electrically neutral. It contains the same number of protons and electrons, so that the atom as a whole has no net charge. Elements with atomic numbers from 1 to 107 have so far been identified. The symbol Z is used to denote the atomic number of an element. Thus, for hydrogen, $Z = 1$.

Henry Moseley (1887-1915), a brilliant English physicist, performed experiments that revealed the atomic numbers of a number of elements. Serving in the military service during World War I, Moseley was killed while still in his twenties.

Neutrons. There are three types of hydrogen atoms. The most common type is called *protium.* Protium has a nucleus consisting of a single particle. That particle is a proton.

The second kind of hydrogen atom is called *deuterium.* Deuterium, too, has a proton in its nucleus, but this nucleus has a mass about twice the mass of protium. The additional mass comes from a particle called a **neutron.** The third kind of hydrogen atom, called *tritium,* has a nucleus consisting of one proton and two neutrons. The chemical properties of all three kinds of hydrogen atoms are virtually the same.

The neutron was discovered in 1932 by James Chadwick, a British

> Protons and neutrons are the best known nucleons, although others (muons, pions, etc.) have been found.

Figure 12-5

The isotopes of hydrogen, showing the nuclei of protium, deuterium, and tritium.

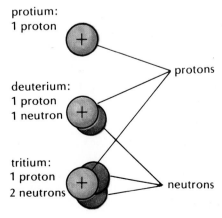

protium:
1 proton

deuterium:
1 proton
1 neutron

tritium:
1 proton
2 neutrons

protons

neutrons

physicist. It has almost the same mass as a proton, but has no electric charge. The properties of the electron, the proton, and the neutron are summarized in Figure 12-6.

Figure 12-6

The particles making up atoms.

	Approximate Mass	Charge	Location in the Atom
Electron	$\dfrac{1}{1837}$ u*	1–	Normally at relatively large distances from the nucleus
Proton	1 u	1+	Part of the nucleus
Neutron	1 u	No charge	Part of the nucleus

*The letter *u* is an abbreviation for *atomic mass unit*. This unit of mass is defined in Section 12-8.

Isotopes. As we have just seen, all atoms of the same element are not necessarily identical. They are alike in those characteristics that determine their chemical properties—that is, in atomic number Z, which is the number of protons in their nuclei. They may differ, however, in the number of neutrons in their nuclei.

Atoms of the same element that have different numbers of neutrons in their nuclei have different masses. Such atoms are called **isotopes** of that element. Protium, deuterium, and tritium are isotopes of hydrogen. In a natural sample of hydrogen, about one atom in every 6000 is an atom of deuterium. Tritium is not found in natural samples of hydrogen. It must be made artificially. It is an unstable, or radioactive, isotope. See Figure 12-5.

Like hydrogen, all the other elements have isotopes. Some occur naturally in samples of the element. Most of the known isotopes, however, have been produced artificially, as in the case of tritium. Only the three isotopes of hydrogen have been given special names. The isotopes of the other elements are identified by their different masses. This will be explained later in this chapter (Section 12-7).

Questions for Sections 12-4 and 12-5

6. What is a discharge tube?
7. What are cathode rays? How did these rays come to have this name?
8. What is the value of (a) the charge of an electron, and (b) the mass of an electron?
9. What are nucleons?
10. How does the proton compare with the electron in terms of (a) electrical charge and (b) mass?
11. What is the atomic number of an atom?
12. How does the neutron compare with the proton in terms of (a) electrical charge and (b) mass?

12-6   The Concept of Atomic Weight

Until the discovery of isotopes, chemists assumed that all the atoms of a particular element have the same mass. In Dalton's time there was no way to determine the actual mass of an individual atom in grams. However, Dalton and other chemists of his time were able to determine the *relative* masses (or "weights") of the atoms of many of the known elements. They were able to determine, for example, that a sulfur atom has twice the mass of an oxygen atom and 32 times the mass of a hydrogen atom. These conclusions were based on experiments that revealed what percentage of the total mass of a compound could be attributed to each element making up the compound.

Figure 12-7

A pile of nuts whose total mass is 500 grams combine with a pile of bolts whose total mass is 1000 grams to produce a pile of "nut-bolt compound." If it is assumed that the compound consists of equal numbers of nuts and bolts, then a bolt must have a mass twice as great as a nut. By this method, we are able to assign a relative mass to the bolt in terms of the mass of a nut: Mass of bolt = 2 x Mass of nut.

Using similar reasoning, early chemists were able to determine the relative masses of the atoms of many elements.

Under the assumption that two nuts get fastened to every bolt, what is the relative mass of a bolt?

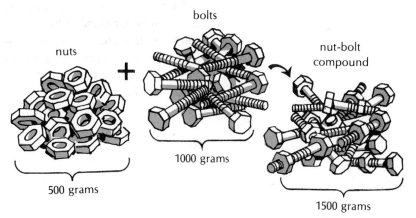

nuts

bolts

nut-bolt compound

500 grams

1000 grams

1500 grams

As a result of these investigations, it soon became clear that the hydrogen atom has the smallest mass of all the elements. Dalton assigned to it a value of 1. Relative masses were then found for the other elements on this basis. For example, an atom that has a mass 12 times the mass of the hydrogen atom would have a mass of 12 on this relative scale. Gradually, the relative masses of the atoms of all the known elements were determined. They were listed in tables of "atomic weights."

12-7   Mass Number

An ordinary hydrogen (protium) atom is made up of one proton and one electron. Practically all the mass of the atom is in its single proton. If the hydrogen atom is given a relative mass value of 1, then the mass of a proton is also very nearly 1. A neutron has very nearly the same mass as a proton; its mass is also very nearly 1. The approximate

Figure 12-8

Naturally occurring oxygen is made up of a mixture of these three isotopes: oxygen-16 ($^{16}_{8}O$), oxygen-17 ($^{17}_{8}O$), and oxygen-18 ($^{18}_{8}O$). The overwhelming number of atoms in this mixture, 99.76% of the total, are oxygen-16 atoms.

Mass No. 16

Mass No. 17

Mass No. 18

8–

8–

8–

8+
8N

8+
9N

8+
10N

OXYGEN–16
99.76%

OXYGEN–17
0.04%

OXYGEN–18
0.20%

relative mass of any atom can therefore be found by simply adding the number of protons and neutrons in its nucleus, since each of these nucleons has a mass of 1. (The mass of the electrons is too small to matter.) The sum of the protons and neutrons in the nucleus of any atom is called the **mass number** of that atom. For example, the most common isotope of carbon has 6 protons and 6 neutrons in its nucleus. The mass number of this isotope is therefore 6 + 6, or 12. This isotope of carbon is called carbon-12 and is represented by the symbol ^{12}C. Another isotope of carbon has 6 protons and 8 neutrons in its atomic nucleus. Its mass number is 14. It is referred to as carbon-14, or ^{14}C.

All isotopes of carbon have the same number of protons in the atomic nucleus—6. This number of protons is the atomic number of carbon. It is the same for all its isotopes. The atomic number is sometimes included in the symbol for an isotope, as a subscript at the lower left. The complete symbol for carbon-12 is $^{12}_{6}C$. (The small numbers used to be placed to the right of the symbol: C^{12}_{6}). Naturally occurring oxygen is a mixture of three isotopes. See Figure 12-8.

We have already stated that Z is used as the symbol for atomic number. The letter A is used as the symbol for mass number. Since Z is the number of protons in the nucleus, and A is the sum of the protons and neutrons, the number of neutrons in any atom can be determined by subtracting Z from A:

$$\text{Number of neutrons} = A - Z$$

For example, in the sodium isotope $^{23}_{11}Na$, $A = 23$ and $Z = 11$. There are $23 - 11$, or 12, neutrons in the nucleus of this atom.

Figure 12-9

When writing symbols for isotopes, the mass number is written as a superscript, the atomic number as a subscript, both to the left of the symbol for the element.

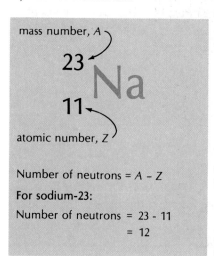

mass number, A

23

Na

11

atomic number, Z

Number of neutrons = $A - Z$

For sodium-23:

Number of neutrons = 23 - 11

$= 12$

12-8   Modern Standard of Atomic Mass

The chemists of the 19th century who were measuring atomic masses believed they were finding the relative masses of individual atoms. For example, the atomic mass of chlorine was found to be 35.5. It was assumed that every atom of chlorine had a mass that was 35.5 times as large as the mass of a hydrogen atom. Today we know there is no single chlorine atom with that relative mass. Natural chlorine is a mixture of two isotopes. About 75% of the atoms in a natural sample of chlorine are the isotope of mass number 35; the other 25% have mass number 37. The *average* mass of this mixture of atoms is 35.5, and this is what the chemists of the nineteenth century were measuring.

Tables of "atomic weights" thus gave an average value for the mixture of isotopes in a natural sample of each element. Different investigators obtained the same values for these atomic weights because the proportions of isotopes in any natural sample of an element are always very nearly the same. The term "atomic weight" is still sometimes used today to mean this average value of the masses of the isotopes in a natural sample of an element. However, the term **atomic mass** is generally preferred and is used in this text.

If natural hydrogen is assigned an atomic mass of exactly 1.000, the atomic mass of oxygen is very nearly, but not quite, 16. For reasons of convenience in determining atomic masses, chemists originally decided to set the atomic mass of natural oxygen at exactly 16.000. (This made the atomic mass of hydrogen 1.008.) The oxygen standard of atomic mass was used as the basis of atomic-mass tables for many years. However, in 1961 a new agreement was reached in which the atom of the isotope carbon-12 became the standard. The atomic mass of carbon-12 was set at exactly 12. This was the first time that the mass of a single isotope was used as a standard rather than the average mass of a mixture of naturally occurring isotopes of an element.

We can think of 1/12 the mass of the ^{12}C atom as being a unit for expressing atomic masses. This unit is called an **atomic mass unit,** and it may be represented by the symbol u*. The atomic mass of the ^{12}C atom is exactly 12 atomic mass units, or 12 u.

Naturally occurring carbon is a mixture of carbon isotopes. More than 98% of this mixture is carbon-12 atoms. The remaining atoms are of greater mass. When the masses of the mixture of naturally occurring isotopes are averaged, a value of 12.011 15 u is obtained for the mass of an "average" carbon atom. This is the mass that is given for carbon in a table of atomic masses such as that found in the back of this book.

Questions for Sections 12-6 through 12-8

15. What atom was used as a standard in Dalton's table of atomic weights?
16. What is the mass number of an atom? What symbol is used to denote mass number?
17. How is mass number used to designate an isotope?
18. Write the symbol for tritium, an isotope of hydrogen having 2 neutrons in the nucleus.

---

*Since the scale of atomic masses is a relative one, many people believe it is incorrect to express relative atomic masses in units of any kind. Therefore, the term atomic mass unit and its symbol u are not always used. Instead, atomic masses are expressed as pure numbers.

19. How many neutrons are present in the isotope of oxygen represented by the symbol $^{17}_{8}O$?
20. What isotope is used as the standard in the modern table of atomic masses?
21. What is an atomic mass unit?

12-9   The Usefulness of Models

Figure 12-10

A *physical* model. This type of model should not be confused with a scientific model, which is a mental picture that helps explain something we cannot see or experience directly.

Scientists often make use of *models* to help them interpret their observations. A scientific model is not like a model car, a doll's house, a globe, or any other small-scale copy of a real thing. A **scientific model** is a mental picture that helps us understand something we cannot see or experience directly. A good model of the atom helps to explain the characteristics and behavior of atoms. But it is not an actual picture of an atom. Until the mid 1970's, no photograph showing individual atoms had ever been made. Today it is possible to produce photographs in which the location of individual atoms is indicated by a blurred spot. There are no details in such pictures.

Scientific models of the atom have changed many times since Dalton first proposed the existence of atoms. The models were changed because they did not account for new discoveries. In each case, a new model was needed that would fit the new facts. Dalton's model of the atom was a solid sphere that could not be broken apart or changed in any way. When electrons were discovered, the model of the atom had to be changed to include them. Since electrons have a negative charge, the model of the atom had to include positive charges to make the atom as a whole neutral. J. J. Thomson proposed a model in which the atom is a positively charged sphere in which the negatively charged electrons are embedded. Rutherford's investigations, as we shall see, led to the idea of a positively charged nucleus at the center of the atom. All models of the atom since Rutherford's time have kept Rutherford's positively charged nucleus. Bohr modified the Rutherford model to overcome some of its shortcomings. The Bohr model is based upon Bohr's theory of energy levels in the atom. Modern quantum mechanics has modified Bohr's atom to give us the model we have today.

12-10   The Rutherford Model of the Atom

Ernest Rutherford was a distinguished British scientist. In 1909, Rutherford and his assistants did a famous experiment that proved that atoms are not like the solid spheres visualized by Dalton and Thomson. The experiment had developed from Rutherford's interest in *alpha particles*. Rutherford had earlier identified alpha particles as being positively charged helium atoms. Alpha particles are one of the types of particles released when uranium and some other radioactive ele-

Lord Ernest Rutherford
(1871-1937)

Born in New Zealand, Rutherford conducted most of his research activities in Cambridge, England. His influence on scientific thought can be compared to that of Faraday and Newton. His investigations of radioactivity, his discovery of the alpha particle, proton, and beta rays, and his development of the nuclear theory of atomic structure laid the groundwork for the science of nuclear physics. He produced the first instance of artificial transmutation when he bombarded nitrogen with alpha particles. Because Bohr adopted Rutherford's nuclear concept in developing his atomic model, the model is often called the Rutherford-Bohr atom.

Rutherford became the recipient of many honors for his many achievements. He received the 1908 Nobel Prize in chemistry, was president of the Royal Society, and in 1931 was made Baron Rutherford. His last 18 years (1919-1937) were spent as professor of experimental physics at Cambridge.

Figure 12-11

The Rutherford experiment: the scattering of alpha particles by a thin gold foil.

ments disintegrate. (Radioactive elements are discussed in Sections 13-16 to 13-21.)

In his experiment, Rutherford used the setup shown in Figure 12-11. As shown in the drawing, Rutherford used a very thin sheet of gold as a target. On one side of the foil was a lead box containing a radioactive substance. A small hole in the box permitted a narrow stream of alpha particles to shoot out. These particles were directed at right angles to the surface of the foil. On the other side of the foil, hanging parallel to the foil, Rutherford suspended a screen coated with zinc sulfide. Each time an alpha particle hit this zinc sulfide coating, a flash of light was produced at the point of contact. By observing these flashes of light it was possible to see if the alpha particles that passed through the foil had been deflected from their straight-line path.

Much to Rutherford's surprise, nearly all the alpha particles passed straight through as though there were no foil there. Rutherford later described this experiment by saying it was like shooting bullets at a ghost. Rutherford interpreted these observations to mean that the atoms in the foil consist mainly of *empty space!* In addition to the many particles that passed straight through the foil, Rutherford also noticed that a few particles were deflected slightly from their straight-line path. Still others were deflected at large angles of 90° or more. Rutherford interpreted these observations to mean that each atom contained a small, dense, positively charged central portion, or nucleus. The positively charged gold nuclei repelled the positively charged alpha parti-

(A)

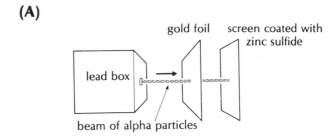

(B)

ENLARGED VIEW

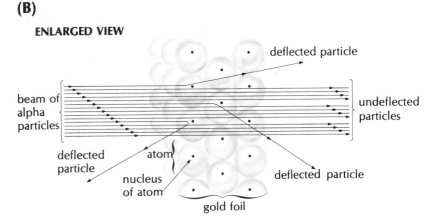

cles, deflecting the alpha particles that came near, much as a steel helmet would deflect a rifle bullet. However, because the nuclei were so small, not many "hits" were scored. Most of the alpha particles passed straight through the "empty" portion of the atoms.

Rutherford repeated this experiment using other metal foils. Each time he got similar results. He concluded that atoms in general consist of small, massive, positively charged nuclei surrounded mainly by "empty" space. In this model, electrons moved about in the empty space that made up most of the atom's volume. The negative charge of the electrons offset the positive charge of the nucleus, thereby accounting for the atom as a whole being electrically neutral.

12-11 The Neutron

Rutherford observed that the pattern of the deflection of alpha particles differed for different metals. He realized that the deflection depends upon the size of the positive charge in the nucleus. Large deflections from the straight-line path are produced by nuclei containing a large positive charge. Rutherford reasoned that the nucleus of the least massive atom, that of hydrogen, is a single particle with a positive charge. He called this particle a *proton*. He then assumed that the nuclei of other atoms contained various numbers of protons. The positive charge of each nucleus depends on the number of protons it contains.

However, if the mass of a proton is 1 (the same as a hydrogen atom), then the protons that account for the positive charge of the other nuclei do not account for their mass. The atomic mass of each element that Rutherford investigated is about twice the mass of the protons it seems to contain. For example, an atom of sodium has 11 protons and an atomic mass of approximately 23 u. Thus, there is a mass of approximately 12 u that is not accounted for by the mass of the protons. Rutherford suggested that there might be tightly bound proton-electron pairs present in the nucleus, in addition to the separate protons. He suggested the name *neutron* for these proton-electron units.

In 1932, James Chadwick, who had worked with Rutherford earlier, shed more light on this question. Chadwick had been bombarding the element beryllium with alpha particles. A new kind of particle was emitted by the beryllium atoms when struck by the alpha particles. See Figure 12-12.

The new particles discovered by Chadwick had a mass about equal to that of a proton. But, unlike protons, they had no charge. They were very penetrating particles that could pass through 10 to 20 centimeters of lead. Chadwick concluded that these single particles were what Rutherford thought might be electron-proton pairs. Chadwick kept the name neutron for the particles. In the modern atomic model, the nuclei of all atoms have neutrons in them with one exception. Only the nucleus of protium, the lightest istope of hydrogen, has no neutrons in it.

Figure 12-12

BEFORE COLLISION

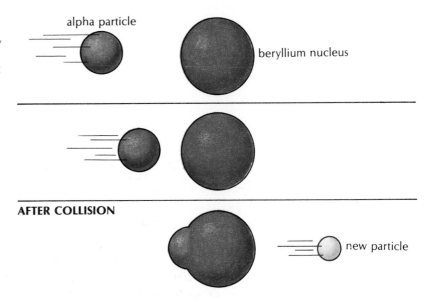

Chadwick's discovery. Chadwick found that when an alpha particle bombarded a beryllium atom, a new particle was emitted that had no charge and a mass about equal to that of a proton. These new particles were called neutrons.

12-12   Shortcomings of Rutherford's Model

As we have seen, Rutherford's model depicted the atom as having a positively charged nucleus of relatively great mass. Traveling around the nucleus were one or more negatively charged electrons of very small mass. Since opposite charges attract, the electrons should be strongly attracted toward the nucleus by electric forces. Rutherford assumed that the motion of the electrons around the nucleus keeps them from falling into the nucleus, just as the motion of the moon around the earth keeps it from falling into the earth.

Figure 12-13

According to the laws of classical physics, charged particles travelling in a curved path radiate energy. If these laws applied to electrons in atoms, the electron would slow up as it circled the nucleus, causing it to spiral in and the atom to collapse. Because this does not happen, Bohr concluded that new laws were needed to describe the behavior of electrons in atoms.

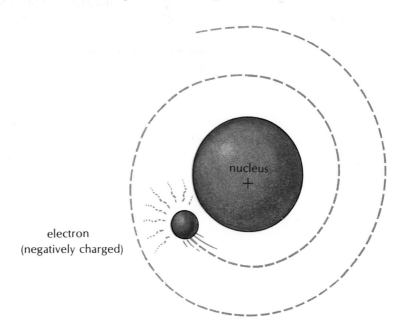

There was a serious flaw in this model. According to the theory of moving electric charges, a charged particle moving in a curved path should give off light or other forms of electromagnetic energy. If an electron traveling around the nucleus were to lose energy, it would gradually fall toward the nucleus. A similar result is observed with artificial earth satellites. As they lose energy through friction with the atmosphere, they drop to lower orbits. Since atoms seem to be very stable structures, an atomic model must explain why the electrons do not give off energy and collapse into the nucleus.

In 1913, the Danish physicist Niels Bohr proposed a model in which the orbiting electrons do not have to lose energy. To understand the Bohr model, we must first consider briefly the theory of light and electromagnetic radiation.

Questions for Sections 12-9 through 12-12

22. What is a scientific model?
23. Briefly describe Dalton's model of the atom.
24. Why has it been necessary to change the scientific model of the atom several times since Dalton's first model?
25. Based on his gold-leaf experiments, how did Rutherford describe the nuclei of gold atoms?
26. What observations led Rutherford to suspect the presence of neutral particles (neutrons) in the nuclei of most atoms?
27. How is the nucleus of a protium (hydrogen-1) atom different from that of all other atomic nuclei?
28. How did Rutherford explain the fact that the negatively charged electrons of his atomic model did not fall into the positively charged, relatively massive nucleus?
29. According to accepted theory, what happens when a charged particle moves in a curved path?

Goldstein - proton

12-13   The Nature of Light

During the 1600's, a controversy began about how light travels away from its source. Sir Isaac Newton, the English physicist and mathematician, suggested that light consists of tiny particles. A beam of light, according to this theory, is a stream of particles. About the same time, Christian Huygens, a Dutch physicist, suggested that light consists of waves. According to Huygens, light travels away from its source in the same way that water waves travel away from a stone that has been dropped in a pond. About 200 years later, in 1864, the Scottish physicist James Clerk Maxwell proposed a theory of light that became widely accepted. Maxwell's theory gives strong support to the idea that light is a wave phenomenon. Later, in the early 1900's, Max Planck, a German physicist, revived the particle theory. Planck had been studying the light and heat given off by a hot body. The only way Planck could explain what he observed was to propose that light is made up of discrete bundles of energy. These bundles of energy he called **quanta** (plural of *quantum*). The amount of energy in each quantum depended upon the color of the light. The energy in a quantum of blue light is greater, for example, than the energy in a quantum of red light. Quanta of light are the fundamental units of light. Quanta of light are also called *photons*. The idea that light energy comes in packets or quanta is known as the **quantum theory.**

The modern theory of light holds that light has a dual nature. It can behave both as waves and particles. In some types of experiments, the wave properties of light are apparent. In other types of experiments, the particle nature of light is apparent. Both ideas are needed for a complete description of the behavior of light.

12-14   Light as Waves

To understand light when it is showing its wave properties, we need to know the terms that are used to describe waves. These terms are wavelength, frequency, and wave velocity.

Wavelength. Shake a wave in a rope. See Figure 12-14. The waves consist of a series of peaks and troughs. The distance between two neighboring peaks or two neighboring troughs is called the **wavelength** of the wave. Wavelength is often represented by the Greek letter lambda, λ. See Figure 12-15.

Figure 12-14

Waves in a rope or on water consist of a series of peaks and troughs.

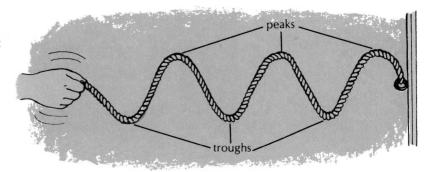

Figure 12-15

The distance between two neighboring peaks or two neighboring troughs is the wavelength of a wave.

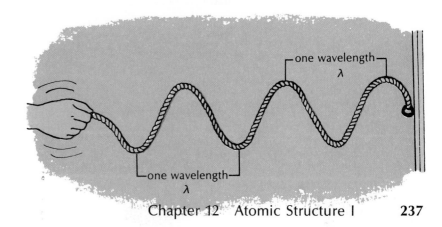

Frequency. The **frequency** of a wave is the number of peaks that pass a given point each second. At one time, frequency was expressed in *cycles per second*. If 1 peak of a wave passed a given point each second, its frequency was described as 1 cycle per second. The unit *cycles per second* has now been replaced by a unit called the **hertz** (abbreviated Hz). A wave in which 1 peak passes a given point each second has a frequency of 1 hertz (1 Hz).

Wave velocity. The **velocity** of a wave is the distance a given peak moves in a unit of time (usually one second). The velocity of a wave is equal to the frequency multiplied by the wavelength. For example, if the frequency is 10 hertz (10 waves per second), a given peak will move a distance of 10 wavelengths in one second. If the wavelength is 5 meters, the velocity is

$$10 \text{ waves/sec} \times 5 \text{ meters/wave} = 50 \text{ meters/sec}$$

If velocity is represented by v, frequency by f, and wavelength by λ, the relationship among these quantities can be stated by the following formula: $v = f \lambda$.

12-15   Continuous Spectrum

When the filament in an electric light bulb is heated, it gives off light. If a narrow beam of this light passes through a prism, the white light will be separated to form a band of colors ranging from red to violet. This band of colors is called a **continuous spectrum.** See Figure 12-16.

Figure 12-16

A continuous spectrum.

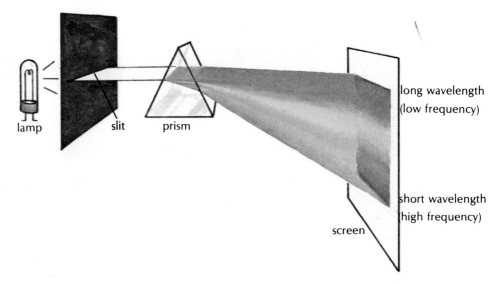

lamp   slit   prism

long wavelength (low frequency)

short wavelength (high frequency)

screen

The red part of the spectrum is made up of many wavelengths of light. The longest wavelength is at the extreme end of red. Going toward orange, the wavelengths become shorter. Proceeding from orange through the other colors to violet, the wavelengths get shorter and shorter.

Frequency and wavelength are inversely proportional. Therefore, in terms of frequency, the red end of the spectrum corresponds to waves of light of lower frequency than violet.

12-16   Bright-line Spectra

If sodium chloride crystals are heated in a flame, the flame develops a yellow color. When this light is passed through a prism, the screen shows something quite different from a continuous spectrum. Instead of a blending of colors, two yellow lines appear. See Figure 12-17.

When lithium chloride crystals are heated an orange-red flame is produced. When this light is passed through a prism, another series of colored lines appear. The lines from sodium chloride do not match the lines from lithium chloride. See Figure 12-17 (C). These lines of color are called *bright-line spectra*. Different elements may give what seems to be the same color to a flame, but when we examine the spectral lines, the set of lines produced by one element always differs from the set produced by any other element. Spectral lines are the fingerprints

Figure 12-17

(A) A continuous spectrum is obtained by passing a band of white light through a prism, as shown in Figure 12-16. (B) A bright-line spectrum of sodium is obtained by sprinkling sodium chloride crystals into the flame of a burner and passing the light through a prism. (C) A bright-line spectrum for lithium is obtained by sprinkling lithium chloride crystals into the flame of a burner and passing the light through a prism. The wavelengths and colors of each line in (B) and (C) can be determined by referring to the scale in (A).

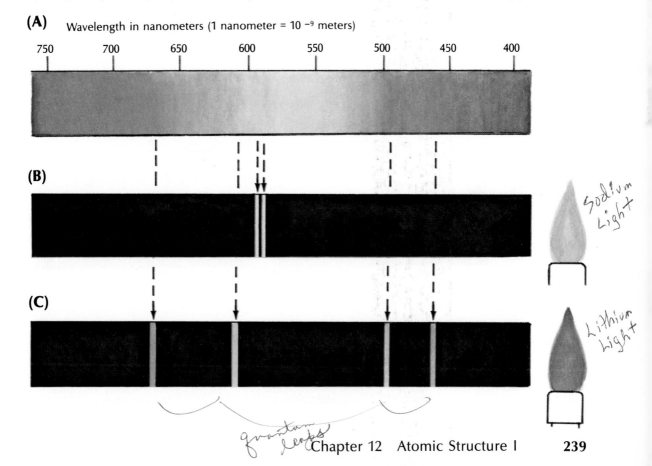

(A)   Wavelength in nanometers (1 nanometer = 10^{-9} meters)

750   700   650   600   550   500   450   400

(B)

(C)

of elements. Each element has its own unique set of lines. This set of lines is called the **bright line spectrum** of the element.

Questions for Sections 12-13 through 12-16

30. How was Planck's theory of light similar to that of Newton? How was it different?
31. What familiar experience did Huygens use to illustrate his concept of how light traveled away from its source?
32. What are quanta?
33. The greek letter *lambda* (λ) is used to represent what property of waves?
34. How would you express the frequency of a wave in which 5 peaks passed a given point each second?
35. How do you determine the velocity of a wave?
36. What do you call the band of colors that is produced when white light is passed through a prism?
37. What is meant by the statement: "Spectral lines are the fingerprints of elements"?

12-17 Electromagnetic Radiation

Figure 12-18

The electromagnetic spectrum. Note that the part that we can see, the visible spectrum, is only a small part of the whole electromagnetic spectrum.

Visible light is one type of what is known as electromagnetic radiation, often simply called *radiation*. Other types of electromagnetic radiation are gamma rays (Section 13-20), X rays, ultraviolet and infrared light, and radio waves. None of these types of radiation can be detected by the human eye. The types of radiation listed above form what is called the **electromagnetic spectrum.** See Figure 12-18.

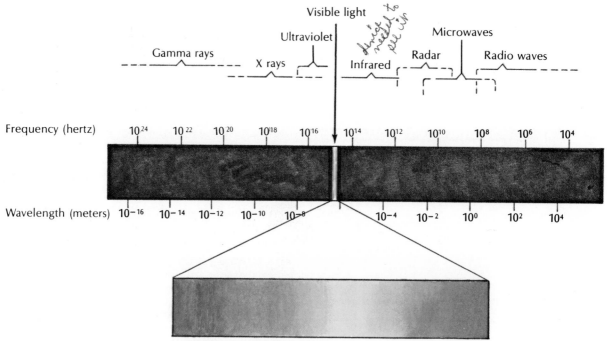

Expanded visible part of the electromagnetic spectrum

Although we cannot see most of the radiations that make up the electromagnetic spectrum, there are other ways of detecting them. There are photographic films, for example, that are affected by gamma rays, X rays, ultraviolet light, and infrared light. Radio receivers can detect waves in the radio region of the electromagnetic spectrum.

All forms of electromagnetic radiation travel through a vacuum at the same speed. This is the speed of light, which is 3.00×10^8 meters per second. The speed of light through air is slightly less than through a vacuum. However, the difference is so slight that 3.00×10^8 meters per second (to three significant figures) is correct for either medium. The small letter c is used to represent the speed of light. For light, the formula $v = f\lambda$ (page 160) has the form: $c = f\lambda$.

12-18   Energy and Light

Scientists can measure the wavelengths corresponding to all the lines in a bright-line spectrum. Each line has a particular frequency. If we know the wavelength of a line, we can calculate its frequency from the formula $c = f\lambda$, where c, the speed of light, is a known constant. For example, if the wavelength of a line is 6.0×10^{-7} meter, then its frequency is:

$$c = f\lambda$$

$$3.0 \times 10^8 \ \frac{m}{sec} = f \times (6.0 \times 10^{-7} \ \frac{meters}{wave})$$

$$f = \frac{3.0 \times 10^8 \ \frac{meters}{second}}{6.0 \times 10^{-7} \ \frac{meter}{waves}}$$

$$= 0.50 \times 10^{15} \ \frac{waves}{second}$$

$$= 5.0 \times 10^{14} \ \text{hertz}$$

Planck derived a formula that expresses the energy of a single quantum (photon) of radiation of any given frequency. The formula states that the energy is directly proportional to the frequency of the radiation. The constant of proportionality is called **Planck's constant,** and is represented by h. The formula is:

$$E = hf \qquad \text{where,}$$

E = the energy (in joules) of a photon of radiation of frequency f

h = 6.6×10^{-34} joule/hertz

For a spectral line whose frequency is 5.0×10^{14} hertz, the energy of a photon of radiation of that frequency is:

$$E = h \times f$$

$$= 6.6 \times 10^{-34} \; \frac{\text{joule}}{\text{hertz}} \times 5.0 \times 10^{14} \; \text{hertz}$$

$$= 3.3 \times 10^{-19} \; \text{joule}$$

Remember that this is the *smallest* quantity of energy that can be transferred by radiation of that frequency.

Questions for Sections 12-17 and 12-18

38. Name several types of electromagnetic radiation.
39. How is it possible to detect invisible forms of electromagnetic radiation?
40. What is the velocity of all forms of electromagnetic radiation? What symbol is used to represent this velocity?
41. How can you determine the frequency of a wave when the wavelength is known?
42. What is the relationship between the energy of a quantum of radiation and the frequency of that radiation?
43. In the formula $E = hf$, what does the letter h represent?

12-19   Electron Energy Levels in the Bohr Model

The key idea in Bohr's model of the atom is that there are certain definite orbits in which an electron can travel around a nucleus without radiating energy. In Bohr's original model, each of these orbits is a circular orbit at a fixed distance from the nucleus. An electron in a given orbit has a certain definite amount of energy. The greater the radius of the shell, or the distance of the electron from the nucleus, the greater the energy of an electron in that shell. Thus, the possible electron orbits are known as **energy levels.**

Bohr proposed that the only way an electron can lose energy is by dropping from one energy level to a lower one. When this happens, the atom emits a photon of radiation corresponding to the difference in energy levels. As long as electrons remain in their orbits, they do not lose energy. Clearly, electrons already in the lowest energy level cannot lose energy. Bohr also worked out rules for the number of electrons that can be at any level at the same time. (These rules will be described in the next chapter.) Electrons in higher levels cannot drop to a lower level if that level is filled. An important point of Bohr's model is that in every atom in its normal state, all the electrons are in the lowest energy levels available. Since no electron can move to a lower level, none of them can lose energy. The atom is, therefore, energetically stable. By suggesting that electrons behave in this manner, Bohr was saying that the laws of physics that describe the behavior of free charged particles in the laboratory do not apply to electrons in atoms.

"Energy levels" of a ladder. Some of the features of the Bohr atom can be compared with a ladder. The rungs of a ladder represent energy levels. As a person climbs a ladder, each higher rung represents a position of greater potential energy. Furthermore, the rungs are the only places on the ladder where a person can be located. We can make a rule that only one person can stand on a rung. A ladder with 10 rungs could have as many as 10 people on it, or it could have fewer than 10. Let us also have one person on the ground steadying the ladder. Suppose there are 5 people on the ladder (and one on the ground). The 5 could occupy any of the 10 rungs, provided they observed the rule of only one person per rung. However, the lowest energy state they could have would be to have the lowest 5 rungs occupied. No one could now move any lower.

12-20   Atoms and Radiation

Figure 12-19

Energy levels within an atom.

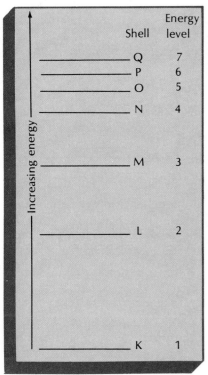

Under normal conditions, the electrons within an atom occupy the lowest energy levels available to them. When all the lowest levels are occupied, the atom is said to be in the **ground state,** or in an unexcited state. However, atoms can absorb energy from an outside source, such as heat from a flame or electrical energy from a source of voltage. When this happens, the absorbed energy can cause one or more of the electrons within the atom to move to higher energy levels. When electrons are in these higher levels the atom is said to be in an **excited state** and it is energetically unstable. It does not remain in that state for long. The electrons return to lower levels very rapidly. As they do so, energy is given off.

In every atom there are many possible energy levels that an electron can occupy. In the Bohr model, the lowest energy level is called the K shell or energy level 1. Successively higher levels are labeled L, M, N, and so on. The energy difference between successive shells is different for each pair of shells. For example, the difference in energy between the K shell and the L shell is greater than that between the L and M shells. See Figure 12-19. Furthermore, the difference between the same two shells in different atoms is different. However, in any given atom, there is an exact amount of energy needed to move an electron from one particular level to a particular higher level. Bohr used the term *quantum* from Planck's theory to describe this definite amount of energy needed to raise an electron from one level to another.

When an electron in an excited state returns to a lower energy level, it gives off a quantum of energy exactly equal to the amount initially needed to raise it to its excited state. In accordance with Planck's theory, this quantum of energy appears as radiation of a definite frequency. It may be in the visible part of the electromagnetic spectrum.

If many atoms in a sample of an element are excited at the same time, they may give off various frequencies of radiation as their electrons drop back to their ground state energy levels. Some of this radiation may well be visible as the characteristic spectrum of the element. A neon sign gives off radiation of this kind. See Figure 12-20.

From the bright-line spectrum of an element, we can now determine the value of the energy levels in its atoms. Each line in the spectrum represents a particular "quantum jump" that an electron can make in that atom. Each line also represents radiation of a definite wavelength and frequency. Planck's formula enables us to calculate the energy of a quantum of radiation of that frequency. This quantum of energy is the energy lost by an electron as it changes levels in the atom. Careful analysis of the spectra of many elements has enabled chemists to put together a detailed picture of the electron energy levels within the atoms of all the elements. We will be looking at that picture in the next chapter.

Questions for Sections 12-19 and 12-20

44. What is the key concept in Bohr's model of the atom?
45. What is the relationship between the amount of energy an electron has and its distance from the nucleus?
46. According to Bohr's theory, under what circumstances can an electron lose energy?
47. When is an atom in the ground state? What is another name for this condition?
48. According to the Bohr theory, how do electrons within an atom move to higher energy levels?
49. What happens when an electron in an excited atom returns to its original energy level?
50. Compare the energy of an electron in the K level of an atom with that of an electron in the M level of the same atom.

CHAPTER SUMMARY

1. The modern atomic theory states that all matter is made up of atoms, and that atoms are composed of smaller (subatomic) particles. Atoms of the same element are the same in their chemical behavior, but may differ in their masses. Atoms of two or more elements may join together in simple, whole-number ratios to form compounds.
2. The fundamental subatomic particles are electrons, protons, and neutrons. These particles differ from each other with respect to their electric charge and mass.
3. The number of protons in the nucleus of an atom is called its atomic number (Z). All atoms of the same element have the same number of protons in their nuclei. Atoms of different elements have different numbers of protons in their nuclei.

4. Atoms of the same element that have different numbers of neutrons in their nuclei are called isotopes of that element.
5. The sum of the protons and neutrons in the nucleus of an atom is called the mass number *(A)* of that atom.
6. The atomic mass of an element is the average mass of the isotopes in a natural sample of that element. The relative scale of atomic masses of the elements is based on the mass of the carbon-12 isotope. Its atomic mass is set at exactly 12.
7. Ernest Rutherford depicted the atom as having a small, dense, positively charged nucleus surrounded by relatively "empty" space. The electrons circled the nucleus as they moved through that empty space.
8. According to the modern theory of light, light has a dual nature—it can behave both as particles and as waves. In his quantum theory, Max Planck proposed that light consist of bundles of energy, called quanta. The amount of energy in a quantum of light depends on the color (wavelength) of the light.
9. Waves are described in terms of wavelength (λ), frequency *(f)*, and velocity *(v)*. The relationship among these quantities is given by the formula: $v = f\lambda$.
10. A continuous spectrum is a band of colors, ranging from red to violet, that is produced when a beam of white light is passed through a prism.
11. A bright-line spectrum is a set of bright lines produced when the light from a glowing substance is passed through a prism. Each element produces a unique bright-line spectrum.
12. Visible light, gamma rays, X rays, ultraviolet and infrared light, and radio waves are all types of electromagnetic radiation.
13. The energy of a single quantum of radiation is directly proportional to the frequency of the radiation, as indicated in the formula $E = hf$ where h is called Planck's constant.
14. Niels Bohr modified Rutherford's model of the atom by defining definite orbits in which electrons can travel around the nucleus. These orbits, called energy levels, represent the only areas in which electrons can be located. Upon absorbing energy from an outside source, electrons can "jump" from lower to higher energy levels. They then "fall" back to their original energy levels, and energy is emitted as they do.

TERMS YOU SHOULD KNOW

law of conservation of matter
law of definite proportions
law of multiple proportions
subatomic particles
discharge tube
cathode rays
charge/mass ratio
electron
nucleus

nucleon
proton
atomic number
neutron
isotope
mass number
atomic mass
atomic mass unit
scientific model
quanta
quantum theory

wavelength
frequency (wave)
hertz
velocity (wave)
continuous spectrum
bright-line spectrum
electromagnetic spectrum
Planck's constant
energy levels
ground state
excited state

Section

12-1
1. Briefly describe the atomic concept of matter as suggested by some early Greek philosophers.
2. How did the continuous theory of matter differ from the atomic concept described in question 1?
3. How did Dalton's theory account for the law of conservation of matter?

12-3
4. Give two examples of the behavior of matter which illustrate that the essential ideas of Dalton's atomic theory are still useful.

12-4
5. Briefly describe the contributions made by each of the following scientists in extending our knowledge of atomic structure: (a) William Crookes (b) J. J. Thomson (c) Robert Millikan.
6. Why is the charge of the electron considered to be the fundamental unit of negative charge?

12-5
7. Briefly describe the structure of the nucleus of an atom.

12-6
8. What did the chemists in Dalton's time know about the masses of atoms?

12-7
9. What is the difference between atomic number and mass number of an atom?
10. What is the (a) mass number and (b) atomic number of an isotope having 11 protons and 13 neutrons in its nucleus?
11. How many neutrons are in the nucleus of the isotope of aluminum represented by the symbol $_{13}^{27}\text{Al}$? What is the name of this isotope?
12. Suppose that a new element is discovered, that it is given the symbol Q, and that researchers have discovered two isotopes of the element. A student claims that he read that the two isotopes are represented by the symbols $_{107}^{243}\text{Q}$ and $_{108}^{244}\text{Q}$. What mistake has the student made?

12-8
13. Explain why the atomic masses of most elements are not simple whole numbers.
14. What is the mass, in atomic mass units, of an atom having 4 times the mass of a carbon-12 atom?

12-9
15. Why is the use of models necessary to the understanding of the nature and structure of atoms?
16. Describe the model of the atom proposed by J. J. Thomson.
17. What feature of Rutherford's model of the atom has continued to appear in all later models of the atom?

12-10
18. Based on the results of his famous gold-foil experiment, what observations led Rutherford to conclude that the gold atoms consist mostly of empty space?
19. Why did Rutherford conclude that atoms contain small, dense, positively charged central portions?
20. Describe Rutherford's model of the atom.

12-11
21. Describe the neutral particles in an atomic nucleus as suggested by Rutherford. Who is credited with discovering and identifying the neutron?

12-12
22. What characteristic of a moving electric charge did the electrons of Rutherford's atomic model fail to show?
23. Explain why Rutherford's model of the atom had to be revised.

12-13   **24.** During the 1600's, there was a basic disagreement among scientists about how light traveled.
(a) Briefly describe the two schools of thought on this topic.
(b) How does the modern theory of light incorporate the ideas of the earlier opposing schools of thought?

25. How did Planck's theory come to be called the quantum theory?

26. According to the quantum theory, what determines the amount of energy in a photon?

12-14   **27.** Define the following terms as they relate to waves: (a) wavelength (b) frequency (c) velocity.

28. Determine the velocity of a wave that has a wavelength of 4 meters and a frequency of 20 hertz.

12-15   **29.** As you move across the continuous spectrum from red to violet, what happens to (a) wavelength? (b) frequency?

12-16   **30.** How does a bright-line spectrum differ from a continuous spectrum?

12-17   **31.** Briefly describe the electromagnetic spectrum.

12-18   **32.** Suppose you were asked to compare the properties of the radiation represented by two different lines, A and B, in a bright-line spectrum, with line A having the longer wavelength. How would the following properties of the two lines compare? (a) frequency (b) velocity (c) energy.

12-19   **33.** Briefly describe the energy levels of the Bohr model of the atom.

34. How did Bohr's theory answer the important question left unanswered by Rutherford's model (Section 12-12)?

12-20   **35.** Explain why atoms in the ground state do not give off energy.

36. By combining the ideas in Bohr's theory and Planck's theory, what can be learned from studying the bright-line spectrum of an element?

FOR FURTHER THOUGHT

12-1   **1.** Figure 12-1 on page 221 shows a procedure for determining the composition of water. List the assumptions on which this procedure depends.

12-7   **2.** (a) Can the atoms of two different elements have the same atomic number? Explain.
(b) Can the atoms of two different elements have the same mass number? Explain.

12-8   **3.** On the present scale of atomic masses, the atomic mass of hydrogen is approximately 1.008 u. Suppose the scale were changed by international agreement to make the atomic mass of hydrogen exactly 1 u. What would be the effect of this change on the atomic masses of the other elements?

4. (a) Are all atomic masses known exactly? Explain.
(b) Is any atomic mass known exactly? Explain.

Atomic Structure—II

Objectives

After you have completed this chapter, you will be able to:
- Explain the use of wave-mechanics in atomic theory.
- Describe the wave-mechanical model of the atom.
- Trace the evolution of the concept of the atom from Dalton to the present.

13-1 Classical Mechanics

Mechanics is the branch of physics that deals with the motions of bodies under the influence of forces. **Classical mechanics** refers to the laws of motion that were worked out by Isaac Newton in the 17th century. These laws, which included the theory of gravitation, are remarkably successful in explaining the observed motions of objects on the earth as well as the motion of the moon around the earth and the motions of the planets around the sun. In the kinetic theory of gases, the laws of classical mechanics are applied to the motions of atoms and molecules. They are very successful in explaining many of the properties and the behavior of gases. At the beginning of the 20th century, most scientists believed that classical mechanics could explain the motions of all bodies large and small.

The first indication that Newton's laws might not apply to all motions came with Einstein's theory of relativity. Einstein showed that Newton's equations do not give correct results when objects are traveling at very high speeds, that is, at speeds close to that of light. Einstein wrote new equations in which Newton's laws of motion were adjusted for the effects of high speed. Einstein's equations are more complicated than Newton's, but they have to be used for objects traveling at speeds near that of light.

The second indication of a possible limit to the use of classical mechanics came in the investigation of the motions of electrons in atoms. Niels Bohr used the laws of classical mechanics to calculate the possible orbits and speeds of an electron in the hydrogen atom. However, in the Bohr model, the electron was allowed to have only certain definite energies. Although an electron could "jump" from one energy level to another, it could not exist in the atom at any energy between

Niels Bohr (1885-1962)

Born in Copenhagen, Denmark, Bohr obtained his doctorate in physics at the University of Copenhagen. Shortly after, he studied at Cambridge under J. J. Thomson and later at the University of Manchester under Ernest Rutherford. He was appointed professor of physics at the University of Copenhagen in 1916 and the director of the Institute for Theoretical Physics in 1920. It was at this time that he advanced his theory of atomic structure for which he was awarded the 1922 Nobel Prize in physics. His theory, which applied Planck's quantum theory to Rutherford's nuclear concept of the atom, laid the groundwork for modern atomic physics.

In 1938, Bohr was invited to the Institute for Advanced Study in Princeton, N.J., where he worked with Einstein and carried out extensive atomic research. He was elected president of the Danish Academy of Science and shortly after acted as adviser to the Manhattan Project, which made the first atomic bomb. Like Einstein, Bohr emphasized the dangers of atomic war and stressed peaceful solutions to international conflicts. He was awarded the Atoms for Peace Award in 1957.

Figure 13-1

Sir Isaac Newton.

Figure 13-2

Albert Einstein.

these levels. There was nothing in classical mechanics to explain why this was so. According to Newton's laws, the kinetic energy of a body always changed smoothly and continuously, not in sudden jumps. The idea of "quantized" energy levels of the Bohr model was an important one. The energy levels explained the existence of atomic spectra. But they did not fit into the classical theory of motion and energy.

Another difficulty with the Bohr model was that it worked well only for the hydrogen atom with its single electron. The Bohr model could not be made to predict the energy levels of electrons in atoms with more than one electron. A new approach to the laws governing the behavior of electrons inside atoms seemed to be needed. Such a new approach was developed in the 1920's by the combined work of many scientists, and it led to the theory of **wave mechanics** (also called **quantum mechanics**). Like Einstein's relativity mechanics, wave mechanics is a theory that is needed only for certain special situations. Relativity mechanics must be used when speeds are very high. Wave mechanics must be used for the motions of subatomic particles.

We cannot present the theory of wave mechanics in its complete form because it uses highly advanced mathematics. We can, however, describe in a general way the model of the atom that this theory produces. In order to do this, we must briefly consider two startling ideas of modern physics—the wave nature of particles and the Heisenberg uncertainty principle.

Chapter 13   Atomic Structure II   **249**

13-2 Wave Character of Particles

As part of his quantum theory, Planck suggested that light has particle-like properties, since it is composed of individual bundles (quanta) of energy. In 1924, Louis de Broglie, a French physicist, suggested that if waves can have a particle-like character, as Planck had suggested, perhaps *particles can have a wave-like character*. In 1927 de Broglie's ideas were shown to be true experimentally when investigators showed that electrons could produce *diffraction patterns*. Diffraction patterns are patterns produced by waves as they pass through small holes or narrow slits.

According to modern physics, all objects have waves associated with them. For objects of large mass, these waves are too short to be detected. As objects become less massive, their wavelengths become longer. But even a particle with the very small mass of an electron has a wavelength of only about the diameter of an atom. However, this is enough to "spread" the electron inside the atom and make it impossible to apply classical mechanics to its motion.

Questions for Sections 13-1 and 13-2

1. With what aspect of physics is the study of mechanics concerned?
2. What theory led to the discovery that the classical laws of mechanics did not apply to the motions of all objects?
3. What was the major shortcoming of the Bohr model of the atom?
4. What theory was developed as a result of the revision of Bohr's atomic model?
5. What is a diffraction pattern?
6. What does the fact that electrons produce diffraction patterns indicate about the character of electrons?

13-3 The Heisenberg Uncertainty Principle

In 1927 Werner Heisenberg (1901-1976), a German physicist, stated what is now called the **uncertainty principle.** This principle states that it is impossible to know both the precise location and the precise velocity of a subatomic particle at the same time. The reason for this is that in order to observe a particle, we must interact with it. For example, we may use photons of light to "see" the particle. But the photon, which has mass and energy, would interact with the particle and change its velocity. So we could not be sure what the velocity was at the moment of observation. Whatever we might do to make one measurement more precise makes another measurement less precise. Some uncertainty must always remain.

The amount of uncertainty may be extremely small. It is much too small to affect observations of ordinary objects. But in the case of electrons inside atoms, the uncertainty in position may be as large as the atom itself.

13-4   Probability Waves

Heisenberg's uncertainty principle gives a meaning to the waves associated with particles. The uncertainty principle tells us that we cannot be sure of the precise location and motion of small particles. We can only state the *probability* of finding a particle at a particular place at a particular time. The equations of wave mechanics give these probabilities for electrons inside the atom. The equations do not enable us to calculate exact orbits for the electrons. They describe, instead, regions of space inside the atom where an electron is likely to be at any time.

These equations are very much like the equations that mathematically describe waves. The equation for a water wave, for example, tells us how the water level changes as a wave goes by and what the wavelength of the wave is. The equations of wave mechanics tell us how the probability of finding an electron at a particular place within the atom changes from place to place. If we plot this changing probability as a graph, it has the shape of a wave. In other words, we can regard the waves associated with particles as waves of probability. There is nothing actually moving in a probability wave. But there is nothing actually moving in a light wave, either. Still, both kinds of wave have definite wavelengths, can interact with other waves, and can interact with matter. Probability waves are just as "real" as light waves or water waves.

13-5   Probability Waves and Electron Energy Levels

The location and motion of an electron inside an atom is described by a probability wave. The theory of wave mechanics states that an electron's probability wave must "fit" inside the atom in such a way that it meets itself without any overlap. A wave that does this is called a **standing wave.** See Figure 13-3. The wavelength of an electron's probability wave depends on the energy of the electron. There are only certain energies for which the wavelengths are just right to form standing waves in the atom. These are the energy levels of the Bohr model. However, the equations of wave mechanics apply to atoms of any complexity. They explain why definite energy levels exist and also tell much about the number and nature of these levels in any atom.

Questions for Sections 13-3 through 13-5

7. It is impossible to know both the precise location and precise velocity of a subatomic or small particle at the same time. What is this principle called and who first stated it?
8. What do the equations of wave mechanics describe?
9. What is a standing wave?

Figure 13-3

Producing a standing wave in a rope.
(A) By moving your hand up and down quickly once, a wave will begin to travel down the rope. (B) Move your hand up and down 40 or 50 times without stopping, very gradually increasing the rate of the up-and-down motion of your hand. When your hand is moving at just the right rate, a standing wave will be produced in the rope. This is happening when one point in the middle of the rope (called a node) is stationary. (C) With the standing wave of (B) in the rope, gradually increase the rate of the up-and-down motion of your hand. This will destroy the standing wave. When you are moving your hand fast enough, two complete waves will be produced in the rope. In this instance, the standing wave has a greater number of whole waves fitting on the rope. Standing waves on a rope are similar to the standing waves of electrons in atoms. The electrons can only have energies corresponding to wavelengths that will fit a whole number of times into the atom.

(A)

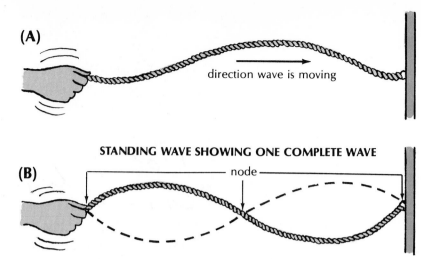

direction wave is moving

STANDING WAVE SHOWING ONE COMPLETE WAVE

(B)

node

STANDING WAVE SHOWING TWO COMPLETE WAVES

(C)

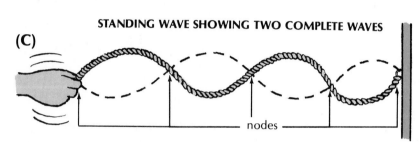

nodes

13-6 Principal Energy Levels of the Wave-Mechanical Model of the Atom

In Chapter 12 we saw how the Bohr model of the hydrogen atom succeeded in explaining the observed spectrum of hydrogen. According to this model, there are a number of orbits that the electron in the hydrogen atom can occupy. The smallest of these orbits represents the lowest energy that the electron can have. With the electron in this smallest orbit, the atom is said to be in the "ground state." By absorbing a quantum of energy of the right amount, the electron can jump to a higher orbit or "energy level" in the atom. With an electron in a higher orbit, the atom is said to be in an excited state. When the atom is in an excited state, the electron may fall back to an orbit of lower energy, emitting a quantum of energy as it does so. The wavelength of the emitted radiation depends on the size of the energy "jump." The wavelength is shorter for jumps of greater energy. Each wavelength in the spectrum of an element corresponds to a particular jump that an electron may make between one orbit and another. See Figure 13-4.

The equations of wave mechanics predict the same energy levels for the hydrogen atom as does the Bohr model. However, in the wave-

Figure 13-4

The Bohr atom and the hydrogen spectrum.

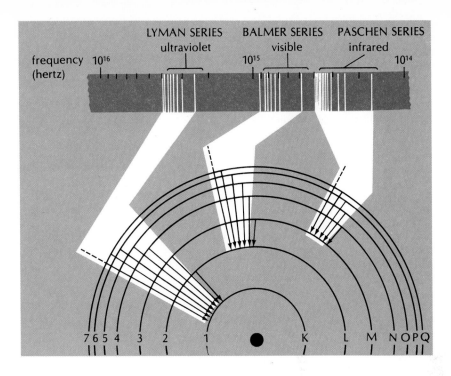

The modern atomic model has the electrons occupying regions of space about the nucleus, not following circular paths as in the Bohr model.

mechanical model the orbit or path of the electron is not a circle with a definite radius. In this model, only the probability of finding the electron in a certain region of the atom is given. The region of highest probability for each energy level is a spherical shell centered on the nucleus. These energy levels or shells in the hydrogen atom are called principal energy levels. They are numbered 1, 2, 3, etc., as in the Bohr model. The number of the shell or principal energy level is called the **principal quantum number.** It is represented by the symbol n.

13-7   Sublevels

The principal energy levels that we have been talking about are the levels that the single electron can occupy in a hydrogen atom. According to wave mechanics, every atom has principal energy levels. And every principal energy level has one or more sublevels within it. The number of sublevels in any principal level is the same as its number n. That is, the first principal energy level ($n = 1$) has 1 sublevel. The second principal energy level ($n = 2$) has 2 sublevels. The third level ($n = 3$) has 3 sublevels, and so on. The existence of sublevels accounts for the abundance of lines in the spectra of atoms other than hydrogen. Bohr's model could not explain these spectra partly because the model has only principal energy levels.

Each electron in a sublevel has a definite energy. The lowest sublevel in each principal level is called the s sublevel. In the first principal level, it is labeled the ls sublevel. In the second principal level, it is the 2s sublevel.

Figure 13-5

The continuous visible spectrum and the bright-line spectra of helium and cadmium. When an electron in an excited atom falls to a lower energy level, radiation is emitted whose energy is equal to the difference between the higher and lower energy levels. When the wavelength of the radiation is in the visible part of the spectrum, a line of color will appear in the bright-line spectrum of the element. Each line of color represents an electron jump between two particular energy levels. No two elements have the same bright-line spectrum because the arrangement of electrons within the atoms of each element is unique.

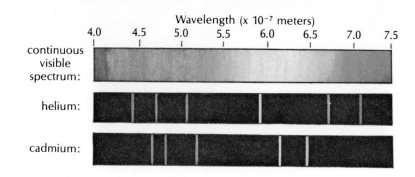

The next higher sublevel is called the *p* sublevel. There is no *p* sublevel when $n = 1$; this principal level has only one sublevel, the *s* sublevel. But for $n = 2$ and higher principal levels, *p* sublevels exist. The two sublevels of the second principal level ($n = 2$) are labeled 2*s* and 2*p*.

When $n = 3$, a third sublevel appears, called the *d* sublevel. When $n = 4$, there is a fourth sublevel, called the *f* sublevel. The additional sublevels for higher values of *n* are not discussed here, because they are not occupied by electrons in the ground state of any atom; but they do exist theoretically. The above statements are summarized in Figure 13-6.

Figure 13-7 is a diagram of the relative energy of the sublevels for the first four principal energy levels. Note the overlapping of energy levels for $n = 3$ and $n = 4$.

Figure 13-6

Sublevels present in each principal energy level.

Principal Energy Level (n)	Sublevels Present
1	1s
2	2s 2p
3	3s 3p 3d
4	4s 4p 4d 4f
5	5s 5p 5d 5f 5 . .
6	6s 6p 6d 6f 6 . . 6 . .

unlettered sublevels

Figure 13-7

The first four principal energy levels and their sublevels. Note that the 3*d* sublevel has higher energy than the 4*s*, producing an overlapping of principal energy levels 3 and 4. Within a given principal energy level, *s* sublevels are lower in energy than *p* sublevels, *p* sublevels are lower than *d* sublevels, and *d* sublevels are lower than *f* sublevels. This diagram should be compared closely with the preceding figure.

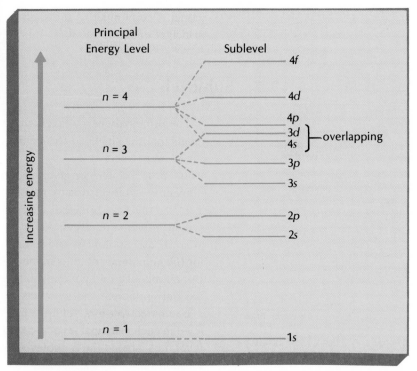

13-8   Orbitals

Each sublevel in an atom represents a possible energy for an electron in that atom. For each sublevel, there are regions of space inside the atom where electrons of that energy may be found. Such a region is called an **orbital.** The model developed from the equations of wave mechanics is called the *orbital model* of the atom.

In this model, each *s* sublevel has a single orbital. Each *p* sublevel has 3 orbitals. Each *d* sublevel has 5, and each *f* sublevel has 7. Electrons have a property called *spin*, which might be likened to the rotation of the earth on its axis. The laws of wave mechanics allow only two electrons to occupy any orbital. The two electrons in an orbital, called an **orbital pair,** must have opposite spins.

With a maximum of two electrons per orbital, the three *p* orbitals can be occupied by a maximum of 6 electrons. The five *d* orbitals can be occupied by a maximum of 10 electrons. The seven *f* orbitals can be occupied by a maximum of 14 electrons.

With the information we now have, we can find the total number of orbitals in each principal energy level and the maximum number of electrons that can be present. The results are summarized in Figure 13-8.

Figure 13-8

The relationship between n, and the number of orbitals and maximum number of electrons in a principal energy level.

Principal Energy Level (n)	Number of Orbitals Present				Total Number of Orbitals (n^2)	Maximum Number of Electrons ($2n^2$)
	s	*p*	*d*	*f*		
1	1	-	-	-	1	2
2	1	3	-	-	4	8
3	1	3	5	-	9	18
4	1	3	5	7	16	32

Note: Theoretically, the number of orbitals and possible number of electrons continue to increase for higher values of *n*. However, no atom actually has more than 32 electrons in any of its principal levels.

Questions for Sections 13-6 through 13-8

10. In the Bohr model of the atom, under what circumstances could an electron "jump" to a higher energy level?
11. What does the term principal quantum number refer to?
12. In the wave-mechanical model of the atom, what modifications were made to the principal energy levels of Bohr's model?
13. How many sublevels may be present in (a) principal energy level 3 (*n* = 3)? (b) principal energy level 6 (*n* = 6)?
14. What is an orbital? How many electrons may occupy an orbital?
15. How would the energy of an electron in the 3*d* sublevel of an atom compare with that of an electron in the 4*s* sublevel of the same atom (see Figure 13-7)?

13-9   The Ground State

The lowest, and most stable, energy state of an atom is known as the **ground state.** For an atom to be in the ground state, its electrons must be in the lowest possible energy levels. No electron can remain in a particular orbital if there is a vacant orbital of lower energy.

13-10   Notation for Electron Configurations

The arrangement of the electrons among the various orbitals of an atom is called the **electron configuration** of the atom. Electron configurations can be written using a special notation that tells the principal energy level, the type of sublevel, and the number of electrons in that sublevel. An example of the notation is the expression $1s^2$. The coefficient 1 refers to the first principal energy level. The letter s refers to the s orbital. The superscript 2 refers to the number of electrons in the orbital. The expression $1s^2$ thus means that there are 2 electrons in the s orbital of principal energy level 1. The expression $2s^1$ means that there is 1 electron in the s orbital of principal energy level 2. The expressions p_x, p_y, p_z refer to the three p orbitals. Therefore, $3p_x^2$ means that there are 2 electrons in one of the p orbitals of energy level 3.

The notation for a neutral boron atom is $1s^2 2s^2 2p_x^1$. This means that boron has 2 electrons in the $1s$ orbital, 2 electrons in the $2s$ orbital, and 1 electron in one of the $2p$ orbitals. For neutral atoms, the sum of the superscripts ($2 + 2 + 1 = 5$ for the boron atom) is the number of electrons in the atom, which is also the atomic number, Z, of the element.

13-11   Electron Configurations for the First Eleven Elements

Using the diagram in Figure 13-7 and the following rules, we will determine the electron configurations for the first 11 elements when their neutral atoms are in the ground state.

RULES FOR DETERMINING ELECTRON CONFIGURATIONS

1. Each added electron enters the lowest energy orbital of the lowest energy shell available.
2. No more than two electrons can be placed in any orbital.
3. Before a second electron can be placed in any orbital, all the orbitals of that sublevel must contain at least one electron. (This is known as **Hund's rule.**) For example, each of the p orbitals in the second energy level receives one electron before any of them receives a second electron.

Hydrogen ($Z = 1$). The single electron of the hydrogen atom must enter the lowest energy level available. As shown in Figure 13-7, this lowest level is the s orbital of the first principal energy level. The notation for hydrogen's electron configuration is $1s^1$.

Helium ($Z = 2$). A helium atom has two electrons. These occupy the lowest energy level available. The first electron occupies the $1s$ orbital, as did the electron in the hydrogen atom. The second electron also enters the $1s$ orbital, since this orbital can accommodate up to two electrons. The notation for helium's electron configuration is $1s^2$. Figure 13-9 shows one way of showing the filled $1s$ orbital in the helium atom and the half-filled $1s$ orbital in the hydrogen atom.

Figure 13-9

One way of showing the half-filled 1s orbital in a hydrogen atom (left) and the filled 1s orbital of the helium atom (right).

Lithium ($Z = 3$). A lithium atom has three electrons. The first two take the positions of the two electrons in helium. That is, they occupy the $1s$ orbital. Orbitals can hold no more than two electrons. Thus, the $1s$ orbital is filled. From Figure 13-7, the next higher orbital is the $2s$ orbital. The third electron enters this orbital. The electron configuration for lithium is $1s^2 2s^1$.

Beryllium ($Z = 4$). A beryllium atom has four electrons. The first three occupy the same orbitals as the electrons in lithium. The fourth electron enters the $2s$ orbital. Beryllium's configuration is $1s^2 2s^2$.

Boron ($Z = 5$). A boron atom has five electrons. The first four enter the orbitals occupied by the electrons in the beryllium atom. These are the $1s$ and $2s$ orbitals. Since these two orbitals both have two electrons in them, they are filled. The fifth electron enters the next highest orbital. From Figure 13-7, this is one of the three $2p$ orbitals. (Recall that the p orbitals are designated p_x, p_y, and p_z.) The electron configuration for boron is $1s^2 2s^2 2p_x^1$.

Carbon ($Z = 6$). By rule 3 (Hund's rule), an electron cannot pair with an electron in a p orbital unless each of the two other p orbitals at the same principal energy level already have at least one electron in them. Therefore, the sixth electron enters either the $2p_y$ or $2p_z$ orbital. Carbon's electron configuration is $1s^2 2s^2 2p_x^1 2p_y^1$.

Nitrogen to *neon* ($Z = 7$ to $Z = 10$). Each of the three $2p$ orbitals can hold two electrons. Thus the $2p$ sublevel can hold a total of six electrons. However, according to rule 3 (Hund's rule), each of the orbitals in any sublevel must contain one electron before any pairing of electrons takes place. Thus, in an atom of nitrogen ($Z = 7$), each of the three p orbitals contains one electron. In oxygen ($Z = 8$), one p orbital pair is formed; in fluorine ($Z = 9$), a second p orbital pair is formed;

Chapter 13   Atomic Structure II   257

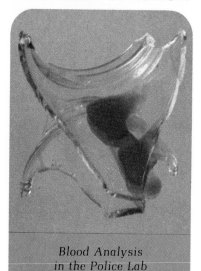

and in neon ($Z = 10$), all three p orbitals are filled. The electron configurations of these elements are as follows:

$$\text{Nitrogen } (Z = 7): \quad 1s^2 2s^2 2p_x^1 2p_y^1 2p_z^1$$
$$\text{Oxygen } (Z = 8): \quad 1s^2 2s^2 2p_x^2 2p_y^1 2p_z^1$$
$$\text{Fluorine } (Z = 9): \quad 1s^2 2s^2 2p_x^2 2p_y^2 2p_z^1$$
$$\text{Neon } (Z = 10): \quad 1s^2 2s^2 2p_x^2 2p_y^2 2p_z^2$$

The notations for electron configurations are usually simplified to show only the total number of electrons in a sublevel, rather than the breakdown into orbitals. For example, the $2p$ sublevel in oxygen would be represented as $2p^4$, and the entire atom would be:

$$1s^2 2s^2 2p^4$$

The abbreviated form of the notations for these four atoms thus becomes:

$$\text{Nitrogen } (Z = 7): \quad 1s^2 2s^2 2p^3$$
$$\text{Oxygen } (Z = 8): \quad 1s^2 2s^2 2p^4$$
$$\text{Fluorine } (Z = 9): \quad 1s^2 2s^2 2p^5$$
$$\text{Neon } (Z = 10): \quad 1s^2 2s^2 2p^6$$

Sodium ($Z = 11$). With the formation of the neon atom, all the available sublevels in the first two principal levels have been filled. The 11th electron needed for the sodium atom must start a third shell, $n = 3$. The electron enters the orbital of lowest energy in this shell, the $3s$ orbital. The electron configuration for sodium is $1s^2 2s^2 2p^6 3s^1$. We have simplified the notation by writing $2p^6$ in place of $2p_x^2 2p_y^2 2p_z^2$. We can simplify the notation still more by observing that $1s^2 2s^2 2p^6$ is the notation for a neon atom. Sodium's configuration can then be written as $[\text{Ne}]\, 3s^1$.

Note that none of the superscripts in an electron configuration can be greater than the capacity of the sublevel. These capacities are 2, 6, 10, and 14 for the s, p, d, and f sublevels, respectively. However, the superscript can be smaller than this maximum number, in which case the superscript indicates that the sublevel is not filled.

Figure 13-10 shows the electron configurations and atomic structure diagrams of the first eleven elements.

Questions for Sections 13-9 through 13-11

16. What is the condition of an atom in the ground state?
17. What is meant by the electron configuration of an atom?
18. What does the notation $3p_x^1$ mean?
19. What is the atomic number (Z) of the element whose neutral atom has the configuration $1s^2 2s^2$?
20. State Hund's rule.
21. How many orbital *pairs* are present in the atom with the electron configuration $1s^2 2s^2 2p^5$?
22. Study this notation for the electron configuration of a nitrogen atom ($Z = 7$): $1s^2 2s^2 2p_x^2 p_y^1$. Is this notation correctly written? If not, what is wrong with it?

Element	Atomic Number	Electron Configuration and Orbital Diagram
hydrogen	1	1s [↑]
helium	2	1s [↑↓]
lithium	3	1s [↑↓] 2s [↑]
beryllium	4	1s [↑↓] 2s [↑↓]
boron	5	1s [↑↓] 2s [↑↓] 2p [↑][ ][ ]
carbon	6	1s [↑↓] 2s [↑↓] 2p [↑][↑][ ]
nitrogen	7	1s [↑↓] 2s [↑↓] 2p [↑][↑][↑]
oxygen	8	1s [↑↓] 2s [↑↓] ₓ 2p p₂ [↑↓][↑][↑]
fluorine	9	1s [↑↓] 2s [↑↓] 2p [↑↓][↑↓][↑]
neon	10	1s [↑↓] 2s [↑↓] 2p [↑↓][↑↓][↑↓]
sodium	11	1s [↑↓] 2s [↑↓] 2p [↑↓][↑↓][↑↓] 3s [↑]

Figure 13-10

The electron configurations and orbital diagrams of the first eleven elements. In the orbital diagrams, each box represents one orbital. An arrow pointing upward represents an electron spinning in one direction. An arrow pointing downward represents an electron spinning in the opposite direction. An orbital can be occupied by no more than two electrons, and when occupied by two electrons, the electrons must have opposite spins.

13-12 Electron Configurations for Elements of Higher Atomic Numbers

The additional electron in a magnesium atom ($Z = 12$) completes the $3s$ sublevel. In building the elements of atomic numbers 13 (aluminum) through 18 (argon), 6 electrons are added to complete the $3p$ sublevel. With the next element, potassium ($Z = 19$), a question arises. Which orbital will the 19th electron enter? That is, which is the orbital with the lowest energy? From Figure 13-7, the s orbital of principal energy level 4 is of lower energy than a d orbital of principal energy level 3. Therefore, in potassium the electron enters the $4s$ orbital, leaving the $3d$ orbitals empty for the time being.

The element following potassium is calcium ($Z = 20$). The 20th electron enters the $4s$ orbital to fill this orbital. Since the $4s$ sublevel is now filled, we must consult Figure 13-7 to determine the next highest level for the element following calcium, which is scandium ($Z = 21$). From Figure 13-7, we see that the $3d$ is the next highest sublevel. Beginning with scandium and continuing to zinc ($Z = 30$), the $3d$ orbitals become filled. The filling of the $3d$ orbitals is sometimes called a belated filling, since the $4s$ orbital fills completely before electrons fill any of the $3d$ orbitals. This belated filling happens because of the overlapping of the sublevels of principal energy levels 3 and 4. See again Figure 13-7.

13-13 Significance of Electron Configurations

Figure 13-7, shows the relative energies of electrons in the sublevels of the first four principal energy levels. For higher principal energy levels ($n = 5$ and higher), the pattern becomes more complicated. In particular, there is a great deal more overlapping of sublevels of the kind illustrated by the $3d$ and $4s$ sublevels in Figure 13-7. As a result, the outermost principal energy level can never have more than 8 electrons. Whenever the p sublevel is filled (making a total of 8 electrons in the principal level), the next electron goes into the s sublevel of the next higher level, thus starting a new shell. You can check this statement by looking closely at Figure 13-11, which shows the electron configurations of all the elements.

The outermost principal energy level is called the **valence shell.** The electrons in the valence shell are called **valence electrons.** From what has just been said you can see that an atom cannot have more than 8 valence electrons. The valence electrons play an important part in the joining of atoms to make molecules and compounds. This will be discussed in the chapters on chemical bonding.

Take a close look at the configurations in Figure 13-11 of the elements known as the *noble gases*. These are the elements whose atomic numbers are 2, 10, 18, 36, 54, and 86. The noble gases (with the exception of helium, $Z = 2$) have 8 electrons in their outermost (valence) shell. The noble gases are the least reactive elements. Evidently, 8 electrons in a valence shell makes an element chemically stable.

ELECTRONIC CONFIGURATIONS OF ALL THE ELEMENTS

Figure 13-11

Electronic configurations of all the elements.

Z	Element	1	2		3			4				5				6				7
		s	s	p	s	p	d	s	p	d	f	s	p	d	f	s	p	d	f	s
1	H	1																		
2	He	2																		
3	Li	2	1																	
4	Be	2	2																	
5	B	2	2	1																
6	C	2	2	2																
7	N	2	2	3																
8	O	2	2	4																
9	F	2	2	5																
10	Ne	2	2	6																
11	Na	2	2	6	1															
12	Mg	2	2	6	2															
13	Al	2	2	6	2	1														
14	Si	2	2	6	2	2														
15	P	2	2	6	2	3														
16	S	2	2	6	2	4														
17	Cl	2	2	6	2	5														
18	Ar	2	2	6	2	6														
19	K	2	2	6	2	6		1												
20	Ca	2	2	6	2	6		2												
21	Sc	2	2	6	2	6	1	2												
22	Ti	2	2	6	2	6	2	2												
23	V	2	2	6	2	6	3	2												
24	Cr	2	2	6	2	6	5	1												
25	Mn	2	2	6	2	6	5	2												
26	Fe	2	2	6	2	6	6	2												
27	Co	2	2	6	2	6	7	2												
28	Ni	2	2	6	2	6	8	2												
29	Cu	2	2	6	2	6	10	1												
30	Zn	2	2	6	2	6	10	2												
31	Ga	2	2	6	2	6	10	2	1											
32	Ge	2	2	6	2	6	10	2	2											
33	As	2	2	6	2	6	10	2	3											
34	Se	2	2	6	2	6	10	2	4											
35	Br	2	2	6	2	6	10	2	5											
36	Kr	2	2	6	2	6	10	2	6											
37	Rb	2	2	6	2	6	10	2	6			1								
38	Sr	2	2	6	2	6	10	2	6			2								
39	Y	2	2	6	2	6	10	2	6	1		2								
40	Zr	2	2	6	2	6	10	2	6	2		2								
41	Nb	2	2	6	2	6	10	2	6	4		1								
42	Mo	2	2	6	2	6	10	2	6	5		1								
43	Tc	2	2	6	2	6	10	2	6	6		1								
44	Ru	2	2	6	2	6	10	2	6	7		1								
45	Rh	2	2	6	2	6	10	2	6	8		1								
46	Pd	2	2	6	2	6	10	2	6	10										
47	Ag	2	2	6	2	6	10	2	6	10		1								
48	Cd	2	2	6	2	6	10	2	6	10		2								
49	In	2	2	6	2	6	10	2	6	10		2	1							
50	Sn	2	2	6	2	6	10	2	6	10		2	2							
51	Sb	2	2	6	2	6	10	2	6	10		2	3							
52	Te	2	2	6	2	6	10	2	6	10		2	4							
53	I	2	2	6	2	6	10	2	6	10		2	5							
54	Xe	2	2	6	2	6	10	2	6	10		2	6							
55	Cs	2	2	6	2	6	10	2	6	10		2	6			1				
56	Ba	2	2	6	2	6	10	2	6	10		2	6			2				
57	La	2	2	6	2	6	10	2	6	10		2	6	1		2				
58	Ce	2	2	6	2	6	10	2	6	10	2	2	6			2				
59	Pr	2	2	6	2	6	10	2	6	10	3	2	6			2				
60	Nd	2	2	6	2	6	10	2	6	10	4	2	6			2				
61	Pm	2	2	6	2	6	10	2	6	10	5	2	6			2				
62	Sm	2	2	6	2	6	10	2	6	10	6	2	6			2				
63	Eu	2	2	6	2	6	10	2	6	10	7	2	6			2				
64	Gd	2	2	6	2	6	10	2	6	10	7	2	6	1		2				
65	Tb	2	2	6	2	6	10	2	6	10	9	2	6			2				
66	Dy	2	2	6	2	6	10	2	6	10	10	2	6			2				
67	Ho	2	2	6	2	6	10	2	6	10	11	2	6			2				
68	Er	2	2	6	2	6	10	2	6	10	12	2	6			2				
69	Tm	2	2	6	2	6	10	2	6	10	13	2	6			2				
70	Yb	2	2	6	2	6	10	2	6	10	14	2	6			2				
71	Lu	2	2	6	2	6	10	2	6	10	14	2	6	1		2				
72	Hf	2	2	6	2	6	10	2	6	10	14	2	6	2		2				
73	Ta	2	2	6	2	6	10	2	6	10	14	2	6	3		2				
74	W	2	2	6	2	6	10	2	6	10	14	2	6	4		2				
75	Re	2	2	6	2	6	10	2	6	10	14	2	6	5		2				
76	Os	2	2	6	2	6	10	2	6	10	14	2	6	6		2				
77	Ir	2	2	6	2	6	10	2	6	10	14	2	6	7		2				
78	Pt	2	2	6	2	6	10	2	6	10	14	2	6	9		1				
79	Au	2	2	6	2	6	10	2	6	10	14	2	6	10		1				
80	Hg	2	2	6	2	6	10	2	6	10	14	2	6	10		2				
81	Tl	2	2	6	2	6	10	2	6	10	14	2	6	10		2	1			
82	Pb	2	2	6	2	6	10	2	6	10	14	2	6	10		2	2			
83	Bi	2	2	6	2	6	10	2	6	10	14	2	6	10		2	3			
84	Po	2	2	6	2	6	10	2	6	10	14	2	6	10		2	4			
85	At	2	2	6	2	6	10	2	6	10	14	2	6	10		2	5			
86	Rn	2	2	6	2	6	10	2	6	10	14	2	6	10		2	6			
87	Fr	2	2	6	2	6	10	2	6	10	14	2	6	10		2	6			1
88	Ra	2	2	6	2	6	10	2	6	10	14	2	6	10		2	6			2
89	Ac	2	2	6	2	6	10	2	6	10	14	2	6	10		2	6	1		2
90	Th	2	2	6	2	6	10	2	6	10	14	2	6	10		2	6	2		2
91	Pa	2	2	6	2	6	10	2	6	10	14	2	6	10	2	2	6	1		2
92	U	2	2	6	2	6	10	2	6	10	14	2	6	10	3	2	6	1		2
93	Np	2	2	6	2	6	10	2	6	10	14	2	6	10	4	2	6	1		2
94	Pu	2	2	6	2	6	10	2	6	10	14	2	6	10	6	2	6			2
95	Am	2	2	6	2	6	10	2	6	10	14	2	6	10	7	2	6			2
96	Cm	2	2	6	2	6	10	2	6	10	14	2	6	10	7	2	6	1		2
97	Bk	2	2	6	2	6	10	2	6	10	14	2	6	10	8	2	6	1		2
98	Cf	2	2	6	2	6	10	2	6	10	14	2	6	10	10	2	6			2
99	Es	2	2	6	2	6	10	2	6	10	14	2	6	10	11	2	6			2
100	Fm	2	2	6	2	6	10	2	6	10	14	2	6	10	12	2	6			2
101	Md	2	2	6	2	6	10	2	6	10	14	2	6	10	13	2	6			2
102	No	2	2	6	2	6	10	2	6	10	14	2	6	10	14	2	6			2
103	Lr	2	2	6	2	6	10	2	6	10	14	2	6	10	14	2	6	1		2
104	Unq	2	2	6	2	6	10	2	6	10	14	2	6	10	14	2	6	2		2
105	Unp	2	2	6	2	6	10	2	6	10	14	2	6	10	14	2	6	3		2
106	Unh	2	2	6	2	6	10	2	6	10	14	2	6	10	14	2	6	4		2
107	Uns	2	2	6	2	6	10	2	6	10	14	2	6	10	14	2	6	5		2
108	Uno	2	2	6	2	6	10	2	6	10	14	2	6	10	14	2	6	6		2
109	Une																			

From the notation for an electron configuration, we can determine the number of valence electrons and the orbitals they occupy. As an illustration, consider the configuration $1s^2 2s^2 2p^6 3s^2 3p^2$. The outermost principal energy level is $n = 3$. The electrons in this outermost level are the valence electrons. There are two s and two p electrons at the $n = 3$ level, making a total of four valence electrons.

The part of the atom exclusive of its valence electrons is called the **kernel** of the atom. The kernel is the atom, including the nucleus, stripped of its valence electrons. In the illustration in the paragraph above, the nucleus plus the $1s^2 2s^2 2p^6$ electrons make up the kernel.

The electron configurations we have looked at thus far have been for neutral atoms in the ground state. Configurations can also be written for atoms when they are excited. For example, $1s^2 2s^2 2p^3 5s^1$ is the configuration for an excited atom. This atom has 8 electrons $(2 + 2 + 3 + 1 = 8)$. The atomic number of this element is therefore 8, and the element is oxygen. The $5s$ electron would be a $2p$ electron for an oxygen atom in the ground state.

13-14 Electron Clouds and the Shapes of Orbitals

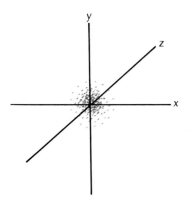

Figure 13-12

An s orbital represented by an "electron cloud." Where the dots are close together, there is a high probability of finding the electron.

Heisenberg's uncertainty principle (Section 13-3) states that it is impossible to know simultaneously the exact position and the exact velocity of an electron. In the wave-mechanical model (orbital model) of the atom, therefore, only the probability of the electron being in a given region of the atom can be estimated. The region where an electron can most probably be found can be represented as a cloud of negative charge. This region is called an **electron cloud.** An electron cloud is dense in regions where there is a high probability of finding an electron and is thin in regions of low probability. For example, Figure 13-12 shows the location of a $1s$ electron in a hydrogen atom at consecutive instants of time. The diagram shows that away from the nucleus, where the dots are more widely separated, there is less chance of finding the $1s$ electron. All s orbitals, regardless of which principal energy level they are a part of, have the same shape. The $1s$, $2s$, $3s$ . . . orbitals are all spherical. The difference between the s orbitals is that one in a higher principal energy level has a larger diameter than one in a lower level.

The shape of a p orbital is more complicated than that of an s orbital. In a p orbital, an electron occupies a region around a straight line that runs through the nucleus. Its shape is sometimes described as being like a dumbbell.

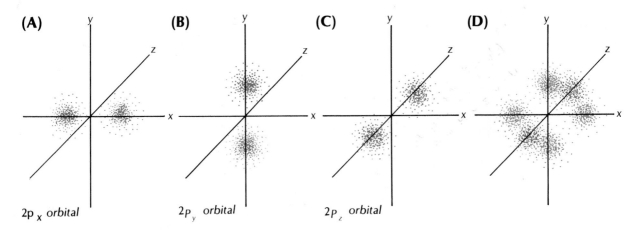

Figure 13-13

The three 2p orbitals. (A) The $2p_x$ orbital. (B) The $2p_y$ orbital. (C) The $2p_z$ orbitals. (D) All three orbitals. The dots show the locations of the electron at consecutive instants of time. Where the dots are closest together there is the greatest probability of finding the electron.

Recall that there are three *p* orbitals. For a particular principal energy level, all three have the same size and shape. Their relationship to each other is best described by referring to a three-dimensional coordinate system in which three straight line axes, *x, y,* and *z,* are at right angles to each other. The nucleus of the atom is at the point where the axes cross. A different *p* orbital lies along each of these axes, as shown in Figure 13-13.

The shapes of the *d* and *f* orbitals are even more complicated than the shape of *p* orbitals. They will not be discussed here.

13-15   The Atom, the Evolution of an Idea

The atomic theory has come a long way from the time of Dalton. In proposing that matter was composed of atoms, Dalton had comparatively little experimental evidence on which to base his ideas. Dalton's conception of the atom gave us a picture in broad strokes. Since Dalton's time, scientists have been filling in the details as more and more experimental evidence has been made available to them. As we saw in the last chapter, a major advance in our understanding of the atom was made in 1898 when J. J. Thomson proposed that electrons were fundamental constituents of atoms. In 1911, Rutherford's work suggested a dense central core at the center of atoms—the nucleus. Bohr in 1932 proposed that the energies of electrons were quantized. Our present view, the quantum-mechanical atom, describes the positions of electrons within an atom in terms of probabilities, giving us electron clouds. These evolving conceptions of the structure of the atom are shown in Figure 13-14.

Figure 13-14

Our ideas about the structure of the atom have gradually changed since Dalton proposed their existence in 1803.

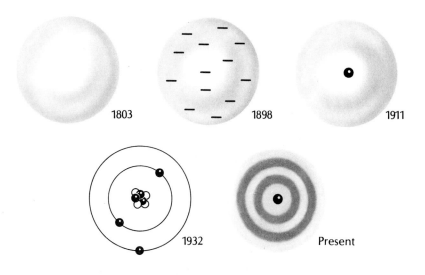

23. Briefly explain what is meant by belated filling. Under what circumstances do belated fillings occur?
24. Once the p sublevel of a principal energy level is filled, where does the next electron go?
25. What is the valence shell of an atom? How many electrons can a valence shell hold?
26. How many valence electrons are in the atom with the electron configuration $1s^2 2s^2 2p^6 3s^1$?
27. What is the kernel of an atom?
28. What is the shape of an s orbital? How does a 1s orbital differ from a 2s orbital in the same atom?

13-16 Changes in the Nucleus

Our discussion of atomic structure has thus far been confined to changes in the atom that take place outside the nucleus. That is, we have discussed electrons, their energies, and what happens when electrons change from one energy level to another. An understanding of the behavior of electrons is important to the chemist because during chemical reactions it is the electrons that are active. The nucleus remains unchanged. However, while they do not take part in chemical reactions, the nuclei of certain elements do undergo changes. Changes that take place in the nuclei of atoms are the subject of the rest of this chapter.

13-17 X Rays

In 1895, Wilhelm Roentgen (1845-1923) discovered that when a metal was struck by cathode rays (Section 12-4), an unknown type of invisible radiation was given off by the metal (Figure 13-15). These new rays could darken photographic film just as light does. They could also pass through some materials that were opaque to visible light. For example, they could affect a photographic plate wrapped in black paper. They could pass easily through flesh, but not through bone. These rays could therefore be used to photograph bones inside the body by passing the rays through the body onto photographic film.

Roentgen called these rays **X rays** because their nature was at first unknown. It was later shown that X rays were electromagnetic waves whose wavelengths were much shorter than the wavelengths of visible light. In general, the shorter the wavelengths of electromagnetic waves, the greater their penetrating power.

Figure 13-15

(A) ***Producing X rays.*** An evacuated glass tube houses the cathode and anode. A current travels through the coiled cathode, making the cathode very hot. Electrons, which have a negative charge, "boil" out of the cathode and are attracted to the positive tungsten anode. When the electrons smash into the tungsten metal, X rays are given off the metal. The X rays will pass through the black paper and will expose the film except for the part lying under the key. (B) ***The film, after it has been developed.***

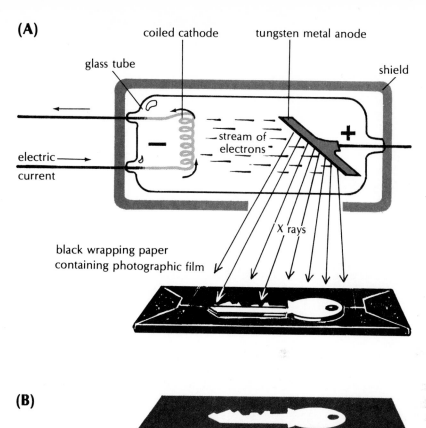

(A)

glass tube

coiled cathode

tungsten metal anode

shield

stream of electrons

electric current

X rays

black wrapping paper containing photographic film

(B)

13-18   Radioactivity

A year after Roentgen's discovery of X rays, Henri Becquerel (1852-1908), a French chemist, made a related observation. Becquerel had samples of ores of the metal uranium. An ore is a rock that contains a large amount of one or more free elements or compounds. Elements or compounds found in the earth are called minerals. Minerals are often mixed with impurities. Becquerel found that the uranium ores emitted radiation that, like X rays, darkened a covered photographic plate. See Figure 13-16. The radiation was at first called Becquerel rays. It was shown later that this radiation was produced when the nuclei of uranium atoms underwent a dramatic change. During this change, uranium atoms changed into the atoms of other elements. Such a change of one element into an entirely different element (or elements) is called **transmutation.** In this case, the element uranium (atomic number 92) spontaneously broke down to produce thorium (atomic number 90) and helium (atomic number 2).

This type of change, in which radiation is produced while the nuclei of certain elements spontaneously disintegrate to produce other elements, is called **radioactivity.** It is also known as **radioactive decay** or **nuclear disintegration.** Most elements have naturally occurring isotopes. Isotopes can be made of the others by artificial means. Many isotopes are radioactive. Those that are not are said to be stable. There

Marie Sklodowska Curie
(1867-1934)

Born in Warsaw, Poland, Marie Sklodowska Curie came to Paris to study physics and chemistry. She married Pierre Curie, a coworker, in 1895. After Becquerel discovered natural radioactivity, the Curies began investigating it. Searching for the source of the intense radiation in uranium ore, they used tons of it to isolate very small quantities of two new elements, radium and polonium, both radioactive. Along with Becquerel, the Curies shared the 1903 Nobel prize in physics. Unfortunately, Pierre died soon afterwards, run over by a heavy street cart. Marie Curie was then chosen to succeed him at the Sorbonne, the first woman professor at this university.

In 1911, she received a second Nobel prize, this one in chemistry, for her work with radium and polonium. She founded the Radium Institute in Paris and became its first director. She devoted much time and effort applying radioactivity to medicine. Her daughter, Irene, and Irene's husband, Frederic Joliet, also carried on research with radioactivity. Both mother and daughter died of leukemia, evidently caused by their exposure to radioactivity.

(A)

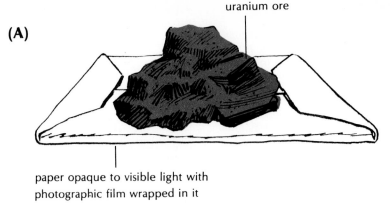

uranium ore

paper opaque to visible light with photographic film wrapped in it

(B)

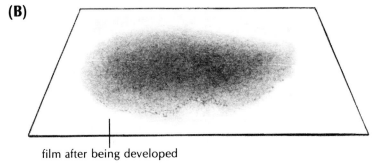

film after being developed

Figure 13-16

(A) *Uranium ore sitting on paper opaque to visible light.* (B) *Film after development is exposed in the area that had been beneath the ore.*

are no stable isotopes of elements with atomic numbers above 83. All such elements as they occur on the earth today are radioactive. All but two of the lighter elements occur on the earth as stable isotopes. Radioactive isotopes of the lighter, stable elements can be made artificially by bombarding the nuclei of stable isotopes with high-energy particles. The radioactive decay of naturally-occurring elements is called **natural radioactivity.** The radioactivity of nuclei made unstable artificially is called **induced radioactivity.**

13-19   Radium

Becquerel rays fascinated Marie Curie, the brilliant young chemist who was Becquerel's assistant. After working with Becquerel, Marie and her physicist husband, Pierre, investigated uranium ores. From these ores the Curies obtained materials that were much more radioactive than pure uranium. They isolated from the uranium ores two new elements—*polonium* and *radium*. Both of these elements were found to be highly radioactive. Radium was found to be much more so than polonium. In fact, radium gave off radiation at a rate two million times as great as that of uranium.

Because the radiation from radium was so intense, the Curies were able to observe additional properties that it had. While passing through air, the radiation made the air a conductor of electricity. That is, it ionized air. It caused phosphorescent substances, such as zinc sulfide, to glow brightly. When exposed to the rays, bacteria and small organisms were killed. The temperature near the radium was several degrees higher than that of the surroundings. This showed that the radium was releasing energy.

13-20 Types of Radiation

Shortly after the Curies made their discoveries, Ernest Rutherford did some experiments with the radiation from various radioactive sources. By directing the rays through electric fields, Rutherford showed that there were three types of radiation. One type of radiation was deflected toward a negatively charged plate. A second type was deflected toward a positively charged plate. The third type was unaffected by charged plates. See Figure 13-17. Rutherford used the Greek letters alpha, beta, and gamma to name these three types of radiation. The rays deflected toward the negative plate were named *alpha rays*. Those deflected toward the positive plate were named *beta rays*. The undeflected rays were called *gamma rays*.

Although alpha and beta rays have properties of both waves and particles, it is simpler, for our purposes, to think of them as being particles and to call them alpha and beta particles. Gamma rays are more definitely a type of electromagnetic radiation.

In general, a naturally radioactive element gives off alpha or beta particles, but seldom both. Gamma radiation usually accompanies the emission of either alpha or beta particles. Uranium and radium are alpha emitters. Thorium is a beta emitter.

Alpha particles. Alpha particles are actually the nuclei of helium atoms. Each alpha particle is made up of two protons and two neutrons, but the two electrons normally present in a neutral helium atom are missing. The absence of the two electrons gives an alpha particle a charge of 2+. The two protons and two neutrons give it a mass of about 4 atomic mass units. The speed of emission of alpha particles varies with the source of radiation. On the average, their speed is about one-tenth the speed of light. Usually they travel only a few centimeters through air. They can be stopped by a single sheet of paper. Alpha particles ionize the air through which they travel.

Beta particles. Beta particles consist of streams of electrons traveling at very high velocities, often approaching the speed of light. Beta particles (electrons) have a small mass (0.000 55 atomic mass units) and a charge of 1−. They have a greater penetrating power than alpha particles but less ionizing ability. Beta particles can be stopped by a thin sheet of aluminum.

Gamma rays. Gamma rays are a type of electromagnetic radiation. They are similar to X rays, but have even shorter wavelengths. They have greater penetrating power than X rays, alpha particles, or beta particles. It can take several centimeters of lead and even a greater thickness of iron to block gamma rays. Gamma rays, like alpha and

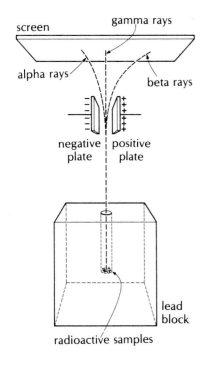

screen

gamma rays

alpha rays

beta rays

negative plate | positive plate

lead block

radioactive samples

Figure 13-17

Three types of radiation. Oppositely charged plates will separate alpha, beta, and gamma rays.

beta particles, ionize the atoms they pass through.

The properties of alpha particles, beta particles, and gamma rays are compared in Figure 13-18.

13-21   Half-Life

The rate at which radioactive decay takes place is fixed for each kind of radioactive nucleus. Nothing can change this rate. The time it takes for one-half of the atoms in a given sample to decay is called the **half-life** of that isotope. In the case of radium-226, the half-life is 1620 years. This means that in a sample of 1000 atoms half the atoms, or 500 of them, will have decayed after 1620 years have passed. If you start with a 20-g sample of radium-226, after 1620 years the sample would contain only 10 grams of radium. After another 1620 years, one-half of that amount, or 5 grams, would remain. Thus, after a period of one half-life, one-half of the original mass of an isotope remains. After two half-lives, one quarter remains. After three half-lives, one-eighth remains, and so on. See Figure 13-19.

As a radium-226 nucleus disintegrates, it gives off an alpha particle. The particle that remains is a nucleus of radon-222. Thus, radium-226 atoms are replaced by alpha particles and atoms of radon-222. This change is part of what is called a radioactive decay series, a subject that is discussed later (in Chapter 31). Of course, as the mass of the radioactive isotope decreases, so too does the amount of radiation given off by it. Half-lives range from billions of years (uranium-238 = 4.15 billion years) to fractions of seconds (polonium-214 = 1.5×10^{-4} second).

Figure 13-18

A comparison of alpha, beta, and gamma rays

Property	TYPE OF RADIATION		
	Alpha Rays or Particles	Beta Rays or Particles	Gamma Rays
Nature	Sometimes behave like particles; sometimes like waves	Same as alpha	Electromagnetic waves of extremely short wavelength
Speed	About 1/10th the speed of light	Approaching the speed of light	Speed of light
Mass	4 atomic mass units	0.0005 at. mass units	0
Penetrating power	Relatively weak (can be stopped by a single sheet of paper)	Greater than alpha	Very penetrating (several centimeters of lead needed to stop them)
Ionizing ability	Will ionize air	Will ionize air	Will ionize the atoms in flesh, causing severe damage to the cells

Figure 13-19

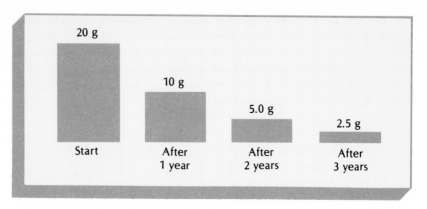

The mass of a radioactive element after the passage of time. The half-life is a unit of time. It is the time it takes for half of the mass of a radioactive element to decay. As an example, suppose there is a 20-gram sample of radioactive element whose half-life is 1 year, the case illustrated. After 1 year, only 10 grams of the element will be left. (The other 10 grams will have turned into one or more other elements.) After another year, only ½ of 10 grams, or 5.0 grams, will remain. After still another year, ½ of 5.0 grams, or 2.5 grams, will remain. (The yellow area represents the mass of new substances that are formed when the radioactive element decays.)

Questions for Sections 13-16 through 13-21

29. Why is an understanding of electron behavior so important to the chemist?
30. What are X rays?
31. What is transmutation?
32. What property do all elements with atomic numbers greater than 83 have in common?
33. Describe some properties of the radiation emitted by radium.
34. Name the three types of radiation described by Rutherford.
35. Describe the behavior of each type of radiation as it passes through an electric field.
36. What is meant by the half-life of an isotope?
37. After a period of four half-lives of a radioactive isotope has passed, what fraction of its original mass will remain?

CHAPTER SUMMARY

1. The theory of wave mechanics (quantum mechanics) was developed to explain the motion and behavior of subatomic particles.
2. The development of the wave-mechanical model of the atom was made possible in large part by the ideas of two men. In 1924, Louis de Broglie suggested that particles displayed some wave-like characteristics, an idea later verified experimentally. In 1927, Werner Heisenberg stated that it is not possible to know both the precise location and velocity of a particle at the same time (the uncertainty principle).
3. The equations of wave mechanics give probabilities for locating electrons in an atom, explain why definite energy levels for electrons exist within atoms, and reveal much about the number and nature of the energy levels.
4. In the wave-mechanical model of the atom, the number of the principal energy level is called the principal quantum number. Each principal energy level has one or more sublevels. The number of sublevels in a principal energy level is equal to the principal quantum number.
5. Orbitals are regions of an energy sublevel where electrons may be found. Each orbital can hold a maximum of two electrons. The two electrons in an orbital are called an orbital pair.

6. By following certain rules, the electron configurations of various atoms can be determined.
7. The outermost energy level of an atom is called its valence shell. The electrons in this energy level are called valence electrons. An atom cannot have more than eight valence electrons. Elements whose atoms have eight valence electrons are chemically stable (unreactive).
8. In the orbital model of the atom, the region where an electron can most probably be found is represented as a cloud of negative charge.
9. Changes in the nucleus of atoms result in the production of one or more entirely different elements. Such changes are accompanied by the emission of radiation. This process is called radioactivity, radioactive decay, or nuclear disintegration.
10. The radiation emitted during nuclear disintegration is of three types—alpha particles, beta particles, and gamma rays.
11. The rate at which radioactive decay takes place is fixed for each kind of radioactive nucleus. The time it takes for one-half of the atoms in a given sample to decay is called the half-life of that isotope.

TERMS YOU SHOULD KNOW

mechanics	orbital pair	radioactivity
classical mechanics	electron configuration	radioactive decay
wave mechanics	Hund's rule	nuclear disintegration
quantum mechanics	valence shell	natural radioactivity
uncertainty principle	valence electrons	induced radioactivity
standing wave	kernel	alpha particles
principal quantum	electron cloud	beta particles
number	X rays	gamma rays
orbital	transmutation	half-life

REVIEW QUESTIONS

Section

13-1
1. What does the term classical mechanics refer to?
2. Briefly describe some of the systems of bodies in motion which are successfully explained by the classical laws of motion.
3. In what situations is it necessary to use the theory of (a) relativity mechanics? (b) wave mechanics?

13-2
4. Describe the relationship between the mass of an object and the wavelength of the waves associated with that object.

13-3
5. Briefly explain *why* it is impossible to know both the precise location and velocity of an electron at the same time.

13-4
6. What characteristics do water waves, light waves, and probability waves have in common?

13-5
7. What do probability waves describe?
8. What determines the wavelength of a probability wave?

13-6
9. In the Bohr model of the atom, under what circumstances may an electron emit energy? What determines the wavelength of the emitted energy?

10. Compare the electron orbits of the Bohr model of the atom with those of the wave-mechanical model.

13-7   **11.** What shortcoming in Bohr's model of the atom was corrected by the sublevels of the wave-mechanical model?

12. Explain why only 4 sublevels (s, p, d, f) have been named when the electrons in many atoms occupy five or more principal energy levels.

13. How is it possible for some electrons in the third principal energy level ($n = 3$) of an atom to have more energy than some electrons in the fourth energy level ($n = 4$) of the same atom?

13-8   **14.** Describe an orbital pair.

15. What is the maximum number of electrons that can be present in an atom having three principal energy levels?

13-9   **16.** What does it mean about the positions of electrons in an atom when the atom is in the ground state?

13-10   **17.** Electron configuration notations, such as $5s^2$, consist of coefficients, letters, and superscripts. What do each of these components represent?

13-11   **18.** Write notations for electron configurations of the following atoms in the ground state: (a) lithium ($Z = 3$) (b) neon ($Z = 10$) (c) aluminum ($Z = 13$) (d) calcium ($Z = 20$)

19. Give the name and atomic numbers of the elements whose atoms in the ground state have the following electron configurations: (a) $1s^2 2s^1$ (b) $1s^2 2s^2 2p_x^2 p_y^1 p_z^1$ (c) $1s^2 2s^2 2p^6 3s^2 3p^4$ (d) $[Ar]4s^2$

13-12   **20.** What are two important consequences of orbital overlapping?

21. Write the notation of the electron configuration of the *kernel* of a sodium atom ($Z = 11$).

22. Which of the following notations shows the electron configuration of a neutral atom in an excited state? Name the element, and explain how you know it is excited: (a) $1s^2 2s^2 2p^1$ (b) $1s^2 2s^2 2p^6 3s^1$ (c) $1s^2 2s^2 2p^6 3s^2 3p^1$

13-18   **23.** What is induced radioactivity? How is it produced?

13-20   **24.** Name and briefly describe the nature and properties of the three types of emanations released during nuclear disintegration.

FOR FURTHER THOUGHT

In each pair of items or statements, which is an observation and which is an inference?

13-2   **1.** (a) Electrons have wavelike properties.
(b) Electrons can produce diffraction patterns.

13-4   **2.** (a) Standing waves in water
(b) Probability waves in atoms

13-6   **3.** (a) The spectrum of hydrogen
(b) The energy levels of electrons in a hydrogen atom

13-17   **4.** (a) X rays are similar to light waves, but of much shorter wavelength.
(b) X rays can pass through opaque paper and darken photographic film.

13-20   **5.** (a) Radioactive elements give off three kinds of radiations.
(b) Radioactive elements have unstable atoms.

6. (a) Gamma rays are electromagnetic radiations.
(b) Gamma rays are the most penetrating of the radiations from radioactive elements.

CHAPTER 14

Chemical Bonding—I

Objectives

After you have completed this chapter, you will be able to:
- Explain the chemical stability of the noble gases.
- Compare ionic and covalent bonding.
- Relate the types of elements to the electron configurations of their atoms.
- Describe metallic bonding and its effects.

14-1 Introduction

A key idea in Dalton's original theory of atoms was that compounds are formed when the atoms of different elements join together. Dalton did not know what the nature of the attachment between atoms might be. The modern quantum theory of the atom does provide an explanation of how atoms are joined in compounds. According to this theory, atoms combine as a result of a transfer or shift of their outer electrons. When such a shift of electrons occurs, a force of attraction develops between the atoms involved. This force that holds two atoms together is called a **chemical bond.** The process by which chemical bonds form is called **chemical bonding,** or just **bonding.** When new chemical bonds form, we say that a **chemical reaction** has taken place. The result is the formation of one or more new substances.

14-2 Valence Electrons and Chemical Bonding

The highest principal energy level in an atom in which there is at least one electron is called the **valence shell.** The electrons in the valence shell are called **valence electrons.** It is these electrons that usually are involved in the making of chemical bonds.

The valence shell is sometimes called the "outermost" shell. It would be more accurate to say that the valence shell is the outermost *occupied* shell of an atom in an unexcited state. If the valence shell in a particular atom is the third energy level, or M shell, this does not mean that higher levels do not exist. It does mean that under normal conditions no electrons are in these higher levels. Therefore, when we speak

Figure 14-1

Considered by many the most elegant way to cross the Atlantic Ocean, this hydrogen-filled airship, the Hindenburg, was carrying a number of wealthy passengers from Germany to the United States when it exploded on May 6, 1937, as it was being pulled to earth at the Naval Air Station, Lakehurst, New Jersey. Later airships used the noble gas helium because helium does not burn.

of the outermost, or valence, shell, we are referring to the outermost shell that has electrons in it.

The chemical properties of an element are determined mainly by the arrangement of the electrons in the valence shell. To understand this relationship between electron structure and chemical reactivity, it will be helpful to consider the structures of the **noble gases.** The noble gases are a group of six elements that do not react with other elements under most conditions. The words stable, inert, and inactive are all used to describe elements that are unreactive.

14-3   Electron Structures of the Noble Gases

Figure 14-2

The electron distributions of the noble gases. The valence shell of each atom is shown against a yellow background.

Figure 14-2 gives the electron distributions of the atoms of the noble gases. Let us look for a similarity in these distributions. The helium atom has 2 electrons in its valence shell. The valence shell for helium is the first energy level, or K shell. The K shell has only one orbital, the s orbital, and it can have a maximum of 2 electrons. Therefore, the

Noble gas	Electron distribution						Electrons in the valence shell
helium	$1s^2$						2
neon	$1s^2$	$2s^22p^6$					8
argon	$1s^2$	$2s^22p^6$	$3s^23p^6$				8
krypton	$1s^2$	$2s^22p^6$	$3s^23p^63d^{10}$	$4s^24p^6$			8
xenon	$1s^2$	$2s^22p^6$	$3s^23p^63d^{10}$	$4s^24p^64d^{10}$	$5s^25p^6$		8
radon	$1s^2$	$2s^22p^6$	$3s^23p^63d^{10}$	$4s^24p^64d^{10}4f^{14}$	$5s^25p^65d^{10}$	$6s^26p^6$	8

Search for a Durable Plastic

The photo shows dyes that are giving off light as a result of the molecules in the dyes being excited with long-wave ultraviolet, or "black" light. This particular reaction is of interest to the scientist because it is believed to be similar to what happens when certain plastics, particularly polyethylene, are exposed to light. Because many plastics undergo destructive changes as a result of exposure to light, the research team of which this scientist is a part is hoping to be able to develop materials that can be added to polyethylene during its manufacture that will reduce the destructive effect of light. A more durable polyethylene will make a better insulation for electric cables.

valence shell for helium is filled to its capacity. The remaining 5 noble gases have 8 electrons (two s electrons and six p electrons) in their valence shells. That is, the s and p sublevels of the valence shells are filled to capacity.

We can now see the distinguishing feature of the electron distributions of the atoms of the noble gases. The s and p orbitals of their valence shell are filled to capacity. The arrangement of two s electrons and six p electrons in a valence shell is called a **stable octet.** According to quantum theory, the formation of the octet of electrons in a valence shell usually releases energy. That is, energy is needed to change an octet of electrons in a valence shell to a different arrangement. Once formed, the octet is difficult to upset. That is what we mean when we say that these octets are stable. We have already noted that when the K shell is the valence shell and is filled with 2 electrons, or when higher valence shells have an octet of electrons, the element so constructed is chemically inactive. We conclude that the inactivity of these elements is due to the stability of their valence shell structures.

All the other elements, other than the noble gases, have 1 to 7 electrons in their valence shells. See Figure 13-11, page 261. These elements with 1 to 7 valence electrons are reactive to varying degrees. When they do react to form chemical bonds, usually electrons shift in such a way that stable octets are formed. In other words, in bond formation, atoms usually attain the stable electron structure of one of the noble gases. There are two ways atoms do this. One way is called *ionic* or *electrovalent bonding.* The other is called *covalent bonding.* Each of these types of bonding will be looked at in some detail.

Questions for Sections 14-1 through 14-3

1. What is a chemical bond?
2. Why are valence electrons important?
3. What is the major factor that determines the chemical properties of an element?
4. What are the noble gases?
5. What is true of the chemical behavior of the noble gases?
6. What are some terms used to describe elements that are not chemically reactive?
7. What is a stable octet?
8. How chemically active is a substance if it is made up of atoms that have a stable octet of electrons?
9. What usually happens to the electrons involved in a chemical reaction?

14-4 Ionic Bonding

Ionic (or **electrovalent) bonding** is the process by which one or more electrons are *transferred* from the valence shell of one atom to the

Atom	Electron distribution
potassium	$1s^2\ 2s^22p^6\ 3s^23p^6\ 4s^1$
chlorine	$1s^2\ 2s^22p^6\ 3s^23p^5$

Figure 14-4

Electron distributions of potassium and chlorine atoms.

valence shell of another atom. We illustrate this kind of transfer by the reaction between potassium and chlorine whose electron distributions before reaction are given in Figure 14-4. Note that the chlorine atom has seven valence electrons. Thus, it needs only one more electron to form a stable octet in its valence shell (energy level 3). Its $3s$ orbital is filled with 2 electrons, and two of the $3p$ orbitals are filled with 2 electrons each. The third p orbital has only 1 electron. One more electron will fill it.

Note that there is a single s electron in the valence shell (energy level 4) of the potassium atom. When potassium reacts with chlorine, this single $4s$ electron in a potassium atom is transferred to the half-filled $3p$ orbital of a chlorine atom, thus filling all three of the p orbitals of the chlorine atom and producing the stable octet formation. A relatively small amount of energy is needed to remove an electron from a neutral potassium atom, less energy than is needed to remove an electron from neutral atoms of most other metals. This in part explains why potassium reacts readily with chlorine.

When an atom of potassium loses an electron in a reaction, its nucleus is not affected. The nucleus still has the 19 protons it had before the reaction. However, the atom has only 18, not 19, electrons. Therefore, the atom as a whole has an excess positive charge of 1 unit. An atom that acquires a charge by losing or gaining electrons is called an **ion.** A **cation** (CAT-i-un) is a positively charged ion formed when a neutral atom loses one or more electrons. An **anion** (AN-i-un) is a negatively charged ion formed when a neutral atom gains one or more electrons. The potassium ion, with its excess positive charge of 1 unit, has the symbol K^+, as you have learned in earlier chapters.

In the reaction between chlorine and potassium, a chlorine atom acquired an extra electron. It now has the same 17 protons in its nucleus, but it has 18 electrons. The atom as a whole has an excess negative charge of 1 unit, and it, too, has become an ion. This ion is the chloride ion. The chloride ion, with its excess negative charge of 1 unit, has the symbol Cl^-, as you learned earlier. See Figure 14-5 on the following page.

When potassium reacts with chlorine, potassium and chloride ions are produced. These ions, having opposite charges, are strongly attracted toward each other. This force of attraction is called an ionic, or electrovalent, bond. The compound formed when potassium and chlorine react and combine is potassium chloride. In this compound, ions of potassium and chlorine are held together by ionic bonds.

Another illustration of ionic bonding is the reaction of magnesium

Figure 14-5

The formation of the compound potassium chloride, KCl, by ionic bonding. An electron in the valence shell of the potassium atom transfers to the valence shell of the chlorine atom, giving the valence shells of each ion a stable octet of electrons. Electrostatic attraction binds the two ions to each other.

BEFORE ELECTRON TRANSFER

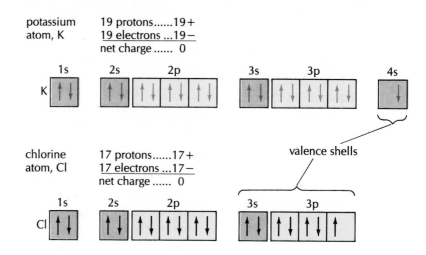

Atom	Electron distribution
magnesium	$1s^2\ 2s^2p^6\ 3s^2$
fluorine	$1s^2\ 2s^2p^5$

AFTER ELECTRON TRANSFER

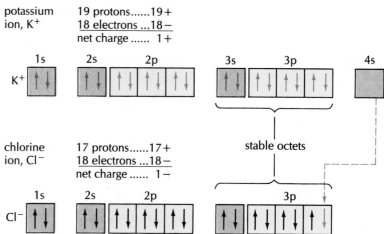

Figure 14-6

The electron distributions of magnesium and fluorine atoms.

with fluorine. The electron distributions of these atoms are given in Figure 14-6.

As in the case of chlorine, the fluorine atom needs only one more electron to complete the octet in its valence shell. The magnesium atom, however, has two electrons in its valence shell. It can therefore furnish enough electrons to complete the octets of two fluorine atoms. When the magnesium atom loses two electrons, becoming a magnesium ion, it acquires an excess positive charge of 2 units. The symbol for the magnesium ion is written Mg^{2+}.

14-5 Ionization Energy

A force of attraction exists between the positively charged protons in the nucleus of an atom and the electrons of the atom, since they have opposite charge. Before an electron can be removed from an atom to form an ion, energy must be supplied to overcome this force of attraction. The amount of energy needed to remove the most loosely held electron from a neutral atom in the gaseous phase is called the **ionization energy** or **ionization potential** of the element. In atoms having a strong attractive force between the nucleus and the electrons, the ionization energy is large. In atoms having a weak attractive force, the ionization energy is small. Metallic elements have small ionization energies. Large ionization energies are typical of nonmetallic elements, including the noble gases.

To remove a second electron from an atom that has had one electron already removed requires more energy than removing the first electron. The amount of energy to remove a second electron is called the *second ionization energy*. Removing a third electron requires more energy than removing the second. This amount of energy is called the *third ionization energy*.

Questions for Sections 14-4 and 14-5

10. What takes place during the process of ionic bonding?
11. What effect does the transfer of electrons have on the nuclei of the atoms involved?
12. What is an ion?
13. How may a neutral atom become an ion with a charge of 2+?
14. The valence shell of a neutral aluminum atom has the structure $3s^2 3p^1$. The valence shell of a neutral chlorine atom has the structure $3s^2 3p^5$. (a) What happens to each of the valence electrons in an aluminum atom when aluminum reacts with chlorine gas to form the compound that is made up of ions of aluminum and chlorine? (b) How would you write the symbol for the aluminum ion? Explain how you arrive at your answer. (c) How would you write the symbol for the chloride ion? Explain.
15. What is meant by the ionization energy of an electron?
16. What is the second ionization energy of an atom and how does it compare to the third ionization energy?

14-6   Electron-Dot Symbols

During a chemical reaction, it is the valence electrons that play an active part in the change. The locations of electrons in lower energy levels usually remain unchanged. Therefore, it is useful to have a way of showing only the valence electrons of an atom. A notation called an **electron-dot symbol** is used to show this information. An electron-dot symbol consists of the symbol of an element surrounded by dots equal in number to the number of valence electrons in an atom. The electron-dot symbols for the elements whose electron distributions are given in Figures 14-4 and 14-6 are:

$$K \cdot \qquad : \ddot{C} l \cdot \qquad Mg : \qquad : \ddot{F} \cdot$$

We understand these symbols to mean:

——Potassium has one valence electron.

——Chlorine has seven valence electrons. Six of these fill three orbitals. The seventh half-fills a fourth orbital.

——Magnesium has two valence electrons that fill one orbital.

——Fluorine has seven valence electrons. Six of these electrons fill three orbitals. The seventh electron half-fills a fourth orbital.

In understanding electron-dot symbols, it is important to remember that electrons fill orbitals of lowest energy level first. Therefore, we expect an *s* orbital to become completely filled (with its maximum of two electrons) before *p* orbitals begin being filled. While *p* orbitals are being filled, each of the three orbitals is occupied by one electron before the orbitals begin filling up with two electrons. Figure 14-7 illustrates these statements with electron-dot symbols for atoms of aluminum, carbon, nitrogen, and bromine.

Figure 14-7

The meanings of the electron-dot symbols.

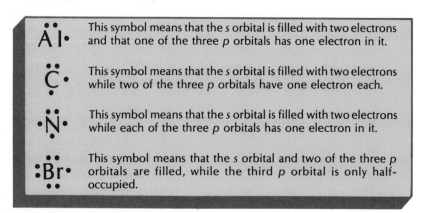

In writing electron-dot symbols, no particular place is assigned for the three *p* orbitals and the one *s* orbital. Therefore, the following symbols all have the same meaning, namely, the *s* orbital and two *p* orbitals are fully occupied, while one *p* orbital is half-occupied:

$$:\overset{..}{\underset{..}{Cl}}\cdot \qquad :\overset{..}{\underset{..}{Cl}}: \qquad \cdot\overset{..}{\underset{..}{Cl}}: \qquad :\overset{..}{\underset{.}{Cl}}:$$

Electron-dot symbols are useful for showing the formation of ionic compounds. The reaction between potassium and chlorine discussed earlier in this chapter can be written:

$$K\cdot \quad + \quad \cdot\overset{..}{\underset{..}{Cl}}: \quad \longrightarrow \quad K^+ \, [\,:\overset{..}{\underset{..}{Cl}}:\,]^-$$

potassium   chlorine   potassium chloride

This equation highlights the essential reaction—the transfer of a valence electron from the potassium to the chlorine atom.

The reaction between magnesium and fluorine can be written:

$$Mg \cdot \overset{\cdot \cdot \quad \cdot \cdot}{\underset{\cdot \cdot \quad \cdot \cdot}{\begin{matrix} F \\ F \end{matrix}}} \longrightarrow Mg^{2+} \begin{bmatrix} \overset{\cdot \cdot}{\underset{\cdot \cdot}{F}} \end{bmatrix}^{-} \begin{bmatrix} \overset{\cdot \cdot}{\underset{\cdot \cdot}{F}} \end{bmatrix}^{-}$$

magnesium   fluorine   magnesium fluoride
atom   atoms

In words, the above equation reads: "One magnesium atom reacts with two fluorine atoms to produce one magnesium ion (with a charge of 2+) and two fluoride ions (each with a charge of 1−).

14-7   Metals, Nonmetals, and Metalloids

Figure 14-8

Most metals have a property called malleability, which means that they can be flattened into thin sheets. Here a craftsman is applying very thin leaves of gold to a form.

Figure 14-9

The dome of the state capitol, Denver, Colorado, was first covered with copper, but later covered with gold. The sheets of gold leaf used for the covering were so thin that it required a piece of gold about the size of an orange to cover the entire dome. (The mass of the gold was 5.7 kg.) A second and third coating of gold were applied in 1950 and 1980.

Elements can be classified on the basis of their atomic structure and their resulting chemical behavior. As will be discussed in Chapter 16, the chemical properties of an element depend chiefly on the number of electrons in the valence shell of its atom. Elements having 1 or 2 electrons in their valence shells are active and easily lose these electrons in chemical action. Such elements show characteristic properties of *metals*. Those with 6 or 7 electrons in their valence shells are also active and easily gain electrons in chemical action to form stable electron distributions. Such elements have *nonmetallic* properties.

The properties of metals and nonmetals are related to their electron distributions. From the chemical viewpoint it is easier to remove electrons from a metal and thereby form positive ions. Nonmetals gain electrons and form negative ions. There are several elements, called **metalloids,** that are neither distinctly metallic nor distinctly nonmetallic in their chemical behavior. Under some conditions, these elements have properties that are characteristic of metals. Under other conditions, their properties are distinctly nonmetallic. Metalloids have

certain unusual properties that make them useful as semiconductors in transistors. Examples of metalloids are boron, germanium, silicon, and antimony.

Questions for Sections 14-6 and 14-7

17. What does an electron-dot symbol show?
18. Write an electron-dot symbol for the element sulfur (S), which has six valence electrons.
19. Write electron-dot symbols for the elements whose electron structures are:
    (a) beryllium, Be $\quad 1s^2\ 2s^2$
    (b) boron, B $\quad 1s^2\ 2s^22p^1$
    (c) oxygen, O $\quad 1s^2\ 2s^22p^4$
    (d) silicon, Si $\quad 1s^2\ 2s^22p^6\ 3s^23p^2$
20. Describe the chemical properties of a metal.
21. Why do nonmetals tend to form negative ions during a chemical reaction?
22. What are metalloids?

14-8 Covalent Bonding

In ionic bonding, electrons leave metallic atoms to join nonmetallic atoms. Very often, however, two atoms combine in such a manner that no complete transfer of electrons takes place. Instead, electrons seem to be held in overlapping orbitals of the atoms. This means that, in effect, the atoms are *sharing* electrons. The shared electrons occupy the valence shells of both atoms at the same time. The attractive force produced as a result of shared electrons is called a **covalent bond.** The process by which the electrons come to be shared is called covalent bonding. In covalent bonding, the atoms acquire a stable octet or fill their valence shells by sharing electrons. The atoms taking part in a covalent bond, therefore, achieve the same end result as the atoms taking part in an ionic bond. However, in covalent bonding, no ions are formed. Substances whose atoms are held together by covalent bonds are called *molecular substances*. Substances formed by ionic bonding are called *ionic substances*. There are far more molecular than ionic substances.

The hydrogen molecule—a simple case of covalent bonding. A hydrogen molecule consists of two atoms bonded by a pair of electrons. Each atom contributes one electron to the pair. According to modern theory, two *s* electron clouds overlap and occupy a common orbital joining the two atoms. The two electrons make up an orbital pair. In this orbital, called a *molecular orbital*, the electrons are in a lower energy level than when they existed in their separate atomic orbitals. See Figure 14-10. The electrostatic force of attraction between the electrons and the positive nuclei bind the two hydrogen atoms together.

Figure 14-10

Two hydrogen atoms combine by covalent bonding to form a diatomic molecule. Each atom contributes one electron to the bond. Each atom shares equally the two electrons in the bond. By sharing electrons, the first energy level of each atom is filled, giving each atom the electron structure of the noble gas helium. The dotted line in the drawing indicates that the electrons are being shared and that a covalent bond exists.

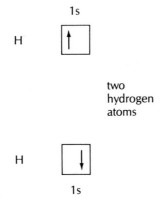

BEFORE FORMING THE COVALENT BOND

two hydrogen atoms

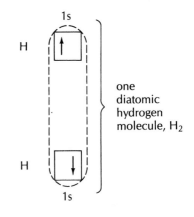

AFTER FORMING THE COVALENT BOND

one diatomic hydrogen molecule, H_2

Figure 14-11

Three ways of representing the hydrogen molecule.

H_2	H:H	H–H
Molecular formula. It shows that there are two atoms of H in the molecule.	*Dot formula.* Each dot represents one valence electron. Each hydrogen atom contributes one valence electron to the bond.	*Dash, or structural, formula.* The dash represents a covalent bond, or one pair of shared electrons.

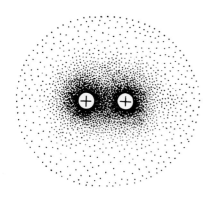

Figure 14-12

The electrons of the two hydrogen atoms appear as electron "clouds" rather than as single points. The sharing process involves an overlapping of these electron "clouds."

A group of atoms held together by covalent bonds is called a **molecule.** The hydrogen molecule can be represented in any of the ways shown in Figure 14-11.

The hydrogen molecule can also be shown as an overlapping of the electron clouds from each of the hydrogen atoms. See Figure 14-12.

Molecules of some other elements. Fluorine and chlorine are examples of other gaseous elements that form **diatomic** (two-atom) **molecules** with a single covalent bond. Their atoms have seven valence electrons. We account for the locations of these seven electrons as follows. Three of the four valence orbitals are each filled with two paired electrons. The fourth orbital is half-occupied with one unpaired electron. The unpaired electron of one atom can be paired with the corresponding unpaired electron of another atom. Thus, two atoms can share a pair of

Figure 14-13

BEFORE FORMING COVALENT BOND

The formation of the covalent bond in the diatomic chlorine molecule. Before the bond is formed, each chlorine atom has only seven electrons in its valence shell (the third energy level). By each atom sharing with the other atom the electron in its half filled *p*-orbital, the valence shell of each atom gains a stable octet of electrons. A covalent bond is thus formed. In the diagram, the dotted line connecting the two *p*-orbitals indicates that the electrons in these orbitals are each shared with the other atom.

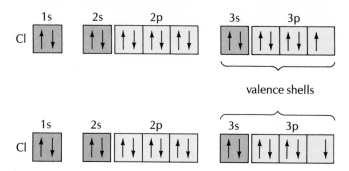

valence shells

AFTER FORMING COVALENT BOND

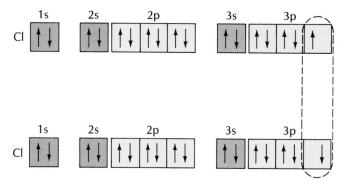

electrons and form a molecule in which the valence shell of each atom is filled with 8 electrons. See Figure 14-13.

Bromine, a liquid at room temperature, and iodine, a solid, are similar in chemical properties to fluorine and chlorine. Their atoms also have seven valence electrons, and both elements also form diatomic molecules with single covalent bonds.

The nitrogen atom has five valence electrons. It forms diatomic molecules by sharing *three* pairs of electrons. The molecule thus has a *triple covalent bond.* The triple bond makes the nitrogen molecule very stable. Each atom in the molecule has acquired the complete octet of electrons. Its structure may be depicted as:

N ≡ N   or   N⋮⋮N

It is significant that noble gases do not form diatomic molecules because their atoms already have complete valence shells. As single atoms they have great stability.

23. What is a covalent bond?
24. How do molecular substances differ from ionic substances?
25. What is a diatomic molecule?
26. Figure 14-13 shows the formation of the diatomic chlorine molecule by covalent bonding. Make a similar drawing for the formation of the diatomic fluorine molecule, which bonds covalently. (The electron structure for neutral fluorine atoms is $1s^22s^22p^5$.)
27. Give the following formulas for the diatomic fluorine molecule: (a) molecular formula (b) dot formula (c) dash, or structural, formula
28. Why is it easier to decompose hydrogen peroxide, H_2O_2, molecules than diatomic oxygen molecules?
29. Why is the diatomic nitrogen molecule especially stable?
30. Which elements are the noble gases? Why do the noble gases consist of monatomic (single atom) molecules rather than diatomic molecules?

14-9   Polyatomic Ions

Some compounds contain groups of covalently bonded atoms that remain unchanged during ordinary chemical reactions. Thus, the behavior of such groups of atoms resembles the behavior of single atoms. These groups of atoms are called **polyatomic ions.** Evidently, the bonds holding atoms together within polyatomic ions are stronger than the bonds that hold the polyatomic ions to the rest of the compound. Polyatomic ions, therefore, are quite stable. When a compound containing a polyatomic ion reacts, none of the covalent bonds within the polyatomic ion are normally broken. During reaction, the arrangement of atoms making up the polyatomic ion remains intact. Examples of polyatomic ions are the hydroxide ion, OH^-, nitrate ion, NO_3^-, sulfate ion, SO_4^{2-}, carbonate ion, CO_3^{2-}, phosphate ion, PO_4^{3-}, and ammonium ion, NH_4^+. Polyatomic ions have a charge because they gained or lost electrons during their formation. See Figure 14-14.

At one time polyatomic ions were called radicals, but using the term radicals to describe polyatomic ions has fallen into disfavor. The term radical is still used to describe certain organic structures, but in organic chemistry the term radical has another meaning, as described in Chapter 29.

Figure 14-14

The diagram accounts for the single negative charge on the hydroxide ion, OH⁻. The 8 protons from the oxygen nucleus and the 1 proton from the hydrogen nucleus give the structure 9 units of positive charge. However, the structure has 10 electrons.

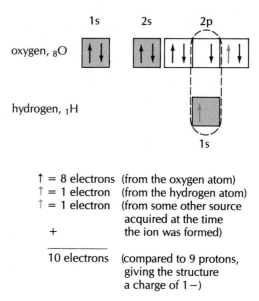

↑ = 8 electrons (from the oxygen atom)
↑ = 1 electron   (from the hydrogen atom)
↑ = 1 electron   (from some other source
                 acquired at the time
 +   the ion was formed)
_____
10 electrons   (compared to 9 protons,
                giving the structure
                a charge of 1−)

Coordinate covalence. A variation of covalent bonding is **coordinate covalent bonding.** Coordinate covalent bonding takes place when the two shared electrons forming a covalent bond are both donated by one of the atoms. Once formed, a coordinate covalent bond is no different from an ordinary covalent bond. The difference is simply in the *source* of the electrons forming the bond. Many ionic radicals are formed by coordinate covalence. The ammonium ion is an example of this kind of radical. When hydrogen chloride gas and ammonia gas are brought into contact with each other, the white solid, ammonium chloride, NH_4Cl, is formed. The ammonium ion, NH_4^+, in the ammonium chloride is formed by coordinate covalence. See Figure 14-15.

Figure 14-15

The ammonium ion forms when molecules of ammonia and hydrogen chloride react. In one of the nitrogen-hydrogen bonds, both electrons came from the nitrogen atom. Once the ammonium ion has been formed, all four nitrogen-hydrogen bonds are identical regardless of where the electrons in the bonds came from.

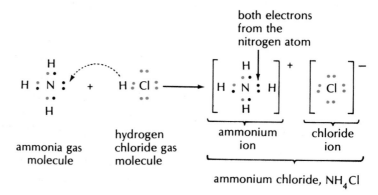

• = valence electrons from the hydrogen atoms
• = valence electrons from the nitrogen atom
• = valence electrons from the chlorine atom

14-10   Metallic Bonding

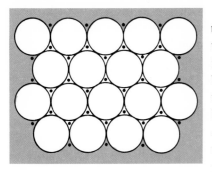

Figure 14-16

Metallic bonding. Positive ions (large circles) are held in regular patterns surrounded by valence electrons (dots) that move about freely within the metal.

Most metals have only one or two valence electrons and low ionization energies. Therefore, their valence electrons are not tightly bound to the atom. These valence electrons do not seem to belong to any individual atoms, but move easily from one atom to another. They can be considered a part of the whole metal crystal. This, in a sense, means that the electrons are shared by *all* the atoms in the metal. Metals can be thought of as positive ions immersed in an "atmosphere" or "sea" of mobile electrons. These mobile electrons exert an attractive force on the positive ions, helping to fix their positions, somewhat the way particles of sand can be glued or cemented into a solid mass. The attractive forces that bind metal atoms together are called **metallic bonds.** The ease with which the valence electrons move distinguishes the metallic bond from the ionic or covalent bond. See Figure 14-16.

The characteristic properties of metals can be explained in terms of their special type of bonding.

1. Metals are good conductors of *heat* and *electricity* because of the mobility of their valence electrons. The valence electrons play a direct part in such conduction.

2. The binding action of the electrons is the basis for the *hardness* of metals.

3. The high luster of metals is the result of the uniform way in which the valence electrons absorb and re-emit light energy that strikes them.

4. The ductility and malleability of most metals is due to the fairly uniform attraction between the electrons and the ions. The ions can change position or "flow" in the "sea" of valence electrons. Metals can therefore be flattened out or stretched into a wire because the electrons and ions can move into other positions without breaking up the essential structure. The attraction between electrons and ions continues even while forces are applied that change the shape of the metal.

14-11   The Strength of a Chemical Bond

The strength of a diatomic chemical bond can be expressed in terms of the amount of energy needed to break the bond and produce separate atoms. The energy required to break a chemical bond is called **bond energy,** and is measured in kilocalories or kilojoules per mole. Bond energy is used as a measure of *bond strength*. For example, the bond strength of hydrogen bromide (HBr) is 87.4 kilocalories per mole. This amount of energy is needed to break all the chemical bonds in a mole (6.02×10^{23} molecules) of hydrogen bromide and produce separate atoms of hydrogen and bromine. The bond strength of hydrogen chloride (HCl) is 103.1 kilocalories per mole. Therefore, the bond between hydrogen and chlorine in HCl is stronger than the bond between hydrogen and bromine in HBr.

Bond strength and stability of compounds. Compounds in which the bonds between atoms are relatively strong are stable compounds. Large amounts of energy must be supplied in order to break these compounds apart into their elements or into simpler compounds. When these stable compounds are formed from their elements, large amounts of energy are given off. Stable compounds are in a relatively low energy state. When the bonds in a compound are weak, relatively little energy is needed to break the compounds down. Such compounds are unstable. They are in a relatively high energy state.

Bond energy and chemical change. Generally, chemical change will take place if the change leads to a lower energy state and, therefore, a more stable structure. Where the difference in energy states between the reactant(s) and product(s) is large, the resulting exothermic reaction releases a large amount of energy. Where the difference in energy

Figure 14-17

The reaction between sodium and chlorine.
(A) A piece of sodium metal at room temperature.
(B) At a relatively low temperature, sodium melts.
(C) The molten metal reacts vigorously with chlorine gas to produce common table salt, NaCl.

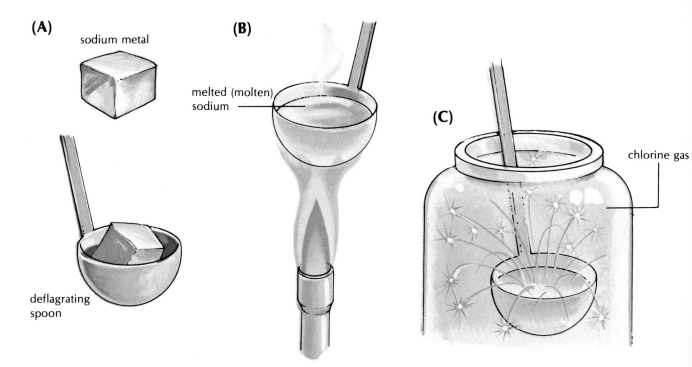

(A) sodium metal

deflagrating spoon

(B) melted (molten) sodium

(C) chlorine gas

states is small, the change from the less stable to the more stable system will release little energy. The energy that may be released in any chemical change is called *chemical energy* and is a form of potential energy stored in chemical substances. Some chemical changes can be made to occur in which the products have a higher potential energy than the reactants. Such reactions are endothermic and require an input of energy to make them occur.

In summary, systems at low potential energy states are more stable than those at high potential energy states. Chemical changes occur more readily if proceeding from higher to lower energy states and hence to more stable structures. Such changes are exothermic. The reverse changes are endothermic.

Figure 14-18

The electrolysis of water. The decomposition of water, an endothermic reaction, takes place only if energy is continuously supplied by a source of electric current.

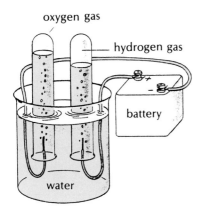

oxygen gas

hydrogen gas

battery

water

Let us apply what we know about energy in chemical systems to a particular reaction. Consider the reaction between sodium and chlorine to form sodium chloride. Recall that chlorine gas is made up of diatomic molecules. During the reaction of sodium with chlorine, the bond must be broken that links one chlorine atom with another in the diatomic chlorine molecule. Breaking the bond requires an input of energy. An input of energy is also required to remove the electron from a sodium atom in the formation of the sodium ion. (Recall that this energy is called the ionization energy.) Thus we see that an input of energy is needed to start the reaction between sodium and chlorine. However, there is an *output* of energy as the electron from the sodium atom attracted by the chlorine nucleus, "falls" into the chlorine atom to form the chloride ion. Finally, there is an additional output of energy as the sodium ions and chloride ions fall into place in the sodium chloride crystal. The formation of sodium chloride is an exothermic reaction because the total output of energy is greater than the total input of energy.

Where the opposite is true, that is, where there is a net input of energy, a reaction is endothermic. The breakdown of water to form oxygen gas and hydrogen gas is an example of such an endothermic reaction. Energy must continuously be supplied to keep this reaction going. The energy supplied may come from an electric current. The net input of energy needed to form oxygen and hydrogen from water is recovered (becomes a net output of energy) when the change is reversed, that is, when the two gases are reacted to produce water.

This has been a brief and simplified discussion of energy and chemical change. The subject is treated more completely in Chapters 19 and 20.

Questions for Sections 14-9 through 14-11

31. What is a polyatomic ion?
32. Which of the following are polyatomic ions?
    Br^-, H_2O, CO_3^{2-}, CO_2, OH^-, H_2SO_4, $C_2H_3O_2^-$, Mg^{2+}
33. How is coordinate covalent bonding different from covalent bonding?
34. How is the metallic bond different from the ionic and covalent bonds?
35. How would you determine if a given substance is a metal?
36. What is meant by bond energy?
37. What is the relationship between the stability of a compound and its bond strength?
38. During the reaction of sodium and chlorine to form sodium chloride, how does the amount of energy supplied to the system (input) compare to the amount of energy released by the system (output)?
39. During an endothermic reaction, how does the net input of energy compare with the net output?

1. The forces that hold atoms together are called chemical bonds.
2. The chemical properties of an element are determined mainly by the arrangement of its valence electrons. Chemical bonds form as a result of a shift or transfer of these valence electrons.
3. The noble gases are a group of six very stable gases. These gases are stable because the valence shells of their atoms are filled to capacity.
4. The arrangement of two s electrons and six p electrons in a valence shell is called a stable octet. All noble gases except helium have this arrangement.
5. When a neutral atom gains or loses one or more electrons, the balance between positive and negative charges (protons and electrons) is upset and the atom acquires an electrical charge.
6. An electrically charged atom is called an ion. Positive ions have more protons than electrons. Negative ions have more electrons than protons.
7. Ionic bonding takes place when one or more electrons from the valence shell of one atom are transferred to the valence shell of another atom.
8. The force of attraction between oppositely charged ions is called an ionic bond.
9. The energy required to remove the most loosely held electron from a neutral atom of an element is called the ionization energy of that element.
10. Electron-dot symbols are used to show the valence electrons of an atom.
11. Elements having 1 or 2 valence electrons are called metals. Metals tend to lose these electrons easily in chemical reactions and thereby form positive ions.
12. Elements having 6 or 7 valence electrons, called nonmetals, tend to gain electrons easily in chemical reactions and form negative ions.
13. A covalent bond is formed when one or more pairs of electrons is shared by two atoms. In an ordinary covalent bond, each atom donates one of the shared electrons. In a coordinate covalent bond, one of the atoms donates both of the shared electrons.
14. A molecule is a group of atoms held together by covalent bonds.
15. Polyatomic ions are groups of covalently bonded atoms that remain unchanged during ordinary chemical reactions.
16. Metallic bonds are the forces that bind metal atoms together. These forces are produced by a "sea" of mobile electrons that move throughout the entire metal crystal.
17. The energy required to break a chemical bond is called bond energy.

TERMS YOU SHOULD KNOW

chemical bond	ionic bonding	ionization potential	polyatomic ion
chemical bonding	electrovalent bonding	electron-dot symbol	coordinate covalent bond
valence shell	ion	metalloids	
valence electrons	cation	covalent bond	
noble gases	anion	molecule	metallic bond
stable octet	ionization energy	diatomic molecule	bond energy

Section

14-1   1. According to the quantum (wave-mechanical) theory of the atom, how do atoms of different elements combine to form a compound?

14-2   2. Why is it not entirely accurate to refer to the valence shell of an atom as the outermost shell?

14-3   3. Most elements whose atoms have 2 electrons in their valence shell, such as magnesium and calcium, are quite active chemically. Why, then, is helium, which also has 2 electrons in its valence shell, chemically stable (unreactive)?

14-4   4. Can a negative ion be formed during a chemical reaction by the loss of one or more protons from the nucleus of an atom? Explain.

        5. What is responsible for the force that makes up an ionic bond?

14-5   6. What force must be overcome in order to remove an electron from an atom?

14-6   7. The electron-dot symbol for the element argon is $:\ddot{A}r:$ (a) How many valence electrons does an argon atom have? (b) What does this fact tell you about the chemical stability or reactivity of argon?

        8. Write electron-dot symbols for the following elements. The number of valence electrons for each atom appears in parentheses: magnesium (2); boron (3); phosphorus (5); sulfur (6); neon (8)

14-8   9. How are molecular orbitals different from atomic orbitals? How are they similar?

       10. Describe the force that binds two hydrogen atoms together in a hydrogen molecule.

       11. Describe the characteristics of a triple covalent bond.

14-9   12. How does a coordinate covalent bond differ from an ordinary covalent bond?

14-10 13. Briefly describe the four physical properties characteristic of metals that are explained by metallic bonding.

14-11 14. Describe the relationship between the bond energy of a molecule and its bond strength.

FOR FURTHER THOUGHT

14-7   1. The following are statements about three different atoms:
        (1) Its third energy level has 7 electrons.
        (2) Its third energy level has 13 electrons.
        (3) Its third energy level has 18 electrons.
        (a) Which of the atoms must be the atom of a metal? (b) Which of the atoms must be the atom of a nonmetal? (c) Which of the atoms could be the atom of a metal, a nonmetal, or a noble gas?

14-11   2. Which of the following statements can be *inferred* from the observation that a relatively large amount of energy is given off when sodium and chlorine react to form sodium chloride. (One or more statements —or none of the statements—may be selected.) (a) Sodium chloride is an ionic compound. (b) Sodium chloride has less potential energy than the sodium and chlorine from which it is formed. (c) Sodium chloride is a very stable compound. (d) Much energy would be required to break down sodium chloride into its elements. (e) Sodium chloride is a solid at ordinary temperatures.

Chemical Bonding—II

15-1   Introduction

Much of the last chapter was devoted to a discussion of ionic bonding and covalent bonding. Ionic bonds form when valence electrons are transferred completely from the atoms of one element to the atoms of another element. Covalent bonds form when valence electrons are shared by the bonded atoms. In a covalent bond between two atoms of the same element, the electrons in the bond are shared equally. However, when unlike atoms are covalently bonded, the electrons in the bond are usually shared unequally. This means that the electrons in the covalent bond are *partially* transferred. They are closer to one atom than to the other. The resulting bond can be described as covalent with *ionic character.*

Although our discussion thus far has concentrated on bonds between atoms and between ions, forces of attraction also exist between one molecule and another, and between molecules and ions. These forces have an effect on the physical properties of many substances.

We begin our study of these topics by seeing what may happen to a covalent bond when the bonding atoms are different elements.

15-2   Electronegativity and Bond Polarity

Electronegativity is a measure of the attraction of an atom for electrons in the covalent bond. In the electronegativity scale devised by Linus Pauling, the most reactive nonmetal is assigned the highest value, because it has the greatest attraction for electrons in other elements. This element is fluorine. Pauling assigned fluorine a value of 4.0. Oxygen is also highly electronegative. It has a value of 3.5. Metals

Figure 15-1

Element	Electronegativity	
fluorine	4.0	⎫
oxygen	3.5	
chlorine	3.0	nonmetals
bromine	2.8	
iodine	2.5	
sulfur	2.5	⎭
carbon	2.5	
phosphorus	2.1	
hydrogen	2.1	
silicon	1.8	
beryllium	1.5	⎫
magnesium	1.2	
lithium	1.0	
sodium	0.9	metals
rubidium	0.8	
cesium	0.7	
francium	0.7	⎭

Electronegativities of some common elements.

do not have much of a tendency to attract electrons to their atoms. In fact, the valence electron in metallic atoms can be removed from the atoms relatively easily. Thus, metals have small electronegativity values, such as 0.9 for sodium and 1.2 for magnesium. Figure 15-1 gives the electronegativities of some common elements.

When two unlike atoms are covalently bonded, the shared electrons will be more strongly attracted to the atom of greater electronegativity. Such a bond is said to be **polar.** Pauling's concept of electronegativity was based on the idea that every covalent bond between unlike atoms has some ionic character. The difference in the electronegativities of two elements can be used to estimate the degrees of covalent and ionic character, or *polarity*, in a bond formed between two of their atoms. A difference of 1.7 or more indicates that a bond has more than 50% ionic character. In fact, such a bond can be described as being ionic. Differences of less than 1.7 indicate that bonds have predominately covalent character. Some exceptions to this rule may be found.

15-3   Polar and Nonpolar Molecules

Figure 15-2

The difference between a covalent bond and a polar covalent bond.
(A) In the chlorine molecule, both chlorine atoms have equal attractions for the two shared electrons. The diagram shows these electrons at the midpoint between the two atoms. The molecule has no polarity because the electron charges are distributed symmetrically. (B) In the hydrogen chloride molecule, the chlorine atom has a greater attraction for the shared electrons than the hydrogen atom. The diagram shows these electrons pulled closer to the chlorine atom. (C) If an oval is used to represent the hydrogen chloride molecule, then the end of the molecule occupied by the chlorine atom develops an excess negative charge. The end of the molecule occupied by the hydrogen atom develops an excess positive charge. Molecules with unequal charge distributions are called dipoles. A dipole molecule as a whole is neutral because the positive charge on one end cancels the negative charge on the other end.

When two atoms form a molecule with a polar covalent bond, there is an uneven distribution of electrical charge in the molecule. The molecule has excess positive charge at one end and excess negative charge at the other end, even though the molecule as a whole is electrically neutral. Such a molecule is called a **polar molecule.** Polar molecules are also known as **dipoles**.

In molecules consisting of like atoms, such as hydrogen, H_2, and chlorine, Cl_2, the bonds are *nonpolar covalent* bonds. The molecules are also nonpolar. Figure 15-2 illustrates the difference between a nonpolar covalent bond and a polar covalent bond.

In some molecules, the individual bonds are polar, but the molecule as a whole is nonpolar. This happens in molecules with a *symmetrical* structure. In such cases, the bond polarities counterbalance each

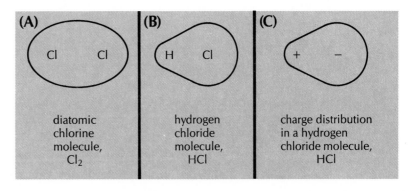

(A)	(B)	(C)
Cl Cl	H Cl	+ −
diatomic chlorine molecule, Cl_2	hydrogen chloride molecule, HCl	charge distribution in a hydrogen chloride molecule, HCl

Chapter 15   Chemical Bonding II   291

Figure 15-3

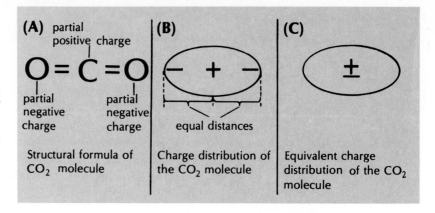

Carbon dioxide, a nonpolar molecule with polar bonds. (A) Because oxygen atoms have a greater attraction for electrons than carbon atoms, the two ends of the molecule have a negative charge and the center has a positive charge. (B) **Charge distribution on the CO_2 molecule.** The negative charge on the left end of the molecule is the same distance from the center as the negative charge on the right. (C) The center of negative charge lies at a point midway between the two negative charges. Therefore, the centers of positive and negative charge coincide. The molecule as a whole has no polarity even though the two bonds are polar.

other. Carbon dioxide, CO_2, is an example of a compound whose bonds are polar but whose molecules are nonpolar. See Figure 15-3.

Water is an interesting case of a substance whose molecules are polar. The hydrogen-oxygen bonds in water are polar because oxygen atoms have a strong attraction for electrons. We might expect the water molecule to have this structure:

H – O – H   (incorrect structural formula for water)

If the molecule were linear, as shown above, it would be nonpolar because of the symmetrical placement of the hydrogen atoms with respect to the oxygen atom.

Experiments show, however, that the real structure of the water molecule is:

O
H   H   (correct structural formula for water)

The lack of symmetry gives a partial negative charge to the end of the molecule at the greatest distance from the hydrogen atoms. At the opposite end there is a partial positive charge. We can show the location of the charge in this way:

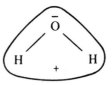

When the polar nature of the water molecule is of importance, the molecule is often represented in the following manner:

The shape and the polarity of the water molecule have important effects on the properties of water, especially as a solvent.

1. Under what conditions are the electrons in a covalent bond shared unequally by the bonded atoms?
2. What is electronegativity?
3. When is a covalent bond considered to be polar?
4. What did Pauling believe to be true about covalent bonds between unlike atoms?
5. What is a polar molecule?
6. How is it possible for a molecule to be nonpolar when its individual bonds are polar?

15-4   Molecular Substances

The **molecule,** by one definition, is the smallest particle of a substance capable of independent existence (or independent motion)*. The separate units that are formed by covalently bonded atoms qualify, therefore, as molecules. Compounds that exist as ionic crystals are *not* made up of molecules, a point that is discussed in more detail later in the chapter.

The molecules in molecular substances may be either polar or nonpolar. If polar, they tend to arrange themselves so that oppositely charged ends are near one another. (See Figure 15-4). The attraction between the opposite charges tends to hold the molecules together. As a result, polar covalent compounds are usually liquids or solids at room temperature. On the other hand, most *nonpolar* covalent substances are gases at room temperature. This is especially true of molecules with few atoms. There are no forces of attraction between their molecules strong enough to keep them from dispersing into the gaseous state at ordinary temperatures. Carbon dioxide (CO_2), oxygen (O_2), hydrogen (H_2), and chlorine (Cl_2) consist of nonpolar covalent molecules. These substances do not change to the liquid or solid phase except at low temperatures and high pressures. In other words, they have low boiling and melting points. However, nonpolar molecules made of many atoms, or of the more massive atoms, may be liquids or solids at room temperature. The reason for this will become clearer as we proceed.

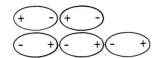

Figure 15-4

Polar molecules tend to arrange themselves so that oppositely charged ends are near one another.

15-5   Network Solids

In **network solids**, also called covalent crystals, covalent bonds extend from one atom to another in a continuous pattern. Diamond, for example, consists of atoms of carbon bonded to one another in a con-

*Recall that in Section 14-8 the molecule was defined as a cluster of atoms held together by covalent bonds.

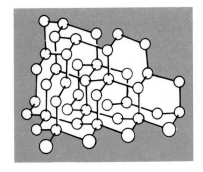

tinuous, three-dimensional pattern. See Figure 15-5. Silicon carbide (carborundum) is a substance in which atoms of silicon and carbon are joined by covalent bonds extending throughout the mass of the compound. Such substances do not have separate, distinct molecules. The entire mass may be considered to be a single giant molecule (macromolecule). Network solids are generally very hard, have very high melting points, and are poor conductors of heat and electricity. These properties of network solids are the result of strong chemical bonds and strongly held electrons.

Figure 15-5 *A network solid.* Atoms in the crystal are joining in regular patterns by covalent bonds extending in two or three dimensions. Diamond is a network solid made of covalently bonded carbon atoms.

15-6   Ionic Crystals

Figure 15-6

The sodium chloride crystal.
(A) A portion of a crystal, showing a sodium ion and the six chloride ions that surround it. (B) A larger portion of the crystal. (C) Another way of representing a sodium chloride crystal. The arrangement of the ions gives sodium chloride crystals their cubic shape. In ionic crystals, the basic units making up the crystals are ions. In the crystal, there are no groups of bonded atoms that fit the definition of a molecule.

Ions, not atoms, are the basic units of matter making up an ionic substance. For example, when sodium and chlorine react to form sodium chloride, large numbers of atoms are involved. During this reaction, sodium ions and chloride ions are formed and packed into a regular pattern resulting from a balance of forces of attraction and repulsion. This regular pattern of ions is called an *ionic crystal*, or a crystal *lattice*. In the sodium chloride crystal, each ion is surrounded by six ions of opposite charge. The result is the cubic shape that is characteristic of sodium chloride crystals, as illustrated in Figure 15-6. The units in the crystals are ions. There are no units that could be labeled as molecules of sodium chloride.

The ions in such a crystal are strongly held in fixed positions by the electrical attractions of surrounding ions. A considerable amount of

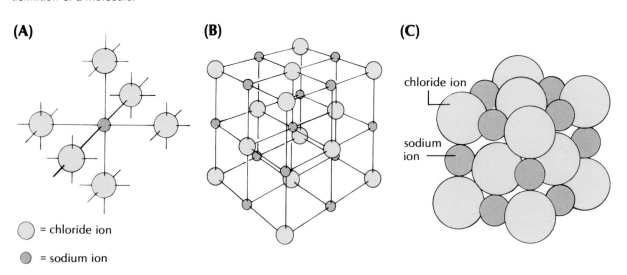

(A)

(B)

(C)

chloride ion

sodium ion

◯ = chloride ion

⬤ = sodium ion

The ionic crystal of sodium chloride has no molecules because no one ion can be considered as being attached entirely to only one other ion.

energy is required to break up such a structure. Thus, ionic crystals have high melting point temperatures. These crystals also cannot conduct the electric current, because the ions are immobile. When melted or dissolved in water, the crystal lattice is destroyed. The ions are thus free to move about. In this condition, the ionic substance will conduct the electric current. These properties—fixed ionic positions, high melting point, and nonconduction of an electric current—are generally possessed by all ionic solids. Additional examples of such solids include calcium chloride, magnesium oxide, and potassium bromide.

Questions for Sections 15-4 through 15-6

7. Give two definitions for the term molecule.
8. In a molecular substance, how do polar molecules tend to arrange themselves?
9. Describe the bonds in a network solid.
10. Describe some of the physical properties of a network solid.
11. Explain why substances that exist as ionic crystals are not considered to be made up of molecules.
12. Describe the arrangement of ions in a crystal lattice of sodium chloride.
13. Describe some of the physical properties of ionic solids.

15-7 Hydrogen Bonding

In compounds such as water (H_2O), ammonia (NH_3), and hydrogen fluoride (HF) the hydrogen atoms are bonded to small atoms of high electronegativity (oxygen, nitrogen, and fluorine, respectively). In such compounds, the hydrogen atom has only a very small share of the electron pair that forms the bond. Such molecules are highly polar. The size of the positive charge on the hydrogen end of these molecules is much greater than that on the positive end of an average dipole. In fact, each hydrogen atom acts largely as an exposed proton. It can be attracted to and form a weak bond with the electronegative atom of a neighboring molecule. Such a bond is called a **hydrogen bond.** It is more than just an electrical attraction between opposite charges. It actually has some covalent character. Hydrogen bonding is often represented by a broken line, as in the diagram of hydrogen bonding in water, Figure 15-7.

Figure 15-7

A hydrogen bond exists between the oxygen atom in a water molecule and the hydrogen atom in an adjacent water molecule.

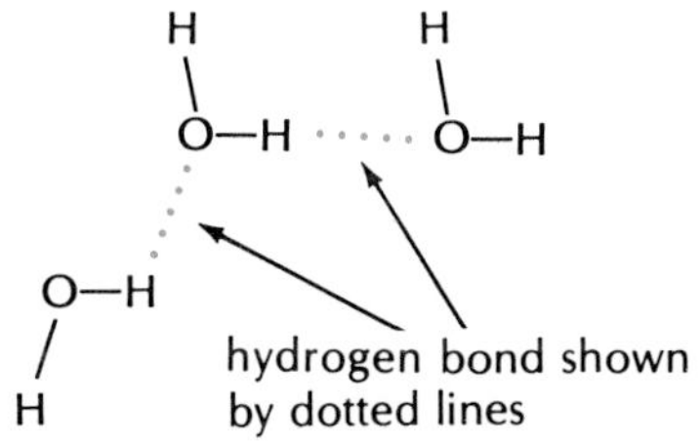

H
H
O—H
O—H
O—H
H
hydrogen bond shown by dotted lines

The hydrogen atom in a hydrogen bond is in effect bonded to two atoms, more weakly to one than the other. However, the hydrogen bond need not be in the same plane as the two covalent bonds in the molecule. The hydrogen bonds may extend into three-dimensional space.

The strength of the hydrogen bond increases with the degree of electronegativity of the atom bonded to the hydrogen. The strength *decreases* with the size of the bonded atom. For example, nitrogen and chlorine atoms have the same electronegativities. However, the hydrogen bond between hydrogen in one molecule and nitrogen in an adjacent one is *much* stronger than the bond between hydrogen and an adjacent chlorine atom. This is because nitrogen atoms are much smaller than chlorine atoms. The negative charge of the electrons in the nitrogen atom is concentrated into a smaller volume, and it therefore exerts a greater attraction for the proton of the hydrogen atom in a neighboring molecule.

15-8 The Effect of Hydrogen Bonds on Physical Properties

Hydrogen bonding is responsible for a number of unusual properties. As an example, consider the four compounds H_2O, H_2S, H_2Se, and H_2Te. Each of the atoms bonded to the hydrogen has six electrons in its valence shell. The molecules are therefore similar in structure, although they have increasing molecular masses. We might expect to find a regular pattern in some of their properties. Figure 15-8 shows the boiling points of H_2S, H_2Se, and H_2Te. We see that these boiling points are fairly low. We notice, also, that the boiling point is highest for the compound of greatest molecular mass ($-2°C$ for H_2Te), and lowest for the compound of least molecular mass ($-62°C$ for H_2S). Since the molecular mass of H_2O is even smaller than that of H_2S, we would expect the boiling point of H_2O to be still lower than $-62°C$. Instead, it is $100°C$, much higher than any of the others. See Figure 15-9.

The explanation is that hydrogen bonding occurs in H_2O, but not in the other compounds to any significant degree. Water must therefore be raised to a much higher temperature before the kinetic energy of its molecules becomes great enough to break the hydrogen bonds of the liquid state and vaporize the substance.

Figure 15-8

The boiling points of H_2S, H_2Se, and H_2Te.

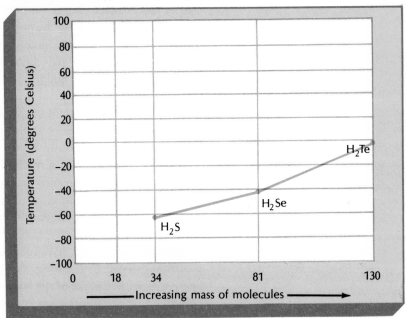

Figure 15-9

If the trend shown by H_2S, H_2Se, and H_2Te held true for H_2O, the boiling point of H_2O would be about $-65°C$, as shown by the dotted line. Instead, water boils at $+100°C$. This unexpectedly high boiling point is caused by hydrogen bonding.

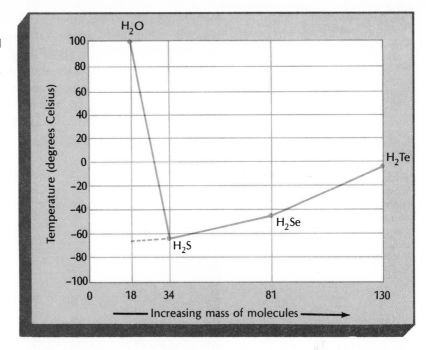

Fluorine (F), chlorine (Cl), bromine (Br), and iodine (I), each with 7 valence electrons, form a group of chemically similar elements. The boiling points of their hydrogen compounds vary in a manner similar to those of the group of compounds described above. In this group, the strong hydrogen bonds are found in hydrogen fluoride, making this substance boil at an unexpectedly high temperature. See Figure 15-10.

Hydrogen bonding also explains why some substances have unexpectedly low vapor pressures, high heats of vaporization, and high melting points. In order for vaporization or melting to take place, molecules must be separated. Energy must be expended to break hydrogen bonds and thus break down the larger clusters of molecules into separate molecules. As with the boiling point, the melting point of H_2O is abnormally high when compared to the melting points of the hydro-

Figure 15-10

The boiling points of the hydrogen compounds of some elements having seven valence electrons. For similar compounds, the boiling point normally is lower for smaller molecules. The abnormally high boiling point of hydrogen fluoride, HF, is the result of strong hydrogen bonding.

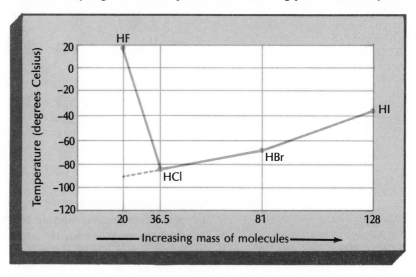

gen compounds of the other elements having six valence electrons, which are chemically similar but which have no appreciable hydrogen bonding. The melting points of the hydrogen compounds of elements with seven valence electrons show the same abnormality. Because of hydrogen bonding, hydrogen fluoride (HF), whose molecules have the smallest mass, melts at a higher temperature than either hydrogen chloride or hydrogen bromide. See Figure 15-11.

Figure 15-11

The melting points of the hydrogen compounds of some elements having seven valence electrons. If HF melted at the expected temperature, the curve would follow the dashed line. The abnormally high melting point of HF is the result of strong hydrogen bonding.

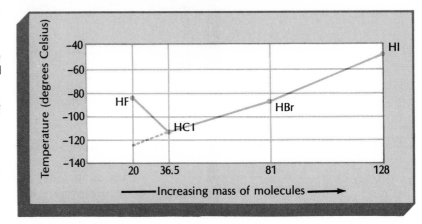

Hydrogen bonding has an effect on the crystal structure of ice. X-ray studies show that the three-dimensional structure caused by hydrogen bonding gives ice crystals a crystalline arrangement with many hexagonal openings. This open structure accounts for the low density of ice. When ice is melted, hydrogen bonds are broken. Then the open structure is destroyed, and molecules move closer together. Therefore, the liquid phase of water is denser than the solid phase. For most substances, the opposite is true. See Figure 15-12.

Figure 15-12

The structures of water in the solid and liquid phases. Hydrogen bonding in ice gives ice a more open structure than the structure of liquid water. Hence, while the solid phase of most substances is more dense than the liquid phase, the opposite is true for water.

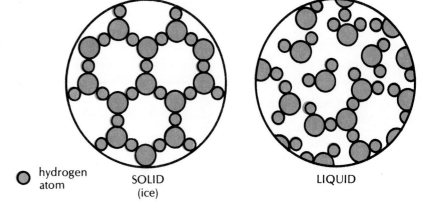

The hydrogen bond in biological systems. Hydrogen bonds occur often in compounds important to life. For example, hydrogen bonding is mainly responsible for the coiled shapes of protein molecules. Hydrogen bonds thus have a direct effect on the properties of proteins.

Hydrogen bonds are found in the important nucleic acids DNA and RNA. DNA makes up the genes, the hereditary units that control the functions of cells and the manufacture of proteins. Hydrogen bonds hold together the double helix structure of DNA and are, therefore, an important factor in heredity.

Questions for Sections 15-7 and 15-8

14. Under what circumstances do hydrogen atoms that are part of a compound resemble exposed protons?
15. How does the magnitude of the charge on the hydrogen end of a molecule that forms hydrogen bonds compare with that on the positive end of an ordinary dipole?
16. How does the presence of hydrogen bonds affect the boiling point of a substance?
17. Name some physical properties other than boiling point that are affected by the presence of hydrogen bonds.

15-9 Van der Waals Forces

Figure 15-13

The van der Waals force. (A) At a particular instant, the electron distribution in molecule 1 becomes unsymmetrical, with more electrons on the right side of the molecule. At that instant the right side will have a slight negative charge with respect to the left side. The negative charge on the right side of molecule 1 repels the electrons in molecule 2, giving the two molecules the same charge distribution. The negative end of molecule 1 and the positive end of molecule 2 attract each other, as shown by the dotted lines. (B) An instant later, as electrons shift again, the left side of molecule 1 may develop a slight negative charge, causing the charge distribution in the neighboring molecule to shift in a similar manner. This electrostatic attraction between molecules, which provides a cohesive force between molecules, is called the van der Waals force.

Molecules are relatively close together in solids, in liquids, and in gases when the gases are under high pressure. When molecules are close together, electrostatic forces of attraction develop between them. These forces are much weaker than those that exist in the chemical bonds between atoms or in hydrogen bonds between certain molecules. These weak forces arise as a result of shifts in the positions of electrons within the molecule. This shifting produces an uneven distribution of charge. One portion of the molecule becomes temporarily negative and, by repelling electrons in a neighboring molecule, it makes the near end of the neighboring molecule temporarily positive. The attraction of these opposite charges acts as a cohesive force on the molecules. Also, the second molecule may have a similar effect on a third molecule. In this manner, the effect spreads. Although the charge distributions are constantly shifting, the net effect is an overall attraction between the molecules. These forces of attraction are known as **van der Waals forces.** Johannes van der Waals was a Dutch scientist who first mathematically analyzed the magnitude of these forces. See Figure 15-13.

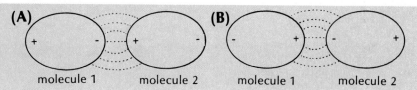

molecule 1   molecule 2   molecule 1   molecule 2

The van der Waals forces are directly related to the number of electrons present. Therefore, the larger the molecules, the stronger is this force of attraction between the molecules. In substances where van der

Waals forces are relatively large, we expect a higher boiling point. Experiments show that where two substances are chemically similar, the one with the larger molecules does, indeed, boil at the higher temperature unless hydrogen bonds exist in the other substance.

The van der Waals forces also increase with a decrease in distance between molecules. This fact is particularly applicable to gases. In gases the normally large distances between molecules can be greatly reduced by lowering the temperature and increasing the pressure. At low temperature and high pressure, even small, nonpolar molecules, such as those of oxygen and hydrogen, can be made to exist as liquids and solids. Van der Waals forces account for the fact that these substances, normally gases, can exist as liquids and solids.

Questions for Section 15-9

18. What are van der Waals forces?
19. How does the magnitude of van der Waals forces compare with those present in chemical bonds or hydrogen bonds?
20. Describe the relationship between van der Waals forces and (a) the number of electrons present; and (b) the distance between molecules.

15-10 Directional Bonding by *s* and *p* Electrons

Figure 15-14

Suppose that a single atom (atom A) has two other atoms (atom B and atom C) bonded to it. An angle will be formed by the two straight lines that connect the nucleus of atom A to the nuclei of atoms B and C. See Figure 15-14. This angle is called the **bond angle.** The bond angle is the angle between any two bonds. For molecules consisting of two atoms, there is no bond angle. There is only a single line connecting the two nuclei in the molecule. A molecule in which all the nuclei are in a straight line is called a *linear* molecule. All two-atom molecules are of course linear.

We wish now to consider bond angles in molecules containing more than two atoms. One factor that determines bond angles is the nature of the valence orbitals taking part in the bonding. The *s* electron cloud is spherical and nondirectional in bonding tendency. See Figure 15-15.

Figure 15-14

The bond angle. In this three-atom molecule, the bond angle between atoms *B* and *C* is formed by the straight lines connecting the nucleus of atom *A* to the nuclei of atoms *B* and *C*. This angle would be referred to as the angle *BAC*.

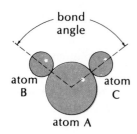

Figure 15-15

(A) ***A plane bisecting a sphere.*** The *x*−, *y*−, and *z*−axes are at right angles to each other and intersect at the center of the sphere. (B) Three axes intersecting at right angles are used to describe the *s* orbital, the region occupied by *s* electrons. Having a spherical shape with the nucleus of the atom at its center, the *s* orbital is nondirectional in bonding. That is, another atom may bond at any point around the sphere.

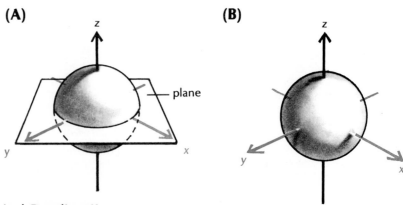

(A)

(B)

But the three p orbitals are oriented at right angles to each other. If no other factors were involved, the directional tendencies of p orbitals would determine bond angles. See Figure 15-16.

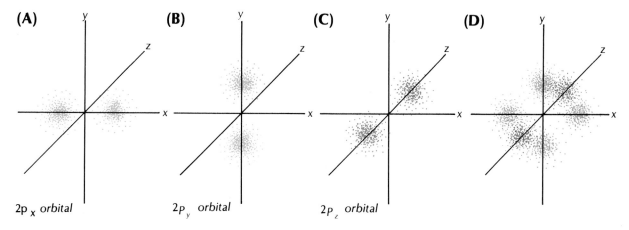

(A) 2p ₓ orbital   **(B)** 2p ᵧ orbital   **(C)** 2pᵤ orbital   **(D)**

Figure 15-16

The three 2p orbitals, each at right angles to the other two. If two of these orbitals are only half-filled, two more atoms may form covalent bonds by each contributing an electron to a half-filled orbital. In the absence of other influences, the bond angle thus formed would be a right angle because of the directional nature of p orbitals.

The effect of p electrons on bond angles can be illustrated with the compound tellurium hydride, TeH₂. The element tellurium, Te, has six valence electrons in the atom, two of them being unpaired p electrons. In its hydrogen compound, H₂Te, the p electrons show that they are oriented at right angles to one another by forming a molecule in which the bond angle is 90°.

H : Te :
    ̤
    H

• = valence electrons of hydrogen atoms

• = valence electrons of tellurium atom

The right angle directional bonding by p electrons is also shown in the compound antimony hydride, SbH₃. The antimony hydride molecule has a pyramidal shape (a pyramid with a three-sided base). The H-Sb-H bond angles have been measured to be 91°, close enough to a right angle to show that the perpendicular axes of the p orbitals have determined the directions of the bonds. See Figure 15-17.

Figure 15-17

(A) Antimony hydride, SbH₃, has a pyramidal shape with a three-sided base (shown by the dotted lines). Each line connecting Sb to an H represents a covalent bond between the antimony atom and a hydrogen atom. (B) Another representation, showing the valence electrons of the atoms of both elements.

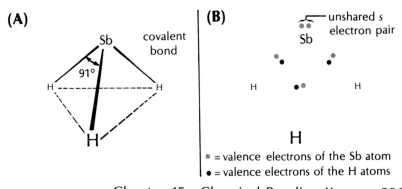

(A)   **(B)**

covalent bond

91°

unshared s electron pair

• = valence electrons of the Sb atom

• = valence electrons of the H atoms

Chapter 15   Chemical Bonding II   **301**

15-11 Hybridization

In a great many compounds, bond angles are not determined simply by the directional orientation of the orbitals involved in the bonding. In some atoms, a rearrangement of electrons in some of the orbitals occurs when bonding takes place. This process, called **hybridization,** changes the shapes of the electron clouds and, hence, the directions of the covalent bonds.

Carbon is one element in which hybridization occurs. The electron configuration of the carbon atom in the *ground state* (Section 13-9) is $1s^2 2s^2 2p^2$. It can be represented as follows:

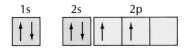

The empty box, of course, is an empty orbital. The diagram shows that a neutral carbon atom has two unpaired electrons and should, therefore, form *two* covalent bonds in its compounds. However, it usually forms *four* covalent bonds. Thus, the carbon atom acts as though it has four unpaired electrons. This can be accounted for if we assume that a $2s$ electron leaves the $2s$ orbital and enters the empty $2p$ orbital when the carbon atom is approached by the atoms of an element with which it will react. By this assumption, the orbital diagram for carbon during its chemical reactions is

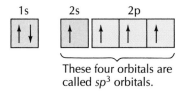

The four half-filled orbitals thus created all have identical energies. These four orbitals are called sp^3 orbitals. The bonding that takes place is called sp^3 hybridization because each of the four valence electrons of the central carbon atom is a hybrid of both s and p bonding characteristics. When hydrogen combines with carbon to form methane, CH_4, the bonding can be represented as shown in Figure 15-18.

Figure 15-18

Orbital diagrams can be used to represent the bonding between carbon and hydrogen atoms to produce the gas methane, CH_4. There are four covalent bonds in the methane molecule. The carbon atom of methane employs sp^3 hybrid orbitals in bonding with the hydrogen atoms.

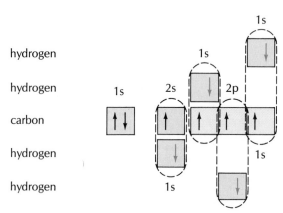

Figure 15-19

The tetrahedral structure of the methane molecule.

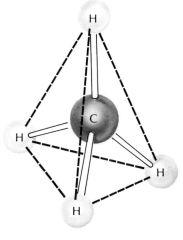

Because the four carbon-hydrogen bonds are identical in CH_4, the carbon atom may be considered to be at the center of a tetrahedron, and all H-C-H bond angles are identical, 109° 28' (almost 109.5°). All instances of sp^3 bonding produce tetrahedral structures. See Figure 15-19.

Questions for Sections 15-10 and 15-11

21. What is the minimum number of atoms that must be present in a molecule to form a bond angle?
22. What is a linear molecule?
23. What bond angles would you expect to find in a molecule in which electron clouds along p orbitals were the only determining factor?
24. What is hybridization?
25. What do the structures of all molecules containing sp^3 hybrid bonds have in common?

CAN YOU EXPLAIN THIS?

The left photo shows a stream of carbon tetrachloride, CCl_4, falling past a plastic rod that was given an electrostatic charge by rubbing the plastic with a piece of cloth.

The right photo shows a stream of water falling past the same plastic rod after it was given an electrostatic charge by rubbing the plastic with the same piece of cloth.

1. Can you explain the difference in behavior of these two liquids?
2. Can you think of any other liquids that you would expect to behave like water?
3. Can you think of any liquids that you would expect to behave like carbon tetrachloride?

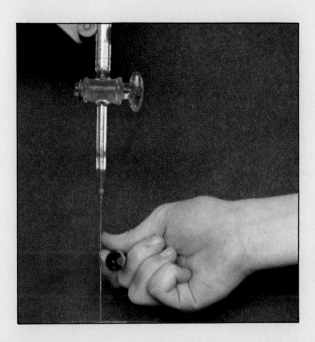

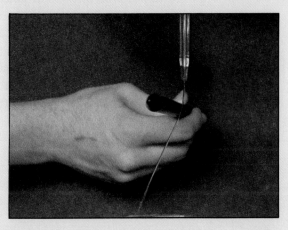

1. Electronegativity is a measure of the attraction of an atom for electrons in the covalent bond. The greater the electronegativity of an element, the stronger its attraction for these shared electrons.

2. When atoms of different elements are covalently bonded, the electrons in the bond will be shared unequally—they will be more strongly attracted to the atom of greater electronegativity. Such a bond is said to be polar.

3. The difference in electronegativity of two elements can be used to estimate the degree of polarity in a bond formed between two of their atoms. A difference of 1.7 or more usually indicates a bond that has more than 50% ionic character.

4. When atoms of two different elements are held together by a polar covalent bond, the molecule formed will have an excess positive charge at one end and an excess negative charge at the other end. Such molecules are called polar molecules.

5. By one definition, the molecule is the smallest particle of a substance capable of independent existence or independent motion.

6. Network solids are substances in which covalent bonds extend from one atom to another in a continuous pattern throughout the structure of the solid. Such substances do not have separate, distinct molecules. The entire mass may be considered to be a single giant molecule (macromolecule).

7. When hydrogen is bonded to a small, highly electronegative atom (O, N, or F), the molecule formed is highly polar. The hydrogen atom is virtually an exposed proton. The force of attraction between the positively charged hydrogen end of one molecule and a negatively charged atom of an adjacent molecule is called a hydrogen bond.

8. Hydrogen bonding is responsible for unexpectedly high boiling and melting point temperatures, low vapor pressures, and high heats of vaporization of some substances.

9. Van der Waals forces are weak forces of attraction between molecules of a substance. These forces are created by the constant shifting of the positions of electrons within the molecules of the substance.

10. The angle between any two chemical bonds is known as the bond angle. In a linear molecule, the bond angle is 180°.

11. One factor that determines bond angle is the nature of the valence orbital involved in the bonding. S orbitals, which are spherical, are nondirectional in bonding tendency. The p orbitals are oriented at right angles to one another and tend to form bond angles of 90°.

12. In some atoms, a rearrangement of electrons in some of the orbitals takes place when bonding occurs. This process, called hybridization, affects the shapes of the electron clouds and, thus, the directions and angles of the bonds.

TERMS YOU SHOULD KNOW

electronegativity	polar molecule	van der Waals forces
polar bond	network solid	bond angle
dipole	hydrogen bond	hybridization

REVIEW QUESTIONS

Section

15-1   **1.** Under what circumstances does a covalent bond have ionic character?

15-2   **2.** Why do chemically active metals have low electronegativity values?

        3. What is a polar bond?

        4. How are electronegativity values used to determine the degree of polarity in a bond formed between atoms of two different elements?

        5. Based on the electronegativity values listed in Figure 15-1, will the bonds in a molecule of magnesium oxide (MgO) be predominantly ionic or covalent?

15-3   **6.** Why does a symmetrical arrangement of polar-bonded atoms produce a nonpolar molecule?

        7. Is it possible for a molecule containing only nonpolar bonds to be polar? Explain your answer.

15-4   **8.** Why is it incorrect to refer to sodium chloride as a molecular substance?

        9. Why are many nonpolar covalent substances gases at room temperature?

15-5   **10.** Explain why network solids are not considered to have separate, distinct molecules.

15-7   **11.** Explain why some hydrogen compounds contain hydrogen bonds while other hydrogen compounds do not.

15-8   **12.** What unusual characteristics of water are explained by the presence of hydrogen bonds?

        13. Are van der Waals forces likely to be greater in the solid, liquid, or gaseous phase of a particular substance? Explain your answer.

15-9   **14.** Why are at least three atoms necessary for the formation of a bond angle?

        15. Why are the angles formed by bonds involving electrons in an *s* orbital nondirectional?

15-10   **16.** Describe what occurs during the process of hybridization.

        17. Why is the bonding in methane called sp^3 hybridization?

FOR FURTHER THOUGHT

15-2   **1.** Xenon, krypton, and radon are noble gases that form only a few compounds, and these compounds are formed only with oxygen and fluorine. Which of the following statements is closely related to the existence of these compounds? Explain your answer.

(a) Oxygen and fluorine are gases.

(b) Oxygen and fluorine form diatomic molecules.

(c) Oxygen and fluorine have the two largest values of electronegativity.

15-9   **2.** It is easier to split wood parallel to the grain than across it. In which direction are van der Waals forces probably the main cohesive force? Support your answer.

        3. Ionic bonds, covalent bonds, hydrogen bonds, and van der Waals forces are four types of chemical bonding. The same basic natural force accounts for all of these bonds. What is this force?

CHAPTER 16

Periodic Table

Objectives

After you have completed this chapter, you will be able to:
- Analyze the arrangement of the periodic table.
- Relate each element's position in the table to its structure and its properties.
- Trace patterns of change in the elements within periods and columns of the periodic table.

16-1   Introduction

There are more than 100 elements. If you were to pick a few elements at random and compare them, you would probably find great differences in their properties. However, there are certain elements that are similar to one another in many ways. During the nineteenth century, when most of the elements were being discovered, many chemists tried to classify the elements according to their similarities. Four of these chemists were Johann Döbereiner and Lothar Meyer, both Germans, John Newlands, an Englishman, and Dmitri Mendeleev, a Russian.

Döbereiner's triads. In 1829, Johann Döbereiner (der-buh-I-ner) (1780-1849) noted a relationship between the properties of certain elements and their atomic masses. Döbereiner knew that chlorine, bromine, and iodine had similar chemical properties. He arranged these elements in order of their atomic masses. Chlorine, the element with the smallest mass, was placed first. Next came bromine. Iodine, with the largest mass, was placed last. Döbereiner noticed that the difference between the masses of chlorine and bromine was about equal to the difference between the masses of bromine and iodine. He observed the same relationship for several other groups of three elements whose properties are similar. One of these groups includes sulfur, selenium, and tellurium. Calcium, strontium, and barium make up another group, as do lithium, sodium, and potassium. These groups of three similar elements are known as *Döbereiner's triads*. See Figure 16-1.

Newlands's law of octaves. In 1864, John Newlands (1837-1898) saw a connection between the properties of elements and their atomic masses. He stated that if the known elements, beginning with lithium,

Figure 16-1

Dobereiner's triads, illustrated with four triads. When the three elements in a triad are put in the order of their atomic masses, the difference in mass between the first and second elements is about equal to the difference in mass between the second and third elements.

Example	Triad	Atomic Mass	Difference in Mass
1	chlorine	35.5	44.5
	bromine	80	47
	iodine	127	
2	sulfur	32	47
	selenium	79	49
	tellurium	128	
3	calcium	40	48
	strontium	88	49
	barium	137	
4	lithium	7	16
	sodium	23	16
	potassium	39	

are arranged in order of increasing atomic mass, the eighth element will have properties similar to the first, the ninth to the second, the tenth to the third, and so on. See Figure 16-2. Newlands called this relationship the law of octaves, comparing the elements to the notes in an octave of the musical scale. Newlands tried to make his law apply to all the elements known at the time. However, because many of the heavier elements had not yet been discovered, many of the known elements did not fit the pattern.

Mendeleev's periodic table. Dmitri Mendeleev (duh-MEE-tree men-duh-LAY-ef) (1834-1907) was unaware of Newlands's work. In 1869, he developed a table that showed a relationship between the properties of elements and their atomic masses. At about the same

Figure 16-2

Newlands's octaves. Newlands lined up the elements in order of their increasing atomic masses, starting with lithium. (Neon, between F and Na, was not listed because the noble gases had not yet been discovered.) Newlands noticed that the first seven elements had different properties, but that the properties began to repeat themselves at 8-element intervals.

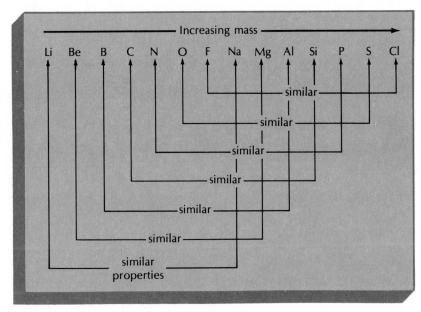

time, Lothar Meyer (1830-1895), without knowing about the work of Mendeleev, wrote about this same relationship. Mendeleev's table was published eight months before Meyer's. It was planned so carefully and in such detail that Mendeleev is given the credit for making the major contribution.

Mendeleev avoided Newlands's mistake of trying to force elements to fit into groups where they obviously did not belong. Although Mendeleev arranged the elements in the order of their atomic masses, he left an empty place in the table if no known element had the expected properties and atomic mass to fit that particular spot. He assumed that elements not yet discovered would fill these places. He even predicted what the properties of these undiscovered elements were likely to be. When predicted elements were actually discovered during his lifetime, Mendeleev's fame was assured. See Figure 16-3.

Mendeleev's table was called the periodic table. It arranged all the known elements in the order of their increasing atomic masses. The elements were placed into horizontal rows in such a way that elements with similar properties fell into the same vertical column. These similar elements were called families. For example, the halogen family has in it the chemically similar elements fluorine, chlorine, bromine, and iodine. Lithium, sodium, potassium, rubidium, and cesium make up another family called the alkali metals.

Figure 16-3

An earlier version of the periodic table. The periodic table has been evolving over the years, the newer tables being more complete than the older ones. Among missing elements in the table shown here are astatine (atomic number 85, discovered in 1940), francium (atomic number 87, discovered in 1939), and promethium (atomic number 61, discovered in 1945).

ПЕРИОДИЧЕСКАЯ СИСТЕМА ЭЛЕМЕНТОВ

ГРУППЫ ЭЛЕМЕНТОВ

ПЕРИОДЫ	РЯДЫ	I	II	III	IV	V	VI	VII	VIII			0
1	I	H 1 1,008										He 2 4,003
2	II	Li 3 6,940	Be 4 9,02	5 B 10,82	6 C 12,010	7 N 14,008	8 O 16,000	9 F 19,00				Ne 10 20,183
3	III	Na 11 22,997	Mg 12 24,32	13 Al 26,97	14 Si 28,06	15 P 30,98	16 S 32,06	17 Cl 35,457				Ar 18 39,944
4	IV	K 19 39,096	Ca 20 40,08	Sc 21 45,10	Ti 22 47,90	V 23 50,95	Cr 24 52,01	Mn 25 54,93	Fe 26 55,85	Co 27 58,94	Ni 28 58,69	
	V	29 Cu 63,57	30 Zn 65,38	31 Ga 69,72	32 Ge 72,60	33 As 74,91	34 Se 78,96	35 Br 79,916				Kr 36 83,7
5	VI	Rb 37 85,48	Sr 38 87,63	Y 39 88,92	Zr 40 91,22	Nb 41 92,91	Mo 42 95,95	Ma 43 —	Ru 44 101,7	Rh 45 102,91	Pd 46 106,7	
	VII	47 Ag 107,88	48 Cd 112,41	49 In 114,76	50 Sn 118,70	51 Sb 121,76	52 Te 127,61	53 J 126,92				Xe 54 131,3
6	VIII	Cs 55 132,91	Ba 56 137,36	La 57 * 138,92	Hf 72 178,6	Ta 73 180,88	W 74 183,92	Re 75 186,31	Os 76 190,2	Ir 77 193,1	Pt 78 195,23	
	IX	79 Au 197,2	80 Hg 200,61	81 Tl 204,39	82 Pb 207,21	83 Bi 209,00	84 Po 210	85 —				Rn 86 222
7	X	87 —	Ra 88 226,05	Ac 89 227	Th 90 232,12	Pa 91 231	U 92 238,07					

* ЛАНТАНИДЫ 58-71

Ce 58 140,13	Pr 59 140,92	Nd 60 144,27	61 —	Sm 62 150,43	Eu 63 152,0	Gd 64 156,9
Tb 65 159,2	Dy 66 162,46	Ho 67 164,94	Er 68 167,2	Tu 69 169,4	Yb 70 173,04	Cp 71 174,99

16-2 The Periodic Law

The original *periodic law,* based on Mendeleev's work, stated that the physical and chemical properties of elements were periodic functions of their atomic masses. This meant that if elements were arranged in order of increasing atomic masses, those with similar properties would show up at regular intervals, or periods.

Mendeleev found that for the lighter elements (those at the top of the chart), the chemical properties repeated at intervals of seven elements. For example, lithium, sodium, and potassium were chemically alike. Sodium was the seventh element after lithium (remember that the noble gases were not known). Potassium was the seventh element after sodium. These three elements were placed in the same vertical column, or family. Similarly, beryllium, magnesium, and calcium had similar properties, and were seven elements apart. They formed part of another family.

For the heavier elements, the scheme of every seventh element did not work. However, Mendeleev found that by having a double set of families in the same vertical column, the heavier elements could be put into their right families. In this part of the table, similar elements occurred 17 elements apart. For example, rubidium is chemically similar to lithium, sodium, and potassium. It came 17 elements after potassium. Strontium, which resembles beryllium, magnesium, and calcium, came 17 elements after calcium. In the halogen family (fluorine, chlorine, bromine, and iodine), chlorine was 7 elements after fluorine, but the next two intervals were 17 each.

Mendeleev realized that there were a few irregularities in his chart. For example, iodine has a smaller atomic mass than tellurium. However, iodine is chemically similar to the elements in the halogen family. If placed in this family on the chart, iodine *follows* tellurium. See Figure 16-4. Mendeleev placed all the elements in families with chemi-

Figure 16-4

A small section of the periodic table, showing an irregularity in the arrangement of atomic masses.
When the elements are arranged in order of increasing atomic number (51, 52, 53, 54), they will also be in order of increasing atomic mass with only a few exceptions, one of which is shown here. Iodine, which follows tellurium, has a smaller rather than a larger atomic mass. Knowing nothing about atomic numbers and believing that the elements should be usually arranged in order of increasing atomic mass, Mendeleev nevertheless placed iodine under chlorine and bromine because the three elements had similar properties.

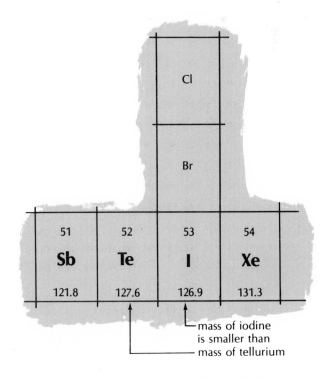

mass of iodine is smaller than mass of tellurium

Dmitri Ivanovich Mendeleev
(1834-1907)

Mendeleev was born in Siberia, but spent most of his life in St. Petersburg (now called Leningrad). He became a professor of chemistry at the Technical Institute in 1864 and at the University of St. Petersburg in 1867. Since he could not find a textbook suitable for his students' needs, he wrote one titled *The Principles of Chemistry*. It became a classic and was used for many years.

Mendeleev's chief claim to fame was the discovery of the periodic classification of the elements (1869). This classification became a cornerstone of chemistry. Mendeleev recognized the combining capacities of elements as a fundamental classifying characteristic and considered the periodic arrangement as a natural law with predictive powers. In fact, he was able to predict the properties of the yet undiscovered elements gallium, scandium, and germanium. In addition to predicting the existence of undiscovered elements, the periodic table called attention to irregularities in the values of certain atomic masses. These irregularities were eventually explained by the discovery of isotopes. During the last years of his life, Mendeleev was director of the Russian Bureau of Weights and Measures.

cally similar elements, disregarding the fact that they occasionally seemed to be out of order with respect to atomic masses. He had the courage to maintain his ideas in spite of these minor disagreements. He believed that an explanation for these irregularities would be found later. Modern theory has proved that he was right.

Today, we know that electron structure is the major factor responsible for the chemical properties of an element. Electron structure is, of course, related to atomic number, not atomic mass. Atomic number, therefore, determines the correct position of an element in the periodic table. The **modern periodic law** states: The properties of the elements are periodic functions of their atomic numbers.

16-3   Reading the Periodic Table

In the modern form of the periodic table, the elements are arranged in horizontal rows in order of increasing atomic numbers. See the periodic table at the back of the book. A modern table shows the symbol for each element, its atomic number, its atomic mass, and the horizontal period and vertical group in which it is located. Much additional information is also usually provided about each element.

Each horizontal row of elements is called a **period.** A period begins at the left of the table. The first element in each period has a single electron in its outermost, or valence, shell. Each period ends at the right of the table with a noble gas, an element with 8 electrons in its outermost shell. Helium, with 2 electrons, is an exception.

Each vertical column of elements is called a **group** or **family.** In going from top to bottom of any group, each element has one more occupied principal energy level than the element above it. Otherwise, their electron structures are quite similar. As a result, the elements in a vertical group have similar chemical properties.

Questions for Sections 16-1 through 16-3

1. All early attempts at classifying the elements according to their chemical similarities made use of what property of the elements?
2. Describe the relationship between similar elements in (a) Döbereiner's triads; (b) Newlands's octaves.
3. Why didn't Newlands's "law" work for the heavier elements?
4. What did Mendeleev's table have in common with the table developed by Newlands?
5. Briefly describe the arrangement of elements in Mendeleev's table.
6. What did the empty spaces in Mendeleev's table represent?
7. What is a family of elements?
8. State the periodic law derived from Mendeleev's work.
9. How does the modern periodic law differ from the original periodic law?
10. In his periodic table, Mendeleev placed iodine after tellurium even though tellurium has a greater mass. Why did he do this?

11. In the modern periodic table (a) what is the interval at which the chemical properties of the lighter elements repeat? (b) at what interval do the heavier elements repeat?
12. Distinguish between a period and a group in the modern periodic table.

16-4   The First Three Periods

The *first period* consists of just two elements, hydrogen and helium. In helium, two electrons complete the first energy level.

The *second period* consists of eight elements, those in which electrons are being added to the second energy level. At the end of this period, in the noble gas neon (atomic number 10), levels $n = 1$ and $n = 2$ are filled to capacity. See Figure 16-5.

Figure 16-5

A section of the periodic table, showing the first two periods. The first period is a short period consisting of only two elements, hydrogen (H) and helium (He). (The atomic number of the element is shown above its symbol. The arrangement of the electrons in the neutral atom is shown below the symbol.)

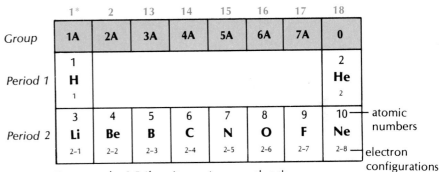

	1*	2	13	14	15	16	17	18
Group	**1A**	**2A**	**3A**	**4A**	**5A**	**6A**	**7A**	**0**
Period 1	1 **H** 1							2 **He** 2
Period 2	3 **Li** 2-1	4 **Be** 2-2	5 **B** 2-3	6 **C** 2-4	7 **N** 2-5	8 **O** 2-6	9 **F** 2-7	10 **Ne** 2-8

atomic numbers
electron configurations

For example, 2-5 (for nitrogen) means that there are 2 electrons in principal level 1 and 5 electrons in principal energy level 2.

In the *third period,* also consisting of eight elements, electrons enter the third energy level. The period ends with argon (atomic number 18), a noble gas with a complete octet in the outermost shell. See Figure 16-6.

Figure 16-6

A section of the periodic table, showing the first three periods. An element in the third period has properties similar to those of the element directly above it in the second period.

	1*	2	13	14	15	16	17	18
Group	**1A**	**2A**	**3A**	**4A**	**5A**	**6A**	**7A**	**0**
Period 1	1 **H** 1							2 **He** 2
2	3 **Li** 2-1	4 **Be** 2-2	5 **B** 2-3	6 **C** 2-4	7 **N** 2-5	8 **O** 2-6	9 **F** 2-7	10 **Ne** 2-8
3	11 **Na** 2-8-1	12 **Mg** 2-8-2	13 **Al** 2-8-3	14 **Si** 2-8-4	15 **P** 2-8-5	16 **S** 2-8-6	17 **Cl** 2-8-7	18 **Ar** 2-8-8

atomic numbers
electron arrangements

*These numbers in blue (1,2, . . . 16, 17, 18) are group numbers approved by the International Union of Pure and Applied Chemistry (IUPAC) in 1984.

16-5   Transition Elements

While reading the following discussion, refer to Figure 13-11, page 261.

The fourth period begins with electrons entering the fourth energy level. One electron is added to the 4s orbital for the potassium atom ($Z = 19$). A second electron is added to the 4s orbital (filling it) for the calcium atom. Beyond calcium, the pattern in which additional electrons are added to the atoms becomes more complicated.

Beginning with scandium and continuing for the next eight elements (from $Z = 21$ to 29), the last electron to be added to the atom *usually* enters the next-to-the-outermost energy level rather than the outermost level. This pattern is not followed by chromium (Cr, $Z = 24$) where we expect 4 electrons in the 3d orbitals but find 5 and where we expect 2 electrons in the 4s orbital and find only 1. Chromium is an exception because having each of its 3d orbitals and its 4s orbital exactly half filled is a more stable arrangement than having 4 electrons occupying the 3d orbitals and 2 electrons occupying the 4s orbital. When the arrangement of electrons in an atom breaks a pattern, one usually finds half-filled orbitals in the atom, an arrangement that gives the atom greater stability. Because differences in electronic arrangements in a next-to-outermost energy level are not as significant as differences in an outermost energy level, the elements from atomic numbers 21 to 29 (scandium to copper) are more similar to each other in their properties than are the other elements in Period 4.

We now turn our attention to the definition of a transition element. There is some disagreement among chemists concerning which elements should be called transition elements. Here we use the definition ap-

Figure 16-7

The transition elements of the fourth period, atomic numbers 21 to 29, and the element with atomic number 30, Zn, do not resemble any of the elements of smaller atomic number and should not be placed under any of these elements. To fit them into the table, the table must first be broken. The location of the Period 4 transition elements is shown in the next figure.

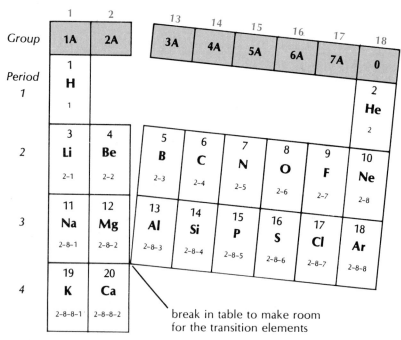

break in table to make room for the transition elements

proved by the International Union of Pure and Applied Chemistry (IUPAC). A **transition element** is an element whose atom has an incomplete *d* subshell or which gives rise to a cation or cations with incomplete *d* subshells. The nine elements in Period 4 having atomic numbers 21 to 29 fit that definition.

These nine transition elements in Period 4 along with zinc (Zn, Z = 30), have properties unlike any of the elements in earlier rows (periods) of the table. Therefore, none of these elements can be placed under any of the elements in the earlier periods since only elements with similar properties go in the columns established by the elements in Periods 2 and 3. To enter these ten elements, the table must be broken between

Figure 16-8

The transition elements are fitted between the two pieces of the table shown in Figure 16-7.

	1	2											13	14	15	16	17	18
	1A	2A											3A	4A	5A	6A	7A	0
Period 1	1 H 1																	2 He 2
2	3 Li 2-1	4 Be 2-2											5 B 2-3	6 C 2-4	7 N 2-5	8 O 2-6	9 F 2-7	10 Ne 2-8
3	11 Na 2-8-1	12 Mg 2-8-2	3 3B	4 4B	5 5B	6 6B	7 7B	8	9 8B	10	11 1B	12 2B	13 Al 2-8-3	14 Si 2-8-4	15 P 2-8-5	16 S 2-8-6	17 Cl 2-8-7	18 Ar 2-8-8
4	19 K 2-8-8-1	20 Ca 2-8-8-2	21 Sc 2-8-9-2	22 Ti 2-8-10-2	23 V 2-8-11-2	24 Cr 2-8-13-1	25 Mn 2-8-13-2	26 Fe 2-8-14-2	27 Co 2-8-15-2	28 Ni 2-8-16-2	29 Cu 2-8-18-1	30 Zn 2-8-18-2						

—————Transition Elements—————

Figure 16-9

The transition elements of Period 4 have 1 or 2 electrons in their outermost energy level, but the number of electrons in the next-to-outermost energy level shows an almost steady increase from left to right. This contrasts with the remaining seven elements in the period, atomic numbers 30 to 36. For these seven elements, the number of electrons in the outermost shell increases from left to right.

	1	2											13	14	15	16	17	18
Group	1A	2A											3A	4A	5A	6A	7A	0
Period 1	1 H 1																	2 He 2
2	3 Li 2-1	4 Be 2-2											5 B 2-3	6 C 2-4	7 N 2-5	8 O 2-6	9 F 2-7	10 Ne 2-8
3	11 Na 2-8-1	12 Mg 2-8-2	3 3B	4 4B	5 5B	6 6B	7 7B	8	9 8B	10	11 1B	12 2B	13 Al 2-8-3	14 Si 2-8-4	15 P 2-8-5	16 S 2-8-6	17 Cl 2-8-7	18 Ar 2-8-8
4	19 K 2-8-8-1	20 Ca 2-8-8-2	21 Sc 2-8-9-2	22 Ti 2-8-10-2	23 V 2-8-11-2	24 Cr 2-8-13-1	25 Mn 2-8-13-2	26 Fe 2-8-14-2	27 Co 2-8-15-2	28 Ni 2-8-16-2	29 Cu 2-8-18-1	30 Zn 2-8-18-2	31 Ga 2-8-18-3	32 Ge 2-8-18-4	33 As 2-8-18-5	34 Se 2-8-18-6	35 Br 2-8-18-7	36 Kr 2-8-18-8

—————Transition Elements—————

Groups 2A and 3A (Groups 2 and 13), and the ten elements placed between these two groups. See Figures 16-7 and 16-8.

After zinc, the next element in Period 4 is gallium (Ga, $Z = 30$). For gallium and the elements in Period 4 beyond gallium, electrons are added to the fourth energy level, the valence shell. The chemical properties of gallium are similar to those of aluminum and boron. Therefore, gallium is put under aluminum and boron. Each of the remaining five elements in Period 4 ($Z = 32$ to 36) is placed under the element of Period 3 to which it is chemically similar. See Figure 16-9.

16-6 The Fifth Period

The *fifth period* is the same length as the fourth. It begins with rubidium (Rb, $Z = 37$). With a single valence electron in the fifth energy level, rubidium is similar to potassium, the first element in the fourth period. Rubidium is, therefore, placed under potassium in the first column. The next element is strontium (Sr, $Z = 38$). Strontium is placed under calcium since strontium is chemically similar to calcium. Next, come nine transition elements. These are placed under the nine transition elements of the fourth period. As was true for the fourth period transition elements, the fifth period transition elements, except for palladium, Pd, have only one or two valence electrons. Also, for practically all of these elements, electrons enter the shell just below the valence shell. These features make the transition elements of both periods similar. The similarity is especially great for elements in the same vertical group.

The next element after silver is cadmium (Cd, $Z = 48$). It falls under zinc. The remaining six elements in Period 5, indium to xenon, fall under elements in Period 4 to which they are chemically similar. The

Figure 16-10

The fifth period of the periodic table.
Nine transition elements are placed below the nine transition elements of the fourth period. For most of the transition elements of both periods, electrons enter the shell just below the valence shell rather than the valence shell itself. The valence shells have just one or two electrons with the exception of Pd. The similarity of the arrangement of electrons in the outer shell make these elements all similar. The similarity is especially striking for pairs of elements, such as scandium and yttrium, that form a vertical group.

	1	2											13	14	15	16	17	18
Group	1A	2A											3A	4A	5A	6A	7A	0
Period 1	1 H 1																	2 He 2
2	3 Li 2–1	4 Be 2–2											5 B 2–3	6 C 2–4	7 N 2–5	8 O 2–6	9 F 2–7	10 Ne 2–8
3	11 Na 2–8–1	12 Mg 2–8–2	3 3B	4 4B	5 5B	6 6B	7 7B	8	9 8B	10	11 1B	12 2B	13 Al 2–8–3	14 Si 2–8–4	15 P 2–8–5	16 S 2–8–6	17 Cl 2–8–7	18 Ar 2–8–8
4	19 K 2–8–8–1	20 Ca 2–8–8–2	21 Sc 2–8–9–2	22 Ti 2–8–10–2	23 V 2–8–11–2	24 Cr 2–8–13–1	25 Mn 2–8–13–2	26 Fe 2–8–14–2	27 Co 2–8–15–2	28 Ni 2–8–16–2	29 Cu 2–8–18–1	30 Zn 2–8–18–2	31 Ga 2–8–18–3	32 Ge 2–8–18–4	33 As 2–8–18–5	34 Se 2–8–18–6	35 Br 2–8–18–7	36 Kr 2–8–18–8
5	37 Rb 2–8–18–8–1	38 Sr 2–8–18–8–2	39 Y 2–8–18–9–2	40 Zr 2–8–18–10–2	41 Nb 2–8–18–12–1	42 Mo 2–8–18–13–1	43 Te 2–8–18–14–1	44 Ru 2–8–18–15–1	45 Rh 2–8–18–16–1	46 Pd 2–8–18–18	47 Ag 2–8–18–18–1	48 Cd 2–8–18–18–2	49 In 2–8–18–18–3	50 Sn 2–8–18–18–4	51 Sb 2–8–18–18–5	52 Te 2–8–18–18–6	53 I 2–8–18–18–7	54 Xe 2–8–18–18–8

Transition Elements (spanning groups 3B–2B)

electrons in these remaining six elements enter the valence shell rather than the shell below it. See figure 16-10.

16-7 The Sixth Period

The *sixth period* begins with cesium (Cs, $Z = 55$). It has one valence electron in the sixth energy level. Chemically similar to rubidium (Rb), cesium is placed under rubidium. The next element, barium (Ba, $Z = 56$) has two valence electrons. Its electron structure and chemical properties match those of strontium. It is, therefore, placed below strontium. The next is lanthanum (La, $Z = 57$). The fourteen elements following lanthanum are called the lanthanoid series. The elements in the lanthanoid series add electrons in a manner not encountered in any of the elements that precede them. The valence shell in these atoms is the sixth energy level. But as atomic number increases, the additional electrons in the atoms of these elements *usually* enter a shell *two* levels below the valence shell. Because a maximum of 14 electrons can enter the seven *f* orbitals, there are a total of 14 lanthanoids. The lanthanoids are transition elements. However, because of the practical difficulty of having a periodic table that is too long, lanthanum and the elements in the lanthanoid series are put in a row below the main section of the periodic table. See Figure 16-11. The lanthanoids are similar not only in the arrangement of electrons in their valence shell but also in the shell below the valence shell. This similarity in electron structure in the two outer energy levels makes the properties of the lanthanoids very similar. It is often hard to tell one lanthanoid from another or to separate a mixture of them.

In addition to the lanthanoids, the sixth period contains eight other transition elements that follow immediately after the lanthanoids. These eight elements are placed in the main body of the table. The first of these is hafnium (Hf, $Z = 72$) and the last is gold (Au, $Z = 79$). After gold is mercury, which goes under cadmium. After mercury come six

	Group 1 / 1A	2 / 2A	3 / 3B	4 / 4B	5 / 5B	6 / 6B	7 / 7B	8	9 / 8B	10	11 / 1B	12 / 2B	13 / 3A	14 / 4A	15 / 5A	16 / 6A	17 / 7A	18 / 0
Period 1	1 H																	2 He
Period 2	3 Li 2-1	4 Be 2-2											5 B 2-3	6 C 2-4	7 N 2-5	8 O 2-6	9 F 2-7	10 Ne 2-8
Period 3	11 Na 2-8-1	12 Mg 2-8-2											13 Al 2-8-3	14 Si 2-8-4	15 P 2-8-5	16 S 2-8-6	17 Cl 2-8-7	18 Ar 2-8-8
Period 4	19 K 2-8-8-1	20 Ca 2-8-8-2	21 Sc 2-8-9-2	22 Ti 2-8-10-2	23 V 2-8-11-2	24 Cr 2-8-13-1	25 Mn 2-8-13-2	26 Fe 2-8-14-2	27 Co 2-8-15-2	28 Ni 2-8-16-2	29 Cu 2-8-18-1	30 Zn 2-8-18-2	31 Ga 2-8-18-3	32 Ge 2-8-18-4	33 As 2-8-18-5	34 Se 2-8-18-6	35 Br 2-8-18-7	36 Kr 2-8-18-8
Period 5	37 Rb 2-8-18-8-1	38 Sr 2-8-18-8-2	39 Y 2-8-18-9-2	40 Zr 2-8-18-10-2	41 Nb 2-8-18-12-1	42 Mo 2-8-18-13-1	43 Te 2-8-18-14-1	44 Ru 2-8-18-15-1	45 Rh 2-8-18-16-1	46 Pd 2-8-18-18	47 Ag 2-8-18-18-1	48 Cd 2-8-18-18-2	49 In 2-8-18-18-3	50 Sn 2-8-18-18-4	51 Sb 2-8-18-18-5	52 Te 2-8-18-18-6	53 I 2-8-18-18-7	54 Xe 2-8-18-18-8
Period 6	55 Cs -18-8-1	56 Ba -18-8-2	*	72 Hf -32-10-2	73 Ta -32-11-2	74 W -32-12-2	75 Re -32-13-2	76 Os -32-14-2	77 Ir -32-15-2	78 Pt -32-17-1	79 Au -32-18-1	80 Hg -32-18-2	81 Tl -32-18-3	82 Pb -32-18-4	83 Bi -32-18-5	84 Po -32-18-6	85 At -32-18-7	86 Rn -32-18-8

Transition Elements (groups 3–12).

— Lanthanoid series —

*	57 La -18-9-2	58 Ce -20-8-2	59 Pr -21-8-2	60 Nd -22-8-2	61 Pm -23-8-2	62 Sm -24-8-2	63 Eu -25-8-2	64 Gd -25-9-2	65 Tb -27-8-2	66 Dy -28-8-2	67 Ho -29-8-2	68 Er -30-8-2	69 Tm -31-8-2	70 Yb -32-8-2	71 Lu -32-9-2

Figure 16-11

The sixth period is made up of 32 elements. It is the longest period. Fourteen of the transition elements of the sixth period are known as the lanthanoid series. The lanthanoids are put below the main body of the table. (In Period 6, electrons in the first two energy levels are not shown.)

elements that complete the sixth period, making a total of 32 elements in the sixth period. These last six elements have properties similar to elements in earlier periods and are placed under the elements to which they are chemically similar.

16-8 The Seventh Period

In the *seventh period*, the valence shell is the seventh energy level. After the first two elements, francium and radium, comes actinium (Ac, Z = 89). Following actinium are 14 elements that are called the actinoid series. All 14 of these elements have 2 electrons in their outermost energy level and either 8, 9, or 10 electrons in their next-to-outermost energy level. In the level below that, the fifth level, we find the primary difference between the actinoids where electrons gradually fill the *f* orbitals of the fifth level. See the inside back cover for a complete periodic table.

The actinoids go below the lanthanoids outside the main body of the table. They have unstable nuclei and are radioactive. In the actinoid series, we reach the last of the elements that occur in nature in any large amount. This element is uranium (U, $Z = 92$). All elements beyond uranium, with the exception of plutonium (Pu, $Z = 94$), are not found in nature. They are unstable and are made in the laboratory. Their atoms spontaneously give off alpha or beta particles and gamma radiation. The instability of elements generally increases as the atomic number increases. For example, a sample of the isotope of element 105 lasts for only a few seconds. Because of the instability of elements with large atomic numbers, it seems unlikely that Period 7 will ever be completed. If new elements can be made with larger atomic numbers, these new elements may not exist long enough to be identified.

Questions for Sections 16-7 and 16-8

21. Why are elements in the lanthanoid series considered to be transition elements?
22. How do transition elements of the lanthanoid series differ from the other transition elements of Period 6?
23. Explain why all the elements of the lanthanoid series exhibit very similar chemical properties.
24. Why is the lanthanoid series of elements placed outside the main body of the periodic table?
25. What do elements of the actinoid series have in common with those in the lanthanoid series?
26. In what respect are most elements in the actinoid series different from all the other elements in the periodic table?

16-9 General Survey of Periodicity in Properties

A study of the periodic table shows certain regularities in the properties of the elements. We have referred to the similarity in properties of elements in the same vertical column. This is the result of their having the same number of valence electrons. An example of these groups is the alkali metal family. The **alkali metals** are all the elements in Group 1A except for hydrogen. See Figure 16-12. Another example of a family is the Group 2A elements, known as the **alkaline earth metals.** The Group 7A elements are the **halogen family.** Group 0 are the **noble gases.** See Figure 16-13. Because of the presence of these families in the vertical "A" groups, similarities in properties recur at regular intervals as we go from left to right in successive periods. Thus, starting with lithium and proceeding to the right in Period 2, active metallic elements are followed by less active ones. The less active metals are followed by increasingly nonmetallic elements. The period ends with a noble gas. Continuing with sodium in the next period, we pass through a similar succession of properties. Thus, in the periodic table, elements with similar properties occur at regular intervals.

Figure 16-12

The alkali metals are all the elements of Group 1A except for hydrogen.

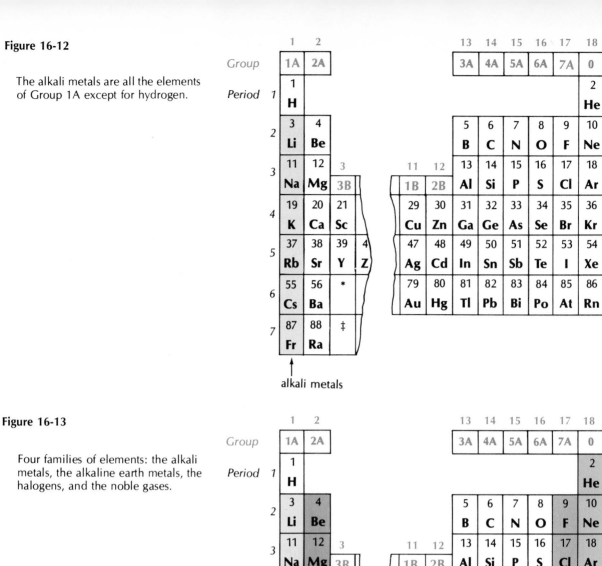

alkali metals

Figure 16-13

Four families of elements: the alkali metals, the alkaline earth metals, the halogens, and the noble gases.

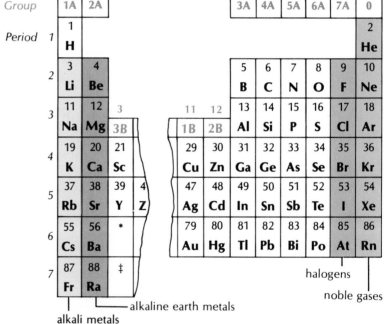

halogens

noble gases

alkaline earth metals

alkali metals

16-10   Covalent Atomic Radius

The **covalent atomic radius** is one-half the measured distance from the nucleus of one atom to that of the next atom in the *solid phase* of an

Figure 16-14

Atomic Radii, Periods 1, 2, and 3

Period 1	H 0.37							He 0.50
Period 2	Li 1.52	Be 1.11	B 0.88	C 0.77	N 0.70	O 0.66	F 0.64	Ne 0.70
Period 3	Na 1.86	Mg 1.60	Al 1.43	Si 1.17	P 1.10	S 1.04	Cl 0.99	Ar 0.94

Note: The numbers in this table are in angstrom units. 1 angstrom = 10^{-10} meter

element. Figure 16-14 gives atomic radii for the elements in the first three periods. As can be seen from the figure, the covalent atomic radius is found to be a periodic property of the elements. Within any one period, the covalent atomic radius decreases as the atomic number increases. (Helium in Period 1 and neon in Period 2 are exceptions to this rule.) This is the result of an increasing positive charge on the nucleus. Nuclei with large positive charges have an increased attraction for the outer electrons. This stronger attraction pulls the outer electrons more tightly around the nucleus. The increased attraction *more than offsets* the repulsion between the added electron and the other electrons in the atom. As a result, the covalent atomic radius is reduced. This pattern is repeated in each period.

The covalent atomic radii increase from top to bottom of any given family of elements. For any such group, the atoms of each successive element have a greater number of occupied energy levels. In other words, elements at the bottom of a column have a greater number of occupied shells. This puts valence electrons in these elements farther from the nucleus. The result is an increase in covalent atomic radius as the atomic number increases within a family. (The increased nuclear charge tends to *decrease* the covalent atomic radius, but this has much less of an effect than the increased number of energy levels occupied by electrons.)

16-11   Ionic Radii

The radius of an *ion* may be larger or smaller than its covalent atomic radius, depending upon the chemical nature of the element. Metals lose electrons when forming ions. Nonmetals gain electrons. Therefore, the ionic radii of metals are smaller than their covalent atomic radii. The ionic radii of nonmetals are larger. (Both atomic and ionic radii are usually measured in angstrom units. **One angstrom** (Å) is equal to 1×10^{-10} meter.) As you move from left to right across a period, ionic radii show decreasing values for the positive ions. These ions usually consist of only the kernel of the atom. A sudden increase in the value of the ionic radius is found where an element forms a negative ion. See Figure 16-15. The radii of negative ions to the right of the first negative ion in a period are smaller because of the effect of the increased nuclear

Figure 16-15

Ionic radii, Periods 2 and 3. In Period 2, note the large increase in ionic radius from the positive nitrogen ion to the negative oxygen ion. A similar large jump occurs in Period 3 from the positive phosphorus ion to the negative sulfur ion.

	H							**He**
								——
Period 2	Li^{1+} 0.68	Be^{2+} 0.35	B^{3+} 0.23	C^{4+} 0.16	N^{5+} 0.13	O^{2-} 1.40	F^{1-} 1.33	**Ne** ——
Period 3	Na^{1+} 0.97	Mg^{2+} 0.66	Al^{3+} 0.51	Se^{4+} 0.42	P^{5+} 0.35	S^{2-} 1.84	Cl^{1-} 1.81	**Ar** ——

Note: The numbers in this table are in angstrom units. 1 angstrom = 10^{-10} meter

charge. In the vertical columns, ionic radii increase in going from top to bottom in any given family. This increase is due to the increase in the number of occupied energy levels that appear in the ions of higher atomic number.

Questions for Sections 16-9 through 16-11

27. How do the chemical characteristics of the elements in a period change as you move from left to right across the periodic table?
28. Define the atomic radius of an element.
29. How does atomic radius change as you move from left to right (atomic number increases) across a given period of the periodic table?
30. Describe the relationship between atomic radius and nuclear charge.
31. How does atomic radius change as you move from top to bottom of any given family of elements?
32. Describe the relationship between atomic radius and number of occupied energy levels.
33. Why are ionic radii of metallic elements smaller than the atomic radii of the same elements?
34. Give the name and numerical value of the unit generally used to measure atomic and ionic radii.
35. What is the general trend displayed by the radii of positive ions as you move from left to right across a period of the periodic table?
36. As you study ionic radii from left to right across a period, what does a sudden increase in the size of an ionic radius indicate?

16-12   Ionization Energy and Boiling Points

The ionization energy or ionization potential of an element is the energy required to remove the most loosely held electron from a neutral atom of the element when a sample of the element is in the gaseous phase. (This energy is also called the first ionization energy. See Section 14-5.) The ionization energy is another periodic property of the elements, as shown in Figure 16-16. Look at the portion of the graph for the elements in the second and third periods (Li to Ne, and Na to Ar). For both periods, the general trend is upward—toward an increase in ionization energy with an increase in atomic number. (The exceptions to the general trend are B and O in Period 2 and Al and S in Period 3.)

There are chiefly two reasons why, within a period, the ionization energy tends to increase as the atomic number increases. The first reason has to do with the nuclear charge. As you go across a period from left to right, the number of protons in the nucleus of each element increases by one. These positively charged particles attract the negatively charged electrons. As the number of protons increases, the force of attraction between the nucleus and the electrons increases. More energy is needed to overcome this force of attraction. Hence, the ionization energy increases.

The second reason why ionization energy tends to increase as you proceed across a period from left to right has to do with the size of the atoms. *Within a period,* atoms get smaller as the atomic number increases. (See again the chart of atomic radii in Figure 16-14.)

If an atom is smaller, it means that the electrons in the atom are closer to the nucleus. At a closer distance, there is more of an attractive force between the protons in the nucleus and the electrons. More energy will be required to force the most loosely held electron out of the atom against this force.

As you proceed down the periodic table within a family, the trend is toward a decrease in ionization energy rather than an increase. See, for example, in Figure 16-16 that the ionization energy for argon (the third noble gas) is less than that for neon (the second noble gas), which is less than that for helium (the first noble gas). Also, look at the positions of these elements in Figure 16-13.

Since atomic numbers are increasing as you proceed down the column from helium to neon to argon, you might expect the increased nuclear

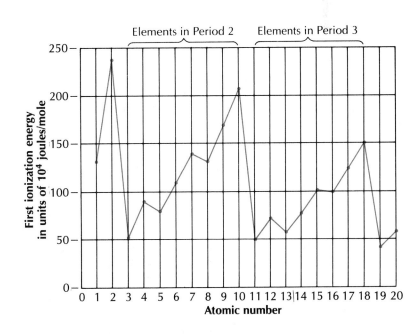

Figure 16-16

The first ionization energies of the first 20 elements plotted against the atomic numbers of these elements. Notice that the pattern produced by the elements in Period 2 is repeated by the elements in Period 3.

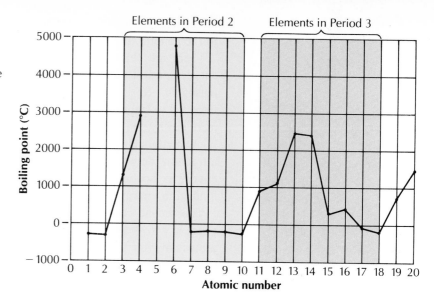

Figure 16-17
The boiling points of the first twenty elements. Note the similarity in the graph for the elements in Periods 2 and 3, where the boiling points of the last four elements in each period are low compared to those of the first four elements. (No boiling point is shown for boron, atomic number 5, because boron sublimes at 2550°C.)

charge to result in increased ionization energies. That this is not the case is the result of another factor that counteracts and predominates over the increase in nuclear charge. That factor is the size of the atoms. While atoms generally get smaller from left to right within a period, they get larger from top to bottom within a column. As described in Section 16-10, going from top to bottom within a column, the atoms of elements get larger because with each new period a new energy level is added. The electrons in that energy level are farther from the nucleus, on average, than the electrons in the outermost energy level of the element directly above. Thus, as you go down a column, you come across two opposing effects. You find that the positive charge in the nucleus of each element is increasing (tending to make ionization energies increase) but so is the size of the atom increasing (tending to have the opposite effect). Because the size of the atom has the greater effect, ionization energies decrease from top to bottom within a column.

See the graph in Figure 16-17 for the periodic trend in the boiling points of the elements in the second and third periods.

16-13   Metals

Most of the elements are metals. A line drawn to the left of boron and continuing downward in a steplike fashion to the left of silicon, arsenic, tellurium, and astatine, would separate the elements that are essentially metals from all the others (to the right of the line). The lanthanoids and the actinoids, at the bottom of the table, are also metals. About 80 of the elements are metals. See Figure 16-18.

The general properties of the metals have been discussed in earlier chapters. Metals have relatively low ionization energies. Therefore, they tend to lose electrons in chemical change, forming positive ions.

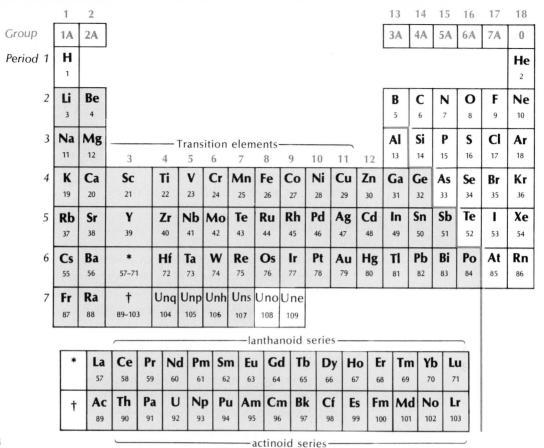

Figure 16-18

Most elements are metals, shown to the left of the blue line.

They have high heat and electrical conductivity, show high metallic luster, and are malleable and ductile. All these properties are explained in terms of the easily detachable electrons in metallic atoms. Except for mercury, metals are solids at room temperature.

The degree of reactivity of a metal is mainly the result of two factors. The first is the amount of positive charge in the nucleus. The second is the number of valence electrons. When going from left to right in a period, the positive charge in the nucleus increases. Thus, the elements to the left have a weaker hold on their valence electrons than those on the right and are more metallic. Also, metals whose atoms have fewer valence electrons to lose are more reactive. Thus, sodium is a more active metal than magnesium. Aluminum, with a higher nuclear charge and 3 electrons to lose from each atom, is less active than magnesium and begins to acquire nonmetallic properties. The rest of the elements in the third period are nonmetals. Their decreasing atomic size and increasing nuclear charge prevent them from losing electrons in chemical change. They are more apt to gain electrons.

Nuclear charge and atomic size also combine to affect the properties of elements within a family. The alkali metal family, Group 1A, is made up of the most active metals. Because of their large size and relatively small nuclear charge, atoms of these elements easily lose their single valence electrons. As we go from top to bottom in the family, from lithium to francium, the nuclear charge becomes much larger. Atoms with large nuclear charges tend to have a greater attraction for valence electrons. However, the addition of a new shell in each successive element increases the atomic size. The *net effect* is a *reduction* in the attraction for valence electrons. In other words, the chemical activity of the metals in Group 1A *increases* with increasing atomic number. For the same reasons, the activities of the metals in Group 2A also increases with increasing atomic number. In general, for any family of elements, the tendency to lose electrons—that is, the metallic character of the elements—increases as you move down the column from lighter to heavier members of the family.

16-14 Nonmetals

Nonmetals consist of atoms that hold their valence electrons by strong nuclear attractions. They have high ionization energies and high electronegativities. Nonmetallic properties are strongest in the elements in the upper right corner of the periodic table. Nonmetals generally gain electrons when combining with metals or share electrons in combination with other elements. They tend to be brittle, have low thermal and electrical conductivities, and lack the luster that is characteristic of metals. At room temperature, nonmetals are gases, molecular solids, or network solids. The exception is bromine, a reddish-brown, volatile liquid. (See photo, page 378.)

The relatively few nonmetals are grouped in the upper right corner of the periodic table. There are only about 20 of them.

In the periodic table, going from left to right, nonmetallic character begins to appear about halfway across a period and becomes stronger to the right. Because of relatively high nuclear charges and small atomic sizes, members of the halogen family, Group 7A, are the most active nonmetals. They gain electrons very readily in chemical change. In fact, fluorine, the first member in the family, is the most active nonmetallic element.

Within a family, the nonmetallic character of the elements decreases (metallic character increases) as you move from top to bottom. This is because of the decreasing attraction for valence electrons. Therefore, in Group 6A the elements undergo gradual change from the very active nonmetal oxygen to the metallic element polonium. Look back at Figure 16-13. The nitrogen family, Group 5A, consists of the nonmetals nitrogen and phosphorus at the top, the metalloid arsenic, and then antimony and bismuth, in order of increasing metallic character.

16-15 Metalloids

As we proceed across periods or down vertical groups, there seems to be a gradual change in the metallic or nonmetallic character of the elements. There is no sharp dividing line between metals and nonmetals. The **metalloids** are elements with borderline behavior. They have some properties characteristic of metals and other properties characteristic of nonmetals. Examples of metalloids are boron, silicon, arsenic, and tellurium.

37. For the elements in the second period of the periodic table, starting with lithium and ending with neon, describe how the ionization energies change.
38. A unit that may be used to state ionization energies is the joule per mole. For example, the ionization energy of lithium may be stated as 313×10^4 joules per mole. Explain what "joules per mole" means as used here.
39. In terms of chemical reactivity, what is a metal?
40. What is an "active" metal?
41. What two factors determine the degree of reactivity of a metal?
42. What is the name of the most chemically active metal? Where is it located in the modern periodic table?
43. Why does metallic character of the elements in a period decrease as you go from left to right across the period?
44. Why does metallic character of the elements in a family increase as you move from top to bottom of the periodic table?
45. Define nonmetal in terms of chemical reactivity.
46. What is an "active" nonmetal?
47. What is the name of the most active nonmetal? Where is it located in the modern periodic table?
48. What is a metalloid?

CHAPTER SUMMARY

1. Most attempts at classifying the elements have involved grouping those elements having similar chemical properties. The best known attempts at classification include Döbereiner's triads, Newlands's octaves, and Mendeleev's periodic table.
2. All early classifications listed the elements in the order of their increasing atomic masses. The modern periodic table lists the elements in the order of their increasing atomic numbers.
3. The modern periodic law states that the chemical properties of the elements are a periodic function of their atomic numbers.
4. Each horizontal row of the periodic table is called a period. The number of a period indicates the number of occupied energy levels in the atoms of each element in that period.
5. Each vertical column of the periodic table is called a group. The elements in groups 1, 2, and 13 to 18 have similar valence electron configurations, and thus have similar chemical properties.
6. A transition element is an element whose atom has an incomplete d subshell or which gives rise to a cation or cations with incomplete d subshells. The transition elements are in groups 3 to 11.
7. The atomic radius of an element is one-half the measured distance from the nucleus of one atom to that of the next atom in the solid phase of the element.
8. Metals form ions by losing electrons. Thus, their ionic radii are smaller than their atomic radii. The reverse situation is true for nonmetals.

9. Ionization energy is a periodic property of the elements. Within a period, first ionization energy tends to increase when moving from left to right. Within a family, first ionization energy tends to decrease when proceeding from top to bottom.

10. The most active metals are situated at the extreme left side of the periodic table. The most active nonmetals are found toward the right side of the table. The most unreactive elements, the noble gases, are a family on the extreme right side of the table.

TERMS YOU SHOULD KNOW

modern periodic law	transition element	halogens
period	alkali metals	atomic radius
group	alkaline earth metals	angstrom
family		metalloid

REVIEW QUESTIONS

Section

16-1   **1.** How did Mendeleev successfully deal with the problem that had made Newlands's law of octaves ineffective for the heavier elements?

16-2   **2.** Why did Mendeleev think of the heavier elements as being members of a "second family" within a vertical group?

3. When arranging the elements in his periodic table, which consideration did Mendeleev think to be more important—following the order of atomic masses exactly, or placing an element in a vertical column with elements of similar properties? Find two examples in the periodic table that support your answer.

4. What is the major factor responsible for the chemical properties of an element?

16-3   **5.** In the modern periodic table, chemical properties of the lighter elements repeat at an interval of 8 elements. In Mendeleev's table this same interval was only 7 elements. Explain why this difference existed.

6. Why do elements in a vertical group have similar chemical properties?

16-4   **7.** Why does Period 1 contain only two elements? What are these elements?

Use your knowledge of the orbital model of the atom and the rules for determining electron configurations to answer questions 8-11.

16-5   **8.** Explain why electrons enter the principal energy level *below* the valence shell in elements with atomic numbers 21-30.

9. In elements with atomic numbers 21-30, what *principal energy level* do additional electrons enter? What *sublevel* do they enter?

10. Starting with element number 31, what energy level do additional electrons enter in the remaining Period 4 elements?

16-6   **11.** In the Period 5 transition elements, what principle energy level and sublevel do additional electrons enter?

12. What Period 4 transition element does silver (Ag) most closely resemble?

13. Why are the chemical similarities of the elements in the lanthanide series greater than the similarities of the transition elements in Periods 5 and 6?

14. What principal energy level and sublevel do electrons enter in the elements of the lanthanide series?

15. What are unstable nuclei?

16. Why is it unlikely that Period 7 will ever be completed?

17. Why do atomic radii increase as you move from top to bottom of a chemical family?

18. Which factor has the greatest influence on atomic radius—nuclear charge or the number of occupied energy levels?

19. How would you answer this question: "Which are larger, atomic radii or ionic radii?"

20. In each of the following pairs of atoms or ions, select the one that you think should have the larger radius and explain the reasons for your choice: (a) O and S (b) O and F (c) O^{2-} and Cl^- (d) Cl and Cl^- (e) Na^+ and F^-

21. In terms of chemical reactivity, differentiate between metals, non-metals, and metalloids.

For 22-25, base your answers on the partial periodic table below.

22. Which element is least likely to form a compound?

23. Which two elements would form the most ionic compound?

24. Which element would have the largest ionic radius?

25. Which element is most likely to be a metalloid?

	1A	2A	3A	4A	5A	6A	7A	0
2	Li							
3		Mg		Si	P	S		Ar
4			Ga				Br	

FOR FURTHER THOUGHT

1. Which of the following was the effect on Mendeleev's periodic table when the existence of isotopes was discovered? Support your answer.
(a) The table had to be greatly revised.
(b) The apparent discrepancies in the table were explained.
(c) The missing elements were discovered and the gaps filled.

2. You wish to determine the covalent atomic radius of an element. One possibly useful piece of information would be the number of atoms occupying a unit volume of the solid element. What physical quantities would enable you to calculate this number?

3. Suppose that the most loosely held electron has already been removed from an atom of an element. How would you expect the energy required to remove the second most loosely held electron (called the *second ionization energy*) to compare with the amount of energy required to remove the first electron? Explain.

Cumulative Review

3-7   **1.** The density of gold is 19.3 g/cm³ and the density of silver is 10.5 g cm³. Which occupies a greater volume, 100 g of gold or 150 g of silver, and by how much?

4-9   **2.** The temperature of 500 g of water changed from 10°C to 40°C. How many calories of heat were absorbed?

6-3   **3.** A mass of hydrogen under a pressure of 700 mm Hg has a volume of 1.00 L. At constant temperature, what will be its volume at standard pressure?

6-5   **4.** A container has 600 mL of air in it at 200°C. Assuming constant pressure, what volume will the air occupy at 25°C?

7-7   **5.** When 2.00 kg of water vapor is condensed to liquid water at 100°C and 1.00 atm, how much heat, in calories, is released?

7-10   **6.** How much heat, in joules, is needed to melt 10.0 g of ice at 0°C?

7-10   **7.** Write formulas for each of the following: (a) aluminum nitrate (b) sodium carbonate (c) calcium phosphate (d) tin(IV) chloride.

8-5   **8.** For each of the following, write two chemical names, one using a prefix and the other using the Stock system: (a) NO (b) CO_2 (c) P_2O_3.

8-7   **9.** Write the names of the following acids: (a) H_2S (b) $HClO$ (c) $HClO_4$.

8-10   **10.** Write formulas for the following acids: (a) chlorous acid (b) hydrofluoric acid (c) sulfurous acid.

       11. (a) What is the numerical value of Avogadro's number? (b) How is this number related to the mole? (c) How is it related to the gram-atom?

9-6   **12.** Find the number of moles in a 408-gram sample of $KHSO_4$.

9-8   **13.** What is the percentage of oxygen in $KHSO_4$?

9-9   **14.** The sugar fructose contains 40.0% C, 6.67% H, and 53.3% O. Its molecular mass is 180 u. (a) What is its empirical formula? (b) What is its molecular formula?

10-3   **15.** Balance the following equations: (a) $CH_4 + O_2 \rightarrow CO_2 + H_2O$ (b) $Fe_2O_3 + H_2 \rightarrow Fe_3O_4 + H_2O$ (c) $MnO_2 + HCl \rightarrow MnCl_2 + H_2O + Cl_2$

10-5   **16.** When nitric acid is exposed to light, it decomposes to produce nitrogen dioxide, oxygen, and water. Write the balanced equation for this reaction.

10-8   **17.** Write balanced formula equations for the following. Next to each equation, write the category of the reaction.
       (a) potassium chlorate $\rightarrow$ potassium chloride + oxygen
       (b) iron + oxygen $\rightarrow$ ferric oxide
       (c) calcium nitrate + sulfuric acid $\rightarrow$ calcium sulfate + nitric acid
       (d) aluminum + copper(II) nitrate $\rightarrow$ aluminum nitrate + copper

10-11 **18.** Omitting spectator ions, write balanced ionic equations for:
       (a) $AgNO_3(aq) + MgCl_2(aq) \rightarrow Mg(NO_3)_2(aq) + AgCl(s)$
       (b) $CuSO_4(aq) + Fe(s) \rightarrow Cu(s) + FeSO_4(aq)$

11-2   **19.** Calcium metal reacts with water as follows:
       $Ca + 2H_2O \rightarrow Ca(OH)_2 + H_2$
       What mass of water reacts completely with 80.0 g of calcium?

11-3   **20.** Explain how the idea of the molar volume of a gas is derived from Avogadro's hypothesis. What is the numerical value of the molar volume?

Cumulative Review

Section

21. The standard density of a gas is 0.714 g/L. (a) What is its molecular mass? (b) The gas is a compound made up of 75.0% C and 25.0% H. What is molecular formula?

11-4
22. How many liters of oxygen are required to burn completely 5.0 L of hydrogen sulfide gas, assuming both volumes are measured at the same temperature and pressure? The products are H_2O and SO_2.

23. Aluminum reacts with hydrochloric acid as follows:

11-5
$$2Al(s) + 6HCl(aq) \rightarrow 2AlCl_3(aq) + 3H_2(g)$$
What mass of aluminum will react with excess acid to produce 200 mL hydrogen at STP?

12-2
24. Explain how Dalton's atomic theory accounts for the law of definite proportions.

12-10
25. According to the Rutherford model of the atom, (a) Where is the chief concentration of the mass of the atom? (b) What constitutes most of the volume of the atom? (c) Why is the uncombined atom electrically neutral?

13-6
26. Compare the path of the electron in the hydrogen atom as described by the Bohr model with the location of the electron as described by the wave-mechanical model.

13-11
27. (a) Write the notation for the electron configuration of the sulfur atom ($Z = 16$) in the ground state. (b) How many electrons are there in the p_X, p_y, and p_z orbitals in the atom's third principal energy level? (c) How many electrons are there in the sulfur atom's valence shell?

13-20
28. Compare the nature and properties of the types of radiations that come from radioactive substances.

14-6
29. (a) Write electron-dot symbols for lithium (atomic number 3) and chlorine (atomic number 17). (b) Use the electron-dot symbols to show how the two elements can combine to form an ionic compound.

14-8
30. Use electron-dot symbols to show how two atoms of bromine (atomic number 35) can bond covalently to form bromine molecules.

14-11
31. When sodium and chlorine react chemically to form sodium chloride, some energy is absorbed by the reactants. How is this energy used?

15-4
32. In both H_2O and CO_2 the bonding is covalent polar. Why is the CO_2 molecule nonpolar while the H_2O molecule is polar?

15-6
33. Explain why an ionic solid, such as NaCl, (a) has no molecules, (b) has a high melting point, and (c) conducts electricity only when dissolved in water or melted.

15-8
34. Explain why the boiling point of water is much higher than that of hydrogen sulfide.

16-3
35. (a) What characterizes the electron structure of the elements in the same group in the periodic table? (b) What type of element is found at the end of each period in the table?

16-9
36. Proceeding from left to right in the third period, (a) how does the type of element change, and (b) what change occurs in the atomic radius?

16-13
37. (a) Describe the change in metallic character when proceeding from top to bottom in group 4A (group 14) in the periodic table. (b) Why is germanium (Ge) considered to be a metalloid?

UNIT 5

Solutions

No dynamite or power drills carved these dramatic rock formations in the Carlsbad Caverns of New Mexico. Not only the cone-shaped stalactites and stalagmites projecting, respectively, from ceiling and floor *but the caves themselves* were formed by the action of water. The ability of water to dissolve solid substances such as this limestone has literally helped to shape the earth.

To the chemist, water, or *aqueous*, solutions hold the key to many reactions involving solids. Many solids simply will not react unless they are dissolved in water. Thus the properties of solutions, which is the subject of this unit, becomes a matter of vital interest to chemists.

Solutions

17-1 Mixtures

Chapters 5, 6, and 7 discussed gaseous, liquid, and solid substances when these substances were pure. However, chemists often work with mixtures. As discussed in Section 3-17, a mixture consists of two or more substances, each of which retains its properties. Mixtures tend to be heterogeneous, especially when they are first being formed. A **heterogeneous mixture** is one in which the substances making up the mixture are not spread uniformly throughout the mixture. This means that samples taken from different parts of the mixture will have different compositions. In a salt-sugar mixture, for example, two samples may have different amounts of salt. One may be 25% salt by mass, another 27%.

When the particles of the substances making up a mixture are small, they can be more uniformly mixed, or intermingled. Thus, there is a relationship between particle size and the uniformity of a mixture. When the particles are small enough and thoroughly enough mixed, the result is a very uniform mixture. Samples from different parts of such a mixture will show the same composition. A mixture in which the components are uniformly intermingled is called a **homogeneous mixture.**

17-2 Solutions

Solutions are homogeneous mixtures made up of very small particles that are, in fact, individual molecules, atoms, or ions. Solutions are important for chemists because solids generally will not react with each other. Solids must usually be dissolved into solutions before reaction will take place to an appreciable extent. In order to understand the typical properties of solutions, let us consider the properties of a common solution—salt water.

1. The solution is a homogeneous mixture if it has been well stirred during its formation. Stirring helps to spread the dissolved particles evenly among the particles of the liquid. A sample taken from one part of a homogeneous solution will have the same relative amounts of salt and water as one taken from any other part of the solution.

2. The dissolved particles (the salt) will not come out of the solution no matter how long the solution is allowed to stand. (This assumes that the solution is covered so that none of the liquid can evaporate.)

3. The solution is clear and transparent. The dissolved particles are too small to be seen. A beam of light passing through the solution cannot be seen. See Figure 17-1.

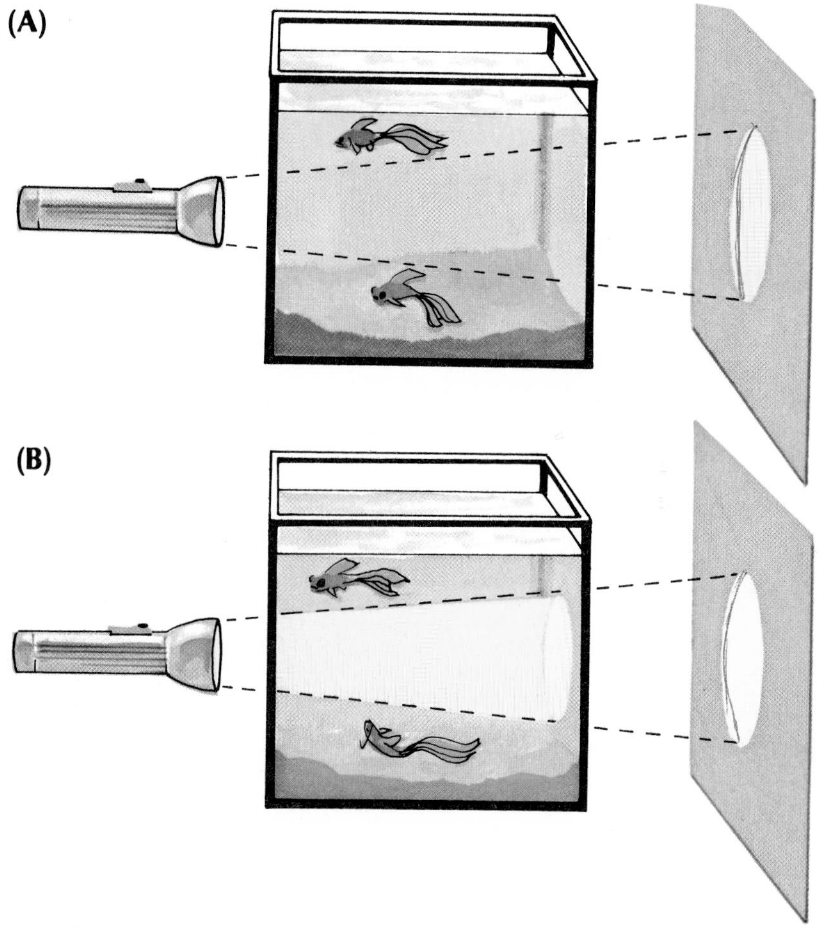

(A)

(B)

Figure 17-1

(A) The aquarium is filled with a solution of salt in water. A beam of light, viewed from the side, cannot be seen as it passes through a solution. (B) The aquarium contains water with tiny particles of clay suspended in it. The tiny suspended particles scatter the light, whereas dissolved particles will not. Hence, the beam of light shows that the lower aquarium contains a suspension rather than a solution.

4. Because of the extremely small size of the dissolved particles, the solution will pass through the finest filters. Therefore, filtration cannot be used to separate one substance making up the solution from another.

5. A solution is a homogeneous mixture that is considered to be a *single* phase even though the components may have been in different

phases before the solution was formed. The salt (sodium chloride) in a salt water solution was originally in the solid phase. In the solution, it is considered to be in the liquid phase.

17-3 Solute and Solvent

Figure 17-2

Iodine is a dark solid (upper photo). When crystals of iodine are dissolved in alcohol, the solution is called a "tincture of iodine."

Many solutions are a mixture of just two substances. Usually, one of the substances is considered to be dissolved *in* the other. The substance that is considered to be the dissolved substance in a solution is called the **solute** (SOL-yoot). The substance in a solution in which the solute is dissolved is called the **solvent.**

In most cases there is little question as to which substance is the solute and which is the solvent. If the two substances were originally in different phases, the one that changed phase is the solute. For example, all solutions made with water are liquid. Any solids or gases that enter the solution, and thus change to the liquid phase, are called solutes. Water is the solvent. The same is true of other liquids, such as alcohol, that are used to make solutions. Solids or gases dissolved in the liquid are the solutes; the liquid is the solvent. When the two substances in a solution were originally in the same phase (for example, two liquids), the substance present in the smaller amount is usually considered the solute. Solutions in which water is the solvent are called aqueous (A-kwee-us or AK-wee-us) solutions. Because water can dissolve many substances, **aqueous solutions** are very common.

When water cannot dissolve a substance, another liquid often will. Carbon tetrachloride (CCl_4) and benzene (C_6H_6) are excellent solvents for fats and oils. For this reason, they are often used to remove grease spots from clothing. Ethyl alcohol (C_2H_5OH) is another widely used liquid solvent. Solutions in which alcohol is the solvent are called **tinctures** (TINK-chers). Tincture of iodine is a solution of iodine (a solid) in alcohol. Acetone (AS-uh-tone) is another common solvent. It is found in some fingernail-polish removers.

17-4 Types of Solutions

Solutions are usually classified as follows:

1. Gaseous solutions. **Gaseous solutions** consist of gases or vapors dissolved in one another. Since all gases mix uniformly with one another, any two or more gases can form a solution. Air is the most common example of a gaseous solution. When dry, it is made up mostly of oxygen gas dissolved in nitrogen gas. Gases consist of molecules that are relatively far apart. Therefore, gaseous solutions can be found in any proportion. Water vapor is one of the components of air that varies widely in its amount. Water vapor is also an example of a substance that has changed its phase (from liquid to gaseous) in

Figure 17-3

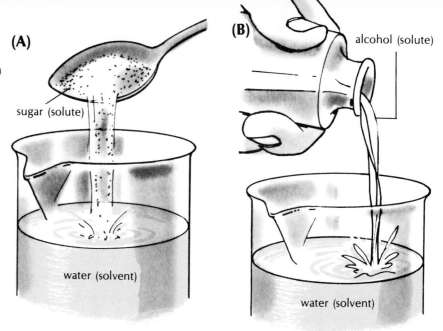

becoming part of a solution. Iodine vapor is another example. Iodine is a solid at room temperature, but it is in the gaseous phase when it becomes part of an air-iodine solution.

2. Liquid solutions. **Liquid solutions** consist of a liquid solvent in which a gas, liquid, or solid is dissolved. Liquid solutions are the most common type. Sugar dissolved in water is an example of a solid dissolved in a liquid. A carbonated beverage is an example of a gas dissolved in a liquid (carbon dioxide gas dissolved in water). Antifreeze solution is an example of a liquid dissolved in a liquid. In a common type of antifreeze, ethylene glycol (ETH-uh-leen GLI-kol), a liquid, is the solute, and water is the solvent. Two liquids that dissolve in each other in all proportions are said to be completely miscible (MISS-uh-bul). Alcohol and water are completely miscible. Liquids that do not dissolve in each other to any appreciable degree are said to be immiscible. Water and oil (which floats on water) are immiscible.

Figure 17-4

When antifreeze is added to the water in the radiator of a car, a solution is formed whose solute and solvent are both liquids.

3. Solid solutions. **Solid solutions** are mixtures of solids uniformly spread throughout one another at the atomic or molecular level. An alloy (AL-oy) is a solid solution of two or more metals. Brass, made of copper and zinc, is a common alloy. Alloys in which one of the metals is mercury are called amalgams (uh-MAL-gums). Although usually a liquid, mercury is considered to be in the solid phase when part of an amalgam. Solutions of gases in solids exist, but are very rare. When tiny hydrogen bubbles stick to finely divided platinum metal, the hydrogen-platinum mixture approaches the nature of a solution.

Questions for Sections 17-1 through 17-4

1. (a) Distinguish between heterogeneous and homogeneous mixtures. (b) What is the relationship between particle size in the mixture and the uniformity of the mixture?
2. State five (5) properties of a typical solution.
3. Define (a) solute (b) solvent (c) aqueous solution.
4. Name the solute in (a) salt water (b) ammonia water (c) water vapor in the air (d) a brass alloy containing 75% copper and 25% zinc (e) 80-proof (40%) alcohol.
5. Define (a) tincture (b) amalgam. Name the (c) solute in tincture of iodine (d) solvent in a silver amalgam that contains 25% silver.
*6. Name a solvent that can be used to dissolve (a) fat (b) fingernail polish (c) sugar crystals.
7. Define and state one example of a (a) gaseous solution (b) liquid solution (c) solid solution.

17-5 Degree of Solubility

The **solubility** (sol-yoo-BIL-uh-tee) of a solute is a measure of how much solute can dissolve in a given amount of solvent. Solubility is usually described in terms of the quantity of the solute that can be dissolved in a definite amount of solvent at a specified temperature. For example, a maximum of 36.0 g of NaCl will dissolve in 100 g of water at 20°C. That is, the solubility of NaCl at 20°C is 36.0 g per 100 g H_2O.

The main factors that have an effect on solubility are:

1. The nature of the solute and solvent. About 1 g of lead (II) chloride can be dissolved in 100 g of water at room temperature. In the same quantity of water and at the same temperature, 200 g of zinc chloride can be dissolved. The great difference in the solubilities of these two substances is the result of differences in their natures.

2. Temperature. The solubilities of many substances change greatly with temperature. Generally, an increase in the temperature of the solution increases the solubility of a solid solute. A few solid solutes, however, are less soluble in a warmer solution.

Figure 17-5

Most liquid solvents can dissolve more solute when the liquids are at a higher temperature.

For all gases, solubility decreases as the temperature of the solution rises. (Warm soda pop, for example, loses its fizz.) Gases may be released from solution, either partially or entirely, by raising the temperature of the solution. Carbon dioxide, sulfur dioxide, and oxygen may be removed from their aqueous solutions by boiling their solutions for a few minutes. Boiled water tastes flat because we are used to drinking water that has some oxygen dissolved in it.

3. Pressure. For solid and liquid solutes, changes in pressure have practically no effect on solubility. For gaseous solutes, an increase in pressure increases solubility, and a decrease in pressure decreases solubility. (When the cap on a bottle of soda pop is removed, pressure is released and the gaseous solute bubbles out of solution.)

The effect of pressure on the solubility of most gases is described by Henry's law. The law gets its name from William Henry, an English chemist. Henry's law states that the mass of a gas dissolved in a given volume of liquid is directly proportional to the pressure of the gas. Henry's law is not obeyed by gases, such as ammonia, that react chemically with the solvent.

Figure 17-6

The effect of temperature on the solubility of a gas. Soda is given its fizz by dissolving carbon dioxide gas, CO_2, in the soda water. (A) The soda in the two bottles are at different temperatures. One is cold, and the other is warm. (B) When the caps are removed, most of the CO_2 in the cold soda remains in solution. In the warm soda, the CO_2 gas rushes out of the warm solution where it is not very soluble, causing the soda to overflow.

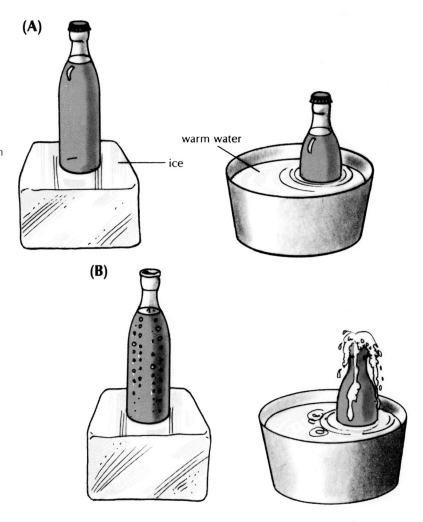

The effect of pressure on gas solubility is used in the preparation of carbonated beverages. Such drinks are bottled under a carbon dioxide pressure slightly higher than one atmosphere. When the bottle is opened and the solution exposed to the lower air pressure, the gas begins to bubble out of solution. This escape of a gas from solution is called **effervescence** (ef-er-VES-ens).

17-6   Factors Affecting the Rate of Solution

The **rate of solution** is a measure of how fast a substance dissolves. It is the quantity of solute that will dissolve during one unit of time. Some of the factors determining the rate of solution are:

1. Size of the particles.   Particle size concerns chiefly solid solutes where the particle size may vary greatly. When a solute dissolves, the action takes place only at the particle surfaces. When the total surface area of the solute particles is increased, the solute dissolves more rapidly. Breaking a solute into smaller pieces increases its surface area and hence its rate of solution.

Figure 17-7

By grinding a solid solute to make particles of a smaller size, the chemist can shorten the time it takes for the solute to dissolve in a liquid solvent.

Figure 17-8

When you make iced tea, sugar will dissolve faster if it is added to the tea while it is still hot. Solid solutes dissolve faster in hotter liquids.

2. Stirring. With liquid and solid solutes, stirring brings fresh portions of the solvent in contact with the solute, thereby increasing the rate of solution.

3. Amount of solute already dissolved. When there is little solute already in solution, dissolving takes place relatively rapidly. As the solution approaches the point where no more solute can be dissolved, dissolving takes place more slowly.

4. Temperature. For liquid and solid solutes, increasing the temperature not only increases the amount of solute that will dissolve but also increases the rate at which the solute will dissolve. In other words, both solubility and rate of solution are increased with an increase in temperature.

For gases the reverse is true. An increase in temperature decreases both solubility and rate of solution.

8. (a) Define *solubility* (b) Describe the solubility of ordinary salt at 20°C.
9. Name three factors that affect the degree of solubility of a solute.
10. How does a rise in temperature affect (a) the solubility of most solids? (b) the solubility of all gases?
11. The caps are removed from a warm and a cold bottle of carbonated beverage. The soda in the cold bottle bubbles (effervesces) only slightly. The soda in the warm bottle shows rapid effervescence. Explain.
12. (a) State Henry's law describing the effect of pressure on gas solubility. (b) What kind of gases do not obey Henry's law?
13. (a) What is meant by the *rate of solution*? (b) Describe, briefly, four factors that determine the rate of solution.

17-7 Solubility and the Nature of Solvent and Solute

Forces of attraction exist between the particles of a substance. These forces give liquids and solids cohesion—that is, they hold the substance together. In order for a solvent to dissolve a solute, the particles of the solvent must be able to separate the particles of the solute and occupy the intervening spaces.

Polar solvent molecules can effectively separate the molecules of other polar substances. (Polar molecules are discussed in Section 15-3.) This happens when the positive end of a solvent molecule approaches the negative end of a solute molecule. A force of attraction then exists between the two molecules. The solute molecule is pulled into solution when the force overcomes the attractive force between the solute molecule and its neighboring solute molecules. Ethyl alcohol (C_2H_5OH) and water are examples of polar substances that readily dissolve in each other.

However, ammonia, water, and other polar substances do not dissolve in solvents, such as benzene, whose molecules are nonpolar. The nonpolar benzene molecules have no attraction for polar molecules and exert no force that can separate the polar molecules of ammonia or water. On the other hand, a nonpolar substance, such as fat, will dissolve easily in benzene. The molecules of both the fat and benzene are held together by forces that are too weak to prevent the molecules from intermingling freely.

In addition to dissolving polar solutes, polar solvents can generally dissolve solutes that are ionic. Water and ethyl alcohol (C_2H_5OH) are examples of such polar solvents. The negative ion of the substance being dissolved is attracted to the positive end of a neighboring solvent molecule. The positive ion of the solute is attracted to the negative end of the solvent molecule. Dissolving takes place when the solvent is able to pull ions out of their crystal lattice. Water is the polar substance

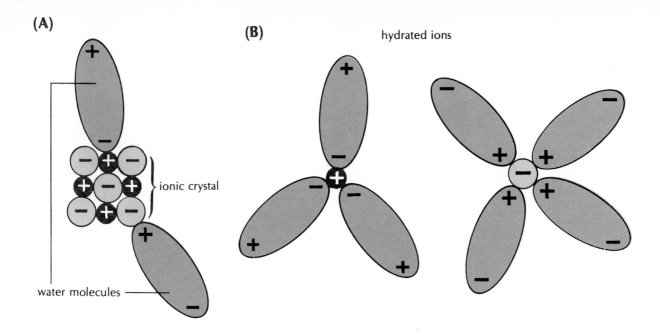

(A)

ionic crystal

water molecules

(B) hydrated ions

Figure 17-9

The hydration of ions. (A) The negative end of the water molecule dipole attaches itself to the positive ion on the surface of the crystal, and the positive end of another water dipole attaches itself to the negative ion. These water molecules pull the ions out of the crystal lattice into solution. (B) Once in solution, water dipoles surround the dissolved ions, creating hydrated ions.

most commonly used as the solvent for ionic compounds. When an ionic compound is dissolved in water, its ions become surrounded by water molecules. Ions surrounded by water molecules are called **hydrated ions.** See Figure 17-9.

The separation of ions by the action of a solvent is called dissociation. Dissociation is described in greater detail in Chapter 23.

The effect of the polarity of molecules is especially noticeable in the case of gases dissolved in water. Hydrogen and oxygen molecules are nonpolar while the molecules of ammonia, hydrogen chloride, and hydrogen sulfide are all polar. The volumes of the nonpolar gases that will dissolve in a liter of water at STP greatly contrast with the volumes for the polar gases. See Figure 17-10.

Figure 17-10

The solubilities of selected gases in water at 0°C and atmospheric pressure. Note that gases having polar molecules dissolve much more readily in water because water molecules are also polar.

GASES WITH POLAR MOLECULES		Volume of gas that will dissolve in 1 volume of water
ammonia,	NH_3	1176
hydrogen chloride,	HCl	507
hydrogen sulfide,	H_2S	4.67
GASES WITH NONPOLAR MOLECULES		
hydrogen,	H_2	0.0215
nitrogen,	N_2	0.0235
oxygen,	O_2	0.0489

17-8 Energy Changes During Solution Formation

When a solid dissolves in a liquid, the solid changes from the solid phase to the liquid phase. As in melting, this change of phase requires energy to overcome the forces that hold the molecules or ions in their positions in the solid. Therefore, in practically all cases where a solid dissolves in a liquid, the change is endothermic. That is, heat is absorbed. The absorbed heat usually comes from the solute-solvent mixture. The temperature of the mixture drops as dissolving takes place. If you are holding a beaker containing a solute and solvent in your hand, you can often feel the beaker getting colder as the solution forms.

A notable exception to this rule is the dissolving of solid NaOH and KOH. In these cases, heat is released. When a concentrated solution of NaOH or KOH is being prepared, the beaker may become too hot to hold.

17-9 Solubility Curves

A **solubility curve** shows how much solute will dissolve in a given amount of solvent over a range of temperatures. Figure 17-11 shows a solubility curve for the solid ionic substance potassium chlorate, $KClO_3$. The curve shows the number of grams of $KClO_3$ that will dissolve in 100 g of water over a temperature range of 0°C to 100°C. To show how the curve is used, let's suppose you want to know the solubility of $KClO_3$ at 50°C. To find the answer, follow up the vertical line from 50°C until this line crosses the curve. At the point where the lines cross, place a ruler so that its straight edge runs horizontally across the page. Follow the straight edge to the left to the vertical axis. The point on the axis where the straight edge of the ruler crosses is slightly above 20. This means that slightly more than 20 g of $KClO_3$ will dissolve in 100 g of water at 50°. In other words, the solubility of $KClO_3$ in water at 50°C is slightly greater than 20 g per 100 g of water.

Figure 17-12 shows the solubility curves for a number of compounds. All the solutes shown are solids except for ammonia, NH_3, which is a gas. For most of the substances shown, the curves sweep up to the right, indicating an increase in solubility with a rise in temperature. The only exceptions are cerium (III) sulfate, $Ce_2(SO_4)_3$, and ammonia. Their solubilities decrease with an increase in temperature.

17-10 Table of Solubilities

The table in Appendix E gives information about the solubilities of many compounds in water. The terms *nearly insoluble* (i), *slightly soluble* (ss), and *soluble* (s) are used. Compounds that decompose in water (d) or those that have not been isolated (n) are also indicated.

Figure 17-11

How to use a solubility curve. To find the solubility of KClO₃ in water at 50°C, go straight up from 50 on the temperature scale. At the point where the straight vertical line intersects the curve, go horizontally over to the left. The curve shows that the solubility of KClO₃ at 50° is slightly greater than 20 grams KClO₃ per 100 grams of water.

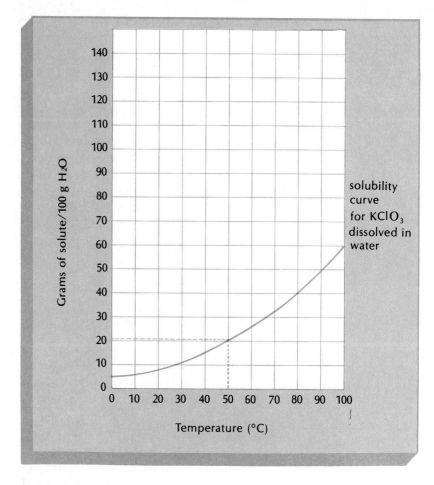

solubility curve for KClO₃ dissolved in water

The names of several metals that normally form positive ions are listed vertically at the left of the table. The positive polyatomic ammonium ion is also listed on the left. Across the top of the table are the names of several nonmetals and clusters of atoms that normally form negative ions. To obtain solubility information about any particular compound included in the table, find the box where the row for the positive ion and the column for the negative ion cross. For example, to get information about aluminum hydroxide, find the box where the aluminum row intersects the hydroxide column. The symbol in this space is "i." This indicates that aluminum hydroxide is not very soluble, or is nearly insoluble.

Questions for Sections 17-7 through 17-10

14. (a) Describe what happens to water molecules and sodium and chloride ions when NaCl dissolves in water. (b) Why doesn't a fat, such as glyceryl stearate, dissolve in water? (c) Why does the fat dissolve in benzene?
15. Explain why ammonia gas is very soluble in water while oxygen is only slightly soluble.

Figure 17-12

Solubility curves for a number of water soluble solutes.

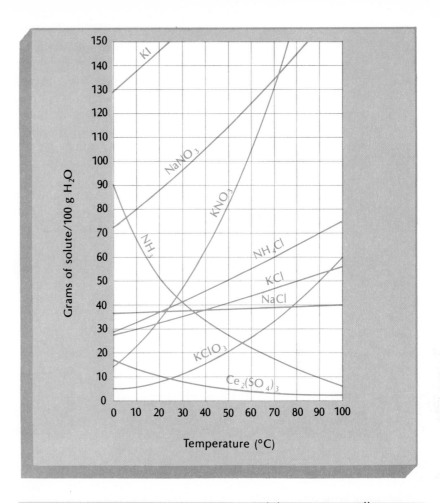

16. Why is the process of dissolving a solid in water usually an endothermic change?
*17. (a) Using the solubility curves, find the solubility of (1) KNO_3 at 70°C (2) NaCl at 100°C (3) NH_4Cl at 90°C. (b) Which of these salts is most soluble at 15°C? (c) Which is least soluble at 15°C?
*18. Using the table of solubilities in App. E, describe the solubility of (a) magnesium chloride (b) copper (II) hydroxide (c) lead iodide.

17-11   Saturated and Unsaturated Solutions

A **saturated solution** is a solution that has dissolved in it all the solute that it can normally hold at the given conditions. For example, at 20°C, an aqueous solution of KCl is saturated when there are 34.7 g of KCl dissolved in 100 g of water. If more KCl is added to this solution, undissolved KCl will settle to the bottom. If an extra gram of KCl is added, then a gram of KCl will sit undissolved on the bottom of the container.

Actually, solute that is added to a saturated solution *will* dissolve, but an equal amount of dissolved solute will come out of solution. When the rate at which undissolved solute goes into solution is equal to

*The answers to questions marked with an asterisk are given in the back of the book.

the rate at which dissolved solute comes out of solution, a condition exists called **solution equilibrium.** Solution equilibrium is the physical state in which there is a continuous interchange between the dissolved and undissolved portions of the solute. As a result of this interchange, there is *no net change* in the amounts of dissolved and undissolved solute. A saturated solution, then, may be defined as one in which the solute in solution is in equilibrium with undissolved solute. See Figure 17-13.

(A)
Before equilibrium
(solution unsaturated)

(B)
At equilibrium (solution saturated)

(C)
Equilibrium disturbed
(solution unsaturated)

(D)
Equilibrium reestablished at higher temperature
(solution saturated)

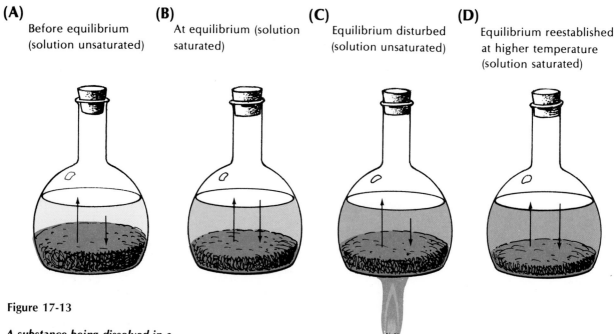

Figure 17-13

A substance being dissolved in a solvent. (A) At first, solid solute dissolves into solution at a faster rate than dissolved solute crystallizes out of solution. (B) At equilibrium, the dissolving of solute into solution and its crystallizing out of solution take place at the same rate. (C) Heating the flask shown in *(B)* upsets the equilibrium. (D) At the higher temperature, equilibrium is finally re-established, but more of the solute is held in solution than in the solution shown in *(B)*.

When describing any saturated solution, the temperature *must* be stated. A saturated solution at one temperature will contain a different amount of dissolved solute than will a saturated solution of the same solute at another temperature. For saturated solutions of gases, both temperature and pressure should be stated. It should also be noted that a solution may contain more than one solute. In such cases, the solution may be saturated with respect to one of the solutes and not saturated with respect to the other. A solution that contains less solute than it can hold at a certain temperature and pressure is said to be **unsaturated.** For example, a solution of KCl containing less than 34.7 g of solute in 100 g of water at 20°C is unsaturated. This solution can continue to dissolve more solute up to the point of saturation.

As mentioned in Section 17-5, the solubility of many solid and liquid solutes in a liquid solvent increases with an increase in the temperature of the solution. For these substances, raising the temperature of a saturated solution will disturb the solution equilibrium. At the higher temperature, the solution can hold more solute. The rate at which the solute dissolves will become greater than the rate at which it crystallizes out. This will continue until enough additional solute dissolves to make the solution saturated at the higher temperature. At this point, equilibrium is reestablished. See Figure 17-13.

Figure 17-14

Types of solutions.

17-12 Supersaturated Solutions

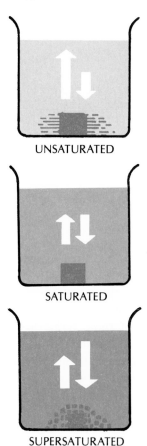

UNSATURATED

SATURATED

SUPERSATURATED

Under special conditions, there are some solutions that can actually hold more solute than is present in their saturated solutions. These solutions are said to be **supersaturated.** Supersaturated solutions are not prepared in the same way as saturated solutions. To make a saturated solution, solute is added until no more will dissolve. To make a supersaturated solution, a saturated solution at high temperature is allowed to cool gradually while it sits undisturbed. Usually, as a saturated solution cools, some solute crystallizes out of solution and drops to the bottom of the container. This happens because the solubility of the solute decreases with a decrease in temperature. For solutes that form supersaturated solutions, the usual course of events does not happen. Instead, all the solute remains in solution as the solution is cooled. By the time room temperature is reached, there will be far more solute in solution than would be present in a saturated solution of the same solute. However, supersaturation is an unstable condition. If a single crystal of solute is added to a supersaturated solution, the excess solute crystallizes out. Only enough solute remains in solution to make the solution saturated at the cooler temperature.

It should be stressed that relatively few solute-solvent mixtures will form supersaturated solutions. Two substances whose aqueous solutions do form supersaturated solutions are sodium acetate ($NaC_2H_3O_2$) and sodium thiosulfate ($Na_2S_2O_3$). Sodium thiosulfate, known as "hypo" to the photographer, is used to develop negatives and to print photos. See Figure 17-14.

17-13 Dilute and Concentrated Solutions

A **dilute solution** is one in which the amount of solute dissolved is small in relation to the amount of solvent. A **concentrated solution** is one in which a relatively large amount of solute is dissolved. For example, a tablespoon of sodium chloride dissolved in a cup of water will produce a fairly concentrated solution. The same amount of solute in a gallon of water will produce a dilute solution. The terms *dilute* and *concentrated* do not tell whether or not a solution is saturated or unsaturated. For example, at 20°C, 144 g of potassium iodide will dissolve in 100 mL of water, while only 0.068 g of lead iodide will dissolve in the same amount of water. Thus, a saturated solution of potassium iodide will be concentrated while a saturated solution of PbI_2 will be dilute.

19. (a) What is a saturated solution? (b) Explain how you would prepare a saturated solution of table salt at room temperature. (c) Describe the equilibrium that exists in this solution. (d) What kind of solution is produced if the solution is heated? Explain.

20. (a) Describe how you would prepare a supersaturated solution of sodium acetate. (b) Explain what happens when an excess crystal of solute is added to the solution.

21. What happens when you stir some crystals of salt in a saturated solution of sugar? Explain.

22. Using potassium nitrate as the solute, explain how you would (a) prepare a dilute solution, and (b) prepare a concentrated solution.

23. Silver sulfate is only slightly soluble in water. Explain why the following solutions of this substance can, or cannot, be prepared: (a) dilute (b) concentrated (c) saturated.

17-14   More Exact Expressions of Concentration

The terms dilute, concentrated, and unsaturated do not tell the actual amounts of solute and solvent in a solution. It is often desirable to know the exact amounts. There are several ways of expressing concentrations quantitatively. We shall consider the following: (1) percentage by mass, (2) molarity, and (3) molality. Each of these terms has advantages in certain situations. Still another unit, normality, will be discussed in Section 25-11. Knowing how to express concentrations accurately will be especially important when we study acid and base titrations in Chapter 25.

17-15   Percentage by Mass

Percentage by mass is a unit of concentration that states the number of parts by mass of solute per hundred parts by mass of solution. A 15% aqueous solution of sodium chloride contains 15 g of salt in 100 g of solution. (Note that if 15 g are salt, then 85 g must be water in every 100-g sample of the solution.) To calculate the percentage by mass of a given solution, first divide the mass of the solute by the mass of the solution. Then multiply the result by 100% to obtain percentage units.

SAMPLE PROBLEM 1

A mass of 25 grams NaCl is dissolved in 200 grams H_2O. What is the concentration of this solution expressed as a percentage by mass?

Solution. Percentage by mass is the mass of the solute divided by the mass of solution, and the answer multiplied by 100% to convert it to a percentage. Note: The mass of the solution is the sum of the masses of solute and solvent.

The *pharmacist's* 10% solution contains 10 g of solute per 100 *milliliters* of solution.

$$\text{Percentage by mass} = \frac{25 \text{ g}}{25 \text{ g} + 200 \text{ g}} \times 100\%$$

$$= 11\%$$

The concentration of the sodium chloride in the solution is 11% by mass.

SAMPLE PROBLEM 2

A solution of sodium chloride (NaCl) dissolved in water is 12.0% sodium chloride by mass. How many grams of sodium chloride are in a 120-gram sample of this solution?

Solution. If a solution is 12.0% NaCl by mass, it means that 12.0% of the mass of any sample of the solution is NaCl.

$$12.0\% \times 120 \text{ grams} = 14.4 \text{ grams}$$

The 120-gram sample of solution contains 14.4 grams of NaCl.

17-16   Calculating the Mass of a Solution

It is much easier to measure the volume of a liquid solution than to measure its mass. To measure volume, we simply pour the solution into a graduated cylinder or similar volume-measuring container. To measure the mass of solution, we have to measure the mass of a container when it is empty, and then with the solution in it. Then we have to subtract the mass of the container to find the mass of the solution. This is a clumsy and time-consuming series of operations.

It is easier to *calculate* the mass of a given volume of solution than to measure it. This can be done if we know the density of the solution. (Density is discussed in Section 3-7.) We use the relationship: Mass = Volume × Density. See Figure 17-15.

Densities of common solutions can be found in science handbooks, such as the *Handbook of Chemistry and Physics*. These handbooks sometimes give the *specific gravity* of the solution, rather than the density. **Specific gravity** is the ratio of the mass of a substance to the mass of an equal volume of water. Specific gravity has no units, but since the density of water is 1.0 g/mL, specific gravity is numerically equal to the density in grams per milliliter. For example, 7.9 is the specific gravity of iron. (This means that any sample of iron has a mass

(A)

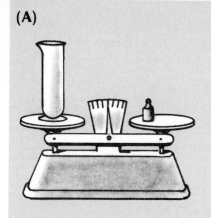

(B)

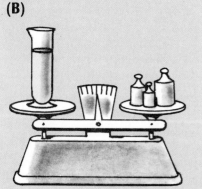

Mass = Mass of container with liquid
minus mass of empty container

(C)

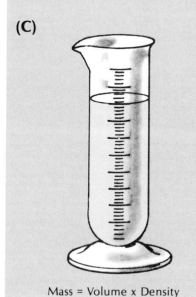

Mass = Volume x Density

Figure 17-15

Two ways of determining the mass of a solution. (A) First determine the mass of an empty container. (B) Then determine the mass of the container with the solution in it. The mass of the solution is the difference. (C) If the density of a solution is known, an easier way to determine the mass of the solution is to multiply the volume of the solution, as measured in a graduated cylinder, by the density of the solution.

7.9 times as great as the mass of an equal volume of water.) If the specific gravity is 7.9, then the density of iron is 7.9 g/mL.

With the above information as a background, let us work a problem that makes use of the concentration of a solution expressed in percentage by mass.

SAMPLE PROBLEM

Suppose that a solution of hydrogen chloride gas dissolved in water has a concentration that is 30% hydrogen chloride by mass. (Recall that an aqueous solution of hydrogen chloride is commonly called hydrochloric acid.) How much solute is there in 100 mL of this solution if the density of the solution is 1.15 g/mL?

Solution

Step 1. Determine the mass of 100 mL of the solution.

$$\text{mass} = \text{density} \times \text{volume}$$
$$= 1.15 \text{ g/mL} \times 100 \text{ mL}$$
$$= 115 \text{ g}$$

Step 2. Determine what mass of HCl gas is dissolved in 115 g of the solution.

$$\text{mass HCl} = 30\% \times \text{mass of solution}$$
$$= 30\% \text{ of } 115 \text{ g}$$
$$= 0.30 \times 115 \text{ g}$$
$$= 34.5 \text{ g}$$

There are 34.5 g of HCl gas dissolved in 100 mL of a solution that is 30% HCl by mass.

Questions for Sections 17-14 through 17-16

24. Why are the terms *dilute, concentrated,* and *unsaturated* sometimes not satisfactory for describing the concentration of a solution?
25. (a) As a unit for solution concentration, what does *percentage by mass* express? (b) What is the percentage by mass of a solution that contains 25 g of KNO_3 in 400 g of water? (c) What is the mass of a 10% solution of NaCl that contains 4.0 g of NaCl?

26. (a) Define *density*. (b) Define *specific gravity*. (c) Distinguish between density and specific gravity.
*27. What is the mass of sulfuric acid in 250 mL of an 88% solution that has a density of 1.80 g/mL?
28. A 14.0% solution of Na_2CO_3 in water has a density of 1.15 g/mL. If an 85.0-mL sample of this solution is evaporated to dryness, what mass of solute remains behind?

17-17   Molarity

Sometimes it is useful for chemists to know the number of molecules or formula units of solute in a given volume of solution. Then it is convenient to express concentrations in terms of molarity. The **molarity** of a solution is the number of moles of solute in 1 liter of solution. A *1 molar* solution (abbreviated *1 M*) has 1 mole of solute in every 1 liter of solution. See Figure 17-16. "One mole of solute" means "1 mole of solute molecules" when referring to molecular substances. It means "1 mole of solute formula units" when referring to nonmolecular substances. For example, a 1 *M* solution of sucrose (common sugar) dissolved in water has 1 mole of sucrose molecules (6.02×10^{23} sucrose molecules) in every liter of solution. A 1 *M* solution of NaCl dissolved in water has 1 mole of formula units of NaCl dissolved in every liter of solution. (Recall that 1 formula unit of NaCl consists of 2 ions—1 sodium ion and 1 chloride ion.)

In equal volumes of all solutions whose molar concentrations are the same, there are the same number of solute molecules or the same number of solute formula units. For example, suppose we have two

*The answers to questions marked with an asterisk are given in the back of the book.

Figure 17-16

How to make a 1 molar solution.
(A) Add 1 mole of solute to less than 1 liter of solvent. (B) After all the solute has dissolved, add additional solvent to the solution to bring the volume up to 1 liter.

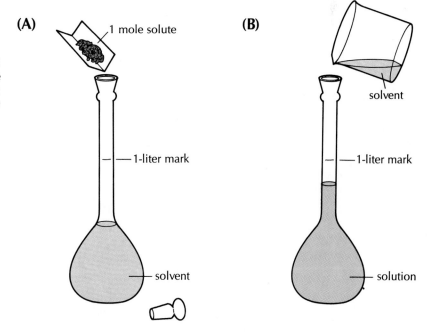

*The Oceans,
a Source of Mineral Wealth*

There are 36 minerals that the United States government considers "strategic," that is, essential for American industry. Some of the better known of these minerals are manganese, cobalt, and chromium. During 1980, about 90% of the cobalt and chromium we used and more than 97% of the manganese had to be imported. Substantial amounts of 20 of the remaining 33 strategic minerals also had to be imported. Our dependence on foreign countries for these minerals is a cause of alarm because many of these countries are in politically unstable regions in Africa and Asia.

One alternate source for strategic minerals is the oceans. Some of the minerals are lying on the ocean floor. Others are dissolved in the water. Obtaining minerals from the ocean poses many technological problems, but the importance of strategic minerals assures that these problems will be attacked with great vigor in the coming years.

aqueous solutions. One contains solute A. The other contains solute B. Assume that the concentrations of both solutions are 0.50 M. In any volume of the solution made with A there are the same number of molecules of A as there are molecules of B in an equal volume of the solution made with B.

Many reactions take place only when the reactants are in solution. Here is why molarity is so useful when the reactants are in solution. Suppose that 1 molecule of A reacts with 1 molecule of B. If the chemist has solutions of A and B of the same molar concentration, then equal volumes of these two solutions will react.

If the molarity and the volume of a solution are known, the mass of the solute can be determined. The concentration in moles per liter (molarity) multiplied by the volume in liters equals the number of moles of solute.

$$\text{moles solute in a solution} = \left(\text{molar concentration of the solution} \right) \times \left(\text{volume of solution in liters} \right)$$

Once the number of moles of solute are known, the number of grams of solute can be determined. This is done by multiplying the number of moles of solute by the number of grams in one mole.

$$\text{grams solute} = \text{moles solute} \times \text{grams/mole}$$

SAMPLE PROBLEM 1

Some sucrose (common table sugar) is dissolved in water. How many moles of sugar are dissolved in 200 mL of solution if its concentration is 0.150 M?

Solution. The concentration 0.150 M means that there is 0.150 mole of sugar dissolved in every liter of solution. But 200 mL is only 200/1000 = 1/5 of a liter. There is, therefore, 1/5 × 0.150 mole = 0.030 mole sugar in 200 mL of solution. Using the formula, the answer would be obtained as follows:

$$\text{moles solute} = (\text{molar conc.}) \times (\text{vol. of solution})$$

$$= \frac{0.150 \text{ mole}}{\text{liter}} \times 0.200 \text{ liter}$$

$$= 0.0300 \text{ mole sugar}$$

There is 0.0300 mole sugar dissolved in 200 mL of a solution whose concentration is 0.150 M.

SAMPLE PROBLEM 2

How many grams of sucrose (common table sugar) are dissolved in 200 mL of a solution whose concentration is 0.150 M? (Note: The formula of sucrose is $C_{12}H_{22}O_{11}$.)

Solution. In Sample Problem 1, we found that there are 0.0300 mole of sucrose in 200 mL of a 0.150 M solution.

To find the number of grams of sucrose in 0.0300 mole of sucrose, we need first to find the number of grams in 1 mole of sucrose, $C_{12}H_{22}O_{11}$.

One mole of sucrose, $C_{12}H_{22}O_{11}$, consists of:

12 moles C atoms × 12 g/mole	=	144 g C
22 moles H atoms × 1 g/mole	=	22 g H
11 moles O atoms × 16 g/mole	=	176 g O
		342 g

One mole of sucrose molecules has a mass of 342 g. Therefore, 0.0300 mole of sucrose will have a mass of:

$$0.0300 \text{ mole} \times \frac{342 \text{ g}}{\text{mole}} = 10.3 \text{ g sucrose}$$

Questions for Section 17-17

29. (a) Define *molarity*. (b) Describe the concentration of a 1.0 M solution of KCl in terms of its gram formula mass. (c) If equal volumes of two solutions of the same molarity exactly react with one another, what relative number of molecules of the solutes are reacting?

*30. (a) How many moles of NaCl are dissolved in 150 mL of solution if the concentration of the solution is 0.360 M? (b) How many grams are dissolved?

31. (a) How many moles of dextrose, $C_6H_{12}O_6$, are dissolved in 320 mL of a 0.250 M solution of this sugar? (b) How many grams of dextrose are in the solution?

32. A mass of 98 g of sulfuric acid, H_2SO_4, are dissolved in water to prepare a 0.50 M solution. What is the volume of the solution, in liters?

*33. A solution of Na_2CO_3 contains 53 g of solute in 200 mL of solution. What is its molarity?

34. What is the molarity of a solution of HNO_3 which contains 12.6 g of solute in 500 mL of solution?

17-18   Molality

Molality is another unit of solution concentration commonly used in chemistry. **Molality** is the number of moles of solute dissolved in one kilogram of solvent.

$$\text{molality} = \frac{\text{moles of solute}}{\text{kilograms of solvent}}$$

Figure 17-17

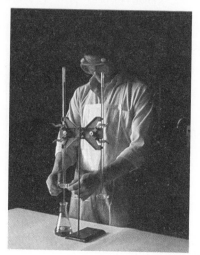

Chemists and technicians who work in medical laboratories must be especially careful that the solutions they work with are of the correct concentration.

Molal concentrations are indicated by the small letter "*m*." For example, the concentration of a 1 molal NaCl solution can be written 1 *m* NaCl.

SAMPLE PROBLEM 1

Suppose that 0.25 moles of sugar are dissolved in 1000 grams of water. What is the molal concentration of this solution?

Solution. Molality is the number of moles of solute dissolved in 1 kilogram of solvent. The problem tells us that 0.25 moles of sugar are dissolved in 1000 grams—which is 1 kilogram—of solvent. Therefore, the molality of the solution is 0.25 *m*.

SAMPLE PROBLEM 2

A mass of 23 grams of ethyl alcohol, C_2H_5OH, is dissolved in 500 mL of water. What is the molal concentration of this solution?

Solution. One mole of C_2H_5OH will have a mass of 46 g as shown below:

$$2 \text{ moles C atoms} \times 12 \text{ g/mole} = 24 \text{ g C}$$
$$6 \text{ moles H atoms} \times 1 \text{ g/mole} = 6 \text{ g H}$$
$$1 \text{ mole O atoms} \times 16 \text{ g/mole} = \underline{16 \text{ g O}}$$
$$46 \text{ g}$$

Therefore, 23 grams of ethyl alcohol is 0.50 mole (23 g ÷ 46 g/mole = 0.50 mole). Since the density of water is 1 g/mL, 500 mL of water has a mass of 500 g, or 0.500 kg. The molal concentration of the solution is:

$$\text{molality} = \frac{\text{moles solute}}{\text{kilograms solvent}}$$

$$= \frac{0.50 \text{ mole}}{0.500 \text{ kg}}$$

$$= 1.0 \text{ molal}$$

Questions for Section 17-18

35. (a) Define *molality*. (b) By what letter is it indicated? (c) What is the essential difference between molarity and molality?
*36. A solution of $Ca(NO_3)_2$ contains 2.05 g of solute in 250 g of water. What is the molality of the solution?
37. What is the mass of water in a 2.5 *m* solution of $Ca(NO_3)_2$ if the mass of solute is 8.2 g?

CAN YOU EXPLAIN THIS?

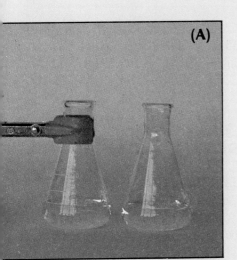

(A)

(A) The flask on the left contains a solution formed by dissolving the white solid lead nitrate, $Pb(NO_3)_2$, in water. The flask on the right contains a solution formed by dissolving the white solid sodium iodide, NaI, in water. (B) A yellow solid was formed when one solution was added to the other. (C) The solution containing the yellow solid was filtered, producing a clear filtrate and a yellow solid. Not shown: The clear filtrate was first heated to 90°C, and then the yellow solid added to it. All the yellow solid dissolved in the hot filtrate. (D) After the hot solution was cooled, crystals of a yellow solid were produced.

1. When the precipitate was filtered from the solution, what substances remained in the filtrate?
2. Why did the yellow solid dissolve into the filtrate when it was heated to 90°C?
3. What is the solid matter shown in the flask in the last photograph?
4. Why did the solid shown in the last photograph form?

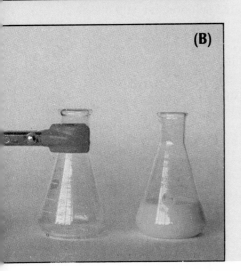

(B)

(C)

(D)

CHAPTER SUMMARY

1. In a heterogeneous mixture, the components are not spread uniformly. In a homogeneous mixture, the components are spread uniformly.
2. Solutions are homogeneous mixtures consisting of very small particles. Solutions are clear and transparent, made up of a single phase, and pass easily through filters. The dissolved particles do not settle out on standing.
3. The solute is the dissolved substance and the solvent is the medium of solution. The solute is usually present in smaller amount. If one of the components changed its phase in becoming part of the solution, it is generally considered the solute.
4. Aqueous solutions are solutions in water. Tinctures are solutions in alcohol.
5. Gaseous solutions are a mixture of gases or vapors. Liquid solutions consist of a liquid solvent in which any other phase is dissolved. Solid solutions are

uniform mixtures of atoms or molecules of solids.

6. The solubility of a solute states the quantity that can be dissolved in a definite amount of solvent at a given temperature and, in the case of gases, at a given pressure.

7. The solubility of a substance depends upon the nature of the solute and solvent, the temperature, and the pressure. With an increase in temperature, the solubility of gases decreases while the solubility of solids generally increases. Change of pressure affects the solubility of gases significantly but has practically no effect on the solubilities of solids or liquids.

8. The rate of solution depends upon the size of the solute particles, stirring, temperature, and the amount of solute already dissolved.

9. Polar solutes dissolve best in polar solvents. Nonpolar solutes dissolve best in nonpolar solvents.

10. In the formation of solutions, changes from solid to liquid, or from liquid to gas, involve an absorption of energy. The opposite is true for the reverse changes in phase.

11. Solubility curves and tables are used to describe solubilities.

12. A saturated solution is a stable solution that has dissolved as much solute as it can under the existing conditions. An unsaturated solution can still dissolve more solute at the given conditions.

13. A supersaturated solution is an unstable solution that has dissolved in it more solute than the saturated solution of the same solute at the same temperature.

14. A dilute solution contains a relatively small amount of solute. A concentrated solution contains a relatively large amount of solute.

15. Concentrations of solutions may be expressed quantitatively by (a) percentage by mass (b) molarity (c) molality.

16. Percentage by mass states the number of parts by mass of solute per hundred parts by mass of solution.

17. The molarity of a solution is the number of moles of solute in one liter of solution.

18. The molality of a solution is the number of moles of solute in 1000 g of solvent.

TERMS YOU SHOULD KNOW

homogeneous mixture	solid solutions	solution equilibrium
heterogeneous mixture	solubility	supersaturated solution
solution	effervescence	dilute solution
solute	rate of solution	concentrated solution
solvent	hydrated ions	percentage by mass
aqueous solutions	solubility curve	specific gravity
tincture	saturated solution	molarity
gaseous solutions	unsaturated solution	molality
liquid solutions		

REVIEW QUESTIONS

Section

17-2   1. In what way does a solution behave differently from a suspension when a beam of light is shined through it?

17-3　**2.** Define and state one example of (a) a solute (b) a solvent (c) a tincture (d) an aqueous solution

17-4　**3.** State one example of a (a) gaseous solution (b) liquid solution (c) solid solution.

17-5　**4.** (a) State three (3) factors that generally determine the degree of solubility of a substance. (b) Describe the effect of temperature change on the solubility of most solids. (c) Describe the effect of temperature change and pressure on the solubility of gases.

　　　5. (a) What do you see when a warm bottle of a carbonated beverage is opened? Explain. (b) What name is used to describe this action?

　　　6. (a) Describe the relationship between the pressure and the solubility of a gas. (b) Why doesn't the gas ammonia follow this rule?

17-6　**7.** What would you do to dissolve a given quantity of large potassium nitrate crystals as quickly as possible?

17-7　**8.** Explain what occurs to the ions of KCl as this salt dissolves in H_2O.

　　　9. Explain what happens when oil particles dissolve in benzene.

　　　10. Why can't benzene dissolve sodium chloride?

　　　11. Hydrogen chloride is very soluble in water; hydrogen is only slightly soluble. How can the difference be accounted for?

17-8　**12.** The top of a flat wooden block is wet with water and a small beaker is then placed on the wet area. Solid ammonium nitrate is placed into the beaker and a small volume of water is added to dissolve it. After a few minutes, it is observed that the beaker is frozen to the block. Explain.

17-9　**13.** Use the solubility curves (Figure 17-12) to describe the solubility of (a) KCl at $80°C$ (b) $KClO_3$ at $90°C$ (c) $NaNO_3$ at $10°C$.

17-10　**14.** Use the table of solubilities to describe the solubility of (a) calcium hydroxide (b) barium carbonate (c) aluminum sulfate.

17-11　**15.** (a) Explain why crystals of salt will dissolve in a saturated solution of sugar. (b) What will happen if a few sugar crystals are stirred in the same solution?

　　　16. Explain the solution equilibrium that exists in a saturated NaCl solution that is in contact with some excess NaCl crystals.

　　　17. Use the information in the answers to question #13, above, to state whether the following solutions are saturated or unsaturated: (a) 50 g of KCl in 100 g of H_2O at $80°C$ (b) 45 g of $KClO_3$ in 100 g of H_2O at $90°C$ (c) 40 g of $NaNO_3$ in 50 g of H_2O at $10°C$.

　　　18. What happens to a saturated solution of KCl at $30°C$ when it is heated to $40°C$?

17-12　**19.** A crystal of solute is added to three different solutions. It dissolves in solution A, remains unchanged in solution B, and causes precipitation of solute in solution C. Describe the nature of each original solution.

17-13　**20.** Saturated solutions of ammonia, potassium chlorate, potassium nitrate, and sodium nitrate are prepared at $10°C$. Which would you label as dilute, and which concentrated? Which is least concentrated? (Consult Figure 17-12 for help in answering this question.)

Section

17-15   1. An aqueous solution of NaOH contains 10.0 g of solute in 500 g of solution. What is the concentration of the solution expressed as a percentage by mass?

2. How many grams of NH_4Cl are dissolved in 70.0 g of solution if the solution's concentration is 20.0% by mass?

3. What is the mass of a 5.00% solution of $Al_2(SO_4)_3$ which contains 17.1 g of solute?

17-16   4. What is the mass of KOH in 200 mL of a 15% solution that has a density of 1.1 g/mL?

5. A 14.0% solution of $Al_2(SO_4)_3$ has a density of 1.30 g/mL. What is the mass of dissolved solute in 90.0 mL of solution?

6. What is the mass of solute in 40.0 mL of a 5.0% solution of $CuSO_4$ if the density of the solution is 1.05 g/mL?

17-17   7. A solution of NaOH contains 19.2 g of solute in 160 mL of solution. What is the molarity of the solution?

8. A solution of HCl is 0.300 M. What mass of acid is dissolved in 150 mL of solution?

9. What is the molarity of a solution of $Mg(OH)_2$ that contains 20.0 g of solute in 325 mL of solution?

17-18   10. A solution of $NaNO_3$ contains 34 g of solute dissolved in 100 g of water. What is the molality of the solution?

11. What mass of $AgNO_3$ is dissolved in 200 g of water if the molality of the solution is 0.300 m?

12. A water solution of NH_4Cl contains 15.0 g of solute in 200 g of solvent. What is the molality of the solution?

13. A water solution of sucrose, $C_{12}H_{22}O_{11}$, contains 10.2 g of the sugar in 200 mL of the solution. The density of the solution is 1.02 g/mL. What is its molality?

FOR FURTHER THOUGHT

17-6   1. A beaker contains a solution made up of a solid completely dissolved in a liquid solvent. For each of the following actions, state whether it will (1) always, (2) sometimes, or (3) never make the solution more concentrated. Explain your answers.
(a) Raise the temperature of the solution.
(b) Add more solute.
(c) Add more solvent.
(d) Stir the solution vigorously.
(e) Allow the solution to stand for 24 hours.

2. The concentration of an aqueous solution of a known solute is given in percentage by mass. Which of the following can be calculated?

17-14   (a) Grams of solute per kilogram of solution.
(b) The solubility of the solute in grams per kilogram of solution.

17-17   (c) The molarity of the solution.

17-18   (d) The molality of the solution.
(e) The number of grams of solute in 100 mL of solution.

The Colligative Properties of Solutions

Objectives

When you have completed this chapter, you will be able to:
- Relate freezing point lowering and boiling point elevation to the vapor pressure of solutions.
- Explain how colligative properties of a solution depend upon molality and the nature of the solvent.
- Determine molecular masses from freezing points and boiling points of solutions.

18-1 Introduction

Some solutions conduct electricity while others do not. One kind of apparatus used to determine the conductivity of a solution is illustrated in Figure 18-1 on the following page. When the switch is closed, the light bulb will light if the solution is a conductor. Substances whose solutions are conductors are called **electrolytes.** The light bulb will stay out if the solution is a nonconductor. Substances whose solutions do not conduct electricity are called **nonelectrolytes.** The discussion in this chapter is limited to solutes that are nonelectroytes.

The last chapter discussed ways of expressing the concentration of a solution. At that time no mention was made of the effects of dissolved substances on the properties of a liquid solvent. These effects are the subject of this chapter. We will be considering three properties of solutions. These properties are (1) vapor pressure, (2) freezing point, and (3) boiling point.

18-2 Vapor Pressure Depression

closed container

The vapor pressure of a liquid is a measure of the tendency of molecules in the liquid phase to escape as gas molecules. Liquids with high vapor pressures evaporate easily and are said to be **volatile.** Liquids with low vapor pressures do not evaporate easily and are said to

Figure 18-1

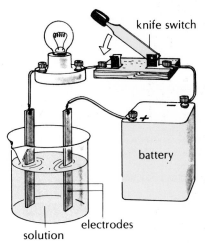

knife switch

battery

electrodes

solution

be nonvolatile. Some liquid solutes are volataile and others are not, while solid solutes are usually nonvolatile.

An increase in temperature will cause an increase in vapor pressure. Therefore, if we want a liquid to evaporate faster, we raise its temperature. Hot water, for example, evaporates faster than cold water.

When a solid is dissolved in a solvent, the vapor pressure of the resulting solution is always lower than the vapor pressure of the pure solvent. We say that the presence of a dissolved solute causes a depression (a lowering) of the vapor pressure of a solvent. **Vapor pressure depression** is the lowering in the vapor pressure of a liquid that occurs when substances are dissolved in the liquid. For solutes that are nonvolatile nonelectrolytes, the amount the vapor pressure is lowered, at a given temperature and pressure, depends upon two factors. (1) One factor is the molal concentration of the solution. (2) The other factor is the nature of the solvent.

For solutes that are nonvolatile nonelectrolytes, the lowering of the vapor pressure does not depend upon the nature of the solute particles, but only upon their molal concentration. The particles of one solute will lower the vapor pressure just as much as the particles of another when their molal concentrations are the same and they are dissolved in the same solvent. If a different solvent is used, the vapor pressure will be lowered by a different amount. Therefore, for a given molal concentration, the vapor pressure lowering depends upon the nature of the solvent.

For solutions of nonvolatile nonelectrolytes in a particular solvent, the vapor pressure depression is directly proportional to the molal concentration of the solutions. This relationship holds well for dilute solutions, but breaks down as concentrations increase. We illustrate these ideas with an example. Suppose that the vapor pressure of a certain pure solvent is 20 mm Hg at room temperature and the existing atmospheric pressure. Enough of a solute is added to a mass of solvent to make a 0.15 molal solution. The vapor pressure is then measured and found to be 18 mm Hg. The solute lowered the vapor pressure by 2 mm Hg (20 mm Hg − 18 mm Hg = 2 mm Hg.) Therefore, we say that the depression of the vapor pressure is 2 mm Hg for a 0.15 molal solution. Suppose that additional solute is added, causing the molal concentration to double to 0.30 m. Then, the depression of the vapor pressure will double to 4 mm Hg. That is, the 0.30 m solution will have a vapor pressure of 16 mm Hg. This lowering of the vapor pressure depends only on the molal concentration. It will be the same for any nonelectrolyte dissolved in that solvent.

Solutions have lowered vapor pressures because of changes in the spacing of solvent molecules. The distances between solvent molecules is increased as more and more solute molecules enter a solution. In other words, as solute concentration increases, solvent concentration decreases. A decrease in solvent concentration evidently reduces the rate at which the solvent evaporates and hence reduces the vapor pressure.

1. Distinguish between electrolytes and nonelectrolytes.
2. (a) Define *vapor pressure*. (b) If a substance is volatile, what is true of its vapor pressure? (c) What effect has an increase in temperature upon vapor pressure?
3. (a) How does a dissolved solid affect the vapor pressure of the solvent? (b) At a given temperature and pressure, what two factors determine the extent of the vapor pressure lowering caused by a solute that is a nonvolatile nonelectrolyte?
4. (a) Compare the vapor pressure lowerings in two solutions where the solvents are the same, the molalities equal, but the solutes (nonvolatile nonelectrolytes) are different. (b) What is the relationship between vapor pressure lowering and the molal concentration for solutions of nonvolatile nonelectrolytes in the same solvent? (c) Compare the accuracy of this relationship in dilute and concentrated solutions.
5. If, for a particular solvent, the vapor pressure depression is 1.3 mm Hg for a 0.24 *m* solution of a nonvolatile nonelectrolyte, what would it be for a 0.96 *m* solution of a different nonvolatile nonelectrolyte?
6. Explain why the vapor pressure of a solution of a nonvolatile solute should be lower than the vapor pressure of the pure solvent.

18-3   Freezing Point Depression

The **freezing point** is the temperature at which the solid and liquid phases of a substance can exist together without any net change in the amount of substance in either phase. For example, at 0°C, the freezing point of water, a piece of ice can float in water (at the same temperature) without the ice appearing to melt or the water appearing to freeze. This situation can exist only so long as no energy is being taken from or given to the water-ice system. Although the ice appears not to melt, some of it actually does melt. However, at the same time an equal mass of water freezes. As a result, the amounts of ice and water remain constant, and it *appears* as though neither the ice is melting nor the water freezing. Equilibrium exists between the solid and liquid phases of a substance at its freezing (melting) point, as discussed in Section 7-10.

The freezing point of a substance is the only temperature at which the solid and liquid phases of a substance have the same vapor pressure. This is shown graphically in Figure 18-2 for water. Notice the point where the vapor pressure curve for water meets the vapor pressure curve for ice. The temperature on the horizontal axis that refers to the point of intersection is the freezing temperature of water.

From the previous section, we saw that the vapor pressure of a solution is lower than the vapor pressure of the pure solvent. Suppose that we add a solute to some water to form a water solution. We then measure the vapor pressure of the solution over a range of tempera-

Figure 18-2

Vapor pressure curves for pure water (unbroken line) and for ice (dashed line). The freezing point of a substance is the only temperature at which the solid and liquid phases of a substance have the same vapor pressure. This temperature is shown on the graph by the point where the curve for ice meets the curve for pure water.

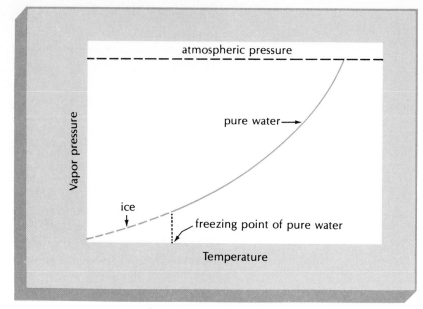

Figure 18-3

Vapor pressure curve for a water solution as well as for pure water and for ice. The freezing point of a solution is the temperature at which the vapor pressure of the solution and the vapor pressure of ice are the same. Note that this temperature is lower than the freezing point of pure water. The freezing point of a solution is lower than the freezing point of the pure solvent from which it is made.

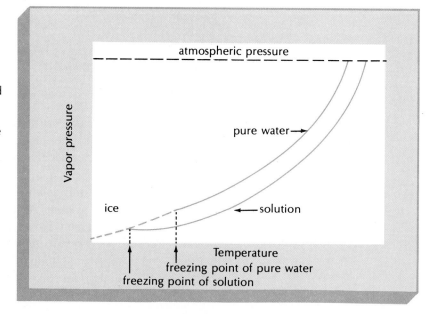

tures between the temperature at which the solution starts to freeze and the temperature at which it starts to boil. The curve we obtain from these measurements is given in Figure 18-3 along with the curve for pure water and the curve for ice. Notice that for every temperature, the vapor pressure of the solution is lower than the vapor pressure of pure water. This agrees with the discussion in the previous section. Dissolved matter causes a depression in the vapor pressure of the solvent. Notice also the point where the curve for the vapor pressure of the solution meets the curve for the vapor pressure of ice. This point is to the left of the point of intersection for pure water and ice. The point corresponds to a lower temperature. In other words, the freezing point of the solution is lower than the freezing point of the pure solvent. Dissolved matter causes a depression in the freezing point of a solution. The **freezing point depression** is the lowering of the freezing point of a liquid that occurs when substances are dissolved in the liquid.

While it is common to speak of "the freezing point of the solution," it is the solvent in the solution that is actually freezing. The solute particles remain dissolved in the liquid phase of the solvent.

The amount the freezing point is lowered by solutes that are nonelectrolytes depends upon the same two factors that affect vapor pressure lowering. (1) One factor is the molal concentration of the solution. (2) The other factor is the nature of the solvent. For solutes that are nonelectrolytes, one solute will lower the freezing point of a solution the same amount as another, provided the solutions are made from the same solvent and their molal concentrations are the same. The freezing point of different solvents is lowered by different amounts. The amount that the freezing point is lowered is characteristic of the solvent. For example, 1-molal water solutions of all nonelectrolytes freeze at 1.86°C below the freezing point of pure water. That is, they all freeze at −1.86°C rather than at 0°C. These same solutes forming 1-molal solutions with a different solvent will lower the freezing point by a different amount.

Car owners put to good use the effect of dissolving substances in a solvent. When water in a closed container freezes, the water expands and can easily break the container. Car owners in cold climates must make certain that the water doesn't freeze in the cooling systems of their cars. By dissolving chemicals in the water, the freezing point of the water can be lowered below the coldest outdoor temperatures. Ethylene glycol is a chemical commonly used as an antifreeze.

18-4   Boiling Point Elevation

Recall from Section 7-5 that the temperature at which the vapor pressure of a liquid equals atmospheric pressure is the boiling point of the liquid. Notice in Figure 18-4 that the vapor pressure curve for pure water and the line for atmospheric pressure intersect at a point corresponding to T_1. Therefore, T_1 is the boiling point of pure water. Figure 18-4 also shows the vapor pressure curve for a solution whose solvent is water and whose solute is a nonvolatile nonelectrolyte. The vapor pressure curve for the solution intersects the line for atmospheric pressure at a point corresponding to T_2. Therefore, T_2 is the boiling point of the solution. T_2 is a higher temperature than T_1, indicating that dissolved matter elevates (raises) the boiling point of the solution. Because of the lowered vapor pressure of the solution, a higher temperature is needed to bring the vapor pressure up to the level of the atmospheric pressure. In general, a solvent boils at a higher temperature when it has a nonvolatile solute dissolved in it. Now we see the full effect of a dissolved nonvolatile solute on a solvent. The freezing point of the solute is lowered and the boiling point is raised. A solvent can,

Figure 18-4

Vapor pressure curves for pure water, ice, and a solution whose solvent is water and whose solute is a nonvolatile nonelectrolyte. The boiling point is the temperature at which the vapor pressure equals atmospheric pressure. The boiling points are T_1 for pure water and T_2 for the solution. The solution boils at a higher temperature than the pure solvent. Notice that the solution is in the liquid phase over a broader range of temperatures than the pure solvent.

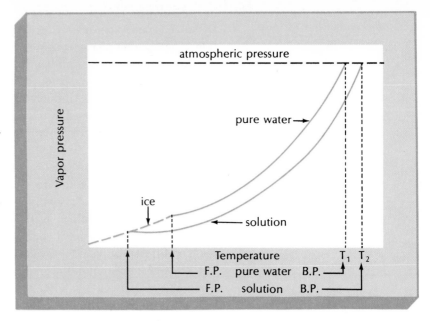

therefore, exist in the liquid phase over a wider range of temperatures if it has something dissolved in it. The increase in the boiling point of a liquid that occurs when substances are dissolved in the liquid is called the **boiling point elevation.**

As was true for vapor pressure depression and freezing point depression, boiling point elevation depends upon the nature of the solvent and the molal concentration of the solution. For example, for solutions whose solutes are nonvolatile nonelectrolytes, solutions of the same molal concentration made from different solvents will have different boiling point elevations. But solutions made from these solutes will all boil at the same elevated temperature provided they are made from the same solvent and their molal concentrations are the same.

Questions for Sections 18-3 and 18-4

7. (a) Define *freezing point.* (b) Describe the equilibrium that exists in an ice-water mixture at 0°C. (c) Compare the vapor pressures of the ice and water in the mixture.
8. Referring to the temperature-vapor pressure curves, show that the freezing point of a solution is lower than that of the pure solvent.
9. (a) What is the freezing point depression of a molal solution of a nonelectrolyte in water? (b) Why is ethylene glycol used in the cooling systems of autos that are driven in cold climates?
10. (a) Using the vapor pressure curves for water and a solution of a nonvolatile nonelectrolyte, compare the temperatures at which the water and the solution reach their boiling points. (b) In terms of the vapor pressure, explain why the solution should have a higher boiling point than the pure solvent.
11. What three properties of solutions depend upon the nature of the solvent and the molal concentration of the solution?

18-5 Molal Freezing Point Constant

It can be shown experimentally that a 1-molal solution of glycerine, sugar, or alcohol will lower the freezing point of water by 1.86°C. The normal freezing point of water is 0°C. Therefore, the freezing point of such a solution is −1.86°C. Moreover, one mole of *any* nonelectrolyte, dissolved in 1000 grams of water, lowers the freezing point by this same amount. This value, 1.86, is called the molal freezing point constant for water. It has the unit °C/molal. The constant, including its units, is 1.86°C/molal. The molal freezing point constant of a solvent is numerically equal to the number of degrees the freezing point of the solvent is depressed by a nonelectrolyte solute at a 1-molal concentration. Figure 18-5 gives the values of the molal freezing constant for several solvents.

The molal freezing point constant is used in the following relationship.

$$\Delta T_f = K_f m \qquad \text{(Eq. 1)}$$

In this relationship, the expression ΔT_f is used to represent *the depression of the freezing point.* The symbol Δ is the Greek letter *delta.* As used in the equation, *delta* means *change in.* Therefore, ΔT_f means *change in the freezing temperature.* In Equation 1, K_f is the *molal freezing point depression constant,* and *m* is the *molal concentration of the solution.*

Equation 1 is simply a mathematical way of expressing a direct relationship between the freezing point depression (ΔT_f) and the molal concentration of the solution (*m*). The **molal freezing point constant, K_f,** is the proportionality constant relating the depression of the freezing point of a liquid to the molal concentration of its solutions. In words, Equation 1 reads: "The depression of the freezing point is directly proportional to the molal concentration of the solution." The relationship expressed by Equation 1 holds well for dilute solutions but becomes less accurate as the concentrations of solutions increase.

A typical problem making use of Equation 1 is given in the sample problem.

Figure 18-5

Molal freezing point constants, K_f, for selected solvents. For solutions made from solutes that are non-electrolytes, K_f tells how much the freezing point of the solution is below the freezing point of the pure solvent when the concentration of the solution is 1 molal.

Solvent	K_f
acetic acid	3.90 °C / molal
benzene	4.90
formic acid	2.77
naphthalene	6.8 - 6.9
phenol	7.40
water	1.86

SAMPLE PROBLEM

How much will the freezing point be lowered if enough sugar is dissolved in water to make a 0.50-molal solution?

Solution. To solve the problem, we use Equation 1: $\Delta T_f = K_f m$. For water, K_f is 1.86°C/molal. The molal concentration, *m*, as given in the problem is 0.50 *m*.

Applying Equation 1,

$$\Delta T_f = K_f m$$

$$= \frac{1.86°C}{molal} \times 0.50 \text{ molal}$$

$$= 0.93°C$$

A 0.50-molal aqueous solution of sugar freezes at 0.93°C below the normal freezing point of water.

Questions for Section 18-5

12. (a) Explain what is meant by the *molal freezing pont constant* of a solvent?   (b) What is the value of K_f for acetic acid, benzene, and phenol (see Figure 18-5).   (c) Indicate the molal freezing point constant for water, including the units.
13. (a) Explain the equation, $\Delta T_f = K_f m$.   (b) How does its accuracy change with an increasing solution concentration?
*14. What is the freezing point of a solution of glycerine dissolved in water if the concentration of the solution is 0.24 *m*?
15. What is the freezing point of a 0.850 *m* aqueous solution of dextrose?
16. What is the freezing point of a solution that contains 68.4 g of sucrose, $C_{12}H_{22}O_{11}$, dissolved in 100 g of water?

18-6   Molecular Mass Determinations by Freezing Point Depression

Equation 1 of the previous section can also be used to determine the molecular masses of certain substances. Recall that Section 11-3 discussed a method for determining the molecular mass of gaseous substances. The method made use of the molar volume (22.4 liters), the volume occupied by 1 mole of gas at STP. Sometimes chemists want to determine the molecular masses of substances that are not gases. Then the method of Section 11-3 can be applied. However, not all substances can be vaporized. Some, while still solids, decompose when heated.

For substances that cannot be vaporized but that do dissolve in a solvent, Equation 1 provides another approach for finding molecular masses. First, a solution is made of the substance whose molecular mass is to be determined. This means adding a carefully measured mass of the substance to a carefully measured mass of the solvent. Then, the temperature of the solution is lowered until the solution begins to freeze. By finding the difference between the freezing points of the pure solvent and the solution, the depression of the freezing point, ΔT_f, can be determined. Knowing ΔT_f and looking up the value of the molal freezing point constant of the solvent, we can use Equation 1 to find the molal concentration of the solution *m*.

If: $\Delta T_f = K_f m$ **(Eq. 1)**

Chemistry in the Kitchen

In one sense, the chef is a chemist whose laboratory is the kitchen. When foods are cooked, chemical reactions take place that transform the raw food materials into their cooked state. Hence, to be a good cook, the cook must have an understanding of certain chemical principles. The most important of these principles is the effect of temperature on the rate of chemical change. Both cook and chemist have ways of carefully controlling temperature. For example, the cook's double boiler is the chemist's water bath.

In addition to an understanding of temperature, the cook must know how to make solutions, separate mixtures, and make accurate measurements of mass and volume — to name only some of the skills that are common to the science of chemistry and the art of cooking.

Then:

$$m = \frac{\Delta T_f}{K_f} \qquad \text{(Eq. 2)}$$

But,

$$m = \frac{\text{the number of moles of solute}}{\text{the number of kilograms of solvent}}$$

We can put this expression for m into Equation 2:

$$\frac{\text{(number of moles of solute)}}{\text{(number of kilograms of solvent)}} = \frac{\Delta T_f}{K_f}$$

or,

$$\left(\begin{array}{c}\text{number of moles}\\\text{of solute}\end{array}\right) = \frac{\Delta T_f}{K_f} \times \left(\begin{array}{c}\text{number of kilograms}\\\text{of solvent}\end{array}\right) \qquad \text{(Eq. 3)}$$

Since all the quantities on the right side of Equation 3 are known, we can calculate the number of moles of solute in the solution. And since we know the mass of the solute in grams, we can find the molar mass by dividing the mass of the solute in grams by the number of moles. The molar mass in grams is numerically equal to the molecular mass of the substance.

This reasoning can be made easier to follow by working a typical problem with actual numbers.

SAMPLE PROBLEM

Suppose that 98.0 grams of a nonelectrolyte are dissolved in 1 kilogram of water. The freezing point of this solution is found to be $-0.465°C$. What is the molecular mass of the solute?

Solution. If the substance freezes at $-0.465°C$, then its molal concentration can be found from the relationship:

$$\Delta T_f = K_f m \qquad \text{(Eq. 1)}$$

$$0.465°C = 1.86°C/\text{molal} \times m$$

$$m = \frac{0.465°C}{1.86°C/\text{molal}}$$

$$= 0.250 \text{ molal, or}$$

$$= 0.250 \text{ mole solute/kg solvent}$$

This molal concentration, $0.250\,m$, tells us that there is 0.250 mole of solute for each kilogram of solvent (water). Since there is 1 kg of water in the solution, there is 0.250 mole of solute in it.

But we know the mass of this solute. It is 98.0 grams. If we divide this mass by the number of moles, we obtain the mass per mole:

$$\frac{98.0 \text{ g}}{0.250 \text{ mole}} = 392 \text{ g/mole}$$

If the mass of one mole is 392 g, then the molecular mass is 392 u.

Chapter 18   The Colligative Properties of Solutions   **365**

17. Write the equation that expresses the number of moles of solute (nonelectrolyte) in a given solution in terms of freezing point lowering, freezing point constant, and the mass of the solvent.

*18. A solution contains 4.50 g of a nonelectrolyte dissolved in 225 g of water and has a freezing point of $-0.310°C$. What is the gram formula mass of the solute?

19. A solution of urea contains 18.0 g of solute in 200 g of water. Its freezing point is $-2.79°C$. What is the gram-molecular mass of urea?

18-7   Molal Boiling Point Constant

Solvent	K_b
acetic acid	3.07
acetone	1.71
benzene	2.53
carbon tetrachloride	5.03
chloroform	3.63
ethyl alcohol	1.22
methyl alcohol	0.83
phenol	3.56
toluene	3.33
water	0.52

Figure 18-6

Molal boiling point elevation constants, K_b, for selected solvents. K_b tells how much the boiling point of the solution is above the boiling point of the pure solvent when the concentration of the solution is 1 molal. The unit for the constants is °C/molal.

As was true for the molal freezing point constant, the molal boiling point constant (K_b) is characteristic of the solvent. For water, its value is 0.52°C/molal. That is, the boiling point of a 1-molal water solution of a nonvolatile nonelectrolyte is 0.52°C above the boiling point of pure water. At standard pressure, these solutions boil at 100.52°C. In general, the molal boiling point constant is numerically equal to the number of degrees the boiling point of the solvent is raised by non-volatile, nonconducting solutes that are at a 1-molal concentration. Values of the constant for several solvents are given in Figure 18-6.

The **molal boiling point constant,** K_b, is the proportionality constant that relates the elevation of the boiling point of a liquid to the molal concentrations of its solutions:

$$\Delta T_b = K_b m \qquad \textbf{(Eq. 4)}$$

Notice the similarity between Equation 1 and Equation 4. Equation 4 can be applied in the same way as Equation 1. However, while boiling point elevations can be used to determine molecular masses, freezing point depressions are a more accurate way to make these determinations. The relationship expressed by Equation 4 is more accurate for dilute solutions, but it breaks down for more concentrated solutions.

18-8   Colligative Properties of Solutions

Vapor pressure depressions, freezing point depressions, and boiling point elevations all have something in common. They are characteristic of the solvent. Their values depend upon the nature of the solvent and the concentration of, but not the nature of, the solute. The word *colligative* means *bound together*. Properties that are bound together under the same rule, law, or hypothesis are referred to by scientists as colligative properties.

20. (a) Explain the significance of the molal boiling point constant. (b) Express its value for water, including appropriate units. (c) What is the boiling point of a 1-molal aqueous solution of a nonvolatile nonelectrolyte at standard pressure?

21. (a) Write the equation relating molality and boiling point elevation. (b) Which property is more accurate for molecular mass determination, freezing point depression or boiling point rise?

*22. (a) What is the molal boiling point constant for carbon tetrachloride? (b) The boiling point of CCl_4 is $76.8°C$. A given solution contains 8.10 g of a nonvolatile nonelectrolyte in 300 g of CCl_4. It boils at $78.4°C$. What is the gram molecular mass of the solute?

23. The molal boiling point constant for ethyl alcohol is $1.22°C/molal$. Its boiling point is $78.4°C$. A solution of 14.2 g of a nonvolatile nonelectrolyte in 250 g of the alcohol boils at $79.8°C$. What is the gram molecular mass of the solute?

24. (a) What name is given to the properties that are bound together under the same rule or law? (b) Name three examples of such properties.

CHAPTER SUMMARY

1. Electrolytes are substances whose solutions are conductors of electricity. Nonelectrolytes are substances whose solutions do not conduct the current.

2. The vapor pressure of a liquid is a measure of the tendency of its molecules to escape into the gaseous phase.

3. An increase in temperature causes an increase in vapor pressure.

4. The depression of the vapor pressure of a solution of a nonelectrolyte depends upon the molal concentration and the nature of the solvent.

5. For solutions of nonvolatile nonelectrolytes in a given solvent, the vapor pressure depression is directly proportional to the molal concentration of the solution.

6. At the freezing point, solid and liquid phases exist in a state of equilibrium.

7. For solutions of nonelectrolytes, the freezing point lowering is proportional to the molal concentration.

8. The molal freezing point constant for water is $1.86°C/molal$.

9. For solutions of nonvolatile nonelectrolytes, the boiling point elevation is proportional to the molal concentration.

10. The molal boiling point constant for water is $0.52°C/molal$.

11. The equation $\Delta T_f = K_f m$ expresses the direct proportionality that exists between the depression of the freezing point and the molal concentration of a solution of a nonelectrolyte. A similar equation, $\Delta T_b = K_b m$, exists for the elevation of the boiling point.

12. The equations for freezing and boiling point changes with molality hold fairly well for dilute solutions but become less accurate as concentrations increase.

13. The equation for freezing point depression is used to make molecular mass determinations for nonelectrolytes. It can be modified to yield the following equation:

Chapter 18   The Colligative Properties of Solutions   367

$$\left(\begin{array}{c} \text{the number of moles} \\ \text{of solute in the solution} \end{array} \right) = \frac{\Delta T_f}{K_f} \times \left(\begin{array}{c} \text{the number of} \\ \text{kilograms of solvent} \end{array} \right)$$

The number of moles of solute in the solution divided into the number of grams of solute in the solution gives the molecular mass of the solute.

14. Vapor pressure depression, freezing point lowering, and boiling point elevation are called colligative properties.

TERMS YOU SHOULD KNOW

electrolyte	vapor pressure	boiling point elevation
nonelectrolyte	depression	molal freezing point
vapor pressure	freezing point	constant
volatile	freezing point	molal boiling point
	depression	constant

REVIEW QUESTIONS

Section

18-1
1. Two solutions are tested to determine their electrical conductivity. A salt solution caused the light bulb to glow brightly. A glycerine solution did not light the bulb at all. Describe each substance with respect to its ability to behave as an electrolyte.

18-2
2. (a) Compare the vapor pressures of alcohol, water, and a heavy lubricating oil. (b) What can be done to the water to increase its vapor pressure? (c) How can its vapor pressure be decreased?

3. Which of the following factors, if changed, will alter the vapor pressure depression of a liquid in which only a nonvolatile nonelectrolyte is dissolved: (1) The nature of the solute (2) the concentration of the solute (3) the nature of the solvent.

4. How is the vapor pressure depression of a solution of a nonvolatile nonelectrolyte related to the molal concentration of the solution?

5. In terms of solvent concentration, explain the vapor pressure depression in a solution of a nonvolatile solute.

18-3
6. (a) Describe the changes that occur in a mixture of ice and water where the temperature remains at 0°C. (b) Compare the vapor pressures of the ice and water in this mixture. (c) What happens when a small amount of heat is applied to the mixture?

7. (a) What is the temperature in a one-molal solution of a nonelectrolyte in water that is cooled until it forms ice particles? (b) What happens if the temperature is changed to 0°C?

8. How is the freezing point depression in a solution of a nonelectrolyte related to the molality of the solution?

18-4
9. Why does a solution of a nonvolatile solute have a higher boiling point than that of the pure solvent?

10. (a) How is the boiling point rise in the solution of a nonvolatile nonelectrolyte related to the molality of the solution? (b) Referring to the vapor pressure-temperature curves, describe the relative temperatures at which the solution and pure solvent reach vapor pressures of 760 mm Hg.

11. Upon what two factors does the extent of the vapor pressure depression, freezing point lowering, and boiling point rise depend?

18-5   12. Explain what is meant by the statement that the molal freezing point constant of water is 1.86°C/molal.

13. Write the equation showing the relationship between the freezing point depression of a solution and its molality.

18-6   14. Using the equation in question 13, derive one that expresses the number of moles of solute in terms of the freezing point depression, molal freezing point constant, and the solvent mass.

18-7   15. The boiling point of benzene is 80°C. Its molal boiling point constant is 2.53°C/molal. Explain the meaning of the constant.

16. Write the equation that relates the boiling point rise to the molality.

18-8   17. (a) Name three colligative properties of solutions. (b) What is the meaning of the term *colligative*, and how is its meaning related to the properties of solutions described in this chapter?

REVIEW PROBLEMS

18-2   1. The vapor pressure lowering of a solution containing 100 g of sucrose in 500 g of water at 25°C is 0.250 mm Hg. What is the vapor pressure lowering of a solution containing 50.0 g of sucrose in 50.0 g of water at 25°C?

18-5   2. What is the freezing point of a solution of ethyl alcohol, C_2H_5OH, that contains 20.0 g of the solute dissolved in 250 g of water?

3. How many grams of ethylene glycol, $C_2H_4(OH)_2$, must be added to 500 g of water to yield a solution that will freeze at −7.44°C?

18-6   4. A solution of 1.00 g of nicotine in 20.0 g of water has a freezing point of −0.574°C. (a) What is the gram molecular mass of the nicotine? (b) If the empirical formula of nicotine is C_5H_7N, what is its molecular formula?

18-7   5. Calculate the mass of a mole of a compound that raises the boiling point of water to 100.78°C at 1 atm when 51 g of the compound are dissolved in 500 g of water.

FOR FURTHER THOUGHT

18-3   1. Methyl alcohol is cheaper than ethylene glycol and its freezing point lowering effect on water is greater. Why isn't it used very much in car radiators?

18-4   2. Ethylene glycol is relatively nonvolatile and is used in auto radiators as an antifreeze. Why is it allowed to remain in the radiator in the warm months?

18-7   3. A solution of sugar in water is boiling at a temperature of 100.9°C. Heat is being supplied at a rate just sufficient to keep the solution boiling.

(a) Describe what will probably happen if a quantity of sugar is quickly stirred into the solution.

(b) What temperature change, if any, would you expect to observe as the heating continues?

(c) Is there any limit to this temperature change? Explain.

UNIT 6

Kinetics and Equilibrium

In chemical plants and factories such as this petrochemical plant in Torrance, California, industrial processes are used to generate useful substances on a large scale. Industrial chemists must be able to control a reaction so that large amounts of the desired product are produced quickly and economically. In order to do so, they apply what are called *equilibrium principles*. The important topics of chemical kinetics—the study of reaction rates and mechanisms—and chemical equilibrium are the subject of this unit.

Chemical Kinetics

19-1 Introduction

Chemical kinetics is the branch of chemistry concerned with the rates of chemical reactions and with the mechanisms of chemical reactions. The **reaction rate,** or velocity, of a chemical reaction is obtained by measuring the number of moles of reactant used up, or the number of moles of products formed, in a unit volume of reaction mixture per unit of time. The meaning of the expression "mechanisms of chemical reactions" will be made clear later in the chapter.

Chemical reactions take place at different rates. For example, consider two extremes. When water solutions of barium nitrate and sulfuric acid are mixed, a white precipitate of barium sulfate is formed. This and other types of precipitation reactions take place at a rapid rate. At the other extreme are the changes that take place as rocks undergo chemical weathering. These types of changes take place so slowly that a human lifetime is often too short a time to observe them.

Figure 19-1

We try to slow down or prevent altogether certain kinds of chemical change. The rusting of iron is a change of this kind.

Figure 19-2

This statue is being attacked by chemical pollutants in the air. Although the chemical change is too slow to observe from one day to the next, the damage occurring over a period of a year is noticeable.

Most chemical changes take place at rates between these two extremes.

Scientists have used the collision theory to explain why reactions take place at different rates. The collision theory states that particles must collide in order for chemical change to occur. These particles may be ions, atoms, or molecules. Suppose that particle *A* and particle *B* react to form particle *C*. As *A* and *B* approach each other, they begin to interact. During this interaction, some electrons shift their positions. As electron shifts occur, old bonds may be broken and new bonds formed. However, for reaction to occur, reacting molecules must collide with each other effectively. An **effective collision** is one in which the colliding particles approach each other at the proper angle and with the proper amount of energy. Thus, how often particles collide and how effective these collisions are determine how much reactant will change to product during a given unit of time. We can compare reacting particles to the interactions between fighters in a boxing ring. The boxer who wants to finish the fight fast knows that it takes more than just a quick series of punches. The punches must have the right amount of force and must fall on the right places to do the job.

There are many reasons for wanting to understand what determines the rate of a chemical reaction. For example, chemical reactions within our bodies must proceed at certain rates if we are to stay healthy. It is important, therefore, to know what controls these reaction rates. Controlling the rates of chemical reactions within our bodies is an area of research in biochemistry. Industrial chemists often want to change the rate of a reaction. They would like to speed up the reaction for the production of ammonia and slow down the rusting of iron. It has been found that there are four main factors that affect the rate of a chemical reaction. These factors are (1) the nature of the reactants, (2) the concentration of the reactants, (3) the temperature, and (4) the use of catalysts.

Questions for Section 19-1

1. (a) Define *chemical kinetics*. (b) Explain what is meant by the rate of a chemical reaction. (c) Give an example of a slow chemical change and one that is rapid.
*2. What are the two characteristics of an effective collision?
3. Why are (a) industrial chemists and (b) biochemists interested in chemical reaction rates?
4. What are the four (4) chief factors that affect the rate of a chemical reaction?

19-2 The Nature of the Reactants

In chemical reactions, some bonds are broken and others are formed. Therefore, the rates of chemical reactions should be affected

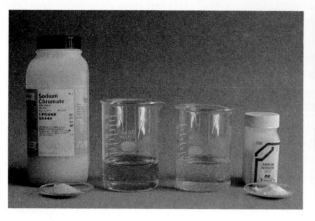

Figure 19-3

The left photo shows the solid substances barium nitrate, $Ba(NO_3)_2$ (watch glass on the right), and sodium chromate, Na_2CrO_4 (watch glass on the left). Also shown are their aqueous solutions. The photo on the right shows the yellow precipitate that is formed instantly when the dissolved ionic substances are mixed.

by the nature of the bonds in reacting substances. Reactions in which there are only slight rearrangements of electrons are usually rapid at room temperature. For example, reactions between ionic substances in aqueous solution may take place in a fraction of a second. Thus, the reaction between solutions of barium nitrate and sodium chromate is very fast. The yellow precipitate of barium chromate (Figure 19-3) appears immediately. In reactions in which many covalent bonds must be broken, reaction usually takes place slowly at room temperature. Hydrogen peroxide solution, for example, is unstable and slowly decomposes to water and oxygen at room temperature. It takes about 17 minutes for half of the peroxide in a 0.50 M solution to decompose. Reacting particles have unique characteristics that affect the speeds of the reactions they take part in.

19-3 The Concentration of the Reactants

Figure 19-4

Moistened steel wool (A) is changed to rust (B) very rapidly (in three days) because the threads of iron in the pad have a large surface area for contact with oxygen in the air. An equal mass or iron in a spherical shape would rust much more slowly because of its small surface area. (C) A rusted pad reduced to a pile of tiny pieces by squeezing it.

(A)

(B)   (C)

An increase in the concentration of any one or more of the reactants *usually but not always* increases the rate of a reaction if the reaction is *homogeneous*. A **homogeneous reaction** is one in which all the reactants are in the same phase. The reaction between hydrogen gas and oxygen gas to produce water is a homogeneous reaction. Reactions between the solutions of two dissolved solids are also homogeneous reactions.

A **heterogeneous reaction** is one which involves reactants in more than one phase. An example is the reaction between oxygen, a gas, and iron, a solid (to produce iron oxide, or rust). When a solid reacts with a gas, reaction will take place faster if the surface area of the solid is increased, since atoms of the gas can react only with those atoms of the solid that are on the surface of the solid. A bar of iron after being cut into small pieces will rust faster than the whole bar, since the surface area increases as the pieces become smaller. See Figure 19-4.

For gaseous and liquid reactants, concentration is often expressed in terms of the mass or number of moles of reactant per unit volume. The concentration of a gaseous reactant can be increased by decreasing the space the gas sample is occupying. Conversely, allowing the sample to expand into a greater volume will decrease the concentration. For reactants dissolved in a liquid solvent, concentration can be increased by removing some of the solvent. This can be done by evaporating some of the solvent. Increasing the mass of dissolved solute in a given volume will also increase the concentration of reactant. Adding more solvent will decrease concentration.

An increase in reaction rate caused by an increase in concentration can be explained by the collision theory. An increase in concentration means that there are smaller spaces between the reacting particles. With less distance to travel between collisions, more collisions will take place during any given unit of time. Hence, increase in concentration increases the frequency of the collisions. See Figure 19-5.

Figure 19-5

(A) *Molecules of two reacting substances represented by spheres of different colors.* (B) Pushing the plunger down forces the molecules closer together, and increases the concentrations of the particles. With the particles closer together, collisions between particles will be more frequent and the rate of the reaction will increase.

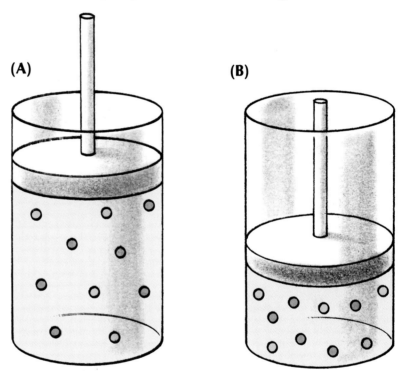

This section began by stating that an increase in concentration *usually but not always* increases the rate of a homogeneous reaction. Later in this chapter we will see why the statement had to be qualified by the phrase *usually but not always*. In the meantime, keep in mind that only an experiment will tell if the concentration of a particular reactant affects the rate of the reaction.

19-4 Temperature

An increase in temperature increases the rate of almost all chemical reactions. For many reactions, a 10°C rise in temperature approximately doubles the speed of the reaction.

An explanation for the effect of temperature on reaction rate can be found in the collision theory. Recall from Section 4-10 that an increase in temperature means that the kinetic energy (and hence the speeds) of the reacting particles has increased. The faster-moving particles collide more often and their greater kinetic energy increases the effectiveness of these collisions.

19-5   Catalysts

A **catalyst** (KAT-uh-list) is a substance that speeds up a chemical reaction without itself being permanently altered. For example, when a test tube containing solid potassium chlorate is heated, oxygen gas is given off. Another solid, potassium chloride, remains in the tube in the place of the potassium chlorate. This reaction takes place much more rapidly if solid manganese dioxide is mixed with the potassium chlorate before heat is applied. When the reaction ends and no more oxygen is given off, none of the potassium chlorate will be left in the tube but all of the manganese dioxide will remain. Because the manganese dioxide speeds up the reaction, it must play some part in the reaction. However, any change it does undergo is only temporary, since all of it can be recovered in its original form at the end of the reaction.

Platinum metal is used as a catalyst in many of the reactions of hydrogen gas. Enzymes are catalysts for many biochemical processes.

There are some substances that slow down chemical reactions. These substances are called inhibitors.

Finding a catalyst for a particular chemical reaction has been largely a matter of trial and error. Some catalysts have been discovered by accident. Chemists hope eventually to learn enough about catalysts to be able to make an effective catalyst for any particular reaction. Catalysis (kuh-TAL-uh-sis), the speeding up of chemical reactions by substances that are not themselves permanently altered during reaction, is the subject of much research nowadays.

Figure 19-6

Research chemists whose special area of interest is catalysts.

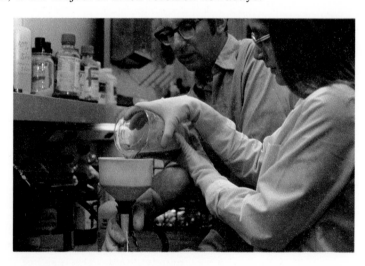

5. Explain why the nature of the reactants is responsible for the reaction rate in a specific reaction which is (a) rapid (b) slow.
6. (a) Explain the difference between a homogeneous and a heterogeneous reaction. (b) How does an increase in concentration usually affect the speed of a homogeneous reaction? (c) Explain why a given mass of iron will rust faster when broken into small pieces than when in the form of a single bar.
*7. How can the concentrations of (a) two reacting gases and (b) two reacting solutions be increased to cause an increase in the rate of reaction?
*8. Why does an increase in reactant concentration cause an increase in reaction rate?
9. In terms of collision theory, explain why the rate of reaction increases when the temperature is increased.
10. Define *catalyst* and state how this definition can be applied to the manganese dioxide used in the preparation of oxygen from potassium chlorate.

19-6 Reaction Mechanisms

The flame of an oxy-acetylene torch reaches a temperature of 3300°C, a temperature hot enough to cut through metals by quickly melting them. As is true of the burning of most fuels, the products of the complete combustion of acetylene are carbon dioxide and water. The balanced equation for the reaction is:

$$2C_2H_2 + 5O_2 \longrightarrow 4CO_2 + 2H_2O \qquad \textbf{(Eq. 1)}$$
acetylene

The balanced equation seems to imply that 2 molecules of acetylene collide with 5 molecules of oxygen to yield the products. Chemists know that for 2 acetylene molecules and 5 oxygen molecules all to reach the same point at the same time is an extremely unlikely event. Collisions of even 3 particles are rare. If a 7-particle collision were necessary for reaction to take place in the gaseous phase, the reaction would never be observed. Since in fact oxygen and acetylene react rapidly, the reaction must proceed through a series of steps. Each step probably involves a collision of only 2 particles.

Figure 19-7

When acetylene, a gas, is burned with oxygen, a very hot flame is produced. The net equation for the reaction, $2C_2H_2 + 5O_2 \rightarrow 4CO_2 + 2H_2O$, does *not* reveal the mechanism of the reaction.

Chemists believe that most chemical reactions, not just that between oxygen and acetylene, take place by means of simple steps. We illustrate this idea with the hypothetical reaction between substances A and B to produce C. The first step in the reaction is the reaction of a particle of A with a particle of B to produce a particle of the substance I. The second step is the reaction of another particle of A with a particle of I to produce a particle of C:

$$\textit{Step 1:} \qquad \underbrace{A + B}_{\text{reactants}} \longrightarrow \underbrace{I}_{\substack{\text{intermediate} \\ \text{product}}}$$

$$\textit{Step 2:} \qquad A + I \longrightarrow \underbrace{C}_{\text{product}}$$

If we add Steps 1 and 2, the intermediate particle I, found on the right in Step 1 and on the left in Step 2, cancels out to produce the net equation:

$$\textit{Net equation:} \qquad 2A + B \longrightarrow C$$

For our hypothetical reaction, a two-particle collision (Step 1) followed by a second two-particle collision (Step 2) produces the product C. It is wrong to interpret the net equation as meaning that the product C is produced from a three-particle collision between two particles of A and one particle of B. When giving the equation for a reaction, the net equation is what is usually given, not the steps that add up to the net equation. In fact, the steps that add up to the net equation are not known for many reactions. All the equations given in this book have been net equations and will be net equations unless otherwise indicated.

The series of steps by which reacting particles rearrange themselves to form the products of a chemical reaction is called the **reaction mechanism.** Determining reaction mechanisms is difficult because the intermediate product or products often have short lives. Produced in Step 1 of a mechanism, they may be used up immediately in Step 2. Trying to isolate and determine the structure of such temporary substances is difficult.

Figure 19-8 (left photo)

The very dark, brown liquid in the beaker and the brown vapor above the liquid are bromine, one of only two elements that are liquids at room temperature and standard pressure. Research has shown that the mechanism for the reaction between hydrogen and bromine involves several steps even though the net equation for the reaction is very simple:
$$H_2 + Br_2 \longrightarrow 2HBr$$

Figure 19-9 (right photo)

Crystals of the element iodine, a solid at room temperature. Although the net equation for the reaction of iodine with hydrogen is similar to the net equation for the reaction of bromine with hydrogen, research has shown that the mechanism for the iodine reaction is much simpler.

A reaction whose mechanism has been studied is the reaction between hydrogen and bromine. The net equation for the reaction is

$$H_2 + Br_2 \longrightarrow 2HBr \qquad \text{(Eq. 2)}$$

Studies show that the path from hydrogen and bromine to hydrogen bromide has several steps. In these steps it is believed that single atoms of hydrogen and bromine as well as their diatomic molecules are reactants.

The net equation for the reaction between H_2 and I_2 is very similar to that between H_2 and Br_2:

$$H_2 + I_2 \longrightarrow 2HI \qquad \text{(Eq. 3)}$$

Since the equations for the two reactions are similar, you might expect similar mechanisms. However, studies of the iodine reaction suggest that its mechanism is much simpler. From the studies of these two reactions, it is clear that a net equation cannot be used to predict the mechanism of a reaction. Only experiments shed light on this question.

19-7   Reaction Mechanisms and Rates of Reactions

In Section 19-3 it was stated that an increase in the concentration of any one or more of the reactants *usually but not always* increases the rate of a homogeneous reaction. We can now explain why we could not say "... *always* increases the rate of a homogeneous reaction."

The different steps in a reaction mechanism take place at different rates. One step in a mechanism may occur almost instantaneously, while another step occurs slowly. The rate of the overall reaction is then determined by the rate of the slowest step. The slowest step in a reaction mechanism is called the **rate-determining step.** An analogy may be helpful in understanding this point. Suppose three people, *A*, *B*, and *C*, team up to send out a mailing. They decide to do the mailing in three steps:

Step 1: Person *A* is to write the addresses of the sender and receiver on the envelopes.
Step 2: Person *B* is to fold the letters and stuff them into the envelopes.
Step 3: Person *C* is to seal and stamp the envelopes.

In this three-step process, the rate-determining step is Step 1, since it takes longer to write two addresses on an envelope than to do either of the other tasks. *B* and *C* will finish an envelope and will then have to

Chemicals for Fighting Fires and Promoting Plant Growth

The photo shows an airplane discharging a fire retarding material used to control brush and forest fires. The material can be applied from fire trucks and backpack pumps as well as from aircraft. In addition to containing a fire retardant, the material also contains a plant nutrient, diammonium phosphate. This chemical helps promote the growth of new trees and vegetation in burned out areas.

wait for *A* to finish addressing the next envelope. If two or three more people are assigned to sealing and stamping, the job will get done no faster. Nor will more people assigned to Step 2 speed up the job. Step 1 is the bottleneck. Only by putting more people to addressing the envelopes will the mailing get out faster.

Let us see how sending out a mailing relates to a reaction with a three-step mechanism. In the first step, two kinds of particles, *A* and *B*, react to produce an intermediate particle, I_1. In the second step, particle *A* reacts with the intermediate to produce a second kind of intermediate particle, I_2. In the third step, a particle *C* reacts with I_2 to produce a particle *D*. These steps are summarized below:

$$\text{Step 1:} \qquad A + B \longrightarrow I_1 \quad \textit{(fast)}$$
$$\text{Step 2:} \qquad A + I_1 \longrightarrow I_2 \quad \textit{(slow)}$$
$$\text{Step 3:} \qquad C + I_2 \longrightarrow D \quad \textit{(fast)}$$
$$\textit{Net equation:} \quad 2A + B + C \longrightarrow D$$

Now suppose that we increase the concentration of C. This will make Step 3 take place even faster than before, but it will have little effect on the speed of the overall reaction since Step 2 is the rate-determining step. However, increasing the concentration of A would speed up the overall reaction since A is a reactant in Step 2, the rate-determining step. Knowing the mechanism of a reaction provides a basis for predicting the effect of the concentration of a reactant on the overall rate of a reaction. If the reaction mechanism is unknown, then experiments must be done to determine the effect of concentration on reaction rate.

Questions for Sections 19-6 and 19-7

11. (a) Why is it more likely for a reaction to take place in a series of steps rather than in one step? (b) Define *reaction mechanism*.
*12. (a) Describe a probable mechanism for the reaction
$$2Na + S \rightarrow Na_2S$$
(b) Can the same mechanism be used to explain all net reactions of the general form: $2A + B \rightarrow C$? (c) What procedure should be followed to determine the mechanism of any specific reaction?
13. Which rate in the steps of a reaction mechanism determines the rate of the net reaction?
14. The reaction $2A + B + C \rightarrow D$, takes place through the following mechanism:

$$\text{Step 1 (fast): } A + B \rightarrow I_1$$
$$\text{Step 2 (slow): } I_1 + A \rightarrow I_2$$
$$\text{Step 3 (fast): } I_2 + C \rightarrow D$$

What is the effect on the rate of the overall reaction of an increase in the concentration of each of the following: (a) Substance *A*. Explain. (b) Substance *B*. Explain. (c) Substance *C*. Explain.

19-8   Activation Energy

The transition-state theory is based on the collision theory. According to the transition-state theory, chemical structures that are unlike the structures of either the reactants or the products exist for brief periods of time while the atoms rearrange themselves during a chemical reaction. These short-lived particles are formed in the following manner. Imagine a reaction between a particle of substance A and a particle of substance B to produce particles of substances C and D. For reaction to occur, A and B must collide. If they approach from the wrong angle or have too little kinetic energy, they will rebound from each other without forming particles C and D. However, if the angle of approach is right and the particles have enough energy, a particle containing all the atoms of both A and B is temporarily formed. This particle is called an activated complex or a transition-state complex. Thus, an **activated complex** is a short-lived particle that will temporarily exist when reacting molecules collide at the proper angle with the proper amount of energy. Activated complexes have short lives because they are unstable. Shortly after the activated complex is formed, it may break apart either to reform the original particles A and B or it may form the product particles C and D. The minimum amount of energy needed to form the activated complex is called the **activation energy.** See Figure 19-10.

Figure 19-10

(A) Two reacting particles approach each other. (B) They form an activated complex. (C) After forming the activated complex, the complex may break apart to reform the original substances, or (D) it may break apart to form one or more new substances.

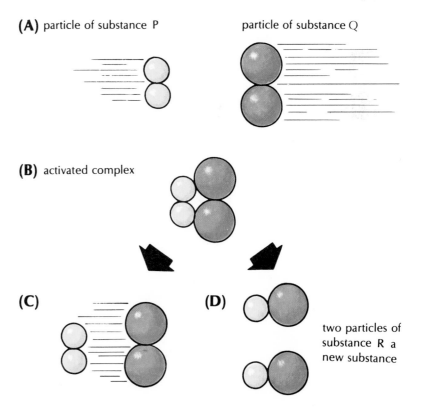

(A) particle of substance P   particle of substance Q

(B) activated complex

(C)

(D)

two particles of substance R a new substance

19-9   Potential Energy Diagram

The relationship between the activation energy and the energy absorbed or given off during a reaction can be shown graphically on a potential energy diagram. On a potential energy diagram, the potential energy of the reactants, activated complex, and products are shown on the vertical axis. The horizontal axis, called the reaction coordinate, shows the progress of the reaction. Figure 19-11 shows a potential energy diagram for the reaction between two substances, A and B, to produce substance C. The flat portion of the graph at the left shows the combined potential energies of the molecules of substances A and B when these molecules are too far apart for any interaction between them to have taken place. Following the curve toward the right, the curve begins to rise as molecules of A and B begin to interact and lose speed. The lost kinetic energy becomes potential energy, which is why the curve begins to rise. At the top of the "hill," potential energy becomes a maximum. This is the potential energy of the activated complex. If the activated complex breaks apart to form the product substance C, the potential energy decreases, as shown by the right-hand side of the curve. At the end of the reaction, molecules of substance C have the potential energy shown by the flat portion of the graph on the extreme right.

Figure 19-11

A potential energy diagram for the reaction between substances A and B to produce substance C. The potential energy (P.E.) of the reactants is shown on the left, and that of the product, on the right. Before reaction can occur, the potential energy of the reactants must increase by the amount shown as the activation energy. The difference between the potential energies of the reactants and the product is ΔH, the heat of the reaction. In this case, the reaction is exothermic—the heat of reaction is given off.

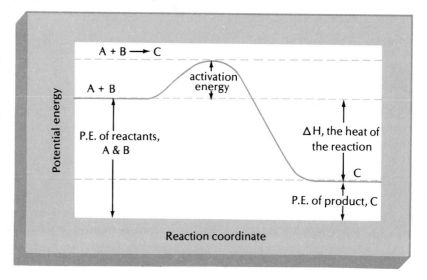

For this particular reaction, there has been a net loss of potential energy. That is, the potential energy of the reactants is greater than that of the product. The potential energy that is lost is released during the reaction. The reaction is exothermic. The difference between the potential energy of the reactants and the potential energy of the product is the heat released during the reaction. This energy is called the **heat of the reaction.** Heats of reaction have the symbol ΔH. They will be discussed in more detail in the next chapter.

For a chemical reaction to take place, the energy of the reactants

Even in an exothermic reaction, the reactants must climb the energy hill before the products can be formed.

must be raised to the highest point of the curve. In other words, enough energy must be supplied to form the activated complex. This energy is, of course, the activation energy.

We have looked at a potential energy diagram for the reaction between substances A and B to form substance C. The reverse reaction can take place. Substance C can be decomposed to form substances A and B. The same potential energy diagram can be used for both the forward and the reverse reactions. For the reverse reaction, the potential energy diagram is read in the reverse direction, reading from right to left. Or, the same information can be replotted, starting on the left with the potential energy of substance C, showing the potential energy of the activated complex, and ending with the potential energy of substances A and B. The replotted graph would, of course, be read in the normal left-to-right direction. See Figure 19-12.

Figure 19-12

The potential energy diagram of Figure 19-11 replotted in the reverse direction to show the decomposition of substance C to form substances A and B. Comparing the diagram shown here with that in Figure 19-11, notice that the activation energy for the decomposition of C is much greater than the activation energy for its formation. **ΔH** is numerically the same in both reactions, but in this reaction the heat is absorbed.

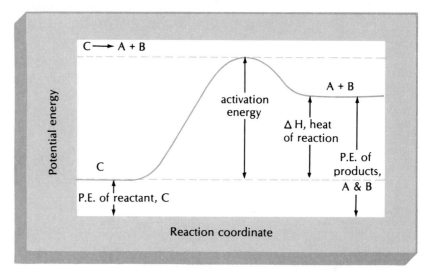

For the decomposition of substance C, the potential energy of the products A and B is higher than the potential energy of the reactant C. This is an endothermic reaction. Energy must be continuously supplied to substance C to keep the reaction going. Note that the activation energy for the decomposition of C is greater than the activation energy for its formation.

19-10 Activation Energy and Temperature

The average kinetic energy of random motion of the molecules in a system is proportional to the temperature. At any temperature, some molecules have less energy than the average, and others have more. The higher the temperature, the greater will be the number of molecules with enough energy to climb the potential energy hill and form the activated complex. Therefore, the higher the temperature, the greater the rate of the reaction.

Figure 19-13

Effect of a catalyst. A catalyst changes the reaction mechanism, producing one that has a lower activation energy. Thus it is possible for the reaction to proceed at a lower temperature or at a faster rate. The net energy change of the reaction is not affected. That is, the difference between the energy of the reactants and the energy of the products remains unchanged.

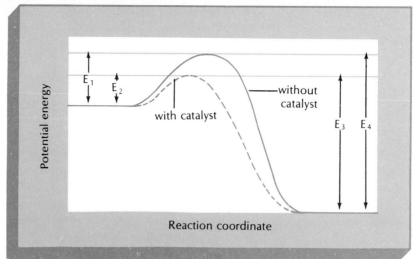

19-11   Effect of Catalysts on Activation Energy

A catalyst increases the speed of a reaction by changing the reaction mechanism. The new mechanism will provide steps with lower activation energies. However, the net energy change for the reaction is not affected. In each case the catalyst can be recovered in its original chemical form at the end of the reaction. See Figure 19-13.

Questions for Sections 19-8 through 19-11

*15. Consider the reaction A + B→C + D. (a) State two reasons why a collision between A and B molecules may not be effective. (b) What is the nature of an activated complex? (c) What paths of reaction may be taken by an activated complex? (d) Define *activation energy.*

16. Refer to the potential energy diagrams for the combination of *A* and *B* to form *C* (Figure 19-11) and for the reverse reaction (Figure 19-12). (a) Which reaction is exothermic and which is endothermic? (b) Compare the heats of reaction. (c) Compare the activation energies.

17. (a) How is the temperature of a substance related to the kinetic energy of its molecules? (b) Why does an increase of temperature increase the rate of a reaction?

18. (a) What is the effect of a catalyst on the activation energy of a reaction? (b) What is its effect on the net energy change of the reaction?

CHAPTER SUMMARY

1. Chemical kinetics is concerned with rates and mechanisms of chemical reactions.

2. The rate of a chemical reaction is a measure of the mass or the number of moles of a substance used up or formed in a unit volume of reaction mixture per unit of time.

CAN YOU EXPLAIN THIS?

The beaker in the photograph contains methyl alcohol, CH_3OH. The wire coil is platinum metal that was first heated over a burner until it became red hot. While still hot, the coil was quickly lowered into the beaker so that its lower end rested just above the surface of the liquid while the upper end was hooked over a glass stirring rod that rested across the top of the beaker. Allowed to remain in this position, the wire stayed red hot for 15 minutes or longer. The smell of formaldehyde, $HCHO$, could be detected in the space around the beaker.

What makes the platinum wire remain red hot while it rests just over the surface of the liquid?

3. The mechanism of a reaction describes the series of steps by which reacting molecules rearrange themselves to form the reaction products.
4. The chief factors affecting the rate of a chemical reaction are the nature and concentration of the reactants, the temperature, and catalysts.
5. The nature of the bonds in the reactants —ionic or covalent, stable or unstable —affect the rate of a chemical reaction.
6. An increase in the concentration of a reactant results in a greater frequency of collisions between reactants. This causes an increase in the rate of reaction.
7. An increase in temperature increases reaction rate because it increases the percentage of effective collisions.
8. Catalysts increase the rates of reactions because they convert the reaction mechanism to a new one that provides steps with a lower net activation energy.
9. The rate of the overall reaction is governed by the rate of the slowest step in the reaction mechanism.
10. In a chemical reaction, the reactants form a particle called an activated complex. It has a temporary existence, changing back into the original reactants or into the final products.
11. The minimum amount of energy needed to form the activated complex is called the activation energy.
12. The potential energy diagram shows the relationship between the activation energy and the net loss or gain of energy during a chemical reaction.
13. For two reactions that are the reverse of one another, the net energy gained in the endothermic reaction is equal to that lost in the exothermic reaction. The activation energies are different.
14. At higher temperatures, the rates of reactions increase because more molecules are provided with the energy needed to form the activated complex.

TERMS YOU SHOULD KNOW

chemical kinetics   heterogeneous reaction   rate-determining step
reaction rate   catalyst   activated complex
effective collision   reaction mechanism   activation energy
homogeneous reaction   heat of reaction

Section

19-1   1. (a) Describe the collision theory of reaction. (b) Complete the statement: The rate of a chemical reaction depends upon the _____ of collisions and how _____ they are.

19-2   2. The reaction between sodium hydroxide and hydrochloric acid at room temperature is rapid, while that between ethyl alcohol and hydrochloric acid is slow. Explain this in terms of the nature of the chemical bonds in the reactants.

19-3   3. Why will a mixture of hydrogen and chlorine react faster when the volume they occupy is decreased?

   4. Explain why (a) iron filings rust faster than iron wire (b) iron will rust faster in an open container than it will if placed in an air-tight container.

   5. Hydrochloric acid reacts with zinc to produce zinc chloride and hydrogen. Why is the hydrogen evolved more slowly when the acid is made more dilute?

19-4   6. Since a 10°C rise in temperature approximately doubles the rate of a chemical reaction, how should we expect the rate at 50°C to compare to the rate of the same reaction at 0°C?

   7. In terms of the frequency and effectiveness of collisions, explain the increase in reaction rate resulting from a temperature increase.

19-5   8. (a) What are two important properties shown by the MnO_2 catalyst used in the preparation of O_2 from $KClO_3$? (b) Experimentation shows that during the reaction the MnO_2 is changed to MnO_4^- (permanganate) ions. What is the probable change that now takes place in this ion?

19-6   9. Outline the probable series of steps that describe the mechanism of the reaction:

$$H_2 + Br_2 \rightarrow 2HBr. \text{ (Hint: The initial step is, } Br_2 \rightarrow 2Br.)$$

   10. The proposed steps for the mechanism of a certain reaction are the following:

$$\text{Step 1: } Cl_2 + AlCl_3 \rightarrow AlCl_4^- + Cl^+$$
$$\text{Step 2: } Cl^+ + C_6H_6 \rightarrow C_6H_5Cl + H^+$$
$$\text{Step 3: } H^+ + AlCl_4^- \rightarrow AlCl_3 + HCl$$

(a) Write the equation for the net reaction. (b) What is the formula of the catalyst?

19-7   11. In the mechanism described in question 10, Step 1 is slow, while Steps 2 and 3 are rapid. Explain the effect on the overall rate of reaction of an increase in the concentration of the (a) C_6H_6 (b) Cl_2.

19-8   12. Suggest a two-step mechanism for the following reaction:

$$2NO + O_2 \rightarrow 2NO_2$$

The activated complex is NO_3.

   13. The decomposition of hydrogen peroxide has the following mechanism:

$$H_2O_2 + I^- \rightarrow H_2O + IO^-$$
$$H_2O_2 + IO^- \rightarrow H_2O + O_2 + I^-$$

What is the formula of the substance that behaves (a) like an activated complex? (b) as a catalyst?

14. (a) Define *activation energy*. (b) Compare the activation energies for the decomposition of water and the decomposition of hydrogen peroxide. (c) Explain the difference.

19-9　15. The potential energy diagram shown below is for the reaction:

$$C \rightarrow A + B$$

Select the number that indicates the (a) activation energy (b) potential energy of the reactant (c) heat of reaction (d) potential energy of the activated complex. (e) Is the reaction endothermic or exothermic?

FIGURE A
(for Question 15)

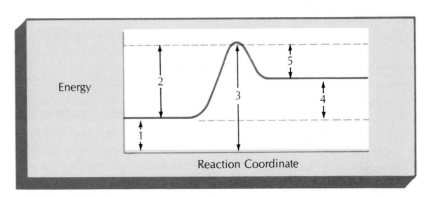

16. (a) Why can an "unstable" substance be stable at room temperature? (b) Why does a rise in temperature cause this substance to decompose?

17. An increase in temperature increases the rate of a given reaction. Explain this increase in terms of the activation energy and activated complex.

19-11　18. (a) What is the effect of a catalyst on the reaction mechanism of a reaction? (b) How does this affect the activation energies of the steps in the mechanism? (c) Why does the net energy change remain the same?

FOR FURTHER THOUGHT

19-3　1. A charcoal grill has air vents that can be adjusted.
(a) As the vent openings are made smaller, what happens to the rate of burning of the charcoal? Why?
(b) Will the temperature of the fire become higher or lower? Why?

19-8　2. When you strike a match, friction produces heat, which then provides activation energy to start the combustion reaction. Is activation energy needed to keep the reaction going? If so, where does it come from? If not, why not?

19-11　3. Sugar is oxidized in the body at 37°C (body temperature). Outside the body, sugar will burn only at a temperature above 600°C. What accounts for the difference?

Chapter 19　Chemical Kinetics　　**387**

Enthalpy and Entropy

20-1 Heat Content or Enthalpy

Every system or sample of matter has energy stored in it. This energy is present in various forms. Some of the energy is stored in chemical bonds. Some is potential energy related to the physical phase of the substance and its pressure and volume. Some is the kinetic energy of the random motion of the atoms and molecules in the material. The total of all these forms of energy is called the heat content, or **enthalpy** (EN-thal-pee), of the substance.

It is not possible to measure or calculate the total heat content of a particular substance. All we can say is that the heat content, or enthalpy, remains constant as long as no energy enters or leaves the material. If energy does enter or leave the substance, then its enthalpy will change by an amount equal to the amount of energy gained or lost.

The capital letter H is the symbol used for heat content, or enthalpy. The symbol may be used with a subscript to indicate a particular substance. For example,

$$H_{H_2O(l)}$$

denotes the heat content of water in the liquid phase. The heat content of water in the solid phase would be represented by

$$H_{H_2O(s)}$$

Since energy must be added to ice to change it to the liquid phase, $H_{H_2O(l)}$ is greater than $H_{H_2O(s)}$. The change in heat content that occurs during any process is represented by ΔH. In the case of the melting of ice to liquid water,

$$\Delta H = H_{H_2O(l)} - H_{H_2O(s)}$$

The actual values of $H_{H_2O(l)}$ and $H_{H_2O(s)}$ cannot be determined. However, it is possible to measure ΔH by measuring the amount of heat absorbed when the change occurs. As we have seen in Section 7-10, ΔH for the melting of ice is 80 cal/g. Note that ΔH in this change is positive. The product of the change, liquid water, has a greater heat content than the ice from which it was formed. A positive value of ΔH indicates a process in which heat is absorbed—an endothermic process. For an exothermic process, such as the freezing of water, ΔH is negative.

In all chemical reactions, there is a change in enthalpy. That is, the total enthalpy of the products is different from the total enthalpy of the reactants. If the reaction is endothermic, the enthalpy increases and ΔH is positive. If the reaction is exothermic, the enthalpy decreases and ΔH is negative. The change in enthalpy is called the **heat of reaction,** and it is usually given in kilocalories.

20-2   Heat of Formation

When one mole of a compound is formed from its elements, the heat of reaction, ΔH, has a special name. It is called the **heat of formation.** Heats of formation are symbolized ΔH_f. The heat of formation of a compound depends on the temperature and pressure at which the reaction occurs. It also depends on the phase of the product. For example, when water is formed by the combination of hydrogen and oxygen, more heat is given off if the water is formed in the liquid phase than if it is formed in the gaseous phase. The difference is the heat that is released when water changes from a gas to a liquid.

The **standard heat of formation,** represented by the symbol ΔH_f°, is the heat of formation when the temperature is 25°C and the pressure is 1 atmosphere. The phases of the reactants and the product must also be stated. The standard heat of formation of liquid water is -68.32 kcal per mole. This means that when 1 mole of liquid water is formed from hydrogen and oxygen at 25°C and 1 atmosphere pressure, 68.32 kilocalories of heat is released.

The equation for the formation of water is:

EXOTHERMIC REACTION

$$H_2(g) + \tfrac{1}{2}O_2(g) \longrightarrow H_2O(l) + 68.32 \text{ kcal} \qquad \textbf{(Eq. 1)}$$

In words, this equation says that 1 mole of hydrogen gas combines with $\frac{1}{2}$ mole of oxygen gas to produce 1 mole of liquid water and to release 68.32 kcal of heat. Since heat is given off, the heat of reaction is -68.32 kcal.

The reverse reaction, that for the decomposition of water, is an endothermic reaction. The equation for the reaction is:

ENDOTHERMIC REACTION

$$H_2O(l) + 68.32 \text{ kcal} \longrightarrow H_2(g) + \tfrac{1}{2}O_2(g) \qquad \textbf{(Eq. 2)}$$

Since heat is absorbed, the heat of reaction is +68.32 kcal.

In writing equations, we indicate whether the reaction is endothermic or exothermic by the position of the energy term. For exothermic reactions, the energy term goes on the right side of the equation. For endothermic reactions, the energy term goes on the left side of the equation. Energy terms in equations are always written as positive numbers regardless of whether the equation is for an endothermic or for an exothermic reaction. Position alone tells which kind of a reaction it is.

In writing the heats of reaction, ΔH, we distinguish between endothermic and exothermic reactions by the sign of the number. When the heat of reaction is written as a positive number ($\Delta H = +68.32$ kcal), the reaction is endothermic. When the heat of reaction is written as a negative number ($\Delta H = -68.32$ kcal), the reaction is exothermic.

Equations are usually balanced with whole-number coefficients, but note that oxygen has a fractional coefficient (½) in the equation showing the formation of water.

$$H_2(g) + \tfrac{1}{2}O_2(g) \longrightarrow H_2O(l) + 68.32 \text{ kcal} \qquad \textbf{(Eq. 3)}$$

Oxygen has a coefficient of ½ because the equation was balanced to make the amount of water formed equal 1 mole. When heats of formation are given for a compound, the equations for those reactions are always written in terms of forming 1 mole of compound. In doing this, coefficients of some other substances may become fractions.

For the above equation, the fractional coefficient for oxygen can be eliminated by doubling all terms:

$$2H_2(g) + O_2(g) \longrightarrow 2H_2O(l) + 136.64 \text{ kcal} \qquad \textbf{(Eq. 4)}$$

Both ways of writing the equation are correct. However, we must keep in mind that the energy term, 136.64 kcal, in the last equation tells the amount of heat evolved when *2 moles* of water are formed rather than 1. Therefore, −136.64 kcal is not the heat of formation of water, since the heat of formation is by definition the heat of the reaction when *1 mole* of compound is formed.

The standard heats of formation for a number of compounds are given in the table in Figure 20-1.

20-3 Stability of Compounds

Some compounds are unstable. This means that they tend to break down easily into simpler substances or into their elements. The stability of a compound is generally related to its heat of formation. A compound with a large negative heat of formation gives off a large amount of energy during its formation. It therefore requires the same input of energy to decompose the compound into its elements. Such a compound is usually very stable. On the other hand, there are compounds that have small negative heats of formation, or even positive heats of formation. These compounds tend to be unstable, because

Name of Compound	Reaction for the Compound's Formation	Standard Heat of Formation, ΔH_f° (kcal/mole of product)
aluminum oxide	$2Al(s) + \frac{3}{2}O_2(g) \longrightarrow Al_2O_3(s)$	-399.1
ammonia	$\frac{1}{2}N_2(g) + \frac{3}{2}H_2(g) \longrightarrow NH_3(g)$	-11.0
carbon dioxide	$C(s) + O_2(g) \longrightarrow CO_2(g)$	-94.1
carbon monoxide	$C(s) + \frac{1}{2}O_2(g) \longrightarrow CO(g)$	-26.4
copper oxide	$Cu(s) + \frac{1}{2}O_2(g) \longrightarrow CuO(s)$	-37.1
magnesium oxide	$Mg(s) + \frac{1}{2}O_2(g) \longrightarrow MgO(s)$	-143.8
nitric oxide	$\frac{1}{2}N_2(g) + \frac{1}{2}O_2(g) \longrightarrow NO(g)$	$+21.6$
nitrogen dioxide	$\frac{1}{2}N_2(g) + O_2(g) \longrightarrow NO_2(g)$	$+8.1$
sodium chloride	$Na(s) + \frac{1}{2}Cl_2(g) \longrightarrow NaCl(s)$	-98.2
sulfur dioxide	$S(s) + O_2(g) \longrightarrow SO_2(g)$	-71.0
water (gaseous phase)	$H_2(g) + \frac{1}{2}O_2(g) \longrightarrow H_2O(g)$	-57.8
water (liquid phase)	$H_2(g) + \frac{1}{2}O_2(g) \longrightarrow H_2O(l)$	-68.3

Figure 20-1

Standard heats of formation for some selected compounds.
(Pressure = 1 atm; temp. = 25°C)

they require little or no net input of energy to cause them to decompose. Explosives are substances that readily decompose into gaseous substances and release energy as they do so. The released heat causes the gaseous substances to expand rapidly.

Carbon dioxide, for example, is a stable compound. It has a standard heat of formation of -94.05 kcal/mole. By contrast, the standard heat of formation of nitric oxide, NO, is $+21.6$ kcal/mole. Nitrogen dioxide, NO_2, is another compound whose standard heat of formation is positive, specifically, $+8.1$ kcal/mole. The positive sign means that the reactions in which these compounds are formed from their elements are endothermic. These compounds are relatively unstable. That is, they are easily decomposed.

Figure 20-2

Explosions, such as the one shown here to bring down this building, are often the result of the breakdown of unstable compounds.

1. (a) What is meant by the term *enthalpy* or heat content? (b) What symbol is used to designate the enthalpy of ice? (c) What is the symbol used to indicate a change in enthalpy?
2. (a) Write the equation showing the change in enthalpy that occurs when water is frozen to ice. (b) Is this change in enthalpy positive or negative? (c) What is another name for the change in enthalpy? (d) What are its usual units?
3. (a) Define *heat of formation*. (b) In what units is it measured? (c) What changes in conditions will cause a change in the value of the heat of formation of a substance?
*4. (a) Define *standard heat of formation* and give the symbol used to represent it. (b) What is its value for water in the liquid phase? (c) What is its value for water vapor? (d) Write the equation for the formation of liquid water from hydrogen gas and oxygen gas, including in the equation a term showing the heat of reaction.
5. (a) What is the usual relationship found between heats of formation of substances and their stabilities? (b) Using the table of standard heats of formation, describe the relative stabilities of MgO, CO_2, NH_3, and NO.

20-4   Hess's Law of Constant Heat Summation

In any series of reactions that start with the same reactants and end with the same products, the net change in energy must be the same. This conclusion follows from the principle of conservation of energy. Consider, for example, the following reaction between copper (II) oxide and hydrogen:

$$CuO(s) + H_2(g) \longrightarrow Cu(s) + H_2O(g) \qquad \Delta H = ? \text{ kcal} \qquad \textbf{(Eq. 5)}$$

This reaction may be expressed as the sum of a series of other reactions. For example, the two simple reactions

$$CuO(s) \longrightarrow Cu(s) + \tfrac{1}{2}O_2(g) \qquad \Delta H_1 = 37.1 \text{ kcal} \qquad \textbf{(Eq. 6)}$$

$$H_2(g) + \tfrac{1}{2}O_2(g) \longrightarrow H_2O(g) \qquad \Delta H_2 = -57.8 \text{ kcal} \qquad \textbf{(Eq. 7)}$$

can be added to produce Equation 5. By Hess's law (stated below), ΔH (the heat of reaction for Equation 5) must equal $\Delta H_1 + \Delta H_2$:

$$
\begin{aligned}
\Delta H_1 &= 37.1 \text{ kcal} \\
+\ \Delta H_2 &= -57.8 \text{ kcal} \\
\hline
\Delta H &= -20.7 \text{ kcal}
\end{aligned}
$$

*The answers to questions marked with an asterisk are given in the back of the book.

Equation 6 is a simple decomposition reaction and Equation 7 is a simple formation (composition) reaction. Therefore, their heats of reaction (37.1 kcal and -57.8 kcal, respectively) could be obtained

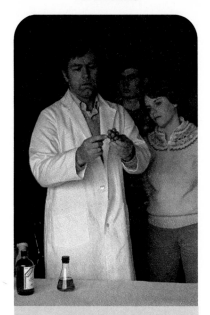

from a table giving heats of formation, such as the table in Figure 20-1. Notice that the sign of ΔH_1 was changed from -37.1 kcal to $+37.1$ kcal because Equation 6 was written as a decomposition, not as a combination.

To sum up, the heat of reaction for Equation 5 is not listed in a table giving heats of formation because Equation 5 is not a simple formation or decomposition. However, Equation 5 can be expressed as the sum of two reactions whose heats of reaction are listed. We can therefore find the heat of reaction for Equation 5 by applying **Hess's Law: When a reaction can be expressed as the algebraic sum of two or more other reactions, then the heat of the reaction is the algebraic sum of the heats of these other reactions.** Tables of heats of formation can thus be used to calculate any heat of reaction by breaking the reaction down into hypothetical combination and decomposition reactions, and then applying Hess's law in the manner illustrated here.

Enthalpy changes for reactions can be obtained in a simpler manner by subtracting the heats of formation of the reactants from those of the products. The arithmetic involved is the same as that used in the method described above, but this procedure is shorter as it eliminates the need for partial equations. In using this method, be sure to multiply the heats of formation by the coefficient of the compound involved. Using this simpler method for the reaction given by Equation 5, we subtract the heat of formation for the reactant (CuO $= -37.1$ kcal) from the heat of formation for the product ($H_2O = -57.8$ kcal):

$$\Delta H = -57.8 \text{ kcal} - (-37.1 \text{ kcal}) = -20.7 \text{ kcal}$$

(In using either method, the heats of formation of all elements are set at zero.)

Questions for Section 20-4

6. (a) What relationship exists between the heat of formation of a compound and its heat of decomposition? (b) ΔH for the decomposition of mercuric oxide is $+43.4$ kcal:

$$2HgO(s) + 43.4 \text{ kcal} \rightarrow 2Hg(l) + O_2(g)$$

What is the ΔH_f for HgO(s)?

7. When iron rusts in air, the following reaction occurs:

$$4Fe(s) + 3O_2(g) \rightarrow 2Fe_2O_3(s)$$

$\Delta H = -393$ kcal. What is the heat of formation of $Fe_2O_3(s)$?

*8. Apply Hess's law of constant heat summation to calculate the heat of reaction for the burning of carbon monoxide:

$$2CO(g) + O_2(g) \rightarrow 2CO_2(g)$$

(Use the partial equations in the table of Heats of Formation.)

*9. For the same reaction as in question 8, calculate the heat of reaction by subtracting the sum of the total heats of formation of the reactants from the total heat of formation of the moles of product.

Chapter 20   Enthalpy and Entropy   **393**

*10. The heat of reaction for the combustion of one mole of ethyl alcohol is -227 kcal.
$$C_2H_5OH(l) + 3O_2(g) \rightarrow 2CO_2(g) + 3H_2O(l) + 227 \text{ kcal}$$
How much heat is evolved when 11.5 g of alcohol are burned?

11. Calculate ΔH for the reaction:
$$Cl_2(g) + 2HBr(g) \rightarrow 2HCl(g) + Br_2(g)$$
ΔH_f° values are: $HCl(g) = -22.1$ kcal/mole
$HBr(g) = -8.70$ kcal/mole

12. The ΔH for the complete combustion of propane is -531 kcal:
$$C_3H_8(g) + 5O_2(g) \rightarrow 3CO_2(g) + 4H_2O(l)$$
Calculate the heat of reaction for the combustion of 11.0 g of propane.

13. The following are some ΔH_f° values: $CH_4(g) = -17.9$ kcal/mole; $CHCl_3(l) = -31.5$ kcal/mole; $HCl(g) = -22.1$ kcal/mole. What is the heat of reaction for the equation:
$$CH_4(g) + 3Cl_2(g) \rightarrow CHCl_3(l) + 3HCl(g)$$

14. Ethylene reacts with hydrogen to form ethane:
$$C_2H_4(g) + H_2(g) \rightarrow C_2H_6(g)$$
The heat of reaction is -32.7 kcal. The ΔH_f° value for $C_2H_4(g)$ is $+12.5$ kcal/mole. What is the heat of formation of $C_2H_6(g)$?

20-5 The Direction of Chemical Change

Water flows spontaneously downhill from a position of greater potential energy to one of less potential energy. This change is spontaneous in the direction of lower energy. Chemical changes can also proceed from higher energy to lower. This is what happens during an exothermic reaction. Since reactions leading to the formation of stronger chemical bonds are generally exothermic, we expect reactions to be spontaneous if they produce stronger bonds.

Consider the exothermic reaction for the formation of mercuric oxide from its elements:

$$Hg(l) + \tfrac{1}{2}O_2(g) \longrightarrow HgO(s) + 21.7 \text{ kcal} \qquad \textbf{(Eq. 8)}$$

The heat content of the product, HgO, is less than that of the reactants, Hg and O_2. We expect mercuric oxide to form spontaneously, proceeding from the higher energy of the reactants to the lower energy of the product. In actual practice, we find that the reaction does proceed spontaneously *at moderate temperatures*. But at temperatures above 400°C, the reaction does *not* take place. Instead, the reverse reaction occurs. Mercuric oxide decomposes:

$$HgO(s) + 21.7 \text{ kcal} \longrightarrow Hg(l) + \tfrac{1}{2}O_2(g) \qquad \textbf{(Eq. 9)}$$

This decomposition is endothermic, yet it occurs spontaneously if the temperature is high enough. Against our expectations, the direction of the change reverses itself at higher temperatures, proceeding spon-

Figure 20-3 Water flows spontaneously from a position of higher to a position of lower gravitational potential energy, as shown by this waterfall on the Yellowstone River in Yellowstone National Park. During an exothermic chemical reaction, chemical potential energy is spontaneously lowered as the reactants are rearranged to form the products.

taneously from lower energy to higher energy. In terms of the flow of water, this is like water reversing direction and flowing uphill. Evidently, a change in energy (from higher to lower) is not the only factor that determines in what direction a chemical change will occur spontaneously. There is another factor that influences the direction of a chemical change. This factor has to do with entropy (EN-tro-pee), the topic of our next section.

20-6   Entropy

Entropy is a measure of the disorder, randomness, or lack of organization of a system. A system has a large entropy if it is in a great state of disorder. Changes tend to go in the direction of increasing entropy.

To illustrate the meaning of entropy, let us consider a situation in which entropy is changed. Picture the Smith family arriving at their vacation cottage in Maine to spend the December holidays. They enter the living room, which is quite cold. In fact, an open window has allowed some snow to pile up in one corner of the room. Mr. Smith soon starts a log fire in the fireplace and boils some water to make hot drinks.

Even if the entropy were not increased by the Smith family, it would normally tend to increase over a period of time: ice melts, water evaporates, wood decays, etc.

Mr. Smith's actions have caused an *increase* in entropy in five instances. (1) The air in the room has been warmed. (2) Cold water has been changed to hot water. (3) The snow in the room has melted. (4) Boiling water has been converted to steam. (5) Some of the wood has been changed to carbon dioxide and water vapor. In the first two instances, the rise in temperature has led to increased molecular motion and, therefore, a less ordered molecular arrangement. In the third and fourth instances, a change of phase has taken place. Molecular arrangement is most orderly in the solid phase and least orderly in the gaseous phase. In the final instance, as the logs burned, a solid (wood) was changed to gases (CO_2 and H_2O vapor). As explained above, the molecular arrangement in gases is less orderly than that in solids.

Entropy is represented by the letter S. A change in entropy is shown by the symbol ΔS and is defined by the equation:

$$\Delta S = S_f - S_i \qquad \textbf{(Eq. 10)}$$

where S_f = the final entropy, the entropy after the change has occurred

S_i = the initial entropy, the entropy before the change has occurred

In terms of the living room, S_f was large, while S_i was small. Therefore, the change in entropy, ΔS, is a positive number. Consider the reverse situation. The fire in the fireplace is extinguished and the Smith family leaves the cottage to return to their permanent home. After some time, the air in the room and some hot water left in the kettle become much colder. Water vapor in the room condenses to a liquid, and some water on the living room floor freezes. From equation 10, subtracting a larger positive number from a smaller one produces a ΔS that is negative. A negative ΔS indicates that there has been a *decrease* in entropy, or disorder. A decrease in disorder means that a more ordered arrangement is achieved. (It is important to understand that the cooling of the room and, therefore, its decrease in entropy, occurs only because heat can leave through the walls to the cold outdoors. The entropy of a completely insulated container could not decrease by itself.)

The chemist is interested in the concept of entropy as it applies to chemical and physical changes. When a substance is in the solid phase, it has a small entropy because the particles of the solid are restricted in their motions. When a solid changes to the liquid phase, its entropy increases. The particles of the liquid have greater freedom of motion. Hence, the liquid is more disordered and disorganized than the solid. When a liquid changes to a gas, the entropy of the substance increases even more. The particles of a gas have very random motions. Gas molecules exist almost totally independently of each other. They spread out to fill their container. Entropy changes when substances change their phase.

What changes in entropy occur when substances react? The formation of a compound from its constituent elements causes a decrease in entropy since the bonding of elements to form a compound creates a more orderly state. When the reverse change takes place, that is, when the compound decomposes, order and organization break down. Entropy increases.

Changes in temperature also cause a change in the entropy of matter. An increase in temperature causes an increase in entropy, since faster-moving particles move more randomly.

20-7 The Effect of Changes in Entropy on the Direction of Spontaneous Change

In Section 20-5 it was mentioned that a change in energy is a factor that influences the direction of a spontaneous change. Specifically, systems tend to go spontaneously from higher energy to lower energy. That is, a decrease in energy favors a spontaneous change. In terms of chemical reactions, energy considerations lead us to expect exothermic reactions to proceed spontaneously. But we also noted that endothermic reactions do take place spontaneously under certain conditions. Therefore, a change in energy cannot be the only factor that influences the direction of a spontaneous change. There is another factor, and that factor is the change in entropy. An increase in entropy (ΔS = a positive number) favors spontaneous change. This fact is sometimes stated by saying that in nature, changes tend to take place that create a greater state of disorder.

To shed light on this idea, let us consider the situation shown in Figure 20-4. At first the valve is closed. Container 1 holds molecules of argon gas and Container 2 is a vacuum. When the valve is opened, the

Figure 20-4

Two containers with a valve connecting them. (A) Container 1 has argon in it. Container 2 is a vacuum. (B) *The two containers after the valve has remained open for some time.* The molecules went from a more ordered state in A to a less ordered state in B when the restraint in A (the closed valve) was eliminated.

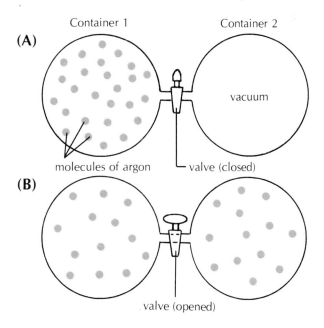

gas flows through the valve until its molecules are evenly distributed in both containers.

The reason for the even distribution is not hard to understand. When the valve was closed, molecules struck the valve and rebounded. When it was opened, molecules striking in the same spot passed through the hole created by opening the valve. Until there were an equal number of molecules in both containers, more molecules passed from Container 1 into Container 2 than in the opposite direction.

The final distribution of the molecules can also be explained in terms of the entropy of the system. Having more molecules in one container than in the other is a special situation. It is more orderly and less random than a uniform distribution. It is an observed law of nature that if a system can change from a more orderly to a more random, or disordered, arrangement, it will tend to do so. Where an arrangement is observed to have a special order, we assume that there must be some reason for it. There must be some restraint on the system that prevents it from assuming a more random arrangement. In Figure 20-4, the closed valve is the restraint that originally kept all the molecules in one container. With the valve open, the restraint was gone. Then the gas spontaneously rearranged itself to a more random state, filling both containers.

The same principle applies to the situation shown in Figure 20-5. In *(A)*, Container 1 holds pure argon. Container 2 holds pure helium. In *(B)*, with the valve open, the gases spontaneously mix until they are present in the same proportions in both containers. The uniform mixture is the least special (or the most random) arrangement possible. Since there is no restraint with the valve open, the arrangement shown in *(B)* results.

Figure 20-5

Two containers with a valve connecting them. (A) Container 1 has argon in it; Container 2, helium. (B) ***The two containers after the valve has remained open for some time.*** The distribution of molecules goes from the more orderly state in *A* to the less orderly state in *B*, illustrating the tendency of systems in nature to assume states that are more random and less organized.

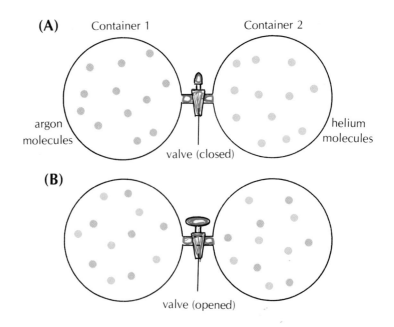

(A) Container 1   Container 2

argon molecules   helium molecules

valve (closed)

(B)

valve (opened)

What happens to gases in the apparatus just referred to is a particular instance of a general phenomenon. In general, any system at constant temperature and pressure tends to undergo a change so that in its final state it has a greater entropy than in its original state. In terms of our equation,

$$\Delta S = S_f - S_i \qquad \text{(Eq. 10)}$$

a value of S_f that is greater than the value of S_i means that the difference, ΔS, will be positive. Therefore, spontaneous changes are favored by positive values for ΔS, that is, by increases in entropy.

We can summarize this section as follows. Two factors influence the direction of spontaneous change. One factor is ΔH and the other is ΔS (the change in energy, or enthalpy, and the change in entropy). Specifically, a negative value for ΔH (decrease in enthalpy) and a positive value for ΔS (an increase in entropy) favor spontaneous change. Based on the enthalpy factor alone, endothermic reactions should never occur because ΔH for these changes is positive. The fact that endothermic changes do occur is the result of the influence of ΔS. If the increase in entropy is great enough, its effect will predominate, and the reaction will proceed even though the change in enthalpy is in the wrong direction for spontaneous change. Figure 20-6 summarizes the effect of changes in enthalpy and entropy in four different situations.

Figure 20-6

The effect of the signs of ΔH and ΔS on spontaneous change.

Situation	Signs of ΔH and ΔS	Comment
1	$\Delta H = -$ (favorable) $\Delta S = +$ (favorable)	Both factors are favorable for spontaneous change. The change can occur.
2	$\Delta H = +$ (unfavorable) $\Delta S = -$ (unfavorable)	Neither factor favors spontaneous change. The change cannot occur.
3	$\Delta H = -$ (favorable) $\Delta S = -$ (unfavorable)	The change in enthalpy is favorable, but the change in entropy is unfavorable. The change can occur only if the effect of the change in enthalpy is greater than the effect of the change in entropy.
4	$\Delta H = +$ (unfavorable) $\Delta S = +$ (favorable)	The change in enthalpy is unfavorable, but the change in entropy is favorable. The change can occur only if the effect of the change in entropy is greater than the effect of the change in enthalpy.

Chapter 20   Enthalpy and Entropy   **399**

15. (a) Why are compounds with large negative heats of formation very stable? (b) Why does a chemical reaction tend to move in the direction of forming stronger bonds? (c) As shown by the spontaneous decomposition of HgO above 400°C, what other factor influences the direction of chemical change?

*16. (a) Explain what is meant by the *entropy* of a system. Why are the following changes considered to be examples of increasing entropy? (b) the evaporation of water; (c) the decomposition of $MgCO_3(s)$ into $MgO(s)$ and $CO_2(g)$; (d) dissolving sugar in water (e) heating air.

17. Two containers, one filled with oxygen and the other with nitrogen, are connected by a tube having a closed valve. When the valve is opened, the gases will flow into one another, forming a mixture in both containers. Why?

18. (a) What algebraic sign is used for ΔS to indicate an increase in entropy? (b) Indicate the signs for the ΔH and ΔS for a change that cannot possibly occur spontaneously.

20-8 The Gibbs Free Energy Equation and its Application to Chemical Change

We wish now to illustrate the situations referred to in Figure 20-6 with some emphasis on the effect of temperature on the interplay of ΔS and ΔH.

An example of Situation 1 in Figure 20-6 is an ordinary combustion, such as the combustion of the liquid fuel pentane, C_5H_{12}.

$$C_5H_{12} + 8O_2 \longrightarrow 5CO_2 + 6H_2O \qquad \text{(Eq. 11)}$$
$$\text{steam}$$

This is an exothermic reaction (ΔH is negative) and the entropy of the products is greater than the entropy of the reactants, since both products are gases. Because the products have greater entropy, S_f is greater than S_i, making ΔS positive. Therefore, both driving forces, ΔH and ΔS, favor combustion.

In Situation 3, ΔH is negative. Thus, the sign of ΔH is favorable to a spontaneous change. If enthalpy alone determined events, the change would occur spontaneously. However, ΔS is also negative, meaning that the entropy decreases as the change proceeds. This effect is unfavorable for change and tends to prevent the change from occurring. What determines whether the unfavorable change in S, tending to prevent change, is great enough to offset the favorable change in H? The relationship that applies was discovered by the American scientist Willard Gibbs (1839-1903). Through a mathematical study of the factors involved, Gibbs showed that the effect of entropy depends upon the temperature. The **Gibbs equation** is:

$$\Delta G = \Delta H - T\Delta S$$ **(Eq. 12)**

where ΔH = the change in enthalpy
T = the Kelvin temperature
ΔS = the change in entropy

The letter G represents a quantity called the free energy. This symbol was chosen in honor of Gibbs's work. Mathematical analysis (beyond the scope of this text) shows that the $T\Delta S$ term is equivalent to the amount of heat that must be transferred to produce a given change of entropy, ΔS, at the temperature T.

Gibbs showed that a change tends to occur spontaneously only if the change in free energy, ΔG, is negative. In other words, it is not enough for ΔH to be negative for a change to be spontaneous. The combination of ΔH and $-T\Delta S$ must be negative; indicating a release of energy. With this in mind, let us take a closer look at Equation 12 for the conditions set forth in Situation 3 (Figure 20-6) when ΔH and ΔS are both negative.

When ΔS is negative, the term $-T\Delta S$ in Equation 12 will be positive. (A negative times a negative equals a positive.) If the value of the expression $-T\Delta S$ is positive, ΔG will be negative only if the value of ΔH is more negative than the value of $-T\Delta S$ is positive.

To clarify these statements, let us look at an example. Suppose that $\Delta H = -37$ kcal and that $\Delta S = -0.06$ kcal/K. This clearly is Situation 3 in Figure 20-6, where both ΔS and ΔH are negative. Now suppose that the temperature is 300°C or 573 K. ΔG can be found from Equation 12:

$$\Delta G = \Delta H - T\Delta S \qquad \text{(Eq. 12)}$$

$$= -37 \text{ kcal} - (573 \text{ K} \times -0.06 \text{ kcal/K})$$

$$= -37 \text{ kcal} - (-34 \text{ kcal})$$

$$= -37 \text{ kcal} + 34 \text{ kcal}$$

$$= -3 \text{ kcal}$$

Since ΔG is negative, the change can take place spontaneously at a temperature of 300°C.

Next, suppose that the temperature is 400°C or 673 K. Again we find ΔG from Equation 12:

$$\Delta G = \Delta H - T\Delta S \qquad \text{(Eq. 12)}$$

$$= -37 \text{ kcal} - (673 \text{ K} \times -0.06 \text{ kcal/K})$$

$$= -37 \text{ kcal} - (-40 \text{ kcal})$$

$$= -37 \text{ kcal} + 40 \text{ kcal}$$

$$= +3 \text{ kcal}$$

Since ΔG is positive, the change cannot occur spontaneously. A temperature of 400°C is too great.

This example illustrates that changes that are accompanied by a decrease in both entropy and enthalpy (ΔS and ΔH both negative) will not occur spontaneously at temperatures that are high enough to make the positive value of the $-T\Delta S$ term predominate over the negative value of the ΔH term, thereby making ΔG positive. At low enough temperatures, the change will occur spontaneously because the $-T\Delta S$ term will have a smaller positive value. Then, the ΔH term will be negative enough to be the dominant factor, making ΔG negative, too.

In Situation 4 (Figure 20-6), both ΔH and ΔS are positive (both enthalpy and entropy are increasing). An increase in entropy favors spontaneous change, but an increase in enthalpy opposes it. The two driving forces of the change are working against each other. Which force wins out will be determined by how large the $-T\Delta S$ term is compared to the value of the ΔH term. The negative value of the $-T\Delta S$ term must be larger than the positive value of ΔH in order to make ΔG negative. This means that ΔG will be negative only when a high temperature, T, gives the $-T\Delta S$ term a large enough negative value. Figure 20-7 summarizes how the change in free energy is affected by temperature and by changes in enthalpy and entropy.

The formation of mercuric oxide from its elements, and the reverse reaction, its decomposition, are examples of Situations 3 and 4 referred to in Figure 20-7.

Figure 20-7

The effect of changes in enthalpy, ΔH, and entropy, ΔS, on the change in free energy, ΔG.

SITUATION 3, FORMATION OF HgO (ΔH is negative, ΔS is negative)

$$2Hg + O_2 \longrightarrow 2HgO \qquad\qquad \text{(Eq. 13)}$$

Situation	Signs of ΔH and ΔS	Signs of terms ΔH and $-T\Delta S$	Comment
1	$\Delta H = -$ (favorable) $\Delta S = +$ (favorable)	$\Delta G = \Delta H - T\Delta S$ $-\quad +$ $-$	Both terms, ΔH and $-T\Delta S$, are negative. Therefore, ΔG is negative at all temperatures T. The change can occur at all temperatures.
2	$\Delta H = +$ (unfavorable) $\Delta S = -$ (unfavorable)	$\Delta G = \Delta H - T\Delta S$ $+\quad -$ $+$	Both terms are positive. Therefore, ΔG is positive at all temperatures T. The change cannot occur at any temperature.
3	$\Delta H = -$ (favorable) $\Delta S = -$ (unfavorable)	$\Delta G = \Delta H - T\Delta S$ $-\quad -$ $+$	ΔG will be positive when T is a high temperature. ΔG will be negative when T is a low temperature. Change can occur only at sufficiently low temperature.
4	$\Delta H = +$ (unfavorable) $\Delta S = +$ (favorable)	$\Delta G = \Delta H - T\Delta S$ $+\quad +$ $-$	ΔG will be negative when T is a high temperature. ΔG will be positive when T is a low temperature. Change can occur only at sufficiently high temperature.

The heat of the reaction, ΔH, is negative because the reaction is exothermic. ΔS is negative because the entropy decreases as the more highly organized compound is formed. Therefore, the reaction can take place only at lower temperatures (below 400°C). Only then will the positive value of the $-T \Delta S$ term be small enough so that the negative ΔH term will predominate, making ΔG negative, too.

SITUATION 4, DECOMPOSITION OF HgO (ΔH is positive, ΔS is positive)

$$2HgO \longrightarrow 2Hg + O_2 \qquad \textbf{(Eq. 14)}$$

The heat of the reaction, ΔH, is positive because the reaction is endothermic. ΔS is positive because entropy increases as the disordered particles of the elements are formed. The reaction can take place only at higher temperatures (above 400°C). Only then will the negative value of the $-T \Delta S$ term be large enough to predominate over the positive ΔH term, thereby making ΔG negative, too.

It should be understood that a negative value of ΔG does not mean that a particular change will actually occur. It means only that the change *can* occur. Remember that for a chemical change to start, a certain amount of activation energy must be provided. Thus, mercury can be kept in an open container at room temperature. Even though the temperature is low enough for the oxidation to proceed spontaneously, it doesn't occur to any noticeable extent. Mercury must be heated to a moderate temperature to provide enough activation energy for the oxidation reaction to proceed at a noticeable rate. However, if the temperature is raised too high (above 400°C), the reaction reverses and the oxide decomposes.

Questions for Section 20-8

19. (a) Write the Gibbs equation and indicate the meaning of each term. (b) Why is the free energy change sometimes called the net driving force of a reaction? (c) What type of free energy change indicates that a reaction is spontaneous?

*20. State the algebraic signs for the ΔH and the $T \Delta S$ terms in each of the following examples: (a) Ordinary combustions; (b) Heating mercury in air at a temperature below 400°C; (c) Heating HgO at a temperature above 400°C.

21. (a) Why does the effectiveness of an entropy change depend upon the temperature? (b) Using the terms of the Gibbs equation, explain why mercury combines with oxygen at temperatures below 400°C but not at higher temperatures.

*22. (a) For a certain reaction, $\Delta H = -22.0$ kcal and $\Delta G = -12.0$ kcal at 25°C. Calculate ΔS. (b) For the same reaction, calculate ΔG when the temperature is 500 K.

20-9 Application of the Free Energy Equation to a Physical Change

We now apply the free energy equation, $\Delta G = \Delta H - T\Delta S$, to a physical change, the freezing of water. When water freezes, heat is evolved. The ΔH term for this exothermic process is negative, favoring spontaneous change. Therefore, from a consideration of enthalpy alone, we would expect water to freeze at all temperatures. It does not freeze at all temperatures because the freezing of water is accompanied by a decrease in entropy as water molecules become more highly organized in the ice crystal. A decrease in entropy (negative ΔS) works against spontaneous change. When ΔS is negative, the term $-T\Delta S$ is positive. Only when this term is small, that is, when temperatures are low, will the negative ΔH term predominate, making ΔG negative, too. Therefore, only at low temperatures will ice freeze.

The situation is quite different at high temperatures. Then, the $-T\Delta S$ term has a large positive value. It predominates over the negative ΔH term, making ΔG positive, too. At high temperatures, water will not freeze.

The free energy equation also explains why ice melts at higher temperatures. The melting of ice is an endothermic process (positive ΔH). The positive value for ΔH works against spontaneous change. From a consideration of the change in enthalpy alone, ice should never melt. However, ΔS is positive, too, since the breakdown of the highly structured ice crystal causes an increase in entropy. The increase in entropy favors spontaneous change and works against the unfavorable change in enthalpy (positive ΔH). At higher temperatures, the $-T\Delta S$ term has a large enough negative value to make ΔG negative, too. At high temperatures, therefore, ΔG is negative for the melting of ice.

As temperature is reduced, the value of the term $-T\Delta S$ becomes less negative, making ΔG less negative. A temperature is finally reached for which $\Delta G = 0$. This is the lowest temperature at which ice will melt. At still lower temperatures, ΔG turns positive and the reverse process, the freezing of water, becomes spontaneous. The temperature that makes $\Delta G = 0$ is the melting point of ice. This is the temperature at which the melting of ice and the freezing of water are in equilibrium with each other. At this temperature, the mass of ice that melts in an ice-water mixture is equal to the mass of water that freezes during any given unit of time. Hence, no net change occurs in the amounts of ice and water. When equilibrium exits between two opposing processes, $\Delta G = 0$.

Figure 20-8

If a change in enthalpy were the only consideration, water could pass only from the liquid phase (higher potential energy) to the solid phase (lower potential energy). The ice in the glass would never melt. That water can change phase in the opposite direction (solid to liquid) is a result of a change in entropy.

20-10 Free Energy of Formation

The free energy of formation of a compound is the change in free energy when one mole of the compound is formed from the constituent elements. It is indicated by the symbol ΔG_f°. Its values are

Name of Compound	Reaction for the Compound's Formation	Standard Free Energy of Formation kcal/mole (ΔG_f^0)
aluminum oxide	$2Al(s) + \frac{3}{2}O_2(g) \longrightarrow Al_2O_3(s)$	-376.8
ammonia	$\frac{1}{2}N_2(g) + \frac{3}{2}H_2(g) \longrightarrow NH_3(g)$	-4.0
carbon dioxide	$C(s) + O_2(g) \longrightarrow CO_2(g)$	-94.3
carbon monoxide	$C(s) + \frac{1}{2}O_2(g) \longrightarrow CO(g)$	-32.8
magnesium oxide	$Mg(s) + \frac{1}{2}O_2(g) \longrightarrow MgO(s)$	-136.1
nitric oxide	$\frac{1}{2}N_2(g) + \frac{1}{2}O_2(g) \longrightarrow NO(g)$	$+20.7$
nitrogen dioxide	$\frac{1}{2}N_2(g) + O_2(g) \longrightarrow NO_2(g)$	$+12.4$
sodium chloride	$Na(s) + \frac{1}{2}Cl_2(g) \longrightarrow NaCl(s)$	-91.8
sulfur dioxide	$S(s) + O_2(g) \longrightarrow SO_2(g)$	-71.8
water (gaseous phase)	$H_2(g) + \frac{1}{2}O_2(g) \longrightarrow H_2O(g)$	-54.6
water (liquid phase)	$H_2(g) + \frac{1}{2}O_2(g) \longrightarrow H_2O(l)$	-56.7

Figure 20-9

Standard heats of free energy for some selected compounds.

listed in tables for the same conditions as the heats of formation, that is, 1 atmosphere pressure and 298 K. At these conditions the substances are in their usual phase of solid, liquid, or gas. The units, as for heats of reaction, are in kcal/mole. Figure 20-9 gives the values of ΔG_f^0 for some selected substances. Free energies of formation may be used to calculate free energy changes for reactions.

The free energy of formation of a compound is always somewhat different from its heat of formation. The difference is the value of the $T\Delta S$ term for the given conditions.

Questions for Sections 20-9 and 20-10

23. (a) A sample of ice melts to water at temperatures above 0°C (273 K). In terms of the items in the Gibbs equation, explain why the ΔG values should be negative for this change above 0°C. (b) Using the Gibbs equation, explain why ΔG is negative for the freezing of water at temperatures below 0°C.

*24. For the reaction $Fe_2O_3(s) + 3CO(g) \rightarrow 2Fe(s) + 3CO_2(s)$, the change in free energy at 25°C and 1 atm ($\Delta G°$) is -7.5 kcal/mole. Calculate the standard free energy of formation of the ferric oxide, Fe_2O_3. ΔG_f^0 values: CO = -32.8 kcal/mole; $CO_2 = -94.3$ kcal/mole.

CHAPTER SUMMARY

1. The total of all the forms of energy stored in a substance or in a system is called the heat content or *enthalpy*. It is given the symbol H.
2. The change in enthalpy is represented by the symbol ΔH.
3. A positive value of ΔH indicates an endothermic change; a negative value is used for an exothermic change.

4. The change in enthalpy for any reaction is called the *heat of reaction.* It is usually measured in kilocalories.

5. The heat of reaction for the formation of one mole of a compound from its elements is called the *heat of formation.* It is given the symbol ΔH_f and is measured in kilocalories/mole.

6. The standard heat of formation is measured at 25°C and 1 atm pressure. Its symbol is ΔH_f^o.

7. Stable compounds have high negative heats of formation. Compounds with small negative, or positive, heats of formation tend to be unstable.

8. Hess's law of constant heat summation states that if a reaction can be expressed as the sum of two or more other reactions, its heat of reaction is the algebraic sum of the heats of reaction of the other reactions.

9. A chemical change tends to proceed spontaneously in the direction of a decrease in enthalpy and an increase in entropy.

10. Entropy is the measure of the disorder, randomness, or lack of organization in a substance or system. It is designated by the letter S.

11. *In general,* gases are in a higher state of entropy than liquids. Liquids have higher entropies than solids. Elements are at higher entropy levels than compounds.

12. A temperature increase raises the entropy level. The product of the Kelvin temperature and ΔS ($T\Delta S$) is the heat equivalent of the ΔS at the temperature T.

13. The Gibbs equation expresses the free energy change in a reaction: $\Delta G = \Delta H - T\Delta S$. The combination of the ΔH and the $-T\Delta S$ values must result in a negative ΔG value if the change is to be spontaneous.

14. An endothermic reaction may be spontaneous if the $-T\Delta S$ is negative enough to outweigh the positive ΔH and thus produce a negative ΔG.

15. The Gibbs equation may be applied to physical as well as chemical changes. For example, the melting of ice takes place at a temperature above 0°C because the high negative value of the $-T\Delta S$ causes the ΔG to be negative even though the ΔH is positive.

16. Free energies of formation are the changes in free energy that occur when a mole of a compound is formed from its elements. They may be used to calculate free energies of reactions.

TERMS YOU SHOULD KNOW

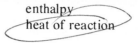

enthalpy
heat of reaction

heat of formation
standard heat of
    formation

Hess's law
entropy
Gibbs equation

REVIEW QUESTIONS

Section 20-1

1. (a) Mention three (3) forms in which energy may be stored in a substance. (b) What name is given to the total of this stored energy? (c) What measurement of the stored energy can be made after a change occurs in a substance or system? (d) Indicate this energy change for the melting of ice.

2. State the nature of the enthalpy change and the algebraic sign for ΔH

in a change that is (a) exothermic (b) endothermic. (c) In what unit is heat of reaction usually measured?

3. (a) What is the algebraic sign of the heat of reaction in an endothermic reaction? (b) How is the energy term indicated in an equation?

20-2   4. (a) Distinguish between heat of reaction and heat of formation. Include the symbols and units for both. (b) Mention the relative values of the heats of formation of the three phases of a substance. (c) Define *standard heat of formation*.

5. (a) Why are coefficients in equations sometimes written in fractional amounts? (b) Including the energy term, write the equation for the combination of hydrogen and oxygen in the usual manner and using a fractional coefficient for the oxygen.

6. When aluminum melts, 94 cal of heat per gram of aluminum are absorbed. What is the ΔH per mole? The mass of one mole of aluminum atoms is 27 g.

7. In the reaction $2Al(s) + 1\frac{1}{2}O_2(g) \rightarrow Al_2O_3(s)$, what is the amount of energy liberated by the oxidation of 6.75 g of Al? The ΔH_f° of Al_2O_3 is -399 kcal/mole.

8. When 1.00 g of methane, CH_4, is burned, 13.3 kcal of heat are evolved. What is ΔH for the combustion of one mole?
$$CH_4(g) + 2O_2(g) \rightarrow CO_2(g) + 2H_2O(l)$$

20-3   9. (a) Describe what kinds of values very stable compounds have for their heats of formation. (b) Why does a reaction tend to move in the direction of the formation of stable compounds? (c) Why do compounds with positive or small negative heats of formation tend to be unstable?

20-4   10. ΔH_f° for $CCl_4(l)$ is -31.5 kcal/mole; for $CH_4(g)$, it is -17.9 kcal/mole. What is ΔH for the reaction,
$$CH_4(g) + 2Cl_2(g) \rightarrow CCl_4(l) + 2H_2(g)$$

11. Calculate the heat of reaction, at 25°C and 1 atm, for the reaction:
$$CaCO_3(s) \rightarrow CaO(s) + CO_2(g)$$
ΔH values: $CaCO_3(s) = -288.4$ kcal/mole; $CaO(s) = -151.9$ kcal/mole; $CO_2(g) = -94.05$ kcal/mole.

12. The heat of reaction for the combustion of acetylene is -621.4 kcal:
$$2C_2H_2(g) + 5O_2(g) \rightarrow 4CO_2(g) + 2H_2O(l) + 621.4 \text{ kcal}.$$
What is the heat of formation of acetylene?

13. ΔH for the combustion of propane is -531 kcal:
$$C_3H_8(g) + 5O_2(g) \rightarrow 3CO_2(g) + 4H_2O(l) + 531 \text{ kcal}$$
What is ΔH_f° for propane?

14. ΔH_f° for $Fe_2O_3(s)$ is -196.5 kcal/mole. What is ΔH for the reaction:
$$Fe_2O_3(s) + 3CO(g) \rightarrow 2Fe(s) + 3CO_2(g)$$

20-5   15. (a) Why do exothermic reactions tend to be spontaneous? (b) State an example of an exothermic reaction that is spontaneous at certain temperatures but not at others. Mention these temperatures. (c) What conclusion must be drawn from the fact that exothermic reactions are not always spontaneous?

20-6   16. Explain the change of entropy represented by each of the following: (a) The detonation of an explosive; (b) Separating the sugar from the water in a sugar solution; (c) Expanding a gas into a vacuum; (d) The decomposition of $NO_2(g)$ into $NO(g)$ and $O_2(g)$; (e) The combination of $H_2(g)$ and $O_2(g)$ to form $H_2O(l)$; (f) Heating water from 20°C to 50°C.

Chapter 20   Enthalpy and Entropy   **407**

17. Why will potassium nitrate dissolve in water to form potassium and nitrate ions even though the ΔH for this change is positive?

18. Once the burning of coal is started, the reaction is spontaneous. Explain this in terms of ΔS and ΔH.

19. In terms of ΔS and ΔH, explain why some endothermic reactions may occur spontaneously.

20. (a) What arithmetical combination in the Gibbs equation describes a spontaneous change? (b) Why does the effectiveness of the entropy change in the equation depend upon the temperature?

21. The decomposition of $KClO_3(s)$ into $KCl(s)$ and $O_2(g)$ is an endothermic reaction. Why is it spontaneous at temperatures above 370°C but not at temperatures below this value?

22. Refer to the Gibbs equation and state what combination of ΔS and ΔH (a) must produce a negative ΔG. Why? (b) must produce a positive ΔG? Why? (c) tends to produce a negative ΔG at low temperatures. Why? (d) tends to produce a negative ΔG at high temperatures. Why?

23. The ΔH of a certain reaction is -30 kcal and the ΔS, -0.08 kcal per kelvin degree. Calculate ΔG at 25°C. Will this reaction occur spontaneously at 500 K?

24. Explain by calculating ΔG, why KCl crystals will dissolve in water at 25°C, although the ΔH is positive.
$$\Delta H = +2.0 \text{ kcal}; \quad \Delta S = +23 \text{ cal/kelvin}.$$

25. For a given reaction, $\Delta H = 20.0$ kcal and $\Delta G = 16.0$ kcal at 25°C. Calculate the value of (a) ΔS (b) ΔG at 800 K.

26. A sample of ice melts to water at a temperature above 0°C. For each of the terms, $\Delta S, \Delta H$, and ΔG, state whether it is positive or negative and give the reason for your answer.

27. (a) Calculate the standard free energy change of the reaction,
$$Fe_2O_3(s) + 3CO(g) \rightarrow 2Fe(s) + 3CO_2(g)$$
(b) What must first be done before the reaction can proceed spontaneously at the standard temperature of 298 K? ΔG_f^0 values are: $Fe_2O_3(s) = -177$ kcal/mole; $CO(g) = -32.8$ kcal/mole; $CO_2(g) = -94.3$ kcal/mole.

FOR FURTHER THOUGHT

1. The heat of formation of O_2 is zero. Is this statement an observation, a calculation, an inference, or a definition? Explain.

2. A certain chemical reaction is exothermic and has a positive free energy change at temperature T.
(a) Will the reaction proceed spontaneously at temperature T? Explain.
(b) Will the reaction proceed spontaneously at all, some, or no temperatures higher than T? Explain.
(c) Will the reaction proceed spontaneously at all, some, or no temperatures lower than T? Explain.

CHAPTER 21

Chemical Equilibrium

Objectives

When you have completed this chapter, you will be able to:
- Distinguish between a reversible reaction that is in equilibrium and one that is not.
- Derive mass-action expressions.
- Calculate equilibrium constants and apply them to reversible reactions.
- Explain and apply Le Chatelier's principle.

21-1   Reversible Reactions

Virtually all chemical reactions are reversible. For example, when TNT explodes, it produces the gases CO_2, H_2O (water in the gaseous phase), and N_2. Under *extra*ordinary conditions—that is, if one is willing to expend enough energy and follow a complicated pathway—it is possible to re-form TNT from the gaseous products. However, under suitable laboratory conditions, the products of many chemical reactions can be *directly* reacted to form the reactants. Sometimes this can happen under the same conditions as the forward reaction. At other times, somewhat different conditions must be used. All such reactions are called **reversible reactions.**

As an example of a reversible reaction, consider the reaction between iron oxide and hydrogen. When the hydrogen is passed over heated magnetic iron oxide (Fe_3O_4), iron and water are produced:

$$Fe_3O_4 + 4H_2 \longrightarrow 3Fe + 4H_2O \qquad \textbf{(Reaction 1)}$$

The reverse reaction can be produced by passing steam over red-hot iron. Magnetic iron oxide is formed and hydrogen is set free.

$$3Fe + 4H_2O \longrightarrow Fe_3O_4 + 4H_2 \qquad \textbf{(Reaction 2)}$$
$$\text{(steam)}$$

If the water (as steam) is allowed to escape from the reaction vessel during Reaction 1, then Reaction 2 cannot take place. Similarly, if the hydrogen formed by Reaction 2 is allowed to escape, the reverse reaction, Reaction 1, cannot take place. However, the situation is different if either reaction is carried out in a closed vessel so that no substances can escape.

Chemical Equilibrium   **409**

Figure 21-1

(A) When hydrogen gas, H_2, is passed over heated Fe_3O_4, water in the form of steam passes out of the reaction tube, leaving iron, Fe, behind. (B) The reverse of this reaction can be carried out by passing steam over finely divided iron (iron filings). The iron changes to iron oxide, Fe_3O_4, and hydrogen passes out of the tube. Note: This procedure is dangerous and should not be attempted without supervision.

(A)

(B)

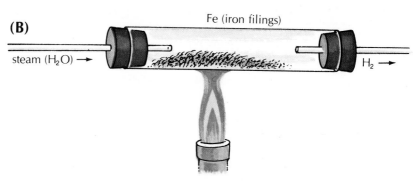

> At 3500°C, the formation and decomposition of water reach a state of equilibrium in a closed system.

Consider what happens if Reaction 1 is carried out in a closed vessel. The reaction will start as soon as the hydrogen gas and magnetic iron oxide are heated to the necessary temperature. The products of the reaction are iron (Fe) and steam (H_2O). But iron in the presence of steam can produce iron oxide and hydrogen by Reaction 2. Therefore, as soon as iron and steam are formed by Reaction 1, they begin combining to produce iron oxide and hydrogen. Reaction 2 will take place at a slow rate at first because not much iron and steam will have been formed. As Reaction 1 continues, more iron and steam are formed. As their concentration increases, Reaction 2 speeds up. Reaction 1 meanwhile slows down as its reactants are used up, causing the concentrations of the reactants to decrease. A point will finally be reached where the two reactions are taking place at the same rate. That is, iron and steam will be used up by Reaction 2 as fast as they are formed by Reaction 1. Magnetic iron oxide and hydrogen will be used by Reaction 1 as fast as they are formed by Reaction 2. Then the concentrations of the substances taking part in the reaction become constant. When the forward and backward reactions are proceeding under the same conditions and at the same rate, a **state of chemical equilibrium** exists. See Figure 21-2. Note that *physical* equilibrium was discussed in Section 7-4.

Rather than writing two separate equations for reversible reactions in a state of equilibrium, it is customary to write one equation using a double arrow. Therefore, the equations for Reactions 1 and 2 can be combined into one equation, written simply:

Figure 21-2

Equilibrium curves. (A) These curves show how the rate of reaction varies with the progress of a reaction toward completion. As the reactants are used up, the rate of the forward reaction decreases. As the products accumulate, the rate of the reverse reaction increases. When the reaction has reached the point at which the two rates are equal, equilibrium occurs. The diagram indicates that equilibrium for this reaction occurs when the forward reaction has gone about 70% toward completion. (B) The reaction rates for the same reaction are here plotted against time from the start of the reaction. This diagram shows more clearly the gradual approach to equilibrium that actually occurs.

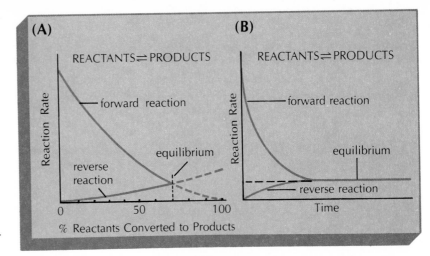

$$Fe_3O_4 + 4H_2 \rightleftharpoons 3Fe + 4H_2O \qquad \text{(Eq. 1)}$$

An equal sign is sometimes used in place of double arrows:

$$Fe_3O_4 + 4H_2 = 3Fe + 4H_2O \qquad \text{(Eq. 2)}$$

When read in the normal left-to-right manner, Equation 1 says that Fe_3O_4 reacts with H_2 to produce Fe and H_2O. This reaction is called the forward reaction. When read in the reverse direction (right to left), Equation 1 says that Fe reacts with H_2O to produce Fe_3O_4 and H_2. This reaction is called the reverse reaction or backward reaction.

21-2 Characteristics of an Equilibrium

An equilibrium is a state of balance in the rates of opposing changes. Vapor-liquid phase equilibrium was discussed in Section 7-4 and solution equilibrium in Section 17-11. These two types of equilibrium are examples of *physical* equilibria. The reactions discussed in the last section are an example of a *chemical* equilibrium. Regardless of whether physical or chemical, an equilibrium is a dynamic state in which change is taking place. Two opposing processes are going on at the same time and at the same rate. Before a state of chemical equilibrium exists, changes occur that are easily observed. For example, there will be changes in the concentrations of substances taking part in the reaction and changes in temperature, and there may be changes in color and pressure. Once a state of chemical equilibrium exists, these changes no longer take place.

A chemical equilibrium can be illustrated by that which exists between the two gases dinitrogen tetroxide, N_2O_4, and nitrogen dioxide, NO_2:

$$N_2O_4 \rightleftharpoons 2NO_2 \qquad \text{(Eq. 3)}$$
$$\text{colorless} \qquad \text{brown}$$

As noted, the one gas is colorless while the other has a brown color. A flask containing these two gases will have a brown color because of the presence of nitrogen dioxide. At any time before equilibrium has been reached, the mixture will be changing color. The mixture will become a darker brown if the forward reaction is proceeding at a faster rate than the reverse reaction. It will become a lighter brown if the reverse reaction is proceeding at the faster rate. But no color change will be observed once equilibrium has been reached. See Figure 21-3.

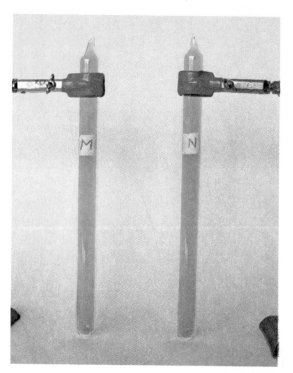

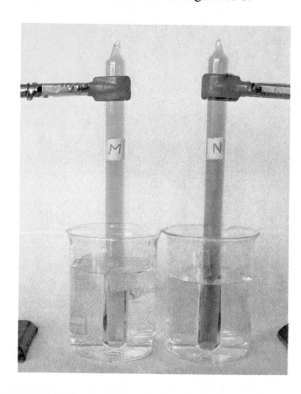

Figure 21-3

In the left photo, both tubes have sealed in them a mixture of the brown gas nitrogen dioxide, NO_2, and the colorless gas dinitrogen tetroxide, N_2O_4. Both tubes were at room temperature. Tube M was then placed in a beaker of ice water, and tube N was placed in a beaker of hot water, as shown in the right photo. How do you account for the difference in the color of the tubes in the right photo?

Questions for Sections 21-1 and 21-2

1. (a) Explain the meaning of *reversible reaction* and mention an example. (b) What name is given to a reversible reaction where both forward and backward reactions occur under the same conditions?
2. (a) When H_2 is passed over heated magnetic iron oxide in a closed vessel, a state of equilibrium is reached. In terms of forward and backward reaction rates, describe what happens leading up to this equilibrium. (b) Write the equation for the equilibrium. (c) Describe the conditions under which the forward reaction may go to completion. (d) Write the equation for this reaction.
*3. (a) For a chemical equilibrium, why is the situation said to be dynamic? (b) Compare the forward and backward rates of reaction during a chemical equilibrium. (c) For the equilibrium $A + B \rightleftharpoons C + D$, which substances may be used as starting materials to produce the equilibrium?
4. Describe the physical equilibrium that can occur in a sealed test tube half-filled with water.
5. How can the colors of N_2O_4 and NO_2 be used to follow the equilibrium that exists between these two gases?

21-3 The Equilibrium Constant

There is a definite relationship between the concentrations of the reactants and products when a reversible reaction has reached a state of equilibrium. This relationship is best illustrated with experimental data. Let us consider the reversible reaction at 490°C between hydrogen and iodine to produce hydrogen iodide:

$$H_2(g) + I_2(g) \rightleftharpoons 2HI(g) \qquad \textbf{(Eq. 4)}$$

At the start of one experiment, 1.00 mole of hydrogen and 1.00 mole of iodine vapor are put into a closed container whose volume is 1.00 liter. The temperature is brought to 490°C. Before reaction begins, then, the concentration of each of these substances is 1.00 mole per liter:

$$[H_2] = 1.00 \text{ mole/liter}$$

$$[I_2] = 1.00 \text{ mole/liter}$$

The brackets are used to indicate that a number refers to a concentration. The expression

$$[H_2]$$

is read "the concentration of hydrogen."

The concentrations of H_2 and I_2 do not remain at 1.00 mole/liter for long. As soon as the two substances come into contact with each other, they begin to react. Eventually, equilibrium is reached when the rate at which hydrogen iodide is being formed is equal to the rate at which it is decomposing. At equilibrium it will be found that the concentrations of both the H_2 and I_2 are 0.228 mole/liter. The concentration of the HI is 1.544 moles/liter. These results are summarized below:

EXPERIMENT 1

Starting Concentrations			Concentrations at Equilibrium		
$[H_2]$	$[I_2]$	$[HI]$	$[H_2]$	$[I_2]$	$[HI]$
1.00	1.00	0	0.228	0.228	1.544

In a second experiment, 1.00 mole of HI is put into the 1-liter reaction vessel at a temperature of 490°C. The hydrogen iodide decomposes to form H_2 and I_2. Because the reaction is reversible, the H_2 and I_2 formed by the decomposition begin to react to re-form HI. Finally, when equilibrium is reached, the concentrations of the substances are found to be:

EXPERIMENT 2

Starting Concentrations			Concentrations at Equilibrium		
$[H_2]$	$[I_2]$	$[HI]$	$[H_2]$	$[I_2]$	$[HI]$
0	0	1.00	0.114	0.114	0.772

Chapter 21   Chemical Equilibrium   **413**

Figure 21-4

Starting and equilibrium concentrations for the reaction between hydrogen and iodine at 490°C.

Experiment	Starting Concentrations			Concentrations at Equilibrium		
	$[H_2]$	$[I_2]$	$[HI]$	$[H_2]$	$[I_2]$	$[HI]$
1	1.00	1.00	0	0.228	0.228	1.544
2	0	0	1.00	0.114	0.114	0.772
3	0	0	1.50	0.171	0.171	1.158
4	0.600	0.400	0	0.245	0.045	0.711
5	0.800	1.200	0	0.090	0.490	1.423

Three more experiments are done with various starting concentrations. The data for all five experiments are shown in Figure 21-4.

Consider the data in Figure 21-4 for the concentrations at equilibrium. There is a relationship among these concentrations that is given by the following equation:

$$\frac{[HI]^2}{[H_2] \times [I_2]} = K \qquad \textbf{(Eq. 5)}$$

Equation 5 states that if the hydrogen iodide concentration is squared, and the result divided by the product of the hydrogen and iodine concentrations, the same number K will be obtained in every case. The way in which this formula is derived will be explained later. Let us first test it with the data given in Figure 21-4:

EXP. 1

$$\frac{(1.544)^2}{(0.228)(0.228)} = 45.9$$

EXP. 2

$$\frac{(0.772)^2}{(0.114)(0.114)} = 45.9$$

EXP. 3

$$\frac{(1.158)^2}{(0.171)(0.171)} = 45.9$$

EXP. 4

$$\frac{(0.711)^2}{(0.245)(0.045)} = 45.9$$

EXP. 5

$$\frac{(1.423)^2}{(0.090)(0.490)} = 45.9$$

The value of the constant is 45.9. This means that no matter what the initial concentrations of the hydrogen, iodine, or hydrogen iodide, their concentrations will adjust themselves until at equilibrium they conform to the relationship given by the equation:

$$\frac{[HI]^2}{[H_2] \times [I_2]} = 45.9 \qquad \textbf{(Eq. 6)}$$

The constant 45.9 is called the equilibrium constant. It is the equilibrium constant for the reversible reaction between hydrogen and iodine. Equilibrium constants are temperature dependent. That is, the constant 45.9 is correct for the reversible reaction between hydrogen and iodine only when the temperature is 490°C. For different temperatures, different constants will apply. For example, at 400°C, the value of the equilibrium constant is not 45.9, but 54.5.

21-4 The Mass-Action Expression

In the last section we saw that Equation 6 stated the relationship between the equilibrium concentrations of the substances taking part in the reversible reaction between hydrogen and iodine when the temperature was 490°C. As was already noted, the number, 45.9, on the right-hand side of Equation 6 is called the equilibrium constant. The left-hand side of Equation 6 is called the mass-action expression. The mass-action expression for a reversible reaction is equal to the equilibrium constant for that reaction at a particular temperature. While the equilibrium constant can only be determined by experiment, the mass-action expression can be derived from the balanced equation for the reaction. We illustrate the derivation below.

Suppose that substances A and B react to produce substances C and D. Since this is a reversible reaction, C and D react to produce A and B. The equation for these reactions can be written:

$$a\text{A} + b\text{B} \rightleftharpoons c\text{C} + d\text{D} \qquad \textbf{(Eq. 7)}$$

The small letters a, b, c, and d represent the coefficients in the balanced equation. The mass-action expression for this equation is

$$\frac{[\text{C}]^c \times [\text{D}]^d}{[\text{A}]^a \times [\text{B}]^b}$$

The numerator (top part) of the mass-action expression is formed from the equilibrium concentrations of substances on the right side of the balanced equation, the concentration of each substance being raised to the power indicated by its coefficient. The denominator (bottom part) of the mass-action expression is formed from the equilibrium concentrations of substances on the left side of the balanced equation, the concentration of each substance being raised to the power indicated by its coefficient. For example, if an equation has the form

$$2\text{A} + \text{B} \rightleftharpoons 3\text{C} + 2\text{D}$$

the mass-action expression would be

$$\frac{[\text{C}]^3 \times [\text{D}]^2}{[\text{A}]^2 \times [\text{B}]}$$

An equation can, of course, have any number of reactants and any number of products. The general case can be represented as follows:

$$a\text{A} + b\text{B} + c\text{C} + \ldots \rightleftharpoons d\text{D} + e\text{E} + f\text{F} + \ldots \qquad \textbf{(Eq. 8)}$$

The mass-action expression for this general case can be written:

$$\frac{[\text{D}]^d \times [\text{E}]^e \times [\text{F}]^f \times \ldots}{[\text{A}]^a \times [\text{B}]^b \times [\text{C}]^c \times \ldots}$$

CHEMISTRY IN ACTION

The Gossamer Albatross

The photo shows the Gossamer Albatross as it was being pedalled 36 kilometers across the English Channel on June 12, 1979, the first flight of a human-powered aircraft across the Channel. This two-hour, 49-minute flight would not have been possible without materials recently developed by the chemical industry. Of special importance to the flight was the tough, thin polyester film used to cover both the wings and the fuselage. The use of this material is one of the reasons that the aircraft, despite its wingspan of more than 29 meters, weighed an incredibly light 25 kilograms (55 pounds) before being boarded by its human engine.

Thus, the **mass action expression** is a fraction formed from the concentrations of the reactants and products of a reaction, each concentration raised to a power indicated by an appropriate coefficient in the balanced equation. The **equilibrium constant** is a temperature dependent constant obtained by evaluating the mass action expression when its concentrations are all equilibrium concentrations.

The reaction

$$H_2 + I_2 \rightleftharpoons 2HI \qquad \textbf{(Eq. 9)}$$

is of the general type

$$aA + bB \rightleftharpoons cC \qquad \textbf{(Eq. 10)}$$

The mass-action expression for Equation 10 is

$$\frac{[C]^c}{[A]^a \times [B]^b}$$

In Equation 9, $a = 1$, $b = 1$, and $c = 2$. Therefore, the mass-action expression for the reaction of Equation 9 is

$$\frac{[HI]^2}{[H_2] \times [I_2]}$$

We saw this expression in Section 21-3 when we noted that its numerical value was 45.9 for five different experiments.

For all reversible reactions at equilibrium, the mass-action expression is equal to a constant at constant temperature. This fact is called the **law of chemical equilibrium.**

The reversible reaction

$$H_2 + I_2 \rightleftharpoons 2HI \qquad \textbf{(Eq. 11)}$$

can also be written in the reverse order:

$$2HI \rightleftharpoons H_2 + I_2 \qquad \textbf{(Eq. 12)}$$

Equations 11 and 12 convey the same information with one difference. Equation 11 implies that equilibrium was reached by reacting hydrogen with iodine. Equation 12 implies that equilibrium was reached by decomposing hydrogen iodide. No matter from which direction equilibrium was reached, the mass-action expression for each equation must obey the law of chemical equilibrium. We illustrate this statement below.

The mass-action expressions for Equations 11 and 12 are

$$\frac{[HI]^2}{[H_2] \times [I_2]} \qquad \textbf{(Eq. 13)}$$

$$\frac{[H_2] \times [I_2]}{[HI]^2} \qquad \textbf{(Eq. 14)}$$

The law of chemical equilibrium tells us that each of these expressions must be equal to a constant when equilibrium has been reached.

$$\frac{[HI]^2}{[H_2] \times [I_2]} = K_1 \qquad \text{(Eq. 15)}$$

$$\frac{[H_2] \times [I_2]}{[HI]^2} = K_2 \qquad \text{(Eq. 16)}$$

The constants K_1 and K_2 cannot have the same numerical values, but they are related. Since the one mass-action expression is the reciprocal of the other, the one constant must be the reciprocal of the other:

$$K_2 = \frac{1}{K_1} \qquad \text{and} \qquad K_1 = \frac{1}{K_2}$$

We already noted that at 490°C, $K_1 = 45.9$. Therefore, $K_2 = \frac{1}{45.9} = 0.0218$. Substituting these values into Equations 15 and 16 gives:

$$\frac{[HI]^2}{[H_2] \times [I_2]} = 45.9 \qquad \text{and} \qquad \frac{[H_2] \times [I_2]}{[HI]^2} = 0.0218$$

At a temperature of 490°C, both of these expressions state the correct relationship between the equilibrium concentrations regardless of the direction from which equilibrium is reached.

Questions for Sections 21-3 and 21-4

6. Consider the following equilibrium that takes place at 490°C:
$$H_2(g) + I_2(g) \rightleftharpoons 2HI(g)$$
(a) What starting substance or substances can be used to bring about the equilibrium in a closed container? (b) With reference to reaction rate, at what point is equilibrium reached? (c) Write the fraction with reaction concentrations that has a constant value at a given temperature. (d) What name is given to this constant?

*7. When 1.00 mole of HI is heated to 510°C in a sealed 1-liter flask until equilibrium is reached, it decomposes to form 0.14 mole of each of the products H_2 and I_2. All reactants are in the gaseous phase. Calculate the equilibrium constant.

8. (a) Write the mass-action expression for the equilibrium,
$$A + 2B \rightleftharpoons 2C + 3D$$
(b) What does the law of chemical equilibrium tell us about this expression?

*9. For the equilibrium $CaCO_3(s) \rightleftharpoons CaO(s) + CO_2(g)$, why is the concentration of the carbon dioxide a constant, assuming the temperature is kept constant?

*10. When 1.0 mole of N_2O_4 is placed into a 5.0 liter container at 100°C, part of it decomposes to form NO_2. At equilibrium, 1.00 mole of NO_2 is present. Calculate K for the reaction $N_2O_4(g) \rightleftharpoons 2NO_2(g)$.

21-5 Significance of the Size of the Equilibrium Constant

At equilibrium, two opposing chemical reactions are going on at the same rate. This statement says nothing about the relative amounts of each substance present at equilibrium. Look once again at the concentrations at equilibrium of hydrogen, iodine, and hydrogen iodide given in Figure 21-4. For each of the five experiments, the amount of hydrogen iodide present is considerably greater than the amount of either the hydrogen or iodine. To indicate that the equilibrium mixture is richer in hydrogen iodide than in either of the other two substances, the equation is sometimes written with a longer arrow pointing in the direction of hydrogen iodide.

$$H_2(g) + I_2(g) \rightleftharpoons 2HI(g) \qquad \text{(Eq. 17)}$$

The size of the equilibrium constant usually indicates the extent to which a reaction proceeds to the right before reaching equilibrium. A small constant, say one whose value is 2×10^{-5}, indicates that at equilibrium relatively little product has been formed. A large value for the constant, say 50 000, indicates that at equilibrium a relatively large amount of product has been formed. See Figure 21-5.

Figure 21-5

The significance of the relative lengths of the double arrows. The arrows in the equation on the left indicate that the equilibrium mixture consists mostly of molecules of substance C. The arrows in the equation on the right indicate that the equilibrium mixture consists mostly of molecules of the substances *A* and *B*.

molecule of substance A   molecule of substance C

molecule of substance B

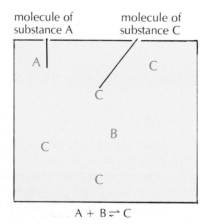

A + B ⇌ C

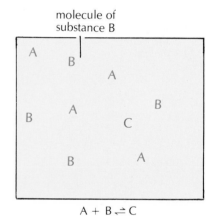

A + B ⇌ C

21-6 Changing the Concentration, Temperature, or Pressure

When a reversible reaction is at equilibrium, both the forward and reverse reactions are proceeding at the same rate. When the temperature, the pressure, or the concentration of a reactant (or product) is changed, a chemical reaction is said to be placed under a **stress**. If a reaction is at equilibrium, a stress will upset the equilibrium. That is, a stress will make the rates of the forward and reverse reactions unequal.

If the forward reaction proceeds faster than the reverse reaction, a greater amount of the products will be formed. If the reverse reaction proceeds faster, a greater amount of the reactants will be formed. When changes in the concentrations of reacting substances takes place following a stress, the equilibrium is said to undergo a **shift** or **displacement.** Eventually, the two reactions will once again take place at the same rate, so that equilibrium will be re-established, but at different concentrations. The rest of the chapter describes how different kinds of stress affect an equilibrium.

(A)

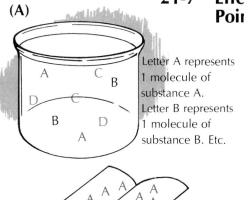

Letter A represents 1 molecule of substance A. Letter B represents 1 molecule of substance B. Etc.

(B)

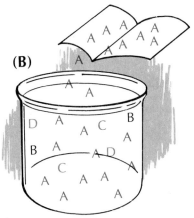

Figure 21-6

(A) *A beaker containing dissolved particles of substances A, B, C, and D in equilibrium with each other as described by the equation:*

$$A + B \rightleftharpoons C + D$$

(B) Solid crystals of substance A being added to the solution from a weighing paper. The probability of a particle A combining with a particle B is now greatly enhanced because of the large increase in the number of particles of substance A. This causes a disturbance in the equilibrium, causing it to shift to the right:

$$A + B \rightleftharpoons C + D$$

21-7 Effect of Concentration of Reactant on the Point of Equilibrium

The effect of changing the concentration of a reactant can be illustrated by the reaction of two solids, A and B. Each substance must first be dissolved in water before it will react with the other to any appreciable extent. When the aqueous solution of A is added to the aqueous solution of B, a reversible reaction takes place in which substances C and D are produced. The equation for the reactions can be written

$$A + B \rightleftharpoons C + D \qquad \text{(Eq. 18)}$$

Now suppose that equilibrium has been reached. Next, some solid, undissolved A is added to the reaction vessel. As the particles of A dissolve in the water, the concentration of A is suddenly increased. Suddenly there are more particles of A than before. The likelihood of a particle of B colliding with a particle of A is suddenly increased. As a result, the forward reaction, that is, the reaction of particle A with particle B, proceeds at a faster rate than before. See Figure 21-6. Since the forward reaction is now proceeding at a faster rate than the reverse reaction, the equilibrium no longer exists. As the forward reaction speeds up, particles of B are consumed, decreasing the concentration of B. At the same time, particles of C and D are being formed at a faster rate than before. Hence, the concentrations of particles C and D increase.

As the number of particles of C and D increases, the likelihood of these particles colliding and reacting increases. Therefore, the reverse reaction begins to speed up. Meanwhile, the forward reaction has begun to slow down because the concentrations of both A and B have been decreasing ever since the forward reaction was speeded up by the addition of A. As the forward reaction continues to slow down, and the reverse reaction continues to speed up, a point is finally reached where the two reactions are once again taking place at the same rate. That is, equilibrium is once again established.

Here we summarize what happens to the equilibrium concentrations of the substances in Equation 18 when solid A is added to the reactants and products at equilibrium:

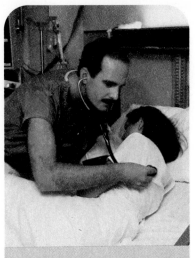
—The concentration of A increases.

—The concentration of B decreases.

—The concentrations of both products, C and D, increase.

We summarize these changes as they apply to the law of chemical equilibrium for Equation 18:

$$\underset{\text{increases}}{\frac{\overset{\text{increases}}{[C]} \times \overset{\text{increases}}{[D]}}{\underset{\text{increases}}{[A]} \times \underset{\text{decreases}}{[B]}} = K} \qquad \textbf{(Eq. 19)}$$

Following the addition of more A, it is clear that the numerator (top part) of the left side of Equation 19 will increase since the concentrations of both C and D have increased. The left side of Equation 19 can maintain the same constant value only if its denominator (bottom part) increases by the same factor. For example, if the numerator doubles, the denominator will have to double, too, if the value of the fraction is to remain unchanged. This means that the concentration of A in Equation 19 must increase enough to outweigh the decrease in the concentration of B. The increase in the concentration of A must be large enough to make the product $[A] \times [B]$ increase over its former value in spite of the decrease in the concentration of B.

The changes referred to in the earlier part of this section can be shown with the following notations:

1. Equation showing the original equilibrium:

$$A + B \rightleftharpoons C + D \qquad \textbf{(Eq. 20)}$$

2. Showing the addition of more of particle A, causing its concentration to increase:

$$A + B \rightleftharpoons C + D \qquad \textbf{(Eq. 21)}$$
$$+$$
$$A$$

3. Showing the removal of particle A, causing its concentration to decrease:

$$\text{Ⓐ} + B \rightleftharpoons C + D \qquad \textbf{(Eq. 22)}$$

4. Showing a shift in the point of equilibrium to the right as a result of the forward reaction temporarily proceeding at a faster rate than the reverse reaction, the shift in this case caused by an increase in the concentration of A:

$$A + B \rightleftharpoons C + D \qquad \textbf{(Eq. 23)}$$
$$+$$
$$A$$

Had the concentrations of either C or D been increased instead of the concentration of A, the reverse reaction would have temporarily been speeded up. This would have driven the point of the equilibrium to the left:

$$A + B \rightleftarrows C + D \qquad \textbf{(Eq. 24)}$$
$$+$$
$$C$$

Had particles of A been removed from the reaction vessel, rather than added, the concentration of A would have decreased. This would have speeded up the reverse reaction, shifting the equilibrium to the left:

$$\textcircled{A} + B \rightleftarrows C + D \qquad \textbf{(Eq. 25)}$$

Questions for Sections 21-5 through 21-7

11. What do the following equilibria tell us about the relative quantities of reactants and products?
    (a) $H_2(g) + I_2(g) \rightleftarrows 2HI(g)$
    (b) $AgCl(s) \rightleftarrows Ag^+(aq) + Cl^-(aq)$

12. What does the size of the equilibrium constant indicate?

*13. At 25°C, three reactions are found to have equilibrium constants of 1.0×10^{16}, 0.015, and 1.8×10^{-11}. (a) Which constant indicates an equilibrium with very little product on the right? Explain. (b) Which reaction can be considered, for practical purposes, to go to completion? Explain.

14. A change of temperature, pressure, or concentration has what general effect on a chemical equilibrium?

15. In the equilibrium mixture $A(aq) + B(aq) \rightleftarrows C(aq) + D(aq)$, more solid A is dissolved. How does dissolving more A affect the concentrations of (a) A (b) B (c) C (d) D? Explain your answers briefly in terms of collision theory.

16. In the reaction $KCl(aq) + NaNO_3(aq) \rightleftarrows KNO_3(aq) + NaCl(aq)$, what is the effect on the point of equilibrium of increasing the concentration of (a) $NaNO_3$ (b) KNO_3?

17. What is the effect on the point of equilibrium of increasing the quantity of AgCl in the reaction $AgCl(s) \rightleftarrows Ag^+(aq) + Cl^-(aq)$?

21-8   Le Chatelier's Principle

By reasoning similar to that in the preceding section it is possible to determine the effect on the equilibrium point of a change in temperature and a change in pressure. The general conclusions of such reasoning are expressed in what is known as Le Chatelier's (luh-

Luis W. Alvarez (1911-   )

Luis Alvarez received the Nobel Prize in Physics (1968) for his discovery of resonance particles. These resonances are elementary particles that may exist only for 10-22 seconds. Alvarez and his colleagues first developed liquid hydrogen bubble chambers and then created new measuring devices and the computer programs needed to detect such elusive particles.

Together with his son, Walter Alvarez, a geologist at the University of California at Berkeley, Luis Alvarez has suggested a theory to explain the disappearance of the dinosaurs. According to their theory, an asteroid collided with Earth about 65 million years ago. The tons of dust thrown into the atmosphere by the impact shielded the Earth from the sun. Green plants that require the sun's energy for photosynthesis died off and so too did the land animals that depended on these plants for food. Alvarez's theory, while still unproven, was used to predict the effect of "nuclear winter" on living things.

SHAT-el-YAY) Principle. **Le Chatelier's principle** states: When a system at equilibrium is subjected to a stress (a change in concentration of a reactant, in temperature, or in pressure), the equilibrium will shift in the direction that tends to counteract the effect of the stress.

Let us consider Le Chatelier's principle as it applies to three kinds of stress.

1. Stress caused by a change in the concentration of a reactant:

SHIFT CAUSED BY AN INCREASE IN CONCENTRATION OF A REACTANT

$$A + B \rightleftharpoons C + D \qquad \text{(Eq. 26)}$$
$$+$$
$$A \qquad \text{(Concentration of A increases)}$$

The stress in this case is an increase in the concentration of substance A. This stress is counteracted by favoring the reaction in which A is consumed. Since A is consumed as a reactant in the forward reaction, the forward reaction is favored. That is, the equilibrium shifts to the right. This agrees with our conclusion in Section 21-7.

SHIFT CAUSED BY A DECREASE IN CONCENTRATION OF A PRODUCT

$$A + B \rightleftharpoons C + D \qquad \text{(Eq. 27)}$$
$$\text{(Concentration of D decreases)}$$

The stress in this case is a decrease in the concentration of D. The stress is counteracted by favoring the reaction in which D is produced, that is, the forward reaction. Had the concentration of either A or B been decreased, the reverse reaction would have been favored.

By simple logic we can understand why Le Chatelier's principle must work as it does in the real world. Suppose that the effect of increasing the concentration of a reactant were the opposite: that is, suppose it favored the reverse reaction. This would mean that increasing the concentration of a reactant would lead to a still further increase in that concentration. That increase would in turn lead to a still further increase. We would have a runaway situation in which no reversible reaction could remain in a stable equilibrium condition. The slightest change in concentration of any substance would drive the equilibrium in the same direction, until the reaction went completely in one direction or the other. If Le Chatelier's principle were not true, no such thing as an equilibrium could ever occur.

The same reasoning applies to other types of stress.

2. Stress caused by a change in temperature:

SHIFT CAUSED BY AN INCREASE IN TEMPERATURE

$$A + B \overset{\text{exo.}}{\underset{\text{endo.}}{\rightleftharpoons}} C + D \qquad \text{(Eq. 28)}$$

The stress in this case is an increase in temperature. The stress is counteracted by favoring the endothermic reaction, since the endothermic reaction absorbs heat. In the above case, the equilibrium shifts to the left.

SHIFT CAUSED BY A DECREASE IN TEMPERATURE

$$A + B \overset{\text{exo.}}{\underset{\text{endo.}}{\rightleftharpoons}} C + D \qquad \text{(Eq. 29)}$$

The stress in this case is a decrease in temperature. The stress is counteracted by a shift in equilibrium that favors the exothermic reaction, since the exothermic reaction releases heat.

Again, logic tells us that this must be the case. If an increase in temperature caused the equilibrium to shift toward a release of heat, that would raise the temperature still higher. That, in turn, would cause a further shift toward a release of heat and a further rise in temperature.

Unlike other stresses, a change in temperature causes both a shift in the point of equilibrium and a change in the numerical value of the equilibrium constant (see the last paragraph in Section 21-3). The mathematical relationship between the temperature and the value of the equilibrium constant is beyond the scope of this book.

3. Stress caused by a change in pressure:

SHIFT CAUSED BY AN INCREASE IN PRESSURE

$$1N_2(g) + 3H_2(g) \rightleftharpoons 2NH_3(g) \qquad \text{(Eq. 30)}$$

| 1 + 3 = 4 moles | 2 moles of |
| of gas molecules | gas molecules |

At constant temperature and constant volume, the pressure exerted by a sample of gas is directly proportional to the number of molecules in the sample. A two-mole sample exerts twice the pressure of a one-mole sample. An increase in pressure can be counteracted by favoring the reaction which reduces the number of molecules. With a smaller number of molecules occupying the constant volume of the reaction vessel, the pressure will tend to decrease. In Equation 30, the forward reaction converts 4 moles of molecules to 2 moles of molecules. Therefore, the forward reaction reduces the number of molecules and is favored by an increase in pressure.

$$1N_2(g) + 3H_2(g) \rightleftharpoons 2NH_3(g) \qquad \text{(Eq. 31)}$$

1 + 3 = 4 moles   2 moles of
of gas molecules   gas molecules

A decrease in pressure can be counteracted by favoring the reaction which produces a greater number of molecules. With a greater number of molecules occupying the constant volume of the reaction vessel, the pressure will tend to increase.

21-9   Effect of a Catalyst on the Point of Equilibrium

Catalysts do not favor one reaction over the other in an equilibrium. They increase the rates of both the forward and reverse reactions equally. Thus, they cause reactions to reach equilibrium more rapidly, but they do not displace the point of the equilibrium.

Questions for Sections 21-8 and 21-9

18. (a) State Le Chatelier's principle. (b) to (e) Consider the reaction for the first step in the Ostwald process for making nitric acid:
$$4NH_3(g) + 5O_2(g) \rightleftharpoons 4NO(g) + 6H_2O(g) + \text{heat}$$
Explain the effect on the equilibrium of (b) increasing the concentration of the oxygen; (c) increasing the pressure; (d) increasing the temperature; (e) removing the NO as it is formed.

19. In the second step of the Ostwald process, the NO reacts with O_2:
$$2NO(g) + O_2(g) \rightleftharpoons 2NO_2(g) + \text{heat}$$
The NO obtained in the first step is quite hot and is cooled before being oxidized to NO_2. Why?

*20. For the following equilibria, explain how the given *stress* affects the equilibrium point:
(a) $N_2(g) + O_2(g) \rightleftharpoons 2NO(g)$ *Increase in pressure.*
(b) $2SO_3(g) + \text{heat} \rightleftharpoons 2SO_2(g) + O_2(g)$ *Increase in temperature.*
(c) Same reaction as in (b)   *Increase in pressure.*
(d) $CaCO_3(s) \rightleftharpoons CaO(s) + CO_2(g)$ *Removal of CO_2.*

21. Explain the effect of using a platinum catalyst in the equilibrium reaction for the oxidation of ammonia (equation in question 18).

21-10   The Haber Process: An Application of Equilibrium Principles

Nitrogen is a component of many important compounds, such as fertilizers and explosives. In its uncombined form nitrogen makes up about 80% of the air. However, uncombined nitrogen is very inert. For many years chemists did not know how to get the large quantities of nitrogen in the air to combine with other elements to form nitrogen compounds. The chemist who wanted to make nitrogen compounds in quantity had to start off with a substance that already had combined nitrogen in it. By one or more reactions, the available nitrogen compound was converted to the desired nitrogen compound.

$$\mathbf{N_2 + 3H_2 \rightleftharpoons 2NH_3}$$

Before World War I, sodium and potassium nitrate were commonly used as a source of combined nitrogen. The munitions industry in Germany relied on these compounds as a source of nitrogen for explosives. Germany had to import sodium and potassium nitrate from South America. When World War I broke out, the Allies put up a naval blockade around Germany to disrupt imports to Germany. The Germans then had to find another source of nitrogen for their explosives. Fritz Haber, a German chemist, provided a solution to the problem. He developed a method for combining nitrogen from the air with hydrogen to produce ammonia gas, NH_3. This method is known as the Haber Process. The Germans used the ammonia obtained from the Haber Process as a source of combined nitrogen for making explosives.

The Haber Process provides a good illustration of the use of equilibrium principles. The reaction is a reversible reaction. The equation for the reaction is:

$$N_2(g) + 3H_2(g) \rightleftharpoons 2NH_3(g) + 22 \text{ kcal} \qquad \textbf{(Eq. 31)}$$

Large quantities of ammonia are made in industry by the Haber Process. The aim of the industrial chemist is to control the reaction so that large amounts of ammonia are produced as quickly as possible. Since raising the temperature will increase the speeds of both the forward and reverse reactions, a high temperature should bring the reaction to equilibrium rapidly. However, raising the temperature favors the endothermic reaction, shifting the equilibrium to the left, lowering the yield of ammonia, and increasing the time needed to obtain a given quantity of ammonia.

SHIFT CAUSED BY A RISE IN TEMPERATURE

$$N_2(g) + 3H_2(g) \underset{\text{endo.}}{\overset{\text{exo.}}{\rightleftharpoons}} 2NH_3(g) \qquad \textbf{(Eq. 32)}$$

In fact, at 500°C, only 0.1% of the mass will be ammonia at equilibrium if the reaction is done at 1 atmosphere pressure. (The other 99.9% is, of course, a mixture of nitrogen and hydrogen.) However, by increasing the pressure, the equilibrium favors the reaction in which fewer molecules are produced, in this case shifting the equilibrium to the right, thus producing an equilibrium mixture that is richer in ammonia.

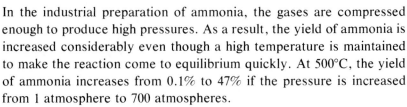

$$1N_2(g) + 3H_2(g) \rightleftharpoons 2NH_3(g) \qquad \text{(Eq. 33)}$$

| 1 + 3 = 4 moles of gas molecules | 2 moles of gas molecules |

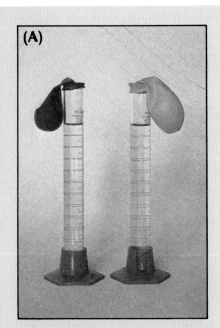

(A)

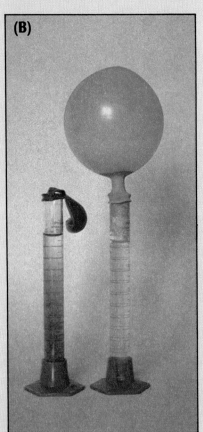

(B)

In the industrial preparation of ammonia, the gases are compressed enough to produce high pressures. As a result, the yield of ammonia is increased considerably even though a high temperature is maintained to make the reaction come to equilibrium quickly. At 500°C, the yield of ammonia increases from 0.1% to 47% if the pressure is increased from 1 atmosphere to 700 atmospheres.

The actual industrial process uses a temperature of 550°C, a pressure of 200 atmospheres, and a catalyst. Under these conditions, about 8% of the nitrogen and hydrogen in the reaction vessel is combined as ammonia. By removing the ammonia as it is formed and feeding in fresh supplies of nitrogen and hydrogen, a satisfactory rate of production of ammonia is achieved.

Questions for Section 21-10

22. Explain the purpose of using the conditions listed below in the Haber process: $N_2(g) + 3H_2(g) \rightleftharpoons 2NH_3(g) + 22$ kcal (a) A pressure of 200 atmospheres. (b) A temperature of 550°C. (c) The removal of ammonia as it is formed. (d) The presence of a catalyst.
*23. What is the value of K at a temperature of 1000 K if the following concentrations are present at that temperature: $[NH_3] = 0.102\ M$; $[N_2] = 1.03\ M$; $[H_2] = 1.62\ M$
24. At 420°C, a liter of Haber reaction mixture is found to consist of 0.50 mole of nitrogen, 0.40 mole of hydrogen, and 0.42 mole of ammonia. Calculate K at this temperature.

CAN YOU EXPLAIN THIS?

(A) The liquids in both cylinders are 2 molar acetic acid solutions, but the solution in the cylinder on the left has also had a quantity of sodium acetate, $NaC_2H_3O_2$, dissolved in it. Each balloon contains the same small quantity of granulated magnesium metal (magnesium metal cut into small pieces).

(B) The balloons were raised at the same time so that the magnesium metal fell into the solutions. The photo shows the setups shortly after the metal entered the solutions.

1. Why was granulated magnesium used?
2. What is causing the balloon shown in Photo B to enlarge? (Explain in terms of an equation for a chemical reaction.)
3. Why is the balloon on the right in Photo B filling up faster than the balloon on the left? (Explain in terms of Le Chatelier's principle as it applies to an equation showing a chemical equilibrium.)

1. A reversible reaction is one in which the products may react, under suitable conditions, to produce the original reactants.
2. When, in a reversible change, the forward and backward changes are going on at the same time, i.e., under the same conditions, the change is said to be in a state of equilibrium.
3. An equilibrium change may be physical or chemical. It is a dynamic state where both forward and backward reactions are going on together at the same rate.
4. The mass-action expression for a chemical equilibrium is a fraction which expresses the ratio between the concentrations of the products (on the right) raised to appropriate powers and the concentrations of reactants (on the left) raised to appropriate powers.
5. The equilibrium constant is the numerical value of the mass-action expression.
6. The combination of the mass-action expression and the equilibrium constant is called the law of chemical equilibrium.
7. The size of the equilibrium constant indicates the extent to which the forward reaction has proceeded at the point of equilibrium.
8. A stress is defined as a change in one of the conditions affecting a chemical change.
9. Le Chatelier's principle states that when a stress is applied to a system in equilibrium, the equilibrium is displaced in the direction that tends to oppose the effect of the stress.
10. Catalysts increase the rates of the forward and backward reactions equally.
11. The Haber process is an example of an equilibrium in which an increase of pressure, a decrease of temperature, and the removal of product favors the formation of an increased percentage of the product. However, the temperature is kept at a moderate level (550°C) to allow the reaction to come to equilibrium more quickly.

TERMS YOU SHOULD KNOW

reversible reactions	mass-action expression	stress
state of chemical equilibrium	equilibrium constant	equilibrium shift or displacement
	law of chemical equilibrium	Le Chatelier's principle

REVIEW QUESTIONS

Section

21-1
1. (a) Distinguish between the terms *reversible reaction* and *equilibrium reaction*. (b) State an example of a reversible reaction that cannot be in equilibrium.
2. Starting with sulfur dioxide and oxygen in a closed vessel, conditions are used which initiate the reaction producing sulfur trioxide. Explain, in terms of reaction rate, how the state of equilibrium is reached.

3. A broken crystal of copper sulfate is placed inside a saturated solution of the compound. A day later, the crystal is seen to be repaired although the mass is unchanged. Explain.

4. A piece of dry ice is placed inside of a closed insulated container. After 24 hours, the solid is found to be only slightly decreased in mass. Explain.

5. A sealed bottle of carbonated water is an example of solution equilibrium. The CO_2 is under pressure in the solution and in the space over the solution. (a) Describe the changes going on. (b) What can you actually observe? (c) How do the rates of the changes compare?

6. Write the mass-action expressions for the following equilibria:
   (a) $2C_2H_6(g) + 7O_2(g) \rightleftharpoons 4CO_2(g) + 6H_2O(g)$
   (b) $4PH_3(g) \rightleftharpoons P_4(g) + 6H_2(g)$
   (c) $4HCl(g) + O_2(g) \rightleftharpoons 2Cl_2(g) + 2H_2O(g)$

7. (a) For the reaction, $2NO(g) + O_2(g) \rightleftharpoons 2NO_2(g)$, write the relationship among the concentrations that will mathematically yield the equilibrium constant for the change. (b) Compare this equilibrium constant with the one obtained if we had started with NO_2 (as the reactant of the forward reaction) to reach equilibrium. (c) Will a change of temperature affect the value of the equilibrium constant?

8. For the equilibrium $2H_2S(g) \rightleftharpoons 2H_2(g) + S_2(g)$, the concentrations at 1130°C are: $[H_2S] = 0.15$ mole/L; $[H_2] = 0.010$ mole/L; $[S_2] = 0.051$ mole/L. Calculate the equilibrium constant.

9. The equilibrium constant for the equilibrium "$A + B \rightleftharpoons C$" is 4.0×10^{-2}. What is the value of this constant for the reverse equilibrium "$C \rightleftharpoons A + B$?"

10. Silver chloride is practically insoluble. When placed into water, it dissolves slightly to form ions: $AgCl(s) \rightleftharpoons Ag^+(aq) + Cl^-(aq)$
    Why is the following expression correct: $[Ag^+] \times [Cl^-] =$ a constant?

11. A total of 3.50 moles of $PCl_5(g)$ is placed into a 500 mL container and heated to 250°C and allowed to reach equilibrium.
    $$PCl_5(g) \rightleftharpoons PCl_3(g) + Cl_2(g)$$
    At equilibrium, 0.270 mole of PCl_3 and 0.270 mole of Cl_2 are present, mixed with the remaining PCl_5. (a) Calculate the concentrations of each of the three substances in moles per liter. (b) Calculate the equilibrium constant.

12. In a one-liter container, a mole of SO_3 is decomposed according to the following equation: $2SO_3(g) \rightleftharpoons 2SO_2(g) + O_2(g)$
    At the equilibrium point, 0.300 mole of oxygen is present. (a) Calculate the concentrations of the SO_2 and SO_3 in moles per liter. (b) Calculate the equilibrium constant.

13. For the reaction $N_2(g) + O_2(g) \rightleftharpoons 2NO(g)$, the equilibrium constant is 1.0×10^{-30} at 25°C and 0.10 at 2000°C. Which reaction, the forward or backward one, (a) goes practically to completion at 25°C? (b) is the one that goes on to a lesser extent at 2000°C?

14. Describe in general terms what will happen to a chemical equilibrium if the temperature, pressure, or concentration of one of the reactants is changed. (One reactant is a gas.)

15. The following equilibrium takes place in a closed vessel at 500°C:
    $$2H_2(g) + S_2(g) \rightleftharpoons 2H_2S(g)$$
    What happens to the point of equilibrium if the concentration of the hydrogen is increased? Explain in terms of the collision theory.

16. For a saturated solution of sodium chloride in contact with excess

solid, an equilibrium exists between the solid and the ions:
$$NaCl(s) \rightleftharpoons Na^+(aq) + Cl^-(aq)$$
(a) What will happen to the equilibrium if silver ions are added to the solution? Explain. (AgCl is insoluble.) (b) What happens to the equilibrium if solid KCl is added to the solution? Explain. (KCl is very soluble.)

21-8   **17.** For the reaction, $N_2(g) + O_2(g) \rightleftharpoons 2NO(g)$, K at 25°C is 4.5×10^{-31}. At 2400°C, K is 3.4×10^{-3}. (a) In which direction is the equilibrium displaced by a rise in temperature? (b) Is the forward reaction exothermic or endothermic? Explain.

18. With reference to the equilibrium,
$$2SO_2(g) + O_2(g) \rightleftharpoons 2SO_3(g) + 45 \text{ kcal,}$$
(a) what stresses will produce an increase in the quantity of SO_3 produced if the temperature is kept constant? (b) What is the effect of a rise of temperature on the equilibrium?

19. Hydrogen peroxide can be decomposed as follows:
$$H_2O_2(l) \rightleftharpoons H_2(g) + O_2(g); \ \Delta H = +44.8 \text{ kcal}$$
Equilibrium is established in a 100-mL flask at room temperature. Predict the direction of the equilibrium displacement if (a) hydrogen gas is added to the flask (b) the temperature is raised to 500°C (c) the entire mixture is compressed into a smaller volume.

21-9   **20.** A platinum catalyst is used in the reaction of SO_2 with O_2 (see equation in question 18, above). What is the effect of the catalyst on (a) the rate of the forward reaction (b) the rate of the backward reaction (c) the equilibrium constant (d) the concentration of SO_3 produced per unit time? (e) Compare the effects on the rates of the forward and backward reactions.

FOR FURTHER THOUGHT

21-4   **1.** All of the following are known about a reversible reaction: its balanced equation, the equilibrium constant at a particular temperature, the concentrations of the reactants at equilibrium. Which of the following can be calculated? Explain.
(a) The concentrations of the products at equilibrium.
(b) The time required to reach equilibrium.
(c) The new equilibrium concentrations if 1 mole of a reactant is added.
(d) The direction in which the equilibrium will shift for any given stress.

21-8   **2.** A reversible reaction has reached equilibrium.
(a) Which of the following will change the equilibrium constant? Explain.
(b) Which will shift the equilibrium (change the concentrations)? Explain.
(1) Adding more of one reactant.
(2) Increasing the concentration of each substance by 10%.
(3) Removing some fraction of the products.
(4) Changing the temperature.
(5) Introducing a catalyst.
(6) Enclosing the reaction vessel in an insulated capsule to prevent heat entering or leaving the vessel and then adding more of one reactant.

The Solubility Product Expression

Objectives

When you have completed this chapter, you will be able to:
- Derive solubility product expressions.
- Determine solubilities from solubility products.
- Predict the formation of precipitates from a knowledge of ion concentrations.
- Describe a way to dissolve insoluble substances.
- Calculate solubility products from solubilities.

22-1 The Solubility Product Constant, K_{sp}

In the saturated solution of an ionic solid, an equilibrium is established between the ions in the solution and the excess solid phase. This kind of equilibrium was discussed in Chapter 17 (Section 17-10). For silver chloride, the equilibrium equation is written

$$AgCl(s) \rightleftharpoons Ag^+(aq) + Cl^-(aq) \qquad \textbf{(Eq. 1)}$$

This equation says that in a saturated solution containing some undissolved solid, the undissolved solid is in equilibrium with dissolved silver and chloride ions. In other words, the solid is dissolving at the same rate at which dissolved ions are re-forming the solid. See Figure 22-1.

According to the law of chemical equilibrium, the mass-action expression for Equation 1 is equal to a constant (the equilibrium constant):

$$\frac{[Ag^+] \times [Cl^-]}{[AgCl(s)]} = K_{eq} \qquad \textbf{(Eq. 2)}$$

The concentration of the solid AgCl is constant, since changing the number of moles of solid by a particular factor will change the volume occupied by the solid by the same factor. That is, the ratio

$$\frac{\text{moles of solid}}{\text{volume occupied by the solid}}$$

remains constant for varying quantities of solid resting on the bottom of the container. Here we use the symbol K to represent the constant concentration of the solid.

$$[AgCl(s)] = K \qquad \textbf{(Eq. 3)}$$

Figure 22-1

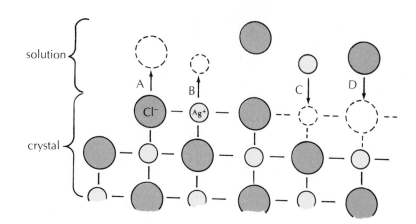

The surface of a crystal of AgCl in contact with a solution containing Ag^+ and Cl^- ions. Equilibrium exists between the solid and dissolved phases when one chloride ion and one silver ion dissolve from the crystal, as shown by the arrows at A and B, for every silver and chloride ion that crystallize out, as shown by the arrows at C and D.

Substituting Equation 3 into Equation 2, we have

$$\frac{[Ag^+] \times [Cl^-]}{K} = K_{eq} \qquad \textbf{(Eq. 4)}$$

Rearranging Equation 4 gives

$$[Ag^+] \times [Cl^-] = K_{eq} \times K \qquad \textbf{(Eq. 5)}$$

The product of two constants, in this case $K_{eq} \times K$, is itself a constant. The new constant, whose value is the product of K_{eq} and K, is given a special name. It is called the solubility product constant, or more simply the solubility product. The solubility product constant is symbolized K_{sp}. Substituting K_{sp} for $K_{eq} \times K$ in Equation 5 gives

$$[Ag^+] \times [Cl^-] = K_{sp} \qquad \textbf{(Eq. 6)}$$

The expression given by Equation 6 is called the solubility product expression for silver chloride. The solubility product expression for silver chloride says that in a saturated solution of silver chloride in contact with silver chloride in the solid phase, the product of the molar concentrations of silver and chloride ions is a constant.

Since solubilities vary with temperature, the solubility product must be given for a specific temperature. This is usually 25°C.

In the equilibrium equation for AgCl (Equation 1), the coefficients of both ions are 1, because their subscripts in the empirical formula of the compound are both 1. If the coefficients of the ions in an equilibrium equation are not 1, then the concentrations in the mass-action expression must be raised to the corresponding powers. Consider, for example, the dissociation of Ag_2SO_4:

$$Ag_2SO_4(s) \rightleftharpoons 2Ag^+(aq) + SO_4{}^{2-}(aq)$$

The mass-action expression for this equation is

$$\frac{[Ag^+]^2 \times [SO_4{}^{2-}]}{[Ag_2SO_4]} = K_{eq}$$

The concentration of the solid phase is a constant. The product of this constant and the equilibrium constant equals the solubility product constant.

Chapter 22   The Solubility Product Expression   **431**

Since $Ag_2SO_4 = K$

$$[Ag^+]^2 \times [SO_4^{2-}] = K \times K_{eq} = K_{sp}$$

The solubility product expression for Ag_2SO_4 is therefore

$$[Ag^+]^2 \times [SO_4^{2-}] = K_{sp}$$

As a final example, let us determine the solubility product expression for calcium phosphate, $Ca_3(PO_4)_2$. Its dissociation equation is

$$Ca_3(PO_4)_2(s) \rightleftharpoons 3Ca^{2+}(aq) + 2PO_4^{3-}(aq)$$

and therefore the solubility product expression is

$$[Ca^{2+}]^3 \times [PO_4^{3-}]^2$$

These examples illustrate the meanings of the terms solubility product constant and solubility product expression. The **solubility product constant** is the constant number that is obtained at a particular temperature when the concentrations of the ions in a saturated solution of a slightly soluble electrolyte are multiplied together, each ion concentration having first been raised to a power equal to its coefficient in the dissociation equation. The **solubility product expression,** or **ion-product,** is the expression that shows what ion concentrations, raised to appropriate powers, produces the solubility product constant. As an example, we can use these terms to label the equality given in the previous paragraph:

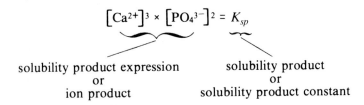

$$[Ca^{2+}]^3 \times [PO_4^{3-}]^2 = K_{sp}$$

solubility product expression
or
ion product

solubility product
or
solubility product constant

Questions for Section 22-1

1. $BaSO_4$ is an "insoluble" substance whose saturated solution in water contains a relatively small concentration of ions:
$$BaSO_4(s) \rightleftharpoons Ba^{2+}(aq) + SO_4^{2-}(aq)$$
Using the mass-action expression for the equilibrium, derive the solubility product expression.
2. Derive the solubility product expression for Ag_2S.
3. Derive the solubility product expression for $Ba_3(PO_4)_2$.

22-2   Meaning of Solubility Product

There are many ionic compounds that are considered to be "insoluble" in water. However, no compound is completely insoluble. Every

Compound	Formula	K_{sp}
aluminum hydroxide	$Al(OH)_3$	5×10^{-33}
barium carbonate	$BaCO_3$	2×10^{-9}
barium chromate	$BaCrO_4$	8.5×10^{-11}
barium sulfate	$BaSO_4$	1.5×10^{-9}
cadmium sulfide	CdS	1.0×10^{-28}
calcium carbonate	$CaCO_3$	4.7×10^{-9}
calcium sulfate	$CaSO_4$	2.4×10^{-5}
copper (I) iodide	CuI	1.1×10^{-12}
iron (II) sulfide	FeS	4×10^{-19}
lead chloride	$PbCl_2$	1.6×10^{-5}
lead chromate	$PbCrO_4$	2×10^{-16}
lead sulfate	$PbSO_4$	1.3×10^{-8}
lead sulfide	PbS	7×10^{-29}
silver bromide	$AgBr$	5.0×10^{-13}
silver chloride	$AgCl$	1.7×10^{-10}
silver iodide	AgI	8.5×10^{-17}

ionic compound dissociates into its ions to some extent when placed in water. The usefulness of the solubility product is that it tells us the *relative* solubilities of electrolytes that are only slightly soluble. For example, the K_{sp} of $CaSO_4$ is 2.4×10^{-5}. This is a small number; in decimal form it is 0.000 024. This is the product of the concentrations of the Ca^{2+} and SO_4^{2-} ions in a saturated solution of $CaSO_4$ in moles per liter. It is not much. But the K_{sp} of $BaSO_4$ is even smaller. It is 1.5×10^{-9}, or 0.000 000 001 5. The solubility product of $AgCl$ is 1.7×10^{-10}. It is more soluble than AgI, whose solubility product is 8.5×10^{-17}. Values such as 1×10^{-53} for mercuric sulfide, HgS, and 1×10^{-35} for CuS indicate extremely low solubilities. Figure 22-2 gives the solubility products for some selected compounds.

The solubility product is useful in another way. It can tell us what will happen when solutions containing different ions are mixed. It enables us to calculate which compounds will precipitate out of such mixtures. This is the topic of the next section.

22-3 Predicting the Formation of Precipitates

The solubility product of silver chloride at 25°C is 1.7×10^{-10}:

$$\left[Ag^+\right] \times \left[Cl^-\right] = 1.7 \times 10^{-10}$$

This means that in any solution at 25°C containing Ag^+ and Cl^- ions, the product of the concentrations of those two ions at equilibrium cannot be greater than 1.7×10^{-10}. It can, of course, be smaller. But if at any time the product of the ion concentrations is greater than 1.7×10^{-10}, Ag^+ and Cl^- ions will combine to form undissociated solid $AgCl$ until the product is brought down to that value. It should also be understood that the presence of other ions has no effect on the solubility product of a particular substance.

Let us suppose that we have two separate solutions. One solution contains 1.00×10^{-3} mole of silver nitrate, $AgNO_3$, per liter. Silver nitrate is quite soluble in water. Over 10 moles can be dissolved in a liter of water at 25°C. Therefore, this solution is far from being saturated, and there will be no detectable solid phase of $AgNO_3$ present.

The other solution consists of 1.00×10^{-2} mole of sodium chloride, NaCl, per liter. Again, the NaCl will be completely dissolved.

Since 1.00×10^{-3} mole of $AgNO_3$ produces 1.00×10^{-3} mole of Ag^+ ion, the concentration of Ag^+ ion in the $AgNO_3$ solution is 1.00×10^{-3} molar. Similarly, the concentration of Cl^- ion in the NaCl solution is 1.00×10^{-2} molar.

Let us now mix together 1.00 liter of each solution. The volume of the mixture will be 2.00 liters. The concentrations of the Ag^+ and Cl^- ions will therefore be halved. That of Ag^+ will be 0.500×10^{-3} molar, or 5.00×10^{-4} molar. That of Cl^- will be 0.500×10^{-2} molar, or 5.00×10^{-3} molar. The product of these two concentrations will thus be:

$$\left[Ag^+\right] \times \left[Cl^-\right] = (5.00 \times 10^{-4})(5.00 \times 10^{-3})$$
$$= 25.0 \times 10^{-7}$$
$$= 2.50 \times 10^{-6}$$

But this product is far greater than 1.7×10^{-10}—about 15 000 times as great. This state of affairs cannot exist for very long. Ag^+ and Cl^- ions will combine to form solid AgCl, which will precipitate, or settle out, of the solution. Only enough Ag^+ and Cl^- ions will remain to make the concentration product equal to 1.7×10^{-10}.

Suppose that the ion product is made less than the solubility product, and that there is undissolved solid solute in the container holding the solution. Then, more solid will dissolve until the ion product equals the solubility product. We can illustrate this phenomenon by considering a saturated solution of calcium carbonate, $CaCO_3$, in contact with solid $CaCO_3$. The equilibrium equation is

$$CaCO_3(s) \rightleftharpoons Ca^{2+}(aq) + CO_3{}^{2-}(aq)$$

If hydrochloric acid, HCl, is added to this solution, the hydrogen ion from the acid combines with the carbonate ion, $CO_3{}^{2-}(aq)$, to produce the hydrogen carbonate ion, $HCO_3{}^-$:

$$H^+(aq) + CO_3{}^{2-}(aq) \longrightarrow HCO_3{}^-(aq)$$

This has the effect of decreasing the concentration of the $CO_3{}^{2-}$ ion. This will reduce the ion concentration product, $[Ca^{2+}] \times [CO_3{}^{2-}]$. As a result, more $CaCO_3$ will dissolve, until enough calcium ion and carbonate ion are present in solution to satisfy the solubility product relationship once again:

$$\left[Ca^{2+}\right] \times \left[CO_3{}^{2-}\right] = K_{sp}$$

where for $CaCO_3$, $K_{sp} = 4.7 \times 10^{-9}$ when the temperature is 25°C.

4. Silver chloride, lead chloride, and barium carbonate are considered to be "insoluble" substances. Explain what is meant by the word "insoluble" as applied to such substances.

5. At 25°C, the K_{sp} for $PbCrO_4$ is 2.0×10^{-16}. For $PbSO_4$, it is 1.3×10^{-8}. For $PbCl_2$, it is 1.6×10^{-5}. Which one of these substances is (a) least soluble, (b) most soluble? (c) Which two of these compounds are closest in their solubilities?

6. What is the concentration of Ag^+ ion that can be present in a solution that is $0.30\,M$ with respect to Cl^- ion? The K_{sp} of AgCl is 1.7×10^{-10}.

*7. Show the calculations that will explain whether or not a precipitate is obtained when 20 mL of $0.010\,M$ NaCl solution are mixed with 20 mL of a $0.000\,10\,M$ solution of $AgNO_3$ (at 25°C).

*8. A solution is $0.20\,M$ in Cl^- ion and $0.20\,M$ in CrO_4^{2-} ion. If finely divided solid silver nitrate is added slowly to the solution and allowed to dissolve after each addition, which will precipitate first, AgCl or Ag_2CrO_4? (The K_{sp} of Ag_2CrO_4 is 1.9×10^{-12}.)

9. The K_{sp} of $CaSO_4$ at 25°C is 2.4×10^{-5}. A concentrated solution of sulfuric acid (H_2SO_4) is added to a saturated solution of calcium sulfate, producing a precipitate of this substance. If the $[SO_4^{2-}]$ in the final solution is $1.2\,M$, what is the $[Ca^{2+}]$ remaining there?

10. Hydrochloric acid is added very slowly to a solution which is $0.30\,M$ in Pb^{2+} ion and 0.30 M in Ag^+ ion. Which will precipitate first, $PbCl_2$ or AgCl? Show calculations.

22-4 Some Sample Problems Involving the Solubility Product

SAMPLE PROBLEM 1

The solubility of $BaSO_4$ at 25°C is 9.09×10^{-4} g per 100 mL of solution. Calculate the solubility product of $BaSO_4$.

Solution. To calculate K_{sp}, we need to write the solubility product expression.

DISSOCIATION EQUATION

$$BaSO_4(s) \rightleftharpoons Ba^{2+}(aq) + SO_4^{2-}(aq)$$

SOLUBILITY PRODUCT EXPRESSION

$$\left[Ba^{2+}\right] \times \left[SO_4^{2-}\right] = K_{sp} \qquad \text{(Eq. A)}$$

To obtain a numerical value for K_{sp}, we must find the molar concentrations of the barium and sulfate ions. We note first that 1 mole of $BaSO_4$

yields 1 mole of Ba^{2+} and 1 mole of SO_4^{2-}. If we find the number of moles of $BaSO_4$ in 100 mL of solution, there will be the same number of moles of Ba^{2+} and SO_4^{2-} in 100 mL of solution. We can then convert this concentration in moles per 100 mL to moles per liter (1000 mL).

To convert 9.09×10^{-4} g to moles, we need to know the mass of 1 mole of $BaSO_4$:

	Atomic mass
Ba =	137
S =	32
O_4 =	64
Molecular mass $BaSO_4$ =	233

The mass of 1 mole of $BaSO_4$ is 233 grams.

To convert from *grams* solute in 100 mL of solution to *moles* solute, the number of grams must be divided by the number of grams per mole:

$$\frac{9.09 \times 10^{-4}g}{233 \text{ g/mole}} = 3.90 \times 10^{-6} \text{ mole}$$

3.90×10^{-6} mole is the number of moles of solute in 100 mL of solution. Next, we convert to the number of moles of solute in 1 liter:

$$\frac{3.90 \times 10^{-6} \text{ mole}}{100 \text{ mL}} \times \frac{1000 \text{ mL}}{1 \text{ liter}} = 3.90 \times 10^{-5} \text{ mole/liter}$$

conversion factor, mL to liters

3.90×10^{-5} mole of $BaSO_4$ consists of 3.90×10^{-5} mole of barium ion and 3.90×10^{-5} mole of sulfate ion. Therefore, their concentrations are

$$\left[Ba^{2+}\right] = 3.90 \times 10^{-5} \ M$$
$$\left[SO_4^{2-}\right] = 3.90 \times 10^{-5} \ M$$

Substituting these concentrations into Equation A above on page 435:

$$\left[Ba^{2+}\right] \times \left[SO_4^{2-}\right] = K_{sp} \qquad \textbf{(Eq. A)}$$
$$(3.90 \times 10^{-5})(3.90 \times 10^{-5}) = K_{sp}$$
$$1.52 \times 10^{-9} = K_{sp}$$

The solubility product of $BaSO_4$ is 1.52×10^{-9} (at 25°C).

SAMPLE PROBLEM 2

The solubility of $Mg(OH)_2$ is 1.3×10^{-4} mole/liter. Calculate the solubility product of $Mg(OH)_2$.

Solution. Derive the solubility product expression.

$$Mg(OH)_2(s) \rightleftharpoons Mg^{2+}(aq) + 2OH^-(aq)$$

(Note that the coefficient of the hydroxide ion is 2, indicating that in magnesium hydroxide there are 2 hydroxide ions for every 1 magnesium ion.)

SOLUBILITY PRODUCT EXPRESSION

$$\left[Mg^{2+}\right] \times \left[OH^-\right]^2 = K_{sp} \qquad \textbf{(Eq. B)}$$

In 1.3×10^{-4} mole of $Mg(OH)_2$, there are 1.3×10^{-4} mole of magnesium ions and twice that many hydroxide ions, making their concentrations:

$$\left[Mg^{2+}\right] = 1.3 \times 10^{-4} \, M \qquad \left[OH^-\right] = 2.6 \times 10^{-4} \, M$$

Substituting these concentrations into Equation B:

$$\left[Mg^{2+}\right] \times \left[OH^-\right]^2 = K_{sp} \qquad \textbf{(Eq. B)}$$

$$(1.3 \times 10^{-4})(2.6 \times 10^{-4})^2 = K_{sp}$$

$$8.8 \times 10^{-12} = K_{sp}$$

SAMPLE PROBLEM 3

The solubility product of silver chromate, Ag_2CrO_4, is 1.1×10^{-12}. Calculate the molar concentration of a saturated silver chromate solution.

Solution. Derive the solubility product expression.

DISSOCIATION EQUATION

$$Ag_2CrO_4(s) \rightleftharpoons 2Ag^+(aq) + CrO_4^{2-}(aq)$$

SOLUBILITY PRODUCT EXPRESSION

$$\left[Ag^+\right]^2 \times \left[CrO_4^{2-}\right] = K_{sp}$$

$$\left[Ag^+\right]^2 \times \left[CrO_4^{2-}\right] = 1.1 \times 10^{-12}$$

Let x be the molar concentration of the Ag_2CrO_4 that dissolves in the saturated solution. According to the dissociation equation, for every x moles that dissociate, $2x$ moles of aqueous silver ions and $1x$ moles of aqueous chromate ions are formed. Therefore, the molar concentrations of these ions in the saturated solution are:

$$\left[Ag^+\right] = 2x \qquad \left[CrO_4^{2-}\right] = x$$

Substituting these values into the solubility product expression and solving for x:

$$\left[Ag^+\right]^2 \times \left[CrO_4{}^{2-}\right] = 1.1 \times 10^{-12}$$

$$(2x)^2 \times \quad x \quad = 1.1 \times 10^{-12}$$

$$4x^3 = 1.1 \times 10^{-12}$$

$$x^3 = 0.275 \times 10^{-12}$$

$$x = \sqrt[3]{0.275 \times 10^{-12}}$$

$$x = 0.65 \times 10^{-4} = 6.5 \times 10^{-5}$$

A saturated solution of silver chromate will have a concentration of 6.5×10^{-5} mole per liter.

Questions for Section 22-4

*11. The saturated solution in equilibrium with a precipitate of Ag_3PO_4 is found to contain 1.6×10^{-5} mole/L of $PO_4{}^{3-}$ ion and 4.8×10^{-5} mole/L of Ag^+ ion. What is the K_{sp} of Ag_3PO_4?

12. A solution of Ag_2S, in contact with excess solid, contains 1.5×10^{-17} mole/L of Ag^+ ion and 4.4×10^{-18} mole/L of S^{2-} ion. Calculate the K_{sp} of Ag_2S.

13. The concentration of lead ion in a saturated solution of PbI_2 at 25°C is 1.3×10^{-3} mole/L. What is its K_{sp}?

*14. The solubility of $SrSO_4$ in its saturated solution is 0.16 g/L at 25°C. Calculate its solubility product.

15. What is the solubility product of AgCl if, at 25°C, 1.88×10^{-3} g dissolves in 1.00 L of water to form a saturated solution?

16. In 100 mL of a saturated solution of CaF_2, at 25°C, 1.6×10^{-3} g of solute is present. What is the K_{sp} of CaF_2?

*17. The solubility product of Ag_2CO_3 is 8.3×10^{-12} at 25°C. Calculate its molar solubility at this temperature.

18. The K_{sp} of $MgCO_3$ at 25°C is 2.0×10^{-8}. What is its molar solubility at this temperature.

CHAPTER SUMMARY

1. The mass-action expression for a slightly soluble ionic compound that is in equilibrium with the saturated solution of its ions includes the concentration of the solid compound in the denominator.

2. Since the concentration of a solid is a constant, it may be combined with the equilibrium constant to produce a new constant called the solubility product

3. Solubility products are usually listed for a temperature of 25°C.

4. Solubility products indicate relative solubilities of slightly soluble electrolytes and also enable us to predict when precipitation will occur when solutions of ions are mixed.

5. Precipitates in contact with their saturated solutions are dissolved when the ion products are made less than the solubility products.

6. Solubility products can be calculated directly from molar solubilities of ions or, indirectly, from solubilities given in terms of grams per unit volume.

solubility product
constant

solubility product
expression

ion product

REVIEW QUESTIONS

Section

$[Mg^+]$

22-1   **1.** (a) Write the mass-action expression for the equilibrium between the ions of $Mg(OH)_2$ and undissolved solid. (b) Equate this expression to an equilibrium constant. (c) Use the equation in (b) to derive the solubility product expression. (d) At what temperature are standard solubility products measured?

2. Write the solubility product expressions for (a) $Fe(OH)_3$, (b) Ag_2CrO_4, (c) $Ca_3(PO_4)_2$.

22-2   **3.** (a) What is the relation between the solubilities of "insoluble" substances and their solubility product constants? (b) Compare the solubilities at 25°C of $BaCO_3$ ($K_{sp} = 2 \times 10^{-9}$), $CaCO_3$ ($K_{sp} = 5 \times 10^{-9}$), $MgCO_3$ ($K_{sp} = 2 \times 10^{-8}$), and $PbCO_3$ ($K_{sp} = 1 \times 10^{-13}$).

22-3   **4.** At 25°C, the K_{sp} of MgF_2 at 25°C, is 8×10^{-8}. The following solutions, all at 25°C, are added to 0.5 L of $1.0 \times 10^{-3} M$ Mg^{2+} ion. (a) 0.5 L of $1.0 \times 10^{-3} M$ F^- ion (b) 0.5 L of $1.0 \times 10^{-2} M$ F^- ion (c) 0.5 L of $1.0 \times 10^{-1} M$ F^- ion. Show by calculations in which case or cases precipitates will form.

22-4   **5.** The solubility of $Pb(OH)_2$ is 4.8×10^{-6} mole/L at 25°C. What is its K_{sp} at this temperature?

6. At 25°C, a saturated solution of $Ce(OH)_3$ contains 5.1×10^{-6} mole of the compound in one liter of solution. What is the K_{sp} of $Ce(OH)_3$?

7. In a saturated solution at 25°C, what are the molar solubilities of (a) CdS ($K_{sp} = 1.0 \times 10^{-28}$ at 25°C), (b) $NiCO_3$ ($K_{sp} = 1.2 \times 10^{-7}$ at 25°C)?

FOR FURTHER THOUGHT

22-3   **1.** A researcher has been working with a solution containing the nitrates of magnesium, potassium, silver, and zinc. Because of the value of silver, the researcher wishes to recover as much pure silver as possible from the solution. Evaporating the solution would recover the silver in the form of its nitrate, but it would be mixed with nitrates of the other metals. She decides to try adding a large amount of sodium chloride to the solution. What effect will this procedure have on the silver in the solution?

2. The researcher carries out the procedure in the preceding question and obtains a precipitate. She filters the precipitate and analyzes its composition. Although it turns out to be mostly silver chloride, about 15% of it is zinc chloride.

(a) What might account for the presence of the zinc chloride in the precipitate?

(b) How could the silver chloride be separated from the zinc chloride?

UNIT 7

Acids, Bases, and Salts

There is something immensely attractive in the idea of two powerful opposites that, in meeting, cancel each other out. Such is the case with the two important classes of chemicals known as *acids* and *bases*. Strong acids such as concentrated sulfuric acid are capable of eating through metal. Strong bases such as lye can be equally corrosive. However, when acids and bases are brought together, they usually neutralize one another, forming a third category of substance called a *salt*. Salts are generally harmless substances lacking the potency of their progenitors.

In the photo, the color of the hydrangeas is a signal flag in the acid/base conflict. When base predominates in the soil, the flowers will be pink. When acid predominates, the flowers will be blue.

The nature of acids, bases, and salts, and the reactions in which they participate, will be the subject of this unit.

Acids, Bases, and Salts I

23-1 Electrolytes and Nonelectrolytes

The water solutions of some substances conduct an electric current. For example, salt water is a good conductor. The apparatus used to test the conductivity of a solution, similar to the one depicted in Chapter 18, is shown in Figure 23-1. Substances whose water solutions conduct an electric current are called electrolytes (ih-LEK-truh-lites). Electrolytes can be gases, liquids, or solids. See Figure 23-2. Sometimes the conducting solutions themselves are called electrolytes.

Figure 23-1

Apparatus for testing the conductivity of solutions. If the bulb lights when the knife switch is closed (pushed down), then the dissolved substance is an electrolyte. Electrolytes are substances whose water solutions conduct electricity.

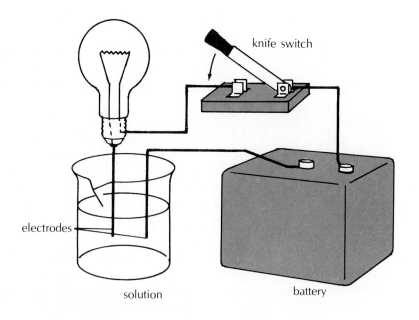

knife switch

electrodes

solution

battery

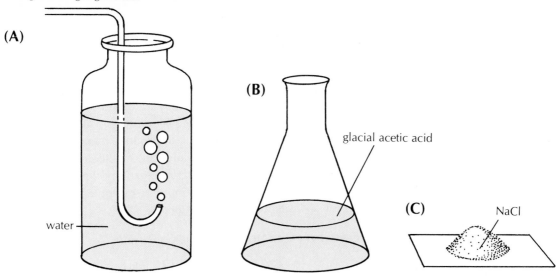

(A)

HCl gas from gas generator

water

(B)

glacial acetic acid

(C)

NaCl

Figure 23-2

Electrolytes may be (A) gases, (B) liquids, or (C) solids. The solution formed when the HCl gas in drawing (A) dissolves in water is called hydrochloric acid.

Substances whose water solutions do not conduct are called nonelectrolytes. A familiar example of a nonelectrolyte is ordinary table sugar (known to chemists as sucrose). A solution of sugar in water will not conduct an electric current.

The conductivity apparatus of Figure 23-1 can be used to determine the strength of an electrolyte. The water solutions of **strong electrolytes** are good conductors of electricity. These solutions conduct electricity well enough to make the bulb light to normal brightness. The water solutions of **weak electrolytes** are poor conductors. In these solutions the bulb of a conductivity apparatus will light only dimly.

23-2   The Theory of Ionization

The ability of some solutions to conduct an electric current is explained by the theory of ionization. The theory of ionization was proposed in 1887 by Svante Arrhenius (ahr-RAY-nee-us) (1859-1927), a Swedish chemist. Arrhenius was led to his theory by his interest in finding an explanation for the abnormal behavior of electrolytes. He found that water solutions of electrolytes showed greater freezing point lowerings than solutions of nonelectrolytes of the same molal concentrations. Since this property is dependent on the concentration of dissolved particles, Arrhenius concluded that electrolytes break down into smaller particles (ions) in solution and that these smaller particles conduct the current. We now know that there are two types of electrolytes. Substances of one type are ionic substances. Substances of the other type are covalently bonded. When ionically bonded electrolytes are added to water, they are said to dissociate. When covalently bonded electrolytes are added to water, they are said to ionize.

23-3   The Dissociation of Ionic Electrolytes

Figure 23-3

When an ionic solid, such as sodium chloride, is dissolved in water, the solution will conduct electricity.

When added to water, the positive ions in an ionic electrolyte attract the negative ends of the water molecules, and the negative ions attract the positive ends of the water molecules. The water molecules then pull the ions out of the solid crystal into solution. As a result, each ion becomes hydrated, that is, surrounded by water molecules, as discussed in Section 17-7 and shown in Figure 17-9 on page 340.

The action of water on ionic solids to produce hydrated ions and to disperse these ions throughout the solution is called **dissociation.** Dissociation is shown by equations. These equations show what ions become dispersed throughout the solution. For example, the dissociation equation for sodium chloride is written:

DISSOCIATION EQUATION FOR SODIUM CHLORIDE

$$NaCl(s) \longrightarrow Na^+(aq) + Cl^-(aq) \qquad \textbf{(Eq. 1)}$$

This equation says that when 1 mole of solid sodium chloride is added to water, 1 mole of sodium and 1 mole of chloride ions making up the solid are hydrated and dispersed throughout the solution. The presence of the water molecules surrounding the ions is indicated by writing *(aq)* after the symbol of each kind of ion.

Notice that dissociation equations are very similar to the equations used to show the equilibrium that can exist between dissolved ions and the undissolved solid in a saturated solution:

**EQUILIBRIUM EQUATION FOR
SATURATED SODIUM CHLORIDE SOLUTION**

$$NaCl(s) \rightleftharpoons Na^+(aq) + Cl^-(aq) \qquad \textbf{(Eq. 2)}$$

The equilibrium equation differs from the dissociation equation only in that it uses a double arrow. The difference is mainly one of emphasis. In the dissociation equation, the emphasis is on what ions are pulled into solution by the water molecules. In the equation showing the equilibrium between dissolved ions and undissolved solid, the emphasis is on the equilibrium that exists if enough solid is present to saturate the solution.

Figure 23-4 gives equations showing the dissociation of four ionic solids.

Pure sodium chloride (dry and without any substance mixed with it)

Figure 23-4

Equations showing the dissociations of four ionic solids.

$$Na_2SO_4(s) \longrightarrow 2Na^+(aq) + SO_4^{2-}(aq)$$
$$(NH_4)_3PO_4(s) \longrightarrow 3NH_4^+(aq) + PO_4^{3-}(aq)$$
$$Pb(NO_3)_2(s) \longrightarrow Pb^{2+}(aq) + 2NO_3^-(aq)$$
$$Al_2(SO_4)_3(s) \longrightarrow 2Al^{3+}(aq) + 3SO_4^{2-}(aq)$$

Figure 23-5

(A) Crystals of an ionic solid will not conduct an electric current. (B) Ionic substances will conduct if they are heated to a high enough temperature to melt them.

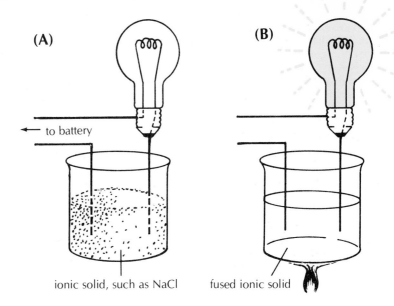

(A)

← to battery

ionic solid, such as NaCl

(B)

fused ionic solid

can be tested in a conductivity apparatus. When this and other ionic solids are tested, the bulb does not light at all, indicating that no current is flowing. However, if these ionic substances are heated until they fuse (melt), the fused ionic substances will conduct. See Figure 23-5. Fused ionic substances conduct a current because in the liquid phase the ions are free to move about. The ions must be mobile if they are to carry a current. In the solid phase, the ions in an ionic substance are locked into a crystal lattice that holds them in place.

23-4 Ionization of Covalently-Bonded Electrolytes

The second type of electrolyte are substances with a molecular structure, that is, substances that are covalently bonded. Pure samples of these substances will not conduct an electric current even when they are liquids or are solids that have been fused. These substances must be mixed with water before they will conduct. Evidently, a reaction takes place between water molecules and the molecules of these substances to form the ions that conduct the current. See Figure 23-6.

The formation of ions caused by the reaction between water molecules and the molecules of a molecular compound is called **ionization.** Acetic acid, a liquid at room temperature, illustrates ionization. Pure acetic acid, containing no trace of water, is called glacial acetic acid. Glacial acetic acid will not conduct a current. When added to water, glacial acetic acid forms hydronium ions and acetate ions according to the reversible reaction:

Figure 23-6

(A) Sulfuric acid, a strong electrolyte, does not conduct when it has no water in it. (B) Diluted with water, sulfuric acid is a good conductor. Water reacts with the undiluted acid to form ions. (Note: If the electrodes are made of an inert metal, such as platinum, they will not react with the acid.)

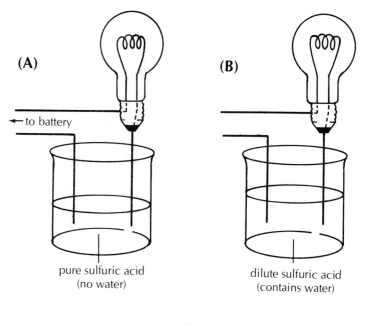

pure sulfuric acid
(no water)

dilute sulfuric acid
(contains water)

$$HC_2H_3O_2 + H_2O \rightleftharpoons H_3O^+ + C_2H_3O_2^- \qquad \textbf{(Eq. 3)}$$

acetic acid

hydronium ion

acetate ion

In the above reaction, the nucleus of the hydrogen atom in the acetic acid molecule separates from the rest of the molecule. This hydrogen ion becomes bonded to a water molecule, forming the hydronium ion, H_3O^+. The shorter arrow to the right in Equation 3 indicates that at equilibrium there are relatively few hydronium and acetate ions present. Therefore, the great bulk of the equilibrium mixture consists of acetic acid molecules and water molecules. Because the concentrations of the hydronium and acetate ions are low in water solutions of acetic acid, acetic acid is a weak electrolyte. That is, solutions of acetic acid make the bulb light only dimly in a conductivity apparatus.

Only a small fraction of the molecules of a weak electrolyte are converted to ions when acted upon by water molecules. This contrasts with the action of water on a strong covalent electrolyte. Water will form ions from a large fraction of the molecules of a strong electrolyte.

We now sum up the difference between the dissociation of an ionic compound and the ionization of a molecular compound. Before water is added to an ionic substance, the ions already exist. The water merely pulls the ions out of the crystal and into solution, making the ions mobile and, therefore, able to conduct current. This process is called dissociation. Ionic compounds are 100% dissociated in water solution.

Before water is added to a molecular substance, no ions exist. However, the molecules of *some* molecular substances react with water molecules to form ions. The formation of ions in this manner is called ionization.

Figure 23-7

Glacial acetic acid is acetic acid that contains no water. Although glacial acetic acid contains no water, its transparency and lack of color make it look like water. A weak electrolyte, glacial acetic acid must be diluted with water before it will conduct.

1. Define and name an example of a (a) strong electrolyte (b) weak electrolyte (c) nonelectrolyte.
2. (a) What is the most important idea in the Arrhenius theory of ionization? (b) What term describes what happens when ionic substances dissolve in water? (c) What term describes the dissolving of covalent electrolytes in water?
*3. (a) Describe the hydration of NaCl as it is dissolved in water. Write dissociation equations for (b) calcium chloride (c) sodium phosphate   (d) aluminum chloride   (e) ammonium sulfate.
4. Explain why (a) dry sodium chloride will not conduct the electric current (b) melted sodium chloride will conduct the current.
5. (a) Describe what happens when glacial acetic acid is dissolved in water. (b) Write the ionization equation for the reaction.

23-5   Acids (Arrhenius's Definition)

According to Arrhenius, an **acid** is a substance that produces hydrogen ions (H⁺) as the only positive ion when the acid is mixed with water. By this definition, the gas hydrogen chloride is an acid.

IONIZATION OF HYDROGEN CHLORIDE GAS

$$HCl(g) \longrightarrow H^+(aq) + Cl^-(aq) \qquad \text{(Eq. 4)}$$

hydrogen   hydrogen   chloride
chloride   ion   ion
gas

$\underbrace{}$
hydrochloric acid

Figure 23-8

Hydrochloric acid, a strong electrolyte, is a solution made by dissolving hydrogen chloride gas in water.

This equation tells us that when hydrogen chloride gas is passed into water, it reacts to form hydrogen ions (as the only positive ion) and chloride ions. In a closed container, an equilibrium exists. However, the concentration of the hydrogen chloride molecules is so low and the concentrations of the ions so high that a single arrow pointing to the right is usually used in the equation. For all intents and purposes, the equilibrium mixture consists almost entirely of ions. The large concentration of ions makes water solutions of hydrogen chloride gas very good conductors of electricity. In other words, hydrogen chloride gas is a strong electrolyte. Aqueous solutions of this gas are called hydrochloric acid.

Experiments done since the time of Arrhenius have shown that in water solutions hydrogen ions (protons) always have water molecules attached to them. That is, hydrogen ions in aqueous solutions are always hydrated. The hydration of the hydrogen ion can be shown by the following equation:

$$H^+ + H_2O \longrightarrow H_3O^+ \qquad \text{(Eq. 5)}$$

hydrogen   hydronium
ion   ion

Hydronium ion is the name of the particle formed by the hydration of a hydrogen ion with a water molecule. Using electron-dot symbols, Equation 5 can be written:

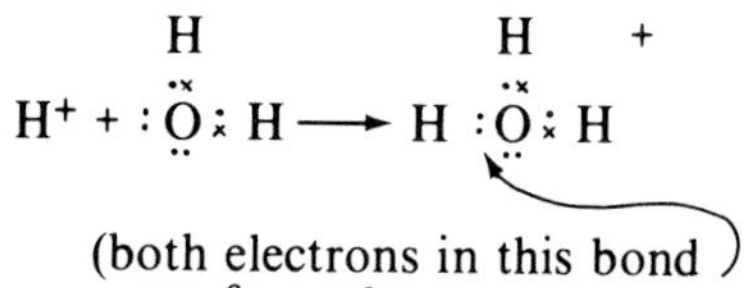

$$H^+ + :\overset{\overset{H}{\cdot\cdot}}{\underset{\cdot\cdot}{O}} : H \longrightarrow H :\overset{\overset{H}{\cdot\cdot}}{O} : H \quad +$$

(Eq. 6)

(both electrons in this bond
come from the oxygen atom,
whereas for each of the other two
bonds, one electron comes from the
oxygen atom and the other from
the hydrogen atom)

Hydronium ions are formed because there is a strong attraction between water molecules and the hydrogen ion, which is nothing more than a bare proton. Physical evidence suggests that in some dilute acid solutions, more than one molecule of water may be attached to the hydrogen ion. Suggested equations showing the formation of the hydrated proton include:

$$H^+ + H_2O \longrightarrow H_3O^+$$

$$H^+ + 2H_2O \longrightarrow H_5O_2^+$$

$$H^+ + 3H_2O \longrightarrow H_7O_3^+$$

$$H^+ + 4H_2O \longrightarrow H_9O_4^+$$

When writing the hydrogen ion in equations, the usual practice is to represent it by the symbol $H^+(aq)$ or to show it hydrated by a single water molecule: H_3O^+. Using the hydronium ion, H_3O^+, the ionization of hydrogen chloride would be shown by the equation below. Compare Equation 7 below with Equation 4 at the beginning of this section.

IONIZATION OF HYDROGEN CHLORIDE GAS

$$HCl + H_2O \longrightarrow H_3O^+ + Cl^-$$

(Eq. 7)

hydrogen
chloride
gas

Equations showing the ionization of five other common acids (in addition to HCl) are shown below:

$$HNO_3 + H_2O \longrightarrow H_3O^+ + NO_3^-$$ **(Eq. 8)**

nitric   nitrate
acid   ion

$$H_2SO_4 + 2H_2O \longrightarrow 2H_3O+ + SO_4^{2-}$$ **(Eq. 9)**

sulfuric   sulfate
acid   ion

$$HCOOH + H_2O \rightleftharpoons H_3O^+ + COOH^-$$ **(Eq. 10)**

formic   formate
acid   ion

$$HC_2H_3O_2 + H_2O \rightleftharpoons H_3O^+ + C_2H_3O_2^- \qquad \textbf{(Eq. 11)}$$

acetic   acetate
acid   ion

$$H_2S + 2H_2O \rightleftharpoons 2H_3O^+ + S^{2-} \qquad \textbf{(Eq. 12)}$$

hydro-   sulfide
sulfuric   ion
acid

The single arrows in the ionization equations for the first two acids, nitric and sulfuric acids, indicate that these substances are strong acids having large concentrations of hydronium ion in dilute solutions. They ionize almost completely. The remaining three acids are weak acids whose equilibrium mixtures contain large concentrations of molecules and small concentrations of ions.

For simplicity, Equations 8 to 12 are often written to show the formation of the hydrogen ion (H^+) rather than the hydronium ion (H_3O^+):

$$HNO_3 \longrightarrow H^+ + NO_3^- \qquad \textbf{(Eq. 8a)}$$

$$H_2SO_4 \longrightarrow 2H^+ + SO_4^{2-} \qquad \textbf{(Eq. 9a)}$$

$$HCOOH \rightleftharpoons H^+ + COOH^- \qquad \textbf{(Eq. 10a)}$$

$$HC_2H_3O_2 \rightleftharpoons H^+ + C_2H_3O_2^- \qquad \textbf{(Eq. 11a)}$$

$$H_2S \rightleftharpoons 2H^+ + S^{2-} \qquad \textbf{(Eq. 12a)}$$

When using these simplified equations, keep in mind that hydrogen ions in water solutions always have water molecules attached to them.

Figure 23-9 gives the names and formulas of some common acids.

Figure 23-9

Some common acids.

Acid	Formula	Common Name
nitric	HNO_3	aqua fortis
hydrochloric	HCl	muriatic acid
sulfuric	H_2SO_4	oil of vitriol
formic	$HCOOH$	----------
acetic	$HC_2H_3O_2$	vinegar
carbonic	H_2CO_3	carbonated water
hydrosulfuric	H_2S	----------

Questions for Section 23-5

6. (a) State the Arrhenius definition of an acid. (b) Write the equation for the ionization of hydrogen chloride. (c) Why is the single arrow usually used in this equation?
7. (a) Why are hydronium ions formed when acids are dissolved in water? Write ionization equations, showing hydronium ion formation, for (b) hydrochloric acid (c) sulfuric acid (d) nitric acid (e) acetic acid. (f) Why are double arrows used in the acetic acid equation?
8. State the chemical names, formulas and common names for 4 acids.

23-6 Ionization Constants for Acids

Where an equilibrium exists between the molecules of an acid and its ions, the law of chemical equilibrium can be applied. For example, consider again the ionization of acetic acid:

IONIZATION OF ACETIC ACID

$$HC_2H_3O_2(aq) \rightleftharpoons H^+(aq) + C_2H_3O_2^-(aq) \qquad \textbf{(Eq. 13)}$$

Applying the law of chemical equilibrium to this equation:

$$\frac{[H^+][C_2H_3O_2^-]}{[HC_2H_3O_2]} = K_a \qquad \textbf{(Eq. 14)}$$

The equilibrium constant for the ionization of an acid is called the **ionization constant** of the acid. These constants are represented by the symbol K_a, as shown in the expression above. It has been determined by experiment that for acetic acid at 25°C, $K_a = 1.8 \times 10^{-5}$.

$$\frac{[H^+][C_2H_3O_2^-]}{[HC_2H_3O_2]} = 1.8 \times 10^{-5} \qquad \textbf{(Eq. 15)}$$

$$(\text{at } 25°C)$$

The numerical value of K_a tells to what extent ions are formed from the molecules of an acid, and, therefore, how strong the acid is. Small values for K_a mean that the water solution has relatively large numbers of molecules and few ions. Figure 23-10 shows ionization equations for several acids and lists their ionization constants. The ionization constants for the strong acids HCl, HNO_3, and H_2SO_4 are so large that there is no usefulness in expressing them numerically. The constants for the weaker acids HF, $HC_2H_3O_2$, and H_2S are small.

Figure 23-10

Ionization equations for several acids and their ionization constants at 1 atm and 298 K.

Acid	Ionization Equation	Ionization Constant
hydrochloric	$HCl \longrightarrow H^+ + Cl^-$	very large
nitric	$HNO_3 \longrightarrow H^+ + NO_3^-$	very large
sulfuric	$H_2SO_4 \longrightarrow H^+ + HSO_4^-$	large
acetic	$HC_2H_3O_2 \rightleftharpoons H^+ + C_2H_3O_2^-$	1.8×10^{-5}
hydrosulfuric	$H_2S \rightleftharpoons H^+ + HS^-$	1.0×10^{-7}
hydrofluoric	$HF \rightleftharpoons H^+ + F^-$	6.7×10^{-4}

SAMPLE PROBLEM 1

One gram of pure H_2SO_4 is diluted to a 1.0-liter volume with water. What will be the molar concentration of the hydrogen ion in this solution?

The person in the photo is eating a piece of Cheddar cheese, which dental researchers at the National Institute of Dental Research think contains one or more substances that prevent tooth decay. This conclusion was reached when it was found that rats fed Cheddar cheese after eating sugary foods developed 80% fewer cavities than the rats in a control group that were fed the sugary foods alone. Once the cavity preventing chemical in Cheddar cheese is isolated and identified, it may be possible for the chemical industry to make the substance readily available for people who have a sweet tooth.

Solution. First determine the number of moles H_2SO_4 in 1.0 gram H_2SO_4. (There are 98 grams H_2SO_4 per mole.)

$$1.0 \text{ g } H_2SO_4 = \frac{1.0 \text{ g}}{98 \text{ g/mole}} = 0.010 \text{ mole } H_2SO_4$$

Sulfuric acid ionizes in two steps. Step 1 is shown in Figure 23-10. If the solution is dilute enough, the ionization is practically 100% complete, and the overall equation is:

$$H_2SO_4 \longrightarrow 2H^+ + SO_4^{2-}$$

we see that for every one molecule of H_2SO_4 that ionizes, two hydrogen ions are formed. Therefore, if 0.010 mole of sulfuric acid is ionized, 0.020 mole of hydrogen ion will be formed. Since this 0.020 mole of hydrogen ion exists in a solution whose volume is 1.0 liter, the molar concentration of the hydrogen ion is 0.020 mole/1.0 liter = 0.020 molar.

SAMPLE PROBLEM 2

A volume of 5.71 mL of pure acetic acid, $HC_2H_3O_2$, is diluted with water at 25°C to form a solution whose volume is 1.0 liter. What is the molar concentration of the hydrogen ion, H^+, in this solution? (The density of acetic acid is 1.05 grams/mL.)

Solution. Molarity is the number of moles of solute per liter of solution. Therefore, we need to work in terms of moles of acetic acid rather than milliliters.

$$\text{mass in grams} = \left(\begin{array}{c} \text{density in} \\ \text{grams/mL} \end{array} \right) \times \left(\begin{array}{c} \text{volume} \\ \text{in mL} \end{array} \right)$$

$$= 1.05 \text{ g/mL} \times 5.71 \text{ mL}$$

$$= 6.0 \text{ g}$$

Converting 6.0 g $HC_2H_3O_2$ to moles $HC_2H_3O_2$:

$$6.0 \text{ g } HC_2H_3O_2 = \frac{6.0 \text{ g}}{60 \text{ g/mole } HC_2H_3O_2}$$

$$= 0.10 \text{ mole } HC_2H_3O_2$$

This problem differs from Sample Problem 1 in that sulfuric acid is a strong acid that ionizes completely, whereas acetic acid is a weak acid that ionizes only slightly, as shown by the small value for its ionization constant ($K_a = 1.8 \times 10^{-5}$). In Sample Problem 1 we knew that the entire 0.010 mole H_2SO_4 ionized to form hydrogen and sulfate ions. In this problem, only a small amount of the 0.10 mole $HC_2H_3O_2$ will ionize. Our approach to this problem must be different. Let x be what we are looking for, the molar concentration of the hydrogen ion in the solution:

$$x = \left[H^+\right]$$

The ionization equation for acetic acid,

$$HC_2H_3O_2 \rightleftharpoons H^+ + C_2H_3O_2^-$$

shows that the H^+ ions and $C_2H_3O_2^-$ ions produced by the ionization of $HC_2H_3O_2$ are equal in number. Therefore, x also equals the concentration of the acetate ion:

$$x = \left[C_2H_3O_2^-\right]$$

In Equation 15,

$$\frac{\left[H^+\right]\left[C_2H_3O_2^-\right]}{\left[HC_2H_3O_2\right]} = 1.8 \times 10^{-5} \qquad \textbf{(Eq. 15)}$$

we now substitute the letter x:

$$\frac{x \cdot x}{\left[HC_2H_3O_2\right]} = 1.8 \times 10^{-5} \qquad \textbf{(Eq. A)}$$

Before we can solve for x in Equation A above, we need to have a value for $[HC_2H_3O_2]$. Because acetic acid is a weak acid, only a relatively few of the acetic acid molecules are converted into hydrogen ions and acetate ions when the acid is added to water as shown by the long arrow to the left in the equation for its ionization. Therefore, the concentration of acetic acid after ionization has occurred is very nearly equal to what its concentration would have been had no ionization taken place. Recall from the early part of the solution to this problem that 5.71 mL of acetic acid is 0.10 mole acetic acid. Since this 0.10 mole $HC_2H_3O_2$ is dissolved in 1 liter of water, we can take the concentration of acetic acid molecules after ionization as being 0.10 molar, even though we know that their concentration is slightly less because of their ionization.

$$[HC_2H_3O_2] = 0.10 \text{ molar}$$

Substituting this value into Equation A:

$$\frac{x \cdot x}{0.10} = 1.8 \times 10^{-5}$$

Solving the above expression for x:

$$x^2 = 0.10 \times 1.8 \times 10^{-5}$$
$$= 1.8 \times 10^{-6}$$
$$x = \sqrt{1.8 \times 10^{-6}}$$
$$x = 1.3 \times 10^{-3} \text{ molar}$$

Our result is that when 5.71 mL of $HC_2H_3O_2$ is diluted to a 1.0-liter volume with water at 25°C, the hydrogen ion concentration of the solution, $[H^+]$, will be 1.3×10^{-3} molar.

Compare the results of these two sample problems:

	Moles of acid used to form 1 liter of solution	Concentration of H^+
Sample Problem 1:	0.010 mole H_2SO_4	0.0200
Sample Problem 2:	0.100 mole $HC_2H_3O_2$	0.0013

Acetic acid, $HC_2H_3O_2$, forms a solution of lower concentration of H^+ ion even though ten times the number of moles of acid were used to make the solution. This difference in behavior is the result of acetic acid being a weak acid and sulfuric acid being a strong acid.

Questions for Section 23-6

9. (a) Using the Arrhenius ionization equation for acetic acid, derive the ionization constant expression for this acid. (b) What is the value of the constant at 25°C?
10. Refer to the K_a values of HF, H_2S, and $HC_2H_3O_2$ in Figure 23-10. (a) Which of these acids is the strongest of the three? (b) Which is weakest? (c) Which, if any, would be considered to be a strong acid?
*11. What is the molar hydrogen ion concentration in a 2.00 liter solution of hydrogen chloride in which 3.65 g of HCl are dissolved?
12. What is the molar concentration of hydrogen ions in a solution containing 4.90 g of H_2SO_4 in 250 mL of solution?
*13. An acetic acid solution is 0.25 M. What is its molar concentration of hydrogen ions?
14. A solution of acetic acid contains 12.0 g of $HC_2H_3O_2$ in 500 mL of solution. What is its molar concentration of hydrogen ions?

23-7 Typical Properties of Acids

1. *Acids are molecular substances that ionize when added to water.* The greater the degree of ionization of an acid, the better will its water solution conduct a current. We have already noted that hydrochloric, sulfuric, and nitric acids ionize almost completely and thus are strong acids. Acetic acid and hydrosulfuric acid ionize only slightly and thus are weak acids.

2. *Acids react with metals that are chemically active to produce hydrogen gas.* Sodium, magnesium, aluminum, and zinc are examples of active metals. Gold, platinum, silver, and copper are examples of inactive metals, that is, metals that do not react with aqueous solutions of acids. A typical equation for the reaction between an active metal and a water solution of an acid is:

$$Zn(s) + 2HCl(aq) \longrightarrow ZnCl_2(aq) + H_2(g) \qquad \textbf{(Eq. 16)}$$

dilute
hydrochloric
acid

*The answers to questions marked with an asterisk are given in the back of the book.

Chapter 23   Acids, Bases, and Salts I   **453**

Figure 23-11

Active metals, such as zinc, magnesium, aluminum, and sodium, react with dilute acids to produce hydrogen gas. Inactive metals, such as copper, gold, platinum, and silver, do not.

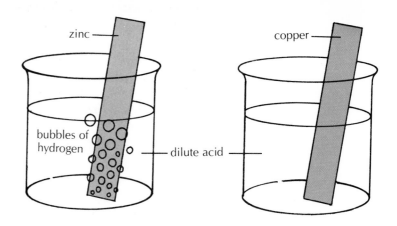

This equation says that zinc metal reacts with dilute hydrochloric acid to produce dissolved zinc chloride and hydrogen gas. The zinc chloride remains in solution as zinc ions and chloride ions while the hydrogen gas bubbles away. See Figure 23-12.

Recall from Section 23-5, Equation 7, that dilute hydrochloric acid consists of hydrated hydrogen ions and chloride ions. It is the hydrogen ions and the zinc metal that are the active ingredients in the reaction between zinc and dilute hydrochloric acid. The chloride ions from the acid are spectator ions. We therefore have another way of conveying the same information shown in Equation 16:

$$Zn(s) + 2H^+(aq) \longrightarrow Zn^{2+}(aq) + H_2(g) \qquad \textbf{(Eq. 17)}$$

-OR-

$$Zn(s) + 2H_3O^+(aq) \longrightarrow Zn^{2+}(aq) + H_2(g) + 2H_2O$$

Figure 23-12

The reaction of zinc metal with dilute HCl. At the start of the reaction, the solution contains H^+ and Cl^- ions. At the end of the reaction, it contains Zn^{2+} and Cl^- ions. The H^+ ions form hydrogen gas that bubbles away. (If excess zinc metal is present at the start, some will be left over at the end of the reaction. If there is excess HCl, some H^+ ions will be left over.)

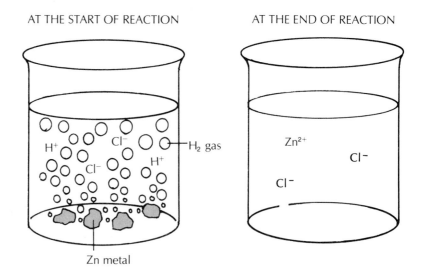

Recall from Section 10-6 that these equations are the ionic equations for the reaction. Dilute sulfuric and dilute nitric acids also contain large concentrations of hydrated protons. Therefore, when these acids react with zinc metal, the same products are produced, namely, aqueous zinc ion and hydrogen gas.

The equation for the reaction between dilute hydrochloric acid and another active metal, magnesium, is:

MOLECULAR EQUATION

$$Mg(s) + 2HCl(aq) \longrightarrow MgCl_2(aq) + H_2(g) \qquad \textbf{(Eq. 18)}$$

-OR-

IONIC EQUATION

$$Mg(s) + 2H^+(aq) \longrightarrow Mg^{2+}(aq) + H_2(g)$$

Sulfuric acid, nitric acid, and hydrochloric acid are all strong acids because they ionize almost completely in water. However, there is an important difference between concentrated sulfuric and nitric acids, on the one hand, and concentrated hydrochloric acid, on the other hand. Concentrated hydrochloric acid is made by bubbling hydrogen chloride gas into water. The gas is very soluble. As more of it dissolves, the hydrochloric acid solution becomes more concentrated. When no more gas will dissolve (when the solution is saturated), about 37% by mass of the solution is hydrogen chloride. The remaining 63% is, of course, water. Therefore, the most concentrated solution of hydrochloric acid that can be obtained is more than 60% water.

The composition of concentrated hydrochloric acid is in marked contrast to the compositions of concentrated sulfuric and concentrated nitric acids. The concentrated solutions of these acids, as obtained from chemical supply companies, contain very little water. A good grade of concentrated sulfuric acid is 95 to 98% sulfuric acid. A good grade of concentrated nitric acid is more than 90% nitric acid. In their concentrated forms, nitric and sulfuric acids have so little water in them that they contain few hydronium ions. Therefore, the concentrated acids will not react with active metals to release hydrogen gas in the manner described by Equation 6. Only their dilute solutions, in which there is a plentiful supply of hydronium ions, react to produce hydrogen gas.

In addition to the first two properties of acids—their reactions with water and with active metals—we can list three other typical properties of acids.

3. *Acids affect the colors of acid-base indicators*. **Indicators** are substances that have one color in an acid solution and another color in a basic solution. (Bases will be discussed shortly.) The effect of dilute acids on indicators is shown in Figure 23-13.

4. *Acids neutralize bases*. Neutralization reactions will be discussed later in this chapter, Section 23-12.

Figure 23-13

The acid and basic colors of three indicators: litmus, phenolphthalein, and methyl orange (M.O.).

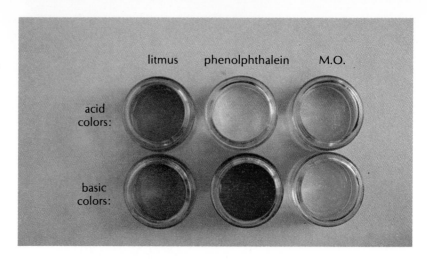

litmus   phenolphthalein   M.O.

acid colors:

basic colors:

Sour milk contains lactic acid; citrus fruits contain citric and ascorbic acids.

5. *Dilute acids have a sour taste.* Citrus fruits, vinegar, and sour milk taste sour because of the presence of dilute acids. Some acids, such as oxalic acid, are poisonous. Because some laboratory chemicals are poisonous, laboratory chemicals should not be tested by tasting them.

We end this section with a caution. Certain concentrated acids—and this is especially true of concentrated sulfuric acid, H_2SO_4—produce large quantities of heat when they are diluted with water. If a small quantity of water is added to concentrated acid, enough heat may be generated to turn the water into steam. Expanding bubbles of steam within the acid can cause the acid to splatter, damaging clothing and causing injury to anyone the acid splatters on. Therefore, great caution should be used in diluting concentrated acids. The proper procedure is to slowly add the concentrated acid to the water. Do NOT do the reverse. The following rhyme may help you remember this:
DO IT THE WAY YOU "OUGHTA" (ought to).
ALWAYS ADD THE ACID TO THE WATER!

23-8   Importance of Acids

Acids play important roles in the life processes that go on inside our bodies. Common foods and fruits contain acids. In citrus fruits, the acid is citric acid. In vinegar, it is acetic acid. In sour milk, it is lactic acid. Grapes contain tartaric acid. The gastric juice in the stomach contains hydrochloric acid. Vitamin C is ascorbic acid.

Many industrial processes use acids. Sulfuric acid is used to make fertilizers, explosives, dyes, and other acids. Hydrochloric acid is used to clean metals, prepare sugar from starch, and in the manufacture of many chemicals. Acetic acid is used in the dyeing of silk and wool and in the manufacture of both rayon and nonflammable film. Other acids are put to other uses. Acids are considered an important class of substances because of their many uses.

15. (a) List five (5) typical properties of acids. What color is given by an acid to the following indicators: (b) litmus (c) phenolphthalein (d) methyl orange?
16. Write the molecular equation for the reaction of (a) magnesium and hydrochloric acid (b) zinc and sulfuric acid.
*17. Using H^+ for the formula of the hydrogen ion, write the ionic equations for the reactions in question 16.
18. Heat energy is produced when acids dissolve in water to produce hydronium ions. Why is more heat produced when a given volume of concentrated sulfuric acid is added to 100 mL of water than when an equal volume of concentrated hydrochloric acid is added to 100 mL of water?
19. Mention the names of acids found in five (5) common substances or foods.
20. State one (1) industrial use of each of the following acids: (a) hydrochloric acid (b) sulfuric acid (c) acetic acid.

23-9   The Preparation of Acids

1. Direct combination of elements. Hydrogen chloride gas may be prepared by burning hydrogen gas in chlorine gas. The equation for the reaction is:

$$H_2(g) + Cl_2(g) \longrightarrow 2HCl(g) \qquad \textbf{(Eq. 19)}$$

When the hydrogen chloride gas is dissolved in water, hydrochloric acid is produced.

2. Reacting a salt of an acid with concentrated sulfuric acid. Salts are ionic compounds whose structures in the solid phase show completely ionic lattices. Salts are the combination of a cation other than the hydrogen ion with an anion other than the hydroxide ion. Nitrates, such as $NaNO_3$, KNO_3, $Mg(NO_3)_2$, are salts of nitric acid, HNO_3. Phosphates, such as Na_3PO_4, K_3PO_4, $Mg_3(PO_4)_2$, are salts of phosphoric acid, H_3PO_4.

When the salt of an acid is reacted with concentrated sulfuric acid, the acid is produced from the anion of the salt and the hydrogen in the sulfuric acid. For example, to make nitric acid, its sodium salt (sodium nitrate) can be reacted with concentrated sulfuric acid:

$$NaNO_3(s) + H_2SO_4(l) \longrightarrow NaHSO_4(s) + HNO_3(g) \qquad \textbf{(Eq. 20)}$$

The sulfuric acid provides the hydrogen needed to make nitric acid. Because concentrated sulfuric acid boils at a high temperature (338°C), the nitric acid can be boiled off as a gas at a low enough temperature so that any unreacted sulfuric acid remains behind. See Figure 23-14.

Figure 23-14

Preparation of nitric acid. Sodium nitrate, $NaNO_3$, and concentrated sulfuric acid, H_2SO_4, are heated in a retort. They react to form nitric acid, which passes out of the reaction mixture as a vapor. The vapor condenses to a liquid that drips out at the end of the retort.

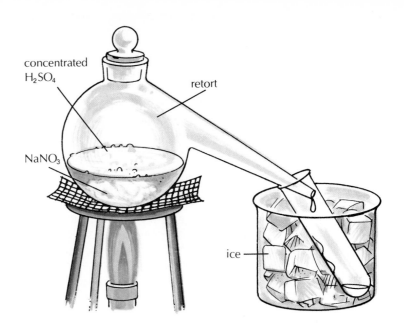

concentrated H_2SO_4

retort

$NaNO_3$

ice

3. *Dissolving an acid anhydride in water.*

An **acid anhydride** is a nonmetallic oxide that will react with water to form an acid as the sole product. Examples of acid anhydrides are CO_2, SO_2, and P_4O_{10}. The following equations show how acid anhydrides react with water to produce acids.

$$CO_2 + H_2O \longrightarrow H_2CO_3 \qquad \textbf{(Eq. 21)}$$
carbon dioxide $\qquad$ carbonic acid

$$SO_2 + H_2O \longrightarrow H_2SO_3 \qquad \textbf{(Eq. 22)}$$
sulfur dioxide $\qquad$ sulfurous acid

$$P_4O_{10} + 6H_2O \longrightarrow 4H_3PO_4 \qquad \textbf{(Eq. 23)}$$
phosphorous pentoxide $\qquad$ phosphoric acid

(P_4O_{10}, the anhydride of phosphoric acid, is called phosphorus *pent*oxide. At the time it was named, its formula was thought to be P_2O_5, hence the prefix *pent-*, meaning five.)

23-10 Naming Acids

The names of acids depend upon the anion the acid is related to. If the anion's name ends in *-ate*, the acid name ends in *-ic*. If the anion is a single element, the name of the acid begins with the prefix *hydro-* and ends with *-ic*. If the anion's name ends in *-ite*, the acid name ends in *-ous*. The way acids are named is summarized in Figure 23-15.

Figure 23-15

The name of an acid is related to the name of the anion from which the acid is derived. (See text for further explanation.)

Formula of Acid	Related Polyatomic Ion	Name of Acid
H_2SO_4	SO_4^{2-} sulfate ion	sulfuric acid
H_3PO_4	PO_4^{3-} phosphate ion	phosphoric acid
HNO_3	NO_3^- nitrate ion	nitric acid
H_2SO_3	SO_3^{2-} sulfite ion	sulfurous acid
HNO_2	NO_2^- nitrite ion	nitrous acid
	Related Monatomic Ion	
HCl	Cl^- chloride ion	hydrochloric acid
HBr	Br^- bromide ion	hydrobromic acid

Questions for Sections 23-9 and 23-10

21. Write equations for the preparation of (a) hydrobromic acid by direct combination (b) hydrogen chloride from sodium chloride and concentrated sulfuric acid (c) nitric acid from magnesium nitrate and concentrated sulfuric acid (d) sulfuric acid from water and sulfur trioxide.
22. Name the following acids: (a) H_2S (b) H_3PO_4 (c) H_2SO_3 (d) H_2CO_3.
23. Write the formulas of (a) hydrobromic acid (b) nitrous acid (c) phosphorous acid (d) sulfuric acid.

23-11 Bases (Arrhenius's Definition)

According to the definition of Arrhenius, a **base** is any hydroxide that dissolves in water to yield hydroxide ions as the only negative ion. By this definition, the following are examples of bases: NaOH (sodium hydroxide), KOH (potassium hydroxide), $Mg(OH)_2$ (magnesium hydroxide), $Ca(OH)_2$ (calcium hydroxide), and NH_4OH (ammonium hydroxide). See Figure 23-16.

Figure 23-16

Some common bases.

Name	Formula	Common Name
sodium hydroxide	NaOH	lye or caustic soda
potassium hydroxide	KOH	lye or caustic potash
magnesium hydroxide	$Mg(OH)_2$	milk of magnesia
calcium hydroxide	$Ca(OH)_2$	slaked lime
ammonium hydroxide	NH_4OH or $NH_3 \cdot H_2O$	ammonia water or household ammonia

23-12   Typical Properties of Bases

1. *Bases are electrolytes.* The aqueous solutions of bases conduct an electric current. Bases such as NaOH and KOH exist as ions in their solid phase. They dissolve readily in water to produce solutions containing large concentrations of ions.

DISSOCIATION EQUATIONS FOR NaOH AND KOH

$$NaOH(s) \longrightarrow Na^+(aq) + OH^-(aq) \qquad \textbf{(Eq. 24)}$$

$$KOH(s) \longrightarrow K^+(aq) + OH^-(aq) \qquad \textbf{(Eq. 25)}$$

Weak bases, such as ammonia water (NH_3 gas dissolved in water) are molecular substances that ionize only slightly in water and are thus poor conductors.

IONIZATION EQUATION FOR AMMONIA GAS, NH_3

$$NH_3 + H_2O \rightleftharpoons NH_4^+ + OH^- \qquad \textbf{(Eq. 26)}$$

2. *Bases cause indicators to turn a characteristic color.* See again Figure 23-13.

3. *Bases neutralize acids.* Concentrated solutions of bases and concentrated solutions of acids are both very corrosive. Concentrated sodium hydroxide, NaOH, for example, is used to clear clogged drain pipes. It will cause severe burns in contact with the skin. Concentrated hydrochloric acid, HCl, can eat through metals and can also cause severe burns. Yet when these two solutions are mixed with each other in the right proportion, a solution of salt dissolved in water is produced.

$$NaOH(aq) + HCl(aq) \longrightarrow \underbrace{NaCl(aq) + H_2O}_{\text{salt water}} \qquad \textbf{(Eq. 27)}$$

The mutual destruction of a base and acid when solutions of the two are mixed is called neutralization. To be more precise, **neutralization** is a chemical reaction between an acid and a base to produce a salt and water. In common usage, the word *salt* is usually taken to mean *table*

Figure 23-17

Sodium hydroxide is commonly sold as small, white spherical masses called sodium hydroxide pellets. The pellets dissolve easily in water to generate much heat and a solution that is very corrosive, especially damaging to the eyes. When sodium hydroxide is neutralized by hydrochloric acid, these two corrosive chemicals are turned into salt water.

Figure 23-18

Some selected neutralization reactions. Solutions of the bases sodium hydroxide and potassium hydroxide will neutralize dilute solutions of the acids shown. In every reaction, one of the products of the reaction is water. The other product is a salt formed from the anion of the acid and the cation of the base.

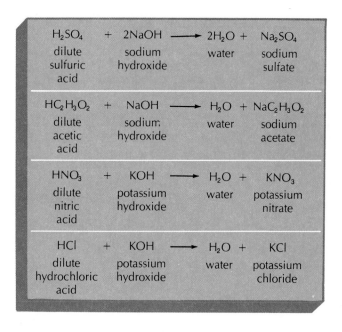

$$H_2SO_4 + 2NaOH \longrightarrow 2H_2O + Na_2SO_4$$

dilute sulfuric acid   sodium hydroxide   water   sodium sulfate

$$HC_2H_3O_2 + NaOH \longrightarrow H_2O + NaC_2H_3O_2$$

dilute acetic acid   sodium hydroxide   water   sodium acetate

$$HNO_3 + KOH \longrightarrow H_2O + KNO_3$$

dilute nitric acid   potassium hydroxide   water   potassium nitrate

$$HCl + KOH \longrightarrow H_2O + KCl$$

dilute hydrochloric acid   potassium hydroxide   water   potassium chloride

salt, which is sodium chloride, NaCl. However, table salt is only one salt among many. Figure 23-18 gives some other neutralization reactions.

4. *Water solutions of bases taste bitter and feel slippery.* As for acids, a taste test should *not* be applied. Many bases are poisonous as well as corrosive to the skin. Concentrated solutions of NaOH or KOH can easily blind a person.

5. *Bases emulsify fats and oils.* The base reacts with the fat or oil to form a soap. The soap solution forms an emulsion with excess fat or oil. (An **emulsion** is a mixture of very fine droplets of two or more liquids that will not dissolve in each other. See Figure 23-19.) Ammonia water is used as a cleanser because it "cuts" grease in this manner.

Questions for Sections 23-11 and 23-12

24. (a) Define a base in terms of Arrhenius theory. (b) Write the chemical names, common names, and formulas of four (4) common bases.
25. (a) State five (5) typical properties of bases. (b) Name the colors shown by litmus, phenolphthalein, and methyl orange in basic solution.
*26. Write equations for the (a) dissociation of calcium hydroxide (b) neutralization of calcium hydroxide by hydrochloric acid (c) neutralization of potassium hydroxide by acetic acid.

Figure 23-19

A water-oil mixture in three stages of separation. Unless an emulsifying agent has been added to it, a water-oil mixture is unstable and will separate, as shown in the photograph. The glass on the left shows the mixture right after the glass was shaken vigorously with a hand covering the mouth of the glass. The glass in the middle had been standing for a while after the mixture had been formed. The glass on the right was allowed to stand long enough for the oil (top layer) to completely separate from the water (bottom layer). Note: Blue food coloring was added to the water to make it easier to see.

23-13   Ionization Constants for Bases

Equation 26 in the last section gave the ionization equation for the weak base ammonia, NH_3. The law of chemical equilibrium can be applied to the ionization of bases as well as to the ionization of acids. For Equation 26, showing the ionization of NH_3, the law gives:

$$\frac{[NH_4^+][OH^-]}{[NH_3][H_2O]} = K_{eq}$$

The concentration of water, $[H_2O]$, varies so little in dilute solutions that it can be considered constant, which we designate here K_1.

$$\frac{[NH_4^+][OH^-]}{[NH_3]K_l} = K_{eq}$$

Rearranging the expression above gives:

$$\frac{[NH_4^+][OH^-]}{[NH_3]} = K_l \times K_{eq}$$

The product of the two constants, $K_1 \times K$, is a third constant called the ionization constant of the base. Ionization constants of bases are represented by the symbol K_b.

$$\frac{[NH_4^+][OH^-]}{[NH_3]} = K_b$$

Generally, the larger the numerical value of K_b, the greater the relative number of ions in solution, including the OH^- ions that give the solution its basic properties. Therefore, when comparing the ionization constants of two weak bases, note that the base whose K_b is a smaller value is usually the weaker base.

Questions for Section 23-13

27. (a) Applying the law of chemical equilibrium, derive the expression which includes the equilibrium constant for the ionization of ammonia in water solution. (b) How can this expression be used to derive the ionization constant of ammonia? (c) At 25°C, the K_b for ammonia is 1.8×10^{-5} and that for methylamine is 5.0×10^{-4}. Which is the weaker base?
*28. What is the concentration of hydroxide ion in a 0.50 M solution of ammonia at 25°C? The ionization constant for ammonia at 25°C is 1.8×10^{-5}.
29. The concentration of hydroxide ion in a solution of ammonia, at 25°C, is 4.0×10^{-4} M. What is the molar concentration of the ammonia in the solution?

23-14   Common Bases

Many bases are commonly found in the home. Ammonia water, lye (sodium hydroxide or potassium hydroxide), and milk of magnesia (magnesium hydroxide) are examples of common bases. Ammonia water is a cleansing agent, lye is used to clean clogged pipes, and milk of magnesia counteracts stomach acidity. Industrially, bases have many uses. They are used in the refining of petroleum, and in the manufacture of rayon, paper, and soap. Refer again to Figure 23-16 for the names of some common bases, their formulas, and common names.

23-15   Preparation of Bases

1. *Reaction between an active metal and water.* Sodium, potassium, and calcium will react with water to form bases and hydrogen gas.

$$2K(s) + 2H_2O \longrightarrow 2KOH(aq) + H_2(g) \qquad \textbf{(Eq. 28)}$$

$$2Na(s) + 2H_2O \longrightarrow 2NaOH(aq) + H_2(g) \qquad \textbf{(Eq. 29)}$$

$$Ca(s) + 2H_2O \longrightarrow Ca(OH)_2(aq) + H_2(g) \qquad \textbf{(Eq. 30)}$$

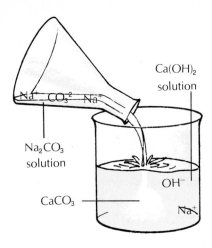

Figure 23-20

Preparing NaOH. When a solution of Na_2CO_3, is added to a solution of $Ca(OH)_2$, the white solid, $CaCO_3$, is formed, leaving Na^+ and OH^- ions in solution. Filtering out the solid will leave a solution containing Na^+ and OH^- ions. If the water is evaporated from the solution, solid NaOH will remain.

2. *Reaction between a salt and a base*. This method may be used to prepare soluble or insoluble bases. The soluble base NaOH may be prepared as follows:

PREPARATION OF NaOH BY THE SODA-LIME METHOD

a salt + a base $\longrightarrow$ a base + a salt

$$Na_2CO_3(aq) + Ca(OH)_2(aq) \longrightarrow 2NaOH(aq) + CaCO_3(s) \qquad \text{(Eq. 31)}$$

The solid, $CaCO_3$, precipitates out, leaving the NaOH (existing as dissolved sodium and hydroxide ions) in solution. The $CaCO_3$ precipitate can be removed by filtration. The water can then be evaporated from the remaining solution, producing solid NaOH. See Figure 23-20. Although most of the commercially prepared NaOH is made by the electrolysis of brine (a concentrated solution of NaCl), a considerable amount is made by the above soda-lime method. Electrolysis will be discussed in a later chapter.

The above method shows the preparation of a soluble hydroxide, the base, sodium hydroxide. An insoluble hydroxide may also be made by the mixing of the solutions of a soluble hydroxide with a soluble salt. For example, the insoluble hydroxide $Fe(OH)_3$ can be made by mixing a solution of one of its soluble salts ($FeCl_3$, for example, is soluble) with a solution of NaOH:

$$3NaOH(aq) + FeCl_3(aq) \longrightarrow Fe(OH)_3(s) + 3NaCl(aq) \qquad \text{(Eq. 32)}$$

By pouring the contents of the reaction vessel through a filter, the insoluble $Fe(OH)_3$ can be separated from the other substances.

3. *Reaction between a basic anhydride and water*. A **basic anhydride** is a metal oxide which reacts with water to form a base. Lime, CaO, is a basic anhydride. It reacts with water to produce slaked lime, $Ca(OH)_2$, a strong base:

$$CaO(s) + H_2O(l) \longrightarrow Ca(OH)_2(s) \qquad \text{(Eq. 33)}$$

calcium   calcium
oxide   hydroxide
(lime)   (slaked lime)

23-16   Definition of a Salt

Salts are ionic compounds containing a positive ion other than the hydrogen ion and a negative ion other than the hydroxide ion. Sodium chloride, NaCl, is a salt composed of the sodium ion, Na^+, and the chloride ion, Cl^-. Aluminum sulfate, $Al_2(SO_4)_3$, is a salt composed of aluminum ions, Al^{3+}, and sulfate ions, SO_4^{2-}. Salts have high melting points. They are, therefore, solids at room temperature. They are good conductors of electric currents either when molten or when dissolved in water. A list of common salts, showing their formulas, common names, and uses, appears in the table in Figure 23-21.

Figure 23-21

Some common salts.

Salt	Formula	Common Name	Important Uses
sodium chloride	NaCl	salt	Manufacture of NaOH, $NaHCO_3$, Na_2CO_3, Cl_2
sodium nitrate	$NaNO_3$	Chile saltpeter	Preparation of explosives. As fertilizer
sodium bicarbonate	$NaHCO_3$	baking soda	In baking powders and fire extinguishers
potassium carbonate	K_2CO_3	potash	In making soap and glass
ammonium chloride	NH_4Cl	sal ammoniac	In dry cells

23-17 Preparation of Salts

There are many methods of preparing salts. The following are some of the more important methods.

1. *Neutralization reactions.* Acids and bases neutralize each other to produce a salt and water. For example,

$$2HCl + Ca(OH)_2 \longrightarrow CaCl_2 + 2H_2O \qquad \text{(Eq. 34)}$$
$$\text{acid} + \text{base} \longrightarrow \text{salt} + \text{water}$$

By evaporating away the water produced in a neutralization reaction, crystals of the salt can be obtained.

2. *Single replacement reactions,* in which an active metal, such as zinc or magnesium, replaces the hydrogen in an acid. For example,

MOLECULAR EQUATION

$$Mg(s) + H_2SO_4(aq) \longrightarrow MgSO_4(aq) + H_2(g) \qquad \text{(Eq. 35)}$$
$$\text{dilute}$$

The acid must be dilute because the reaction is between the metal and the hydronium ion, found only in acids containing a significant amount of water. The ionic equation shows the nature of the reaction more clearly:

IONIC EQUATION

$$Mg(s) + 2H^+(aq) \longrightarrow Mg^{2+}(aq) + H_2(g) \qquad \text{(Eq. 36)}$$

The hydrogen gas bubbles out of solution, leaving magnesium ions and chloride ions (the latter as spectator ions) in aqueous solution. Solid $MgSO_4$ may be obtained by evaporating the water.

3. *Direct combination of elements.* An example of this method of making a salt is the combination of iron and sulfur to make ferrous sulfide.

$$Fe + S \longrightarrow FeS \qquad \text{(Eq. 37)}$$
$$\text{iron} \quad \text{sulfur} \qquad \text{iron (II) sulfide}$$
$$\text{(ferrous sulfide)}$$

Chapter 23   Acids, Bases, and Salts I   **465**

Figure 23-22

Powdered sulfur (left) and small pieces of iron (middle) are mixed to form the mixture on the right. When the mixture is heated vigorously in a test tube, the iron and sulfur combine to form iron (II) sulfide, FeS.

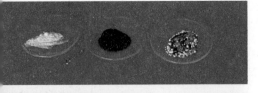

In this reaction, small pieces of iron mixed with powdered sulfur are heated strongly. See Figure 23-22.

4. *Double replacement reaction.* When solutions of two soluble salts are mixed, a precipitate will form if the anion from one of the salts and the cation from the other salt form an insoluble compound. For example,

$$BaCl_2(aq) + (NH_4)_2SO_4(aq) \longrightarrow 2NH_4Cl(aq) + BaSO_4(s) \quad \textbf{(Eq. 38)}$$

In the above reaction, barium ions and sulfate ions combine to form the solid precipitate of $BaSO_4$. The other product of the reaction, NH_4Cl, is also a salt. The two can be separated from each other by filtration.

5. *Reaction of a metallic oxide with a nonmetallic oxide.*

$$MgO \ + \ SiO_2 \ \longrightarrow \ MgSiO_3 \qquad \textbf{(Eq. 39)}$$

magnesium oxide   silicon dioxide   magnesium silicate
(a metallic oxide)   (a nonmetallic oxide)   (a salt)

6. *Reaction of a salt with an acid.*

$$salt \ + \ acid \ \longrightarrow \ salt \ + \ acid$$

$$BaCO_3 + 2HCl \longrightarrow BaCl_2 \ + \ H_2CO_3 \qquad \textbf{(Eq. 40)}$$

(carbonic acid,
an unstable substance)

The carbonic acid is unstable and, upon formation, decomposes into water and carbon dioxide:

$$H_2CO_3 \longrightarrow H_2O \ + \ CO_2 \qquad \textbf{(Eq. 41)}$$

Equations 40 and 41 are usually written as a single equation:

$$BaCO_3 \ + \ 2HCl \longrightarrow BaCl_2 \ + \ H_2O \ + \ CO_2 \qquad \textbf{(Eq. 42)}$$

Questions for Sections 23-14 through 23-17

30. State one commercial use of each of the following bases: (a) ammonia water (b) lye (c) magnesium hydroxide.
31. Write equations for the reaction of (a) calcium and water (b) sodium carbonate and calcium hydroxide (c) sodium hydroxide and aluminum chloride (d) potassium oxide and water.
32. (a) Define *salt.* (b) State three properties of salts.
33. Write the formula, common name, and one use of (a) sodium chloride (b) sodium nitrate (c) sodium bicarbonate (d) ammonium chloride.
34. Write equations showing the preparation of a salt by the (a) neutralization of iron (II) hydroxide by nitric acid (b) reaction of zinc with hydrochloric acid (c) direct combination of calcium and bromine (d) reaction between solutions of silver nitrate and magnesium chloride (e) combination of barium oxide and carbon dioxide (f) reaction of calcium carbonate and hydrochloric acid.

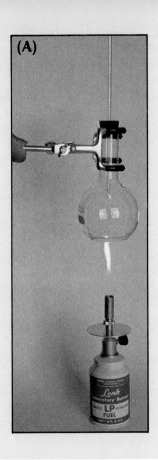

(A)

CAN YOU EXPLAIN THIS?

In Photo A, a small quantity of ammonia water in the bottom of a flask is being heated over a burner. In the neck of the flask there is a one-hole rubber stopper containing a piece of hollow glass tubing. In Photo B, the flask has been inverted and lowered over a large jar of water to which a few drops of phenolphthalein have been added. The end of the tubing is just below the water line. As soon as the end of the tubing made contact with the water, the water rose up the tubing and began squirting into the flask. At the same time, the water took on a reddish color. The water continued to squirt into the flask until the flask was more than ¾ full.

1. How is ammonia water prepared? (Hint: Page 459.)
2. What happened to the ammonia water as it was heated? (Hint: Page 337.)
3. Why did the water rise up the glass tubing?
4. Why did the water take on the reddish color?

(B)

CHAPTER SUMMARY

1. Substances whose water solutions conduct electricity are called electrolytes. Solutions of nonelectrolytes do not conduct the current.
2. The Arrhenius theory proposes that molecules of electrolytes form ions when in solution.
3. When ionic electrolytes are dissolved in water, their ions are hydrated and dissociated.
4. When covalently bonded electrolytes are dissolved in water, they react with the water to form ions. This process is called ionization.
5. When in solution, the ions from ionic or covalent electrolytes are mobile and conduct the current.
6. According to the Arrhenius theory, acids are substances that produce hydrogen ions as the only positive ion when dissolved in water.
7. According to modern theory, the hydrogen ion cannot exist in water as such because it is a bare proton with a high charge density. It combines with water to form the hydronium ion.
8. An ionization constant can be derived for a weak acid. It is equal to the product of the concentrations of the ions, these concentrations being raised to powers indicated by the subscripts in the acid's formula, divided by the concentration of the unionized acid molecule.
9. Acids may be described as substances that form hydronium ions in solution,

Chapter 23 Acids, Bases, and Salts I   **467**

release hydrogen when reacted with active metals, neutralize bases, have a sour taste, and give characteristic colors to indicators.

10. Some common acids present in foods are citric acid, lactic acid, ascorbic acid, tartaric acid, and acetic acid. Some of the more important industrial acids are sulfuric acid, hydrochloric acid, nitric acid, and acetic acid.

11. Acids may be prepared by direct combination, the reaction of a salt of the acid with concentrated sulfuric acid, and the reaction of an acid anhydride with water.

12. According to Arrhenius, a base is a compound that yields the hydroxide ion as the only negative ion when dissolved in water.

13. Bases neutralize acids, taste bitter, give characteristic colors to indicators, and emulsify fats and oils.

14. An ionization constant can be obtained for a weak base and is equal to the product of the concentrations of its ions, raised to powers indicated by the subscripts in the formula of the base, divided by the concentration of the undissociated unit.

15. Examples of some common bases are ammonia water, sodium hydroxide, potassium hydroxide, magnesium hydroxide, and calcium hydroxide.

16. Bases may be prepared by the reaction between an active metal and water, a salt and a base, and a basic anhydride and water.

17. Salts are solids with an ionic lattice, consisting of a metal (or metallic group) combined with a nonmetallic ion, excluding the hydroxide ion. Ordinary salt is NaCl.

18. Salts may be prepared by the direct combination of elements or the combination of metallic and nonmetallic oxides.

19. A single replacement reaction between an active metal and an acid produces a salt and hydrogen.

20. Salts can be produced by double replacement reactions, such as the reaction between an acid and a base (neutralization), the reaction between a salt and an acid, and the reaction between two salts.

TERMS YOU SHOULD KNOW

strong electrolyte	hydronium ion	neutralization
weak electrolyte	ionization constant	emulsion
dissociation	indicator	lye
ionization	acid anhydride	basic anhydride
acid	base	salt

REVIEW QUESTIONS

Section

23-1   1. (a) Using Figure 23-2 as reference, name three electrolytes, each existing in a different phase at ordinary conditions. (b) For each, state whether its solution is a strong or weak electrolyte.

23-2   2. (a) According to Arrhenius, what happens to electrolytes when they are dissolved in water? (b) According to the modern theory, what class of substances *produce* ions when dissolved in water? (c) What class of substances possess ions which become dissociated when these substances are dissolved in water?

23-3   3. NaCl consists of oppositely charged ions that strongly attract one another in the solid phase. Describe the forces that separate these ions when salt is dissolved in water.

        4. Write dissociation equations for (a) calcium nitrate (b) iron (III) chloride (c) ammonium sulfate (d) potassium phosphate.

        5. NaCl is ionic and conducts the electric current when melted or dissolved. In these two conditions, (a) how are the ions alike? (b) how do they differ?

23-4   6. (a) What causes acetic acid to ionize in solution? (b) State one way in which the dissociation of NaCl is similar to the ionization of $HC_2H_3O_2$, and state one way in which they are different.

23-5   7. (a) Write the equations for the ionization of hydrochloric and acetic acids, showing the formation of hydronium ions. (b) What is the essential difference in these equations? Explain.

        8. Write ionization equations, showing the water as a reactant, for the following acids: (a) phosphoric acid (b) hydrobromic acid (c) hydrosulfuric acid

23-6   9. Using the equation for the reaction between acetic acid and water to form hydronium and acetate ions, derive the ionization constant expression for acetic acid.

        10. What is the molar concentration of hydrogen ions in a solution of acetic acid in which 3.0 g of $HC_2H_3O_2$ are dissolved in 250 mL of solution?

        11. What is the molar concentration of hydrogen ions in a solution of nitric acid in which 6.3 g of HNO_3 are dissolved in 500 mL of solution?

23-7   12. Write the molecular and ionic equations for the reaction of (a) Al and HCl (b) Mg and dilute H_2SO_4. Use the hydronium ion in the ionic equations.

        13. State the common names of the following acids: (a) hydrochloric acid (b) nitric acid (c) sulfuric acid (d) acetic acid.

        14. Why is a higher temperature reached when water is added to concentrated sulfuric acid than when the acid is added to the water?

23-8   15. Name the acid found in (a) lemons (b) vinegar (c) sour milk (d) vitamin C (e) gastric juice.

        16. What acid is used (a) to make dyes and explosives (b) to clean metals (c) to manufacture rayon (d) to make other acids?

23-9   17. Write equations for the preparation of (a) hydrosulfuric acid by a direct combination reaction (b) acetic acid from a salt and concentrated sulfuric acid (c) carbonic acid from the acid anhydride (d) phosphoric acid from sodium phosphate and concentrated sulfuric acid.

23-10   18. Write the formulas of (a) chloric acid (b) chlorous acid (c) sulfurous acid (d) hydrofluoric acid.

        19. Name the following acids: (a) H_3PO_3 (b) HNO_2 (c) HBr (d) H_3BO_3. (BO_3^{3-} is the borate ion.)

23-11   20. $Bi(OH)_2NO_3$ has basic properties. Why doesn't the Arrhenius definition of a base include this substance?

21. What is the formula of the base in (a) caustic soda (b) milk of magnesia (c) slaked lime?

23-12 **22.** Write equations for the (a) dissociation of barium hydroxide (b) ionization of ammonia (c) neutralization of sodium hydroxide by phosphoric acid.

23. Why does ammonia water act as a cleaning agent?

23-13 **24.** The following organic compounds are weak bases: aniline ($K_b = 4.6 \times 10^{-10}$); hydrazine ($K_b = 9.8 \times 10^{-7}$); pyridine ($K_b = 1.5 \times 10^{-9}$). Which of these bases is the (a) weakest? (b) strongest?

25. The concentration of ammonium ion in a given solution of ammonia is $2.0 \times 10^{-3}\ M$. What is the molar concentration of the NH_3 in this solution? (K_b for ammonia at 25°C is 1.8×10^{-5}.)

26. What is the concentration of hydroxide ion in a solution of ammonia that is $0.250\ M$? (K_b for ammonia at 25°C is 1.8×10^{-5}.)

23-14 **27.** Name three (3) bases commonly found in the home and state their uses.

23-15 **28.** Write equations for the reaction of (a) sodium and water (b) magnesium chloride and calcium hydroxide (c) iron (III) chloride and potassium hydroxide (d) barium oxide and water.

23-16 **29.** Write the formulas of (a) Chile saltpeter (b) baking soda (c) potash (d) sal ammoniac.

23-17 **30.** Write equations for the preparation of calcium chloride by (a) a neutralization reaction (b) a single replacement reaction (c) direct combination of the elements (d) a double replacement reaction between two salts (e) the reaction of a carbonate with an acid.

31. Write equations for the preparation of the following salts by reactions between metallic and nonmetallic oxides: (a) calcium sulfite (b) magnesium carbonate (c) barium sulfate (d) sodium silicate.

FOR FURTHER THOUGHT

23-6 **1.** A certain number of moles of an acid is added to a flask of water and stirred thoroughly. Assume that you know the ionization equation for the acid. What additional information do you need to calculate the number of moles of H^+ in the solution, if (a) the acid is strong? (b) the acid is weak?

23-7 **2.** Each of the following pairs of statements is an observation. If observation (1) is true, state whether observation (2) is necessarily true, possibly true, or not possible.

(a) (1) A given liquid does not conduct an electric current.
(2) The liquid will neutralize a basic solution.

(b) (1) A given solution does not conduct an electric current.
(2) When zinc is placed in the solution, hydrogen gas is released.

(c) (1) When zinc is placed in a certain solution, hydrogen gas is released.
(2) The solution will turn blue litmus red.

23-12 (d) (1) A given solution conducts an electric current.
(2) The solution will neutralize an acid solution.

(e) (1) A given solution turns red litmus blue.
(2) The solution will neutralize an acid solution.

CHAPTER 24

Acids, Bases, and Salts-II

Objectives

When you have completed this chapter, you will be able to:
- Compare two theories of acids and bases.
- Analyze acid-base reactions.
- Calculate (a) hydrogen and hydroxide ion concentrations and (b) pH and pOH values.
- Explain the actions of buffer solutions and amphoteric substances.

24-1   Operational and Conceptual Definitions

A definition based on *directly observable properties* or effects is called an **operational definition.** An acid may be defined operationally as a substance with a sour taste that neutralizes bases and turns litmus paper red.

A definition based on the *interpretation of observed facts* is called a **conceptual definition.** An acid may be defined conceptually as a substance that produces hydrated hydrogen ions as the only positive ions in its aqueous solutions.

Notice that we can make direct observations to test the operational definition. That is, we can taste a solution suspected of being an acid to see if it tastes sour. (CAUTION: As you have learned, many acids are poisonous, and—like all laboratory chemicals—should never be tasted.) For another test, we can add the solution of a base to the suspected acid solution to see if neutralization occurs. We can see if the solution makes blue litmus turn red. We cannot directly observe hydrated hydrogen ions, the basis of the conceptual definition of an acid. It cannot even be demonstrated that they exist. Nevertheless, a conceptual definition has important advantages over an operational definition. The conceptual definition explains why certain substances are acids. It enables chemists to *predict* that certain substances are acids before tests are run to observe their properties. For example, knowing its formula, chemists could predict that HBr is an acid because a polar diatomic molecule containing hydrogen and one other element should react with water to form hydrated hydrogen ions. This prediction could be made in advance of running tests on solutions of HBr to determine if these solutions have acid properties.

24-2 The Brønsted-Lowry Definition of Acid and Base

In 1923, J. H. Brønsted, a Danish chemist, and T. M. Lowry, an English chemist, proposed independently a new conceptual defintion of an acid. The new concept is known as the Brønsted-Lowry theory. According to this theory, an acid is a substance, either molecule or ion, that can *donate* a proton (a hydrogen atom without its single electron) to another substance. A base, according to the theory, is any substance that can *accept* a proton from another substance. Thus, an acid is a **proton donor,** and a base is a **proton acceptor.** We can illustrate these definitions with the equation for the ionization of hydrogen chloride gas.

IONIZATION OF HCl GAS

$$HCl(g) \; + \; H_2O(l) \longrightarrow H_3O^+(aq) \; + \; Cl^-(aq) \qquad \textbf{(Eq. 1)}$$

an acid	a base	hydronium	chloride
(a proton	(a proton	ion	ion
donor)	acceptor)		

In this reaction, the HCl molecule donates a proton (H^+) to the water molecule, thus forming a hydronium ion. (The proton, with its single positive charge, is what gives the hydronium ion its positive charge.) By accepting the proton, the water molecule acts like a Brønsted-Lowry base.

Another example of the Brønsted-Lowry definition is the reaction for the ionization of ammonia gas. Ammonia gas is very soluble in water, and ionizes slightly in solution.

IONIZATION OF AMMONIA GAS, NH_3

$$NH_3(g) \; + \; H_2O(l) \leftrightarrows NH_4^+(aq) \; + \; OH^-(aq) \qquad \textbf{(Eq. 2)}$$

base	acid	acid	base

In this reaction, a water molecule donates a proton to an ammonia molecule. The loss of a proton, H^+, from a water molecule leaves behind a hydroxide ion, OH^-. The gain of a proton by an ammonia molecule, NH_3, produces an ammonium ion, NH_4^+. In the reverse reaction, the NH_4^+ donates a proton which the OH^- ion accepts. Hence, NH_4^+ is an acid in the reverse reaction, and OH^- is a base.

Notice that in the ionization of ammonia (Equation 2), water functions as an acid, but in the ionization of hydrogen chloride (Equation 1), it functions as a base. Whether water donates or accepts protons depends upon what substance it reacts with. Substances with a strong tendency to donate protons (that is, substances with loosely held protons) make water a proton acceptor, while substances with a strong attraction for protons make water a proton donor.

When acids ionize in water, the hydrated hydrogen ions that are produced are acids by the Brønsted-Lowry definition, and the negative ion is a base. We can illustrate this with the ionization of acetic acid.

$$HC_2H_3O_2(l) \ + \ H_2O(l) \ \rightleftharpoons \ H_3O^+(aq) \ + \ C_2H_3O_2^- \ (aq) \qquad \textbf{(Eq. 3)}$$

acid   base   acid   base

In the forward reaction, the acetic acid molecule is the acid (the proton donor) and the water molecule is the base (the proton acceptor). In the reverse reaction, the hydronium ion, H_3O^+, is the acid and the acetate ion, $C_2H_3O_2^-$, is the base.

Figure 24-1 compares the Arrhenius definitions of an acid and a base with the Brønsted-Lowry definitions.

Figure 24-1

The acid-base theories of Arrhenius and Brønsted-Lowry.

	Theory	
	Arrhenius	*Brønsted-Lowry*
Definition of an acid	Any substance that releases H^+ ions as the only positive ion in aqueous solutions	Any substance that donates a proton
Definition of a base	Any substance that releases OH ions as the only negative ion in aqueous solutions	Any substance that accepts a proton

Questions for Sections 24-1 and 24-2

1. (a) Differentiate between operational and conceptual definitions. (b) Define a base from the operational viewpoint. (c) What is the Arrhenius conceptual definition of a base? (d) Which type of definition can be tested by direct observation? (e) State two (2) advantages of the conceptual definition of acid and base.

2. (a) Compare the Brønsted-Lowry and Arrhenius definitions of acid and base. (b) Write an equation showing hydrogen chloride acting as a Brønsted acid. (c) Write an equation showing ammonia acting as a Brønsted base. (d) In the following equations, label the *reactants* as Brønsted acids or bases:

$$NH_4^+ + OH^- \rightarrow NH_3 + H_2O$$

$$C_2H_3O_2^- + H_3O^+ \rightarrow HC_2H_3O_2 + H_2O$$

*3. (a) Why do both the Arrhenius and Brønsted-Lowry theories consider NaOH to be a base? (b) Why does the Brønsted-Lowry theory consider the CO_3^{2-} ion to be a base, while the Arrhenius theory does not?

24-3 Conjugate Acid-Base Pairs

Acid-base reactions are reversible. Where a strong acid and base are involved, the reversibility is very slight, but it exists. According to the Brønsted-Lowry theory, acid-base reactions are reactions in which protons are donated and accepted. The acid on either side of the equation loses protons to become the base on the other side. The base on either side gains protons to become the acid on the other side. Each acid-base pair, therefore, is related by the transfer of a proton. These acid-base pairs are called conjugate acid-base pairs, or simply **conjugate pairs.** One member of a conjugate pair differs from the other by a proton. This is illustrated by the following equation:

$$HCl + H_2O \rightleftharpoons H_3O^+ + Cl^- \qquad \textbf{(Eq. 4)}$$

HCl is the conjugate acid of the base Cl^-.

H_2O is the conjugate base of the acid H_3O^+.

H_3O^+ is the conjugate acid of the base H_2O.

Cl^- is the conjugate base of the acid HCl.

Here is another example:

$$NH_3 + H_2O \rightleftharpoons NH_4^+ + OH^- \qquad \textbf{(Eq. 5)}$$

A strong acid in the Brønsted-Lowry theory is one that loses protons easily. A strong base is one that has a strong attraction for protons. Recall that when an acid gives up a proton, the remaining substance is its conjugate base. If an acid is strong, it follows that its conjugate base is weak. That is, the conjugate base has little attraction for a proton. That is why the acid can so easily give up a proton.

Likewise, when a base accepts a proton, the substance formed is the conjugate acid of the base. If the base is strong, it follows that its conjugate acid is weak. That is, the conjugate acid has little tendency to lose a proton. That is why the base holds the proton so strongly.

For example, in Equation 4 above, hydrogen chloride is a strong acid and loses protons easily. Its conjugate base, Cl^-, therefore has very little attraction for protons. It is a weak base. It has little tendency to remove protons from the hydronium in the reverse reaction. Likewise, the acid H_3O^+ is weak. It has little tendency to give up a proton and form its conjugate base H_2O. Hence, the point of the equilibrium is to the right, as indicated by the longer "yield" arrow.

Questions for Section 24-3

4. (a) Describe the difference in the composition of the members of a conjugate acid-base pair. (b) How is one formed from the other? (c) Describe the relative acid and base strengths in the pair.
*5. (a) Write the formulas of the conjugates of the following acids: HSO_3^-, HS^-, H_2O, H_3PO_4. (b) Write the formulas of the conjugates of the following bases: NO_3^-, Cl^-, SO_4^{2-}, H_2O.
6. Select the conjugate acid-base pairs in each of the following equations: (All reactions are in aqueous medium.)
    (a) $HC_2H_3O_2 + H_2O \rightleftharpoons H_3O^+ + C_2H_3O_2^-$
    (b) $NH_4^+ + OH^- \rightleftharpoons NH_3 + H_2O$
    (c) $CO_3^{2-} + H_2O \rightleftharpoons HCO_3^- + OH^-$
    (d) $Cl^- + H_3O^+ \rightleftharpoons HCl + H_2O$
    (e) $HPO_4^{2-} + H_2O \rightleftharpoons PO_4^{3-} + H_3O^+$

24-4   The Ionization of Water

We tend to think of water as being a substance made up entirely of molecules. However, a sensitive ammeter will show that pure water does contain some ions, although there are relatively few of them. See Figure 24-2. These ions are the result of a reaction that occurs when two water molecules collide effectively. The products of the collision are a hydronium ion and a hydroxide ion:

$$H_2O + H_2O \rightleftharpoons H_3O^+ + OH^- \qquad \text{(Eq. 6)}$$

The long arrow to the left in Equation 6 indicates that the number of water molecules in any sample of water far outnumbers the number of H_3O^+ and OH^- ions. It also indicates that for every one hydronium ion in a sample of pure water there is one hydroxide ion. These ions are equal in number in all samples of pure water.

Figure 24-2

Water does not contain enough ions to light up a household bulb in a conductivity apparatus. However, a sensitive ammeter in the circuit shows that a current is flowing.

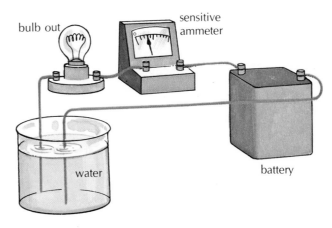

To simplify matters, Equation 6 can be rewritten without showing the water molecule attached to the hydrogen ion:

$$H_2O \rightleftharpoons H^+ + OH^- \qquad \text{(Eq. 7)}$$

The equilibrium shown by Equations 6 and 7 is true of all samples of water whether or not substances are dissolved in the water. Applying the law of chemical equilibrium to Equation 7 gives:

$$\frac{[H^+] \times [OH^-]}{[H_2O]} = K_{eq} \qquad \text{(Eq. 8)}$$

Multiplying Equation 8 by the molar concentration of water, H_2O, gives:

$$[H^+] \times [OH^-] = K_{eq} \times [H_2O] \qquad \text{(Eq. 9)}$$

In pure water, the concentration of water molecules, $[H_2O]$, is constant at constant temperature. In dilute water solutions, their concentration varies very little from their concentration in pure water. Therefore, for practical purposes, $[H_2O]$ is a constant not only in pure water but also in dilute water solutions. The right side of Equation 9 is, then, the product of two constants. The product is itself a constant called the **ion product for water.** The ion product for water is represented by the symbol K_w:

$$K_{eq} \times [H_2O] = K_w \qquad \text{(Eq. 10)}$$
$$\text{ion product for water}$$

Substituting Equation 10 into 9 gives:

$$[H^+] \times [OH^-] = K_w \qquad \text{(Eq. 11)}$$

In pure water at 25°C, there are about a half billion water molecules for every one hydrogen ion and one hydroxide ion.

Equation 11 says that the product of the hydrogen ion concentration and the hydroxide ion concentration in any dilute aqueous solution or in pure water is a constant, K_w. At 25°C, the value of K_w has been found by experiment to be 1.0×10^{-14}. At 25°C, Equation 11 becomes:

$$[H^+] \times [OH^-] = 1.0 \times 10^{-14} \qquad \text{(Eq. 12)}$$
$$\text{(at 25°C)}$$

Equation 12 can be used to calculate the molar concentrations of the hydrogen ion and the hydroxide ion in samples of pure water at 25°C. According to Equation 7, the concentrations of these two ions are equal. Let x be the molar concentration of each of these ions in a sample of pure water at 25°C. Substituting x into Equation 12 gives:

$$[H^+] [OH^-] = 1.0 \times 10^{-14} \qquad \text{(Eq. 13)}$$
$$x \cdot x = 1.0 \times 10^{-14}$$
$$x^2 = 1.0 \times 10^{-14}$$
$$x = \sqrt{1.0 \times 10^{-14}}$$
$$x = 1.0 \times 10^{-7} \text{ molar}$$

Our result tells us that the concentrations of both the H^+ and OH^- ions in samples of pure water at 25°C are $1.0 \times 10^{-7} M$.

Let us consider what happens when a strong acid is dissolved in water. An acid is a substance whose water solution contains a large concentration of hydrogen ions. But at 25°C, Equation 13 must always be true. If the concentration of H^+ goes up, the concentration of OH^- must go down proportionally in order for the ion product to remain constant at 1.0×10^{-14}.

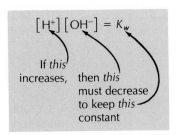

By similar reasoning, a water solution of a base has a large concentration of OH^- and a small concentration of H^+. The sample problem illustrates this effect.

SAMPLE PROBLEM

A mass of 4.0 grams NaOH (0.10 mole NaOH) is dissolved in water to make a solution whose volume is 1.0 liter. What is the molar concentration of the hydrogen ion in this solution?

Solution. NaOH is a strong base that dissociates completely. According to the dissociation equation for NaOH,

$$NaOH(s) \longrightarrow Na^+(aq) + OH^-(aq)$$

1 mole of NaOH dissociates to give 1 mole of Na^+ ions and 1 mole of OH^- ions. Therefore, 4.0 grams NaOH, or 0.10 mole NaOH, dissociates to give 0.10 mole Na^+ ions and 0.10 mole OH^- ions. In a solution whose volume is 1 liter, the concentration of the hydroxide ions would be:

$$[OH^-] = \frac{0.10 \text{ mole}}{1 \text{ liter}} = 0.10 \ M$$

If we substitute this value for $[OH^-]$ in Equation 13 we get:

$$[H^+][OH^-] = 1.0 \times 10^{-14} \qquad \textbf{(Eq. 13)}$$

$$[H^+](0.10) = 1.0 \times 10^{-14}$$

$$[H^+] = \frac{1.0 \times 10^{-14}}{0.10}$$

$$= 1.0 \times 10^{-13} \ M$$

Our result tells us that when 4.0 grams of NaOH is dissolved in 1.0 liter of solution, the increased concentration of OH$^-$ causes the concentration of H$^+$ to decrease to $1.0 \times 10^{-13}\,M$ from its value in pure water of $1.0 \times 10^{-7}\,M$.

Questions for Section 24-4

7. (a) Using the H$^+$ symbol, write the equation showing the slight ionization of water. (b) From this equation, derive the ion-product expression for water. (c) What is the value of the ion-product constant for water at 25°C?
8. Calculate the concentrations of both hydrogen and hydroxide ions at 25°C in (a) pure water (b) 10 M NaOH solution (c) 1.0 M KOH solution (d) 0.10 M HCl solution (e) 10 M HCl solution.
*9. A mass of 1.4 g of KOH is dissolved in water to form 500 mL of solution. What is the concentration, expressed in molarity, of the hydrogen ion in this solution if the temperature of the solution is 25°C?
10. A mass of 4.0 g of NaOH is dissolved in water to form 500 mL of solution whose temperature is 25°C. What is the hydrogen ion concentration in the solution?

24-5   The pH of a Solution

Hydrogen ion concentrations are often expressed in scientific notation. Some examples are:

$$\left[H^+\right] = 1.0 \times 10^{-14}\,M$$

$$\left[H^+\right] = 2.5 \times 10^{-9}\,M$$

$$\left[H^+\right] = 6.3 \times 10^{-6}\,M$$

In scientific notation, the first factor is a number falling between 1 and 10, and the second factor is 10 raised to some power. The hydrogen ion concentrations of solutions can be expressed more conveniently by what is called the pH of the solution. The **pH of a solution** is the negative logarithm, to the base 10, of the hydrogen ion concentration:

$$pH = -\log\left[H^+\right]$$

The meaning and use of logarithms is usually learned in algebra courses, and it is not easy to remember. Therefore, you may not be sure what the expression above means. It is, however, easy to understand when the hydrogen ion concentration is simply 1 times some power of 10. The logarithm, to the base 10, of a power of 10 is equal to that power. For example,

$$\log 10^6 = 6$$

$$\log 10^{-8} = -8$$

Figure 24-3

When the hydrogen ion concentration, $[H^+]$, is simply 1 times a power of 10, then the pH is the power of 10 with its sign changed. The following table gives some examples.

Hydrogen Ion Concentration	pH
1.0×10^{-4}	+4
1.0×10^{-8}	+8
1.0×10^{-12}	+12

Thus we see that if $[H^+]$ is 10^{-7}, then $\log 10^{-7} = -7$, and $-\log 10^{-7} = +7$. Therefore, in a solution whose $[H^+]$ is 10^{-7}, the pH is +7. This is the pH of pure water at 25°C. Since pure water is neutral, a neutral solution has a pH of +7 at 25°C. See Figure 24-3.

In acid solutions, $[H^+]$ is larger than 10^{-7}. For example, it may be 10^{-4}. (Remember that 10^{-4} is 1000 times as large as 10^{-7}.) The pH of such a solution is then +4. We see that in an acid solution, the pH is less than 7. In a basic solution, the pH is greater than 7.

Figures 24-4 and 24-5 give the pH's of some common liquids and some common chemical solutions.

Appendix C shows a calculation for converting a hydrogen ion concentration into a pH when the first factor in the hydrogen ion concentration is a number other than 1.0.

Figure 24-4

The pH of some common liquids.
(Values are approximate.)

Liquid	pH
digestive juices in the stomach	2.0
lemon juice	2.3
vinegar	2.8
carbonated drinks	3.0
grapefruit juice	3.1
orange juice	3.5
tomato juice	4.2
rainwater	6.2
milk	6.5
pure water	7.0
blood	7.4
seawater	8.5
milk of magnesia	11.1

Figure 24-5

The pH of the 0.1 molar solutions of some common substances.

Substance	pH
hydrochloric acid, HCl	1.0
acetic acid, $HC_2H_3O_2$	2.9
sodium bicarbonate, $NaHCO_3$	8.4
ammonia water, $NH_3 \cdot H_2O$	11.1
sodium hydroxide, NaOH	13.0

24-6 The pOH of a Solution

The **pOH** is the negative logarithm of the hydroxide concentration:

$$pOH = -\log[OH^-]$$

If the concentration of hydroxide ion is 10^{-9} M, then the pOH of the solution is +9. From the equation

$$[H^+][OH^-] = 1.0 \times 10^{-14} \qquad \text{(Eq. 14)}$$
$$\text{(at 25°C)}$$

the following relationship can be derived:

$$pH + pOH = 14.00 \qquad \text{(Eq. 15)}$$
$$\text{(at 25°C)}$$

In other words, the sum of the pH and pOH of an aqueous solution at 25°C must always equal 14.00. For example, if the pOH of a solution is 9.00, then its pH must be 5.00 (assuming that the temperature of the solution is 25°C).

SAMPLE PROBLEM

What is the pOH of a solution whose pH is 3.0?

Solution. This problem can be solved by substituting 3.0 for the pH in the expression

$$pH + pOH = 14.0$$
$$3.0 + pOH = 14.0$$
$$pOH = 14.0 - 3.0$$
$$= 11.0$$

Questions for Sections 24-5 and 24-6

11. (a) Define pH. (b) Define pOH. (c) What is the arithmetical relationship between the pH and pOH of an aqueous solution at 25°C? (d) With reference to the pH of pure water at 25°C, where do the acid pH values fall?
12. Consult Figures 24-4 and 24-5. Which is more acid, (a) a carbonated beverage or orange juice? (b) rainwater or seawater? (c) Is sodium bicarbonate acid or basic? (d) How is the pH of acetic acid affected by the addition of a small amount of strong acid?
*13. What is the pH at 25°C of a solution of nitric acid which (a) is $1.0 \times 10^{-4}\,M$? (b) has a pOH of 9.00? (c) has 6.3 g of solute dissolved in 1.00 L of solution?
14. (a) What is the pH at 25°C of a solution that contains 3.65 g of HCl in 1.00 L of solution? (b) What is its pOH?
*15. What is the $[H^+]$ of a solution which has a pH of 10.00 at 25°C?
16. What is the $[H^+]$ of a solution which has a pOH of 9.00 at 25°C?

24-7 Buffer Solutions

There are many situations in which it is desirable to hold the pH of a solution close to a particular value, even though the quantities of acids

or bases in the solution are changing. It is important, for example, that the blood maintain an almost constant pH between 7.3 and 7.5. If the pH of the blood drops below 6.9 or rises above 7.7, a person will die. Acids and bases that enter the bloodstream following the digestion of foods have little effect on the pH of the blood because the blood contains substances called buffers. **Buffers** are mixtures of chemicals that make a solution resist a change in its pH. Solutions that have a resistance to changes in their pH because of the presence of buffers are called buffer solutions.

To understand how buffers work, consider first a solution of a weak acid, such as acetic acid. This acid ionizes slightly according to the following equilibrium:

$$HC_2H_3O_2 \rightleftharpoons H^+ + C_2H_3O_2^- \qquad \text{(Eq. 16)}$$
$$\text{acetic acid} \qquad\qquad \text{acetate ion}$$

The ionization constant for this equilibrium is 1.8×10^{-5} at room temperature. At equilibrium there are relatively few H^+ and $C_2H_3O_2^-$ ions present. Suppose that a small amount of a fairly strong acid is added to this solution. The concentration of H^+ ion will then greatly increase, thus upsetting the equilibrium of Equation 15. The product of H^+ ion and $C_2H_3O_2^-$ ion concentrations will be too large for the ionization constant. The increase in the H^+ ion concentration will make the equilibrium shift to the left:

$$HC_2H_3O_2 \rightleftharpoons H^+ + C_2H_3O_2^- \qquad \text{(Eq. 17)}$$
$$+$$
$$H^+ \left\{ \begin{array}{l} \text{addition of strong acid,} \\ \text{causing the equilibrium} \\ \text{to shift to the left} \end{array} \right.$$

However, the shift in equilibrium shown above will have little effect on the H^+ ion concentration. There were so few $C_2H_3O_2^-$ ions to begin with that when nearly all of them combine with H^+ ions, there will still be a large excess of H^+ ions. The pH of the solution will therefore become much more acid. This is the situation in an *un*buffered solution.

Suppose, though, that to begin with the solution contained not only acetic acid but also a large excess of acetate ions. The excess acetate ions could be provided by adding a soluble salt of acetic acid, such as sodium acetate, $NaC_2H_3O_2$. Now when a small amount of a strong acid is added to the solution, there will be plenty of acetate ions to combine with the excess hydrogen ions. As equilibrium is being restored, a large number of the hydrogen ions from the strong acid will combine with acetate ions to form acetic acid molecules. Nearly all of the hydrogen ions from the strong acid will be consumed in this manner, tending to make the pH of the solution remain close to its original value.

The solution of acetic acid and sodium acetate will also maintain its pH when a small amount of base is added. In this case, the OH^- ions added to the solution tend to combine with H^+ ions to form water, thus at first tending to reduce the H^+ ion concentration and raise the pH. However, the decrease in the concentration of the H^+ ions causes more of the acetic acid to ionize, thus restoring the H^+ ion concentration to near its original value:

$$HC_2H_3O_2 \rightleftharpoons H^+ + C_2H_3O_2^- \qquad \text{(Eq. 18)}$$

combine with OH^- to make H_2O, causing the equilibrium to shift to the right

In this example, a combination of acetic acid and sodium acetate acts as a buffer. These two substances together make the solution a buffered one. See Figure 24-9.

Figure 24-6

An acetic acid/acetate buffer may be made by dissolving acetic acid and one of its salts in water. Sodium acetate is often used as the salt. The pH of the solution typically falls between 3 and 6, the exact pH depending upon how much of each chemical is used.

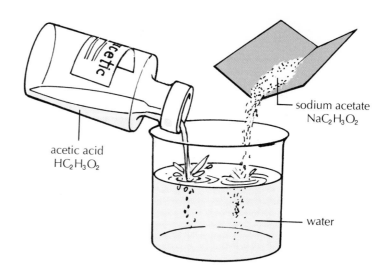

sodium acetate
$NaC_2H_3O_2$

acetic acid
$HC_2H_3O_2$

water

In general, buffers are made up of (1) a weak acid and one of its soluble salts, or (2) a weak base and one of its soluble salts. An example of (2) is an ammonia-ammonium chloride buffer solution. Buffers of the first type buffer a solution in the acid range. Buffers of the second type buffer a solution in the basic range. Both kinds of buffers make solutions in which an equilibrium exists that shifts in response to the addition of acid or base so as to allow only small changes in the hydrogen ion concentration. It should be noted that buffer pairs are actually conjugate acid-base pairs.

24-8 Amphoteric Substances

Some substances, such as the HCO_3^- ion, the HSO_4^- ion, the H_2O molecule, and the NH_3 molecule, can act as either proton donors (acids) or proton acceptors (bases), depending upon what substances they come into contact with. These substances are said to be **amphoteric** (am-fuh-TER-ik) or **amphiprotic** (am-fuh-PRO-tik). Amphoteric substances donate protons in the presence of strong bases.

They accept protons in the presence of strong acids. The two-sided nature of amphoteric substances can be illustrated by the reactions of the bisulfate ion, HSO_4^-:

In the presence of strong acid, H^+, the HSO_4^- ion accepts a proton:

$$HSO_4^- + H^+ \rightleftharpoons H_2SO_4 \qquad \text{(Eq. 19)}$$

In the presence of strong base, OH^-, the HSO_4^- ion donates a proton:

$$HSO_4^- + OH^- \rightleftharpoons SO_4^{2-} + H_2O \qquad \text{(Eq. 20)}$$

Questions for Sections 24-7 and 24-8

17. (a) What is the general function of buffer mixtures? (b) Why are buffers essential in the bloodstream?
18. Describe what happens in a buffer solution of sodium acetate and acetic acid upon the addition of a small quantity of (a) 0.10 M HCl (b) 0.10 M NaOH.
19. (a) Write the equation for the equilibrium reaction that exists in a buffer solution of ammonia and ammonium chloride. What displacement occurs (b) when a small amount of a strong acid is added, and (c) when a small amount of strong base is added?
20. (a) What is an amphoteric substance according to Brønsted-Lowry theory? Write equations showing how the following substances act amphoterically: (b) HCO_3^- ion (c) HS^- ion.

CHAPTER SUMMARY

1. A definition that is based on properties that can be directly observed is called *operational*. One that is based on the interpretation of observed facts is called *conceptual*.
2. The Brønsted-Lowry definitions of acid and base are conceptual. Acids are proton donors. Bases are proton acceptors.
3. Conjugate acid-base pairs are formed reversibly from one another in a reaction where protons are donated and accepted. The conjugates differ in composition by a hydrogen ion. Example: NH_4^+ is the conjugate acid of the base NH_3.
4. If the acid member of a conjugate pair is strong, then the base is weak. The reverse is also true.
5. Water ionizes slightly to form the hydrogen (hydronium) ion and the hydroxide ion.
6. The product of the concentrations of the hydrogen and hydroxide ions in any aqueous solution is a constant. It is called the ion-product constant and is equal to 1.0×10^{-14} at 25°C.
7. In a neutral aqueous solution at 25°C, the concentrations of both hydrogen and hydroxide ions are equal to 1.0×10^{-7} M.
8. The pH of a solution is equal to the negative log (to the base 10) of the hydrogen ion concentration.

9. In acid solution, the $[H^+]$ is greater than $1.0 \times 10^{-7}\,M$ (at 25°C). The pH is, therefore, below 7.00.

10. In basic solution, the $[H^+]$ is less than 1.0×10^{-7} (at 25°C). The pH is greater than 7.00.

11. At 25°C the sum of the pH and pOH is equal to 14.00.

12. Buffer solutions are mixtures that resist a change in pH. They contain either a weak acid and a soluble salt of this acid, or a weak base and a soluble salt of this base.

13. One of the buffer components is acid and neutralizes small amounts of added base. Another component is basic and neutralizes small amounts of added acid.

14. An amphoteric substance is one that may act as a proton donor in one of its reactions and as a proton acceptor in another reaction.

TERMS YOU SHOULD KNOW

operational definition
conceptual definition
proton donor
proton acceptor

conjugate pair
ion-product for water
pH
pOH

buffers
amphoteric
amphiprotic

REVIEW QUESTIONS

(Unless otherwise stated, assume a 25°C temperature for pH and pOH problems.)

Section

24-1

1. (a) Define *acid* from the operational viewpoint. (b) What is the conceptual definition of an acid? (c) What does the conceptual definition predict about the polar diatomic molecule HF?

24-2

2. (a) How are base and acid defined by the Brønsted-Lowry theory? (b) Why does the Brønsted-Lowry theory consider NH_3 to be a base while the Arrhenius theory does not? (c) Label the four (4) substances in the following equilibrium reaction as acid or base, as defined by the Brønsted-Lowry theory:
$$CO_3^{-2} + H_2O \rightleftharpoons HCO_3^- + OH^-$$

3. In the following equilibria, label *all* reactants as Brønsted-Lowry acids or bases:
   (a) $NH_3 + H^- \rightleftharpoons NH_2^- + H_2$ (in liquid ammonia)
   (b) $HNO_2 + OH^- \rightleftharpoons H_2O + NO_2^-$
   (c) $HClO_4 + H_2O \rightleftharpoons H_3O^+ + ClO_4^-$
   (d) $F^- + H_2O \rightleftharpoons HF + OH^-$

24-3

4. (a) What is a conjugate acid-base pair? (b) Write the formulas of the conjugates of the following acids: H_3O^+, H_2SO_3, HCO_3^-, HOCl, NH_4^+. (c) Write the formulas of the conjugates of the following bases: I^-, SO_3^{2-}, PO_4^{3-}, $C_2H_3O_2^-$, $H_2BO_3^-$.

5. The following equation represents the ionization of the strong acid perchloric acid: $HClO_4 + H_2O \rightleftharpoons H_3O^+ + ClO_4^-$

   (a) Select the two conjugate acid-base pairs. (b) Of the two bases, which is the stronger one in this reaction? (c) Of the two acids, which is the stronger one?

6. Select the conjugate acid-base pairs in the following reactions:
  (a) $HNO_2 + H_2O \rightleftharpoons H_3O^+ + NO_2^-$
  (b) $HPO_4^{2-} + H_2O \rightleftharpoons H_3O^+ + PO_4^{3-}$
  (c) $H_2SO_3 + OH^- \rightleftharpoons H_2O + HSO_3^-$
  (d) $H_2CO_3 + SO_4^{2-} \rightleftharpoons HCO_3^- + HSO_4^-$

24-4 **7.** (a) The value of the K_w for water at 25°C is 1.0×10^{-14}; its value at 100°C is 1×10^{-12}. What does this indicate about the degree of ionization of water with increasing temperature? (b) Is it possible for water to have a $[H^+] = 1 \times 10^{-6}\,M$? Calculate the concentrations of both hydrogen and hydroxide ions in (c) $0.20\,M$ HCl solution (d) $0.50\,M$ NaOH solution when the solutions are at 25°C.

8. A nitric acid solution contains 25.2 g of solute in 500 mL of solution. What is the hydrogen ion concentration expressed in molarity?

9. A solution of $Ba(OH)_2$ contains 8.55 g of solute in 1.0 L of solution. What is the molar concentration of the hydroxide ion?

24-5 **10.** (a) What is the pH of a solution of HCl which is $2.0\,M$? (b) What is the pH of a $3.0\,M$ KOH solution? (c) What is the pH of a sulfuric acid solution that is $5.0 \times 10^{-3}\,M$?

11. What is the concentration of hydrogen ions in a solution that has a pH of 7.50?

24-6 **12.** Calculate the pOH of (a) a solution whose pH is -0.75 (b) a $1.0 \times 10^{-2}\,M$ NaOH solution (c) a $1.0 \times 10^{-5}\,M$ HCl solution.

13. Calculate the concentration of H^+ ions in a solution whose pOH is (a) 2.00 (b) -1.00 (c) 11.50.

14. What is the pOH of a solution which contains 7.30 g of HCl in 1.00 L of solution?

24-7 **15.** (a) What is the general composition of a buffer solution? (b) What is the pH range in normal human blood? (c) Why does human blood contain bicarbonate, phosphate, and hemoglobin buffers?

16. (a) Why is the HSO_4^- ion considered to be an amphoteric substance? (b) Write two (2) equations to show its amphoteric nature.

17. Water is an amphoteric compound. Write an equation in which water acts as a (a) proton donor (b) proton acceptor.

FOR FURTHER THOUGHT

24-2 **1.** (a) Explain why the Brønsted-Lowry definition of an acid is a conceptual one.
  (b) Why can there be no operational definition of a Brønsted-Lowry acid?

2. For each of the following statements, state whether is is always true, sometimes true, or never true. Give reasons for your answers.
  (a) A substance that is an acid by the Brønsted-Lowry definition is also an acid by the Arrhenius definition.
  (b) A substance that is an acid by the Arrhenius definition is also an acid by the Brønsted-Lowry definition.
  (c) Arrhenius acids neutralize Arrhenius bases.
  (d) Brønsted-Lowry acids neutralize Brønsted-Lowry bases.
  (e) By the Arrhenius definition, a substance that is an acid under some given condition is an acid under all conditions.

Acid-Base Titration

Objectives

When you have completed this chapter, you will be able to:
- Explain why indicators change color.
- Analyze the results of hydrolysis of salt solutions.
- Select appropriate indicators for acid-base titration.
- Solve problems involving acid-base solutions.

25-1 Acid-Base Indicators

Chemists often need to know how acid or basic a solution is. An electrical instrument called a pH meter will give an accurate measurement of the acidity of a solution. If less accuracy is needed, an acid-base indicator can be used to measure acidity. Indicators change color over a relatively narrow pH range. The pH ranges for three common indicators are shown in Figure 25-1. Thus, if a given solution makes methyl orange turn yellow and blue litmus turn red, then the solution has a pH of between 4.4 and 4.7. Chemically treated paper called pH paper can also be used to tell the approximate acidity of a solution. When a pH paper is wetted with a solution, it turns to a particular color that is characteristic of the acidity of the solution. See Figure 25-2.

An indicator is usually a weak acid that, like other acids, ionizes in water to produce the hydrogen ion, H^+, and a negative ion. The negative ion of one indicator is, of course, different from the negative ion of another indicator, but generally these ions are complicated structures containing many atoms. For simplicity, the symbol In^- is used as the general formula for the negative ions of indicators, and HIn as the general formula for the molecules themselves. The ionization of indicator molecules is written:

Figure 25-1

The pH ranges of three common indicators.

Indicator	pH Range	Color Below Lower pH	Color Above Higher pH
methyl orange	3.1 to 4.4	red	yellow
litmus	4.7 to 8.2	red	blue
phenolphthalein	8.3 to 10.0	colorless	red

Figure 25-2

When a pH test paper is dipped into an aqueous solution, the wetted portion of the paper develops one of the colors shown by the color patches. The color is characteristic of a particular pH ranging from pH = 1 (extreme left) to pH = 11 (extreme right). What was the pH of the solution tested with the test paper shown on the right in the photo?

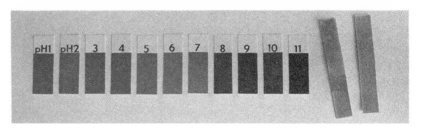

IONIZATION OF INDICATOR, HIn

$$HIn \rightleftharpoons H^+ + In^- \qquad \textbf{(Eq. 1)}$$

The feature that distinguishes an indicator from other weak acids is that the molecules of an indicator have one color and its anions have another color:

$$HIn \rightleftharpoons H^+ + In^- \qquad \textbf{(Eq. 2)}$$

one   another
color   color
(acid color)   (basic color)

The mass action expression for the ionization equation must equal the ionization constant, K_a, of the acid:

$$\frac{[H^+] \times [In^-]}{[HIn]} = K_a$$

In applying this relation, $[H^+]$ must be the total hydrogen ion concentration, including the H^+ ions from the water and from any acids in the solution. In a neutral solution, the ionization will be small where the indicator is a weak acid. That is, in Equation 2, the arrow will be far to the left, indicating a relatively large number of HIn molecules compared to the number of In^- ions. The solution will, therefore, have the color of the HIn molecules (the acid color).

Suppose that a few drops of indicator solution are added to a highly basic solution, say, one with a pH of 12. We know that the H^+ ion concentration in such a solution is 10^{-12} molar—a very small concentration. Since at 25°C,

$$[H^+] \times [OH^-] = 10^{-14}$$

then $[OH^-]$ must be 10^{-2} when $[H^+]$ is 10^{-12}. We can compare these concentrations by dividing the one by the other:

$$\frac{[OH^-]}{[H^+]} = \frac{10^{-2}\,M}{10^{-12}\,M} = 10\,000\,000\,000$$

Thus, the concentration of OH^- ions is 10 000 000 000 times as great as the concentration of H^+ ions in a solution whose pH is 12.

In such a solution, any H^+ ions from the ionization of the indicator acid will immediately react with OH^- ions to form water. This decrease

Chapter 25   Acid-Base Titration   **487**

in H^+ ion concentration will cause the equilibrium to be shifted to the right:

$$HIn \rightleftharpoons (H^+) + In^- \qquad \textbf{(Eq. 3)}$$

acid color   basic color

combine with OH^- ions
to form water

If the concentration of H^+ ions is kept low by the excess OH^- ions, the shift in equilibrium will continue until nearly all the HIn is ionized. A basic solution will therefore show the color of the indicator anion, In^-. This color is the basic color.

Suppose that a strong acid is now added to the solution a little at a time. Its H^+ ions will gradually neutralize the excess OH^- ions originally present. The OH^- concentration and the pH will decrease, while the H^+ concentration will increase. As $[H^+]$ increases, the equilibrium given by Equation 2 will shift to the left. That is the direction in which indicator molecules, HIn, are formed. Eventually, at some value of pH characteristic of that indicator, the solution will take on the color of the indicator molecules. The solution thus changes to the acid color.

Figure 25-3 shows the acid and basic colors of some selected indicators and the pH ranges in which the color changes occur.

There are some acid-base indicators that are weak bases rather than weak acids. Weak base indicators, whose general formula is written InOH, work on the same general principles as weak acid indicators.

25-2   Acid-Base Neutralization

Neutralization may be described as an acid-base reaction between the conjugate acid and base of amphoteric water.

The typical properties of water solutions containing a dissolved acid are due to the hydronium ions (hydrated hydrogen ions). The typical properties of water solutions containing a dissolved base are due to the hydroxide ions. When these two kinds of solutions are mixed, the H_3O^+ ions from the acid combine with the OH^- ions from the base to produce water:

$$H_3O^+ + OH^- \rightleftharpoons 2H_2O$$

When all the H_3O^+ ions from the acid have combined with all the OH^- ions from the base, the acid and base are said to have neutralized each other. Thus, a neutralization reaction is the reaction between the solutions of an acid and a base to produce water. After a neutralization reaction has occurred, the resulting solution may be neutral (pH = 7), but it is sometimes slightly acid or slightly basic. The solution will be slightly acid or basic if *one* of the substances, either the acid or the base, is a weak electrolyte. The pH *may* also be slightly acid or basic if *both* substances are weak electrolytes. The reason why a neutralized solution may not be exactly neutral is discussed later in Sect. 25-5.

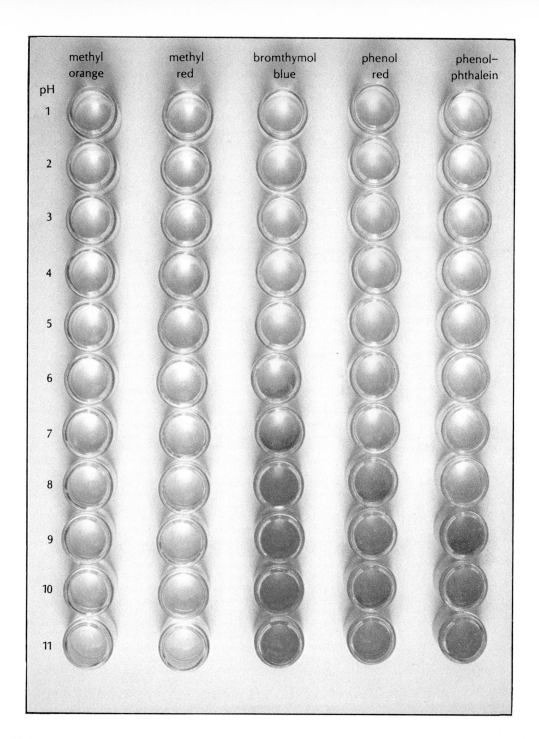

Figure 25-3

The colors of six acid-base indicators when placed in solutions whose pH's range from pH = 1 (top row) to pH = 11 (bottom row).

Questions for Sections 25-1 and 25-2

1. (a) A given solution turns methyl orange indicator yellow, turns litmus blue, and turns phenolphthalein red. What is the approximate pH of the solution? (b) What instrument can be used to supply a more accurate measurement of pH?

(continued, next page)

2. (a) Use the general formula, HIn, for a weak acid indicator and write the equation for its ionization. (b) What color properties of this indicator makes it useful for testing pH values? (c) How is the equilibrium equation in *(a)* affected by the addition of a small quantity of a strong acid? (d) How is the equilibrium equation in *(a)* affected by the addition of a small quantity of base?

*3. What colors are given to methyl orange, litmus, and phenolphthalein, respectively, when testing (a) vinegar (pH of 3), (b) seawater (pH of 8), (c) a saturated $Mg(OH)_2$ solution (pH of 10.5)?

4. (a) Define *neutralization reaction.* (b) Write the general word equation for such a reaction. (c) After all the hydronium ions of the acid have reacted with all the hydroxide ions of the base, is the resulting solution always neutral? Mention one example to support your answer.

25-3 Acid-Base Titration

An **acid-base titration** is a laboratory procedure used to determine the acidity or basicity of a solution. In such a titration, an acid solution whose concentration is known is added to a basic solution of unknown concentration. Or a basic solution of known concentration is added to an acidic solution of unknown concentration. The solution whose concentration is known is called a **standard solution.** An indicator is usually used to signal when enough of the standard solution has been added to neutralize the solution of unknown concentration. By keeping a record of the volume of the standard solution needed to neutralize a measured volume of the solution whose concentration is unknown, the unknown concentration can be determined. We illustrate how this is done in the second of the sample problems that follow.

Figure 25-4

An acid being titrated into a base. The indicator is phenolphthalein.

SAMPLE PROBLEM 1

The concentration of a 0.200-liter hydrochloric acid solution is 0.80 molar. How many moles of HCl are in this solution? How many grams of HCl is this?

Solution. The volume of a solution *in liters* multiplied by its molar concentration gives the number of moles of solute in the solution:

$$\text{moles of solute} = \left(\begin{array}{c}\text{volume of}\\\text{the solution}\\\text{in liters}\end{array}\right) \times \left(\begin{array}{c}\text{molar concentration}\\\text{of the solution}\end{array}\right)$$

Substituting the numbers given in the problem into the above expression gives:

$$\text{moles of solute} = 0.200 \text{ liter} \times 0.80 \text{ moles/liter}$$

$$= 0.16 \text{ mole}$$

Our result is that 0.200 liter of a 0.80 M HCl solution contains 0.16 mole of HCl. To convert to grams, we note that

$$0.16 \text{ moles HCl} = 0.16 \text{ mole} \times \frac{36.5 \text{ g HCl}}{\text{mole}}$$

$$= 5.8 \text{ g HCl}$$

SAMPLE PROBLEM 2

A volume of 20.0 mL of an aqueous solution of strontium hydroxide, $Sr(OH)_2$, has a drop of indicator added to it. (The volume of the drop can be ignored because it is so much smaller than the volume of the solution.) The solution turns color after 25.0 mL of a standard 0.0500 M HCl solution is added. What was the original concentration of the $Sr(OH)_2$ solution, and how many grams of $Sr(OH)_2$ were dissolved in the 20-mL sample?

Solution

Note: In solving this problem, the following abbreviations are used.

V_a = Volume of acid solution in liters
V_b = Volume of basic solution in liters
M_a = Molar concentration of the acid solution
M_b = Molar concentration of the basic solution

Step 1. Write the balanced equation for the reaction and determine the mole relationship.

BALANCED EQUATION

$$2HCl \quad + \quad Sr(OH)_2 \longrightarrow SrCl_2 + 2H_2O$$

2 moles   1 mole

MOLE RELATIONSHIP

number of moles of acid is twice the number of moles of base

moles of acid = 2 (moles of base)

mole factor

Step 2. From the mole relationship, find the molar concentration of the $Sr(OH)_2$ solution.

Note that from Sample Problem 1, we found that:

moles of acid = $V_a M_a$
moles of base = $V_b M_b$

Substitute these products into the mole relationship.

moles of acid = 2 (moles of base)

$$V_a M_a = 2 V_b M_b \qquad \textbf{(Eq. A)}$$

Solving Equation A for M_b:

$$M_b = \frac{V_a M_a}{2 V_b}$$

$$= \frac{0.0250 \text{ liter} \times 0.0500 \text{ mole/liter}}{2 \times 0.0200 \text{ liter}}$$

$$= 0.0312 \text{ mole/liter}$$

$$= 0.0312 \, M$$

Step 3. Determine the number of grams of $Sr(OH)_2$ in the solution. (1 mole $Sr(OH)_2$ = 122 grams)

$$\text{\# grams} = \left(\begin{array}{c} \text{mass in} \\ \text{grams of} \\ \text{1 mole} \end{array} \right) \times (\text{\# of moles neutralized})$$

$$= \left(\begin{array}{c} \text{mass in} \\ \text{grams of} \\ \text{1 mole} \end{array} \right) \times V_b \, M_b$$

$$= 122 \text{ g/mole} \times 0.0200 \text{ L} \times 0.0312 \text{ moles/L}$$

$$= 0.0761 \text{ gram}$$

Questions for Section 25-3

5. (a) Define *acid-base titration*. (b) Define *standard solution*. (c) Describe briefly how you can use a standard acid solution to determine the unknown concentration of a base.

*6. (a) What is the molarity of a solution of HCl if 25.0 mL are titrated to an endpoint by 10.0 mL of a 0.200 M solution of NaOH? (b) How many grams of HCl are there in the 25.0 mL of HCl solution?

*7. What is the molar concentration of a solution of $Ba(OH)_2$ if 50.0 mL are titrated to an endpoint by 15.0 mL of a solution of HCl that is 0.00300 M?

8. (a) What is the molarity of a nitric acid solution if 21.0 mL are needed to completely neutralize 25.0 mL of 0.300 M NaOH solution? (b) How many grams of HNO_3 are dissolved in the 21.0 mL of acid?

9. What is the molar concentration of a solution of KOH if 45.0 mL are completely neutralized by 15.0 mL of 0.500 M H_2SO_4 solution in a reaction in which K_2SO_4 is one of the products?

25-4 Salts Classified According to the Bases and Acids from which They Are Derived

As previously stated, salts are ionic compounds whose solid structures show ionic lattices. They can be classified according to the bases and acids from which they are derived. One kind of salt is composed of the cation of a strong base and the anion of a weak acid. Sodium acetate, $NaC_2H_3O_2$, is an example of this kind of salt:

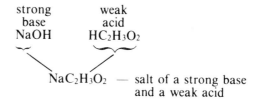

strong base NaOH   weak acid $HC_2H_3O_2$

$NaC_2H_3O_2$ — salt of a strong base and a weak acid

Potassium acetate and sodium and potassium carbonate (Na_2CO_3 and K_2CO_3) are, like $NaC_2H_3O_2$, the salts of strong bases and weak acids.

Another kind of salt is composed of the cation of a weak base and the anion of a strong acid. Ammonium sulfate is an example of this kind of salt:

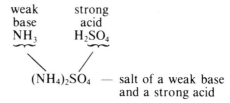

weak base NH_3 strong acid H_2SO_4

$(NH_4)_2SO_4$ — salt of a weak base and a strong acid

Salts can also be composed of the cations and anions of bases and acids that are both strong. Sodium chloride, NaCl, is an example of this kind of salt:

strong base NaOH   strong acid HCl

NaCl — salt of a strong base and a strong acid

Finally, a salt may be derived from a weak base and a weak acid. Ammonium acetate, $NH_4C_2H_3O_2$, is an example:

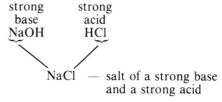

weak base NH_3 weak acid $HC_2H_3O_2$

$NH_4C_2H_3O_2$ — salt of a weak base and a weak acid

25-5 Hydrolysis of Salts

When the salt of a strong acid and strong base, such as NaCl, is dissolved in water, the solution is neutral. However, the salt of a weak base and strong acid produces an acidic solution. The salt of a strong base and weak acid produces a basic solution. The salt of a weak base and weak acid can produce a solution that is either acidic, basic, or neutral, depending on the nature of the salt's ions. That these salt solutions can be acidic or basic means that a reaction takes place between water molecules in the solution and the anion from the weak acid or the cation from the weak base. Such reactions are one type of hydrolysis reaction. A **hydrolysis** reaction is the reaction of a substance with water.

Salts of strong acids and strong bases form hydrated ions in aqueous solution, but, unlike the ions of the other kinds of salts, the anions of strong acids and cations of strong bases are not hydrolyzed (do not react with water molecules).

25-6   Hydrolysis of the Salt of a Strong Base and Weak Acid

Sodium acetate, $NaC_2H_3O_2$, is the salt of the strong base NaOH and the weak acid $HC_2H_3O_2$. We use this salt to illustrate the reaction between salts of this kind and water. When $NaC_2H_3O_2$ dissolves in water, the solution contains $Na^+(aq)$ and $C_2H_3O_2^-(aq)$ ions. It also contains a relatively small number of H^+ and OH^- ions from the ionization of some of the water molecules. There is no attraction between the cations of the salt, Na^+, and the anions, OH^-, from the ionization of the water. This is another way of saying that NaOH is a strong base. When added to water, it dissociates completely, as indicated by the single arrow pointing to the right:

DISSOCIATION OF NaOH

$$NaOH(s) \longrightarrow Na^+(aq) + OH^-(aq) \qquad \textbf{(Eq. 4)}$$

However, attractions do exist between the anion of the salt, $C_2H_3O_2^-$, and the cations present in water, H^+. We have already seen the equilibrium reaction in which these ions play a part:

$$H^+ + C_2H_3O_2^- \rightleftharpoons HC_2H_3O_2 \qquad \textbf{(Eq. 5)}$$

Equation 5 is simply the equation for the ionization of acetic acid written backwards. Equation 5 tells us that some of the hydrogen ions in water are attracted to and will combine with acetate ions to form molecules of the weak acid, acetic acid. In so doing, the hydrogen ions are removed from the solution. This has the effect of decreasing the concentration of hydrogen ions. In order to maintain the ion product of water, additional H_2O will ionize, thus increasing the concentration of the OH^- ion:

$$H_2O \rightleftharpoons (H^+) + OH^- \qquad \textbf{(Eq. 6)}$$

removed by combining
with $C_2H_3O_2^-$

The shift in equilibrium produces more H^+ and OH^- ions, but only the H^+ ions are consumed, as shown by Equation 6. The OH^- ions remain in solution. As a result, the number of OH^- increases, making the solution basic.

A single equation can be written showing the hydrolysis of sodium

Figure 25-5

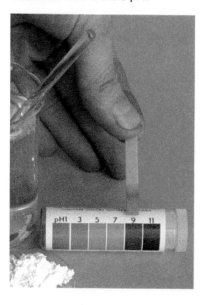

Sodium acetate, $NaC_2H_3O_2$, is the salt of a weak acid and strong base. Its crystals dissolve in water to produce a solution with a basic pH.

acetate. The equation is simply the sum of Equations 5 and 6.

$$H^+ + C_2H_3O_2{}^- \rightleftharpoons HC_2H_3O_2 \qquad \text{(Eq. 5)}$$

$$+ \quad \underline{H_2O \rightleftharpoons H^+ + OH^-} \qquad \text{(Eq. 6)}$$

$$C_2H_3O_2{}^- + H_2O \rightleftharpoons HC_2H_3O_2 + OH^- \qquad \text{(Eq. 7)}$$

Equation 7 indicates that acetate ions (in this case from the salt sodium acetate) react with water to produce acetic acid molecules and OH^- ions. It is the OH^- ions, of course, that make the solution of the salt $NaC_2H_3O_2$ basic. See Figure 25-5.

The law of chemical equilibrium can be applied to the equilibrium given by Equation 7:

$$\frac{[HC_2H_3O_2]\,[OH^-]}{[C_2H_3O_2{}^-]\,[H_2O]} = K \qquad \text{(Eq. 8)}$$

Since the concentration of water in dilute solutions varies so little that it can be considered a constant, we replace $[H_2O]$ with a constant, K_1:

$$\frac{[HC_2H_3O_2]\,[OH^-]}{[C_2H_3O_2{}^-]\,K_1} = K$$

Rearranging the expression above gives:

$$\frac{[HC_2H_3O_2]\,[OH^-]}{[C_2H_3O_2{}^-]} = K \times K_1$$

The product of the two constants, $K \times K_1$, is a constant called the hydrolysis constant, designated K_h:

$$\frac{[HC_2H_3O_2]\,[OH^-]}{[C_2H_3O_2{}^-]} = K_h$$

Notice that $[OH^-]$ appears in the numerator of the above expression. This means that a salt of a strong base and weak acid with a relatively large value for K_h will produce an aqueous solution that is more basic than a similar salt with a small value for K_h.

Questions for Sections 25-4 through 25-6

10. Name the four types of salts, classified according to the bases and acids from which they are derived.
11. Name the classification of each of the following salts: (a) KNO_3, (b) $(NH_4)_2CO_3$, (c) $Mg(C_2H_3O_2)_2$, (d) Na_2SO_4.
12. (a) What is meant by the hydrolysis of a salt? (b) What classes of salts react with water to produce solutions that are not neutral? (c) What happens to the ions of the salt of a strong base and strong acid when the salt is dissolved in water?
*13. When sodium acetate is dissolved in water, (a) what ion chemically reacts with the water? (b) what ion is hydrated? (c) Write the equation for the reaction in (a). (d) Why is the sodium acetate solution basic?

25-7 Hydrolysis of the Salt of a Weak Base and Strong Acid

When dissolved in water, salts of a weak base and a strong acid form acid solutions. Ammonium chloride, NH_4Cl, is an example of such a salt.

When NH_4Cl is dissolved in water, the following ions exist in the water: NH_4^+, Cl^-, H^+, and OH^-. (The last two ions are, of course, from the ionization of the water.) There is no attraction between the hydrogen ions, H^+, and the chloride ions, Cl^-, from the salt, since HCl is a strong acid that ionizes almost completely. However, attractions do exist between ammonium ions and the polar water molecules. The ammonium ion donates a proton to the negative oxygen end of the water molecule to produce a hydronium ion:

$$NH_4^+ + H_2O \rightleftharpoons H_3O^+ + NH_3 \qquad \textbf{(Eq. 9)}$$

The excess hydronium ions make the solution acid. See Figure 25-6.

The hydrolysis constant for Equation 9 is given by the expression:

$$\frac{[NH_3][H_3O^+]}{[NH_4^+]} = K_h$$

Figure 25-6

Ammonium chloride, NH_4Cl, is the salt of a strong acid and weak base. Its crystals dissolve in water to produce a solution with an acid pH.

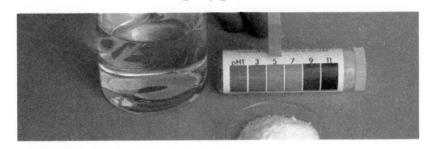

25-8 Hydrolysis of the Salt of a Weak Base and Weak Acid

Salts derived from bases and acids that are both weak produce solutions that may be acid, basic, or neutral, depending upon how strongly the ions of the salt are hydrolyzed. For example, ammonium carbonate, $(NH_4)_2CO_3$, is the salt of a weak base and a weak acid. The hydrolysis reactions for each of the ions in this salt are

$$NH_4^+ + H_2O \rightleftharpoons NH_3 + H_3O^+ \qquad \textbf{(Eq. 10)}$$

$$CO_3^{2-} + H_2O \rightleftharpoons HCO_3^- + OH^- \qquad \textbf{(Eq. 11)}$$

Laboratory measurements show that the relative number of OH^- ions produced by the second reaction happen to be greater than the relative number of H_3O^+ ions produced by the first reaction. Hence, water solutions of this salt are slightly basic. Ammonium acetate, $NH_4C_2H_3O_2$, dissolves in water to make a neutral solution, while an aqueous solution of ammonium sulfite, $(NH_4)_2SO_3$, is acidic.

25-9   Choice of Indicators

In beginning chemistry, indicators are usually used to signal when enough standard solution has been added to cause the acid and base to react completely with one another. When exactly the right amount of standard solution has been added, chemists say that the end point or equivalence point of the neutralization reaction has been reached.

Titrations can be classified according to the strengths of the acids and bases. We list here three types of titrations.

THREE TYPES OF TITRATIONS

Titration between:

Type 1: Strong acid and strong base
Type 2: Strong acid and weak base
Type 3: Weak acid and strong base

In choosing an indicator for a titration, we want one that will change color when enough of the one substance (acid or base) has been added to use up exactly all of the other. When this exact equivalence point has been reached, the solution will be neutral (pH = 7) if the titration is of type 1. However, if the titration is of type 2, a hydrolysis reaction will make the solution at the equivalence point slightly acidic. If the titration is of type 3, a hydrolysis reaction will make the solution at the equivalence point slightly basic.

In type 1 titrations, where both acid and base are strong, practically any indicator can be used. This is because the addition of *one* drop of either reagent will change the pH at the equivalence point by about 6 units. For type 2 titrations, we need an indicator, such as methyl orange, which will change its color in the acid region. (Methyl orange changes color between pH of 3.1 and 4.4.) In type 3 titrations, we should use an indicator that changes color at a basic pH. Phenolphthalein is suitable for this purpose since it changes color between a pH of 8.3 and 10.0.

Questions for Sections 25-7 through 25-9

14. (a) Write the equation for the hydrolysis that takes place when ammonium chloride is dissolved in water. (b) Why is the solution acid? (c) Write the hydrolysis constant expression for the equation in *(a)*.
15. (a) Solutions of weak acid-weak base salts vary in their reactions to litmus. Some are acid, some are basic, and some are neutral. Why? In terms of the strengths of the acid and base produced in hydrolysis, why is a solution of (b) ammonium carbonate basic? (c) ammonium acetate neutral? (d) ammonium sulfite acid?
*16. If litmus, methyl orange, and phenolphthalein are made available, what indicator would you use in the titration of (a) acetic acid by sodium hydroxide? (b) ammonia solution by hydrochloric acid? (c) sodium hydroxide by hydrochloric acid?

25-10   Gram Equivalent Masses

A special quantity, the gram equivalent mass, is used in calculating acid-base titrations. **Gram equivalent masses** are useful because the quantity is defined so that in a particular chemical reaction, 1 gram equivalent mass of one reactant will completely react with 1 gram equivalent mass of another reactant. This simple 1 to 1 correspondence always holds for gram equivalent masses. When masses are expressed in moles, a 1 to 1 relationship sometimes holds, but often does not. For example, 1 mole of NaOH will neutralize 1 mole of HCl but it will neutralize only ½ mole of H_2SO_4. The gram equivalent mass relationship is thus a simpler one than the mole relationship, and it makes acid-base calculations easier.

We now define the gram equivalent mass for both acids and bases.

Gram equivalent mass of an acid. The gram equivalent mass of an acid is the mass in grams of 1 mole of the acid divided by the number of protons donated by each molecule of the acid during neutralization.

Below is the derivation of the gram equivalent masses of three acids when they transfer *all* their protons in a neutralization reaction.

Acid	Number of protons donated	Mass in grams of one mole	Gram equivalent mass
HCl	1	36.5 g	36.5 g ÷ 1 = 36.5 g
H_2SO_4	2	98 g	98 g ÷ 2 = 49 g
H_3PO_4	3	98 g	98 g ÷ 3 = 32.7 g

(Note that if an acid, such as H_2SO_4 or H_3PO_4, transfers only one proton in its reaction with a base, its gram equivalent mass is the same as the mass of one mole.)

Gram equivalent mass of a base: The gram equivalent mass of a base is the mass in grams of 1 mole of the base divided by the number of protons accepted by each formula unit of the base during neutralization.

Below is the derivation of the gram equivalent masses of three bases.

Base	Number of protons accepted	Mass in grams of one mole	Gram equivalent mass
NaOH	1	40 g	40 g ÷ 1 = 40 g
KOH	1	56 g	56 g ÷ 1 = 56 g
$Mg(OH)_2$	2	58 g	58 g ÷ 2 = 29 g

25-11   Normality

Calculations for acid-base titrations are easier if concentrations are expressed in a unit called normality. Normality is a unit based on gram equivalent masses. Normality and molarity are very similar units. In fact, the normality and molarity of many solutions are the same. For example, a hydrochloric acid solution whose concentration is 0.15 molar is also 0.15 normal. The capital letter N is used as an abbreviation for normal. Thus, 0.15 N means 0.15 normal.

Normality. The normality of a solution is the number of gram equivalent masses of solute dissolved in 1 liter of solution.

$$\text{normality} = \frac{\left(\begin{array}{c}\text{number of gram equivalent}\\ \text{masses of solute}\end{array}\right)}{\text{volume of solution in liters}}$$

Since molarity is the number of *moles* of solute dissolved in 1 liter of solution, the molar and normal concentrations of a solution will be the same whenever 1 mole of a substance equals 1 gram equivalent mass of the substance.

SAMPLE PROBLEM

A solution whose volume is 500 mL is made by dissolving 98 grams of H_2SO_4 in water. What is the normal concentration of this solution?

Solution. Assume that the sulfuric acid donates 2 protons in the neutralization reaction being considered. Therefore, 1 gram equivalent mass of H_2SO_4 is the mass in grams of 1 mole divided by 2:

$$1 \text{ gram equivalent mass } H_2SO_4 = \frac{\left(\begin{array}{c}\text{mass in grams of}\\ 1 \text{ mole } H_2SO_4\end{array}\right)}{2}$$

$$= \frac{98 \text{ grams}}{2}$$

$$= 49 \text{ grams}$$

In making up the solution, 98 grams H_2SO_4, or 2.0 gram equivalent masses of H_2SO_4 were dissolved in 500 mL, or 0.500 liters, of solution. Therefore, the normality of the solution is:

$$\text{normality} = \frac{\text{number of gram equivalent masses}}{\text{volume of solution in liters}}$$

$$= 2.0 \text{ gram eq.}/0.500 \text{ liters}$$

$$= 4.0 \text{ gram eq.}/\text{liter}$$

$$= 4.0 \text{ normal, or } 4.0 \ N$$

17. (a) What numerical relationship exists between the number of gram equivalent masses of acid and base that completely react with one another? (b) How is the gram equivalent mass of an acid determined? (c) The molar mass of sulfuric acid is 98 g. What is its gram equivalent mass when it reacts with NaOH to form Na_2SO_4?

18. (a) How is the gram equivalent mass of a base determined? Compare gram molecular mass with the gram equivalent mass for each of the following: (b) NaOH, (c) $Ca(OH)_2$, (d) $Al(OH)_3$. (Assume that all hydroxide groups are changed to water.)

19. (a) Define *normality*. (b) Under what circumstances will the normality and molarity of a solution be the same?

*20. In the reaction $H_2SO_4 + 2NaOH \rightarrow Na_2SO_4 + 2H_2O$ what is the normality of the sulfuric acid if it contains 24.5 g of solute in 200 mL of solution?

21. For the reaction $Ca(OH)_2 + 2HCl \rightarrow CaCl_2 + 2H_2O$ what is the normality of the calcium hydroxide solution if it contains 1.48 g of solute in 500 mL of solution?

*22. What mass of sodium hydroxide must be dissolved in 100 mL of solution to make a 3.00 N solution?

23. For the reaction $Ba(OH)_2 + 2HNO_3 \rightarrow Ba(NO_3)_2 + 2H_2O$, what mass of barium hydroxide must be dissolved in 200 mL of solution to make a solution that is 0.200 N?

25-12 Usefulness of Normal Concentrations in Titrations

In the Sample Problem 2 of Section 25-3, a formula was used that had the form:

$$M_a V_a = p M_b V_b \tag{Eq. 12}$$

p is the mole factor

In Equation 12, the letter p is derived from the balanced equation and expresses the mole relationship between acid and base in a neutralization reaction. For Sample Problem 2 in Section 25-3, p was equal to 2 because it required twice as many moles of acid to neutralize a given number of moles of base. Whereas 2 moles of an acid may be needed to neutralize 1 mole of a base, it is always true that 1 gram equivalent mass of an acid will exactly neutralize 1 gram equivalent mass of a base. This 1 to 1 correspondence follows from the definitions of the gram equivalent masses of acids and bases. In neutralization reactions,

equal numbers of gram equivalent masses of acid and base will have consumed each other when complete neutralization has occurred.

At neutralization:

$$\begin{pmatrix} \text{Number of} \\ \text{gram equivalent} \\ \text{masses of acid} \end{pmatrix} = \begin{pmatrix} \text{Number of} \\ \text{gram equivalent} \\ \text{masses of base} \end{pmatrix} \quad \textbf{(Eq. 13)}$$

However, the product:

(normality of solution) × (volume of solution in liters)

equals the number of gram equivalent masses of acid or base in the stated volume of the solution. We abbreviate the product as $N_a V_a$ for the acid, and $N_b V_b$ for the base. Then, Equation 13 can be written:

$$N_a V_a = N_b V_b \quad \textbf{(Eq. 14)}$$

Equation 14 should be compared with Equation 12 at the beginning of this section. Note that by using normal concentrations instead of molar concentrations, p, the mole factor, has been eliminated. This simplification is often used by chemists and technicians working in medical laboratories who want to make their work easier.

SAMPLE PROBLEM

A 240-mL solution of standard 0.200 N HCl completely neutralizes a 180-mL solution of NaOH of unknown concentration. What is the normal concentration of the NaOH solution?

Solution. For this problem,

$$N_a = 0.200 \ N$$
$$V_a = 0.240 \ \text{L}$$
$$N_b = ?$$
$$V_b = 0.180 \ \text{L}$$

Substituting these values into Equation 14 of this section:

$$N_a V_a = N_b V_b \quad \textbf{(Eq. 14)}$$

$$(0.200 \ \text{N}) \ (0.240 \ \text{L}) = N_b \ (0.180 \ \text{L})$$

$$N_b = \frac{(0.200 \ \text{N}) \ (0.240 \ \text{L})}{(0.180 \ \text{L})}$$

$$= 0.267 \ N$$

The normality of the NaOH solution is 0.267 N.

24. (a) What information is obtained by multiplying the normality of a solution by its volume in liters? (b) What relationship exists between the number of moles of sulfuric acid and sodium hydroxide that completely react to form sodium sulfate and water? (c) What relationship exists between the gram equivalent masses of these substances in this same reaction?

*25. If only 2.00 mL of a solution of hydrochloric acid are required to neutralize 6.00 mL of a 0.100 N solution of $Ba(OH)_2$, what is the normality of the acid?

26. What is the normality of a solution of NaOH if 36.0 mL are required to completely neutralize 27.0 mL of a 0.300 N solution of HCl?

CAN YOU EXPLAIN THIS?

CIRCUIT DRAWING

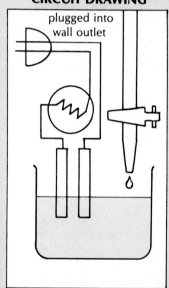

plugged into wall outlet

(A)

(B)

(A) The beaker contains a solution of barium hydroxide, $Ba(OH)_2$, dissolved in water. The burette contains sulfuric acid diluted with water. **(B)** When the sulfuric acid is added to the beaker from the burette, a white precipitate forms.

As more of the acid is run into the beaker, the light gets dimmer and finally goes out. As still more of the acid is run into the beaker, the bulb begins to light up again, finally reaching its original brightness.

1. What kind of substance is barium hydroxide if the light bulb lights when the electrodes are dipped into its aqueous solution? (Write an equation showing what happens when solid $Ba(OH)_2$ is added to water.)

2. As more and more acid is added to the beaker, why does the bulb at first get dimmer, then go out, and finally light up again to its original brightness?

1. Fairly accurate measurements of pH can be made by the pH meter. However, less accurate ones, made by acid-base indicators, can be quite useful.
2. Most acid-base indicators are weak acids in which the negative ion has a color different from that of the neutral molecule.
3. Adding acid to the weak acid indicator displaces the ionization equilibrium to the left, emphasizing the color of the neutral molecule. Adding base displaces the equilibrium to the right, producing the anion color.
4. In an acid-base neutralization, all of the hydronium ions of the acid are combined with all of the hydroxide ions of the base.
5. In an acid-base titration, a standard solution of one of the reactants is used to determine the unknown concentration of the other reactant.
6. Salts may be classified according to the bases and acids from which they are derived. The four classes are: strong acid-strong base, strong acid-weak base, weak acid-strong base, and weak acid-weak base.
7. Except for the strong acid-strong base type, salts are hydrolyzed in water solution to produce a neutral, acid, or basic reaction. This reaction depends upon the relative strengths of the acid and base involved.
8. In salt hydrolysis, the reaction may be one in which the positive ion of the salt forms a weak base or where the negative ion of the salt forms a weak acid (or both).
9. Hydrolysis constants can be derived from hydrolysis equations. The value of the constant indicates the relative extent of the hydrolysis.
10. The nature of the indicator used in an acid-base titration depends upon the kind of salt produced. For example, if the salt is of the type that produces a basic reaction in solution, an indicator such as phenolphthalein, which changes color at a pH in the basic region, is used.
11. The gram equivalent mass of an acid is obtained by dividing the molar mass by the number of protons lost by one molecule of the acid in the reaction being considered.
12. The gram equivalent mass of a base is obtained by dividing the molar mass by the number of protons gained by one molecule of the base in the reaction being considered.
13. The normality of a solution is equal to the number of gram equivalent masses of solute per liter of solution.
14. In any acid-base titration, the product of the normality and volume of the acid is equal to the product of the normality and volume of the base. Volume units must be the same.

TERMS YOU SHOULD KNOW

acid-base titration	gram equivalent mass of	gram equivalent mass of
hydrolysis	an acid	a base
gram equivalent mass	standard solution	normality

Section 25-1

1. Using the formula HIn for a weak acid indicator, explain, in terms of equilibrium displacement, why addition of acid gives the indicator the color of the neutral molecule, while addition of base produces the anion color.

2. The following table shows the pH ranges and colors for various indicators:

Indicator	Acid Color	Basic Color	pH Range Over Which the Color Changes from the Acid Color to Basic Color
methyl red	red	yellow	4.8 to 6.2
thymol blue	yellow	blue	8.0 to 9.6
alizarin yellow	yellow	red	10.1 to 12.0

What is the approximate pH of a solution that is (a) yellow in methyl red, yellow in thymol blue, and yellow in alizarin yellow? (b) yellow in methyl red, blue in thymol blue, and red in alizarin yellow?

3. What colors are produced in the indicators in question 2 by (a) rain water whose pH is 6.3? (b) 0.1 M ammonia water whose pH is 11.2?

25-2

4. (a) At what point is it accepted that an acid and base have neutralized each other? In what type of neutralization is the final solution found to be (b) acid? (c) basic?

25-3

5. Given an appropriate indicator and a standard solution of KOH, describe how you would determine the unknown concentration of a nitric acid solution.

6. If 25 mL of a 0.10 M NaOH solution are required to neutralize 15 mL of a solution of HCl, (a) what is the molarity of the acid? (b) how many grams of hydrogen chloride are dissolved in the 15 mL of acid?

7. A standard solution of H_2SO_4 has 15.0 g of solute dissolved in 200 mL of solution. It is used to titrate a KOH solution, producing K_2SO_4 as the salt product. What is the molarity of the base if 35.0 mL of it are neutralized by 15.0 mL of the acid?

25-4

8. Classify the following salts according to the bases and acids from which they are derived: (a) $CaCl_2$, (b) $KC_2H_3O_2$, (c) $(NH_4)_2SO_4$, (d) $(NH_4)_2S$, (e) $NaNO_3$.

25-5

9. (a) What is the pH of the solution resulting from a strong acid-strong base neutralization? (b) What types of salts are hydrolyzed by water? (c) What type of salt is hydrolyzed to produce an acid or basic or neutral solution, depending upon the specific salt involved?

25-6

10. (a) When Na_2CO_3 is dissolved in water, the solution shows a small concentration of HCO_3^- ion. Write the equation for the equilibrium reaction that produces this ion. (b) Why is the solution basic?

11. The following reaction takes place in a solution of NaHS:
$$HS^- + H_2O \rightleftharpoons H_2S + OH^-$$
The K_h for this reaction is 9.1×10^{-8}. (a) Write the hydrolysis constant expression for this reaction. (b) What is the $[OH^-]$ of a 0.10 M solution of NaHS? (c) What is the $[H^+]$? (d) What is the pH?

12. (a) Write the hydrolysis constant expression for the hydrolysis of sodium acetate: $C_2H_3O_2^- + H_2O \rightleftharpoons HC_2H_3O_2 + OH^-$
(b) Show that this expression is equal to the ion-product of water expression divided by the ionization constant expression for acetic acid. (c) The ion-product of water is 1.0×10^{-14}, and the ionization

constant of acetic acid is 1.8×10^{-5}. What is the hydrolysis constant for the hydrolysis of acetate ion?

13. (a) Calculate the $[OH^-]$ of a $0.10\,M$ solution of sodium acetate, assuming that the K_h of the acetate ion hydrolysis is 5.6×10^{-10}. (b) What is the $[H^+]$? (c) What is the pH?

25-7   14. (a) Write the equation for the hydrolysis of ammonium chloride. (b) Write the hydrolysis constant expression for this reaction. (c) If $K_h = 5.6 \times 10^{-10}$, what is the $[H_3O^+]$ of a $0.40\,M$ solution of NH_4Cl? (d) What is the pH of this solution?

15. (a) A number of weak base-weak acid salts are tested by indicators. What reactions to these indicators may be expected from such salts? (b) Why does a solution of ammonium cyanide (NH_4CN) show a basic reaction? (c) Why does a solution of NH_4F show an acid reaction? (d) The ionization constant of formic acid (HCOOH) is 1.8×10^{-4}. The K_b for ammonia is 1.8×10^{-5}. Will a solution of ammonium formate be acid or basic? Explain.

25-9   16. What indicator could be used effectively in the titration of (a) nitrous acid ($K_a = 4.5 \times 10^{-4}$) by potassium hydroxide? (b) sulfuric acid by ammonia solution? (c) potassium hydroxide by sulfuric acid?

25-10   17. Calculate the gram equivalent mass of the acid in each of the following reactions:
(a) $H_2SO_4 + NaOH \rightarrow NaHSO_4 + H_2O$
(b) $H_3PO_4 + 2KOH \rightarrow K_2HPO_4 + 2H_2O$

18. Calculate the gram equivalent mass of the base in each of the following reactions:
(a) $Bi(OH)_3 + HCl \rightarrow Bi(OH)_2Cl + H_2O$
(b) $Pb(OH)_2 + HNO_3 \rightarrow Pb(OH)NO_3 + H_2O$

25-11   19. For the reaction $H_2SO_4 + 2KOH \rightarrow K_2SO_4 + 2H_2O$, what is the normality of the (a) sulfuric acid, if it contains 10.0 g of H_2SO_4 dissolved in 300 mL of solution? (b) potassium hydroxide solution, if it contains 15.0 g of KOH in 200 mL of solution?

25-12   20. What is the normality of a calcium hydroxide solution if 30.0 mL are completely neutralized by 10.0 mL of a $0.020\,N$ HCl solution?

FOR FURTHER THOUGHT

25-1   1. A student is trying to determine the approximate pH of a solution. He tests the solution with red litmus paper, and it remains red. He tests the solution with blue litmus paper, and it remains blue. He decides that litmus is not sensitive enough, so he tries both methyl orange and phenolphthalein.
(a) What observations would you expect him to make?
(b) What additional information, if any, will these observations provide? Explain.

25-5   2. (a) Which of the following equations represent reactions that occur to a measurable extent?
(1) $NaC_2H_3O_2\,(s) + H_2O\,(l) \rightarrow HC_2H_3O_2\,(aq)\,Na^+\,(aq) + OH^-\,(aq)$
(2) $NaCl\,(s) + H_2O\,(l) \rightarrow HCl\,(aq) + Na^+\,(aq) + OH^-\,(aq)$
(3) $NH_4Cl(s) + H_2O\,(l) \rightarrow NH_3\,(aq) + H_3O^+\,(aq) + Cl^-\,(aq)$
(b) What observations could be made to support your answers?

Cumulative Review

Section

4-9   **1.** A mass of water is heated from 20.0°C to 70.0°C. During this process 41800 joules of heat is added to the water. How much water was heated?

6-3   **2.** A quantity of helium gas under a pressure of 600 mm Hg has a volume of 400 mL. (a) What will be its volume at 900 mm Hg, if the temperature does not change? (b) At what pressure will its volume be 300 mL, again at the same temperature?

6-5   **3.** A quantity of oxygen gas occupies a volume of 35.0 liters at 77°C. At what temperature will its volume to 30.0 liters, at constant pressure?

6-6   **4.** At a temperature of 150°C, a gas exerts a pressure of 800 mm Hg. What pressure will the gas exert at 127°C, assuming the volume of the gas doesn't change?

6-8   **5.** When measured at STP, a mass of nitrogen gas has a volume of 15 liters. Determine its volume at 27°C and 2.0 atmospheres pressure.

6-16   **6.** (a) Define the term *mole*. (b) Why is 22.4 liters at STP called the molar volume of a gas? (c) How many oxygen molecules are there in 22.4 liters of oxygen gas at STP?

7-7   **7.** What mass of steam at 100°C will release 1.43×10^5 calories of heat when the vapor is condensed to liquid water at 100°C and 1.0 atm?

7-10   **8.** How much heat, in joules, is released when 40 grams of water at 0°C turns into ice at the same temperature?

8-7   **9.** Write Stock system names for each of the following: (a) N_2O_5 (b) HgS (c) P_2O_3 (d) CCl_4 (e) $Fe_2(SO_4)_3$ (f) $CuNO_3$

9-5   **10.** (a) What is the meaning of *gram atomic mass*? Use the element sulfur as an example in your answer. (b) What is the meaning of *gram formula mass*? Use the compound water as an example in your answer.

9-8   **11.** Determine the percentage composition of nitrogen dioxide, NO_2.

9-9   **12.** A certain hydrocarbon is made up of 85.6% C and 14.3% H. Its molecular mass is 56.1 u. (a) Find its empirical formula. (b) What is its formula?

11-2   **13.** What mass of hydrogen is formed when 72.0 g HCl reacts with zinc in the following reaction: $Zn(s) + 2HCl(aq) \rightarrow ZnCl_2(aq) + H_2(g)$?

11-3   **14.** At STP, 2.0 L of a gaseous element has a mass of 2.86 g. What is its molecular mass?

11-4   **15.** If 50.0 L of butane gas, C_4H_{10}, burns in oxygen gas under standard conditions, what volume of CO_2 will form? The other product of the reaction is H_2O. (a) Write the balanced equation. (b) Find the answer.

11-5   **16.** In the reaction $2HgO(s) \rightarrow 2Hg(s) + O_2(g)$, what mass of HgO is decomposed when 1000 mL of O_2 are produced at STP?

13-7   **17.** How did the wave-mechanical model of the atom modify and improve upon the Bohr model?

14-11   **18.** What happens to the energy that is used in changing liquid water to oxygen gas and hydrogen gas? How can this energy be recovered?

15-8   **19.** How does hydrogen bonding explain the fact that water at 0°C has a lower density than water at 4°C?

16-12   **20.** In the periodic table, where are each of the following situated: (a) the most active metals (b) most active nonmetals (c) the noble gases (d) the transition metals.

Cumulative Review

Section

17-10   **21.** Use the solubility curve for $KClO_3$ on page 343 to help answer the following. (a) Suppose 20 g of $KClO_3$ are dissolved in 50 g of water at 100°C, and the solution is then cooled. At what temperature is the solution saturated? (b) At 0°C, how much solute will settle out? (c) At 0°C, is the solution dilute or concentrated? Is it saturated or unsaturated?

17-15   **22.** What is the mass of H_2SO_4 in 50.0 mL of a 60% solution that has a density of 1.50 g/mL?

17-17   **23.** A solution of sodium oxalate, $Na_2C_2O_4$, contains 33.5 g of solute in 100 mL of solution. What is the molarity of the solution?

17-18   **24.** A water solution of glucose, $C_6H_{12}O_6$, contains 0.0900 g of solute in 5.00 g of water. What is the molality of the solution?

18-3   **25.** If the outside temperature is 0°C, and salt is spread on a layer of ice on the pavement, the ice will melt. Explain.

21-10   **26.** Consider the equilibrium in the Haber reaction:
$$N_2(g) + 3H_2(g) \rightleftharpoons 2NH_3(g) + \text{heat}$$
(a) Explain the effect of increased pressure on the equilibrium point. (b) Explain the effect of increased temperature on the equilibrium point. (c) How does increased temperature affect the rates of the forward and backward reactions? (d) What is the value of the equilibrium constant at 700 K, if the following concentrations exist at equilibrium: $[NH_3] = 0.600\ M$; $[N_2] = 0.700\ M$; $[H_2] = 1.10\ M$.

23-6   **27.** What is the molar concentration of hydrogen ions in a solution of H_2SO_4 in which there is 4.9 g of H_2SO_4 in 250 mL of solution?

23-7   **28.** Write molecular and ionic equations for the reaction of (a) Al + dilute H_2SO_4 and (b) Mg and HCl in water solution. Use the hydronium ion in the ionic equations.

24-3   **29.** What is the formula of the conjugate base of (a) HNO_2 (b) HS^- (c) $H_2AsO_4^-$ (d) NH_4^+ (e) HOBr? (f) Under what condition may NH_3 act as a Brønsted acid? Write the formula of the conjugate base.

24-6   **30.** (a) At 25°C, what are the concentrations of hydrogen ions and hydroxide ions in a 0.020 M solution of HCl? (b) What is the pH of the solution? (c) What is its pOH?

25-3   **31.** How many grams of solute are there in 35.0 mL of a solution of $Ca(OH)_2$ that can be completely neutralized by 15.0 mL of 0.100 M H_2SO_4?

25-6   **32.** If acetic acid and sodium hydroxide solutions are reacted in equivalent quantities, what color will the resulting solution impart to a solution of (a) phenolphthalein (b) litmus (c) methyl orange?

UNIT 8

Redox and Electrochemistry

The lightning we see strike at Waterton Lakes National Park in British Columbia results from the rapid discharge of electrical energy. This energy is stored in clouds, upon which charged particles have accumulated. We know that atoms consist of charged particles. Therefore it should come as no surprise to learn that underlying all chemical change is the absorption or release of electrical energy.

In this unit we will examine how charges shift within and between atoms as a chemical reaction proceeds. Then we will go on to study both the process of electrolysis—in which an electrical current brings about a chemical change—and its converse, as in the operation of a battery—in which a chemical reaction generates electricity. Thus, the interconnection of chemical change and electrical energy is evident.

CHAPTER 26

Oxidation-Reduction Reactions

Objectives

When you have completed this chapter, you will be able to:
- Apply rules for assigning oxidation numbers to elements in various states.
- Analyze oxidation-reduction reactions.
- Balance redox equations by the oxidation-number method.
- Solve problems involving redox reagents.

26-1 Introduction

In the early days of chemistry a substance was said to be oxidized after it reacted with oxygen. The reaction itself was called oxidation. In this sense, a familiar example of oxidation is the rusting of iron. In this reaction, iron in the presence of moisture reacts with oxygen from the air to produce iron oxide (rust). Rust is the result of iron being oxidized. Another example is the burning of a fuel. When coal burns, the oxygen in the air combines with the carbon and hydrogen in the coal to produce water and the oxides of carbon. The burning of coal is an oxidation reaction.

Today, the term oxidation is used in the same sense, but it is also used in a second sense that gives the term a broader meaning. Later in

Figure 26-1

When wood burns, the hydrogen in the wood is oxidized to H_2O and the carbon to CO and CO_2.

the chapter, we will get back to the second sense of the term oxidation. First, it is useful to explain what is meant by the oxidation number of an element.

26-2 Oxidation Numbers

The **oxidation number,** or **oxidation state,** of an atom is the charge that the atom is assumed to have in a particular molecule or ion. Certain rules have been developed for determining what the oxidation number of an atom is in any given case. In this section we will gradually put together this set of rules.

We begin with those cases in which atoms actually have a charge as the result of acquiring or losing electrons during chemical combination. The compound NaCl consists of two types of charged atoms, sodium ions (Na^+) with a charge of $1+$, and chloride ions (Cl^-) with a charge of $1-$. The first rule for determining oxidation numbers is that the oxidation number of a monatomic ion is the same as the charge on the ion. Therefore, in NaCl, the oxidation number of sodium is $1+$, and the oxidation number of chlorine is $1-$. Another example is the compound magnesium bromide, $MgBr_2$. This compound is made up of magnesium ions (Mg^{2+}) and bromide ions (Br^-). Therefore, in this compound the oxidation number of magnesium is $2+$ and the oxidation number of bromine is $1-$. Figure 26-2 lists some compounds made up of monatomic ions and gives the oxidation numbers of the elements in each compound.

Figure 26-2

The oxidation numbers of elements appearing in ionic compounds made up of monatomic ions.

Compound	Ions Making Up the Compound	Oxidation Numbers of Elements in the Compound
magnesium bromide, $MgBr_2$	Mg^{2+} Br^-	$2+$ $1-$
sodium sulfide, Na_2S	Na^+ S^{2-}	$1+$ $2-$
aluminum chloride, $AlCl_3$	Al^{3+} Cl^-	$3+$ $1-$

Let us now consider the hydrogen atoms in a diatomic hydrogen molecule, H_2. The electron-dot formula for the molecule reminds us that the electrons in the bond are shared equally between each atom. That is, there is no reason why the electrons in the bond should be nearer one atom than the other, since both atoms are atoms of the same element. Neither hydrogen atom can be said to have gained or lost an electron, or to have acquired a partial charge of any kind. Therefore,

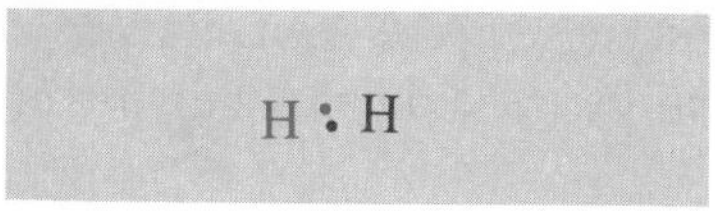

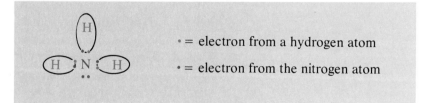

H : H

Figure 26-3

The two electrons in the covalent bond in the diatomic hydrogen molecule are shared equally by each atom. On the average, each electron is as near to the nucleus of one atom as to the nucleus of the other.

the apparent charge of each atom—that is, the oxidation number of hydrogen in H_2—is taken to be zero. See Figure 26-3.

In general, the oxidation number of any element is zero when the atoms of that element are in an elemental state. An atom is in an elemental state when its atoms are not chemically combined with the atoms of another element.

A sodium atom, then, has an oxidation number of zero when we are talking about the pure, uncombined metal, while a sodium atom in the ionic compound NaCl has an oxidation number of 1+. The oxidation number of a chlorine atom is zero when that atom exists in chlorine gas, which is chlorine in its elemental state. However, it has an oxidation number of 1− when the atom exists as a chloride ion, Cl^-, in the ionic compound NaCl.

What are the oxidation numbers of hydrogen and oxygen in the compound H_2O? To answer this question, it is useful to consider an electron-dot formula for water. See Figure 26-4. Since oxygen is highly electronegative, the two bonding electrons from the hydrogen atoms are held closer to the oxygen atom than to the hydrogen atoms. For the purposes of assigning oxidation numbers, the two electrons are treated as though they have been transferred to the oxygen atom. The oxygen atom is assumed to have a charge of 2−, and it therefore has an oxidation number of 2−. Each atom of hydrogen is treated as though it has lost an electron. It is assumed to have a charge of 1+, and it therefore has an oxidation number of 1+.

Figure 26-4

Electron-dot representation of a water molecule. The electrons in the two covalent bonds are shown closer to the nucleus of the oxygen atom than to the nuclei of the hydrogen atoms to indicate the greater electronegativity of the oxygen atom. The oxygen atom thus partially gains two electrons, one from each of the hydrogen atoms. This gives oxygen in water an oxidation number of 2−.

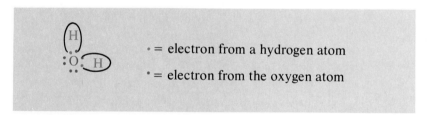

• = electron from a hydrogen atom

• = electron from the oxygen atom

A general rule for assigning oxidation numbers is that in a covalent compound of two elements, the more electronegative element has a negative oxidation number. The other element has a positive oxidation number. For the more electronegative element, we determine the number itself by counting the number of valence electrons being drawn toward one of its atoms. If 3 valence electrons are drawn nearer, the oxidation number of the more electronegative element is 3−. The less electronegative element has a positive oxidation number equal to the number of its valence electrons being drawn away from one of its atoms. We can illustrate this rule with nitrogen and hydrogen in am-

Figure 26-5

Electron-dot representation of an ammonia molecule. The electrons in the three covalent bonds are shown closer to the nucleus of the nitrogen atoms than to the nuclei of the hydrogen atoms in order to indicate the greater electronegativity of nitrogen. The nitrogen atom thus partially gains three electrons, one from each hydrogen atom. This gives nitrogen in ammonia an oxidation number of 3−.

• = electron from a hydrogen atom

• = electron from the nitrogen atom

monia, NH_3. Nitrogen is the more electronegative element. Each valence electron from the 3 hydrogen atoms is drawn nearer to the nitrogen atom, as shown in Figure 26-5. The oxidation number of nitrogen in ammonia is, therefore, $3-$. Since each hydrogen atom is partially losing one electron, the oxidation number of hydrogen in ammonia is $1+$.

26-3 Oxidation Numbers of Hydrogen and Oxygen

It is useful to consider in some detail the oxidation numbers of oxygen and hydrogen when these elements appear in compounds. In almost all cases, oxygen, a very electronegative element, draws 2 valence electrons from a bonding element nearer to itself, as is the case in H_2O. This leads to the following generalization. The oxidation number of oxygen in compounds is usually $2-$. An exception occurs in compounds called peroxides. In peroxides, two oxygen atoms are bonded to each other as well as to the atoms of another element. The electrons that form a covalent bond between the two oxygen atoms are shared equally. Valence electrons from the atoms of the other element are drawn closer to the oxygen atoms, one electron for each oxygen atom, to form a second covalent bond to each oxygen atom. Therefore, the oxidation number of oxygen in peroxides is $1-$ rather than the usual $2-$. See Figure 26-6.

Figure 26-6

Electron-dot representation of a hydrogen peroxide molecule.
In the oxygen-oxygen covalent bond, the electrons are shared equally. The electrons in the two hydrogen-oxygen covalent bonds are shown closer to the oxygen atom to indicate the greater electronegativity of oxygen. Each oxygen atom partially gains one electron. This gives oxygen in hydrogen peroxide an oxidation number of $1-$.

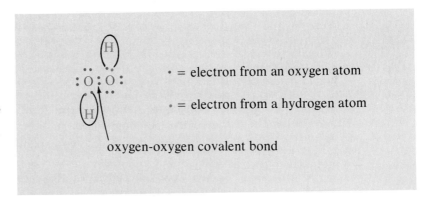

• = electron from an oxygen atom

· = electron from a hydrogen atom

oxygen-oxygen covalent bond

As for hydrogen, its oxidation number in compounds is almost always $1+$ because it usually combines with elements that are more electronegative than it is. It, therefore, usually partially loses its 1 valence electron. An exception to this rule occurs in compounds called hydrides. In a hydride, hydrogen is bonded to a metal that is even *less* electronegative than hydrogen. The less electronegative metal partially loses its valence electron to the hydrogen. This gives the hydrogen atom an apparent charge, or oxidation number, of $1-$ rather than its usual $1+$.

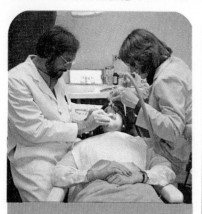

Dentist

Dentistry is a career that requires a good understanding of the basic sciences, including chemistry. The person who is "all thumbs" should look to some other career, since dentistry requires good manual dexterity.

To be a dentist, a person must have two years of college training before being admitted to an accredited school of dentistry. Many people complete a full four-year program at a college or university before going on to dental school. At the dental school, four years of training are required for graduation. The graduate must then be licensed by the licensing board of the state in which he or she is going to practice.

If a person wants to specialize in a branch of dentistry, such as oral surgery or orthodontics, even more education is required.

SAMPLE PROBLEM 1

Give the oxidation numbers of each element in the following equation:

$$2H_2 + O_2 \longrightarrow 2H_2O$$

Solution. The oxidation numbers are written below each element.

$$2H_2 + O_2 \longrightarrow 2H_2O$$

$$\begin{array}{ccc} 0 & 0 & 1+ \ 2- \end{array}$$

Explanation: Hydrogen and oxygen on the left side of the equation are in the elemental state. That is, they are not combined in compounds. Therefore, their oxidation numbers are zero. In water, hydrogen and oxygen have the oxidation numbers they usually have in compounds, 1+ and 2−, respectively.

SAMPLE PROBLEM 2

Give the oxidation numbers of each element in the following equation:

$$Zn + CuCl_2 \longrightarrow Cu + ZnCl_2$$

Solution.

$$Zn + CuCl_2 \longrightarrow Cu + ZnCl_2$$

$$\begin{array}{cccccc} 0 & 2+ & 1- & 0 & 2+ & 1- \end{array}$$

Explanation: Zn and Cu are in the elemental state. Their oxidation numbers are, therefore, zero. $CuCl_2$ and $ZnCl_2$ are compounds made up of the monatomic ions Cu^{2+}, Cl^-, and Zn^{2+}. The oxidation numbers of the elements in these compounds is the same as the ionic charges.

Questions for Sections 26-1 through 26-3

1. (a) Define *oxidation number* (oxidation state). (b) What is the relationship between the charge on a monatomic ion and its oxidation number? (c) Indicate the oxidation state of each of the following: potassium ion, aluminum ion, calcium ion, sulfide ion, bromide ion, chloride ion.
2. In terms of shared electrons, explain why the oxidation number of (a) each hydrogen atom in H_2 is zero, (b) each hydrogen atom in water is 1+, (c) the oxygen atom in water is 2−.
3. (a) Briefly state the general rule for assigning oxidation numbers to the elements in a two-element (binary) covalent compound. (b) Apply this rule to the nitrogen and hydrogen in ammonia.

4. (a) What is the oxidation number of magnesium both before and after reaction in the following reaction?
$$2Mg + O_2 \rightarrow 2MgO$$
(b) What is the oxidation number of iron both before and after reaction in the following reaction?
$$4Fe + 3O_2 \rightarrow 2Fe_2O_3$$

5. (a) Why is the oxidation number of oxygen in its compounds usually 2−? (b) Why is it 1− in peroxides?

6. (a) Why is the oxidation state of hydrogen in its compounds usually 1+? (b) Why is it 1− in hydrides?

*7. For the following equations, indicate the initial and final oxidation states of each element:
(a) $4Al + 3O_2 \rightarrow 2Al_2O_3$
(b) $Fe + SnCl_2 \rightarrow FeCl_2 + Sn$
(c) $2Na + Br_2 \rightarrow 2NaBr$

26-4   Sum of Oxidation Numbers in a Compound

In every compound in the sample problems of the preceding section, the sum of the oxidation numbers of all the atoms in the compound is zero. In $ZnCl_2$, for example, there is one zinc atom with an oxidation number of 2+ and two chlorine atoms, each with an oxidation number of 1−. The total oxidation number of the two chlorine atoms is 2−. The sum of 2+ and 2− is zero. This is to be expected, since oxidation numbers are equivalent to electric charges, and every compound as a whole is electrically neutral.

A general rule is that the algebraic sum of the oxidation numbers of all the atoms in a compound must be zero. In polyatomic ions, the algebraic sum of the oxidation numbers must equal the charge of the ion. As we will see in the next section, these rules usually enable us to assign oxidation numbers to any atom in any compound or ion.

26-5   Elements with Varying Oxidation Numbers

In the compounds of chlorine, oxidation numbers of 1−, 1+, 3+, 4+, and 5+ are found.

*The answers to questions marked with an asterisk are given in the back of the book.

The oxidation numbers of hydrogen and oxygen are fixed. In all compounds except hydrides, the oxidation number of hydrogen is 1+. In hydrides, it is 1−. In all compounds except peroxides, the oxidation number of oxygen is 2−. In peroxides, it is 1−. There are, however, some elements whose oxidation numbers can vary, even in combination with the same element. In Section 8-7, for example, we saw that nitrogen has a different oxidation number in each of its five oxides. In Section 8-10 we saw that chlorine has a different oxidation number in each of its four polyatomic ions containing oxygen.

To determine the oxidation numbers of such elements in any given compound, we apply the rules of Section 26-4. We add the known oxidation numbers of the other atoms in the compound and then find the unknown oxidation number by subtraction. Sample Problem 1 shows how this is done.

SAMPLE PROBLEM 1

What is the oxidation number of sulfur in H_2SO_4?

Solution. The oxidation number of hydrogen in its compounds is $1+$. (Hydrides are an exception that does not apply here.) The oxidation number of oxygen in its compounds is $2-$. (Peroxides are an exception that does not apply here.) To find the oxidation number of sulfur, we apply the rule that the sum of the negative and positive oxidation numbers for all atoms in the formula of a neutral compound must equal zero.

Since there are two hydrogen atoms in the formula, the sum of the oxidation numbers for both hydrogen atoms is $2+$. Since there are four oxygen atoms, the sum of the oxidation numbers for the oxygen atoms is $8-$. Therefore, the oxidation number of sulfur must be $6+$ if all three numbers are to add up to zero. The above reasoning is summarized in Figure 26-7.

Figure 26-7

Determining the oxidation number of sulfur in H_2SO_4. The letter x *is* used in place of the oxidation number of sulfur. The value of x is determined by applying the following rule: *The sum of the positive and negative oxidation numbers of all atoms in the formula of a neutral compound must equal 0.*

	Hydrogen	Sulfur	Oxygen
Oxidation number:	1+	x	2−
Number of atoms indicated in the formula H_2SO_4:	2	1	4
Product: (Total of the oxidation numbers for all atoms indicated in the formula)	2+	x	8−
Applying the rule:	(2+) +	(x) +	(8−) = 0
			x = 6+

In polyatomic ions, the algebraic sum of all positive and negative oxidation numbers for all atoms in the formula must equal the charge on the ion. Sample Problem 2 illustrates the application of this rule.

SAMPLE PROBLEM 2

What is the oxidation number of chromium, Cr, in the dichromate ion, $Cr_2O_7^{2-}$?

Solution. We let the letter x represent the oxidation number of chromium, and we apply the rule that the sum of the positive and negative oxidation numbers for all atoms in the formula must equal the charge on the ion.

	Chromium	Oxygen
Oxidation number:	x	2–
Number of atoms indicated in the formula $Cr_2O_7^{2-}$:	2	7
Product: (Total of the oxidation numbers of all atoms indicated in the formula)	$2x$	14–

Rule for charged particles: Sum of total = charge on ion

Applying rule:

$$(2x) \quad + \quad (14-) \quad = (2-)$$

$$2x = (2-) - (14-)$$

$$2x = 12+$$

$$x = 6+$$

The oxidation number of chromium in the dichromate ion, $Cr_2O_7^{2-}$, is 6+.

In a compound containing the dichromate ion, the same result is obtained for the oxidation number of chromium. Sample Problem 3 shows how this result is arrived at.

SAMPLE PROBLEM 3

What is the oxidation number of chromium in potassium dichromate, $K_2Cr_2O_7$?

Solution. Potassium in this compound is the monatomic potassium ion, K^+. Its oxidation number is, therefore, the same as the charge on the ion, 1+. The oxidation number of oxygen is, as usual, 2–. To solve the problem, we let the letter x stand for the oxidation number of chromium, and we apply the rule that in a neutral compound the sum of the positive and negative oxidation numbers for all atoms in the formula must equal zero.

	Potassium	Chromium	Oxygen
Oxidation number:	1+	x	2–
Number of atoms indicated in the formula $K_2Cr_2O_7$:	2	2	7
Product: (Total of the oxidation numbers for all atoms indicated in the formula)	2+	$2x$	14–

Rule for neutral cpds.: Sum of total = 0

Applying rule: $(2+) + (2x) + (14-) = 0$

$$2x = 12+$$

$$x = 6+$$

The oxidation number of chromium in potassium dichromate, $K_2Cr_2O_7$, is 6+. Compare this result with the result obtained in Sample Problem 2.

Questions for Sections 26-4 and 26-5

8. (a) What is the general rule that is applied to the sum of the oxidation numbers of the atoms in a compound? (b) Apply this rule to Al_2O_3. (c) How is the sum of the oxidation numbers of the atoms in a polyatomic ion related to the charge on the ion? (d) Explain this using the SO_4^{2-} ion as an example.
*9. What is the oxidation number of (a) the sulfur atom in $CaSO_4$? (b) the nitrogen atom in KNO_3? (c) each sulfur atom in $Na_2S_2O_3$?
10. What is the oxidation number of (a) bromine in the BrO_3^- ion? (b) nitrogen in the NH_4^+ ion? (c) chlorine in the ClO_4^- ion?
11. What is the oxidation number of (a) chlorine in $NaClO$? (b) sulfur in H_2SO_3? (c) arsenic in the AsO_4^{3-} ion?

26-6 Summary of Rules for Finding Oxidation Numbers

Rule 1. The oxidation number of a one-atom ion is the same as the charge on the ion. Example: In NaCl, the oxidation number of sodium is 1+ and the oxidation number of chlorine is 1–, since sodium chloride consists of the monatomic ions Na^+ and Cl^-.

Rule 2. The oxidation number of an element in the elemental state is zero. Example: The oxidation number of hydrogen in an H_2 molecule is zero. The oxidation number of sodium in sodium metal is zero. The oxidation number of chlorine in chlorine gas (Cl_2) is zero.

Rule 3. In a covalent compound of two elements, the more electronegative element is given a negative oxidation number and the other element is given a positive oxidation number.

Rule 4. The oxidation number of oxygen in most of its compounds is $2-$. In peroxides, an exception to the rule, its oxidation number is $1-$.

Rule 5. The oxidation number of hydrogen in most of its compounds is $1+$. In hydrides, an exception to the rule, its oxidation number is $1-$.

Rule 6. In neutral compounds, for all atoms represented by the formula, the sum of the positive oxidation numbers must equal the sum of the negative oxidation numbers. Stated another way, for a neutral compound, the algebraic sum of the positive and negative oxidation numbers of all atoms represented by the formula of the compound must equal zero. Example: The oxidation number of sulfur in sodium sulfite, Na_2SO_3, must be $4+$:

$$Na_2SO_3$$

Oxidation number of one atom in the formula: $\quad (1+) + (x) + (2-)$

Number of atoms in the formula: $\quad\quad 2 \quad\quad 1 \quad\quad 3$

All atoms: $\quad (2+) + (x) + (6-) = 0$

$$x = 4+$$

Rule 7. In a polyatomic ion, the algebraic sum of the positive and negative oxidation numbers of all atoms in the formula must equal the charge on the ion. Example: The oxidation number of sulfur in the sulfite ion, SO_3^{2-}, must be $4+$:

$$SO_3^{2-}$$

Oxidation number of one atom in the formula: $\quad (x) + (2-)$

Oxidation number of all atoms: $\quad (x) + (6-) = 2-$

charge on ion

$$x = 4+$$

It is also helpful to realize that active metals with 1 valence electron (Group 1A elements) have oxidation numbers of $1+$ in their compounds. This statement follows from Rule 1, since the active metals of Group 1A form monatomic ions with a charge of $1+$. Active metals with 2 valence electrons (Group 2A elements) have oxidation numbers of $2+$. These metals form monatomic ions whose charges are $2+$.

*12. For each of the following elements, give the oxidation number of an atom of the element and tell which rule you used to arrive at your answer.
*(a) oxygen in KNO_3, (b) oxygen in O_2, (c) sodium in $NaCl$, (d) sodium in sodium metal, Na, (e) chlorine in $KClO_3$, (f) manganese in the permanganate ion, MnO_4^-, (g) chlorine in Cl_2, (h) hydrogen in H_3PO_4.

26-7   Oxidation and Reduction

Early in the chapter it was stated that the term oxidation is used in two senses. In one sense, oxidation is a reaction in which a substance reacts with oxygen. We now turn our attention to the other sense of the term. In its other sense, oxidation refers to a chemical change in which an element increases its oxidation number. In the reaction of sodium with chlorine, sodium is oxidized in the second sense.

$$2Na + Cl_2 \longrightarrow 2NaCl \qquad \textbf{(Eq. 1)}$$
oxidized

We begin to analyze this reaction by determining the oxidation numbers of each element in the equation. First, look at the reactants, sodium and chlorine. Their oxidation numbers are both zero, because both are elements in the elemental state (Rule 2). The product of the reaction, $NaCl$, is a substance made up of the monatomic ions Na^+ and Cl^-. Therefore, by Rule 1, the oxidation numbers of sodium and chlorine in $NaCl$ are $1+$ and $1-$, respectively. It is useful to write the oxidation numbers under each element in the equation.

$$2Na + Cl_2 \longrightarrow 2NaCl \qquad \textbf{(Eq. 2)}$$
$$\quad 0 \qquad 0 \qquad\quad 1+ \;\; 1-$$

During the reaction, the oxidation number of sodium changes from 0 to $1+$. That is, the oxidation number of sodium increases by 1. The oxidation number of chlorine changes from 0 to $1-$. That is, it decreases by 1. These changes can be indicated on Equation 2 in the following manner:

$$2Na + Cl_2 \longrightarrow 2NaCl \qquad \textbf{(Eq. 3)}$$
$$\quad 0 \qquad 0 \qquad\qquad 1+ \;\; 1-$$
decrease of 1
increase of 1

During a chemical reaction, an increase in oxidation number by one element is always accompanied by a decrease by another. In this case, sodium undergoes an increase in its oxidation number. An increase in oxidation number is said to be an oxidation. **Oxidation** represents a loss of, or decreased hold on, electrons. Thus, sodium, in changing from the pure element to the ion, is oxidized. A decrease in oxidation number is said to be a **reduction.** Reduction represents a gain of, or an increase hold on, electrons. Chlorine, in changing from the pure element to the ion is reduced.

Because *red*uction and *oxi*dation always go together in the same reaction, these reactions are sometimes called **redox** reactions, a name that puts some stress on the fact that both processes must take place at the same time. The two must occur together because one element cannot lose electrons (or undergo a decrease in apparent negative charge) without another element gaining electrons (or undergoing an increase in apparent negative charge).

Two more definitions are useful at this time. (1) The element that undergoes a decrease in its oxidation number is called an **oxidizing agent.** In Equation 3, Cl_2 is an oxidizing agent. Note that the oxidizing agent is the substance that is reduced. (2) The element that undergoes an increase in its oxidation number is called the **reducing agent.** In Equation 3, sodium is the reducing agent. The reducing agent is the substance that is oxidized.

Questions for Section 26-7

13. (a) Define oxidation and reduction in terms of the change in oxidation number. (b) Define oxidation and reduction in terms of the loss or gain of electrons.
14. Use the definitions in question 13 to describe what happens to calcium and bromine in the reaction $Ca + Br_2 \rightarrow CaBr_2$.
15. What name is given to a reaction to indicate that during the reaction both reduction and oxidation are going on together?
16. In terms of the loss and gain of electrons, define (a) oxidizing agent, (b) reducing agent.
*17. Name the oxidizing and reducing agents in the following equation and use their definitions to justify your answers:

$$4HCl + O_2 \rightarrow 2H_2O + 2Cl_2$$

18. In the reaction

$$MnO_2 + 4HCl \rightarrow MnCl_2 + Cl_2 + 2H_2O,$$

(a) Select the elements that change their oxidation states, indicate these changes, and indicate the number of electrons lost or gained per atom. (b) Which element is oxidized and which reduced? (c) Name the element (or compound) that is the oxidizing agent and the one that is the reducing agent.

26-8 Balancing Redox Equations Using Oxidation Numbers

PEOPLE IN CHEMISTRY

Reatha Clark King (1938-)

Reatha Clark King had planned to be a home economics teacher in her hometown of Pavo, Georgia. But her career, although closely linked with education, took a different turn.

Reatha King continued her study of chemistry after college at the University of Chicago. Later, she did research in high temperature chemistry at the National Bureau of Standards in Washington, D.C.

During the 1970s she was professor of chemistry and associate dean for academic affairs at York College of the City University of New York.

At present, Dr. King is the president of Metropolitan State University in St. Paul, Minnesota. Throughout her career, Dr. King has been involved in important changes in both science and education.

In Chapter 10, Section 10-8, a scheme was presented for classifying chemical reactions. This scheme lists four types of chemical reactions. In the first three of those listed in Section 10-8, atoms undergo changes in their oxidation numbers. Three of the four types of reactions in the scheme are, then, redox reactions. Only in the last type, that called exchange of ions (or, double replacement) do atoms undergo no changes in their oxidation numbers. Thus, there are many reactions that are redox reactions. Many of these are not as easy to balance as those listed in Chapter 10. In fact, some are quite difficult to balance by the method described there. However, in a correctly balanced redox reaction, the total decrease in oxidation numbers must be equal to the total increase in oxidation numbers. This fact is the basis for a method of balancing redox equations that would otherwise be very hard to balance. The sample problem illustrates the method.

SAMPLE PROBLEM

Balance the following equation:

$$Zn + HNO_3 \longrightarrow Zn(NO_3)_2 + NO_2 + H_2O$$

Solution

Step 1. Determine which atoms are changing their oxidation numbers.

Zn is changing from the elemental state to a zinc ion, Zn^{2+}. Its oxidation number, therefore, changes from 0 to 2+.

Hydrogen has an oxidation number of 1+ in both HNO_3 and H_2O. Its oxidation number, therefore, is not changing.

Nitrogen has an oxidation number of 5+ in HNO_3, but an oxidation number of 4+ in NO_2.

Oxygen has an oxidation number of 2− in all substances in which it occurs in the reaction.

Step 2. Indicate on the equation which atoms undergo a change in oxidation numbers as reactants change to products.

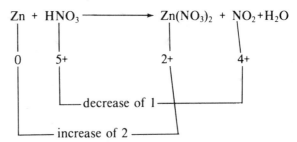

Step 3. Pick coefficients that make the increase and decrease the same. If 2 atoms of nitrogen undergo a decrease of 1, the total decrease will be 2. This will balance the increase of 2 for zinc. To make 2 atoms of nitrogen undergo the change, we need coefficients of 2 for both HNO_3

Figure 26-8

When a rocket fuel burns, a chemical change takes place in which reacting elements undergo a change in their oxidation numbers.

and NO_2. The coefficients that govern zinc must remain as they are. That is, the coefficients of Zn and $Zn(NO_3)_2$ must remain 1 (understood).

$$(1)Zn + 2HNO_3 \longrightarrow (1)Zn(NO_3)_2 + 2NO_2 + H_2O$$

Step 4. Nitrogen appears in two substances on the right side of the equation. The coefficient for HNO_3 on the left must provide for both the nitrogen that is being reduced (that in NO_2) and for the nitrogen whose oxidation number is remaining unchanged (that in $Zn(NO_3)_2$). Two atoms of nitrogen are represented by the formula $Zn(NO_3)_2$ on the right side of the equation. To balance these 2 atoms of nitrogen, the coefficient for HNO_3 must be increased by 2 (from $2HNO_3$ to $4HNO_3$):

$$(1)Zn + 4HNO_3 \longrightarrow (1)Zn(NO_3)_2 + 2NO_2 + H_2O$$

Step 5. By inspection, adjust the coefficient or coefficients of the remaining substances. In this case, only the coefficient for H_2O has not yet been determined. Since 4 atoms of hydrogen are represented by the expression $4HNO_3$ on the left, the coefficient of H_2O must be 2:

$$(1)Zn + 4HNO_3 \longrightarrow (1)Zn(NO_3)_2 + 2NO_2 + 2H_2O$$

This last equation is the correctly balanced equation. As a check, see if the number of oxygen atoms on both sides are equal.

Questions for Section 26-8

*19. (a) For the following equation, indicate the oxidation number of each element:
$$HNO_3 + H_2S \rightarrow NO + S + H_2O$$
(b) Indicate which atoms are undergoing a change in their oxidation numbers and how much of a change is taking place for 1 atom of the element.
(c) Adjust the coefficients to make the total increase equal to the total decrease and write a completely balanced equation.

*20. Balance by making use of changes in oxidation numbers:
(a) $KMnO_4 + HCl \rightarrow KCl + MnCl_2 + H_2O + Cl_2$
(b) $Cu + HNO_3 \rightarrow Cu(NO_3)_2 + H_2O + NO$
(c) $K_2Cr_2O_7 + H_2O + S \rightarrow SO_2 + KOH + Cr_2O_3$

21. Balance by making use of changes in oxidation numbers:
(a) $KNO_3 + C \rightarrow CO_2 + NO_2 + K_2O$
(b) $HNO_3 + I_2 \rightarrow HIO_3 + NO_2 + H_2O$
(c) $Cr_2O_3 + KClO_3 + NaOH \rightarrow Na_2CrO_4 + KCl + H_2O$

26-9 Gram Equivalent Masses for Oxidizing and Reducing Agents

Acids and bases are not the only substances that can be titrated against each other. So can oxidizing and reducing agents. Recall from

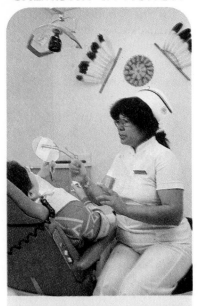

The End of Tooth Decay

Few people visit the dentist with any emotion other than anxiety. With advances in dental care, however, we may soon be able to face these visits without fear.

Since fluorides have been added to drinking water, the number of cavities in people under 17 years old has decreased dramatically. Fluorides can also be applied directly to the surface of teeth. The fluoride ion strengthens tooth enamel and makes it less vulnerable to the bacteria that cause decay. In an experimental procedure called iontophoresis, a weak electric current sends the fluoride ions and their protection through the enamel and into the pulp of the tooth.

Synthetic resins are another product of dental research. Used to fill holes or cracks in molars, these sealants help prevent cavities on chewing surfaces.

These and other advances may mean the end of tooth decay for people under 50 by the end of the century.

Section 25-12 that it is convenient in an acid-base titration to express concentrations in normality. Normal units are also convenient for expressing the concentrations of oxidizing and reducing agents in a redox titration. Since the normality of a solution is the number of gram-equivalent masses of solute divided by the volume of the solution in liters, we need to know how to determine the gram equivalent mass of an oxidizing and reducing agent. The **gram-equivalent mass of an oxidizing agent** is the mass in grams of 1 mole divided by the change in oxidation number of the oxidizing agent during the reaction. The **gram equivalent mass of a reducing agent** is the mass in grams of 1 mole divided by the change in oxidation number of the reducing agent during the reaction. The sample problem illustrates these definitions.

SAMPLE PROBLEM 1

What are the gram equivalent masses of iron (II) sulfate, $FeSO_4$, and potassium permanganate, $KMnO_4$, in the following redox reaction:

$$10FeSO_4 + 2KMnO_4 + 8H_2SO_4 \longrightarrow 2MnSO_4 + 5Fe_2(SO_4)_3 + K_2SO_4 + 8H_2O$$

Solution. The oxidation number of iron in iron (II) sulfate changes by 1, and the oxidation number of manganese in potassium permanganate changes by 5, as shown below:

$$10FeSO_4 + 2KMnO_4 + 8H_2SO_4 \longrightarrow 2MnSO_4 + 5Fe_2(SO_4)_3 + K_2SO_4 + 8H_2O$$

$$2+ \qquad 7+ \qquad\qquad 2+ \qquad 3+$$

— decreases by 5 —

— increases by 1 —

Applying the definitions:

$$\text{gram equivalent mass of iron (II) sulfate} = \frac{\text{mass in grams of 1 mole } FeSO_4}{\text{change in oxidation number}}$$

$$= \frac{152 \text{ grams}}{1}$$

$$= 152 \text{ grams}$$

$$\text{gram equivalent mass potassium permanganate} = \frac{\text{mass in grams of 1 mole } KMnO_4}{\text{change in oxidation number}}$$

$$= \frac{158 \text{ grams}}{5}$$

$$= 31.6 \text{ grams}$$

SAMPLE PROBLEM 2

What is the normality of a solution that contains 15.2 grams of $FeSO_4$ dissolved in 0.500 L of solution if the $FeSO_4$ is reacted with $KMnO_4$ according to the equation given in Sample Problem 1?

Solution. For the reaction referred to in Sample Problem 1, it was determined that the gram equivalent mass of $FeSO_4$ is 152 grams. If 152 grams $FeSO_4$ is 1 gram equivalent, then 15.2 grams $FeSO_4$ is 0.100 gram equivalent.

$$normality = \frac{number\ of\ gram\ equivalents}{volume\ of\ solution\ in\ liters}$$

$$= \frac{0.100\ gram\ equivalent}{0.500\ liters}$$

$$= 0.200\ gram\ equivalent/liter$$

$$= 0.200\ normal$$

Questions for Section 26-9

(Note: The following questions are based on the equations listed for questions 20 and 21 of the previous section, Section 26-8.)

*22. Calculate the gram equivalent mass of
 (a) $KMnO_4$ in part *(a)* of question 20
 (b) HNO_3 in part *(b)* of question 20
 (c) S in part *(c)* of question 20

23. Calculate the gram equivalent mass of
 (a) KNO_3 in part *(a)* of question 21
 (b) I_2 in part *(b)* of question 21
 (c) $KClO_3$ in part *(c)* of question 21

*24. What is the normality of the solution of $KMnO_4$ in the reaction of part *(a)* of question 20, if it contains 4.74 g of solute in 1.00 L of solution?

25. What is the normality of the solution of HNO_3 in part *(b)* of question 21, if the solution contains 25.2 g of solute in 0.500 L of solution?

CHAPTER SUMMARY

1. The oxidation number, or oxidation state, is the charge an atom is assumed to have when it is free or part of an ion or neutral molecule.
2. The oxidation number of an uncombined element, i.e., an element in the neutral state, is zero.
3. The oxidation number of a monatomic ion is the same as the charge on the ion.
4. The oxidation number of oxygen in most of its compounds is $2-$. In peroxides, its oxidation state is $1-$.
5. The oxidation number of hydrogen in most of its compounds is $1+$. In hydrides, it is $1-$.
6. In a covalent binary compound, the more electronegative element has a negative oxidation number.

7. In any neutral compound, the algebraic sum of the oxidation numbers of all the atoms in the formula must equal zero. In other words, the sum of all the positive oxidation numbers must equal the sum of all the negative oxidation numbers.

8. In polyatomic ions, the algebraic sum of all the positive and negative oxidation numbers of the atoms in the ion must equal the charge on the ion.

9. Oxidation is a chemical change in which an element loses, or loosens its hold on, electrons and thus increases its oxidation number.

10. Reduction is a chemical change in which an element gains, or increases its hold on, electrons and thus decreases its oxidation number.

11. Reduction and oxidation go on together in the same reaction and, for this reason, the change is called a redox reaction.

12. In a redox reaction, the element (or compound) that is oxidized is the reducing agent. The element (or compound) that is reduced is the oxidizing agent.

13. To balance redox equations, we first use coefficients that make the total decrease in oxidation number equal to the total increase. This balances the oxidized and reduced atoms. Coefficients may then have to be modified to balance all other atoms.

14. The gram equivalent mass of an oxidizing or reducing agent is equal to the gram-molecular mass divided by the change in oxidation number for a molecule of the agent being considered.

15. Titrations may be carried out using redox reactions. Normality-volume formulas may be used similar to those used in acid-base titrations.

TERMS YOU SHOULD KNOW

oxidation number or oxidation state
oxidation in terms of oxidation state

reduction in terms of oxidation state
redox reaction
oxidizing agent

reducing agent
gram equivalent mass of oxidizing or reducing agent

REVIEW QUESTIONS

Section

26-1   **1.** (a) How was oxidation defined in the early days of chemistry? (b) State one example of an oxidation conforming to this definition.

26-2   **2.** (a) What term is used to describe the charge that an atom is assumed to have in a molecule or ion? (b) How are the oxidation states of monatomic ions determined? What is the oxidation state of the (c) oxide ion? (d) barium ion? (e) fluoride ion? (f) sodium ion?

3. (a) Compare the oxidation states of hydrogen in H_2 and H_2O. (b) Explain why they are different. (c) Compare the oxidation states of sodium in the pure metal and in sodium chloride. (d) Explain the difference.

4. (a) Why is the oxidation number of oxygen in water equal to $2-$? (b) What is the general rule for assigning oxidation numbers to binary covalent compounds?

5. What is the oxidation state of the nitrogen atom in (a) NH_3, (b) NO_2, (c) Ca_3N_2, (d) NI_3?

26-3
6. (a) Why is the oxidation state of the oxygen atom equal to 1− in Na_2O_2? (b) Why is the hydrogen oxidation state 1− in CaH_2? Indicate the oxidation state of oxygen in (c) BaO_2, (d) CO_2. What is the oxidation state of hydrogen in (e) NaH, (f) CH_4?

7. State the change in oxidation state for each element in the reaction,
$$SnCl_4 + Fe \rightarrow SnCl_2 + FeCl_2$$

26-4
8. (a) What is the numerical result obtained by taking the algebraic sum of the oxidation numbers of all the atoms in any neutral compound? What is the oxidation state of (b) N in Mg_3N_2? (c) As in Na_3AsO_4? (d) S in H_2SO_3? (e) P in P_4O_6?

9. (a) How is the charge on a polyatomic ion related to the oxidation numbers of the atoms in the ion? What is the oxidation state of (b) P in PO_4^{3-}, (c) Cr in CrO_4^{2-}, (d) S in SO_3^{2-}, (e) C in HCO_3^-?

26-5
10. State the oxidation numbers of the (a) Cl atom in $NaClO_4$, $NaClO_3$, $NaClO$, and $NaCl$; (b) Mn atom in $MnCl_2$, MnO_2, $KMnO_3$,

26-6
11. Using the equation $2Zn + O_2 \rightarrow 2ZnO$, explain why this reaction is considered to be an oxidation both in terms of the older definition of oxidation and the modern definition.

26-7
12. For the equation $2KClO_3 \rightarrow 2KCl + 3O_2$, (a) state the changes that occur in oxidation states and (b) indicate what element is considered to be oxidized. Why? (c) For the same equation, indicate what element is reduced. Why?

13. Using oxidation numbers, explain why the following are *not* redox equations: (a) $SO_3 + H_2O \rightarrow H_2SO_4$ (b) $P_4O_{10} + 6H_2O \rightarrow 4H_3PO_4$

14. In terms of electron loss and gain, explain why chlorine undergoes both oxidation and reduction in the reaction:
$$3Cl_2 + 6KOH \rightarrow 5KCl + KClO_3 + 3H_2O$$

15. Balance the following redox equations:
(a) $Zn + HNO_3 \rightarrow Zn(NO_3)_2 + NH_4NO_3 + H_2O$
(b) $NaI + H_2SO_4 \rightarrow H_2S + I_2 + Na_2SO_4 + H_2O$
(c) $NF_3 + AlCl_3 \rightarrow N_2 + Cl_2 + AlF_3$
(d) $H_3AsO_3 + NaBrO_3 \rightarrow NaBr + H_3AsO_4$

FOR FURTHER THOUGHT

1. State whether each of the following statements is true or false, and give reasons for your answers.
26-6
(a) Oxidation numbers can be measured experimentally.
(b) In every chemical reaction, the oxidation number of every atom changes.
(c) In a binary compound, the oxidation number of one element must be equal to that of the other, but opposite in sign.
26-7
(d) An atom that is reduced (gains electrons) in a chemical reaction always acquires a negative oxidation number.
(e) In a redox reaction, the oxidizing and reducing agents are on opposite sides of the equation for the reaction.
26-8
2. In a balanced chemical equation, does the sum of the oxidation numbers of the atoms on one side equal the sum on the other side? Explain.

CHAPTER 27

Electrochemistry I—Electrolysis

Objectives

When you have completed this chapter, you will be able to:
- Describe the operation of an electrolytic cell.
- Write equations showing the reactions that occur when several compounds are electrolyzed.
- Explain the operation of a setup for electroplating with metals.

27-1 The Electric Current

Any flow of electric charge is an **electric current.** In metals, the current consists of the movement of valence electrons of atoms. This is called **metallic conduction.** It occurs in power lines, in the wires of household circuits, and in many electric appliances such as toasters, broilers, and electric lights. Electron flow is not limited to metals. It also occurs in all electronic devices such as vacuum tubes and transistors.

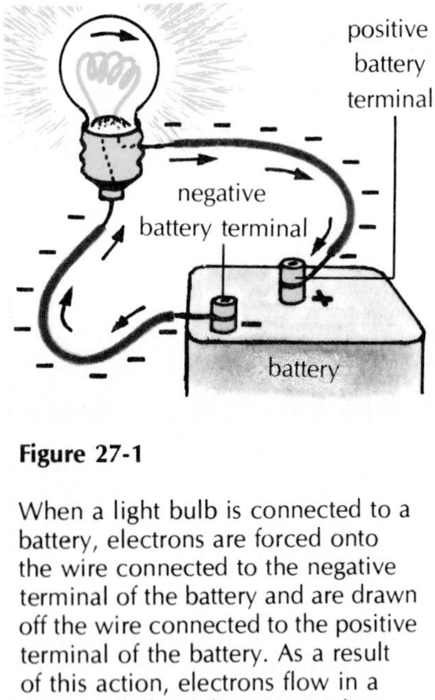

Figure 27-1

When a light bulb is connected to a battery, electrons are forced onto the wire connected to the negative terminal of the battery and are drawn off the wire connected to the positive terminal of the battery. As a result of this action, electrons flow in a direct path from the negative battery terminal, first through the conducting wire and the filament of the bulb in the direction shown by the arrows, and finally back into the battery at the positive terminal. Currents such as that produced by batteries are called direct currents.

An electric current also exists when positive and negative ions move along a path. This kind of current is called **ionic conduction.** In neon signs, both electrons and ions carry the current. During an electrolysis, the topic of this chapter, the electric current is carried by both electrons in metals and ions in solutions.

Electrons and ions do not flow through a conductor spontaneously. They must be caused to flow by applying electric forces to them. One way of doing this is with a battery. Figure 27-1 shows a battery connected to a light bulb. A battery has two terminals marked − and +. The terminal marked −, called the negative terminal, has an excess of negative charge. The terminal marked +, called the positive terminal, has an excess of positive charge. The negative charge at the negative terminal of the battery repels electrons and drives them into one end of the filament of the light bulb. The positive charge at the positive terminal attracts electrons and draws them out of the other end of the filament. The result is a continuous flow of electrons, or electric current, through the filament. Currents that are produced by batteries are direct currents. A **direct current** travels through a conductor in one direction only. (Ordinary house current is alternating current, a subject discussed in physics texts.)

The electric current traveling through the filament of a light bulb causes the filament to glow brightly. The energy for driving the electric current and producing light and heat in the filament comes from chemical reactions in the battery. In the next chapter we will examine these reactions and see how they release electrical energy.

27-2   Current Through an Electrolyte

Suppose that we now connect the battery to a solution of an electrolyte, using two electrodes immersed in the solution, as shown in Figure 27-2. You recall from Chapter 23 (Section 23-1) that the solution of an electrolyte conducts an electric current. Here, the negative terminal of the battery drives electrons into one electrode (making it the negative electrode). The positive terminal draws electrons out of the other electrode, making it the positive electrode.

Figure 27-2

Electrons are forced out of the battery through the negative battery terminal, giving the attached electrode in the beaker a negative charge. Electrons are drawn into the battery through the positive battery terminal, leaving fewer electrons in the atoms of the electrode than there are protons.

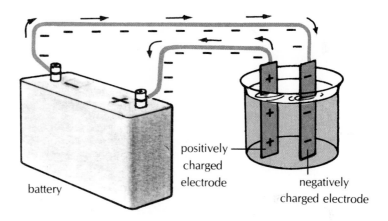

positively charged electrode

battery

negatively charged electrode

We know that if we had the light bulb in the circuit (as in Figure 18-1, page 358) it would light up, showing that a continuous current was flowing through the solution. You might think, then, that the electrons entering the solution at the negatively charged electrode were flowing through the solution to the positively charged electrode. However, this is not what actually happens. Instead, a chemical reaction takes place at each electrode.

At the negative electrode, electrons are accepted by a molecule or an ion. You recall from Chapter 26 that a substance that acquires electrons is reduced. Thus, a reduction reaction takes place at the negative electrode. At the positive electrode, an oxidation reaction occurs. Here, a molecule or ion gives up electrons to the electrode.

We see, then, that electrons flowing into the negative electrode from the battery are taken up by a reduction reaction. Electrons being drawn away from the positive electrode are replaced by electrons given up by an oxidation reaction. By removing electrons at the cathode and replacing them at the anode, the reactions in the solution keep the electrons flowing in the external circuit. There is also an internal flow of current. Positive ions are repelled by the positive electrode and attracted toward the negative electrode. These ions therefore move from the positive to the negative electrode. At the same time, negative ions move, for similar reasons, from the negative to the positive electrode. This movement of ions through the solution is an electric current. It completes the electric path, or circuit, from one battery terminal to the other.

When a current is made to flow through an electrolyte, the electrolytic solution is called the **internal circuit.** The current that travels through the internal circuit is made up of ions in solution. The rest of the setup—that is, the electrodes, the wires connecting the electrodes to a source of current, and the source of current itself— is called the **external circuit.** The current that travels through the electrodes and the attached wires is made up of moving electrons. The internal and external circuits are not two different circuits. They are rather two parts of the same circuit.

Questions for Sections 27-1 and 27-2

1. (a) What is an electric current? (b) Distinguish between conduction in metals and conduction in solutions.
2. (a) Describe briefly how the negative and positive terminals of a battery make an electric current flow through a light bulb that is connected to the battery. (b) What name is given to current that travels in only one direction?
*3. Two electrodes are connected to battery terminals and immersed in a solution of an electrolyte. (a) Which ions are attracted to the negative electrode? (b) What happens to these ions when they reach this electrode? (c) What name is given to such a reaction?
4. Referring to the same conditions as in question 3, (a) which ions are attracted to the positive electrode? (b) Describe what happens at this electrode. (c) What name is given to this type of reaction?
5. (a) When an electric current is made to flow through an electrolyte, what do the terms *internal circuit* and *external circuit* refer to? (b) Explain why there is a continuous flow of electrons in the external circuit when current is being sent from a battery into a solution of an electrolyte. (c) Describe the flow of current inside the solution of the electrolyte.

27-3   Electrolysis

We have just seen that when an electric current flows through the solution of an electrolyte, a reduction occurs at the negative electrode and an oxidation reaction occurs at the positive electrode. These reactions are actually two parts of a single redox reaction. However, the two parts are occurring in different places, one at the cathode and the other at the anode. This process, by which an electric current brings about a redox reaction in a conducting liquid or solution, is called **electrolysis.**

The redox reaction produced by electrolysis would not occur spontaneously under the conditions in the solution. The reaction occurs because energy is supplied by the source of the electric current—in this case, chemical reactions in the battery. In the next few sections, typical electrolysis reactions will be examined in detail. The discussion will help you understand the process more completely.

27-4   Electrolysis of Molten Sodium Chloride

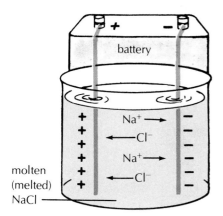

Figure 27-3

When molten sodium chloride is electrolyzed, the positively charged sodium ions are attracted to the negatively charged electrode, and the negatively charged chloride ions are attracted to the positively charged electrode. (The positive charge on the electrode is the result of the positive charges in the metal atoms of the electrode being more numerous than the electrons, a situation that arises when valence electrons in atoms of the electrode move to the battery during the flow of current.)

As you know, solid sodium chloride consists of sodium and chloride ions in a rigid crystal lattice. When sodium chloride is raised to a high enough temperature, it melts. In the liquid state, the ions become free to move. The molten sodium chloride can then be electrolyzed. (CAUTION: This is a dangerous procedure and should not be attempted.) As soon as the current is switched on, the positive sodium ions, Na^+, are attracted toward the negative electrode. The negative chloride ions, Cl^-, move in the opposite direction toward the positive electrode. See Figure 27-3.

When the sodium ions make contact with the negative electrode, they pick up electrons from the electrode. The electrons reduce the sodium ion, forming sodium metal. The sodium metal becomes coated on the electrode. The chemical change can be represented by the equation:

$$Na^+ \ + \ e^- \longrightarrow Na \qquad \textbf{(Eq. 1)}$$

sodium ion	an electron	atom of sodium metal

Notice that Equation 1 balances with respect both to numbers of atoms and to charge. The minus charge from the electron balances the positive charge from the sodium ion, making a net charge of zero on both sides of the arrow.

While sodium ions are moving toward the negative electrode, chloride ions are moving in the opposite direction toward the positive electrode. When chloride ions reach the positive electrode, they give up electrons to the electrode. Each chloride ion gives up one electron, thus becoming oxidized to a neutral chlorine atom. Pairs of these atoms then join to form molecules of chlorine gas. The chemical change can be represented by the equation:

$$2Cl^- \longrightarrow Cl_2 \ + \ 2e^- \qquad \textbf{(Eq. 2)}$$

chloride ions	chlorine gas molecule	two electrons

Equation 2 is balanced with respect to numbers of atoms and to charge.

Current Through a Polymer

Because they are good insulators, plastics are used to cover electrical wires. The wires themselves are made of a metal that conducts electricity. To be a conductor, a substance must have electrons that are free to move from one atom to another. Plastics usually do not have these free electrons.

A new polymer formed from acetylene, however, can conduct electricity as well as any metal. The polymer molecule is made up of groups of carbon and hydrogen atoms. In the carbon chain, single bonds alternate with double bonds. When iodine is added to the molecule, it removes one of the electrons from a double bond. An electron from an adjacent carbon atom can now move over to take its place. This movement of electrons can continue along the length of the molecule.

Batteries made from the new conducting plastic are being tested. Because they are lighter and charge faster than conventional types, the plastic batteries may help to make an electric-powered car a practical reality.

Equation 1 is a reduction, as shown by the decrease in oxidation number:

REDUCTION

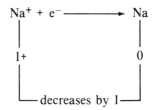

Equation 2 is an oxidation, as shown by the increase in oxidation number:

OXIDATION

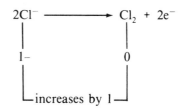

Equations 1 and 2 may appear to be the equations for two different reactions, but they are actually two parts of the same reaction—the decomposition of NaCl. (Recall that oxidation and reduction go together. A substance that loses electrons must lose them to another substance that gains them.) Because Equations 1 and 2 are the two parts of the same reaction, they are called half-reactions. The complete reaction can be obtained by adding the two half-reactions. Thus, a **half-reaction** is the oxidation or the reduction that is part of a redox reaction.

Before we can add Equation 1 and Equation 2, we need to modify one of them. Notice that only 1 electron is gained in Equation 1 (the reduction) while 2 are lost in Equation 2 (the oxidation). The number of electrons must be equal in the half-reactions before they can be added. The number can be equalized by doubling all terms in Equation 1.

$$2(Na^+ + e^- \longrightarrow Na)$$

or,

$$2Na^+ + 2e^- \longrightarrow 2Na \qquad \text{(Eq. 3)}$$

Now the half-reaction of Equation 3 can be added to the half-reaction of Equation 2 to produce the equation for the reaction.

$$2Na^+ + 2e^- \longrightarrow 2Na$$
$$+ \quad 2Cl^- \longrightarrow Cl_2 + 2e^-$$
$$\overline{2Na^+ + 2Cl^- + 2e^- \longrightarrow 2Na + Cl_2 + 2e^-} \qquad \text{(Eq. 4)}$$

Canceling out the two electrons on both sides of the arrow gives:

$$2Na^+ + 2Cl^- \xrightarrow{\text{elec.}} 2Na + Cl_2 \qquad \textbf{(Eq. 5)}$$

$$\underbrace{}_{\text{molten NaCl}} \qquad \underbrace{}_{\substack{\text{sodium} \\ \text{metal}}} \quad \underbrace{}_{\substack{\text{chlorine} \\ \text{gas}}}$$

In discussing electrolyses, it is helpful to be able to distinguish between the two electrodes. The electrode where oxidation occurs is called the **anode.** The electrode where reduction occurs is called the **cathode.** One way to pair these terms correctly is to remember that in simple reactions the *anion* is oxidized at the anode and the *cation* is reduced at the cathode.

Questions for Sections 27-3 and 27-4

6. (a) Define *electrolysis*. (b) Name the two parts of the redox reaction that occur in an electrolysis and state where each part occurs.
7. In the electrolysis of molten sodium chloride, (a) describe what happens at the negative electrode. (b) Write the equation for the reaction at this electrode. (c) What happens at the positive electrode? (d) Write the equation for this reaction.
8. Referring again to the electrolysis of molten sodium chloride, (a) why is the reaction at the negative electrode called a reduction, (b) why is the reaction at the positive electrode an oxidation, (c) why is the negative electrode the cathode, (d) why is the positive electrode the anode?
*9. Write the equations for the half-reactions in the electrolysis of molten NaCl and add them together to obtain the complete redox equation.

27-5 Electrolysis of Water

If you place the electrodes of an electrolysis apparatus into pure water, nothing happens. This is not surprising. For electrolysis to occur, there must be ions available to carry electric charge through the liquid. Although water is slightly ionized into H^+ and OH^- ions, the concentration of these ions is far too small to produce any observable change at the electrodes. However, if just a small amount of sodium sulfate is dissolved in the water, a dramatic change is observed. Bubbles of hydrogen gas are released at the negative electrode and bubbles of oxygen gas at the positive electrode. The addition of many other electrolytes to water will have the same effect. See Figure 27-4.

Some light is shed on what is taking place during these reactions if an indicator, such as litmus, is added to the solution, and the electrodes are put into separate compartments. See Figure 27-5. The litmus gives the solution the purple color characteristic of neutral solutions. After the current has been running for some time, the solution in the com-

Figure 27-4

When water is electrolyzed, bubbles of hydrogen gas are given off at the negative electrode and bubbles of oxygen gas are given off at the positive electrode.

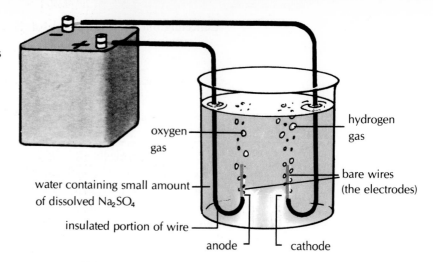

oxygen gas

hydrogen gas

water containing small amount of dissolved Na_2SO_4

bare wires (the electrodes)

insulated portion of wire

anode   cathode

Figure 27-5

The same set-up as that shown in Figure 27-4 but with addition of the two inverted test tubes to collect the gases produced at the electrodes. The neutral purple color of the litmus changes to the pink acid color in the tube where oxygen is given off and to the blue basic color in the tube where hydrogen is given off.

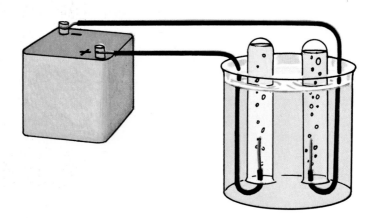

partment where hydrogen is being formed turns blue. This change indicates that the solution has accumulated an excess of OH^- ions in this compartment. The solution in the other compartment turns red, indicating an excess of H^+ ions. When the current is turned off after running for some while, it will be found that the mass of the sodium sulfate present in the solution is the same as it was at the beginning. In other words, the sodium sulfate is not consumed during the reaction. We conclude that the hydrogen and oxygen released by the electrolysis have come from the water.

From the observations that free hydrogen is released at the negative electrode (the cathode) and OH^- ion is formed there, we can write the following reduction half-reaction:

HALF-REACTION AT THE CATHODE (reduction)

$$4H_2O + 4e^- \longrightarrow 2H_2\uparrow + 4OH^- \qquad \textbf{(Eq. 6)}$$

makes the cathode compartment basic

Likewise, we can account for the free oxygen and H^+ ion at the positive electrode (the anode) by the following oxidation half-reactions: half-reactions:

HALF-REACTION AT THE ANODE (oxidation)

$$2H_2O \longrightarrow O_2 + 4H^+ + 4e^- \qquad \text{(Eq. 7)}$$

makes the anode compartment acidic

The complete reaction can be obtained by adding the two half-reactions:

$$6H_2O \longrightarrow 2H_2 + O_2 + 4H^+ + 4OH^- \qquad \text{(Eq. 8)}$$

At the end of the reaction, if the solutions in the anode and cathode compartments are mixed, the hydrogen ions and hydroxide ions combine to form water molecules according to the equation:

$$4H^+ + 4OH^- \longrightarrow 4H_2O \qquad \text{(Eq. 9)}$$

If the electrolysis is done with both electrodes in the same compartment (that is, without separate compartments for the electrodes), the hydrogen and hydroxide ions form water molecules as soon as they are formed. Then, the equation for the complete reaction is simply that obtained by adding Equations 8 and 9:

$$6H_2O \longrightarrow 2H_2 + O_2 + 4H^+ + 4OH^- \qquad \text{(Eq. 8)}$$

$$+4H^+ + 4OH- \longrightarrow 4H_2O \qquad \text{(Eq. 9)}$$

$$2H_2O \xrightarrow{\text{elec.}} 2H_2 + O_2 \qquad \text{(Eq. 10)}$$

If the electrolysis reactions involve only the water, why was the sodium sulfate necessary for the electrolysis to proceed? The reason is that when the electrolysis of water starts, negative hydroxide ions quickly accumulate near the negative electrode (see Equation 6) and positive hydrogen ions accumulate near the positive electrode (see Equation 7). These large amounts of like charge near each electrode act to prevent the further flow of electrons from the battery into the cathode and out of the anode to the battery. That is, the current stops flowing almost as soon as it starts, and the reaction comes to a halt, or proceeds extremely slowly. However, when there are other ions present in the solution, they can quickly shift position to neutralize the excess charges. Positive sodium ions are attracted toward the negative charge of the cathode, and negative sulfate ions are attracted toward the positive charge of the anode. As we have already noted, this movement of ions constitutes an electric current. It completes the electric circuit through the solution and allows the reactions to continue at a rapid rate.

Sodium sulfate is not the only electrolyte that speeds up the electrolysis of water. Any electrolyte will have the same effect if its ions do not themselves react at one of the electrodes. Sulfuric acid is often used. Sodium chloride, however, is not appropriate. As we will see in the next section, the chloride ion, Cl^-, is more readily oxidized at the anode than water. Chlorine gas would be formed there instead of oxygen.

Questions for Section 27-5

*10. For the electrolysis of water, using sodium sulfate as the catalyst, (a) Write the equation for the anode reaction. (b) Write the equation for the cathode reaction. (c) Equating the loss and gain of electrons, add the equations in *(a)* and *(b)* to produce the complete redox reaction. (d) Combine the H^+ and OH^- ions on the same side of the equation and eliminate an equal number of water molecules on each side of the equation in order to obtain the final net equation.

11. (a) If a catalyst is not used in electrolyzing water, what ions would accumulate at the negative electrode and what ions at the positive electrode? (b) What is the effect of such ion accumulation at each electrode? (c) How does the addition of sodium sulfate create an ionic current in the solution?

12. (a) What electrolyte, besides sodium sulfate, may be used as a catalyst in the electrolysis of water? (b) Why can't NaCl be used for this purpose?

27-6 Electrolysis of Concentrated Sodium Chloride Solution (Brine)

A solution of sodium chloride contains sodium ions, Na^+, chloride ions, Cl^-, and water molecules, H_2O. (Very dilute concentrations of hydrogen ion and hydroxide ion are also present from the ionization of the water.) Water molecules are more easily reduced than sodium ions. Therefore, the reaction that takes place at the cathode is the same as the reaction that occurs in the electrolysis of water. Hydrogen gas bubbles off the cathode.

However, chloride ions in moderate concentrations are more easily oxidized than water molecules. Therefore, chlorine gas, rather than oxygen gas, is formed at the anode. The half-reactions are:

HALF-REACTION AT THE CATHODE (reduction)

$$2H_2O + 2e^- \longrightarrow H_2 + 2OH^- \qquad \textbf{(Eq. 11)}$$

HALF-REACTION AT THE ANODE (oxidation)

$$2Cl^- \longrightarrow Cl_2 + 2e^- \qquad \textbf{(Eq. 12)}$$

The equation for the complete reaction is obtained by adding the two half-reactions. The equation is:

IONIC EQUATION, ELECTROLYSIS OF BRINE

$$2H_2O + 2Cl^- \longrightarrow H_2\uparrow + Cl_2\uparrow + 2OH^- \qquad \textbf{(Eq. 13)}$$

The hydrogen gas, H_2, and chlorine gas, Cl_2, bubble out of the solution. An excess of hydroxide ions, OH^-, accumulate in the solution. The sodium ions, Na^+, that were originally in the solution are spectator ions that remain in solution. They undergo no chemical change, although they do carry charge through the solution. As the electrolysis continues, more and more chloride ions are used up, and more and more hydroxide ions are formed. If the electrolysis goes on for long enough, practically all of the chloride ions, Cl^-, will be oxidized. What started out as a NaCl solution will wind up as a NaOH solution. By evaporating the water from the solution, solid NaOH can be recovered. The electrolysis of brine is in fact the method used by industry to prepare NaOH. (Of course, hydrogen gas and chlorine gas are obtained at the same time.)

The molecular equation for the electrolysis of brine can be obtained by adding the spectator sodium ions, Na^+, to both sides of Equation 13. When this is done, the Cl^- ions on the left of Equation 13 combine with the Na^+ ions to form NaCl. The OH^- ions on the right of Equation 13 combine with the Na^+ ions to form NaOH:

MOLECULAR EQUATION, ELECTROLYSIS OF BRINE

$$2H_2O + 2NaCl \longrightarrow H_2 + Cl_2 + 2NaOH \qquad \textbf{(Eq. 14)}$$

27-7   Electroplating

The use of electrolysis to coat a material with a layer of metal is called **electroplating.** Often the object to be plated is made of a cheap metal, and a more expensive metal, such as silver, is plated over it. In order to electroplate, the object to be plated must conduct an electric current. Metals, of course, are conductors. If the object to be plated is made of a nonconducting substance, its surface can be made a conductor by dusting the object with graphite. Graphite is a crystalline form of carbon, and it is a good electrical conductor. The object to be plated is placed into a solution that has dissolved in it ions of the plating metal. For example, silver nitrate, $AgNO_3$, can be used to silverplate because it dissolves in water to form a solution in which the cation is the silver ion, Ag^+.

Figure 27-6

Electroplating a fork. The object to be plated, the fork, is given a negative charge by connecting it to the negative battery terminal. Dissolved metallic ion, in this case the silver ion, is in the solution. These positively charged ions are attracted to the object, where reduction occurs, forming a layer of the plating metal on the object. Ions removed from the solution in this manner are replaced by the oxidation of the metal atoms that make up the anode.

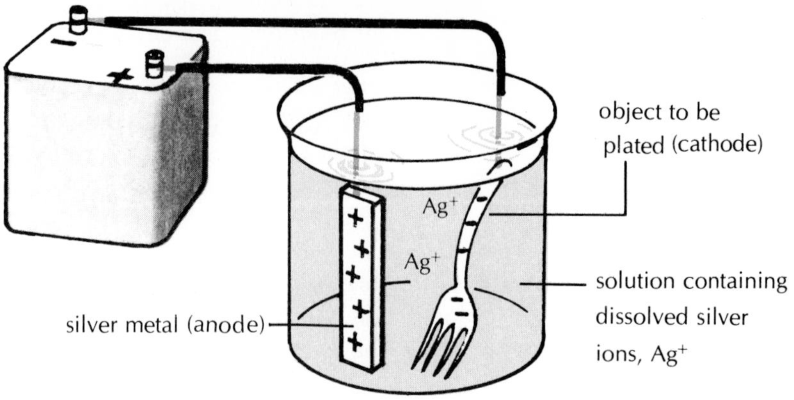

object to be plated (cathode)

silver metal (anode)

solution containing dissolved silver ions, Ag^+

Electroplating is used to increase the value of an object, improve its appearance, or protect it against corrosion.

The object to be plated is connected to the negative terminal of the battery or other source of direct current. Thus, the object to be plated is made one of the electrodes. A bar of the plating metal is made the other electrode. See Figure 27-6. When the current is switched on, the positive metal ions in the solution are attracted to the object. The attraction exists because the object develops a negative charge when connected to the negative terminal of the battery. When the metal ions make contact with the object, they are reduced. That is, they accept electrons and change from ions to neutral metal atoms. These atoms gradually form a metallic coating on the object. Because the metallic ions are reduced, the object to be plated is the cathode. For a silver-plating solution, the cathode half-reaction would be:

HALF-REACTION AT THE CATHODE (reduction)

$$Ag^+ + e^- \longrightarrow Ag \qquad \text{(Eq. 15)}$$

At the anode, oxidation occurs, but in the case of electroplating, the anode itself is oxidized rather than a molecule or ion in the solution. During a silver-plating operation, the silver anode "dissolves" (is oxidized) according to the half-reaction:

HALF-REACTION AT THE ANODE (oxidation)

$$Ag \longrightarrow Ag^+ + e^- \qquad \text{(Eq. 16)}$$

The silver ions that are formed by the half-reaction at the anode replace those that are plated onto the object during the half-reaction at the cathode. Thus, the half-reaction at the anode assures a constant supply of metal ions.

What happens during electroplating makes it clear that the nature of the electrodes affects the results of an electrolysis. An anode that is silver metal is the proper material for silver plating. But silver would be a bad material for the anode if a sodium chloride solution was to be electrolyzed. The reason is that neutral silver atoms are oxidized more easily than chloride ions. When electrolyzing a sodium chloride solution, silver ions, Ag^+, would be produced at the anode rather than chlorine gas, Cl_2, if the anode was silver metal.

Unless there is a good reason to do otherwise, chemists use inactive materials for electrodes. For laboratory or other small-scale operations, platinum electrodes are used because platinum is so inactive. However, it is expensive. For commercial purposes, the much less expensive graphite is commonly used. When graphite is used as an anode, CO_2 is formed as part of the oxidation reaction. However, it does not generally interfere with the formation of the other products of the electrolysis.

Questions for Sections 27-6 and 27-7

13. (a) What three substances are present in relatively high concentrations in a concentrated solution of sodium chloride (brine)? Consider the electrolysis of this solution and write the equation for the (b) cathode reaction, (c) anode reaction, (d) overall ionic reaction that represents the sum of the half-reactions.
14. (a) Name three (3) products obtained in the electrolysis of brine. (b) Which product is obtained by evaporation of the final solution? (c) Write the molecular equation for the electrolysis.
15. (a) What is *electroplating?* (b) What is the general purpose of electroplating? (c) Name two metals that are often used to electroplate other metals.
16. In electroplating, (a) which electrode is made of the object to be plated? (b) Of what substance is the other electrode composed? (c) What can be done if the object to be plated is a nonconductor? (d) What ions must be present in the electroplating solution?
*17. (a) In electroplating a metal spoon by silver, what is the composition of the anode, cathode, and electrolyte? (b) Write the equation for the cathode reaction. (c) Write the equation for the anode reaction. (d) How many silver atoms go into solution for each silver atom that plates out on the spoon?

CHAPTER SUMMARY

1. An electric current may consists of a flow of electrons or a flow of ions.
2. An electric cell, or a battery of cells, can be used as a source of a continuous flow of electrons in one direction (a direct current).
3. When a direct current is passed through a solution of an electrolyte, the positive ions are attracted to the negative electrode where they gain electrons; the negative ions are attracted to the positive electrode where they lose electrons.
4. There is a complete electrical circuit operating during electrolysis. The current in the external circuit consists of a flow of electrons; the current in the solution consists of a flow of ions.
5. The electrode at which ions are reduced (gain electrons) is called the cathode; the electrode at which ions are oxidized (lose electrons) is called the anode. Anions are oxidized at the anode; cations are reduced at the cathode.
6. In the electrolysis of molten sodium chloride, sodium ions are reduced at the cathode, producing the neutral metal. Chlorine ions are oxidized at the anode, producing chlorine gas.

7. The equations for the half-reactions at each electrode may be added to yield a net equation. Before adding, the number of electrons in the half-equations must be made equal.

8. Pure water will not conduct the electric current. The presence of a catalyst, such as sulfuric acid or sodium sulfate, is needed to produce the ionic current.

9. The net equation in the electrolysis of water shows that water is decomposed to form hydrogen gas at the cathode and oxygen gas at the anode.

10. The electrolysis of brine yields sodium hydroxide, hydrogen, and chlorine.

11. In electroplating, the object to be plated is made the negative electrode; the plating metal is made the positive electrode. The electrolyte contains a compound which supplies ions of the plating metal.

12. The metal ions in solution are reduced at the cathode and plate it. The anode is oxidized and forms metal ions to replace those that plate the cathode.

TERMS YOU SHOULD KNOW

electric current	internal circuit	half-reaction
metallic conduction	external circuit	anode
ionic conduction	electrolysis	cathode
direct current		electroplating

REVIEW QUESTIONS

Section

27-1
1. (a) Distinguish between metallic and ionic conduction and state one example of each. (b) Mention the kind(s) of conduction that occurs in neon signs.

2. (a) Describe the electrical charge at each terminal of a battery. (b) If the battery is connected to a light bulb, in which direction are the electrons moving at each terminal?

27-2
3. A direct current is sent through a solution of electrolyte. Describe (a) the electron transfer at the negative electrode, (b) the electron transfer at the positive electrode, (c) the movement of positive and negative ions in the solution.

27-3
4. Describe the oxidation and reduction reactions in a typical electrolysis, mentioning the electrode at which each occurs.

27-4
5. Define (a) anode, (b) cathode, (c) anion, (d) cation.

6. (a) Draw the diagram of the electrolysis cell that can be used for the electrolysis of molten KBr. Use graphite electrodes, labeling the anode and cathode. Include the direction of movement of the ions and electrons. (b) Write the equations for the half-reactions and for the overall net reaction.

27-5
7. When a dilute solution of sodium nitrate is electrolyzed, hydrogen appears at the cathode and oxygen at the anode. (a) Write the equations for the half-reactions. (b) Write the equation for the complete overall reaction.

8. In the electrolysis of $NaNO_3$ solution (question 7, above), a porous diaphragm is used, separating the anode and cathode compartments.

Litmus solution is placed in each compartment. (a) What color does the litmus acquire in the cathode compartment? Why? (b) What color does it acquire in the anode compartment? Why? (c) What eventually happens to the ions causing the litmus colors?

9. Explain why the $NaNO_3$, in the electrolysis of question 7, makes it possible for a current to flow through the solution.

10. Two electrodes are connected to a battery and placed into a container of pure water. Explain why an accumulation of OH^- ions at the negative electrode and H^+ ions at the positive electrode prevent any current from flowing through the water.

27-6 11. In the electrolysis of brine, (a) why aren't sodium ions reduced at the cathode, (b) why is chlorine gas obtained at the anode instead of oxygen gas? (c) Write the ionic equation for the complete electrolysis reaction.

12. In the electrolysis of brine, how many moles of hydroxide ion are produced for every mole of (a) chlorine obtained, (b) chloride ion consumed?

13. (a) An iron bar is to be electroplated with zinc. Describe the composition of the electrodes and electrolyte in the electrolytic cell. (b) Write the ionic equations for the anode and cathode reactions.

27-7 14. Alternating current (A.C.) is electric current that moves in one direction and then the opposite one, many times a second. If, in a typical silver electroplating cell, where a spoon is to be plated, A.C. is used instead of D.C. (direct current), (a) what happens at the silver anode, (b) what happens at the spoon electrode, (c) what is the net effect on the electrodes?

15. (a) What would happen in the electrolysis of brine if the anode were made of silver? (b) State two (2) reasons why graphite electrodes are often used in commercial electrolysis.

FOR FURTHER THOUGHT

27-2 1. When electric current flows through a solution of an electrolyte, electrons are carried into the solution through one electrode and electrons leave the solution through the other electrode. Do electrons move through the solution from one electrode to the other? Explain.

27-4 2. (a) In an electrolysis, how many half-reactions are involved? (b) Where do they occur? (c) What will happen if one half-reaction of an electrolysis cannot occur?

3. Given the reaction: $2NaCl\ (l) + 196.4\ kcal \rightarrow 2Na(s) + Cl_2(g)$
   (a) Is this a redox reaction? Why?
   (b) Does it occur spontaneously at room temperature?
   (c) Can it occur at all? Explain.

27-5 4. A current is flowing through an acid electrolyte. What will be the effect on the current if
   (a) a salt of the acid is added to the solution?
   (b) a base is gradually added to the solution?

Electrochemistry II—Galvanic Cells

> ## Objectives
>
> When you have completed this chapter, you should be able to:
> - Describe the operation of a galvanic cell.
> - Determine net voltage obtained when standard half-cells are paired in a galvanic cell.
> - Predict reaction products by using standard reduction potentials and an activity series.
> - Use half-reactions to write redox equations.

28-1   Introduction

In the last chapter, it was shown that a source of direct current could be used to bring about redox reactions during an electrolysis. A common source of direct current is a battery. There is a similarity between the operation of a battery and an electrolysis cell. In both cases, redox reactions take place at electrodes. The main difference between a battery and an electrolysis cell is that the reactions that occur in a battery occur spontaneously, without any external source of energy, whereas those that occur during electrolysis do not occur spontaneously. In this chapter, attention is shifted to redox reactions that occur spontaneously and that are arranged in such a way that an electric current is produced.

Before proceeding further, it is useful to describe the difference between an electrochemical cell and a battery. A battery is two or more cells arranged so that they operate together. People often refer to the two *batteries* in their flashlight, but it would be more proper to refer to them as two electrochemical cells, or simply two cells.

28-2   The Galvanic, or Electrochemical, Cell

If a strip of zinc is placed in a solution of a copper salt, such as copper (II) sulfate, $CuSO_4$, a reaction takes place, as shown by the following equations:

MOLECULAR EQUATION

$$Zn + CuSO_4 \longrightarrow Cu + ZnSO_4 \qquad \text{(Eq. 1)}$$

Figure 28-1

IONIC EQUATION

$$Zn + Cu^{2+} \longrightarrow Cu + Zn^{2+} \qquad \text{(Eq. 2)}$$

The upper photo shows a strip of zinc metal just after it was placed in a water solution of copper sulfate, $CuSO_4$. Three days later (lower photo) the blue color of the aqueous copper (II) ion, Cu^{2+}, has disappeared. All the Cu^{2+} ions have reacted with the zinc, forming copper metal, seen as the dark mass in the photo. Only a small amount of the zinc metal strip remains. Most of the zinc has been "eaten up" by the reaction. That is, most of the zinc metal has changed to zinc ion, Zn^{2+}, which is dissolved in the clear solution.

This reaction is simply a single replacement reaction (Section 14-8) in which neutral zinc replaces copper. That is, neutral zinc atoms become zinc ions, and copper ions become neutral copper atoms. See Figure 28-1.

The reaction expressed by Equations 1 and 2 is a redox reaction. The reaction can be shown as two half-reactions:

ZINC HALF-REACTION (oxidation)

$$Zn \longrightarrow Zn^{2+} + 2e^- \qquad \text{(Eq. 3)}$$

COPPER ION HALF-REACTION (reduction)

$$Cu^{2+} + 2e^- \longrightarrow Cu \qquad \text{(Eq. 4)}$$

The electrons given up in Equation 3 equal the number acquired in Equation 4. That is, zinc atoms are giving up electrons. The same number of electrons are taken on by copper ions during any particular period of time.

The reaction between neutral zinc atoms and copper (II) ions can be used to make an electrochemical cell if the electrons that leave the zinc atoms are first made to travel through a wire before reducing the copper ions. In order to do this, the half-reactions must take place in separate compartments, as shown in Figure 28-2. Figure 28-2 shows a strip of copper metal in a porous clay cup containing aqueous Cu^{2+} and SO_4^{2-} ions that were obtained by dissolving crystals of $CuSO_4$ in water. The porous cup is sitting in a beaker containing a strip of zinc metal immersed in an aqueous solution of Zn^{2+} and SO_4^{2-} ions that were obtained by dissolving crystals of $ZnSO_4$ in water.

With the porous cup inside the beaker of $ZnSO_4$ solution, no direct reaction will occur because the porous cup keeps the Cu^{2+} ions from coming into contact with the zinc strip. An equilibrium, however, is

Figure 28-2

A different setup (from that shown in Figure 28-1) for the reaction between Zn metal and copper (II) ions, Cu^{2+}. With this setup, contact between Cu^{2+} ions and Zn metal is prevented, and no reaction will take place. However, as will shortly be described, reaction will take place when only a small modification is made in the setup.

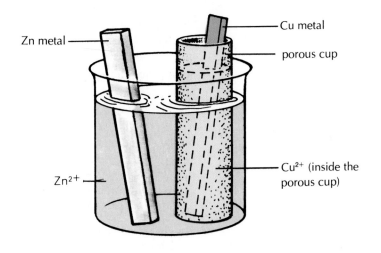

Zn metal —
Cu metal —
porous cup —
Cu²⁺ (inside the porous cup) —
Zn²⁺ —

established between each strip of metal and its dissolved ions. These equilibria can be represented by the following equations:

$$Zn \rightleftharpoons Zn^{2+} + 2e^-$$ (Eq. 5)

$$Cu \rightleftharpoons Cu^{2+} + 2e^-$$ (Eq. 6)

When a zinc atom from the metal strip becomes a zinc ion in the solution, it leaves two electrons behind on the metal. The reaction to the right in Equation 5 thus tends to give the zinc strip a negative charge. The reaction to the right in Equation 6 likewise tends to give the copper strip a negative charge.

Now suppose that a conducting wire is used to join the two strips of metal, as shown in Figure 28-3. It is found by experiment that electrons

Figure 28-3

The same setup as that shown in Figure 28-2 except that a wire now connects the one metal electrode with the other. (The connection is made through the filament of the light bulb.) The lighted bulb indicates that electrons are traveling through the wire and that a chemical reaction is taking place at the electrodes.

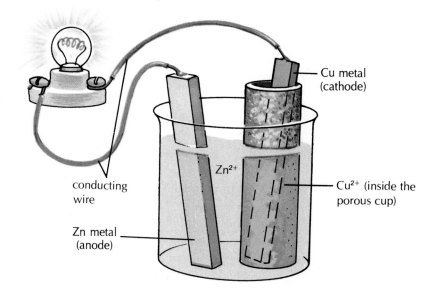

conducting wire

Zn metal (anode)

Zn^{2+}

Cu metal (cathode)

Cu^{2+} (inside the porous cup)

flow from the zinc through the wire to the copper. A light bulb inserted in the circuit can be made to light by this flow of current. The fact that the electrons flow from the zinc to the copper, rather than from the copper to the zinc, means that zinc atoms have a greater tendency to give up electrons and form ions than copper atoms have. That is, in this setup, the zinc strip becomes more negatively charged than the copper strip. Electrons are therefore driven from the zinc to the copper through the connecting conductor.

As a result of this flow of electrons, the number of excess electrons on the copper strip increases, causing the equilibrium in Equation 6 to shift to the left, the direction that causes electrons to be removed from the copper strip. That is, the shift in equilibrium causes Cu^{2+} ions in the solution to pick up electrons from the copper strip and become neutral copper atoms. Hence, adding the wire enables neutral zinc atoms to reduce Cu^{2+} ions even though the zinc atoms are at some distance from the copper ions.

The neutral copper atoms that are formed by the reaction become part of the copper strip, causing its mass to increase. As electrons leave the zinc strip through the wire, the equilibrium in Equation 5 is upset, causing it to shift to the right so as to replace the electrons that leave the strip. That is, more neutral zinc atoms go into solution as Zn^{2+} ions, leaving on the zinc strip the electrons the neutral atoms give up. As more and more neutral zinc atoms become ions and go into solution, the mass of the zinc strip becomes less and less.

The electrons that pass through the wire carry energy and can do useful work, such as lighting flashlight bulbs or ringing doorbells. When the light bulb in Figure 28-3 is replaced with a voltmeter, the voltmeter will indicate the electrical voltage being generated by this combination of half-reactions. See Figure 28-4. The voltage depends on the temperature, on the kinds of metals that are used for the strips, and on the concentrations of the ions in solution. At 25°C, zinc and copper strips immersed in solutions of Zn^{2+} and Cu^{2+} whose concentrations are 1 molar give a voltage of 1.10 volts. By way of comparison, the voltage of an ordinary flashlight cell is 1.5 volts.

Figure 28-4

The same setup as that shown in Figure 28-3 except that the light bulb has been replaced by a voltmeter. The arrows show the direction of electron movement. The voltmeter deflects to the right of the zero mark (as shown) when electrons enter the meter through the negative terminal. They deflect to the left when the electrons enter through the positive terminal.

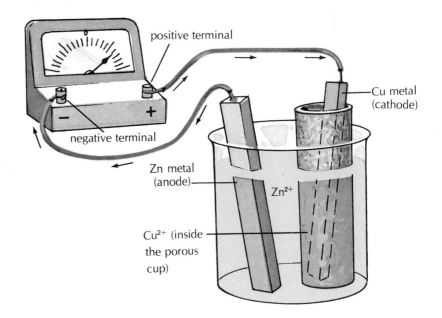

positive terminal

negative terminal

Cu metal (cathode)

Zn metal (anode)

Zn^{2+}

Cu^{2+} (inside the porous cup)

Voltage is sometimes called electromotive force, or emf. The **electromotive force,** or **voltage,** is a measure of the difference in electrical potential energy between two points in an electric circuit. In practical terms, a source of electromotive force, such as a battery, supplying a larger voltage will force a larger current through a particular circuit. A source of electromotive force supplying a smaller voltage will force a smaller current through the same circuit. See Figure 28-5. A more detailed discussion of electromotive force can be found in physics texts.

Chapter 28 . Electrochemistry II—Galvanic Cells   545

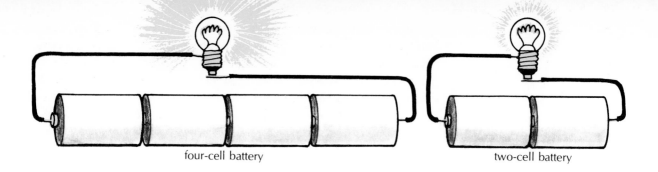

four-cell battery

two-cell battery

Figure 28-5

The four-cell battery provides twice the emf, or voltage, of the 2-cell battery. The larger voltage drives twice as much current through the circuit, making the bulb burn more brightly.

Many combinations of half-reactions can be used to produce electromotive forces. In all cases, when these reactions are arranged properly in a completed circuit, redox reactions take place. The electrons that are lost by the oxidation reaction are made to travel through a wire before being gained in the reduction reaction. Any device that makes use of a redox reaction to produce an electric current is called an **electrochemical cell.** Such a device is also called a **galvanic** (gal-VAN-ik) **cell** or a **voltaic** (vol-TAY-ik) **cell** after the Italian scientists Luigi Galvani (1737-1798) and Count Alessandro Volta (1745-1827).

An electrochemical cell that uses zinc metal dipped into a solution of zinc ions and copper metal dipped into a solution of copper (II) ions is called a Daniell cell.

Much of the same terminology applies to both galvanic and electrolytic cells. Both cells have electrodes. In both cases, the anode is the electrode where oxidation takes place. The cathode is the electrode where reduction takes place. However, the cathode is negative and the anode is positive in an electrolysis, while the opposite is true of a galvanic cell.

In a galvanic cell, the half-reactions that take place at the electrodes are called half-cell reactions. For example, in the Daniell cell, the half-cell reactions are:

HALF-CELL REACTION AT THE ANODE (Daniell cell)

$$Zn \longrightarrow Zn^{2+} + 2e^-$$ **(Eq. 7)**

HALF-CELL REACTION AT THE CATHODE (Daniell cell)

$$Cu^{2+} + 2e^- \longrightarrow Cu$$ **(Eq. 8)**

The complete equation for the reaction is obtained by adding the equations for the two half-cell reactions, which in this case gives:

COMPLETE REACTION (Daniell cell)

$$Zn + Cu^{2+} \longrightarrow Zn^{2+} + Cu$$ **(Eq. 9)**

The terms internal circuit and external circuit, used to discuss electrolysis cells, are also used in discussing galvanic cells. As in the case of electrolysis cells, the **internal circuit** is the solution through which passes a current of positive and negative ions. The rest of the galvanic cell is the external circuit. The **external circuit** is made up of the electrodes and their attached wires, and any device (such as a light bulb) that is powered by the galvanic cell. Electrons travel through the external circuit from one electrode to the other.

Questions for Sections 28-1 and 28-2

1. Compare a galvanic cell with an electrolysis cell and state in which one (or both?) (a) direct current is consumed, (b) direct current is produced, (c) reactions occur spontaneously, (d) reactions go on when energy is applied, (e) an oxidation reaction occurs at one electrode and a reduction reaction at the other.
2. Write the two half-reactions and the net molecular equation for the reaction that occurs when a zinc strip is placed inside a copper (II) sulfate solution.
*3. (a) Describe the porous cup and beaker setup that makes use of the reaction between zinc metal and copper (II) ions to produce an electric current. (b) What ionic reaction occurs at the zinc strip? (c) What ionic reaction occurs at the copper strip? (d) Why do excess electrons flow from the zinc strip to the copper strip? (e) Write the equation for the complete ionic reaction that takes place.
4. (a) What three names can be applied to a cell that uses a redox reaction to produce an electric current? (b) Define *voltage* or *electromotive force*. (c) What is the voltage of a cell, at 25°C, that uses a zinc strip in a 1 molar $ZnSO_4$ solution and a copper strip in a 1 molar solution of $CuSO_4$?
5. In the Daniell cell, which uses the $Zn + CuSO_4$ reaction, (a) why is the negative zinc electrode called the anode, (b) why is the positive copper electrode called the cathode? (c) Compare the charges on these electrodes with those on the anode and cathode in an electrolysis cell.

28-3 The Porous Cup and Salt Bridge

You may be wondering what the purpose of the porous cup is. What would happen if the copper and copper sulfate solution were simply placed in another beaker outside the zinc and zinc sulfate solution, as in Figure 28-6? Experiments show that no current flows in such a set-up. There must be some way for the charges that collect around each electrode to be neutralized by a flow of ions from one solution to the other. That is why a porous cup is used. Ions can gradually pass through the wall of the cup in either direction. When the two solutions are in separate beakers, electrical neutrality cannot be maintained. The reaction in the zinc-zinc sulfate beaker tends to increase the number of positive zinc ions, upsetting the balance of charge. See Equation 7. Meanwhile, in the copper-copper sulfate beaker, the reaction tends to consume positive copper ions, upsetting the balance of charge there, too. See Equation 8.

Figure 28-6

The same set-up as that shown in Figure 28-4 except that the porous cup has been removed from the beaker. When this is done, the current immediately stops flowing, and the voltmeter registers a voltage of zero.

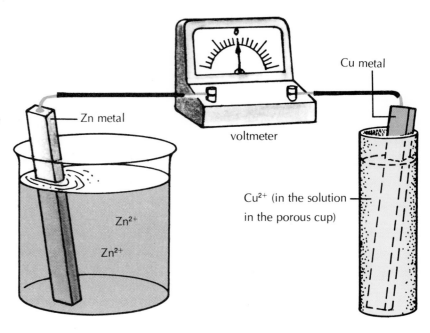

Cu metal

Zn metal

voltmeter

Cu^{2+} (in the solution in the porous cup)

Zn^{2+}

Zn^{2+}

Figure 28-7

A U-tube being prepared for use as a salt bridge. The tube is first filled to overflowing with an electrolyte such as Na_2SO_4 solution. The ends are then plugged so that the electrolyte will not run out of the ends of the tube when it is in use in a galvanic cell.

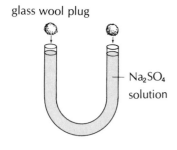

glass wool plug

Na_2SO_4 solution

When the porous cup is in the beaker, positively charged zinc ions gradually pass from the beaker, through the wall of the porous cup, and into the cup. As the zinc ions enter the porous cup, they replace some of the positively charged copper ions that are reduced. Electrical neutrality is also maintained by the passage of negative sulfate ions from the porous cup, through the cup wall, into the beaker. These negatively charged sulfate ions help neutralize the positive charge of the zinc ions formed at the zinc strip.

A passage for ions between one solution and the other can also be provided by what is called a salt bridge. A salt bridge can be made by filling a glass U-tube with the solution of an ionic salt, such as Na_2SO_4. See Figure 28-7. To use the salt bridge in a galvanic cell, the ends of the U-tube are first plugged with wads of glass wool. The U-tube is then inverted, and each end placed in a beaker containing the solutions for one of the half-reactions. Figure 28-8 shows how a salt bridge is used in a Daniell cell. Electrical neutrality of both solutions is maintained by the positive and negative ions within the bridge diffusing into the solutions in the beakers. In making the salt bridge, a salt must be chosen whose ions do not interfere with the reactions at either electrode.

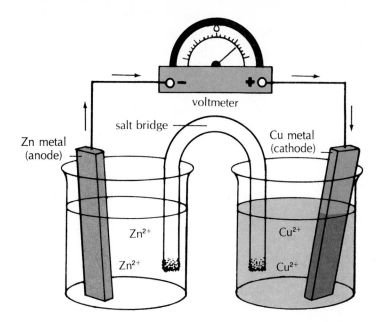

Figure 28-8

The use of a salt bridge in a Daniell cell. Once the bridge is lowered into the two beakers, a voltage develops between the two metals as shown by the voltmeter. The arrows show the direction of electron flow.

Questions for Section 28-3

6. A zinc strip is placed inside a beaker containing dilute $ZnSO_4$ solution; a copper strip is placed inside another beaker containing concentrated $CuSO_4$ solution. The strips are connected by a metal wire. Why is there only a relatively small flow of electrons in the external circuit, and why does this current last for only a brief instant?

*7. (a) If the Cu strip and $CuSO_4$ solution of question 6 were placed inside a porous cup and this cup placed inside the beaker containing the Zn and $ZnSO_4$, what ionic diffusion would occur? (b) How does this diffusion make it possible for electrons to flow through the external circuit?

8. How can a salt bridge serve to maintain electrical neutrality in the solution of a Daniell cell?

28-4 The Ag/Ag⁺ Half-Cell Reaction

There are many half-cell reactions that can be combined to make a galvanic cell. For example, consider the half-cell reaction for a strip of silver metal dipped into a solution of silver ions:

THE SILVER-SILVER ION HALF-CELL REACTION

$$Ag^+ + e^- \rightleftharpoons Ag \qquad \text{(Eq. 10)}$$

Suppose that a galvanic cell were made of this half-cell reaction teamed up with the copper half-cell reaction of the previous section:

THE COPPER-COPPER (II) ION HALF-CELL REACTIONS

$$Cu^{2+} + 2e^- \rightleftharpoons Cu \qquad \text{(Eq. 11)}$$

Figure 28-9 shows the setup for the cell. When the switch is closed, the chemical reaction will begin, and the voltmeter will show a voltage. In one half-cell, oxidation will occur. In the other, reduction will occur. But which will occur where? Here are the two reactions, only one of which will actually happen:

Either . . .
REACTION 1 — Cu^{2+} reduced, Ag oxidized

$$Cu^{2+} + 2e^- \longrightarrow Cu$$

$$2Ag \longrightarrow 2Ag^+ + 2e^-$$

or . . .
REACTION 2 — Ag^+ reduced, Cu oxidized

$$2Ag^+ + 2e^- \longrightarrow 2Ag$$

$$Cu \longrightarrow Cu^{2+} + 2e^-$$

Which reaction takes place depends upon which ion has a greater tendency to be reduced. Worded another way, it depends upon which metal has a greater tendency to be oxidized. A metal is more easily oxidized if its neutral atoms tend to give up electrons more readily. Experiments show that Reaction 2 is the one that actually takes place. This means that Ag^+ ions are more easily reduced than Cu^{2+} ions and that copper metal is more easily oxidized than silver metal. When the temperature is 25°C, and the concentrations of Cu^{2+} and Ag^+ ions in the solutions are both 1 molar, the voltage across the electrodes is 0.46 volt. The copper electrode in this case is negative, and the silver electrode is positive. See Figure 28-9.

When referring to half-cells, it is common practice to call them by the reducing agent and oxidizing agent of which they are made. For

Figure 28-9

The setup for the galvanic cell composed of the Cu/Cu^{2+} and Ag/Ag^+ half-cells. Compare this figure with Figure 28-8. In this figure, copper metal is the stronger reducing agent, making it the anode. Electrons therefore travel into the meter through the meter's positive terminal, making the needle deflect in the opposite direction. In Figure 28-8, Zn metal was the stronger reducing agent, making the electrons flow in the opposite direction.

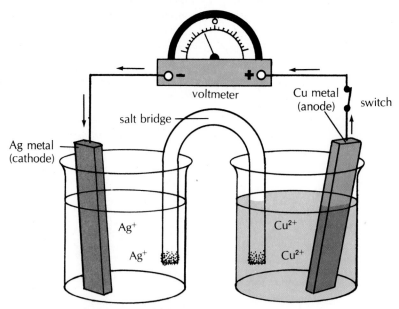

example, the half-cell made of a strip of copper metal dipped into a solution of copper (II) ions is called the *copper/copper (II) ion* half-cell. Using chemical symbols, the *copper/copper (II) ion* half-cell is written Cu/Cu^{2+}. The half-cell made of a strip of silver metal in a solution of silver ions is called the *silver/silver ion* half-cell. It is symbolized Ag/Ag^+.

Questions for Section 28-4

9. A galvanic cell is made up of the Cu/Cu^{2+} and Ag/Ag^+ half-cells. Write the ionic equation for (a) the reaction at the anode, (b) the reaction at the cathode, (c) the complete ionic reaction.
*10. For the galvanic cell in question 9, (a) which electrode is negative, (b) which electrode is positive, (c) which is the cathode? (d) What is the direction of the flow of electrons in the external circuit? (e) Account for the direction of flow of the electrons.

28-5 The Standard Hydrogen Half-Cell

The half-reaction,

$$2H^+(aq) + 2e^- \rightleftharpoons H_2(g) \qquad \text{(Eq. 12)}$$

has a special significance in electrochemistry. Its significance will become apparent as we proceed. The half-reaction shows dissolved hydrogen ions in equilibrium with hydrogen gas. When this reaction is used as one of the two half-cell reactions in a galvanic cell, it is called a **standard hydrogen half-cell** if the concentration of hydrogen ions is 1 molar, the temperature is 25°C, and the hydrogen gas is at 1 atmosphere pressure. The half-reaction in Equation 12 is a reduction if it proceeds from left to right. It is an oxidation if it goes in the reverse direction. The direction it proceeds in is determined by the particular half-cell with which it is connected. For example, when connected to a Cu/Cu^{2+} half-cell (one of the half-cells in the Daniell cell), the reaction proceeds in the reverse direction. That is, hydrogen gas, H_2, loses electrons to produce hydrogen ions, H^+. When connected to a Zn/Zn^{2+} half-cell (the other half-cell in a Daniell cell), the forward reaction occurs. Hydrogen ions react to produce hydrogen gas.

The significance of the standard hydrogen half-cell is that its potential energy has arbitrarily been chosen at zero. The potential energies of all other half-cell reactions are determined by measuring the voltage that develops between these other half-cell reactions and the standard hydrogen half-cell. The potential energies of all other half-cell reactions are then stated in terms of how much greater or how much less they are than the potential energy of the standard hydrogen half-cell. This practice is similar to the arbitrary assignment of zero to the elevation of sea level, and then to the stating of all other elevations in terms of their distances above or below sea level.

Chapter 28   Electrochemistry II—Galvanic Cells   551

Figure 28-10

The standard hydrogen electrode.
Hydrogen gas at standard pressure is bubbled over a platinum electrode that is immersed in a solution whose hydrogen ion concentration is 1 molar. Hydrochloric acid is often used as a source of the hydrogen ion. (The dashed line shows the position of the salt bridge when the half-cell is connected to another half-cell to form a voltaic cell.)

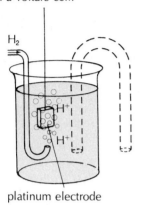

platinum electrode

We will come back to the subject of how a standard hydrogen half-cell is used, but first you may be wondering how a half-cell can be constructed from hydrogen gas and dissolved hydrogen ions. Up to this point, a metal has always been part of a half-cell reaction, and the metal has served as an electrode. In the standard hydrogen half-cell, there is an electrode, but the electrode is not a reactant. It is a platinum strip coated with a finely divided form of platinum called platinum black. Platinum is inactive, reacting with neither hydrogen gas nor dissolved hydrogen ions. However, the platinum black has the ability to hold (adsorb) concentrated portions of hydrogen gas on its surface in an active form. Reaction occurs between the active form of hydrogen and the hydrogen ions in solution. When the forward reaction is taking place (Equation 12), hydrogen ions "withdraw" electrons from the platinum electrode and form hydrogen gas. When the reverse reaction is taking place, the electrons that are given up by the hydrogen gas are "deposited" on the platinum electrode. During the operation of a standard hydrogen half-cell, hydrogen gas at 1 atmosphere pressure is continuously bubbled over the surface of the platinum electrode to assure a constant supply of it. See Figure 28-10.

28-6   Standard Reduction Potentials

The potential energies of many half-cell reactions have been determined by running the half-reactions in galvanic cells in which the standard hydrogen half-cell is the other half-cell.* In all cases, the temperature is kept at 25°C, 1 molar concentrations of all ions are used, and gases, if such take part in the reactions, are kept at 1 atmosphere pressure. These conditions are called **standard conditions.**   **Standard electrode potential** is the name given to the voltage that is obtained at standard conditions when a given half-cell is run in combination with the standard hydrogen electrode. Standard electrode potentials are represented by the symbol $E°$.

Tables have been made that show standard electrode potentials. To show how such a table is made, three galvanic cells will be discussed. In all three cases, the standard hydrogen half-cell is one of the half-cells.

The first half-cell is silver metal dipped into a solution of silver ions, Ag/Ag$^+$. When this half-cell is in combination with a standard hydrogen half-cell, only one of the following two reactions will take place:

---

*Although the standard hydrogen electrode is the universal standard to which all other electrode potentials are related, it is rather inconvenient to use. It is much easier to use the normal calomel (mercurous chloride) electrode. This has a standard reduction potential of 0.28 volt and is based upon the reaction: $Hg_2Cl_2 + 2e^- \rightarrow 2Hg + 2Cl^-$

REACTION 1 — Hydrogen ion, H^+, is reduced:

$$2H^+ + 2e^- \longrightarrow H_2 \qquad \text{(reduction)}$$

$$Ag \longrightarrow Ag^+ + e^- \qquad \text{(oxidation)}$$

REACTION 2 — Silver ion, Ag^+, is reduced:

$$Ag^+ + e^- \longrightarrow Ag \qquad \text{(reduction)}$$

$$H_2 \longrightarrow 2H^+ + 2e^- \qquad \text{(oxidation)}$$

Experiments show that Reaction 2 is what actually happens. Silver ion is reduced. Evidently, it is easier to reduce silver ions than hydrogen ions. A voltmeter shows that the voltage for the reduction of silver ion is +0.80 volt.

The second half-cell is the *copper/copper (II) ion* half-cell, Cu/Cu^{2+}. Only one of two reactions can take place when this half-cell is connected to a standard hydrogen half-cell:

REACTION 1 — Hydrogen ion, H^+, is reduced:

$$2H^+ + 2e^- \longrightarrow H_2 \qquad \text{(reduction)}$$

$$Cu \longrightarrow Cu^{2+} + 2e^- \qquad \text{(oxidation)}$$

REACTION 2 — Copper (II) ion, Cu^{2+}, is reduced:

$$Cu^{2+} + 2e^- \longrightarrow Cu \qquad \text{(reduction)}$$

$$H_2 \longrightarrow 2H^+ + 2e^- \qquad \text{(oxidation)}$$

Experiments show that Reaction 2 is what actually happens. Once again the metallic ion, in this case Cu^{2+}, is reduced rather than the hydrogen ion. However, the voltage for this galvanic cell is only +0.34 volts. The smaller voltage indicates that copper (II) ions are not as easily reduced as silver ions.

We can begin listing these oxidizing agents in order of the ease with which they can be reduced. Since silver ions can be reduced more easily than copper ions, the silver ions should go first:

$$Ag^+$$
$$Cu^{2+}$$
$$H^+$$

The table is more useful if it shows the half-reactions in which these ions play a role:

$$Ag^+ + e^- \longrightarrow Ag$$

$$Cu^{2+} + 2e^- \longrightarrow Cu$$

$$2H^+ + 2e^- \longrightarrow H_2$$

It is also helpful to show the voltages between the standard hydrogen half-cell and the metal/metallic ion half-cells:

	$E°$
$Ag^+ + e^- \longrightarrow Ag$	+0.80 volt
$Cu^{2+} + 2e^- \longrightarrow Cu$	+0.34 volt
$2H^+ + 2e^- \longrightarrow H_2$	0.00 volt

The point needs to be stressed that the voltages are those obtained when each metal/metallic ion half-cell is connected to the standard hydrogen half-cell at standard conditions. The reaction for hydrogen and its ion has a voltage of 0.00 volt because the hydrogen half-cell was selected as a standard and arbitrarily assigned this voltage.

We now look at the third half-cell. This half-cell is made up of zinc metal dipped into a solution of zinc ions: Zn/Zn^{2+}. When this half-cell is connected to a standard hydrogen half-cell, one of the following reactions takes place:

REACTION 1 — Hydrogen ion, H^+, is reduced:

$$2H^+ + 2e^- \longrightarrow H_2 \quad \text{(reduction)}$$

$$Zn \longrightarrow Zn^{2+} + 2e^- \quad \text{(oxidation)}$$

REACTION 2 — Zinc ion, Zn^{2+}, is reduced:

$$Zn^{2+} + 2e^- \longrightarrow Zn \quad \text{(reduction)}$$

$$H_2 \longrightarrow 2H^+ + 2e^- \quad \text{(oxidation)}$$

Reaction 1 is what actually happens. Unlike the other two cases, hydrogen ion is reduced rather than the metallic ion. The reading of the voltmeter indicates that something is different this time, because it now shows electron flow in the opposite direction from the other two cases. For the Zn/Zn^{2+} half-cell, the EMF is 0.76 volt. However, since the flow of electrons in this half-cell is in the other direction, we assign it a negative value, or -0.76 v. This indicates that H+ ions are reduced more readily than are Zn2+ ions. The more negative the E° value of a half-cell, the more difficult it is for reduction to occur. The result is the table in Figure 28-11.

Figure 28-11

Standard reduction potentials for some selected half-cells.

Reduction Half-Reactions		Standard Reduction Potential, E°
Oxidizing Agents	Reducing Agents	
$Ag^+ + e^- \longrightarrow$	Ag	+0.80 volt
$Cu^{2+} + 2e^- \longrightarrow$	Cu	+0.34 volt
$2H^+ + 2e^- \longrightarrow$	H_2	0.00 volt
$Zn^{2+} + 2e^- \longrightarrow$	Zn	−0.76 volt

Rather than titling Figure 28-11 "Standard Electrode Potentials," we have titled it "Standard Reduction Potentials," since it lists oxidizing agents in order of the ease with which they can be reduced. Of the four oxidizing agents listed, Ag^+ can be reduced most easily. The zinc ion, Zn^{2+}, is the most difficult to reduce.

Questions for Sections 28-5 and 28-6

11. (a) Describe the structure of the standard hydrogen electrode. (b) Write the ionic equation for its half-reaction. Does this half-reaction go in the direction of an oxidation or reduction when connected with the (c) Zn/Zn^{2+} half-cell, (d) Cu/Cu^{2+} half-cell?

*12. (a) What are the standard conditions at which standard electrode potentials are measured? (b) What is the standard potential, $E°$, of the hydrogen electrode? (c) Write the equations for the half-reactions that go on when the hydrogen electrode is paired with a Ag/Ag^+ half-cell.

13. (a) What does the positive voltage of a metal/metallic ion half-cell indicate about the ease of reduction of the metallic ion as compared with the hydrogen ion? (b) The standard reduction potentials for the hydrogen, copper, zinc, and silver electrodes are, respectively, 0.00, 0.34, −0.76, and 0.80 volt. Arrange the ions of these elements in the order of their abilities to be reduced, the most easily reduced placed first. (c) Write the equation for the half-reaction that occurs at the zinc electrode when it is paired with the hydrogen electrode, at standard conditions.

28-7 Voltages of Galvanic Cells not Containing the Standard Hydrogen Half-Cell

$E°$ values tell the voltage developed between a half-cell and the standard hydrogen half-cell. However, they can also be used to determine the voltage developed between any two half-cells listed in the table when these half-cells are at standard conditions. Let us see how this is done for the galvanic cell operating at standard conditions that is made up of the two half-cells:

$$Ag^+ + e^- \longrightarrow Ag \qquad E° = +0.80 \text{ volt}$$

$$Zn^{2+} + 2e^- \longrightarrow Zn \qquad E° = -0.76 \text{ volt}$$

The $E°$ values show that the potential energy of the Ag/Ag^+ half-cell is 0.80 volt *above* the potential energy of the standard hydrogen half-cell. (The *plus* sign indicates *above* zero.) The potential energy of the Zn/Zn^{2+} half-cell is 0.76 volt *below* the potential energy of the standard hydrogen half-cell. (The *minus* sign indicates *below* zero.) A galvanic cell composed of these two half-cells would register a voltage that is the difference between the two:

$$+0.80 \text{ volt}$$
$$(-) \ -0.76 \text{ volt}$$
$$\overline{1.56 \text{ volts}}$$

Notice that the mathematics is algebraic. It works just like elevations: If Point A is 1000 meters *above* sea level (+1000 meters) and Point B is 500 meters *below* sea level (−500 meters), then the difference in their elevations is 1500 meters. That is, Point A is 1500 meters above Point B.

$$+1000 \text{ meters}$$
$$(-) - 500 \text{ meters}$$
$$\overline{1500 \text{ meters}}$$

Several other points about the table (Figure 28-11) of standard reduction potentials should be noted. The substances to the left of the arrow in each reduction half-reaction are oxidizing agents. The substances to the right of the arrow are reducing agents. Any oxidizing agent will react with any reducing agent that appears below it in the table. For example, Cu^{2+} will oxidize hydrogen gas or metallic zinc,

$$Cu^{2+} + H_2 \longrightarrow Cu + 2H^+$$

$$Cu^{2+} + Zn \longrightarrow Cu + Zn^{2+}$$

but will not oxidize metallic silver, since metallic silver, Ag, is above Cu^{2+} in the table of Figure 28-11.

With this information in hand, we can go back to the galvanic cell mentioned earlier in this section, that made up of the half-cells Ag/Ag^+ and Zn/Zn^{2+}. We already determined that the voltage of this galvanic cell is 1.56 volts at standard conditions. However, we did not say what would reduce what, or what would oxidize what. Since Ag^+ is above Zn in the table in Figure 28-11, we know that Ag^+ will be reduced by zinc, rather than Ag reducing Zn^{2+}. This same information can be stated in terms of oxidation. Since Ag^+ is above Zn, Zn will be oxidized by Ag^+, rather than Ag being oxidized by Zn^{2+}.

Which half-reactions occur in a galvanic cell can also be determined from the $E°$ values of its half-reactions. Suppose a half-reaction proceeds in the reverse direction, from right to left, so that it describes an oxidation rather than a reduction. Then, the $E°$ value as given in a table of standard reduction potentials must have its sign changed. If the algebraic sum of the $E°$ values for two half-reactions is positive, it means that the half-reactions take place spontaneously. If the sum of the $E°$ values is negative, it means that the half-reactions will not take place spontaneously. The sample problem illustrates this concept.

SAMPLE PROBLEM

Maria Goeppert Mayer
(1906-1972)

Maria Geoppert Mayer was born and educated in Göttingen, Germany. In this university town she began work in quantum mechanics under Max Born. Later she and Born published an article on the lattice theory of crystals.

Throughout her career, Mayer continued to be associated with distinguished scientists. At the suggestion of Harold Urey, she joined the Manhattan Project, the U.S. government's secret research on the atomic bomb.

In 1947, Mayer began a study of the elements with Edward Teller. Teller soon gave up the research but Mayer kept on with it, determined to understand the orderly arrangement of nuclear particles in stable elements. As a result of her study, Mayer proposed a shell structure for the nucleus.

Many scientists thought the theory was wrong, but Enrico Fermi was convinced that it was correct. He and others persuaded Mayer to publish an account of her work. At almost the same time, another physicist, Hans Jensen, published his own paper outlining the same theory.

Maria Goeppert Mayer, Hans Jensen, and Eugene Wigner shared the Nobel Prize for Physics (1963). She was the first woman to receive the prize in theoretical physics.

A silver-silver ion half-cell and a zinc-zinc ion half-cell at standard conditions are connected to make a galvanic cell. What reactions will take place and what will the voltage be?

Solution. The equations for the half-reactions, as obtained from Figure 28-11, are:

$$Ag^+ + e^- \longrightarrow Ag \qquad E° = +0.80 \text{ volt}$$

$$Zn^{2+} + 2e^- \longrightarrow Zn \qquad E° = -0.76 \text{ volt}$$

Since both the half-reactions show a reduction, one of them must be reversed (to show an oxidation). Let us suppose that the oxidation occurs in the silver/silver ion half-cell. Then, the equation must be reversed, and we must remember to change the sign of $E°$ at the same time:

$$Ag \longrightarrow Ag^+ + e^- \qquad E° = -0.80 \text{ volt}$$

Now we double all terms to make electrons in both half-reactions equal, and combine the two equations for the half-reactions:

$$2Ag \longrightarrow 2Ag^+ + 2e^- \qquad E° = -0.80 \text{ volt}$$

$$+ \quad Zn^{2+} + 2e^- \longrightarrow Zn \qquad\qquad + \qquad E° = -0.76 \text{ volt}$$

$$\overline{2Ag + Zn^{2+} \longrightarrow 2Ag^+ + Zn} \qquad \overline{\text{voltage} = -1.56 \text{ volts}}$$

Note that when the terms in the silver/silver ion half-reaction were doubled, the voltage was left unchanged. The voltage was not changed because it depends upon the nature of the reacting materials, the temperature, and the concentration of the ions. The voltage is not affected by the number of moles of substances reacting. That the voltage is negative means that the half-reactions will not proceed spontaneously in the directions shown. This means that each half-reaction must proceed spontaneously in the opposite direction. Therefore, we rewrite the equations in the reverse directions, being careful to remember to change the signs of the voltages:

$$2Ag^+ + 2e^- \longrightarrow 2Ag \qquad E° = +0.80 \text{ volt}$$

$$+ \quad Zn \longrightarrow Zn^{2+} + 2e^- \qquad\qquad + \qquad E° = +0.76 \text{ volt}$$

$$\overline{2Ag^+ + Zn \longrightarrow 2Ag + Zn^{2+}} \qquad \overline{\text{voltage} = +1.56 \text{ volts}}$$

That the voltage is now positive indicates that the half-reactions do proceed spontaneously in the directions shown. At standard conditions, the voltage of the cell is 1.56 volts.

Suppose that these half-reactions proceed for a while. As silver ions are reduced, their concentration decreases. At lower and lower concentrations of silver ion, the voltage becomes less and less. Eventually, the voltage of the cell will become zero. The cell will have become "run down."

Chapter 28 Electrochemistry II—Galvanic Cells

14. In Figure 28-11, the reduction half-reactions and standard reduction potentials are given for the silver, copper, hydrogen, and zinc electrodes. Indicate four (4) redox pairs in each of which the oxidizing agent can react with the reducing agent.

*15. What is the standard potential of the half-reaction,
   (a) $Cu \rightarrow Cu^{2+} + 2e^-$
   (b) $Zn^{2+} + 2e^- \rightarrow Zn$
   (c) What is the sum of the potentials in (a) and (b)?
   (d) Using the answer in (c), would you predict that the reactions, as written in (a) and (b), would take place in a galvanic cell made with zinc and copper electrodes? Explain.

16. Using Figure 28-11, calculate the standard voltage of the galvanic cells formed by joining together the following half-cells: (a) Ag/Ag^+ and Zn/Zn^{2+}, (b) Ag/Ag^+ and Cu/Cu^{2+}, (c) Zn/Zn^{2+} and H_2/H^+.

17. For the galvanic cell, based upon the reaction
$$2Ag^+ + Zn \rightarrow Zn^{2+} + 2Ag$$
(a) what happens to the silver ion concentration as the cell is used, (b) how does the change in Ag^+ ion concentration affect the cell voltage, (c) what will eventually happen to the cell voltage after continuous use?

28-8   The Expanded Table of Standard Reduction Potentials

The table of standard reduction potentials in Figure 28-12 lists the four half-reactions given in Figure 28-11 plus many more half-reactions. It should be emphasized that each line in both tables gives a *half*-reaction, and it takes two *half*-reactions in order for chemical change to occur. Thus fluorine gas, F_2, the oxidizing agent, whose half-reaction is the first entry in Figure 28-12, does not become fluoride ions, F^-, all by itself. This can only happen when an appropriate reducing agent is present. Recall from the last section that reducing agents are to the right of the arrows and that an oxidizing agent can react only with a reducing agent that is below it in the table. Thus fluorine, F_2, can become fluoride ions, F^-, only if there is a reducing agent present that fluorine is capable of oxidizing. For example, this half-reaction

$$F_2 + 2e^- \longrightarrow 2F^- \qquad \text{(Eq. 13)}$$

can take place only if a reducing agent, such as lithium, Li, is present. The last entry in the table is the half-reaction in which lithium occurs:

$$Li^+ + e^- \longrightarrow Li \qquad \text{(Eq. 14)}$$

But notice that the oxidizing agent, fluorine (F_2), oxidizes the reducing agent, lithium (Li), *not* the oxidizing agent, lithium ion (Li^+). Therefore, Equation 14 should be reversed if it is to show what happens when fluorine comes into contact with lithium:

$$Li \longrightarrow Li^+ + e^- \qquad \text{(Eq. 15)}$$

Figure 28-12

Standard reduction potentials.
(Water solutions in which ion concentrations are 1 molar, temperature is 298 K, and gas pressures are 1 atmosphere.)

Half-Reactions	$E°$
Oxidizing Agents Reducing Agents	(volts)
$F_2(g) + 2e^- \longrightarrow 2F^-$	+2.87
$MnO_4^- + 8H^+ + 5e^- \longrightarrow Mn^{2+} + 4H_2O$	+1.52
$Au^{3+} + 3e^- \longrightarrow Au(s)$	+1.50
$Cl_2(g) + 2e^- \longrightarrow 2Cl^-$	+1.36
$Cr_2O_7^{2-} + 14H^+ + 6e^- \longrightarrow 2Cr^{3+} + 7H_2O$	+1.33
$MnO_2(s) + 4H^+ + 2e^- \longrightarrow Mn^{2+} + 2H_2O$	+1.28
$\frac{1}{2}O_2(g) + 2H^+ + 2e^- \longrightarrow H_2O$	+1.23
$Br_2(l) + 2e^- \longrightarrow 2Br^-$	+1.06
$NO_3^- + 4H^+ + 3e^- \longrightarrow NO(g) + 2H_2O$	+0.96
$\frac{1}{2}O_2(g) + 2H^+(10^{-7}M) + 2e^- \longrightarrow H_2O$	+0.82
$Ag^+ + e^- \longrightarrow Ag(s)$	+0.80
$\frac{1}{2}Hg_2^{2+} + e^- \longrightarrow Hg(l)$	+0.79
$Hg^{2+} + 2e^- \longrightarrow Hg(l)$	+0.78
$NO_3^- + 2H^+ + e^- \longrightarrow NO_2(g) + H_2O$	+0.78
$Fe^{3+} + e^- \longrightarrow Fe^{2+}$	+0.77
$I_2(s) + 2e^- \longrightarrow 2I^-$	+0.53
$Cu^+ + e^- \longrightarrow Cu(s)$	+0.52
$Cu^{2+} + 2e^- \longrightarrow Cu(s)$	+0.34
$SO_4^{2-} + 4H^+ + 2e^- \longrightarrow SO_2(g) + 2H_2O$	+0.17
$Sn^{4+} + 2e^- \longrightarrow Sn^{2+}$	+0.15
$2H^+ + 2e^- \longrightarrow H_2(g)$	0.00
$Pb^{2+} + 2e^- \longrightarrow Pb(s)$	−0.13
$Sn^{2+} + 2e^- \longrightarrow Sn(s)$	−0.14
$Ni^{2+} + 2e^- \longrightarrow Ni(s)$	−0.25
$Co^{2+} + 2e^- \longrightarrow Co(s)$	−0.28
$2H^+(10^{-7}M) + 2e^- \longrightarrow H_2(g)$	−0.41
$Fe^{2+} + 2e^- \longrightarrow Fe(s)$	−0.44
$Cr^{3+} + 3e^- \longrightarrow Cr(s)$	−0.74
$Zn^{2+} + 2e^- \longrightarrow Zn(s)$	−0.76
$2H_2O + 2e^- \longrightarrow 2OH^- + H_2(g)$	−0.83
$Mn^{2+} + 2e^- \longrightarrow Mn(s)$	−1.18
$Al^{3+} + 3e^- \longrightarrow Al(s)$	−1.66
$Mg^{2+} + 2e^- \longrightarrow Mg(s)$	−2.37
$Na^+ + e^- \longrightarrow Na(s)$	−2.71
$Ca^{2+} + 2e^- \longrightarrow Ca(s)$	−2.87
$Sr^{2+} + 2e^- \longrightarrow Sr(s)$	−2.89
$Ba^{2+} + 2e^- \longrightarrow Ba(s)$	−2.90
$Cs^+ + e^- \longrightarrow Cs(s)$	−2.92
$K^+ + e^- \longrightarrow K(s)$	−2.92
$Rb^+ + e^- \longrightarrow Rb(s)$	−2.93
$Li^+ + e^- \longrightarrow Li(s)$	−3.00

Let us double the terms in Equation 15 (to double the number of electrons):

$$2Li \longrightarrow 2Li^+ + 2e^- \qquad \textbf{(Eq. 16)}$$

Then, the half-reaction for the reduction of fluorine (Equation 13) can be added to the half-reaction for the oxidation of lithium (Equation 16) to get the complete reaction:

$$F_2 + 2e^- \longrightarrow 2F^- \qquad \textbf{(Eq. 13)}$$

$$+ \; 2Li \longrightarrow 2Li^+ + 2e^- \qquad \textbf{(Eq. 16)}$$

$$\overline{\quad 2Li + F_2 \longrightarrow 2Li^+ + 2F^- \quad} \qquad \textbf{(Eq. 17)}$$

A few points should be noted about the table of standard reduction

Chapter 28   Electrochemistry II—Galvanic Cells   **559**

Emma Perry Carr (1880-1972)

The Garvan Medal is an award given to American women who distinguish themselves in the field of chemistry. The first of these honors went to Emma Perry Carr.

Working at Mount Holyoke College, Emma Carr carried out a research project to learn why groups in a molecule absorb certain wavelengths of light and what happens within the molecule when the light is absorbed.

She was among the first scientists in a U.S. institution to use absorption spectra to study the structure of a molecule.

Besides doing research at the college, Carr was also professor of chemistry and department head until her retirement in 1946. Through the research program she started, a record number of women went on to higher degrees and to jobs in science.

potentials in Figure 28-12. In a number of the half-reactions listed, you will see the hydrogen ion, H^+. The reduction of the dichromate ion, $Cr_2O_7^{2-}$, fifth entry in the table, is an example. The hydrogen ion is present because the dichromate ion can be reduced to the chromium (III) ion, Cr^{3+}, only if the solution is acidic. The presence of the hydrogen ion in a half-reaction means that the half-reaction will proceed as shown only if the solution containing the oxidizing and reducing agent is made acidic.

Another point to note about Figure 28-12 is that fluorine, F_2, the first entry, is the most powerful oxidizing agent. It can react with all the reducing agents in the table. Lithium, Li, the last entry in the table, is the most powerful reducing agent in the list. It can react with all the oxidizing agents. In fact, the last eleven metals in the table are such powerful reducing agents that they can react with water (can reduce water) to produce hydrogen gas. (The reduction of water is the 12th half-reaction from the bottom of the table.)

SAMPLE PROBLEM

Use the table of standard reduction potentials (Figure 28-12) to determine the products of the reaction between lithium, Li, and water, H_2O. Symbolically, the problem can be stated:

$$Li + H_2O \longrightarrow ?$$

Solution. From Figure 28-12, note that water can act as either an oxidizing agent (12th half-reaction from the bottom) or as a reducing agent (7th half-reaction from the top). Only as an oxidizing agent can water react with lithium metal, Li, the strongest reducing agent in the table (last half-reaction). The two entries are:

$$2H_2O + 2e^- \longrightarrow 2OH^- + H_2(g) \qquad \textbf{(Eq. 18)}$$

$$Li^+ + e^- \longrightarrow Li \qquad \textbf{(Eq. 19)}$$

Since the oxidizing agent, H_2O, is above the reducing agent, Li, an oxidation-reduction reaction will take place in which the products of the reaction are the right side of Equation 18 and the left side of Equation 19. We need to reverse Equation 19 so that the products go on the right side:

$$Li \longrightarrow Li^+ + e^- \qquad \textbf{(Eq. 20)}$$

We need also to double all terms to make the number of electrons transferred in the reduction (Equation 18) equal the number transferred in the oxidation (Equation 20):

$$2Li \longrightarrow 2Li^+ + 2e^- \qquad \textbf{(Eq. 21)}$$

To obtain the complete equation, add Equations 18 and 21:

$$2H_2O + 2e^- \longrightarrow 2OH^- + H_2 \qquad \textbf{(Eq. 18)}$$

$$+ \ 2Li \longrightarrow 2Li^+ + 2e^- \qquad \textbf{(Eq. 21)}$$

$$\overline{2Li + 2H_2O \longrightarrow 2Li^+ + 2OH^- + H_2} \qquad \textbf{(Eq. 22)}$$

Equation 22 is an ionic equation. Written as a molecular equation, it becomes:

$$2Li + 2H_2O \longrightarrow 2LiOH + H_2 \qquad \textbf{(Eq. 23)}$$

The lithium hydroxide, LiOH, is in aqueous solution. It can be recovered as a solid by evaporating the water.

Notice that both the ionic equation (Equation 22) and the molecular equation (Equation 23) balance with respect to both numbers of atoms and with respect to charge. This balance is assured when the number of electrons in both half-reactions is made equal.

Questions for Section 28-8

18. In the table of standard electrode potentials (Figure 28-12), (a) which substance is the strongest oxidizing agent, (b) which substance is the strongest reducing agent? (c) Write the complete redox equation involving these two substances. (d) At standard conditions, what is the voltage of the galvanic cell using this reaction?
19. Using Figure 28-12 to obtain the products, write the equation for the reaction between (a) potassium and water, (b) barium and water.
*20. Determine the standard net voltage of the cell formed from the following half-cells: (a) Ca/Ca^{2+} and Fe/Fe^{2+}, (b) Na/Na^+ and Cu/Cu^{2+}, (c) Cl^-/Cl_2 and Fe^{2+}/Fe^{3+}.
*21. (a) At standard conditions, a given galvanic cell has a net potential of 0.49 volt. One of the half-reactions in this cell is,
$$Ni^{2+} + 2e^- \rightarrow Ni(s)$$
What is the standard reduction potential of the other electrode? It is included in the table in Figure 28-12. (b) Write the equation for the half-reaction that occurs at this electrode.

28-9   The Chemical Activities of Metals

The reaction that is commonly used in the laboratory to prepare hydrogen gas is a single replacement reaction in which an "active" metal reduces the hydrogen ion, H^+, that occurs in dilute acid solutions. Zinc is often used as the reducing agent and dilute H_2SO_4 as the source of hydrogen ions. The equations for the reaction are:

MOLECULAR EQUATION

$$Zn + H_2SO_4 \longrightarrow ZnSO_4 + H_2 \qquad \textbf{(Eq. 24)}$$

IONIC EQUATION

$$Zn + 2H^+ \longrightarrow Zn^{2+} + H_2 \qquad \textbf{(Eq. 25)}$$

The table of standard reduction potentials, Figure 28-12, tells which metals, in addition to zinc, can be used to prepare hydrogen by this

gold, Au	
silver, Ag	
mercury, Hg	
copper, Cu	
lead, Pb	
tin, Sn	
nickel, Ni	
iron, Fe	
chromium, Cr	
zinc, Zn	
aluminum, Al	
magnesium, Mg	
sodium, Na	
calcium, Ca	
strontium, Sr	
barium, Ba	
cesium, Cs	
potassium, K	
rubidium, Rb	
lithium, Li	

(Greater chemical activity →)

method. Figure 28-12 shows that the reduction half-reaction for the H^+ ion, for which $E°$ is 0.00, is about halfway down the table.

REDUCTION OF HYDROGEN ION

$$2H^+ + 2e^- \longrightarrow H_2 \qquad E° = 0.00$$

All the metals that appear below this half-reaction will reduce the hydrogen ion. For example, nickel, Ni, iron, Fe, and aluminum, Al, will all reduce H^+. However, metals above the hydrogen half-reaction will not react with the hydrogen ion in dilute acids. Copper, Cu, and silver, Ag, for example, will not react. The table of standard reduction potentials, Figure 28-12, can be used to rank metals in the order of their chemical activities. Figure 28-13 gives such a table.

As a footnote to this section it should be added that the metals at the bottom of the table in Figures 28-12 and 28-13 are so active that they are not used in the laboratory preparation of hydrogen. Their reactions with dilute hydrogen ion are vigorous enough to be dangerous.

Figure 28-13 *Metals listed in the order of their reactivity.* The least active in the list is given first. The most active is given last. All metals below copper are more active reducing agents than hydrogen gas and will produce hydrogen gas in the presence of dilute acids.

28-10   The Galvanic Cell and the Corrosion of Metals

Corrosion technically means the change of a metal to a compound. The most common example of iron corrosion is rusting.

The corrosion of metals is usually an electrochemical process that takes place when a small galvanic cell is formed between a metal and some metallic impurities in the presence of moisture. The atoms of the metal are oxidized and go into solution as ions. Iron metal is oxidized to rust in the presence of moisture and oxygen. The chemist prevents corrosion in several ways:

1. By coating the metal with paint, lacquer, enamel, or grease to seal off the metal from contact with water, oxygen, or other possible reactants.

2. By covering the metal with another metal that is less subject to corrosion. Electroplating with chromium or zinc is an example of applying a protective metal. Zinc may also be applied by dipping the metal to be protected in molten zinc. Any method of applying a zinc coating is called galvanizing.

3. By alloying the metal in such a way that its resistance to corrosion is increased. An alloy is a metal that contains one or more other metals, usually in small quantity. Stainless steel is iron with a small amount of chromium. The chromium prevents the iron from rusting.

4. By making the metal to be protected the cathode in a chemical cell, while making an expendable piece of metal the anode in the same cell. Since metals are corroded (eaten away) by oxidation, the expendable metal is eaten away (corroded) instead of the metal that is being protected.

22. Using the table of standard reduction potentials (Figure 28-12), (a) Name four (4) metals that will not reduce the hydrogen ion. (b) Name four (4) metals that will set hydrogen free from dilute acids. (c) Rank the above eight (8) metals in the order of their activities as reducing agents, placing the most active ones at the top of the list.

23. (a) Which of the following metals would be practical ones to use in a laboratory experiment to prepare hydrogen from dilute hydrochloric acid: iron, sodium, zinc, copper, lithium. (b) Explain why the others should not be used.

*24. (a) A sample of iron with tin impurity forms a galvanic cell in the presence of acid rain. (Acid rain is water that contains dissolved oxygen and sulfur dioxide.) Name the anode, cathode, and electrolyte in this cell. (b) Why does the iron become oxidized instead of the tin?

25. (a) Mention four (4) methods that the chemist uses to prevent the corrosion of iron. (b) Why can magnesium be used as an expendable metal to prevent iron from rusting?

28-11   Balancing Redox Equations by the Use of Half-Reactions (Ion-Electron Method)

Section 26-8 described a method for balancing redox equations that are difficult to balance by inspection. Many of these same equations can be balanced by making use of the information given by the equations for half-reactions. We have already combined the equations for half-reactions on a number of occasions. In each case we took care to make the number of electrons equal before adding the equations for the half-reactions. By equalizing the electrons before adding, we were assured that the equation for the complete reaction would be balanced. Equalizing electrons, then, provides a general method for balancing the equations for redox reactions that can be expressed as the sum of two half-reactions. The sample problem in Appendix F shows how the method is applied.

Question for Section 28-11

*26. Using the half-reaction in Figure 28-12, write the balanced ionic equations for the following reactions (include all steps):
(a) Silver + dilute nitric acid. The gas NO is one of the products. (Hint: What ions are present in dilute nitric acid?) (b) The oxidation of concentrated hydrochloric acid, HCl, by dichromate ion, $Cr_2O_7^{2-}$. (Hint: What ions are present in hydrochloric acid? Which of these ions can be oxidized?)

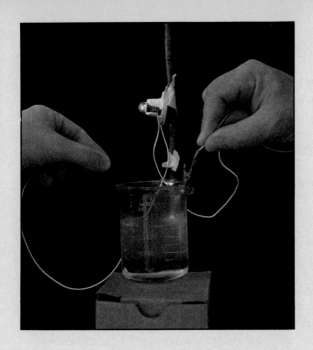

CAN YOU EXPLAIN THIS?

The photograph shows a coil of copper wire on the left and a coil of magnesium ribbon on the right being immersed in a solution of dilute (3 molar) sulfuric acid, H_2SO_4. The two coils are connected by wires to a 1½-volt flashlight bulb, which is being lighted by the chemical reaction taking place. (Below the photo is a line drawing showing the wire connections.)

1. Bubbles are coming out of the solution surrounding the magnesium ribbon. What are these bubbles?

2. Why do you think the light bulb lights? Write a chemical equation for the reaction. Explain your answer to the question in terms of loss and gain of electrons during the reaction.

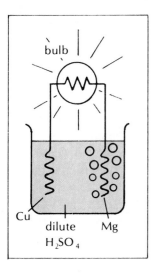

CHAPTER SUMMARY

1. The reactions in both the galvanic cell and electrolysis cell are of the redox type. However, in the galvanic cell, the reactions occur spontaneously; in the electrolysis cell, the reactions are dependent upon an external supply of current.

2. The galvanic cell utilizes two half-reactions as a source of its current. Electrons are released by the half-reaction at the anode and travel through an external conductor to the cathode where they are absorbed in the half-reaction at that electrode.

3. Positive ions accumulate at the anode and negative ions at the cathode. An internal ionic current results as positive and negative ions flow in opposite directions.

4. A porous partition or a salt bridge can be used to permit ionic diffusion.

5. A galvanic cell can be constructed using two metals as electrodes and solutions of ions of these metals as electrolytes. The more active metal becomes the anode and the less active one, the cathode.

6. The standard hydrogen half-cell has a platinum strip coated with finely divided platinum (platinum black). Hydrogen gas is bubbled over this electrode. The half-cell is a standard for electrode potentials and is assigned a value of 0.00 volt.

7. Standard electrode potentials of half-cell reactions are determined by measuring the potential of a galvanic cell in which the tested half-cell is paired with a standard hydrogen half-cell.

8. All standard potentials are measured at standard conditions, e.g., a temperature of 25°C, 1 molar concentration of ions, and 1 atmosphere pressure of gases that take part in the reaction.

9. The voltage of a galvanic cell can be obtained by taking the difference of the reduction potentials of the two half-reactions. The cell voltage is always positive, indicating that a spontaneous reaction is occurring.

10. Using the voltage of a galvanic cell at standard conditions and the standard reduction potential of one of the half-reactions, the standard reduction potential of the other half-reaction can be calculated.

11. The table of standard potentials can be used to determine the products of reactions between the oxidizing and reducing agents shown in the table.

12. Metals can be ranked in the order of their chemical activities on the basis of their positions in the table of standard potentials.

13. The corrosion of metals is due to a chemical reaction that occurs in the galvanic cell formed from the metal, impurities, and moisture.

14. The chemist tries to prevent corrosion of metals by covering them with rust-resistant substances such as paint, lacquer, enamel, and rust-resistant metals. Corrosion is also prevented by connecting the metal with a more active, expendable metal which becomes the anode in the galvanic cell that is formed.

15. Redox equations may be balanced by combining the equations for the oxidation and reduction half-reactions found in the table of standard electrode potentials.

TERMS YOU SHOULD KNOW

electromotive force or
    voltage
electrochemical cell
galvanic cell

voltaic cell
internal circuit
external circuit
standard conditions

standard hydrogen
    half-cell
standard electrode
    potential

REVIEW QUESTIONS

Section

28-1
1. (a) Compare a battery with an electrolysis cell, mentioning one similarity and two differences. (b) Differentiate between a battery and a flashlight cell. (c) What practical application can be made of spontaneous redox reactions?

28-2
2. A given galvanic cell, made of two compartments separated by a porous partition, is based upon the reaction,

$$Cu + 2AgNO_3 \rightarrow Cu(NO_3)_2 + 2Ag$$

(a) Describe the composition of the electrodes and electrolytes. (b) Write the equations for the half-reaction that occurs at each electrode. (c) Describe the direction of flow of electrons in the external circuit. (d) Describe the flow of ions in the internal circuit.

3. What would happen if the porous partition of the cell in question 2 were removed?

4. Define (a) voltage, (b) electrochemical cell, (c) internal circuit, (d) external circuit, (e) Upon what conditions does the value of the voltage of a galvanic cell depend?

5. (a) A current is sent through an electrolysis cell containing $ZnCl_2$ solution. Write the equation for the half-reaction at the cathode. (b) Write the equation for the half-reaction at the cathode of a Daniell

Chapter 28   Electrochemistry II—Galvanic Cells   **565** cell. (c) Compare the charge on the cathode in *(a)* and in *(b)*.

28-3 6. A zinc strip is placed into a dilute $ZnSO_4$ solution in one beaker and a copper strip is placed into a concentrated $CuSO_4$ solution in another beaker. The two strips are connected by a metal wire but no flow of current is observed. Explain (a) what happens at the zinc strip, (b) what happens at the copper strip, (c) why no electrons flow in the external circuit.

7. If the same electrodes and solutions of question 6 are simply kept apart by a porous partition, electrons will flow in the external circuit. (a) Explain the changes at each electrode that now make possible the external flow of electrons. (b) What can be used instead of a porous partition to achieve the same result?

28-4 8. (a) Sn^{2+} ions are more easily reduced than Fe^{2+} ions. Describe the structure of a galvanic cell using the Sn/Sn^{2+} and the Fe/Fe^{2+} half-reactions. (b) Write the equations for the half-reactions that occur at each electrode during the operation of the cell. (c) Which electrode is the anode and which, the cathode? (d) Which electrode is negative and which, positive? (e) Write the ionic equation for the complete reaction.

28-5 9. (a) What is the function of the platinum black that coats the platinum strip in the standard hydrogen half-cell? (b) What is the potential of this cell?

28-8 10. At standard conditions, a hydrogen half-cell is paired with a Fe^{2+}/Fe^{3+} half-cell. Write the (a) half-equation for the anode reaction, (b) half-equation for the cathode reaction, (c) the equation obtained by adding the two half-reactions.

11. (a) At what specific conditions does the Ag/Ag^+ half-cell have a potential of 0.80 volt? (b) What is the standard potential of the galvanic cell in question 10? (c) What is the standard potential of the galvanic cell consisting of the Mn/Mn^{2+} half-cell paired with the hydrogen half-cell?

12. A galvanic cell, based on the Zn/Zn^{2+} and Ag/Ag^+ half-reactions at standard conditions, has a net potential of 1.56 volts. If the silver nitrate electrolyte is made more dilute by the addition of water, (a) what change occurs in the half-cell potential of the silver electrode? Explain. (b) What change occurs in the complete cell potential? Explain.

13. If the Ag/Ag^+ half-cell were chosen as the standard and its standard reduction potential set at zero, what would be the standard reduction potential of the (a) Cu/Cu^{2+} half-cell, (b) H_2/H^+ half-cell, (c) Sn/Sn^{2+} half-cell, (d) Fe/Fe^{2+} half-cell, (e) Au/Au^{3+} half-cell?

14. The net equation for a given galvanic cell is,
$$Sn(s) + 2Ag^+ \rightarrow Sn^{2+} + 2Ag(s)$$
(a) What is the net potential of the cell, assuming standard conditions? (b) What is the net potential after each of the separate half-reactions reaches a state of equilibrium? (c) Write the equation for the half-reaction at the tin electrode. (d) What is oxidized during the operation of the cell? (e) What is the reducing agent?

15. At standard conditions, a given galvanic cell has a net potential of 0.59 volt. One of the half-reactions is:
$$Fe \rightarrow Fe^{2+} + 2e^-$$

(a) Find the standard reduction potential of the other electrode, using the table in Figure 28-12. (b) Write the equation for the half-reaction at this electrode.

16. Use the standard reduction potentials of Figure 28-12 to decide whether, at standard conditions, Br^- ions can be oxidized to Br_2 by the following: (a) Cl_2, (b) H^+ ions, (c) Ni^{2+} ions, (d) MnO_4^- ions in acid solution.

17. Calculate the voltages of the cells made of the following electrode pairs, at standard conditions: (a) Mg/Mg^{2+} and Zn/Zn^{2+}, (b) Al/Al^{3+} and Cl^-/Cl_2 (Pt electrode), (c) Fe^{2+}/Fe^{3+} (Pt electrode) and Br^-/Br_2 (Pt electrode).

18. Based upon the half-reactions in the table of standard reduction potentials, what are the formulas of the products of the complete reaction between (a) MnO_2 and Br^- ions in acid medium, (b) Zn and Fe^{3+} ions, (c) Rb and H_2O.

19. The following express the results obtained upon bringing some metals and ionic solutions together:
$$Mn(s) + Zn^{2+} \rightarrow Zn(s) + Mn^{2+}$$
$$Fe(s) + Co^{2+} \rightarrow Fe^{2+} + Co(s)$$
$$Fe(s) + Zn^{2+} \rightarrow \text{no reaction}$$

28-9 20. Arrange the ions in decreasing order of their attraction for electrons. Which ion is the strongest oxidizing agent? Which is the weakest? Refer to half-cell potentials to determine whether the following reactions will proceed spontaneously at standard conditions. (Justify each answer.)
(a) $3Mg(s) + 2Al^{3+} \rightarrow 3Mg^{2+} + 2Al(s)$
(b) $Sn(s) + Fe^{2+} \rightarrow Sn^{2+} + Fe(s)$
(c) $2KI + Br_2 \rightarrow 2KBr + I_2$
(d) $Cr_2O_7^{2-} + 14H^+ + 2Cl^- \rightarrow 2Cr^{3+} + 7H_2O + Cl_2$

28-10 21. During the corrosion of impure iron, (a) what acts as the anode, (b) what is the cathode? (c) How does attaching a block of zinc to an iron pipe keep the iron from rusting?

FOR FURTHER THOUGHT

28-2 1. Consider the setup in Figure 28-3 on page 544. Classify each of the following statements about this setup as either an observation or an inference. Explain your answers.
(a) The zinc electrode gradually loses mass.
(b) The amount of zinc in solution gradually increases.
(c) Zinc atoms become zinc ions.
(d) The bulb lights.
(e) Electric current flows through the external circuit.
(f) Electrons flow from the zinc through the wire of the external circuit into the copper.
(g) Ions pass through the walls of the porous cup.

28-7 2. When half-cell A is combined with half-cell B in an electrochemical cell, the cell produces a voltage of 0.94 volts. When half-cell B is combined with half-cell C, the voltage produced is 0.66 volts. What would be the voltage of a cell in which half-reaction A is combined with half-reaction C?

UNIT 9

Organic Chemistry

Originally associated exclusively with living organisms, carbon compounds were labeled *organic*. Although we have learned to synthesize such compounds in the laboratory independent of living things, the mystique and value of such compounds is in no way diminished. The variety and complexity of carbon compounds is unrivalled in nature. Their importance to humanity is unequalled. Without the petroleum formed from plants and animals millions of years ago, and being extracted from the oil wells shown in the photo, transportation and manufacturing would virtually cease. Without the synthetic organic compounds used in medicines, plastics, and so on, our standard of living would be radically altered.

The subject of this unit is the nature of organic compounds and the structural formulas and naming systems that have been developed to deal with their extraordinary variety and complexity.

CHAPTER 29

Organic Chemistry—I

Objectives

When you have completed this chapter, you will be able to:
- List some general properties of organic compounds.
- Relate the bonding of carbon to the formation of many compounds.
- Compare the general formulas of hydrocarbon series and apply the IUPAC system to name their members.
- Explain how different types of polymers are formed.

29-1   The Nature of Organic Compounds

All living things are composed mainly of organic compounds. Organic compounds are the compounds of carbon. The term *organic* originally came from the belief that such compounds could be produced only by living organisms and could be obtained only from living organisms or their remains. Living things were considered to have a "vital force" that was needed to create these compounds.

In 1776 Karl Scheele (1742-1786), the German chemist credited with the discovery of chlorine, prepared an organic compound, oxalic acid, by reacting sugar with nitric acid. This showed that an organic compound could be made in the laboratory. However, it was argued that the vital force for the creation of this compound came from the sugar, which had once been part of a living sugar cane plant.

In 1828, another German chemist, Friedrich Wöhler (1800-1882), discovered that urea, an organic compound found in animal urine, could be produced from the reaction between two inorganic substances. These substances are ammonium chloride, NH_4Cl, and silver cyanate, AgOCN. This discovery prompted other chemists to experiment with the synthesis of organic substances from inorganic ones. Soon acetic acid and several other organic substances were prepared from inorganic materials. Chemists then accepted the fact that organic compounds can be prepared from materials that never were a part of a living organism. Rather, the factor common to all such compounds was the element carbon. Thus, **organic compounds** are now defined simply as compounds of carbon. Organic chemistry is the branch of chemistry that deals with the study of carbon compounds. Only a few carbon compounds, such as the carbonates and the oxides of carbon, are still considered to be inorganic.

29-2 General Properties of Organic Compounds

Carbon is unique among the elements because of its ability to combine with itself and other elements to form an almost limitless number of compounds. Over two million organic compounds are known, and the number is being increased by over 100 000 each year. In contrast, there are only about 60 000 known inorganic compounds—that is, compounds that do not contain carbon.

Two factors account for many of the properties of organic compounds. First, the bonding in an organic compound is usually covalent. Second, the typical organic molecule is nonpolar. Because of these characteristics, organic molecules are held together chiefly by the weak van der Waals forces. Therefore, the compounds usually exist as gases, liquids, or low-melting solids. (Inorganic compounds are predominantly high-melting solids.) Because of the weak intermolecular forces, organic liquids generally have high vapor pressures. The high vapor pressures account for their strong odors and low boiling points. Acetone, ether, and benzene are examples of organic liquids with strong odors and low boiling points. Most organic solids have melting points that range from slightly above room temperature to about 400°C. These temperatures are extremely low compared to the much higher melting points of most inorganic solids. (NaCl, for example, melts at 801°C.)

The nonpolar nature of the molecules explains why organic liquids or solutions do not conduct an electric current. This is in marked contrast to the conductivity of inorganic acids, bases, and salts, many of which are strong electrolytes. Also, organic compounds with nonpolar molecules are insoluble in polar solvents, such as water. The fact that oil (a mixture of organic compounds) floats on water illustrates the insolubility of organic substances in water. However, organic substances readily dissolve in nonpolar solvents. Those relatively few organic compounds whose molecules are somewhat polar, such as acetic acid and ethyl alcohol, do dissolve in water.

Most organic compounds will ignite and burn when heated to a high enough temperature in air. Carbon tetrachloride, CCl_4, and chloroform, $CHCl_3$, are exceptions. Heating in the absence of air will break down (decompose) many organic compounds because organic molecules are easily disrupted at high temperatures. The decomposition of an organic compound by heat produces two or more simpler compounds.

The covalent bonding in organic compounds affects their speed of reaction, which is usually slow compared to the speed of reaction between inorganic compounds. A reaction involving inorganic acids, bases, or salts starts almost instantaneously because of the forces of attraction between oppositely charged ions. In a reaction between two typical organic compounds, no ions are involved. Moreover, the strong covalent bonding does not allow the molecules to form activated complexes easily. Random collisions do not provide enough energy to reach the high activation energies needed for most organic reactions. All of these facts account for the slowness of reaction between organic compounds.

29-3   Bonding in Organic Compounds

Figure 29-1

Structural and electron-dot formulas for methane. (Recall that in three-dimensional space, the shape of a methane molecule is tetrahedral, as shown in Figure 11-19.)

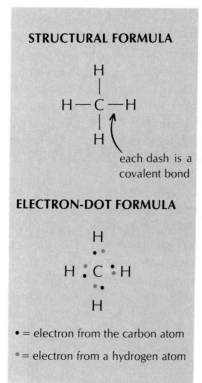

STRUCTURAL FORMULA

each dash is a covalent bond

ELECTRON-DOT FORMULA

• = electron from the carbon atom

⦁ = electron from a hydrogen atom

In the periodic table, carbon occupies a position about halfway between the positive-ion-forming alkali metals and the negative-ion-forming halogens. A carbon atom has four electrons in its valence shell. As a result of sp^3 hybridization (Section 11-11), each of these four electrons forms an equivalent covalent bond. For example, in the compound methane, CH_4, each of the four hydrogen atoms is attached to the carbon atom by the same kind of covalent bond. The structural formula for methane is shown in Figure 29-1.

In methane, each hydrogen atom shares its one electron with the carbon atom. A total of four bonds are formed, each one consisting of a pair of electrons. As Figure 29-1 shows, the carbon atom has a hold on eight electrons in its valence shell, thus resembling the stable structure of the noble gas neon. Each hydrogen atom is associated with the two electrons. Thus, its structure resembles that of the noble gas helium. Since the arrangement of hydrogen atoms about the carbon atom is symmetrical, and all of the bonds are covalent, the molecules of methane are nonpolar and nonionic.

The bonds of carbon atoms usually extend into three-dimensional space at equal angles to each other. Such bonding produces a tetrahedral structure. In this structure, the carbon atom is at the center, and the atoms bonded to the carbon atom are at the corners, as shown in Figure 29-2.

Carbon atoms form covalent bonds with other carbon atoms as well as with atoms of other elements. While some organic molecules contain only one or two carbon atoms, there are "giant" molecules that may contain hundreds or even thousands of carbon atoms. This ability of carbon atoms to bond to other carbon atoms is one of the reasons there are so many organic compounds.

Figure 29-2

(A) ***The tetrahedral shape of a methane molecule, CH_4.*** The carbon atom is at the center and hydrogen atoms are located at the corners. (B) Propane, C_3H_8, consists of a "chain" of tetrahedrons. (C) ***The way chemists often write a structural formula for propane.*** Structural formulas are often written in a straight line which ignores the bond angles between carbon atoms. (D) ***A structural formula for propane that more closely resembles the model shown in (B).***

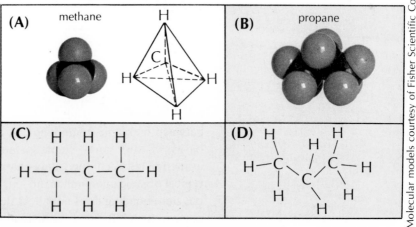

1. (a) What type of compounds are studied in organic chemistry? (b) Which compounds are exceptions and are studied together with inorganic compounds? (c) What is the origin of the term "organic"?

2. (a) What is the chief reason for the existence of so many carbon compounds? (b) What two factors account for the general properties of organic compounds? (c) Mention one property of organic liquids and one of organic solids due to the weak van der Waals forces between the molecules.

*3. What are two properties of most organic liquids that are due to the nonpolar nature of the molecules?

4. What happens to many organic compounds when heated to a high temperature (a) in air, (b) in the absence of air? (c) What property of organic compounds accounts for the fact that speeds of reaction are usually slow?

*5. (a) Write the structural formula of methane. (b) The structural formula of methane, the answer to (a), can give a mistaken impression of the shape of the methane molecule. Explain. (c) State two (2) reasons why molecules of methane are nonpolar and nonionic. (d) What geometric structure is produced in methane because of the equal C-H bond angles (109°28′)? (e) What is wrong with this structural formula: H−C−H
   |
   H

6. (a) Write the electron-dot formula of methane. What noble gas structure is shown in the methane molecule by (b) the carbon atom, (c) the hydrogen atom?

29-4 Usefulness of Structural Formulas

A molecule consisting of two carbon atoms, six hydrogen atoms, and one oxygen atom is represented by the molecular formula C_2H_6O. Often two or more organic compounds have the same molecular formula. In the case of C_2H_6O, there are two organic compounds with this formula. The structural formulas of these compounds are shown in Figure 29-3.

Figure 29-3

Two compounds, each of which has the molecular formula C_2H_6O: ethyl alcohol and dimethyl ether. Structural formulas for these substances reveal different structures and explain why each compound has a different set of properties.

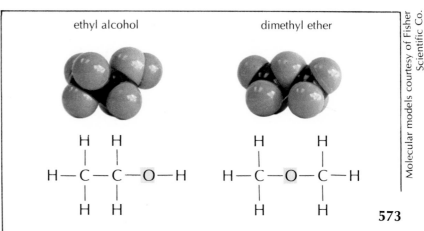

ethyl alcohol   dimethyl ether

Molecular models courtesy of Fisher Scientific Co.

573

Compared to the molecular formula, the structural formula has the advantage of showing the approximate geometric arrangement of the atoms. However, structural formulas take up a large amount of space. Where chemists wish to show structure while using a minimum of space, they write molecular formulas in a way that shows, to a certain degree, how the atoms are arranged in a molecule. For example, ethyl alcohol, whose structural formula is given at the top of Fig. 29-4, can also be represented more briefly by the formulas CH_3CH_2OH and C_2H_5OH.

The reason the oxygen and hydrogen atoms on the right of the molecule remain in place in all three formulas is that this group gives the molecule properties that are common to a large group of compounds called alcohols. Do not confuse the $-OH$ group (the alcohol group) in an organic molecule with the hydroxide ion, OH^-, present in inorganic bases such as NaOH and KOH. The hydroxide ion gives basic properties to water solutions that the ion is dissolved in. The $-OH$ group in an organic molecule gives these substances altogether different properties. Unlike water solutions of the hydroxide ion, alcohols do not taste bitter, do not have a slippery feeling, and do not turn red litmus blue. Alcohols have an entirely different set of properties, as will be seen in the next chapter. Ethyl alcohol, the compound in Fig. 29-4, is only one compound belonging to this group. Another common alcohol is methyl alcohol, whose structural formula is

Figure 29-4

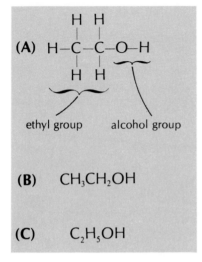

(A) ethyl group alcohol group

(B) CH_3CH_2OH

(C) C_2H_5OH

H—C—O—H

methyl group   alcohol group

The structure of a methyl alcohol molecule can be shown in an abbreviated manner by writing the formula as follows:

CH_3OH

methyl group   alcohol group

The compound dimethyl ether

H—C—O—C—H

methyl group   methyl group

$$CH_3OCH_3$$

Figure 29-5

The structure of a diethyl ether molecule can be represented by any of the formulas shown. Its molecular formula, $C_4H_{10}O$, tells nothing about its structure. That is, it tells nothing about how the 4 carbon atoms, 10 hydrogen atoms, and 1 oxygen atom are arranged to form a molecule.

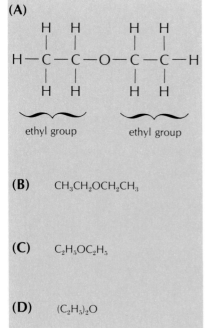

(A)

ethyl group   ethyl group

(B) $CH_3CH_2OCH_2CH_3$

(C) $C_2H_5OC_2H_5$

(D) $(C_2H_5)_2O$

Dimethyl ether is only one of a number of compounds that are members of the ether family. The distinguishing feature of an ether is the presence of an oxygen atom to which two carbon atoms are bonded. Diethyl ether can be represented by the formulas shown in Figure 29-5.

While molecular formulas of the type shown here can often be used to show the structures of simpler molecules, this is not generally true of large, complex molecules. For complex molecules, only structural formulas can be used to show structure.

Isomers. Compounds that have the same molecular composition but different structures are called **isomers.** Ethyl alcohol and dimethyl ether, the compounds shown in Figure 29-3, are isomers. Butane and isobutane are another example of isomers. Both have the same molecular composition (82.8% carbon and 17.2% hydrogen by mass). Both have the same molecular mass, 58 atomic mass units. A molecule of each substance consists of 4 atoms of carbon and 10 atoms of hydrogen. But each substance has its own unique structure and hence its own unique set of properties. See Figure 29-6.

Figure 29-6

Butane and isobutane have the same molecular formula, C_4H_{10}, but they have different structures. Compounds having the same molecular formula but different structures are called isomers. Either compound may be said to be an isomer of the other.

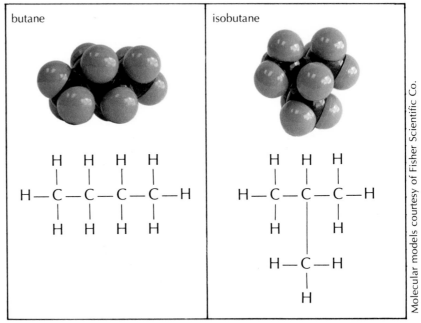

Molecular models courtesy of Fisher Scientific Co.

The number of possible isomers that an organic compound can form increases greatly as the number of carbon atoms increases. The compound whose molecular formula is $C_{15}H_{32}$ could have over 400 isomers. Many of these isomers have in fact been prepared.

29-5   Saturated and Unsaturated Compounds

Figure 29-7

Saturated compounds have only single bonds between carbon atoms. Unsaturated compounds have at least one double or one triple bond between carbon atoms.

The nature of the bonds between each pair of carbon atoms in an organic compound will determine whether the compound is saturated or unsaturated. Saturated compounds are those in which the four covalent bonds of each carbon atom are utilized to the fullest extent in holding other atoms. The bonds between the carbon atoms in a **saturated** compound are single bonds, indicating the sharing of one pair of electrons by a pair of neighboring carbon atoms. In an **unsaturated** compound, the bonds between neighboring carbon atoms are double bonds or triple bonds. In a double bond, two neighboring carbon atoms share two pair of electrons. In a triple bond, they share three pair of electrons. See Figure 29-7.

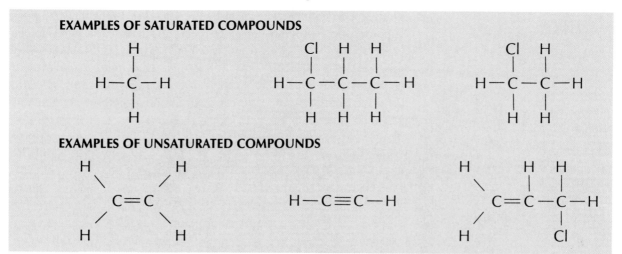

EXAMPLES OF SATURATED COMPOUNDS

EXAMPLES OF UNSATURATED COMPOUNDS

Questions for Sections 29-4 and 29-5

7. (a) Write the structural formula of an organic compound whose molecule has 1 chlorine atom, 3 hydrogen atoms, and 1 carbon atom. Note: Both hydrogen and chlorine form 1 covalent bond when bonding with other elements in organic compounds. (b) If you are able, write another structural formula for a different organic molecule composed of 1 chlorine atom, 3 hydrogen atoms, and 1 carbon atom. (c) Why is it necessary to use structural formulas to represent most organic compounds rather than molecular formulas? (d) Was a structural formula necessary for making clear the structure of the substance referred to in part *(a)* of this question? Explain.
8. (a) Write the names and formulas of three (3) groups, or radicals, that are parts of organic compounds. (b) What distinguishes the formula of the basic hydroxide group from the alcohol group?
*9. (a) Write the formulas of ethyl alcohol and dimethyl ether showing, as units, the groups of which they are composed. (b) Why are these compounds considered to be isomers?
10. (a) Describe double and triple bonds in terms of shared electrons. (b) Define *saturated compound*. What type of bonding characterizes (c) saturated compounds, (d) unsaturated compounds?

29-6　Homologous Series

Figure 29-8

A homologous series, called the alkanes. The first four members of the series are shown. The general formula of an alkane is C_nH_{2n+2} where n = the number of carbon atoms. The increment is not a chemical substance. The increment, CH_2, is part of a molecule, not a complete molecule. Hence, there is no substance whose formula is CH_2.

Organic compounds can be classified into groups having the same general formula and related structures and properties. Such a group is called a family or **homologous** (ho-MOL-uh-gus) **series.** Each member of such a series differs in formula from the member before it by the same number and kind of atoms. This formula difference between consecutive members of a homologous series is called the **increment.** The meaning of the term *increment* will become clear to you if you study Figure 29-8, which shows the first four members of the homologous series known as the alkanes.

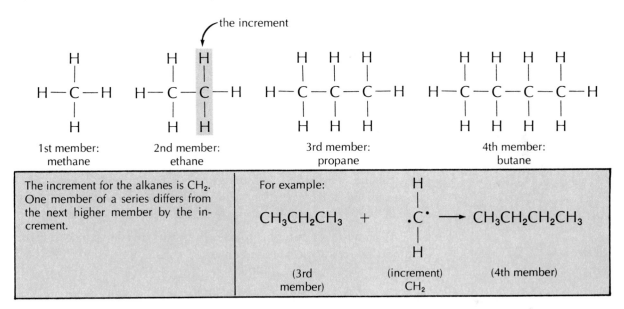

| 1st member: methane | 2nd member: ethane | 3rd member: propane | 4th member: butane |

The increment for the alkanes is CH_2. One member of a series differs from the next higher member by the increment.

For example:

$$CH_3CH_2CH_3 \ + \ .\overset{\displaystyle H}{\underset{\displaystyle H}{C}}. \longrightarrow CH_3CH_2CH_2CH_3$$

| (3rd member) | (increment) CH_2 | (4th member) |

29-7　Hydrocarbons

Almost all organic compounds contain hydrogen in addition to carbon. A large number of organic compounds also contain a third element, oxygen, and a fourth element, nitrogen. Various other elements may also be present. This section is concerned with the organic compounds that contain only the two elements carbon and hydrogen. These compounds are called **hydrocarbons.** The most abundant sources of hydrocarbons are petroleum and natural gas. Hydrocarbons may have structures that are **straight-chain, branched-chain,** or **cyclic.** Straight-chain and branched-chain structures are called open-chain structures. Open-chain hydrocarbons are also called **aliphatic** hydrocarbons. See Figure 29-9.

Hydrocarbons vary greatly in the size of their molecules. The number of carbon atoms in a molecule may range from one atom to thousands. Under normal conditions of temperature and pressure, compounds made up of small molecules tend to be gases. Those made up of long molecules tend to be solids. Compounds whose molecules

Figure 29-9

Hydrocarbons may be straight-chain hydrocarbons, branch-chain hydro-carbons, or cyclic hydrocarbons.

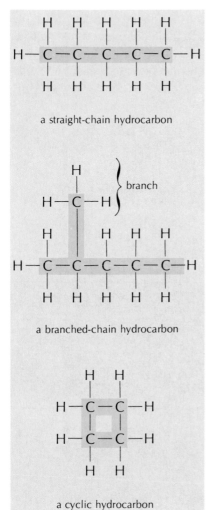

a straight-chain hydrocarbon

a branched-chain hydrocarbon

a cyclic hydrocarbon

Figure 29-10

The first three members of the alkane family.

are of intermediate size tend to be liquids. This simply means that as molecules become larger, boiling and melting points tend to increase as a result of an increase in van der Waals forces in larger molecules. But the melting points of solid organic compounds made up of even very large molecules tend to be considerably lower than the melting points of inorganic compounds.

Hydrocarbons will burn in air or oxygen. They are very much in demand as fuels for cooking, heating, and other applications requiring heat energy. Gasoline is a mixture of various saturated and unsaturated liquid hydrocarbons.

29-8 Classification of Hydrocarbons

Hydrocarbons are classified into several different series of compounds. The grouping is based mainly on the type of bonding that exists between carbon atoms. The five most important hydrocarbon series are alkanes (al-KANES), alkenes (al-KEENS), alkynes (al-KINES), alkadienes (AL-kuh-di-EENS), and aromatics (ar-uh-MAT-iks).

Alkanes are aliphatic, or open-chain, hydrocarbons in which only single bonds are present. The alkanes are saturated compounds. Figure 29-8 shows the formulas of the first four members of the series.

Alkenes are aliphatic hydrocarbons in which a single pair of carbon atoms in each molecule are connected by a double bond. See Figure 29-11.

Alkynes are aliphatic hydrocarbons in which a pair of carbon atoms of each molecule are connected by a triple bond. See Figure 29-12.

Alkadienes are aliphatic hydrocarbons in which two separate pairs of carbon atoms are connected by double bonds. See Figure 29-13.

Aromatics are ring, or cyclic, hydrocarbons in which six carbon atoms are arranged in a closed ring. Aromatics, as the name suggests, often have strong odors. Molecules of these structures are usually represented as having alternate single and double bonds between the carbon atoms. See Figure 29-14.

Much of the remainder of this chapter is devoted to a more thorough discussion of these five classes of hydrocarbons.

methane   ethane   propane

Figure 29-13

Figure 29-11

Three members of the alkene family. Members of this family all have a double bond between one pair of carbon atoms.

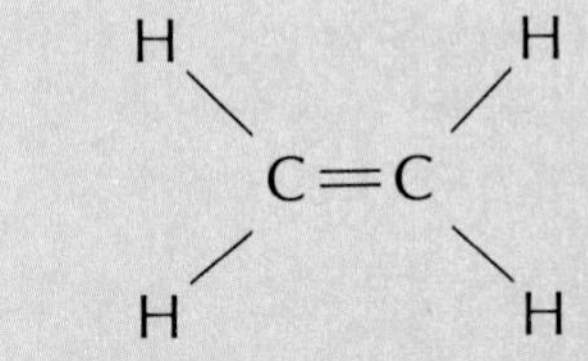

ethene

propene

2-butene

Figure 29-12

Three members of the alkyne family. Members of this family have a triple bond between one pair of carbon atoms.

ethyne
(acetylene)

propyne

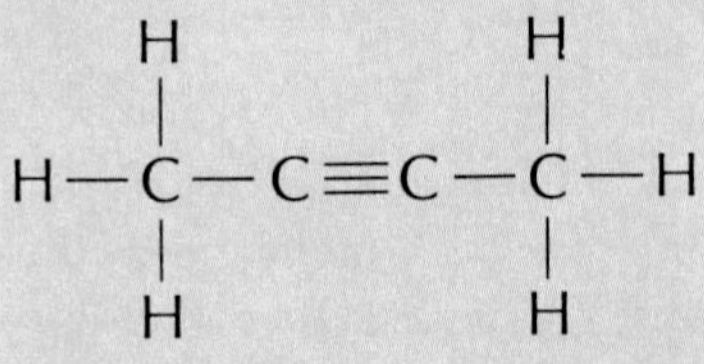

2-butyne

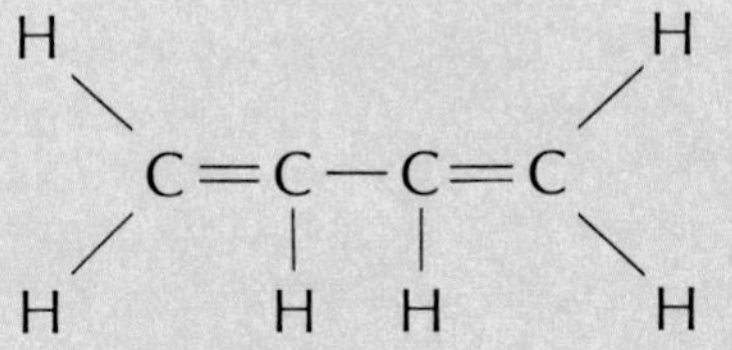

Three members of the alkadiene family. Members of this family have double bonds between two pairs of carbon atoms. In alkadienes, the two double bonds are always separated by at least one pair of carbon atoms joined by a single bond.

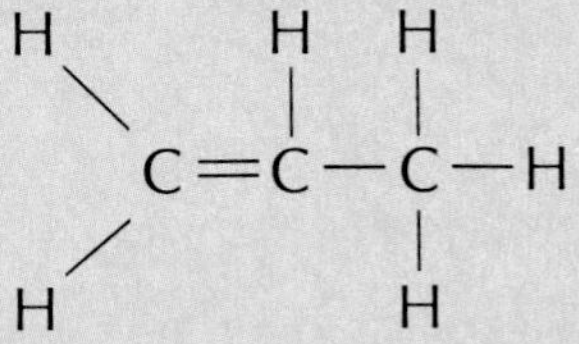

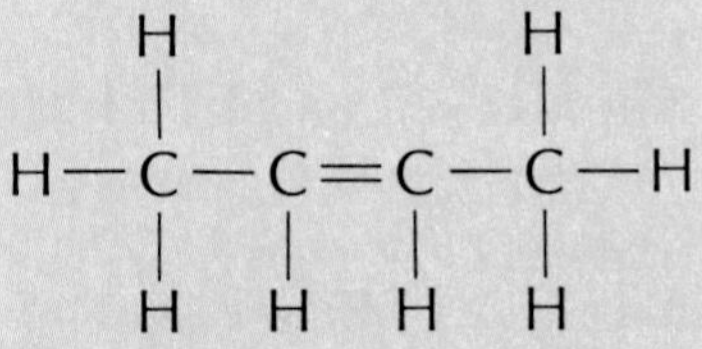

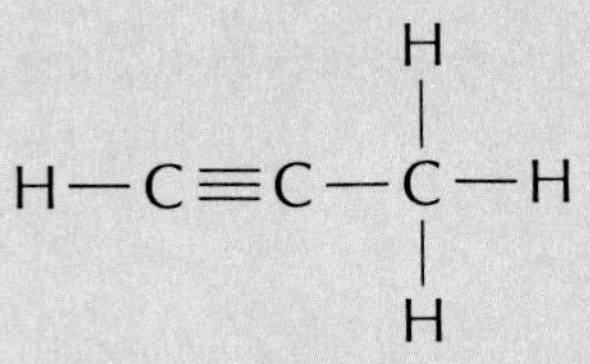

butadiene

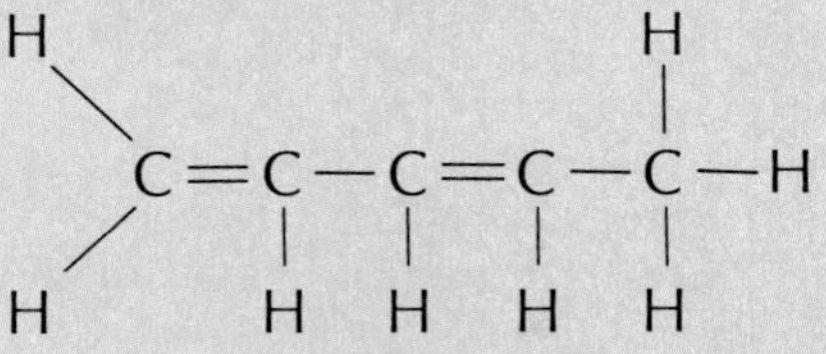

1,3-pentadiene

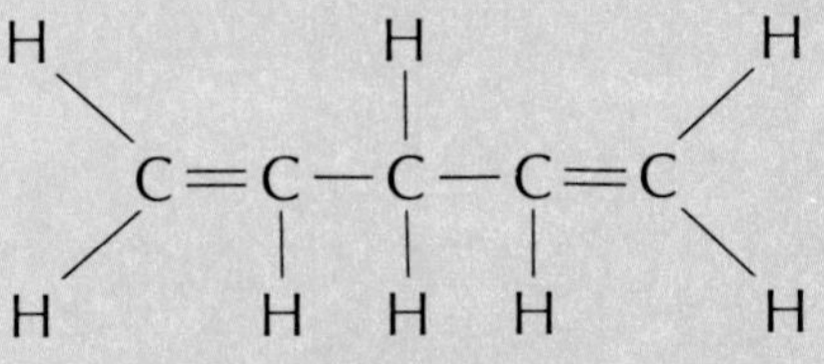

1,4-pentadiene

Figure 29-14

Three aromatic compounds. Aromatic compounds are benzene and the compounds derived from it.

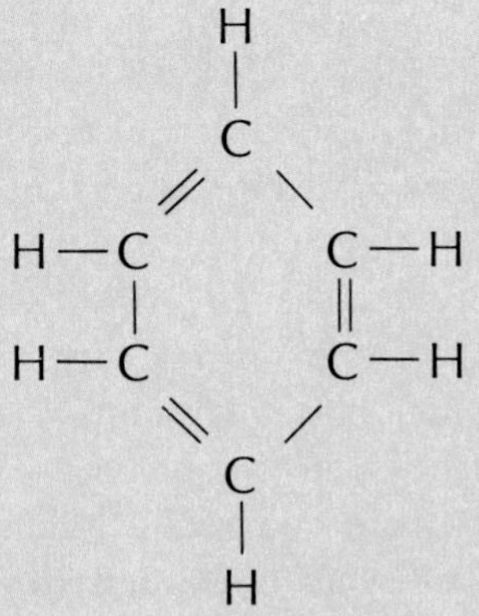

benzene

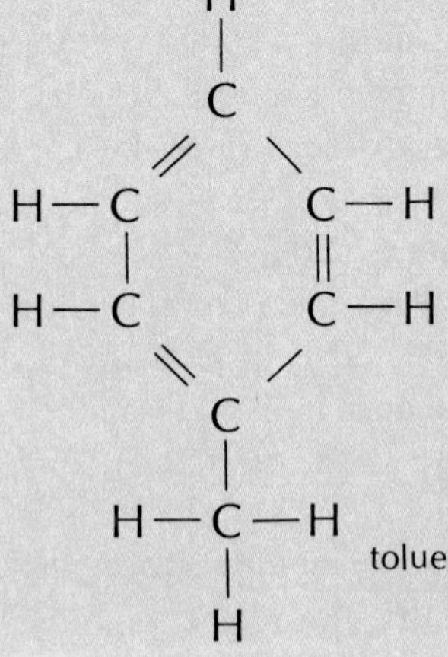

toluene

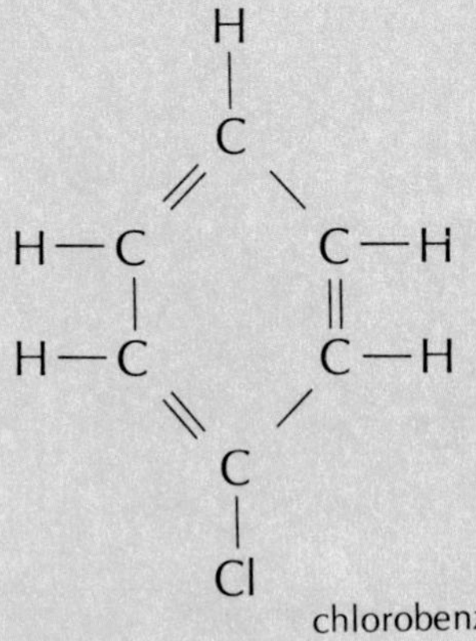

chlorobenzene

11. Define (a) homologous series, (b) increment. (c) What is the formula of the increment in the alkane series?
12. (a) What are *hydrocarbons?* (b) What are their chief sources? (c) What three (3) types of structures are found in hydrocarbons? (d) Describe open-chain structures.
13. (a) Relate the normal phases of hydrocarbons to their relative molecular sizes. (b) Why do boiling points and melting points tend to increase with an increase in the molecular sizes of hydrocarbons? (c) What is the chief use of hydrocarbons?
14. (a) Write the names and structural formulas of an alkane, an alkene, and an alkyne. (b) How do the structures in these three classes of hydrocarbons differ from one another?
15. Describe the structures of an (a) alkadiene, (b) aromatic. Write the structural formulas of (c) butadiene, (d) benzene.

29-9   Saturated Hydrocarbons—The Alkanes

The alkane series of hydrocarbons consists of compounds that have the general formula C_nH_{2n+2}, where "*n*" represents the number of carbon atoms. All members of this series have names ending in *-ane*. The series is sometimes called the **paraffin series.** *Paraffin* comes from the Latin *parum affinis,* meaning "little affinity." Paraffins do not react readily and are unaffected by many reagents. Paraffin wax is a mixture of compounds from this series. The relative inactivity of alkane compounds is the result of their saturation. All the carbon atoms are attached to each other by single bonds.

Under ordinary conditions, the first four members of the alkane series are gases, the next twelve are liquids, and the higher members are solids. As stated previously, the bonding is covalent nonpolar, and the molecules are attracted to each other only by the weak van der Waals forces. Since these forces become more effective as the number of electrons per molecule increases, boiling and melting points of the alkanes increase as the molecular mass increases.

All members of the alkane series are open-chain (aliphatic) compounds. Thus, the alkanes can be divided into two groups. One group of alkanes is the unbranched, or straight-chain, compounds. The other group is the branched, or branched-chain, compounds. Simple, unbranched members of this series are known as **normal alkanes.** Branched members form just one of the classes of compounds that fall into the group of compounds called *alkane derivatives*. This group is discussed in more detail later in this section.

Figure 29-15

Two compounds that contain the methyl group CH₃–, one of the alkyl groups. The first compound is methyl alcohol. The second compound is methyl amide.

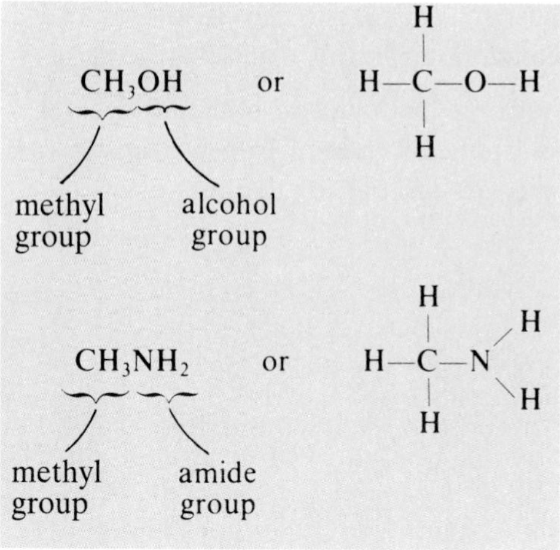

Figure 29-16

The two isomers of butane. The molecular formula of both compounds is C_4H_{10}. Both compounds have the same composition (82.8% carbon and 17.2% hydrogen by mass), but the different arrangements of atoms in each molecule give a different set of properties to each substance.

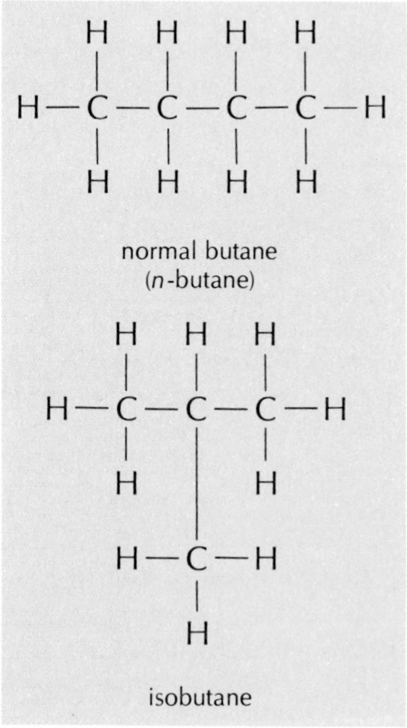

Normal alkanes. The names of the normal alkanes are composed of a prefix, which denotes the number of carbon atoms, and the suffix *-ane*, which signifies that the compound contains only single bonds, and is thus saturated. The first four members of this series are methane, ethane, propane, and butane. The prefix *meth-* indicates a compound with one carbon atom in its molecule. *Eth-* indicates two carbon atoms. *Prop-* indicates three carbon atoms. *But-* (pronounced *byoot* to rhyme with *root*) indicates four carbon atoms. (See Figure 29-5.)

Starting with the fifth compound in the series, Greek and Latin prefixes are used to indicate the number of atoms present. The prefixes *pent-*, *hex-*, *hept-*, *oct-*, *non-*, and *dec-* mean respectively five, six, seven, eight, nine, and ten. These prefixes are derived from the Greek except for the prefix *non-* which comes from the Latin *nonus*. Pentane, then is the five-carbon alkane.

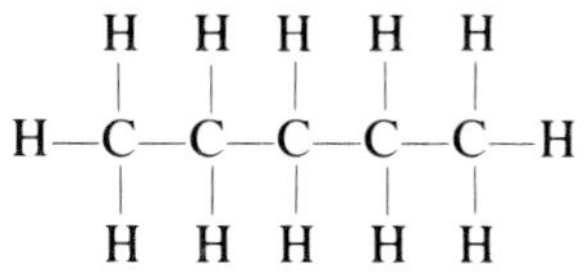

Hexane is the six-carbon alkane:

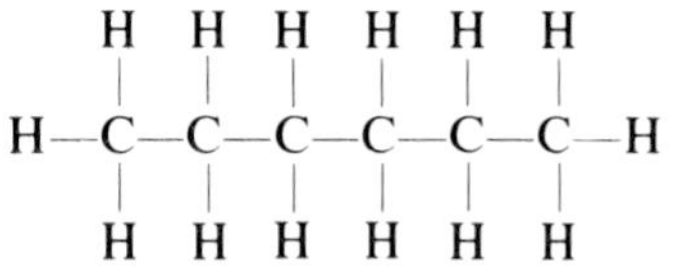

Alkyl groups. If a hydrogen atom is removed from a terminal carbon atom of any alkane compound, the remaining portion of the alkane is called an **alkyl group** or **alkyl radical**. The general formula for such a group is C_nH_{2n+1}. Alkyl groups are named by replacing the *-ane* ending of the alkane compound with the ending *-yl*. Examples of alkyl groups include the methyl group, CH_3—, the ethyl group, C_2H_5—, the propyl group, C_3H_7—, and the butyl group, C_4H_9—. These various groups of atoms show up in many organic compounds. They are merely parts of compounds. Thus, there is no compound with the formula CH_3 or C_2H_5. Two examples of compounds that contain the methyl group, CH_3, are methyl alcohol and methyl amide. See Figure 29-15.

Alkane isomers. As described in Section 29-4, isomers are compounds that have the same composition but different structural arrangements and properties. The three simplest alkanes—methane, ethane, and propane—exist only in their normal forms. That is, they have no isomers. Butane is the first alkane that exists in isomeric form. The structural formulas for its two isomers are shown in Figure 29-16.

As the number of carbon atoms in the molecule increases, the number of different possible arrangements of those atoms in space also increases. Therefore, the higher the member is in the series, the greater its number of isomers. Pentane has 3 isomers, hexane has 5, heptane has 9, and octane has 18. The structures and names of the three isomers of pentane are shown in Figure 29-17. The straight-chain, or unbranched, alkane isomers are known as *normal* isomers. Thus, the straight-chain isomer of butane is normal butane, or *n*-butane. The straight-chain isomer of pentane is normal pentane, or *n*-pentane. The branched-chain isomers are considered to be *derivatives*, a term which is described below. The method of assigning names to these isomers and other organic compounds is explained later in this chapter.

Figure 29-17

The three isomers of pentane. Although these substances have different structures, they all have the same molecular formula: C_5H_{12}

Alkane derivatives. An **alkane derivative** is a compound obtained by substituting an atom or group of atoms for one or more hydrogen atoms in a normal alkane. All branched-chain hydrocarbons are derivatives of normal hydrocarbons.

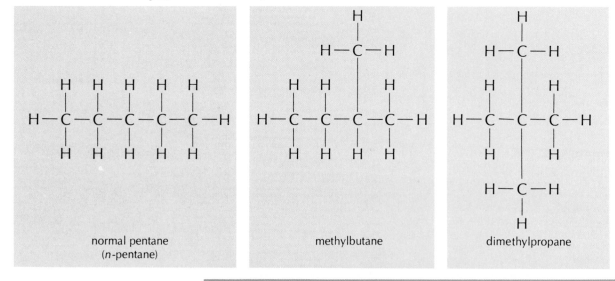

normal pentane
(*n*-pentane)

methylbutane

dimethylpropane

Questions for Section 29-9

16. (a) What is the general formula for alkanes? (b) Why are the alkanes generally slow to react with many reagents? (c) What type of bonding exists within the molecules of alkanes? (d) Why are their boiling and melting points relatively low?

17. (a) What is the rule that is generally followed in naming alkanes? (b) Mention five (5) prefixes used in alkane names and state what each one indicates. (c) What is the molecular formula of hexane?

18. (a) What is an alkyl group? (b) What is its general formula? (c) Write the formulas and names of alkyl groups containing 1 to 4 carbon atoms. (d) What is the molecular formula of pentyl alcohol?

19. (a) What similarities and what differences make it correct to refer to the following two substances as isomers of each other:

$$CH_3CH_2CH_2CH_3 \qquad CH_3CHCH_3$$
$$| $$
$$CH_3$$

(b) Which of the following alkanes has the most isomers: octane, heptane, pentane, or hexane?

20. (a) What is an alkane derivative? (b) Write the structural formula of *n*-pentane. (c) Write the structural formula of a derivative of *n*-pentane having the molecular formula C_6H_{14}.

29-10 IUPAC System for Naming Alkane Derivatives

Figure 29-18

An illustration of Rule 1. Two possible chains are the 4-carbon chain shown by arrow 1 and the 5-carbon chain shown by arrow 2. In naming the compound by IUPAC rules, the compound bears the name of the longest chain. Hence, it is a pentane (5-carbon chain) rather than a butane (4-carbon chain). As will be explained by other rules, the name of the compound is 3-methylpentane. The correct structural formula shows the 5-carbon parent chain in a straight line.

(A hydrogen atom is understood to be located at the end of each dash, but, for the sake of simplicity, these atoms are not written in the formula.)

Figure 29-19

An illustration of Rule 2. The longest chain has 4 carbon atoms. Hence, the molecule is a butane. By Rule 2, the carbon atoms in the chain are numbered from right to left in order to put the methyl group on the carbon atom with the lower number. The compound is therefore called 2-methylbutane. Had the carbon atoms been incorrectly numbered from left to right, the compound would have the incorrect name 3-methylbutane.

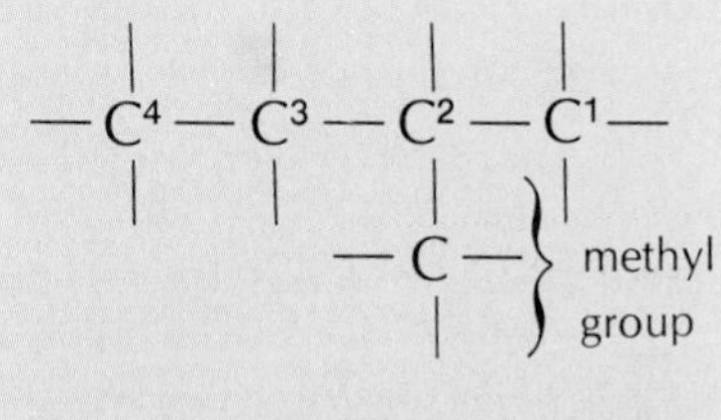

(A hydrogen atom is understood to be located at the end of each dash.)

As the study of organic chemistry developed, many compounds acquired more than one name. Common names were developed and used over the years. New names were often given to a particular compound, but the old name or names were still used. For example, C_2H_5OH is commonly known as alcohol. It is also called grain alcohol, ethyl alcohol, and ethanol. Many other compounds acquired two, three, or even four names.

As more and more isomers were discovered and isolated, the need for greater precision and uniformity in naming these compounds became greater. In 1892, a group of chemists met in Geneva, Switzerland, and developed a simplified system for naming organic compounds. This conference produced the Geneva System of nomenclature. (*Nomenclature* is defined as a system of names used in a science or art.) This system was modified somewhat and adopted by the International Union of Chemistry in 1930. The present name of this organization is the International Union of Pure and Applied Chemistry. The rules are now referred to as the **IUPAC System** of nomenclature. (IUPAC is pronounced I-yoo-pak.)

Applications of the IUPAC System. To understand the IUPAC System of nomenclature, let us first discuss the rules as they apply to the alkanes. Later, as we study other types of organic compounds, similarities in the rules and their application will simplify the naming of the new compounds.

As you study the application of the IUPAC rules in this section, keep in mind that the term alkane is a general name for the saturated open-chain hydrocarbons. A name ending in *-ane* indicates that the substance is a normal alkane or an alkane derivative. Actually, the rules for naming the normal (unbranched) alkanes have already been discussed. These rules consist of adding the appropriate prefix (*meth-*, *eth-*, *prop-*, etc.) to the suffix *-ane*. The IUPAC rules given below are used in naming alkane derivatives, especially branched alkanes.

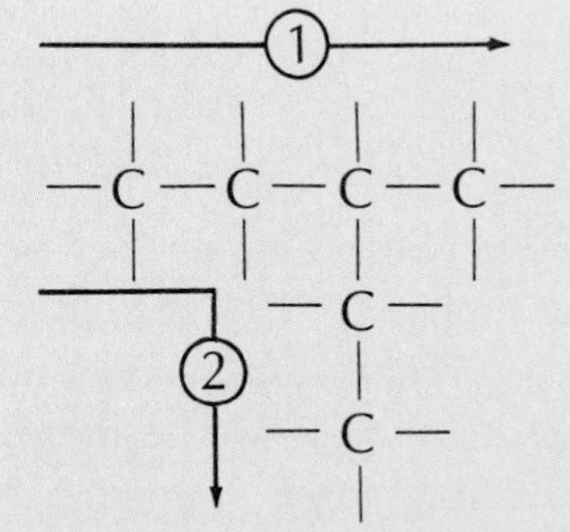

Rule 1. The compound bears the name of the longest carbon chain, or sequence. This sequence is called the parent chain, or parent alkane. Even for branched-chain compounds, the formula must show the parent chain in a straight-line. Study the examples in Figure 29-18.

Rule 2. Number consecutively the carbon atoms of the longest chain in order to establish the position of each atom in the chain. These numbers are used to indicate where, along the chain, branching (or substitution) takes place. That is, the numbers are used to indicate to which carbon atoms the alkyl groups, or other groups, are attached. The direction of the numbering is chosen so that the lowest numbers possible are given to the side chains, as shown by the example in Figure 29-19.

Rule 3. Determine the name(s) of the group(s) attached to the carbon atoms in the parent chain. The numbers designating the carbon atoms in that chain are used to prefix the names of the groups attached to the chain.

Rule 4. The complete name of the compound is obtained by first naming the attached groups, each one being prefixed by the number of the carbon atom to which it is attached. The final part of the name consists of the name of the parent alkane. Study the examples given in Figure 29-20.

Figure 29-20

Illustrations of the IUPAC system for naming alkane derivatives.

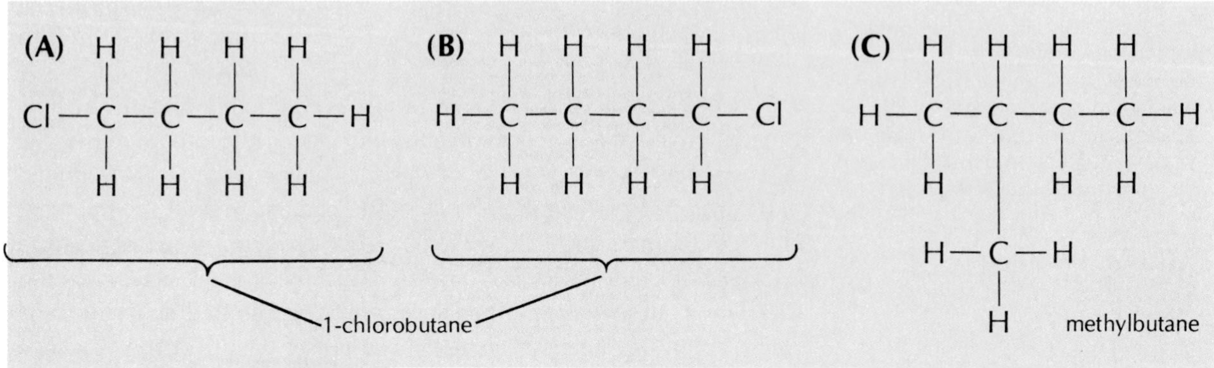
(A)
(B)
(C)
1-chlorobutane
methylbutane

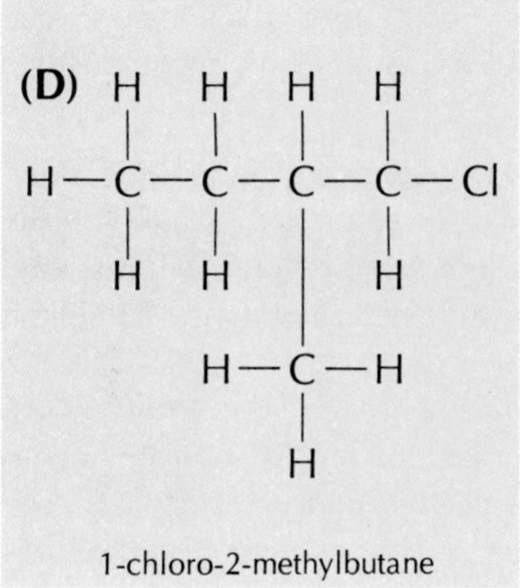
(D)
1-chloro-2-methylbutane

Rule 5. For compounds in which a particular group appears more than once, use the appropriate numerical prefix (di-, tri-, etc.) to indicate how many times the group appears. A carbon atom number must be used to indicate the position of each such group. If two (or more) of the same group are attached to the same carbon atom, the number of the carbon atom is repeated. See Figure 29-21 for some illustrations.

Rule 6. Halogen groups and other nonalkyl groups are also named from their positions along the carbon chain.

Rule 7. If there are 2 or more different substituted groups in a name, they are arranged alphabetically. See Figure 29-23.

Example 1. Let us apply the above rules to the compound commonly called isobutyl bromide:

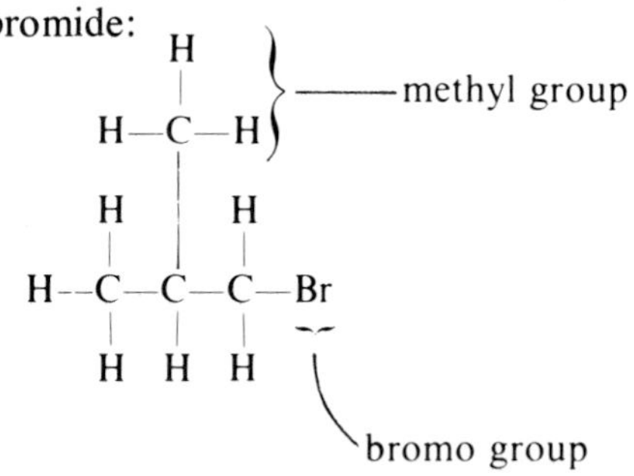
methyl group
bromo group

The longest sequence of attached carbon atoms is three. Thus, the parent alkane is propane. A bromine atom (bromo group) is attached to one carbon, and a methyl group to another. If the carbon atoms were numbered from left to right, the compound would be named 3-bromo-methylpropane. If the numbering is done from right to left (the correct way in this instance), the name is 1-bromo-2-methylpropane. This is the correct name because it has the smaller numbers. (See Rule 2.)

Following are some additional examples:

Example 2. An isomer of hexane, C_6H_{14}, has the structural formula shown in Figure 29-22. As shown in the figure, the longest sequence of bonded carbon atoms is four, making the parent alkane butane. Two methyl groups are attached to the *same* carbon atom. Therefore, the name of the isomer is 2,2-dimethylbutane.

Example 3. The structure shown in Figure 29-23 is somewhat more complex. The name of the compound is 1,1-dichloro-3-ethyl-2,4-dimethylpentane.

Example 4. No number is needed in the name methylpropane (an isomer of butane) to show the position of the substituted methyl group, since only one such position is possible for this substance. See Figure 29-24.

Figure 29-21

Illustrations of the IUPAC system for naming alkane derivatives.

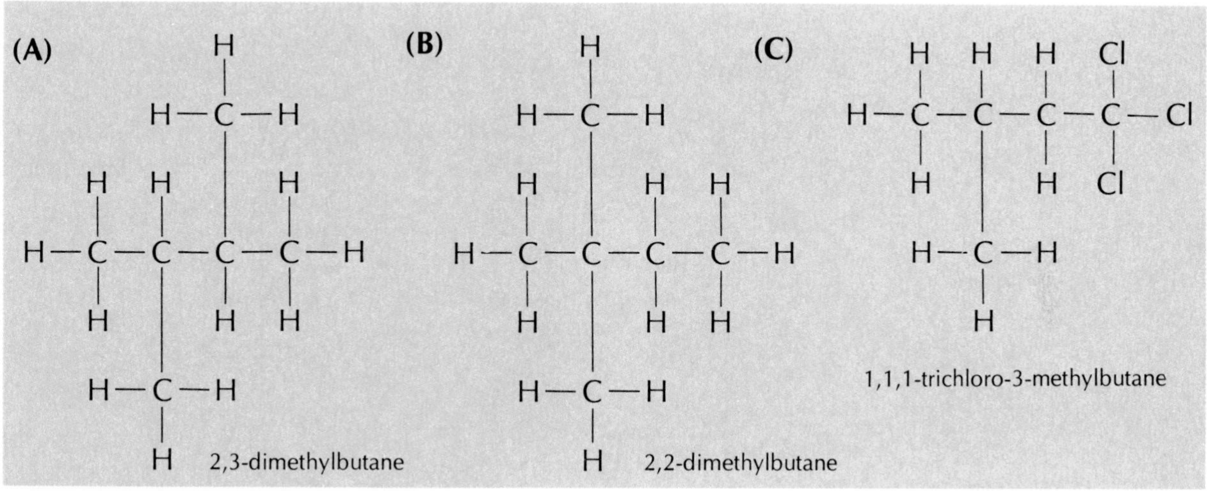

(A) 2,3-dimethylbutane

(B) 2,2-dimethylbutane

(C) 1,1,1-trichloro-3-methylbutane

Figure 29-22

2,2-dimethylbutane.

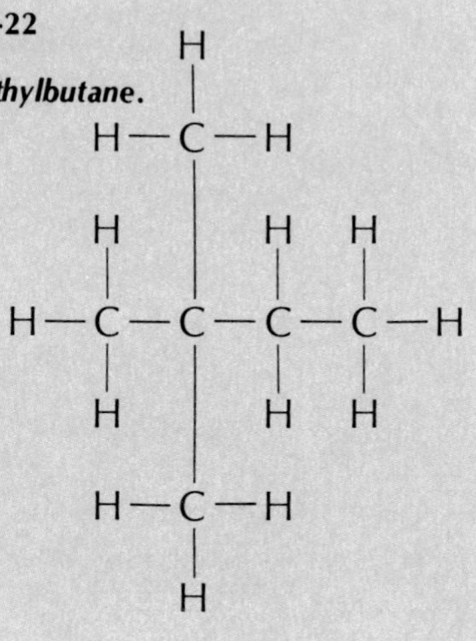

Figure 29-23

Structural formula for 1,1-dichloro-3-ethyl-2,4-dimethylpentane.

ethyl group

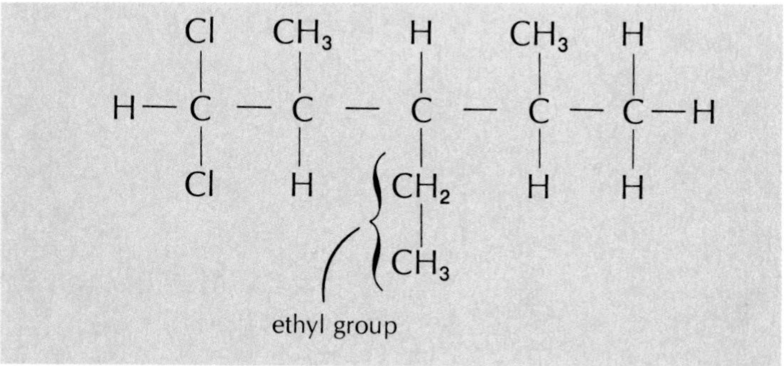

Figure 29-24

On a propane molecule (A), a methyl group can be substituted only onto the #2 carbon atom and still have the molecule remain a propane, as shown in (B). If the methyl group is substituted onto either end carbon atom, the molecule becomes that of normal butane. In naming the compound, it is not necessary to state that the methyl group is attached to the #2 carbon since no other possibility exists. The name of the compound is simply "methylpropane."

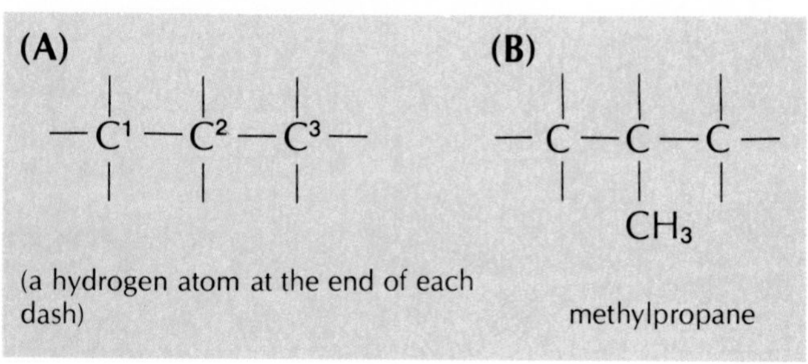

(A) (a hydrogen atom at the end of each dash)

(B) methylpropane

Example 5. The IUPAC System favors assigning the simplest name possible to a structure. Thus, the three isomers of pentane shown in Figure 29-25 are *n*-pentane, methylbutane, and dimethylpropane. It is not necessary to include numbers for the carbon atoms to which the alkyl groups are attached because only one structure is possible for each of the branched isomers. For example, if the methyl group of methylbutane is attached to an end carbon, the resulting structure is *n*-pentane. If the methyl group is attached to either of the two internal carbon atoms, that atom would be considered to be carbon number 2 in the sequence, and the structure would be 2-methylbutane. Thus, the 2 is not necessary in naming the compound, and it is omitted.

Figure 29-25

The three isomers whose molecular formula is C_5H_{12}.

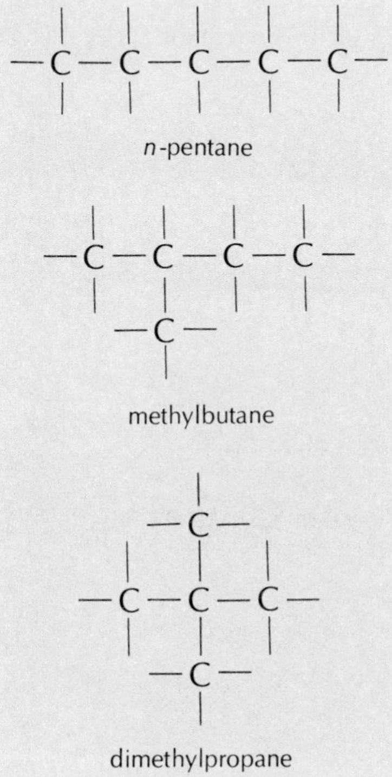

n-pentane

methylbutane

dimethylpropane

Questions for Section 29-10

21. (a) Why was it important to develop a standard system of nomenclature for organic compounds? (b) What rule does the IUPAC system of nomenclature apply in naming normal alkanes?
22. (a) What is the parent chain in a branched alkane? (b) How is the direction of numbering the carbon atoms in a parent chain chosen? (c) How are these numbers used in naming a branched alkane?
*23. Name the following compounds according to IUPAC rules:

$$
\begin{array}{c}
\quad\quad\quad CH_3 \\
\text{*(a) } CH_3{-}C{-}CH{-}CH_2{-}CH_3 \\
\quad\quad\quad CH_3 \; CH_3
\end{array}
$$

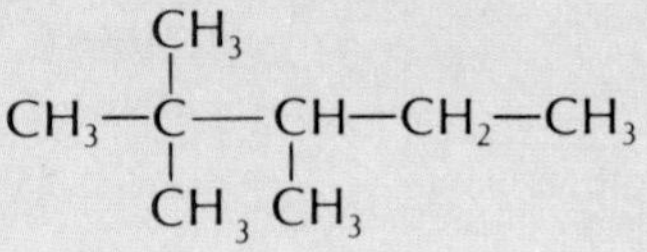

$$
\begin{array}{c}
\text{(b) } CH_3{-}CH_2{-}CH{-}CH_2{-}CH{-}CH_2{-}CH_3 \\
\quad\quad\quad\quad\quad CH_3 \quad\quad\quad CH_2 \\
\quad\quad\quad\quad\quad\quad\quad\quad\quad\quad CH_3
\end{array}
$$

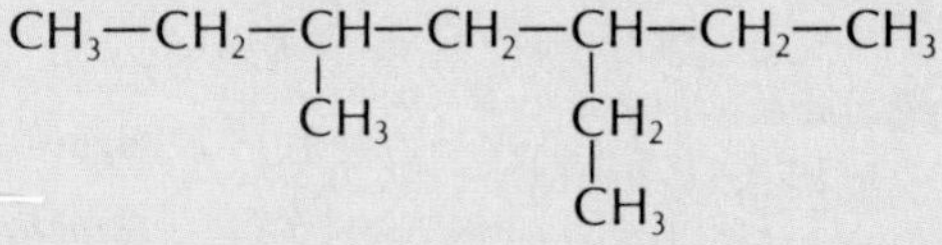

$$
\begin{array}{c}
\text{(c) } CH_3{-}CH{-}CH_2{-}CH_3 \\
\quad\quad\quad CH_2 \\
\quad\quad\quad CH_2 \\
\quad\quad\quad CH_3
\end{array}
$$

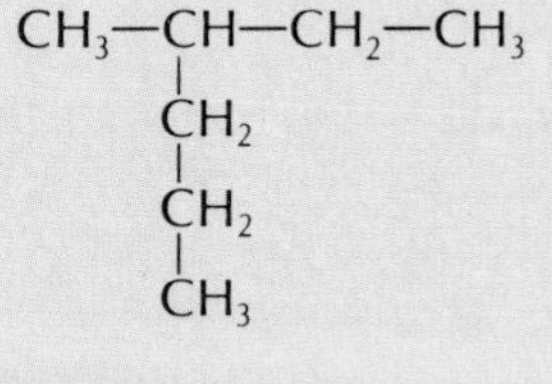

*24. Write the structural formulas of: *(a) 3-ethyl-2,4-dimethylpentane (b) 2,2,3-trimethylbutane (c) 4-ethyl-2,3-dimethylhexane

29-11 Unsaturated Aliphatic Hydrocarbons: Alkenes, Alkynes, Alkadienes

Saturated compounds, such as the alkanes, cannot directly combine with other atoms because their valence electrons are fully used. However, unsaturated compounds—those containing double or triple bonds—*can* directly attach additional atoms. The reason for this greater reactivity of unsaturated compounds is that the electrons in multiple bonds are not held as strongly as are those in single bonds. Thus, one bond of a double bond can be broken quite easily, and the electron used to form a covalent bond with another atom or radical. Similarly, one or two bonds of a triple bond can be broken.

Alkenes. The alkene, or ethylene, series is a family of unsaturated hydrocarbons. Each member of the series has a structure in which one pair of carbon atoms is connected by a double bond. Such a bond indicates the sharing of two pairs of electrons. The general formula for the alkenes is C_nH_{2n}. The first member of this series is commonly called ethylene. Its IUPAC name is ethene. Its formula is C_2H_4:

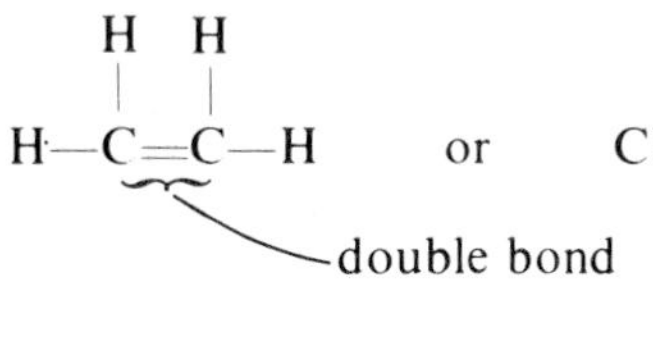

$$H-C=C-H \qquad \text{or} \qquad CH_2=CH_2 \qquad \text{or} \qquad C_2H_4$$

double bond

ethylene
(ethene)

The following equation shows that ethylene can add atoms, such as chlorine atoms, directly to its structure:

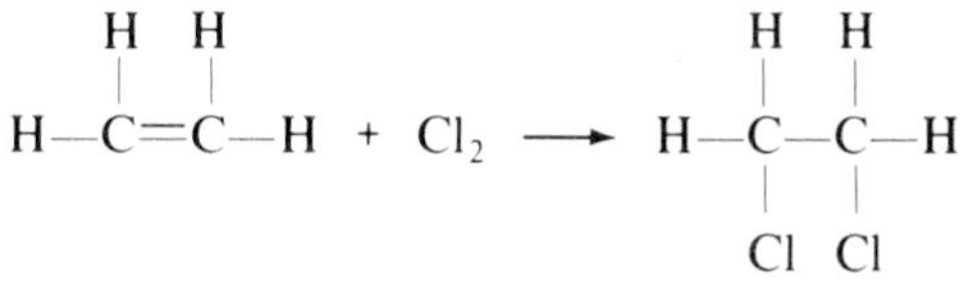

$$H-C=C-H \ + \ Cl_2 \ \longrightarrow \ H-C-C-H \qquad \textbf{(Eq. 1)}$$

ethylene
(ethene)

1,2-dichloroethane

The reaction given by Equation 1 is called an addition reaction. Notice that the reaction (addition) involves the double-bonded carbon atoms. One bond of the double bond is broken, and each of the carbon atoms then forms a covalent bond with a chlorine atom.

The halogen compounds formed by addition reactions with alkenes are usually oily liquids. Thus, the alkene series is also known as the **olefin** (oil-former) series. Ethylene (ethene) serves as the starting point for the production of the plastic polyethylene and the antifreeze ethylene glycol.

The formulas of the higher members of the alkene series are obtained by the addition of the increment,—CH_2—, just as in the alkane series. The second member has the formula C_3H_6, and is propylene (IUPAC name: propene). Its structural formula is shown in Figure 29-26.

Propylene is used in the manufacture of the much-used plastic polypropylene. Following propene in the alkene series are butene, C_4H_8, pentene, C_5H_{10}, hexene, C_6H_{12}, heptene, C_7H_{14}, and so forth.

IUPAC rules state that the names of the alkenes must end in -*ene* and that the position of the double bond must be shown by a number preceding the name. This number indicates the first carbon atom in the double bond pair. The carbon atoms are numbered from the end of the

Figure 29-26

The formula for propylene, the second member of the alkene series.

propylene
(propene)

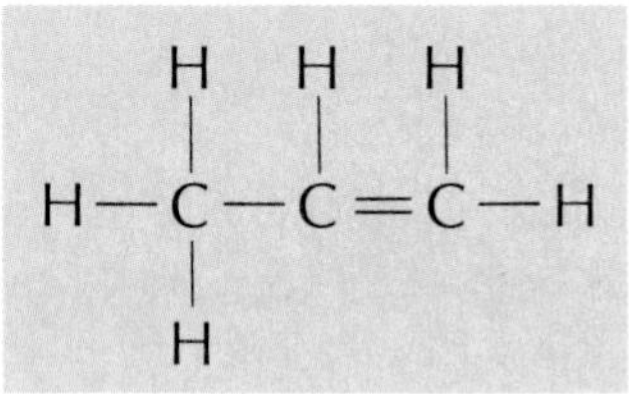

$$H-C-C=C-H$$

or

$$CH_3CH=CH_2$$

Figure 29-27

Some illustrations of the IUPAC rules for naming members of the alkene series.

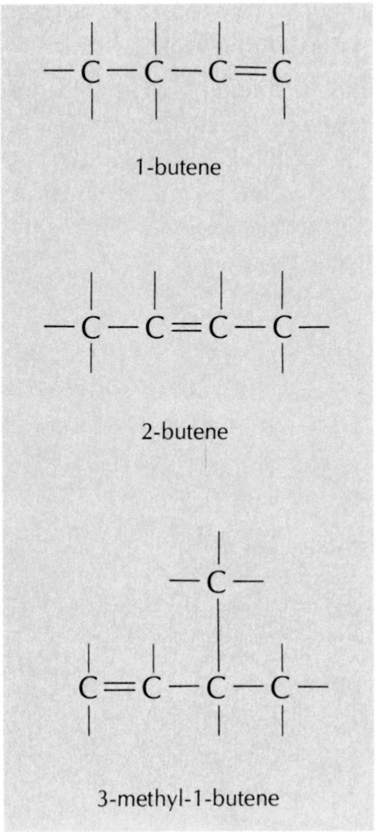
1-butene
2-butene
3-methyl-1-butene

chain nearest the double bond. The rules for naming derivatives are similar to those used for naming alkanes. See Figure 29-27.

There are no isomers for ethene and propene. Only one structure is possible for these two- and three-carbon members of the alkene series. Therefore, no number is needed to indicate where the double bond is located.

Alkynes. Members of the alkyne series are unsaturated hydrocarbons that contain a triple bond. Such bonds represent the sharing of three pairs of electrons by two neighboring carbon atoms in the hydrocarbon chain. Compounds in this series are, therefore, more unsaturated than those in the alkene series. The general formula for the alkyne series is C_nH_{2n-2}.

The common name for the alkyne series is the acetylene series, named after its first member, acetylene, C_2H_2. Acetylene burns with a hot flame and is used in the oxyacetylene blowtorch for cutting and welding metals. It is also the starting point in the production of many important substances such as artificial rubber, neoprene, and vinyl plastics.

In accordance with IUPAC rules, alkynes are named by adding the suffix *-yne* to the usual hydrocarbon prefixes. Thus, the IUPAC name for acetylene, with its two carbon atoms, is ethyne. Some of the other compounds in this series are propyne, C_3H_4, butyne, C_4H_6, and pentyne, C_5H_8.

The structural formulas for the first two alkynes are:

$$H{-}C{\equiv}C{-}H \qquad H{-}C{\equiv}C{-}CH_3 \quad \text{or} \quad CH_3{-}C{\equiv}C{-}H$$

ethyne — propyne

These two alkynes have no isomeric forms. The two structural formulas shown for propyne are the same. They are simply written with the methyl group (CH_3) at opposite ends.

The next higher alkyne, butyne, has two isomers. As with the alkenes, IUPAC rules state that the position of the triple bond must be shown by a number preceding the name. This number indicates the first carbon atom in the triple bond pair. The two isomers of butyne are 1-butyne and 2-butyne:

$$CH{\equiv}C{-}CH_2{-}CH_3 \qquad CH_3{-}C{\equiv}C{-}CH_3$$

1-butyne — 2-butyne

Alkadienes. As implied by the *-diene* ending, alkadienes are unsaturated hydrocarbons with *two* double bonds between two pairs of carbon atoms. Alkadienes are isomeric with the alkynes. They have the same molecular formulas as the alkynes and, therefore, cannot be distinguished from those compounds on the basis of the molecular formula alone. For example, although their structures are different, both butyne and butadiene have the same molecular formula: C_4H_6. The double bonds in alkadienes do not occur consecutively in the molecule.

Dietitian

Dietitians plan menus to provide people with the nutrition they need for good health. Many dietitians work in hospitals where they arrange diets that are compatible with the patients' medical conditions. Equally important, the dietitian must make certain that patients do *not* receive foods that may aggravate their illness or retard their recovery from an operation. Dietitians know how to plan meals that will promote either the loss of weight, or, if desirable, its gain. In addition to hospitals, dietitians are employed in schools, colleges, summer camps, and industry.

To become a dietitian, a person usually completes a four-year program in a college or university. The program includes chemistry, biology, foods, nutrition, and practical courses acquainting the aspiring dietitian with the operations of institutions that hire dietitians. Most dietitians spend some time working as interns under the supervision of a practicing dietitian.

Thus, the minimum number of carbon atoms in an alkadiene is generally four.

The first, and most important, member of the series is butadiene, C_4H_6. As already mentioned, it is an isomer of butyne. The structural formula of butadiene is $CH_2=CH-CH=CH_2$. To emphasize the locations of the double bonds, it could be named 1,3-butadiene. However, the name butadiene is usually used and is sufficient because it does not have an isomer in the -*diene* family. The next higher homolog has the molecular formula C_5H_8. An important member of this class is isoprene. The structural formula of isoprene is

$$CH_2=C-CH=CH_2 \qquad \text{isoprene}$$
$$| $$
$$CH_3$$

The IUPAC name of isoprene is 2-methyl-1,3-butadiene. Butadiene and isoprene are best known for their use as raw materials in the manufacture of synthetic rubber. Isoprene is also the simple molecular unit found in natural rubber. Synthetic and natural rubber are polymers. Polymers are giant molecules formed by the union of small identical molecules. From 1000 to 45 000 isoprene units are joined to form the long, coiled chains in the natural rubber polymer. The synthetic rubber made from isoprene is Coral rubber or Ameripol.

Questions for Section 29-11

25. (a) What is the general formula of an alkene? (b) What is characteristic of the structure of any alkene? (c) Write the molecular formulas and names of the first five (5) members of the ethylene series.
26. (a) Why can alkenes undergo addition reactions while alkanes cannot? (b) Write a structural formula equation showing the addition of chlorine to ethylene. (c) What is the IUPAC name for the product of this reaction? (d) Why are alkenes also called olefins?
27. Write the structural formula of (a) 2-pentene, (b) 3-methyl-2-pentene. (c) What is the correct IUPAC name for a compound incorrectly called 4-methyl-1-butene?
*28. (a) What characteristic bond is found in alkynes? (b) What is the general formula for the alkyne series? (c) Write the molecular formulas and names of the first four (4) members of this series. (d) Write the structural formulas for propyne and 1-butyne.
29. (a) Describe the bonds characteristic of alkadienes. (b) What is the general formula of this series? (c) Write the structural formulas of butadiene and isoprene. (d) What is the IUPAC name for isoprene?
30. Name or describe a commercial product made from (a) ethylene, (b) propylene, (c) acetylene, (d) butadiene, (e) isoprene.

29-12 Alicyclic Hydrocarbons

All of the hydrocarbons discussed to this point have been aliphatic—that is, open-chain hydrocarbons with either straight or branched structures. Hydrocarbons in which the carbon atoms are arranged in a closed, or ring, structure are called cyclic hydrocarbons. The two main groups of cyclic hydrocarbons are the alicyclic hydrocarbons and the aromatic hydrocarbons. Aromatic hydrocarbons are discussed in the next section.

In **alicyclic** hydrocarbons, the carbon atoms are linked by single or double bonds and are arranged in a closed structure. As with the aliphatic hydrocarbons, the alicyclic hydrocarbons are classified into several different series of compounds. The grouping is based mainly on the type of bonding that exists between carbon atoms. Included among these series are cycloalkanes, cycloalkenes, and cycloalkadienes, as well as other more complex groups.

The names of the three series mentioned above consist of the prefix *cyclo-* attached to the names of different series discussed under the aliphatic hydrocarbons. As you might expect, there is a definite relationship between the structures of the compounds in a cyclic series and those in the chain series bearing the same name. The relationship is in the number of carbon atoms in the main structure and the type of bonding that exists between these carbon atoms.

Like the alkanes, **cycloalkanes** are saturated hydrocarbons. That is, these compounds contain only *single* bonds between carbon atoms. Since the minimum number of carbon atoms that can form a closed structure is three, the first member of this series is cyclo*propane*. The names and structural formulas of the first three members of the cycloalkane series are shown in Figure 29-28.

Figure 29-28

Structural formulas for the first three members of the cycloalkane series.

cyclopropane   cyclobutane   cyclopentane

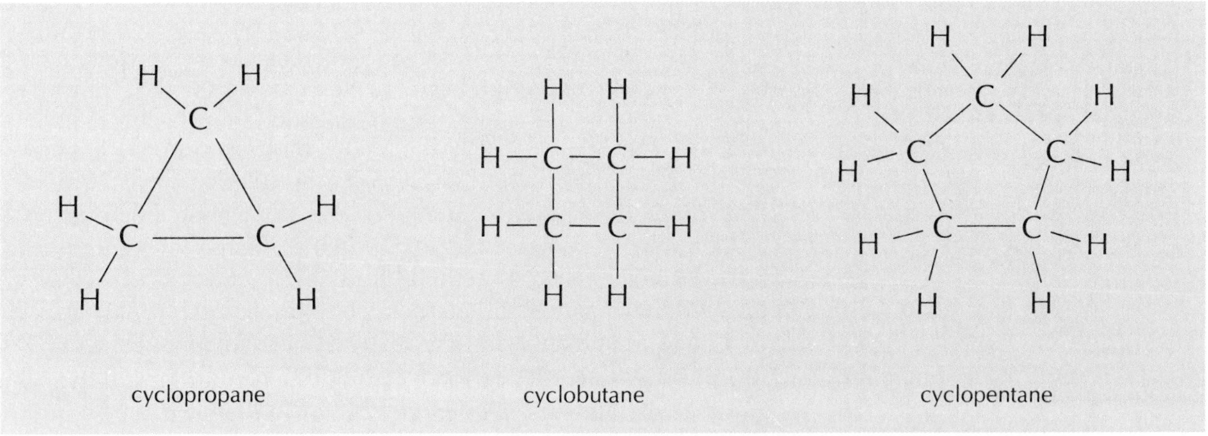

Similarly, **cycloalkenes** contain one double bond between a pair of carbon atoms in the ring structure. **Cycloalkadienes** contain two double bonds between two different pairs of carbon atoms. Figure 29-29 gives structural formulas for one cycloalkene and one cycloalkadiene.

29-13   Aromatic Hydrocarbons—The Benzene Series

Aromatic hydrocarbons are by far the best known and widely studied class of hydrocarbons. The name aromatic indicates that many of the compounds in this series have pleasant and/or distinctive odors.

Figure 29-29

(A) *Structural formulas of a member of the cycloalkene family and (B) a member of the cycloalkadiene family.* Note that in naming a cycloalkadiene, the carbon atoms must be numbered in order to specify the locations of the two double bonds.

Figure 29-30

Structural formula for benzene.

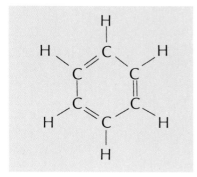

Figure 29-31

Chemists often use a hexagon with a circle inside to represent a benzene molecule (Figure 29-30). Whereas Figure 29-30 gives some people the mistaken impression that in benzene the carbon-carbon bonds are half double bonds and half single bonds, the hexagon-with-circle representation shown here makes it more apparent that all six carbon-carbon bonds are identical.

(A)

cyclopentene

(B)

1,3-cycloheptadiene

The general formula for members of this series is C_nH_{2n-6}.

All of the aromatic hydrocarbons have structures that are related to or derived from that of benzene, the simplest of the series. The molecular formula of benzene is C_6H_6. Its structural formula (shown in Figure 29-30) contains a ring of six carbons with alternating single and double bonds. On paper, the structure looks like just another unsaturated alicyclic compound. However, as we will see, the chemical behavior of the bonds in benzene indicates that those bonds are different from the bonds in other cyclic compounds we have been examining.

Benzene is an excellent solvent and is widely used as such. It is also used as the starting point for the synthesis of dyes, explosives, and such drugs as aspirin and sulfa drugs. Benzene is one of the products obtained in the fractional distillation of coal tar. Fractional distillation is the process of separating two or more liquids from a mixture by means of successive distillations. This process is described in more detail later in the chapter. Coal tar is a thick, black mixture of organic compounds produced when coal is heated in the absence of air. This mixture is rich in aromatic hydrocarbons.

Many benzene compounds are obtained by the fractional distillation of coal tar and petroleum. These compounds are used in industry as solvents and in the manufacture of dyes, drugs, explosives, and plastics. The explosive TNT is produced by the reaction of toluene with nitric acid in the presence of concentrated sulfuric acid.

As we have already stated, the structure shown in Figure 29-30 would suggest that benzene is an unsaturated hydrocarbon. However, much research into the nature of the bonds in benzene indicates that all the carbon-carbon bonds are equivalent to one another and intermediate in character between a single bond and a double bond. The true distribution of electrons is somewhere between that found in a single bond and that found in a double bond. This is known as a resonance hybrid bond.

In its reactions, then, benzene displays properties that are typical of both saturated and unsaturated hydrocarbons. To indicate the equivalency of the carbon-carbon bonds, the structural formula for benzene is often written as a hexagon with a circle inside. See Figure 29-31.

The second member of the benzene series is toluene, C_7H_8. The IUPAC name of toluene is methylbenzene. Its structure is represented as shown in Figure 29-32.

The third member of the benzene series is xylene, C_8H_{10}. The IUPAC name of xylene is dimethylbenzene. Its three isomeric forms are discussed in the following section. See Figure 29-33.

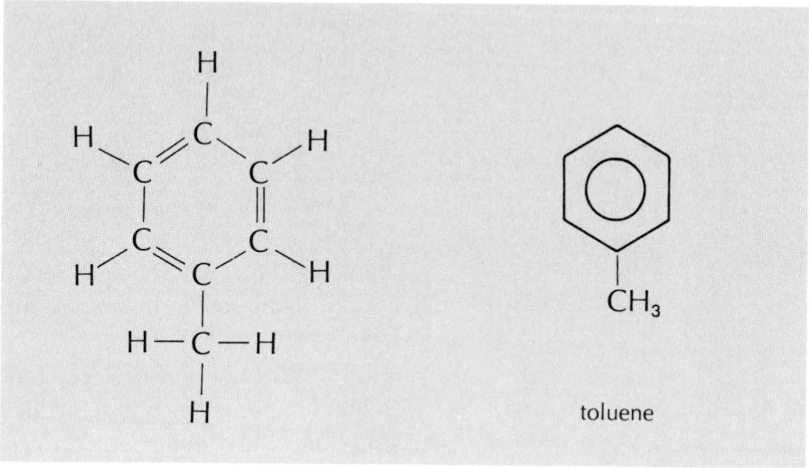

Figure 29-32

Two ways to represent a molecule of toluene.

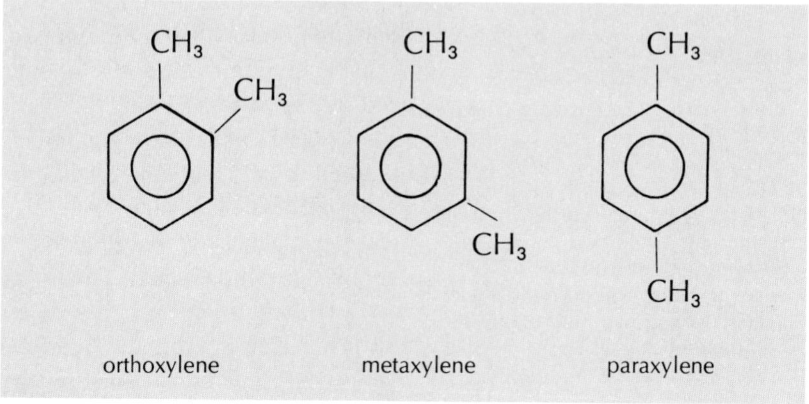

toluene

Figure 29-33

The three xylene isomers, C_8H_{10}. The prefix *ortho-* means that the substituted groups are on neighboring carbon atoms. *Meta-* means that the substituted groups are separated by one carbon atom; *para-*, that they are separated by two carbon atoms.

orthoxylene   metaxylene   paraxylene

29-14   Naming Benzene Derivatives

The IUPAC rules for naming benzene derivatives are similar to those used in naming chain compounds. Prefixes are attached to the "parent" name, benzene. The prefixes identify the group(s) that have been substituted for hydrogen atoms on the benzene ring. Thus, in the methylbenzene (toluene) molecule, one methyl group has been substituted for a hydrogen atom.

As with chain compounds, the IUPAC system of naming benzene derivatives involves numbering the carbon atoms in the ring in order to pinpoint the locations of the side chains. However, if only two groups are substituted in the benzene ring, the compound formed will be a benzene derivative having three possible isomeric forms. In such

Figure 29-34

cases, the prefixes *ortho-*, *meta-*, and *para-* may be used to name the isomers. The three prefixes are abbreviated *o-*, *m-*, and *p-*. In the **ortho-** structure, the two substituted groups are located on adjacent carbon atoms. In the **meta-** structure, they are separated by one carbon atom. In the **para-** structure, they are separated by two carbon atoms. Figure 29-33 gives the structural formulas and the common and IUPAC names for the three isomers of xylene, C_8H_{10}.

Figure 29-34 gives the names and the structural formulas of several benzene derivatives. By studying each example, you should be able to determine how the IUPAC system is applied in naming compounds in the benzene series.

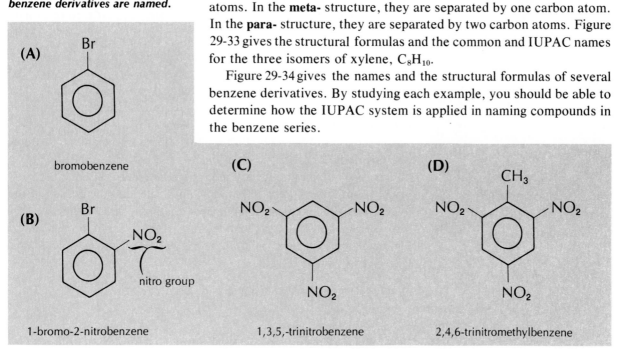

(A) bromobenzene

(B) 1-bromo-2-nitrobenzene / nitro group

(C) 1,3,5,-trinitrobenzene

(D) 2,4,6-trinitromethylbenzene

Questions for Sections 29-12 through 29-14

31. (a) What is the chief structural difference between aliphatic hydrocarbons and cyclic hydrocarbons? (b) Describe the general structure of alicyclic hydrocarbons. Describe the structure of a typical (c) cycloalkane, (d) cycloalkene, (e) cycloalkadiene.
32. Write the structural formula for (a) cyclobutane, (b) cyclobutene, (c) 1,3-cyclopentadiene.
*33. (a) Describe the characteristic structure present in benzene and other aromatic hydrocarbons. (b) What is the general formula for the members of the benzene series? (c) Write the structural formula for benzene, showing the double bonds. (d) What is the richest natural source of aromatic hydrocarbons? (e) Name four (4) classes of commercial products made from aromatic hydrocarbons.
34. (a) Describe the carbon-carbon bonds in benzene. (b) What kind of properties are shown by benzene because of this hybrid bond?
35. Write the structural formula of (a) toluene, (b) metaxylene, (c) nitrobenzene, (d) 1-bromo-3-chlorobenzene, (e) 2,4,6-trinitrotoluene (TNT).

29-15   Reactions of the Hydrocarbons

General activity. The alkanes are relatively inactive and, under ordinary conditions, will not react with acids, bases, and metals. They will

Stephanie Louise Kwolek
(1923-   )

Born in New Kensington, Pennsylvania, Kwolek received her B.S. degree in chemistry from the Carnegie Institute of Technology. She joined Du Pont's Textiles Fibers Department as a chemist. Her preliminary work at Du Pont served as a basis for the large-scale preparation of Lycra and Nomex fibers and of Kepton film.

In 1965, she presented a thin opalescent solution of a polymer to a laboratory technician and asked that he spin it into fibers. When he expressed doubt that it could be done, she insisted that it be done. The product was Kevlar aramid fiber, the most important synthetic fiber since nylon. Its outstanding stiffness and tenacity make it ideal for use in aircraft interiors, rockets, high performance boats, passenger car tires, ropes, cables, and conveyor belts. It was found to stop bullets from handguns and, today, more than a quarter of a million police officers are protected by vests reinforced by Kevlar. (See photo, page 597.)

Kwolek was given awards and citations from the American Chemical Society, The American Institute of Chemists, the Franklin Institute, and the American Society for Metals. Du Pont has promoted her to the high rank of Research Associate.

not react with halogens in the absence of light, but will react with them in sunlight. Because of their unsaturated structures, the alkenes and alkynes are much more reactive. These unsaturated structures will readily react with molecules, such as Cl_2, Br_2, and HCl, to form new compounds.

Combustion. Although inactive, alkanes will burn in air or oxygen. Propane is bottled in metal containers and commonly sold as a fuel for cooking and for heating water where natural gas is not available. The alkenes and alkynes are also sold as fuels. Acetylene, for example, is used in the oxyacetylene torch.

The products obtained by burning hydrocarbons depend on the temperature and the concentration of oxygen present. When there is plenty of air present (excess oxygen) and a high temperature, combustion is usually complete. Complete combustion means that the carbon in the hydrocarbons is oxidized to its highest oxidation state, producing CO_2 (in which carbon has an oxidation state of 4+). The hydrogen in the hydrocarbon is oxidized to H_2O. The equation for the complete combustion of methane, CH_4, is:

COMPLETE COMBUSTION OF CH_4

$$CH_4 + 2O_2 \longrightarrow CO_2 + 2H_2O \qquad \text{(Eq. 2)}$$

Incomplete combustion takes place at relatively low temperatures and in a limited amount of oxygen. Incomplete combustion means that the carbon in the hydrocarbons is oxidized to an intermediate oxidation state, producing CO (in which carbon has an oxidation state of 2+). The equation for the incomplete combustion of methane is:

INCOMPLETE COMBUSTION OF CH_4

$$CH_4 + \frac{3}{2}O_2 \longrightarrow CO + 2H_2O \qquad \text{(Eq. 3)}$$

Comparing Equations 2 and 3, you will see that in the incomplete combustion, a smaller amount of oxygen combines with 1 mole of methane. Complete combustion releases a greater amount of heat from a fuel, and is thus a more efficient use of the fuel. Incomplete combustion is not only a less efficient use of the fuel, but it can also be dangerous because CO is a poisonous gas. The exhaust fumes of automobiles contain CO because not all the hydrocarbons in the gasoline are completely burnt up.   This is why a car engine should never be run in a closed garage.

In addition to CO, very small particles of carbon are often produced when combustion is incomplete. The black soot that comes from some candle flames consists of tiny particles of carbon resulting from the incomplete combustion of the hydrocarbons in the wax.

Substitution. When one or more hydrogen atoms of a hydrocarbon are replaced by some other element or group, the chemical change is called **substitution**. The added group or element is called a substituent. The alkanes react with the halogens in sunlight to form substitution products called halogen derivatives. The reaction is difficult to control and produces a mixture of reaction products. Thus, when methane reacts with chlorine, a mixture of chloromethane, CH_3Cl, dichloromethane, CH_2Cl_2, trichloromethane, $CHCl_3$, and tetrachloromethane, CCl_4, is obtained. (HCl is also formed.) Figure 29-35 lists some common halogen derivatives of methane.

Figure 29-35

Some common halogen derivatives of methane, CH_4.

Common Name	IUPAC Name	Formula	Chief Uses
methyl chloride	chloromethane	CH_3Cl	Local anesthetic
chloroform	trichloromethane	$CHCl_3$	General anesthetic; solvent
iodoform	tri-iodomethane	CHI_3	Antiseptic
carbon tetra-chloride	tetrachloromethane	CCl_4	Solvent; dry cleaning; fire extinguisher
Freon	dichlorodifluoro-methane	CF_2Cl_2	Refrigerant

When chlorine reacts with ethane, a mixture of halogen substitution products is also obtained. Two of the products are the following isomers:

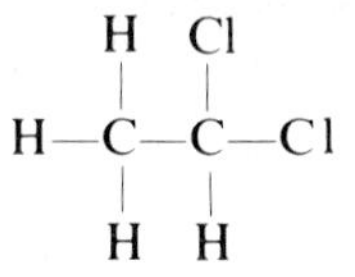

1,1-dichloroethane 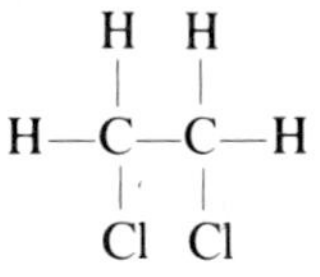   1,2-dichloroethane

Substitution products are characteristic of reactions involving saturated hydrocarbons. Although such products may also be obtained in reactions of unsaturated hydrocarbons, addition products (see below) are more characteristic. Addition products cannot be produced from saturated hydrocarbons.

Addition. Since only a single bond is needed to join two carbon atoms, alkenes and alkynes can add atoms or groups at the double or triple bond, opening it up and changing it to a single bond. This is called addition. The products of an **addition reaction** are called addition compounds. Addition reactions are much faster than substitutions and may continue until the compound is completely saturated.

Ethylene, as a representative alkene, will readily add bromine or chlorine, but will not add the less reactive element iodine. Ethylene will, however, react with a concentrated solution of hydrogen iodide. The equation for the reaction of ethylene with bromine is:

AN ADDITION REACTION (BROMINE ADDS TO THE MOLECULE AT THE DOUBLE BOND)

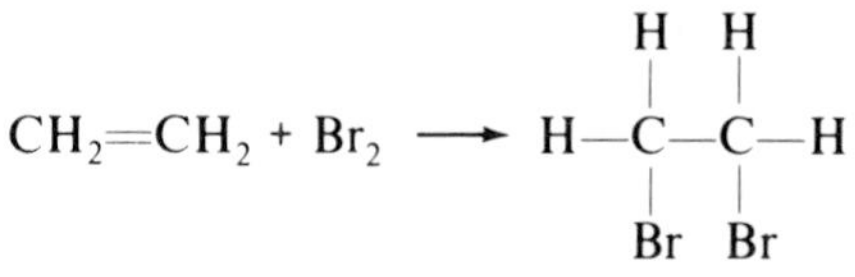

$$CH_2{=}CH_2 + Br_2 \longrightarrow \begin{array}{c} H \quad H \\ | \quad\; | \\ H{-}C{-}C{-}H \\ | \quad\; | \\ Br \;\; Br \end{array} \qquad \textbf{(Eq. 4)}$$

1,2-dibromoethane

Ethylene reacts with chlorine in the same manner to form the addition product 1,2-dichloroethane.

When ethylene reacts with hydrogen iodide, iodoethane is formed:

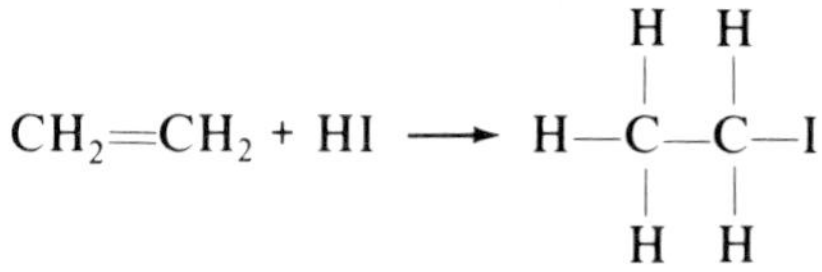

$$CH_2{=}CH_2 + HI \longrightarrow \begin{array}{c} H \quad H \\ | \quad\; | \\ H{-}C{-}C{-}I \\ | \quad\; | \\ H \;\; H \end{array} \qquad \textbf{(Eq. 5)}$$

iodoethane

The halogen derivative 1,2-dichloroethane is commonly known as ethylene chloride. It is used commercially as a solvent and in the preparation of Thiokol, an artificial rubber, and ethylene glycol, an antifreeze. The bromine addition product 1,2-dibromoethane (Equation 4), is a heavy colorless liquid, commonly called ethylene bromide. It is used with lead tetraethyl in high-octane gasolines in order to form an easily vaporized lead compound.

The triple bond, like the double bond, is also chemically reactive. The reaction of acetylene with chlorine produces a mixture of two halogen derivatives. Their formation can be shown by the following equations:

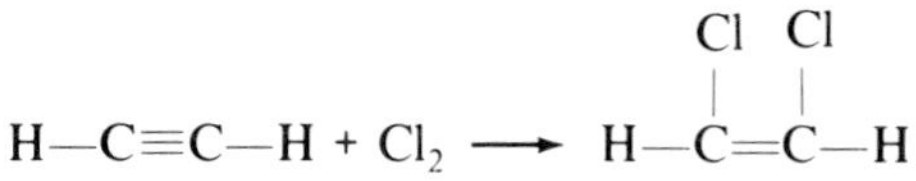

$$\underset{\text{acetylene}}{H{-}C{\equiv}C{-}H} + Cl_2 \longrightarrow \underset{\text{1,2-dichlorethene}}{\begin{array}{c} Cl \;\; Cl \\ | \quad\; | \\ H{-}C{=}C{-}H \end{array}} \qquad \textbf{(Eq. 6)}$$

$$\begin{array}{c} Cl \;\; Cl \\ | \quad\; | \\ H{-}C{=}C{-}H \end{array} + Cl_2 \longrightarrow \begin{array}{c} Cl \;\; Cl \\ | \quad\; | \\ H{-}C{-}C{-}H \\ | \quad\; | \\ Cl \;\; Cl \end{array} \qquad \textbf{(Eq. 7)}$$

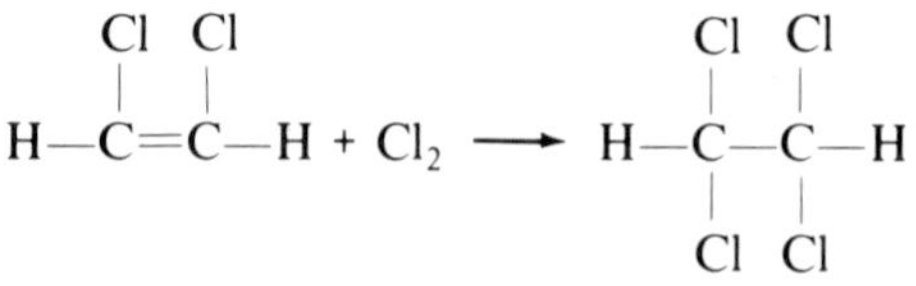

1,1,2,2-tetrachloroethane

Alkenes and alkynes can add hydrogen to their molecules in the presence of suitable catalysts, such as platinum, palladium, or nickel. The temperature at which these reactions occur is dependent upon the catalyst used and may vary from room temperature to about 250°C.

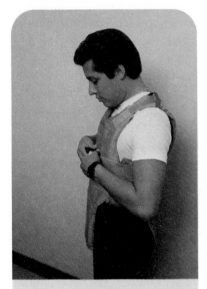

*Chemistry
in the Service of Law Enforcement*

The photo shows a bullet-proof vest made of a synthetic organic chemical that is five times as strong as steel, kilogram for kilogram. Because the material is so strong, bullet-proof vests made of it can be considerably lighter than those made from metal, and police officers are more inclined to wear the lighter vests. In use since the 1970's, these vests have already saved a number of lives and prevented a number of serious injuries.

Polyvinyl chloride, or vinyl, is an addition polymer used to make floor tiles, pipes, and film for food packaging. Starch and cellulose are examples of condensation polyers.

The process is called catalytic hydrogenation. By this process, ethylene can be reduced to ethane, or acetylene can be reduced to ethylene (which in turn can be reduced to ethane):

$$H-C\equiv C-H + H_2 \longrightarrow CH_2=CH_2 \qquad \textbf{(Eq. 8)}$$
$$\text{acetylene} \qquad\qquad \text{ethylene}$$

$$CH_2=CH_2 + H_2 \longrightarrow CH_3-CH_3 \qquad \textbf{(Eq. 9)}$$
$$\text{ethane}$$

Polymerization. As stated earlier, **polymers** are giant molecules formed by the joining of simple molecules into long chains. The simple units are called monomers, and the process by which large numbers of small units combine is called polymerization (po-LIM-er-i-ZAY-shun). For example, the double bond in an ethylene molecule, $CH_2=CH_2$, can be broken, to form a unit whose structure can be represented:

$$\cdot\, CH_2-CH_2\, \cdot \qquad \text{ethylene monomer}$$

When two of these units combine with each other, the result is:

$$\cdot\, CH_2-CH_2\cdot \;+\; \cdot\, CH_2-CH_2\cdot \;\longrightarrow\; \cdot\, CH_2-CH_2-CH_2-CH_2\cdot$$

To the four-carbon particle still other monomer units can add on until finally a very long molecule is produced made up of the monomer units. These giant polymer molecules are called polyethylene.

Polymers may consist of a linkage of hundreds or thousands of monomers. Examples of natural polymers are cotton, wool, silk, and natural rubber. Synthetic rubbers, plastics, and many textiles (Dacron, Orlon, etc.) are manufactured polymers.

Many polymers are made by addition reactions between molecules of an unsaturated hydrocarbon or derivatives of such a hydrocarbon. The formation of polyethylene, referred to above, is the result of an addition reaction. To make the ethylene monomer units combine, a catalyst must be used, and the temperature must be elevated somewhat. Polymers formed by addition reactions are called addition polymers.

Some polymers are made by addition reactions between unsaturated molecules of more than one substance. Such polymers are called copolymers. Butyl rubber, the synthetic rubber made from isobutylene and isoprene, is a copolymer.

Other polymers, called condensation polymers, are made by reactions between molecules of two different monomers. In these reactions, a small molecule, usually water, is eliminated. For example, nylon is formed by the condensation reaction between molecules of hexamethylene diamine and adipic acid; a molecule of water is eliminated. Bakelite and protein are other examples of condensation polymers.

29-16　Petroleum

Petroleum is the principal source of aliphatic (straight- and branched-chain) hydrocarbons, and an important source of aromatic hydrocarbons. This very important raw material consists chiefly of saturated hydrocarbons, but may also contain unsaturated and aromatic hydrocarbons and derivatives, depending upon the source.

Petroleum is refined by **fractional distillation.** In this process, successive distillations are carried out at increasingly higher temperatures. The distillate (the vapor that is condensed) is collected in several portions or fractions. The first fraction is the richest in the petroleum components that have the lowest boiling points. The later fractions have components with the higher boiling points. The fractions include such substances as gasoline, kerosene, furnace oil, naphthas, and lubricating oils. These fractions are usually purified before they are distributed commercially.

The most important fraction, gasoline, is used chiefly as a fuel in the internal combustion engines in cars. A rather large number of hydrocarbons, varying from six to ten carbon atoms per molecule, constitute most of the types of commercial gasolines. However, in the fractional distillation of petroleum, only about 20% of the crude oil comes over as gasoline. This amount would supply only a small fraction of the world demand. Moreover, this gasoline has some undesirable features, such as poor antiknock qualities. Therefore, other processes are used to increase the supply and quality of gasoline. The most important of these is cracking.

Cracking. Cracking is the process in which higher molecular mass hydrocarbon molecules, which are unsuitable for direct use in gasoline, are broken down into smaller molecules that are more easily evaporated and, therefore, more suitable for gasoline. The two chief cracking processes are thermal cracking and catalytic cracking. In thermal cracking, the higher molecular mass molecules, usually obtained from the kerosene fraction, are heated under pressure. These molecules, containing 10 to 16 carbon atoms each, are decomposed chiefly into alkanes and alkenes of lower molecular mass. The alkenes are present in larger quantities than the alkanes and are superior in antiknock qualities. Catalytic cracking usually uses high temperatures and some increase in pressure in addition to a catalyst. The product of catalytic cracking is superior to that obtained by thermal cracking. This is so because catalytic cracking produces not only alkenes, but also a greater amount of branched-chain and ring compounds. These compounds increase octane ratings and therefore improve the antiknock qualities of the gasoline.

Questions for Sections 29-15 and 29-16

36. (a) Compare the chemical activity of alkanes with that of unsaturated hydrocarbons. (b) Write the equation for the complete combustion of CH_4 in oxygen. (c) In addition to water, what are two

products of the incomplete combustion of hydrocarbons?

37. (a) Describe the nature of a substitution reaction. (b) What are the names and formulas of three (3) chlorine substitution products of methane? (c) Write the formula and the IUPAC name of the refrigerant Freon.

*38. Write the structural formula and IUPAC name of the addition product obtained when ethylene reacts with (a) Cl_2 (b) HI. Write the structural formula and IUPAC name of the addition product formed when a molecule of acetylene reacts with (c) one molecule of chlorine, (d) two molecules of chlorine.

39. Define (a) polymer, (b) monomer. Mention one example of (c) an addition polymer, (d) a copolymer. (e) Name the monomers present in the copolymer mentioned in (d).

40. Describe (a) the composition of a typical petroleum, (b) fractional distillation. (c) What are five (5) products of the fractional distillation of petroleum? (d) Which is the most important product?

41. (a) Describe the process of cracking. (b) What is its chief purpose? What conditions are used in (c) thermal cracking, (d) catalytic cracking? (e) Why is the gasoline obtained by catalytic cracking superior in octane rating to that obtained by thermal cracking?

*The answers to questions marked with an asterisk are given in the back of the book.

CHAPTER SUMMARY

1. All living things are composed chiefly of organic compounds, i.e., compounds of carbon.
2. Organic chemistry deals with the study of carbon compounds.
3. The chief reason for the existence of so many carbon compounds is the ability of carbon atoms to bond to one another.
4. The molecules of most organic compounds are nonpolar and show covalent bonding. These characteristics account for many of the properties of these compounds.
5. Because of sp^3 hybridization, the four electrons of a carbon atom form equivalent covalent bonds. These bonds extend at equal angles into space (109°28') and produce tetrahedral structures.
6. Many carbon compounds are isomers of one another, i.e., they have the same molecular composition but different structures and different properties. Structural formulas are used to distinguish them from one another.
7. In saturated compounds, the four covalent bonds of carbon are fully utilized and are represented by single lines. In unsaturated compounds, double or triple bonds are present, indicating that valence bonds can still be used for adding other atoms to the molecule.
8. Hydrocarbons are organic compounds consisting of hydrogen and carbon only. They may have structures that are straight-chain, branched-chain, or open-chain.
9. Melting points and boiling points of hydrocarbons increase with the increase in molecular size.
10. Alkanes are open-chain hydrocarbons with single bonds and the general formula C_nH_{2n+2}. The name of a normal alkane consists of a prefix, which indicates the number of carbon atoms, and the suffix, and the suffic -ane.

11. Alkyl groups (or alkyl radicals) are parts of compounds and have the general formula C_nH_{2n+1}.

12. The straight-chain alkane isomers are known as normal isomers; the branched-chain isomers are considered to be derivatives.

13. The IUPAC system names organic compounds according to definite rules.

14. The alkene series is a family of unsaturated hydrocarbons whose general formula is C_nH_{2n}. The alkene molecule has a double bond.

15. Alkynes are unsaturated hydrocarbons whose molecules have triple bonds. The general formula of the series is C_nH_{2n-2}; their names end in *-yne*.

16. Alkadiene molecules have two double bonds between two pairs of carbon atoms. They form important addition polymers and are isomeric with alkynes.

17. Alicyclic hydrocarbons have ring structures linked by single or double bonds. They include cycloalkanes, cycloalkenes, cycloalkadienes, and other more complex groups.

18. Aromatic hydrocarbons have the general formula C_nH_{2n-6}. Their structures include the benzene ring which has 6 carbon atoms with alternating single and double bonds.

19. The carbon-carbon bonds in benzene are intermediate in character between a single and double bond; the compound shows properties of both saturated and unsaturated hydrocarbons.

20. All hydrocarbons, including the relatively inactive alkanes, will burn in air or oxygen. Incomplete combustion produces the element carbon and the poisonous gas carbon monoxide.

21. All hydrocarbons may undergo substitution reactions; addition reactions are more characteristic of the unsaturated hydrocarbons.

22. Polymers are giant molecules formed by the joining of simple molecules (monomers) into long chains.

23. Many polymers, such as polyethylene, are made by addition reactions between molecules of unsaturated hydrocarbons or derivatives of such hydrocarbons.

24. By cracking, high molecular mass molecules are broken down into smaller molecules that can be used in gasoline.

TERMS YOU SHOULD KNOW

organic chemistry	aliphatic	cycloalkane
structural formula	alkane	cycloalkene
isomer	alkene	cycloalkadiene
saturated compound	alkyne	ortho-
unsaturated compound	alkadiene	meta-
homologous series or	aromatic	para-
family	paraffin series	substitution reaction
increment	normal alkane	substituent
hydrocarbon	alkyl group	addition reaction
straight-chain	alkane derivative	polymer
branched-chain	IUPAC system	fractional distillation
open-chain	olefin	cracking
cyclic	alicyclic	

Section

29-1   **1.** (a) What was the original meaning of the word "organic" when applied to chemical compounds? (b) How did Wöhler's synthesis of urea lead to a change in definition?

29-2   **2.** (a) What two factors account for the bonding of organic molecules by van der Waals forces? (b) Describe the melting points, boiling points, and vapor pressures that result from such bonding.

  3. (a) What test can be used to show that gasoline, an organic fuel, is made of nonpolar molecules? (b) Explain how the covalent bonding in organic compounds accounts for the slowness of their reaction speeds.

29-3   **4.** (a) The carbon atom in the free state holds two s and two p electrons in the outermost principal energy level. Why are there four equivalent bonds in methane? (b) How does the carbon atom in methane resemble the noble gas neon? (c) Why does methane have a tetrahedral structure?

29-4   **5.** (a) What is the advantage of the structural formula over the molecular formula? (b) How can we condense the amount of space needed for a structural formula? (c) Explain your answer to (b) by using some specific example.

  6. (a) Write the structural formulas of methyl alcohol, ethyl alcohol, and diethyl ether, using formula groups. (b) Mention one similarity and one difference in the characteristic group present in alcohols and bases.

  7. Why are the substances

$$CH_3\!-\!O\!-\!C_2H_5 \quad \text{and} \quad CH_3\!-\!\underset{\underset{OH}{|}}{\overset{\overset{H}{|}}{C}}\!-\!CH_3$$

considered to be isomers?

29-5   **8.** (a) Why is an organic compound whose formula has single bonds only considered to be saturated? (b) Why is a compound which has a double bond in its formula considered to be unsaturated?

29-6   **9.** Write the formula of the missing compound in each of the following sequences: (a) C_3H_8, C_4H_{10}, C_6H_{14} (b) C_2H_2, C_3H_4, C_5H_8.

29-7   **10.** (a) Name two types of open-chain structures. (b) What is another name for open-chain structures? (c) Write the structural formula of a cyclic hydrocarbon.

  11. (a) Compare the average melting points of solid organic and inorganic substances. What is the most probable phase of a hydrocarbon with the formula (b) C_3H_8, (c) $C_{10}H_{22}$, (d) $C_{18}H_{38}$?

29-8   **12.** (a) Name the five (5) important hydrocarbon series. (b) For each series, state what is characteristic about the structure of a typical member. (c) Write the name and structural formula for any one compound in each of the series.

29-9   **13.** (a) Write the molecular formulas of alkanes containing 7, 8, and 9 carbon atoms. (b) What general chemical property is a result of the saturated bonding in alkanes? (c) Why do van der Waals forces become stronger with the increase of the molecular mass of an alkane?

14. (a) Distinguish between a hydrocarbon that is a normal alkane and one that is an alkane derivative. (b) Write the molecular formulas for pentane, hexane, and decane. (c) What is the normal phase for the compounds in *(b)*?

15. (a) Write the structural formulas of normal propyl chloride and normal butyl chloride. (b) Write the structural formula of isopropyl chloride, the isomer of normal propyl chloride.

16. Write the structural formulas of the three isomers of pentane. (Use the formula CH_3 to indicate the methyl group.)

29-10 17. Write the structural formula of (a) 2,2-dichloro-3-methylbutane, (b) 2,3,3-trimethylpentane, (c) 3-ethyl-3-methylhexane.

18. Write the structural formulas of the following halogen derivatives: (a) 1,1,2-trichloroethane, (b) 2-bromo-2-chloro-1,1,1-trifluoroethane, (c) 1,4-dibromo-3-ethylhexane.

19. None of the following names adhere to IUPAC rules. Write the structural formula of each and state the correct IUPAC name: (a) 3,3,4-trichloropentane, (b) 2,6-dichlorohexane, (c) 3-*n*-propylbutane.

20. The following are structural formulas of two pairs of molecules: (Some are written incorrectly.)

Pair 1: $CH_3-CH_2-CH-CH_3$ and $CH_3-CH_2-CH-CH_2-CH_3$
$\qquad\qquad\quad\;\; | \qquad\qquad\qquad\qquad\qquad\qquad\;\; |$
$\qquad\qquad\quad C_2H_5 \qquad\qquad\qquad\qquad\qquad\quad CH_3$

Pair 2: $CH_3-CH_2-CH_2-CH_2$ and $CH_3-CH-CH_3$
$\qquad\qquad\qquad\qquad\qquad | \qquad\qquad\qquad\qquad\; |$
$\qquad\qquad\qquad\qquad\quad CH_3 \qquad\qquad\qquad\quad C_2H_5$

(a) Which pair represents only one substance? (b) Which pair represents isomers? (c) Write the correct IUPAC names and structural formulas for the three formulas that are written incorrectly.

29-11 21. Write the structural formulas of (a) 2,4,4-trimethyl-2-pentene (b) 4-bromo-3-methyl-1-pentyne (c) 2,3-dimethyl-1,3-butadiene (d) 2,4-hexadiene.

22. Write the structural formulas of the following isomer pairs: (a) 1-butene and 2-butene (b) 2,3-dimethyl-1,3-butadiene and 3-methyl-1-pentyne (c) 3-ethyl-4-methyl-1-hexene and 4-methyl-2-octene.

23. State the IUPAC names of   (a) $CH_2-CH_2-CH=CH-CH_3$
$\qquad\qquad\qquad\qquad\qquad\qquad\qquad\qquad\quad |$
$\qquad\qquad\qquad\qquad\qquad\qquad\qquad\qquad\quad Cl$

(b)
$\qquad\qquad\qquad Br$
$\qquad\qquad\qquad |$
$CH\equiv C-C-CH_2-CH_3$
$\qquad\qquad\quad |$
$\qquad\qquad\quad Br$

(c)
$\qquad\qquad\qquad\qquad CH_3$
$\qquad\qquad\qquad\qquad |$
$CH_3-CH_2-C-C=C-CH_3$
$\qquad\qquad\quad |\;\; |\;\; |$
$\qquad\qquad\quad Cl\; Cl\; Cl$

24. When the compound 2-butanol $CH_3CHCH_2CH_3$
$\qquad\qquad\qquad\qquad\qquad\qquad\qquad\qquad |$
$\qquad\qquad\qquad\qquad\qquad\qquad\qquad\qquad OH$

is treated with warm, concentrated H_2SO_4, a molecule of water is eliminated. Write the name and structural formula of the alkene produced when the water molecule is formed by the combination of the -OH group and the hydrogen atom on (a) carbon atom 1, (b) carbon atom 3.

29-12   **25.** For each of the following structural formulas, mention the name of the substance represented and the family of hydrocarbons to which it belongs:

(a)   (b)   (c)

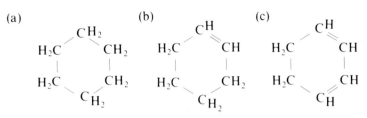

29-13   **26.** (a) Describe the nature of the hybrid bonds in benzene. (b) Write the structural formula of benzene that indicates the relationship of the carbon-carbon bonds. (c) What two types of hydrocarbons does benzene resemble in its reactions?

29-15   **27.** Using the molecular formulas, write the equation for the complete combustion of (a) butane, (b) octane. (c) Write an equation for the incomplete combustion of propane if the products are H_2O and CO.

28. Using structural formulas, write equations for the following substitutions:
(a) methane + chlorine, producing dichloromethane and HCl,
(b) ethane + bromine, producing ethyl bromide and HBr,
(c) ethane + chlorine, producing 1,1-dichloroethane and HCl.

29-16   **29.** (a) Of what type of hydrocarbon is petroleum the principal source? Compare fractional distillation and cracking with respect to the (b) nature of the process used, (c) chief product obtained.

FOR FURTHER THOUGHT

1. Classify each of the following statements as either (1) a definition, (2) an observation, or (3) an inference.

29-1   (a) All organic compounds are compounds of carbon.

29-3   (b) In a structural formula, each dash represents a covalent bond.

(c) In a structural formula, each dash represents a pair of shared electrons.

29-4   (d) Organic compounds may have the same molecular formula but different structural formulas.

(e) Isomers have the same molecular formula but different structural formulas.

(f) Alcohols contain a hydroxyl group ($-OH$).

(g) Alcohols do not turn red litmus blue.

(h) Alcohols do not produce OH^- ions.

29-5   (i) Unsaturated compounds contain pairs of carbon atoms sharing more than one pair of electrons.

29-9   (j) The alkanes are saturated compounds.

29-15   **2.** In a certain reaction, one of the reactants is a hydrocarbon. One product of the reaction is a hydrocarbon with the same number of carbon atoms as the reacting hydrocarbon, but with a larger number of hydrogen atoms. What can you conclude about the reacting hydrocarbon?

CHAPTER 30

Organic Chemistry—II

Objectives

When you have completed this chapter, you will be able to:
- Identify and write formulas for functional groups.
- State the formulas and IUPAC names for types of organic compounds, and describe their properties.
- Write equations for various organic reactions.
- Explain the nature of enzymes and their role in biochemical reactions.

30-1 Introduction

The last chapter was concerned with various families of organic compounds all of which are hydrocarbons. This chapter is devoted to a number of other important classes of organic compounds. These classes of compounds include alcohols, aldehydes (AL-duh-hides), ketones (KEE-tones), ethers, carboxylic (car-bok-SIL-ik) acids, esters, carbohydrates, and soaps.

Functional Groups. As mentioned in Chapter 29, there are various groups of atoms, called **functional groups,** that give organic compounds characteristic properties. For example, the -OH group referred to in Section 29-4 is a functional group. The -OH group gives these compounds, called alcohols, certain properties in common that are characteristic of alcohols. From the standpoint of nomenclature and organization, it is convenient to consider many organic compounds as being composed of one or more functional groups attached to a hydrocarbon unit. Although the IUPAC system names these compounds as though they were hydrocarbon derivatives, they are not necessarily prepared from hydrocarbons. Some of the functional groups are listed in Figure 30-1.

30-2 Alcohols

Alcohols make up the class of organic compounds in which one or more hydrogen atoms of a hydrocarbon have been replaced by an -OH group. For example, if one hydrogen atom is removed from the structural formula for a molecule of methane, and a hydroxyl group, -OH, is

FUNCTIONAL GROUP

Name of Group	Structure	Examples of the Group in a Compound	
hydroxyl, or alcohol group (occurs in organic compounds called alcohols)	$-OH$	methanol (methyl alcohol)	ethanol (ethyl alcohol)
aldehyde group (occurs in aldehydes)		methanal (formaldehyde)	ethanal (acetaldehyde)
carbonyl group (occurs in ketones)		propanone (methyl ketone)	3-pentanone (ethyl ketone)
ether group (occurs in ethers)		dimethyl ether	diethyl ether
carboxyl group (occurs in carboxylic acids)		methanoic acid (formic acid)	ethanoic acid (acetic acid)

(A)

$$H-\underset{\underset{\displaystyle H}{|}}{\overset{\overset{\displaystyle H}{|}}{C}}-H \quad \text{methane}$$

(B)

$$H-\underset{\underset{\displaystyle H}{|}}{\overset{\overset{\displaystyle H}{|}}{C}}-OH \quad \text{methyl alcohol}$$

(C) CH_3OH methyl alcohol

Figures 30-2

The structure of methyl alcohol.
(A) A molecule of the hydrocarbon methane. (B) When one of the hydrogen atoms on methane is replaced by a hydroxyl group, $-OH$, the result is methyl alcohol. (C) A shorter way of showing the structure of methyl alcohol.

put in its place, the result is the formula for methyl alcohol. See Figure 30-2.

It should be stressed that the alcohol group (also called the hydroxyl group) in an alcohol does not function the same way as the OH^- ion in an inorganic base. In an inorganic base, the hydroxide group is ionically bonded. In alcohols, the hydroxyl group is covalently bonded. Thus, alcohols do not dissociate to form hydroxide ions in water solution as do inorganic bases. Therefore, alcohols do not have the properties associated with the OH^- ion.

The general formula for alcohols is usually represented as ROH, where R represents an alkyl group and OH represents the functional group. R, for example, represents CH_3 in methyl alcohol, CH_3OH. It represents CH_3CH_2 in ethyl alcohol, CH_3CH_2OH.

Monohydroxy Alcohols. Monohydroxy alcohols contain only one hydroxyl group per molecule. Methyl alcohol, CH_3OH, and ethyl alcohol, CH_3CH_2OH, are both monohydroxy alcohols.

Monohydroxy alcohols belong to one of three groups. They can be either primary, secondary, or tertiary alcohols, depending upon the number of carbon atoms directly bonded to the carbon atom holding the -OH group. A **primary alcohol** is one in which the carbon holding the -OH group is bonded to only one other carbon atom. In a **secondary alcohol,** the carbon holding the -OH group is bonded to two other carbon atoms. In **tertiary alcohols,** the carbon holding the -OH group is bonded to three other carbon atoms. See Figure 30-3. The only exception to these definitions is methyl alcohol. It contains only one carbon atom in its molecule (and, therefore, that carbon atom is attached to no other carbon), but it is still considered to be a primary alcohol. Primary

Figure 30-3

(A) The carbon atom bonded to the $-OH$ group is bonded to one other carbon atom in a primary alcohol, (B) to two other carbon atoms in a secondary alcohol, and (C) to three other carbon atoms in a tertiary alcohol.

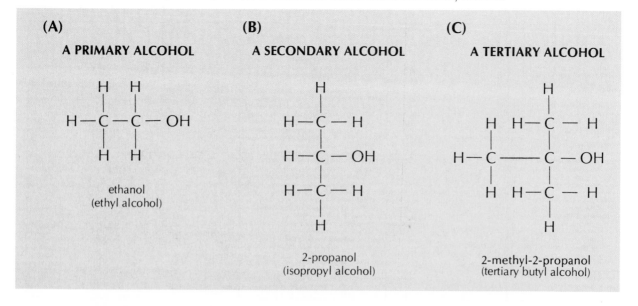

(A)
A PRIMARY ALCOHOL

ethanol
(ethyl alcohol)

(B)
A SECONDARY ALCOHOL

2-propanol
(isopropyl alcohol)

(C)
A TERTIARY ALCOHOL

2-methyl-2-propanol
(tertiary butyl alcohol)

alcohols are also defined as being alcohols in which the -OH group is attached at the end of the hydrocarbon chain. Thus, by this definition, the end group of a primary alcohol has the structural formula:

$$
\begin{array}{c}
\text{H} \\
| \\
-\text{C}-\text{OH} \\
| \\
\text{H}
\end{array}
$$

Methyl alcohol does qualify as a primary alcohol by this definition.

The manner in which an alcohol reacts to mild oxidation can be used to distinguish primary, secondary, and tertiary alcohols. When warmed in the presence of potassium permanganate and sulfuric acid (a mild oxidizing combination), primary alcohols are oxidized first to aldehydes and then to organic acids. (Aldehydes and organic acids are families of compounds that are discussed later in this chapter.) With the same oxidizing mixture, secondary alcohols are oxidized to ketones (also discussed later in the chapter). Tertiary alcohols are not changed by mild oxidizing mixtures. If stronger oxidizers are used, tertiary alcohols are broken down into smaller molecules. Thus, one can distinguish between primary, secondary, and tertiary alcohols by seeing how an alcohol behaves in the presence of oxidizing agents.

Under the IUPAC system, monohydroxy alcohols are named by replacing the final -e of the parent hydrocarbon with -ol. Methyl alcohol is related to the hydrocarbon methane. By removing the final e from methane and adding ol, we get the IUPAC name for methyl alcohol: methanol. The IUPAC name for the alcohol derived from ethane, CH_3CH_3, is ethanol, CH_3CH_2OH.

The Prefix *Iso-.* Although not a part of the IUPAC system, the prefix iso- is sometimes used in the naming of organic compounds. This prefix is used to indicate that there is a methyl branch in a carbon chain. For example, consider the structure of isobutyl alcohol. See Figure 30-4. The normal compounds and the compounds described by the prefix *iso-* are isomers. Thus, normal butyl alcohol, $CH_3CH_2CH_2CH_2OH$, and isobutyl alcohol have the same molecular formula, $C_4H_{10}O$, and are isomers. The *iso-* prefix is used in naming compounds containing a variety of functional groups, not just those containing the alcohol group. When the prefix is used, the methyl branch must be on the next to the last carbon atom in the chain, counting away from the functional group. The following structural formulas illustrate the use of the term:

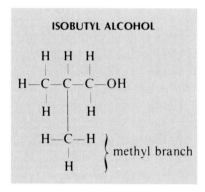

Figure 30-4

ISOBUTYL ALCOHOL

$$
\begin{array}{cccc}
\text{H} & \text{H} & \text{H} \\
| & | & | \\
\text{H}-\text{C}-\text{C}-\text{C}-\text{OH} \\
| & | & | \\
\text{H} & & \text{H} \\
& | \\
& \text{H}-\text{C}-\text{H} \\
& | \\
& \text{H}
\end{array}
$$
} methyl branch

$$
\begin{array}{cc}
CH_3CHCH_2CH_2OH & \quad CH_3CHCH_2CH_2CH_2OH \\
| & \qquad | \\
CH_3 & \qquad CH_3 \\
\text{isopentyl alcohol} & \quad \text{isohexyl alcohol}
\end{array}
$$

Two Common Monohydroxy Alcohols: Methanol and Ethanol. The simplest alcohol, methanol, can be obtained from wood by heating the wood in the absence of air. This process, called **destructive distillation,** breaks the wood down into simpler substances, one of which is methanol. See Figure 30-5. Since methanol was originally prepared this way, it was given the name wood alcohol, a name that is still used today. Methanol is now prepared by the catalytic combination of carbon monoxide and hydrogen.

Figure 30-5

The destructive distillation of wood. The wood splints are heated by the burner *in the absence of air.* Gases that are formed during the process pass into the condensing tube. Those that boil at temperatures above that of the cold water turn into liquids in the condensing tube. Those that boil below the temperature of the cold water pass out of the condensing tube into the air. When wood is burned *in air,* entirely different products are formed.

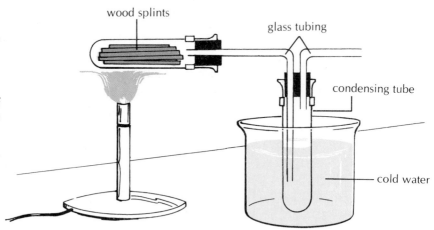

Methanol tastes like ethanol, but is extremely poisonous when swallowed. Unfortunately, it is sometimes mistaken for ethanol, the alcohol present in beer, wine, and hard liquors. Methanol attacks the nervous system, especially the optic nerves. Many cases of blindness, and even death, have resulted from drinking wood alcohol. Commercially, methanol is used as a solvent in lacquers and varnishes. It is also used as a fuel and in the manufacture of formaldehyde.

Ethanol, or ethyl alcohol, is the most common and familiar of the alcohols. It is also known as grain alcohol because it can be prepared from corn or other grain plants. When prepared from corn, the starch in the corn is first converted into a fermentable sugar. The sugar is then fermented to produce ethanol. Any sweet fruit juice can be fermented to produce ethanol. Fermentation is a chemical change brought about by enzymes, which are catalysts produced by living organisms. The ethanol is removed from the fermented mixture by distillation. The term *proof* is used in the liquor trade to indicate the proportion of ethanol in a beverage. The **proof** is equal to twice the percentage of alcohol by volume. Thus, 90 proof means 45% alcohol by volume. Pure alcohol is 200 proof and is called absolute alcohol. Ethanol intended for commercial use is often **"denatured,"** or rendered unfit to drink, by the addition of methanol.

Ethanol is a volatile, colorless, flammable liquid with an odor that many people find pleasant. It is an excellent solvent and fuel. Besides its use in alcoholic beverages, ethanol is used as a solvent for lacquers,

Figure 30-6

The structure of ethylene glycol. Having two hydroxyl groups, ethylene glycol is a dihydroxy alcohol.

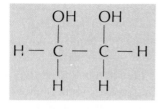

or

CH₂OHCH₂OH

1,2-ethanediol
(ethylene glycol)

Figure 30-7

The structure of glycerine. With three hydroxyl groups, glycerine is a trihydroxy alcohol.

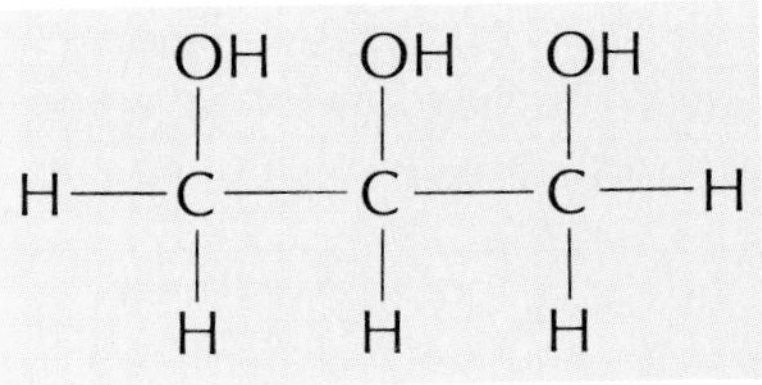

$$OH \quad OH \quad OH$$
$$H-C-C-C-H$$
$$H \quad H \quad H$$

or

$$CH_2OHCHOHCH_2OH$$

1,2,3-propanetriol
(glycerine or glycerol)

Figure 30-8

The hydroxyl group, present in both water and methyl alcohol, makes both substances similar with regard to certain properties. Molecules of both substances have considerable polarity, making each substance completely soluble in the other.

WATER

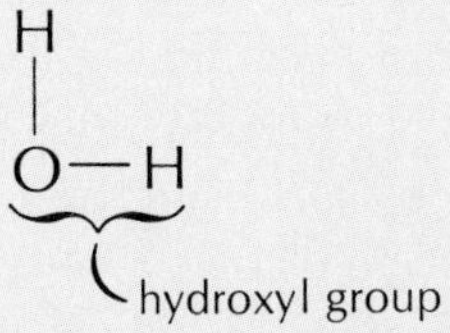

$$H$$
$$O-H$$
hydroxyl group

METHYL ALCOHOL

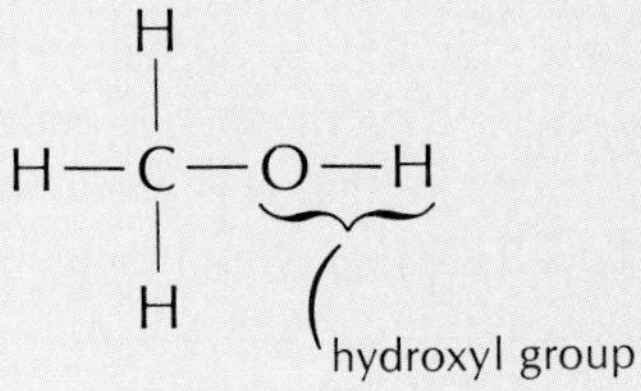

$$H$$
$$H-C-O-H$$
$$H$$
hydroxyl group

and in the preparation of extracts, ether, drugs, and perfumes.

Dihydroxy Alcohols. Dihydroxy alcohols, commonly called glycols, are alcohols whose molecules have two hydroxyl groups. The best known of these is ethylene glycol, $C_2H_4(OH)_2$. See Figure 30-6.

The IUPAC names for ethylene glycol are 1,2-dihydroxyethane or 1,2-ethanediol. The *-diol* ending indicates that there are two hydroxyl groups per molecule. Ethylene glycol is a common antifreeze for car radiators.

Trihydroxy Alcohols. Trihydroxy alcohols have three hydroxyl groups per molecule. The most important trihydroxy alcohol is glycerine, $C_3H_5(OH)_3$. See Figure 30-7.

Glycerine is a viscous, sweet-tasting liquid obtained as a by-product in the manufacture of soap. It is used to make plastics, drugs, cosmetics, foods, and nitroglycerine. Glycerine's IUPAC name is 1,2,3-trihydroxypropane or 1,2,3-propanetriol.

Some General Properties of Alcohols. Alcohol molecules have both polar and nonpolar properties. The -OH group is polar, while the hydrocarbon part of an alcohol molecule is nonpolar in character. Methyl alcohol is similar to water in that the hydroxyl group is a considerable part of the total molecule. Therefore, it is quite polar and completely soluble in water in all proportions. See Figure 30-8.

Ethyl and propyl alcohols are also polar enough to be completely miscible with water. However, the next higher member of the series, the four-carbon butyl alcohol, is more hydrocarbon in nature. It is not completely soluble in water. Longer chain alcohols are even less soluble. See Figure 30-9.

Figure 30-9   **1-BUTANOL**

As the hydrocarbon portion of an alcohol molecule becomes longer, the alcohol becomes less soluble in water. The 4-carbon alcohol whose formula is shown is not completely soluble in water, whereas the 1-, 2-, and 3-carbon monohydroxy alcohols are all completely soluble.

$$H \quad H \quad H \quad H$$
$$H-C-C-C-C-OH$$
$$H \quad H \quad H \quad H$$

hydrocarbon portion of the molecule

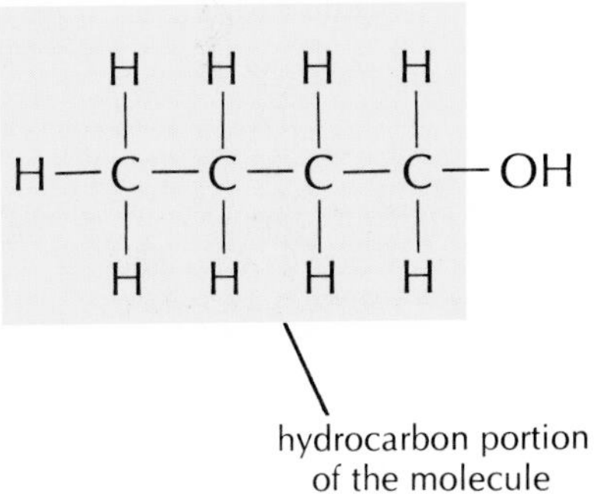

The polarity (and hence water solubility) of an alcohol is also affected by the number of -OH groups in its molecule. As this number increases, the polarity of the molecule increases. Ethylene glycol and glycerine (Figures 30-6 and 30-7) are completely soluble in water. Even longer chain glycols, such as 1,4-butanediol, 2,3-butanediol, and three of the five pentadiols, are completely soluble in water.

Alcohols react with organic acids to produce compounds belonging to the ester family. This reaction will be discussed later in the chapter after organic acids are described.

1. (a) What is the nature of a functional group? (b) Write the names and formulas of five (5) functional groups found in organic compounds.
2. (a) Describe the composition of an alcohol. (b) Write the general formula of a monohydroxy alcohol. (c) Write the formula and name of the alcohol obtained by replacing one hydrogen atom of ethane with the alcohol group.
*3. (a) Define *primary alcohol* and write the name and structural formula of one example. Do the same for (b) a secondary alcohol, (c) a tertiary alcohol.
4. What types of compounds are produced by the oxidation of (a) primary alcohols, (b) secondary alcohols?
*5. What is the IUPAC name for (a) CH_3OH, (b) C_2H_5OH? Mention two additional names that are used for (c) CH_3OH, (d) C_2H_5OH.
6. State three (3) important properties and three (3) uses of (a) methyl alcohol, (b) ethyl alcohol. (c) Why is methyl alcohol sometimes called wood alcohol? (d) Describe its preparation by a synthesis reaction.
7. Define or describe (a) fermentation, (b) proof, (c) denatured alcohol, (d) absolute alcohol. (e) What percentage of alcohol is present in a liquor that is 30 proof?
8. State the IUPAC and common name of a (a) dihydroxy alcohol, (b) trihydroxy alcohol. (c) State one use for ethylene glycol. (d) State two uses for glycerine.
9. (a) Why do alcohols possess both polar and nonpolar properties? (b) Why is butyl alcohol less soluble in water than ethyl alcohol? (c) Why is glycerine more polar than ethylene glycol?

Figure 30-10

Some common aldehydes.

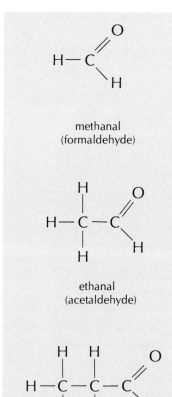

methanal
(formaldehyde)

ethanal
(acetaldehyde)

propanal

30-3 Aldehydes

The functional group of an **aldehyde** (AL-duh-hide) has the structural formula

aldehyde group

Examples of common aldehydes are shown in Figure 30-10.

Formaldehyde and acetaldehyde are the common names for the aldehydes shown in Figure 30-10. The IUPAC names are obtained by replacing the *-e* ending of the related hydrocarbon with *-al*. For example, the one-carbon aldehyde whose formula is HCHO is related to the one-carbon hydrocarbon methane, CH_4. By removing the *-e* ending from methane and replacing it with *-al*, the name methanal is produced. Hence, the IUPAC name for formaldehyde, HCHO, is methanal. By the same reasoning, the IUPAC name for acetaldehyde is ethanal.

The position of the aldehyde group in all aldehydes is at the end of the carbon chain. Therefore, it is not necessary to use a number in the name of an aldehyde to reveal where the aldehyde group is located. Members of the aldehyde family with four or more carbon atoms have isomeric forms.

Methanal (formaldehyde) is a colorless gas with a pungent, irritating odor. It is used as a germicide and disinfectant. It is very soluble in water. A solution composed of 37% formaldehyde in water, called formalin, is used to preserve dead animal specimens, as an antiseptic, and in the manufacture of rayon. Methanal is also used in the manufacture of plastics. Bakelite is one such plastic.

Ethanal is used to make aniline dyes, synthetic rubber, and many important organic compounds. Some of these compounds are acetic acid, acetone, ethyl acetate, and 1-butanol.

Figure 30-11

Alcohols are more soluble in water than aldehydes whose molecules have the same number of carbon atoms because the hydroxyl group is more polar than the aldehyde group.

Solubility in Water. The addition of the aldehyde group to the parent group gives only moderate polarity to the molecule. Therefore, aldehydes are relatively less soluble in water than alcohols. See Figure 30-11.

SOLUBILITIES IN 100 GRAMS OF WATER AT 20°C			
Alcohols		Aldehydes	
3-carbon molecule: $CH_3CH_2CH_2OH$	completely soluble	CH_3CH_2CHO	20 g
4-carbon: $CH_3CH_2CH_2CH_2OH$	20 g	$CH_3CH_2CH_2CHO$	3.7 g
5-carbon: $CH_3CH_2CH_2CH_2CH_2OH$	8.3 g	$CH_3CH_2CH_2CH_2CHO$	very slightly soluble
6-carbon: $CH_3(CH_2)_5OH$	2.6 g	$CH_3(CH_2)_4CHO$	insoluble

Aldehydes as Reducing Agents. Aldehydes are very easily oxidized to carboxylic acids (discussed in Section 30-6). The general reaction is shown in Figure 30-12.

Figure 30-12

The general reaction showing the oxidation of an aldehyde to a carboxylic acid. In the formulas, R represents alkyl groups, such as CH_3-, CH_3CH_2-, etc.

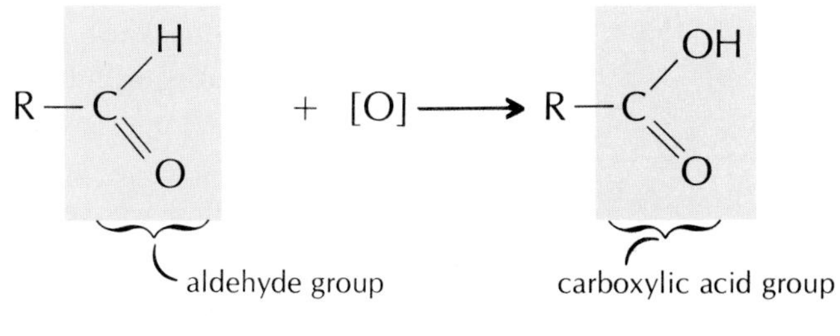

[O] is used to indicate oxygen from an oxidizing agent

Since aldehydes can be oxidized to organic acids, it means that they are themselves reducing agents. If a substance whose identity is unknown is suspected of being an aldehyde, one identifying test is to attempt to oxidize the unknown. Benedict's solution and Fehling's solution both contain the oxidizing agent $Cu(NH_3)_4^{2+}$. In this polyatomic ion (the copper-ammonia complex ion), the copper is in an oxidation state of 2+. Aldehydes will reduce the copper to a state of 1+ or even 0 (metallic copper). If the test solutions have a basic pH, a reddish precipitate is formed if an aldehyde is present. The reddish precipitate consists of copper (I) oxide and metallic copper. This test is useful in identifying glucose and other sugars possessing the aldehyde group. (Sugars are discussed later in the chapter.)

Aldehydes can also reduce the silver-ammonia complex ion, $Ag(NH_3)_2^+$, to metallic silver. When a solution of silver nitrate and ammonia water are mixed, the silver-ammonia complex ion is formed. If this solution is warmed gently with a formaldehyde solution in a test tube, a silver mirror will appear on the walls of the test tube. This reaction may be used as a test for aldehydes. This is the reaction used to produce mirrors by depositing silver on glass plates.

30-4   Ketones

Ketones are organic compounds containing the functional group

carbonyl group

Neither of the atoms that attaches to the sides of a carbonyl group can be a hydrogen atom. A hydrogen atom in that position would make the group an aldehyde group. Carbonyl groups are never found, therefore, at either end of a carbon chain. They are always found in the interior part of a chain with hydrocarbon radicals to either side. See Figure 30-13.

The IUPAC system names ketones by replacing the *-e* ending of the related hydrocarbon with *-one*. Where necessary, a number is used to show the position of the carbonyl group. For example, the ketone whose structural formula is shown in (B) of Figure 30-13 is related to the five-carbon alkane named pentane. Removing the final *-e* from pentane and substituting *-one* gives pentanone. The number 2 carbon is part of the functional group. Therefore, the name of the compound is 2-pentanone.

The compound whose structural formula is shown in (C) of Figure 30-13 has the IUPAC name 4-methyl-3-hexanone. Note that the carbonyl carbon is given the lower number in relation to substituted groups. For the molecule shown in Figure 30-13(C), this requires numbering carbon atoms from right to left rather than in the reverse direction.

The simplest ketone has the structural formula shown in (A) in Figure 30-13. The IUPAC name of this substance is propanone. No number is needed because there is only one interior carbon atom for

Figure 30-13

Three ketones. In a ketone, the carbonyl group, highlighted by the yellow color below, is never at the end of a carbon chain. It always occupies an interior position in the chain.

(A)

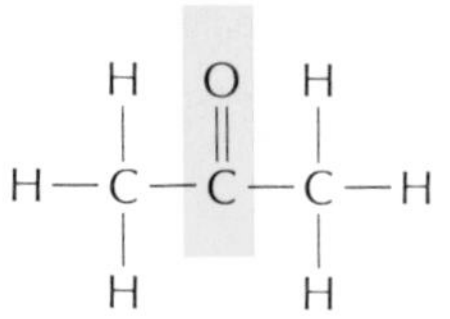

propanone
(acetone)

(B)

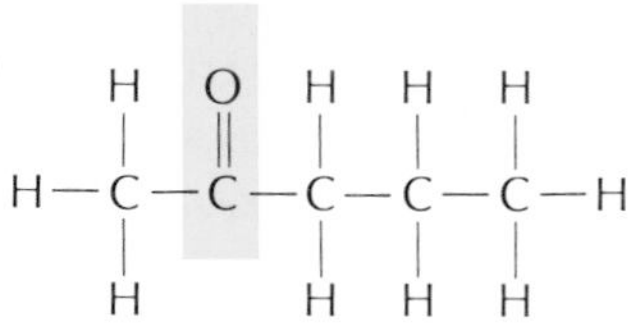

2-pentanone

(C)

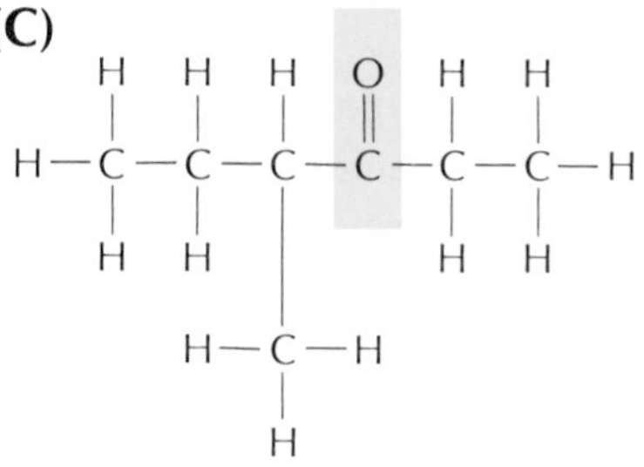

4-methyl-3-hexanone

the carbonyl group. The common name of propanone is acetone. Acetone is a colorless liquid that boils at 56°C and has a characteristic sweetish odor. Its odor is well known to those who have used it as a solvent to remove nail polish. It is a good solvent for organic compounds and is widely used to dissolve varnishes, plastics, and paints. Acetone is made commercially by oxidizing the secondary alcohol 2-propanol.

FORMATION OF ACETONE BY OXIDATION OF 2-PROPANOL

$$CH_3CHCH_3 + [O] \longrightarrow CH_3CCH_3 + H_2O \qquad \text{(Eq. 1)}$$

2-propanol

oxygen
from the
oxidizing agent

propanone
(acetone)

The middle carbon atom in 2-propanol has an oxidation number of 0. In propanone, it has an oxidation number of $2+$, an increase of 2. Hence, Equation 1 shows 2-propanol being oxidized to propanone.

Questions for Sections 30-3 and 30-4

10. Write the structural formula, IUPAC name, common name, and two uses of the aldehyde whose formula contains (a) one carbon atom, (b) two carbon atoms.
11. Write the equation for the general reaction showing the oxidation of an aldehyde to an acid.
*12. What is the composition of the solid produced when an aldehyde is treated with (a) Fehling's solution, (b) a solution of the silver-ammonia complex ion? (c) What property is shown by the aldehyde in these tests?
*13. Write the structural formulas of (a) acetone, (b) butanone. (c) What is the IUPAC name for acetone? (d) What is its chief use?
14. Write the equation, including structural formulas, for the preparation of acetone from 2-propanol.

30-5   Ethers

Ethers are organic oxides with the general formula ROR′, where R and R′ are alkyl groups that may be the same or different. Examples of ethers are shown in Figure 30-14.

The best known ether is diethyl ether, also called ethyl ether or just plain ether. At one time, ether was commonly used in surgery as a general anesthetic. Today, because it has several drawbacks, ether is seldom used in surgery except with laboratory animals. One of its drawbacks is its great flammability. Another is the irritation it causes

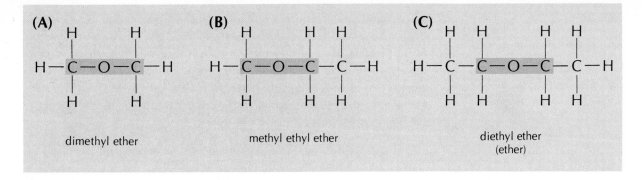

(A) dimethyl ether

(B) methyl ethyl ether

(C) diethyl ether
(ether)

Figure 30-14

Ethers have an oxygen atom to which two carbon atoms are bonded. They are organic oxides with the general formula ROR′, where R and R′ are alkyl groups that may be the same or different.

the respiratory tract. Still another is the nausea many people feel as they awake from ether. To a large extent, halothane, used together with nitrous oxide, has replaced ether in the operating room. Industrially, ether is used as a solvent for gums, fats, and waxes.

The normal boiling point of ether (34.6°C) is below normal body temperature (37°C). Its great volatility makes it a much greater fire hazard than many other flammable (but less volatile) liquids. Students are cautioned to stay away from ether unless they fully understand the safety precautions that should be followed when using it.

30-6   Carboxylic Acids

Although there are other types of organic acids, the most common organic acids belong to a group called carboxylic acids. Many fruits and vegetables contain carboxylic acids. One such acid is the familiar citric acid found in lemons, oranges, and other citrus fruits. Oxalic acid is found in rhubarb. Tartaric acid is found in grapes.

The functional group of a **carboxylic acid** is the carboxyl (car-BOK-sil) group:

$$-C\diagup_{\diagdown O}^{OH}$$ carboxyl group

This structure is written in an abbreviated form as -COOH.

The IUPAC system names organic acids by replacing the final -e of the parent hydrocarbon with -oic. For example, the simplest organic acid is the one-carbon acid commonly called formic acid:

$$H-C\diagup_{\diagdown O}^{OH}$$ methanoic acid
(formic acid)

This one-carbon organic acid is related to the one-carbon alkane methane. Removing the final -e from methane and replacing it with -oic

Figure 30-15

Three common carboxylic acids.

(A)

acetic acid,
CH_3COOH

(B)

oxalic acid,
HOOCCOOH

(C)

citric acid,
$C_3H_4(OH)(COOH)_3$

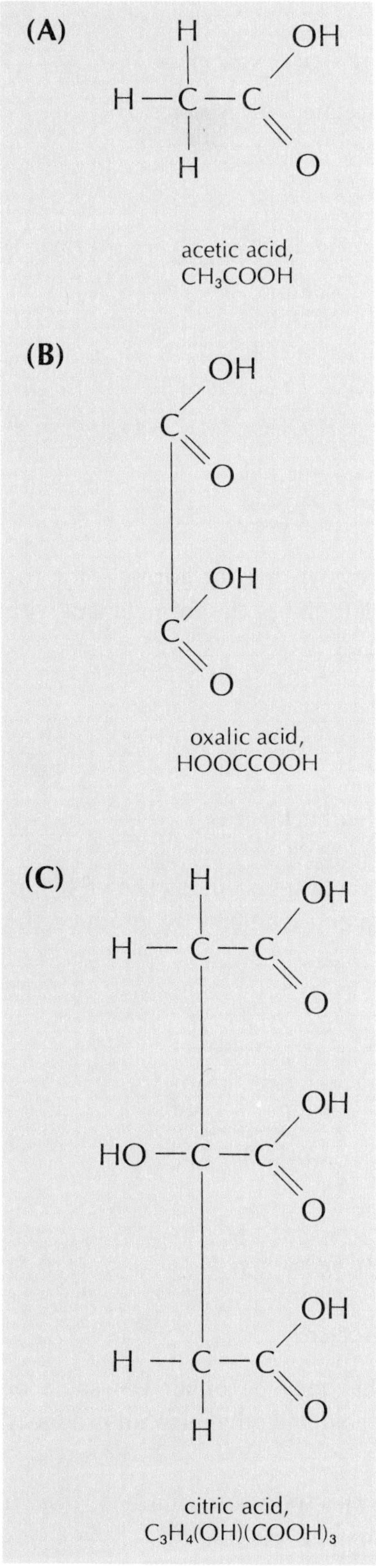

gives methanoic. Thus, the IUPAC name for formic acid is methanoic acid. The two-carbon acid

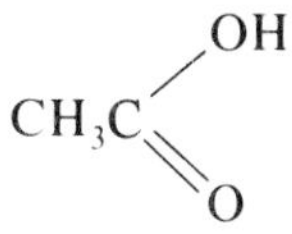

ethanoic acid

is related to the two-carbon alkane ethane. The IUPAC name for this acid is ethanoic acid.

Ethanoic acid is the acid called acetic acid throughout this book. Up to this point, the formula for acetic acid has been written

$$HC_2H_3O_2 \qquad \text{acetic acid}$$

rather than

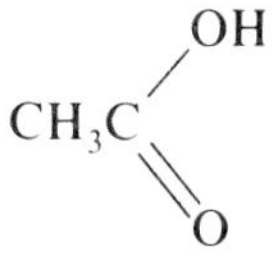

acetic acid

This second way of writing the formula for acetic acid is more revealing because it clearly shows that the substance is an acid containing the carboxyl group. The organic chemist is likely to write the formula of acetic acid in the more abbreviated form

$$CH_3COOH \qquad \begin{array}{l}\text{acetic acid} \\ \text{(ethanoic acid)}\end{array}$$

carboxyl group

The formula for propanoic acid is

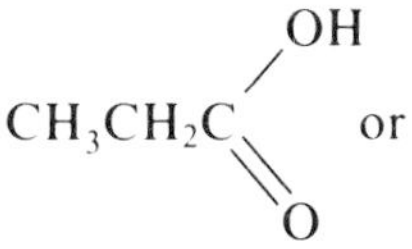

or CH_3CH_2COOH or C_2H_5COOH

Some acids contain more than one carboxyl group. Oxalic acid has two carboxyl groups. Some common carboxylic acids are shown in Figure 30-15.

Saturated organic acids having one carboxyl group have the general formula $C_nH_{2n+1}COOH$. They may be considered to be derivatives of the alkanes, where one hydrogen atom is replaced by the carboxyl group. These acids form a homologous series called the **fatty acid** series because so many of its members occur in natural fats.

General Properties of Carboxylic Acids. Like inorganic acids, soluble carboxylic acids produce hydronium ions in aqueous solution and react with bases to produce salts. Carboxylic acids, however, are generally weak, ionizing only slightly. Carboxylic acids react with alcohols to form compounds called **esters.** This kind of reaction is called **esterification** (ess-TER-uh-fuh-KAY-shun). The following equations, in which

Chapter 30   Organic Chemistry II   615

Percy L. Julian (1899-1975)

Percy L. Julian was an outstanding American research chemist. He created a drug used to treat glaucoma (a serious eye ailment), found an inexpensive method of manufacturing the important drug cortisone, and synthesized progesterone, a female hormone. Julian made many new products from soybeans, among them a firefighting solution that saved many lives in World War II. He owned more than 100 chemical patents.

Julian was a student at De Pauw University, graduating the highest ranking student in his class (class of 1920). Julian earned a master's degree at Harvard University (1928) and a doctorate at the University of Vienna (1931). In 1953, he founded the Julian Laboratories, a pharmaceutical company with branches in Mexico and various countries of South America.

For some years Julian was active in education, teaching chemistry at the Fisk University, West Virginia State College, and Howard University. He received 18 honorary doctorate degrees and many academic and civic citations.

acetic acid is used as a representative acid, describe some reactions that are typical of carboxylic acids:

IONIZATION:

$$CH_3COOH + H_2O \rightleftharpoons CH_3COO^- + H_3O^+ \qquad \textbf{(Eq. 2)}$$

acetic   acetate   hydronium
acid   ion   ion

NEUTRALIZATION:

$$CH_3COOH + NaOH \longrightarrow CH_3COONa + H_2O \qquad \textbf{(Eq. 3)}$$

sodium
acetate

ESTERIFICATION:

$$CH_3COOH + CH_3OH \rightleftharpoons CH_3COOCH_3 + H_2O \qquad \textbf{(Eq. 4)}$$

methyl   methyl
alcohol   acetate
            (an ester)

Esterification is sometimes shown by writing the formula for the alcohol with the alcohol group on the left end of the formula and with the group written HO rather than OH:

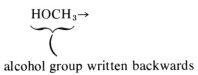

$$HOCH_3\rightarrow$$

alcohol group written backwards

As a result of the reaction, a water molecule splits out, as shown by the dashed lines, and the remaining fragments combine to produce the ester:

$$CH_3COOH + HOCH_3 \rightleftharpoons H_2O + CH_3COOCH_3 \qquad \textbf{(Eq. 5)}$$

acetate   methyl
group   group

methyl acetate

The general equation for esterification is

$$RCOOH + R'OH \rightleftharpoons RCOOR' + H_2O \qquad \textbf{(Eq. 6)}$$

a carboxylic   an   an
acid   alcohol   ester

where R and R' are alkyl radicals that may be either the same or different. The reaction between acetic acid and ethyl alcohol produces ethyl acetate:

$$CH_3COOH + CH_3CH_2OH \rightleftharpoons CH_3COOCH_2CH_3 + H_2O \qquad \textbf{(Eq. 7)}$$

acetic   ethyl   ethyl   water
acid   alcohol   acetate

Esterification bears some resemblance to neutralization in that water is one of the products of the reaction. An important difference is that in neutralization, hydrogen ions and hydroxide ions combine to form water. In esterification, these ions do not exist. To bring about esterification, the organic acid and alcohol are warmed in the presence of concentrated sulfuric acid, which acts catalytically. The sulfuric acid absorbs the water by forming the hydrate $H_2SO_4 \cdot H_2O$. Removal of the water in this manner (water is a product of the reaction) drives the equilibrium to the right, favoring the formation of more ester.

An ester can be broken up to form the original alcohol and carboxylic acid from which it is made by heating the ester in water that contains a small amount of a strong acid. We illustrate this reaction, called the hydrolysis of an ester, with ethyl acetate.

HYDROLYSIS OF ETHYL ACETATE

$$CH_3COOCH_2CH_3 + HOH \xrightarrow[\text{heat}]{H^+} CH_3CH_2OH + CH_3COOH \qquad \textbf{(Eq. 8)}$$

ethyl   ethyl   acetic
acetate   alcohol   acid

The general equation for this ester hydrolysis is:

$$\text{ester} + \text{water} \longrightarrow \text{alcohol} + \text{acid}$$

Polarity in Carboxylic Acids. The carboxyl group gives considerable polarity to the acid molecule. As with alcohols and aldehydes, as the length of the carbon chain in the molecule increases, the solubility in water decreases. Methanoic acid, ethanoic acid, propanoic acid, and one of the isomers of butanoic acid are completely miscible with water. Pentanoic acid is soluble to the extent of 3.7 g in 100 g of water. The higher acids are practically insoluble.

Attractive forces exist between the oppositely charged ends of polar molecules. As a result, polar substances tend to have higher boiling points than nonpolar substances. Therefore, carboxylic acids have higher boiling points than their corresponding nonpolar hydrocarbons. Methane, ethane, propane, and butane are gases at room temperature. At the same temperature, methanoic, ethanoic, propanoic, and butanoic acids are liquids.

Questions for Sections 30-5 and 30-6

*15. (a) What is the general formula for an ether? (b) Write the structural formula of diethyl ether. (c) Why has the use of ether as an anesthetic in surgery been largely discontinued? (d) What is its chief industrial use?

 16. Write the formulas of (a) methanoic acid, (b) ethanoic acid. (c) What are the common names of these acids? (d) Write the structural formula of oxalic acid.

 17. (a) What is the general formula of a fatty acid? (b) Why is it given this name?

*18. (a) Mention two chemical properties of carboxylic acids which are also typical of inorganic acids. (b) What reaction involves carboxylic acids and alcohols? (c) Write the equation for the reaction in which ethyl acetate is formed from the acid and alcohol. (d) What are two conditions used to bring about this reaction? (e) Write a balanced equation for the hydrolysis of methyl acetate. Give the name of each product formed.

19. (a) What part of the carboxylic acid molecule gives it polarity? (b) Why do the solubilities of carboxylic acids decrease with the increase of carbon atoms in the molecule? (c) Why do carboxylic acids have higher boiling points than the hydrocarbons which have the same number of carbon atoms per molecule?

30-7 Esters

As described in the last section, esters are formed when a carboxylic acid reacts with an alcohol. Esters can also form when an *in*organic acid reacts with an alcohol. A rather unusual type of ester, from the standpoint of its properties, is made by the reaction between glycerine and nitric acid. See Figure 30-16.

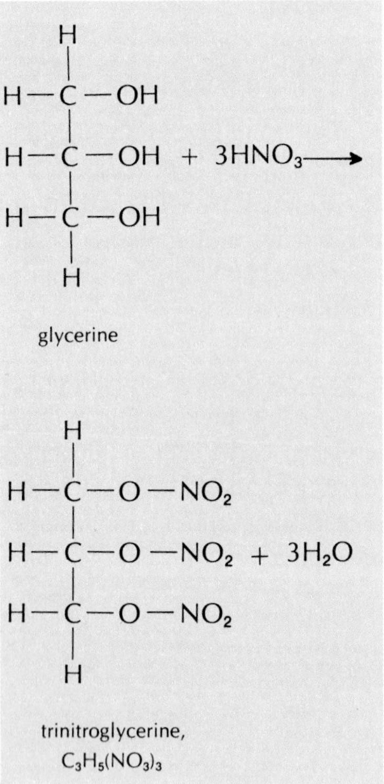

The ester product of the reaction is glyceryl nitrate, commonly known as nitroglycerine. It is an oily liquid that explodes very easily when heated or bumped. Nitroglycerine is safer to handle when the oily liquid is absorbed into wood pulp or porous earth. The product is called dynamite.

Esters made from alcohols and organic acids of low molecular mass are colorless liquids that have agreeable, fruity odors. Many of the odors in flowers come from esters. Esters are, therefore, used in the preparation of perfumes and synthetic flavors. Methyl acetate gives nail polish its odor.

Fats are glyceryl esters of carboxylic acids of relatively high molecular mass. At room temperature, saturated fats are solids while unsaturated fats are liquids.

30-8 Carbohydrates

A **carbohydrate** is a compound of carbon, hydrogen, and oxygen in which the hydrogen and oxygen atoms are present in the same ratio as in water. Its general empirical formula may be written as $C_y(H_2O)_x$, where x and y may be the same or different numbers. (Recall that an empirical formula is derived from experimentation. It is nonstructural and represents the simplest ratio of atoms in the compound.) This formula seems to indicate that the substance is a hydrate of carbon and accounts for the use of the name *carbohydrate*. Experiments show that carbohydrates contain hydroxyl groups and aldehyde or ketone groups. See Figures 30-17 and 30-18.

When concentrated sulfuric acid is poured onto a carbohydrate, the sulfuric acid decomposes the carbohydrate by removing water from it. Carbon remains in an uncombined form. Heating a carbohydrate will also remove water (as steam) from it, leaving uncombined carbon behind. See Figure 30-19.

Figure 30-16

The formation of the explosive trinitroglycerine from the reaction between glycerine and nitric acid.

glycerine

trinitroglycerine,
$C_3H_5(NO_3)_3$

Figure 30-17

Representations of the structural formulas of glucose and fructose, two carbohydrates that are sugars, both of which have the molecular formula $C_6H_{12}O_6$. In these carbohydrates, as in all carbohydrates, the ratio of hydrogen to oxygen atoms is 2 to 1, the same ratio that exists in water.

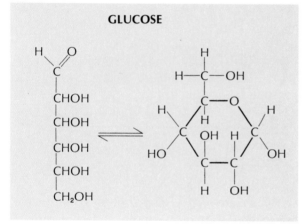

GLUCOSE

aldehyde group

hydroxyl groups

FRUCTOSE

ketone group

hydroxyl groups

Figure 30-18

Both glucose and fructose have straight-chain structures that can exist in equilibrium with ring structures.

GLUCOSE

FRUCTOSE

Figure 30-19

The left photo shows sugar just after concentrated sulfuric acid was poured over it. The right photo shows the same beaker several minutes later.

The most important types of carbohydrates are sugars, starches, and cellulose.

The common sugar sold in food stores is cane sugar. Chemists call cane sugar sucrose (SOO-krose, pronounced to rhyme with "too close"). Sucrose has the empirical formula $C_{12}H_{22}O_{11}$. Sucrose is obtained from sugar cane and sugar beets. It is also found in fruits and other vegetables, often with glucose and fructose, but not in large enough amounts to make these foods a commercial source of sucrose.

Sucrose can be hydrolyzed to produce an equal number of molecules

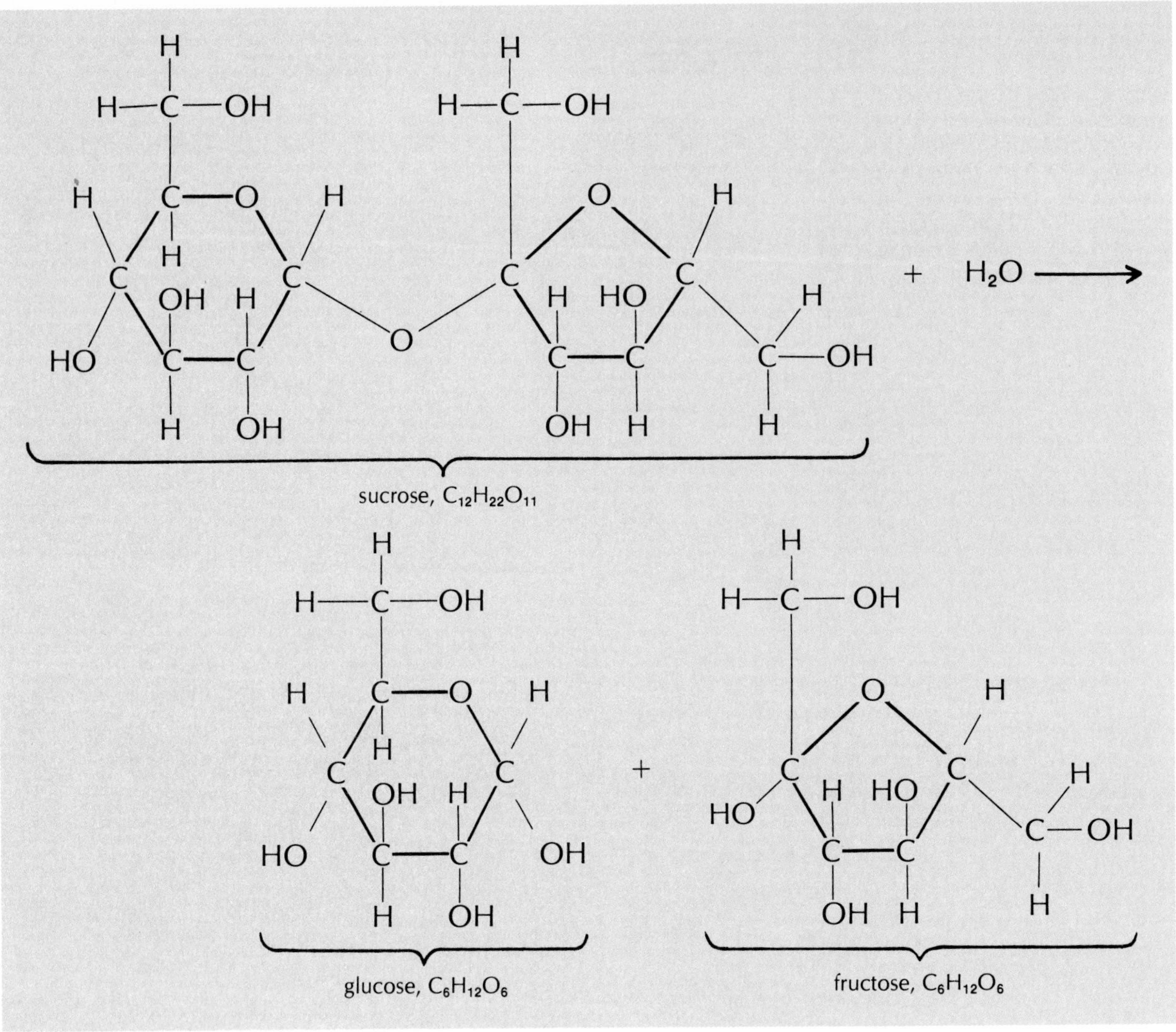

sucrose, $C_{12}H_{22}O_{11}$

$+ \; H_2O \longrightarrow$

glucose, $C_6H_{12}O_6$

$+$

fructose, $C_6H_{12}O_6$

Figure 30-20

When sucrose is hydrolyzed (reacts with water), its molecule splits to produce the simpler sugars glucose and fructose.

of glucose and fructose. See Figure 30-20. The hydrolysis is done in the laboratory by heating an aqueous solution of sucrose in the presence of acid. It is also done in the body during the digestion of sucrose. Because digestion takes place at body temperature, the reaction would be too slow were it not for substances produced within the body that catalyze the reaction. This type of catalyst is called an **enzyme.** Enzymes enable **biochemical reactions** (reactions in living organisms) to take place at a useful speed in spite of the relatively low temperatures that exist within the body.

Fermentation. One of the important reactions of glucose is its chemical change to ethyl alcohol and carbon dioxide. This reaction takes place in the presence of zymase (ZI-mase), the enzyme that catalyzes this reaction. Zymase comes from yeast cells, which are widely found in nature. They grow rapidly in any moist medium containing certain nutrients. Glucose is one such nutrient. Therefore, any sample of moist glucose in the presence of yeast will generally be changed to alcohol.

A chemical reaction that is catalyzed by an enzyme is called a **fermentation.** Fermentations are generally exothermic reactions that do not require the presence of air. During fermentation, organic compounds are decomposed into simpler substances. The reaction of glucose in the presence of zymase is called alcohol fermentation. Alcohol fermentation is used to prepare   alcoholic beverages and to produce the carbon dioxide that makes bread rise. The equation for the reaction is:

ALCOHOL FERMENTATION

$$C_6H_{12}O_6 \longrightarrow 2C_2H_5OH + 2CO_2 \qquad \text{(Eq. 9)}$$

glucose   ethanol

Figure 30-21

The yeast added to bread and cake dough contains enzymes that cause the sugar in the dough to undergo alcohol fermentation, a chemical reaction in which one of the products of the reaction is CO_2 gas. As the CO_2 is formed, it makes tiny bubbles in the dough, causing the dough to rise.

Questions for Sections 30-7 and 30-8

20. (a) Why is nitroglycerine considered to be an ester? (b) How does it differ in method of formation from an ester such as ethyl acetate? (c) Write the structural formula of nitroglycerine. (d) Why are many esters used in the preparation of perfumes and synthetic flavors?
21. (a) Define *carbohydrate*. What functional group characterizes the (b) glucose molecule, (c) fructose molecule? (d) What product is left behind when a carbohydrate is heated with concentrated sulfuric acid?
22. (a) Name three (3) important types of carbohydrates. (b) What is the molecular formula of sucrose? (c) Name the products obtained by the hydrolysis of sucrose.
*23. (a) Define *fermentation*. (b) Write a balanced equation, using molecular formulas, for the fermentation of glucose. (c) What catalyst is required for this reaction?

Figure 30-22   # 30-9   Soaps and Detergents

(A) *The formula for stearic acid.* (B) *The stearate ion, an anion.* (C) *The sodium ion, a cation.* (D) *A common soap, sodium stearate, the sodium salt of stearic acid.*

(A)	$CH_3(CH_2)_{16}COOH$
(B)	$CH_3(CH_2)_{16}COO^-$
(C)	Na^+
(D)	$CH_3(CH_2)_{16}COONa$

Soaps. From a chemical point of view, a soap is a metallic salt of a higher carboxylic acid. These salts contain about 12 to 18 carbon atoms in the carbon chain making up the anion of the salt. For example, the most common soap is the sodium salt of stearic acid. See Figure 30-22.

Soaps commonly used in cleansing are the stearates and palmitates of sodium and potassium. The sodium soaps are hard and more widely used than the potassium soaps. The potassium soaps, being softer, tend to lather more easily than the sodium soaps. They have many special uses in creams, and cosmetics, and as liquid soaps.

There are certain compounds that are soaps—that is, that are metal-

Chapter 30   Organic Chemistry II   **621**

lic salts of higher carboxylic acids—but have no cleansing properties. These are insoluble salts of higher carboxylic acids obtained when a common soap, such as sodium stearate, is dissolved in water containing certain metallic ions. For example, calcium stearate, an insoluble substance, will precipitate out of solution if a sodium stearate soap is used in water containing dissolved calcium ions:

$$Ca^{2+}(aq) + 2C_{17}H_{35}COONa(aq) \longrightarrow (C_{17}H_{35}COO)_2Ca(s) + 2Na^+(aq) \quad \textbf{(Eq. 10)}$$

                sodium stearate   calcium stearate
                (common soap)   precipitate

In addition to calcium ions, dissolved magnesium ions and dissolved ferrous ions will combine with the stearate anion to form insoluble substances. Water containing these metallic ions is called **hard water.** These ions have to be removed from the water—that is, the water must be softened—before ordinary soap is able to form a lather and carry out its cleansing action. Some insoluble "soaps" do have practical uses. Magnesium stearate, for example, is used in body powders. Some insoluble soaps are used as lubricants.

Saponification. Soaps are made by boiling oils or solid fats with solutions of either sodium hydroxide or potassium hydroxide. Oils and fats are esters. During saponification, the part of the oil or fat molecule derived from an alcohol is split from the part derived from a carboxylic acid. Thus, saponification resembles the ordinary hydrolysis of an ester (Section 30-6), and the term is broadly applied to describe the alkaline hydrolysis of any ester. The following equation shows the formation of sodium stearate:

SYNTHESIS OF SOAP FROM A FAT BY ALKALINE HYDROLYSIS

$$(C_{17}H_{35}COO)_3C_3H_5 + 3NaOH \longrightarrow C_3H_5(OH)_3 + 3C_{17}H_{35}COONa \quad \textbf{(Eq. 11)}$$

    glyceryl stearate   glycerine   sodium stearate
       (a fat)   (common soap)

When the reaction is complete, a concentrated solution of NaCl is added. The soap is not very soluble in a water solution of NaCl. The soap, therefore, separates from the mixture. It rises to the top where it can be skimmed off. This way of separating the soap from the mixture is called *salting out.* The valuable by-product glycerine, $C_3H_5(OH)_3$, is removed by steam distillation. In this step, steam is passed through the remaining mixture to vaporize the glycerine, which is then condensed by cooling.

Although soap is still manufactured in most parts of the world by saponification, a new process has been developed in the United States. Fats are hydrolyzed at high temperature in the presence of a catalyst. The following equation shows the hydrolysis of glyceryl stearate:

$$(C_{17}H_{35}COO)_3C_3H_5 + 3H_2O \longrightarrow 3C_{17}H_{35}COOH + C_3H_5(OH)_3 \quad \textbf{(Eq. 12)}$$

    glyceryl stearate   stearic acid   glycerine

During the Middle Ages, soaps were made by boiling animal fat or olive oil in water containing ashes from wood or seaweed. These ashes contain sodium and potassium bases.

The resultant fatty acid is drawn out at the top of the tower and the glycerine at the bottom. The fatty acid is purified and treated with the correct amount of alkali (NaOH or KOH) to change the acid to soap. The process is an improvement over the older one because it is continuous and allows more effective separation and purification of the glycerine and fatty acids.

Saponification is sometimes used to remove greases that collect in drain pipes. Commercial products, containing lye, are made into concentrated solutions that are poured into the clogged drain. In theory, the lye should saponify the greases and fats and thus clear the drain. Actually, the lye may not be very effective because of the slowness of its action. Extreme care should be used in handling lye, since it is very caustic and can cause severe burns. To avoid the possibility of blinding oneself, safety glasses should be worn when handling lye.

Detergents. The term detergent simply means cleansing agent. Detergents are synthetic preparations that are not soaps but that act as soaps in their cleansing action. Like soaps, detergent molecules are made up of a polar and a nonpolar unit. They make up the usual commercial dishwashing and laundering cleansing agents. One advantage that detergents have over soaps is that they will lather just as well in hard water as in soft water.

Questions for Section 30-9

24. (a) Define *soap*. (b) State the chemical names of four (4) common soaps. (c) In what two respects do potassium soaps differ from sodium soaps? (d) What is the molecular formula of the most commonly used soap, sodium stearate?
25. (a) What three (3) ions are usually present in hard water? (b) What happens when a soluble soap is added to hard water? (c) Why is this effect economically undesirable?
*26. (a) Why is saponification called an alkaline hydrolysis? (b) What are the products of the saponification of the fat, glyceryl stearate, by sodium hydroxide solution? (c) What is meant by *salting out*?
27. (a) Name the products obtained by the catalytic hydrolysis of glyceryl stearate. (b) How is one of the products changed to a soap in a commercial process? (c) What are the advantages of this process over the one using alkaline hydrolysis for soap manufacture?
28. (a) What are detergents? (b) What is their advantage over soaps?

CHAPTER SUMMARY

1. Alcohols are organic compounds in which one or more hydrogen atoms of a hydrocarbon have each been replaced by an —OH group.
2. Monohydroxy alcohols, such as methyl and ethyl alcohols, contain only one hydroxyl group in a molecule. They may be primary, secondary, or tertiary alcohols, depending upon the number of carbon atoms bonded to the carbon atoms holding the -OH group.

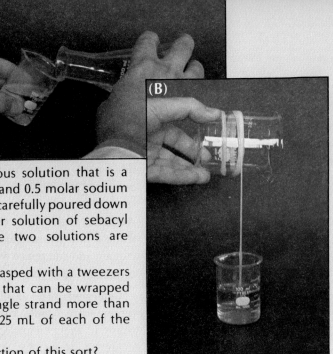

(A)

(B)

CAN YOU EXPLAIN THIS?

The beaker in Photo A contains an aqueous solution that is a mixture of 0.5 molar hexamethylene diamine and 0.5 molar sodium hydroxide. The flask whose contents are being carefully poured down the side of the beaker contains a 0.25 molar solution of sebacyl chloride dissolved in hexane. Because the two solutions are immiscible, they form two layers.

When the film between the two layers is grasped with a tweezers and pulled upward, the film forms a thread that can be wrapped around a beaker, as shown in Photo B. A single strand more than 10 meters long can be formed from about 25 mL of each of the two solutions.

1. What possible use might be made of a reaction of this sort?
2. What kinds of tests would you do to determine if the reaction could really be used for the purpose you have suggested?

3. When oxidized by potassium permanganate in acid solution, primary alcohols at first form aldehydes and then form acids; secondary alcohols form ketones. Tertiary alcohols are not affected by such oxidation, but are broken down into smaller molecules by stronger oxidizing agents.

4. The IUPAC system names monohydroxy alcohols by replacing the final -e of the parent hydrocarbon with -ol. In dihydroxy and trihydroxy alcohols, the IUPAC system indicates the positions of the alcohol groups by the numbers of the carbon atoms to which they are attached. For example, ethylene glycol becomes 1,2-ethanediol.

5. Methyl alcohol (wood alcohol) can be synthesized from CO and H_2 in the presence of a catalyst. It is also obtained by the destructive distillation of wood.

6. Ethyl alcohol can be prepared by the fermentation of sugar.

7. The polarity of alcohols increases with the increase in the number of -OH groups in the molecule. It decreases as the number of carbon atoms increases in the hydrocarbon part of the molecule.

8. The functional group in aldehydes is the $-C\begin{smallmatrix}O\\H\end{smallmatrix}$ group. The IUPAC names of aldehydes are obtained by replacing the -e ending of the parent hydrocarbon with -al.

9. The aldehyde group gives less polarity to the molecule than the alcohol group. Aldehydes are, therefore, less soluble in water than alcohols with the same number of carbon atoms.

10. Aldehydes act as reducing agents, forming organic acids in the process.

11. Ketones have the $C=O$ functional group. In the IUPAC system, they are named by replacing the -e ending of the parent hydrocarbon with -one. The ketone group is located by the number of its carbon atom.

12. The general formula of ethers is ROR', where R and R' are alkyl groups.

13. The chief type of organic acid is the weak carboxylic acid. Its functional group is the carboxyl group, $- C\overset{\displaystyle\nearrow O}{\underset{\displaystyle\searrow OH}{}}$

14. The IUPAC system names carboxylic acids by replacing the final -e of the parent hydrocarbon with -oic.

15. The saturated carboxylic acids that have one carboxyl group in the molecule form a homologous series called the fatty acid series because a number of its higher members occur in fats. The general formula for the series is $C_nH_{2n+1}COOH$

16. Typical reactions of carboxylic acids are ionization, neutralization, and esterification.

17. The carboxyl group of an acid is polar; the hydrocarbon chain is nonpolar. Therefore, as the molecular mass of the acid increases, the solubility in water decreases. Because of their polar molecules, the boiling points of acids are higher than those of hydrocarbons with the same number of carbon atoms to the molecule.

18. Esters are compounds formed when an alcohol reacts with an acid. The reaction is reversed when the ester is hydrolyzed.

19. Carbohydrates are compounds of carbon, hydrogen, and oxygen where the hydrogen and oxygen atoms are present in the ratio of two atoms to one. The most important types are starches, sugars, and cellulose.

20. A fermentation is a chemical reaction catalyzed by an enzyme. In the alcohol fermentation, glucose, in the presence of zymase, changes to alcohol and carbon dioxide.

21. A soap is a metallic salt of a higher carboxylic acid. Sodium and potassium soaps are soluble and used for cleansing; calcium, magnesium, and ferrous soaps are insoluble.

22. Saponification is the alkaline hydrolysis of an ester. When a fat is saponified in the presence of NaOH, a sodium soap is formed.

TERMS YOU SHOULD KNOW

alcohol	dihydroxy alcohol	esterification
functional group	trihydroxy alcohol	carbohydrate
monohydroxy alcohol	aldehyde	enzyme
primary alcohol	ketone	biochemical reactions
secondary alcohol	ether	fermentation
tertiary alcohol	carboxylic acid	soap
destructive distillation	fatty acid	hard water
proof	ester	saponification
denatured		

REVIEW QUESTIONS

Section 30-1   **1.** In what type of organic compound do we find the (a) hydroxyl group (b) carbonyl group (c) carboxyl group?

30-2   **2.** (a) Write the structural formula of the primary monohydroxy alcohol derived from ethane. (b) Write the structural formula and name of the initial product obtained by its mild oxidation. (c) Why is it called a primary alcohol?

3. (a) Write the formula of 2-propanol. (b) To which group of mono-hydroxy alcohols does it belong? (c) Write the structural formulas and names of the products obtained by its mild oxidation.

4. (a) Write the equation for the synthesis of methanol from carbon monoxide and hydrogen. (b) What alcohol does methanol resemble in taste? (c) What danger is there in drinking methanol? (d) Why is it called *wood alcohol?* (e) How is it used commercially?

5. (a) What are three names applied to ethanol in addition to its IUPAC name? (b) Why is absolute alcohol said to be 200 proof? (c) Why is alcohol often sold in the denatured form? (d) Mention two (2) important uses of ethanol.

6. Write the structural formulas of (a) 2,2,4-trimethylhexanol (b) 3-methyl-2-butanol (c) 2,3,4-pentanetriol (d) 3-methyl-2,4-pentanediol.

7. (a) Write the structural formula for ethylene glycol. (b) What are the two IUPAC names that can be applied to this substance? (c) Why is it used as an antifreeze in car radiators?

8. (a) Write the structural formula for glycerine. (b) What are two possible IUPAC names for glycerine? (c) What part of its structure is responsible for its complete solubility in water?

9. (a) Which is more soluble in water and why? (a) methyl alcohol or butyl alcohol, (b) ethyl alcohol or ethylene glycol?

10. Write the structural formulas and IUPAC names of the four (4) isomers that are alcohols and have the formula C_4H_9OH. For each, state whether it is a primary, secondary, or tertiary alcohol.

30-3   11. (a) Write the structural formulas of propanal and 2-methylpropanal. (b) Why is it unnecessary to indicate the position of the aldehyde group in the name of any aldehyde? (c) Why are aldehydes less soluble in water than the corresponding alcohols? (d) What is the name and formula of the compound to which acetaldehyde is changed after its reaction with Fehling's solution?

12. Write the structural formula and name of the aldehyde formed by the oxidation of (a) methyl alcohol, (b) 2-methylpropanol, (c) 3,3-dimethylbutanol.

13. Methyl alcohol can be oxidized to formaldehyde, which can be oxidized to formic acid, which can be oxidized to carbon dioxide, as shown in the following sequence: $CH_3OH \rightarrow HCHO \rightarrow HCOOH \rightarrow CO_2$ (a) List the oxidation states in the order in which they occur in each compound. (b) In terms of these states, why is each change considered to be an oxidation?

30-4   14. (a) Write the structural formula of (a) 5-methyl-3-hexanone, (b) the ketone formed by the oxidation of 2-butanol, (c) propanone. (d) What is the name of the alcohol from which propanone is made commercially?

15. The names of ketones often include the names of the alkyl groups to which the carbonyl group is bonded. What is the IUPAC name of (a) diethyl ketone (b) methyl ethyl ketone (c) ethyl isopropyl ketone (d) diisopropyl ketone?

30-5   16. Name the ether that is (a) an isomer of propanol, (b) formed when a dehydration reaction removes one molecule of water from two molecules of ethanol, (c) used industrially as a solvent for gums and fats.

17. Ethanol and dimethyl ether are isomers. Ethanol is a liquid that boils at 78.5°C. Dimethyl ether is a gas whose boiling point is −24°C. Account for the difference in boiling points.

30-6 **18.** Compare the chemical properties of a carboxylic acid, such as acetic acid, with an inorganic acid, such as hydrochloric acid, mentioning two similarities and two differences.

19. (a) Butyric acid is so-named because it is found in rancid butter. Write its structural formula and IUPAC name. (b) Do the same for a propanoic acid that is isomeric with butyric acid.

30-8 **20.** (a) What is the general empirical formula of a carbohydrate? (b) Write the structural formula of a 6-carbon sugar containing the ketone group. (c) What is the empirical formula and name of a 12-carbon sugar?

21. (a) Define *enzyme*. (b) What enzyme catalyzes the fermentation of glucose? (c) Why does a baker often use sugar and yeast in preparing bread? (d) Starch has the empirical formula $C_6H_{10}O_5$. How can a combination of hydrolysis and fermentation produce alcohol from starch?

22. With respect to the temperature and catalyst used, compare the hydrolysis of sucrose in the laboratory with this hydrolysis as it takes place in the human body.

30-9 **23.** (a) What is a soap? (b) Name an example of a hard soap, a soft soap, and an insoluble soap. (c) Write the equation for the formation of a sodium soap by the alkaline hydrolysis of the fat glyceryl stearate, whose formula is $(C_{17}H_{35}COO)_3C_3H_5$. (d) Name the process used to remove the glycerine by-product.

FOR FURTHER THOUGHT

Select from the list the statement that completes the definition in each question. Then find a statement that describes an observation that could be made in each case.

List of Statements

(A) Substance X contains carbon, hydrogen, and oxygen, with hydrogen and carbon in the ratio of 2 atoms of H to 1 atom of O.

(B) Substance X produces an ester and water when reacted with a carboxylic acid.

(C) Substance X contains an —OH group bonded to a carbon atom.

(D) Substance X contains the —COOH group.

(E) Substance X produces uncombined carbon when treated with concentrated sulfuric acid.

(F) Substance X reduces copper ions in Benedict's solution.

(G) Substance X produces water when it reacts with an alcohol.

(H) Substance X contains the —CHO group.

30-2 **1.** (a) Definition: Substance X is an alcohol if _____.
(b) Observation: _____.

30-3 **2.** (a) Definition: Substance X is an aldehyde if _____.
(b) Observation: _____.

30-6 **3.** (a) Definition: Substance X is a carboxylic acid if _____.
(b) Observation: _____.

30-8 **4.** (a) Definition: Substance X is a carbohydrate if _____.
(b) Observation: _____.

UNIT 10

Nuclear Chemistry

Chemistry had its origins in alchemy—the ancient search for the secret of changing "base" metals, such as lead, to the "noble" metals silver and gold. However, the development of the atomic theory, with its concept of unchangeable atoms, made such transmutation of elements seem to be an impossible dream. Yet transmutation of elements is precisely what is occurring inside these towers of a nuclear power plant in Sacramento, California.

In power plants like this, something far more useful than gold or silver is produced. It is energy —huge amounts of energy. It is energy that comes not from the simple rearrangement of outer electrons but from changes in the very heart of the atom—its nucleus. In the process, the atom itself is transformed and one element is changed into another.

This unit explores the kinds of changes that can occur in the nuclei of atoms and the astounding results of such changes.

Nuclear Chemistry

Objectives

When you have completed this chapter, you should be able to:
- Write equations for various nuclear reactions.
- Compare natural and induced radioactivity.
- Distinguish between nuclear fission and fusion, and describe devices and reactors of both types.
- Describe and discuss the benefits and problems of nuclear energy.

31-1   Natural Radioactivity

As described in Chapter 13 (Sections 13-16 to 13-21), some of the isotopes of the elements found in nature are not stable. These unstable isotopes are called **radioactive isotopes** or **radioisotopes.** Samples of these radioisotopes continually emit alpha particles or beta particles, usually along with gamma radiation. For example, a sample of uranium gives off alpha particles and gamma radiation. The alpha or beta particles that are emitted from unstable elements come from the nuclei of the atoms. The emission of an alpha or beta particle from the nucleus of an atom alters the composition of the nucleus. The altered nucleus is no longer the nucleus of the original element but is instead the nucleus of another element. This change of one element into another, as stated in Section 13-18, is called transmutation.

Over a period of time, it is found that the amount of uranium in a sample of material containing that element decreases as more and more alpha particles are emitted. A sample that starts out as pure uranium gradually becomes ''polluted'' with atoms of the element thorium. Evidently, thorium is the element that is produced when a uranium atom emits an alpha particle. This change can be shown by a nuclear equation:

WORD EQUATION: ALPHA EMISSION FROM A URANIUM ATOM

$$\text{uranium atom} \longrightarrow \text{thorium atom} + \text{alpha particle} \qquad \textbf{(Eq. 1)}$$

This word equation can be expressed as a symbol equation if we know what symbols to use to represent the various kinds of particles. Before arriving at the symbols for the particles, it needs to be emphasized that Equation 1 is not an equation for a chemical change. A chemical reaction shows how atoms rearrange themselves to form one or more new

PEOPLE IN CHEMISTRY

Ignacio Tinoco, Jr. (1930-)

Ignacio Tinoco was born in El Paso, Texas. As an undergraduate he attended the University of New Mexico. The University of Wisconsin awarded him a Ph.D. in chemistry in 1954.

At present, Dr. Tinoco is professor of chemistry at the University of California at Berkeley. His research is in the area of biophysical chemistry. Dr. Tinoco tries to answer questions such as: How do chemicals cause mutations? How is DNA, a long polymer, folded to fit into a virus? How does DNA form a chromosome?

Dr. Tinoco has several honorary degrees and has received several awards for his research.

substances. It shows, for example, how the atoms in water molecules can rearrange themselves to form molecules of oxygen and hydrogen. Equation 1 is the equation for a nuclear reaction, not a chemical reaction.

A **nuclear reaction** is one that involves changes in the nuclei of atoms. In these changes, both the charge and the mass of a nucleus may change. Therefore, the equation for a nuclear reaction must show the charge and the mass of each nucleus before and after reaction.

When we say that a uranium atom produces a thorium atom and an alpha particle, we need to know what particular isotope of uranium undergoes this change. (Not all isotopes of uranium do.) The answer comes from experiment. Experiments show that the nuclei of an isotope of uranium whose mass number (Section 12-7) is 238 spontaneously emit alpha particles. As a result of alpha emission, each nucleus of a uranium-238 atom changes to the nucleus of a thorium atom. All isotopes of uranium have 92 protons in their nuclei. Therefore, the nuclear charge on all uranium nuclei is 92+. The mass number and the charge on a uranium-238 isotope are shown in the following symbol:

$$_{92+}^{238}\text{U}$$

Notice that the charge, 92+, is written as a subscript and that the mass number, 238, is written as a superscript. Each of these numbers is written before the symbol of the element.

We now substitute this symbol for a uranium-238 atom into the word equation:

$$_{92+}^{238}\text{U} \longrightarrow \text{thorium} + \text{alpha particle} \qquad \textbf{(Eq. 2)}$$

To arrive at the complete symbol equation, we need to have the correct symbols for the particular thorium isotope that is produced and for the alpha particle. We already know (Section 13-20) that an alpha particle is a helium nucleus containing two neutrons and two protons. This particle, therefore, has a mass number of 4 and a charge of 2+. Its symbol is

$$_{2+}^{4}\text{He}$$

Substituting this symbol into Equation 2 gives:

$$_{92+}^{238}\text{U} \longrightarrow \text{thorium} + _{2+}^{4}\text{He} \qquad \textbf{(Eq. 3)}$$

The symbol equation will be complete when we know what particular isotope of thorium is produced. Experiment will reveal the answer but it can also be derived from Equation 3. Nuclear equations must balance with respect both to mass and to charge. The total charge on the left of Equation 3 is 92+. The total charge on the right must be the same. If the alpha particle has a charge of 2+, then the thorium isotope must have a charge of 90+. (Of course, all isotopes of thorium have the same nuclear charge, 90+, which is the number of protons in the nucleus, or the atomic number.) As to balancing mass, the mass on the left of Equation 3 is 238. If the alpha particle has a mass 4, then the thorium

Chapter 31   Nuclear Chemistry   **631**

isotope must have a mass of 234. That is, the thorium isotope is thorium-234. Its symbol is:

$$_{90+}^{234}\text{Th}$$

Substituting this symbol into Equation 3 gives the completed symbol equation:

$$_{92+}^{238}\text{U} \longrightarrow _{90+}^{234}\text{Th} + _{2+}^{4}\text{He} \qquad \text{(Eq. 4)}$$

In writing nuclear equations, it is common to omit the plus signs showing charge. Equation 4 may also be written

$$_{92}^{238}\text{U} \longrightarrow _{90}^{234}\text{Th} + _{2}^{4}\text{He} \qquad \text{(Eq. 5)}$$

31-2   The Uranium-238 Decay Series

The thorium-234 isotope referred to in the last section is itself unstable. Its nuclei begin to emit beta particles very soon after they are produced by alpha emission from a uranium-238 isotope. The equation for the emission of an electron (a beta particle) from thorium-234 can be written as follows, where a question mark is used in the place of the new element that is produced:

EMISSION OF AN ELECTRON FROM THORIUM-234

$$_{90}^{234}\text{Th} \longrightarrow \; ? + _{1-}^{0}\text{e} \qquad \text{(Eq. 6)}$$

symbol for an electron
or beta particle

In Equation 6, notice that the mass of the electron, or beta particle, is written as zero. An electron does have mass, but its mass is taken to be zero because it is so small compared to the masses of the nuclei and nuclear particles that take part in nuclear changes. Without resorting to an experiment (or without consulting someone who has done the experiment), we can derive the charge and mass of the atom represented by the question mark. According to Equation 6, the charge of the new atom must be 91+, since 91+ and the charge on the electron, 1−, must add up to 90+, the charge on the thorium atom:

$$_{90}^{234}\text{Th} \longrightarrow _{91}? + _{1-}^{0}\text{e}$$

A periodic table shows that the element whose atomic number is 91 is protactinium, Pa. The mass number of the protactinium isotope must be 234 in order to make the masses balance:

$$_{90}^{234}\text{Th} \longrightarrow _{91}^{234}\text{Pa} + _{1-}^{0}\text{e} \qquad \text{(Eq. 7)}$$

You may wonder how an electron (or beta particle) can be emitted from a thorium-234 nucleus if its nucleus (like the nuclei of all atoms) is made up only of neutrons and protons. Scientists believe that a neutron in a nucleus can emit an electron and change to a proton. This change is represented by the following equation:

$$\underset{0}{^{1}}\text{n} \longrightarrow \underset{1}{^{1}}\text{H} + \underset{-1}{^{0}}\text{e} \qquad \textbf{(Eq. 8)}$$

neutron   proton   electron
or
beta particle

Notice that the charges of both particles on the right side of the equation add up to zero, the charge on a neutron. The masses of both particles on the right add up to 1, the mass of a neutron.

The protactinium isotope shown in Equation 7 is also unstable. Its nucleus emits a beta particle to produce uranium-234:

$$\underset{91}{^{234}}\text{Pa} \longrightarrow \underset{92}{^{234}}\text{U} + \underset{-1}{^{0}}\text{e} \qquad \textbf{(Eq. 9)}$$

beta particle

Note that the loss of an electron (a beta particle) increases the nuclear charge by one unit. It goes from 91 in protactinium to 92 in uranium.

Uranium-234, in Equation 9, is also unstable, and produces thorium-230 by alpha emission:

$$\underset{92}{^{234}}\text{U} \longrightarrow \underset{90}{^{230}}\text{Th} + \underset{2}{^{4}}\text{He} \qquad \textbf{(Eq. 10)}$$

Thorium-230, also unstable, produces radium-226 by alpha emission:

$$\underset{90}{^{230}}\text{Th} \longrightarrow \underset{88}{^{226}}\text{Ra} + \underset{2}{^{4}}\text{He} \qquad \textbf{(Eq. 11)}$$

The five nuclear transmutations referred to above can be summarized as follows, where the particle that is emitted is written over the arrow:

$$^{238}\text{U} \xrightarrow{\alpha} {}^{234}\text{Th} \xrightarrow{\beta} {}^{234}\text{Pa} \xrightarrow{\beta} {}^{234}\text{U} \xrightarrow{\alpha} {}^{230}\text{Th} \xrightarrow{\alpha} {}^{226}\text{Ra}$$

The formation of new elements does not stop with radium-226. It, too, is unstable. In fact, in addition to the five transmutations shown above, nine more occur (making a total of 14) as an unstable isotope of one element emits an alpha or beta particle to produce an unstable isotope of another element. The last transmutation in the 14-step series is the formation of lead-206. Because lead-206 is stable (is non-radioactive), no new transmutations are derived from it. The process ends. This chain of transmutations, starting with uranium-238 and ending with lead-206, is called **a radioactive series.** Specifically, it is the uranium series, named for the first element in the chain. In addition to the U-238 series, there are two other series among elements found in nature. These are the U-235 series and the Th-232 series. Each

Figure 31-1

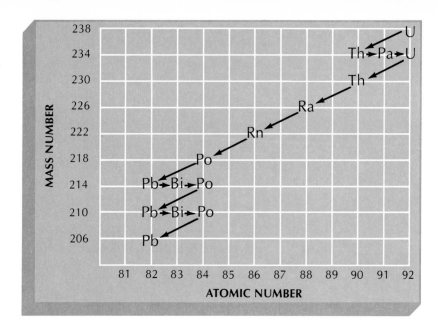

Figure 31-1

The uranium-238 decay series. The series starts with uranium-238, upper right, and proceeds through 14 steps to lead-206, a stable isotope on the lower left of the graph. Each arrow pointing to the right shows a transmutation by beta emission. The arrows pointing diagonally down to the left show transmutations by alpha emission. How does alpha emission differ from beta emission in its effect on the mass number and atomic number of a decaying nucleus?

series begins with a heavy radioactive element having a long half-life (Section 13-21) and ends with a stable isotope of lead.

Figure 31-1 shows all 14 steps in the uranium-238 decay series.

Questions for Sections 31-1 and 31-2

1. (a) Define *nuclear reaction*. How does the emission of an alpha particle affect the (b) mass number of an atom, (c) nuclear charge? (d) Write the symbol of an alpha particle and of a U-238 atom, showing the mass number and atomic number.
2. (a) State one similarity and one difference between the ordinary chemical equation and the nuclear equation. (b) Write the nuclear equation for the radioactive change of U-238 to an isotope of thorium and an alpha particle.
*3. (a) What change in the nucleus of an atom is responsible for the emission of an electron? (b) What effect does the emission of an electron from the nucleus have upon the mass number and nuclear charge of an atom? (c) When Th-234 decays, it emits an electron and leaves behind the element protactinium. Write the nuclear equation for this reaction.
4. Name the particle emitted when an atom of (a) $^{234}_{91}Pa$ changes to $^{234}_{92}U$, (b) $^{230}_{90}Th$ changes to $^{226}_{88}Ra$.
5. (a) What is a radioactive series? (b) Name three (3) such series. (c) What is the final element formed in all these series?

31-3 Artificial Radioactivity (Induced Radioactivity)

As was discussed in Section 31-1, some elements that occur in nature are unstable and spontaneously emit alpha or beta particles. Nothing needs to be done to get unstable elements to decay by alpha or beta emission. Unstable elements do this by themselves at a rate that cannot be changed by conditions normally obtainable in laboratories.

While scientists play no part in the transmutation of naturally occurring unstable isotopes, they have learned how to transmute elements that are normally stable. In 1919, while working with a radioactive substance that was an alpha emitter, Ernest Rutherford discovered that stable nitrogen gas could be transmuted into oxygen gas when the alpha particles were allowed to shoot into a sample of nitrogen. The equation for this change is:

TRANSMUTATION OF NITROGEN-14 INTO OXYGEN-17 BY ALPHA EMISSION

$$^{14}_{7}N + {}^{4}_{2}He \longrightarrow {}^{17}_{8}O + {}^{1}_{1}H \qquad \textbf{(Eq. 12)}$$

alpha particle

symbol for a proton
the nucleus of the most common isotope of hydrogen

This was the first instance of artificially produced nuclear transmutation. This event marked the beginning of many experiments in which various elements were made by bombarding the nuclei of other elements with fast-moving atomic or subatomic particles. Among the particles used for this purpose are electrons, protons, neutrons, alpha particles (helium nuclei), and deuterons (nuclei of deuterium atoms, Section 12-5).

Although the oxygen produced in Rutherford's experiment was a rare isotope, it was stable. In fact, O-17 makes up about 0.04% of natural oxygen. For many years thereafter, all isotopes produced by nuclear transmutation were likewise stable. In 1934, however, Irene Joliot-Curie (1897-1956), the daughter of Pierre and Marie Curie, and her husband Frederic (1900-1958), were studying the effects of alpha particle bombardment on some of the lighter elements. When aluminum was bombarded by alpha particles, they observed the emission of other particles, as usual in such experiments. However, when the alpha bombardment was stopped, the aluminum sample continued to give off radiations. In other words, a radioactive isotope had been produced. Investigation revealed that the initial bombardment had transformed the aluminum nuclei to nuclei of phosphorus-30. This isotope of phosphorus is radioactive. It decays by beta emission to an isotope of silicon. The two steps of the reaction can be represented as follows:

$$^{4}_{2}He + {}^{27}_{13}Al \longrightarrow {}^{30}_{15}P + {}^{1}_{0}n \qquad \textbf{(Eq. 13)}$$

$$^{30}_{15}P \longrightarrow {}^{30}_{14}Si + {}^{0}_{1}e \qquad \textbf{(Eq. 14)}$$

a positron

The radioactive phosphorus-30 (Equation 14) is the first radioactive isotope to be made in a laboratory. Radioactivity produced in an element by a laboratory technique is called **artificial radioactivity** or **induced radioactivity.**

The particle in Equation 14 having the symbol ${}^{0}_{1}e$ has the same mass as an electron but carries one unit of positive charge rather than one unit of negative charge. These particles are called **positrons** or positive electrons.

31-4   Radioisotopes Produced from Stable Isotopes of the Same Element

In the Joliot-Curie experiment just described, a radioactive isotope of phosphorus is produced, but the target element is aluminum. Because the bombarding particles are charged, the charge of the new nuclei, and hence their atomic number, is different from that of the target nuclei. Atoms of one element become atoms of another element. In another type of nuclear change, the non-radioactive isotope that is bombarded becomes a radioactive isotope of the same element. One way to accomplish this result is to use uncharged "bullets," particularly neutrons. When the Joliot-Curies bombarded common table salt, NaCl, with neutrons, both radioactive sodium and radioactive chlorine were produced:

$$\underset{\substack{\text{neutron}}}{{}^{1}_{0}n} + \underset{\substack{\text{non-radioactive}\\\text{sodium in NaCl}}}{{}^{23}_{11}Na} \longrightarrow \underset{\substack{\text{radioactive}\\\text{sodium in NaCl}}}{{}^{24}_{11}Na} \qquad \textbf{(Eq. 15)}$$

$$\underset{\substack{\text{non-radioactive}\\\text{chlorine in NaCl}}}{{}^{1}_{0}n + {}^{37}_{17}Cl} \longrightarrow \underset{\substack{\text{radioactive}\\\text{chlorine in NaCl}}}{{}^{38}_{17}Cl} \qquad \textbf{(Eq. 16)}$$

(Note that Cl-37 makes up about 25% of natural chlorine, the remaining 75% being Cl-35.) Because the target nuclei absorb the uncharged neutrons, the mass number increases, but the atomic number remains the same. That is, ordinary sodium (or chlorine) becomes a radioactive isotope of the same element. Thus, Equations 15 and 16 do not show transmutations, but rather the formation of a radioactive isotope from a stable isotope *of the same element*.

Neutrons are used in a variety of nuclear reactions. The speed of the neutron "bullets" depends upon their source. Neutrons have relatively high penetrating power because of their lack of charge. Charged particles are deflected from their straight-line paths by their interactions with the positively charged nuclei of atoms. Neutrons, having no charge, are not.

Hundreds of radioisotopes have been prepared in the laboratory and many of them have important uses in such areas as medical diagnosis and treatment, geology, biochemistry, analytical chemistry, metallurgy, agriculture, and scientific research. The usefulness of radioisotopes is partly the result of their having the same chemical properties as stable isotopes of the same element. That is, they undergo the same chemical changes. When a radioactive isotope is substituted for a stable isotope of the same element, a Geiger counter or other radiation counter can be used to trace the path of the

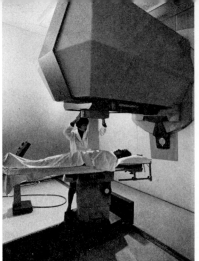

Figure 31-2

Radiations from radioactive isotopes are used to destroy cancer cells.

radioisotope as it moves through a living thing into which it has been placed. For example, radioactive phosphorus mixed with ordinary phosphorus can be fed to the roots of a plant. A Geiger counter placed alongside a leaf will tell the experimenter how much of the phosphorus is reaching the leaf and how long it takes to get there. A radioisotope whose movements are followed by a radiation counter is called a **tracer.**

There are other properties that make radioisotopes useful. Those that emit gamma radiation can be used to destroy bacteria. This property has application in medicine and in food preservation. Gamma rays are also able to destroy or arrest the growth of cancerous tissue. Radioactive cobalt is commonly used to treat such malignant growths. Radioisotopes are used in industry to detect flaws in metals. Gamma rays and other emissions are absorbed at known rates as they pass through sheets of different materials, such as metals, paper, and plastics. Thus, radioisotopes can be used to measure the thickness of such materials.

Questions for Sections 31-3 and 31-4

*6. (a) Name the element changed and the element produced in the first case of artificial transmutation. (b) Who accomplished this? (c) How was the change brought about? (d) Write the equation for the nuclear reaction involved.

7. (a) Name the scientists who caused a transmutation by bombarding aluminum with alpha particles. (b) What element was produced? (c) Describe a significant difference in properties between this element and the one produced by Rutherford.

8. Write the nuclear equation for (a) the bombardment of $_{13}^{27}\text{Al}$ by alpha particles, (b) the decay of the product to $_{14}^{30}\text{Si}$. (c) Describe the positron.

9. (a) What "bullets" can be used to make a nonradioactive isotope change into a radioactive one of the same element? (b) Write the nuclear equations showing the effect of such "bullets" on the $_{11}^{23}\text{Na}$ and $_{17}^{37}\text{Cl}$ atoms in common table salt.

10. (a) What are radioisotopes? (b) Name four (4) areas in which radioisotopes are used. (c) Name four (4) specific applications of radioisotopes.

31-5 Radioactive Dating

One of the most interesting applications of radioactivity is its use in determining the ages of rocks and in dating relics and past events. This application is called **radioactive dating.** An estimate of the age of the earth can be made by determining the ages of various minerals. The determination is based on the assumption that the earth must be at least as old as the oldest rocks and minerals in its crust. Any one of the three natural radioactive series can be used for this purpose. For example, the uranium series may be used. U-238 has a half-life of 4.5×10^9 years.

The annual rings in redwood trees have been used as a check on ages arrived at by the carbon dating method.

The end products of the series are Pb-206 and helium. After one half-life, a one-gram sample of uranium will have decayed to produce 0.43 g of Pb-206 and 0.07 g of helium. One-half of the original amount of U-238, 0.50 g, will still be present in the sample. By comparing the amount of U-238 to the amount of Pb-206 or helium present in any uranium mineral, the age of the mineral can be estimated. Many such measurements have yielded an age of at least 4 billion years for the earth's crust. Other radioactive pairs, such as K-40/Ar-40 and Sr-87/Rb-87, have been used for similar dating.

The half-life of C-14 is about 5700 years. Because this time span is much shorter than the half-life of U-238, C-14 has proved valuable in dating the remains of organic material up to an age of about 40 000 years. A small percentage of the carbon dioxide in the atmosphere contains radioactive C-14. The stable isotope of carbon is C-12. C-14 is a beta emitter and decays to form N-14 (nitrogen-14):

$$\begin{array}{c} ^{14}_{6}C \end{array} \longrightarrow \begin{array}{c} ^{14}_{7}N \end{array} + \begin{array}{c} 0 \\ _{1-}e \end{array} \qquad \textbf{(Eq. 17)}$$

In any living organism, the ratio of C-14 to C-12 is the same as it is in the atmosphere, because of the constant interchange of materials between the organism and its surroundings. When an organism dies, this interchange stops and the C-14 gradually decays to nitrogen. By comparing the relative amounts of C-14 and C-12 in the remains, we can calculate how long ago the organism died. Thus, if an old piece of wood has a ratio of C-14 to C-12 that is half as great as the ratio in the atmosphere, the age of the wood is 5700 years (one half-life). In other words, the old wood emits half as much beta radiation per gram of carbon as that emitted by living plant tissue or by newly formed wood. As an example, this method was used to determine the age of the Dead Sea Scrolls (about 1900 years old). A new technique developed in 1977 by Professor Harry Gove and fellow researchers at the University of Rochester uses a Van de Graaff particle accelerator to separate the C-14 and C-12 atoms. It can be used with very small samples and can date articles as old as 75 000 years.

In 1972 radioactive dating of ancient bones discovered in East Africa extended man's ancestry more than a million years earlier than had previously been believed. Three different dating methods were used to determine the age of the bones. In one, a sample of volcanic debris associated with the bones was analyzed to determine the ratio of a radioactive isotope of potassium to that of argon. Another dating method was based on the decay of a uranium radioisotope. A third technique was based on reversals in the earth's magnetic field over the last few million years. The three results agreed with each other within the range of permissible error. This agreement increases our confidence in the effectiveness of these dating methods.

Figure 31-3

The age of the Dead Sea Scrolls was determined by analyzing the amount of radioactive carbon-14 in the Scrolls.

31-6   Particle Accelerators

As described earlier, artificial transmutations are produced by bombarding "target" nuclei with fast-moving particles. Atomic scientists have developed a number of machines that produce beams of high-energy atomic or subatomic particles. Called **particle accelerators,** these machines take a supply of charged particles, such as alpha particles from a radioactive substance or electrons emitted by a heated cathode, and accelerate them to desired speeds by means of electric and magnetic fields. In the **cyclotron,** particles circle millions of times inside a pair of charged metal D-shaped shells, called *dees*. An electromagnet makes the particles gain additional energy each time they go around. The cyclotron was the first truly effective "atom smasher" used in research. It was invented by Ernest Lawrence, a professor of physics at the University of California. He received the Nobel Prize for this achievement in 1939. (Element 103, lawrencium, was named in his honor.) The **synchrotron** is an improved type of cyclotron that focuses the beams of the accelerated particles by means of a series of electromagnets.

The **linear accelerator** does not use magnetic fields. It consists of long sections of tubing in which the positive ions are accelerated by means of synchronized fields of electric force. Accelerators are now available that can produce enormous particle energies. Particle accelerators have proved to be indispensable for studying the ultimate structure of matter.

Questions for Sections 31-5 and 31-6

11. (a) What is meant by the term *radioactive dating*? (b) U-238 has a half-life of 4.5×10^9 years, and its radioactive series forms Pb-206 and helium as end-products. Describe briefly how the age of a mineral can be determined by the use of this series.

*12. (a) Write the nuclear equation for the decay of $^{14}_{6}C$ to $^{14}_{7}N$. (b) The half-life of C-14 is about 5 700 years. How can the ratio of C-14 to C-12 be used to determine the age of dead organic materials? (c) Up to approximately what age can such substances be dated by this method?

13. (a) Who invented the cyclotron? (b) Why is it called a particle accelerator?

14. (a) Why is the synchrotron an improvement over the cyclotron? (b) What are scientists trying to find out from their experiments with particle accelerators?

31-7   Nuclear Energy: The Mass-Energy Relation

In 1905, Albert Einstein (1879-1955) published his Theory of Relativity. At that time, he demonstrated mathematically that mass and energy are equivalent. He also showed that, theoretically, mass could be converted into energy and vice versa. Einstein's formula stating the **mass-energy relation** is a simple one:

$$E = mc^2$$

where E is the quantity of energy equivalent to a mass m, and c is the speed of light. If the speed of light is expressed in meters per second and the mass is expressed in kilograms, then the energy is given in joules.

The important fact about this relation is that the speed of light is a large number (3×10^8 meters per second), and its square, the quantity that appears in the formula, is still larger (9×10^{16}). The energy equivalent to 1 kilogram of mass is therefore 9×10^{16} joules. This is the amount of energy that would be obtained if 1 kg of matter were completely changed to energy. It is about the amount of energy released by the burning of 3 billion kilograms of coal!

According to the Einstein relation, whenever energy is released by any physical or chemical change, an equivalent amount of mass disappears. For example, when 1 kilogram of coal is burned, about 3×10^7 joules of energy are given off. An equivalent amount of mass should be missing from the products of the reaction. However, a calculation using the Einstein formula shows that the amount of mass lost will be 0.000 000 3 gram! Obviously, a change in mass so small could never be detected. The Einstein relation between mass and energy was, therefore, considered to be purely theoretical, with no hope of ever testing it in a real experiment.

This view of the Einstein relation remained until the discovery of nuclear reactions. The energies involved in these reactions, relative to the masses involved, are enormously greater than they are in ordinary chemical reactions. Using modern instruments of great sensitivity, it is possible to detect and measure the changes in mass that occur during nuclear reactions. These measurements show that the Einstein relation is true.

31-8 Changes of Mass in a Nuclear Reaction

Figure 31-4 shows some of the mathematics pertaining to the conversion of mass to energy in a nuclear reaction. In this reaction, a proton strikes a lithium nucleus, producing two helium nuclei and energy. Precise measurements have been made of the masses involved in this reaction. As the arithmetic below the equation shows, the total mass of one proton and one lithium nucleus is greater than the mass of two helium nuclei by 0.018 09 atomic mass unit. Yet, the two helium nuclei are the only particles of matter produced by the proton-lithium collision. Evidently, the mass that "disappears" is converted into the energy that is released as a product of the reaction. This energy has been measured and found to agree with the amount predicted by the Einstein formula.

Even if the amount of mass changed to energy is only a fraction of 1% of the total mass involved, the amount of energy released *per gram* of reacting substance is enormous. For example, one gram of lithium in the reaction just described yields about 230 billion (2.3×10^{11}) joules. This reaction is an example of a fusion reaction, a type of reaction that will be discussed later in the chapter. Such reactions are believed to account for the high temperatures and tremendous energy output of the sun and other stars.

Figure 31-4

When a proton collides with a lithium-7 nucleus, two helium-4 nuclei are formed. Their total mass is less than the total mass of the proton and lithium nucleus by 0.018 09 atomic mass unit. This mass is accounted for by the amount of energy that is released.

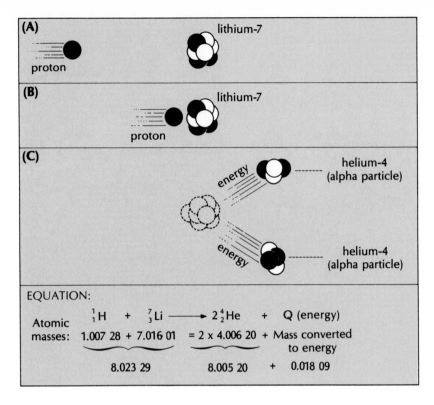

31-9 Nuclear Fission

The term "fission" means "splitting." **Nuclear fission** refers to the splitting of an atomic nucleus into fragments of about the same mass. This splitting results in the release of large amounts of energy. In a **fission reactor,** the nuclear splitting is controlled, so that the released energy can be harnessed to do useful work. Two important discoveries helped to make controlled atomic fission possible.

One of the discoveries was made by Enrico Fermi (1901-1954) in 1934. He found that a greater amount of neutron-induced radioactivity was produced when paraffin, a rather inactive compound of carbon and hydrogen, was placed between the neutron source and the target. He explained that the neutron beam was *slowed down* by repeated collisions with hydrogen nuclei in the paraffin. These slower neutrons were more easily captured by the nuclei of target atoms. The captured neutrons caused a greater amount of induced radioactivity.

In 1939, Otto Hahn (1879-1968) and Fritz Strassmann (1902-   ) discovered that an isotope of barium was produced when naturally-occurring uranium was bombarded with neutrons. Lise Meitner, a colleague of Hahn, advanced the explanation that "the uranium nucleus, after neutron capture, divided itself into nuclei of roughly equal size." Later investigations showed that uranium, as found in nature, consists of 99.3% of U-238 and 0.7% of U-235. Only the U-235 atoms were found to be fissionable. It is only this small fraction of the uranium that is split by neutron bombardment, in some instances producing barium

Figure 31-5

The fission of a uranium-235 nucleus. (A) and (B) A neutron approaches a uranium-235 nucleus. (C) If the neutron strikes the nucleus with the right amount of energy and in the right place, the nucleus will split. In addition to the release of energy, two smaller atomic nuclei are produced along with two or three neutrons. In the equation, the symbol Q is used to represent energy.

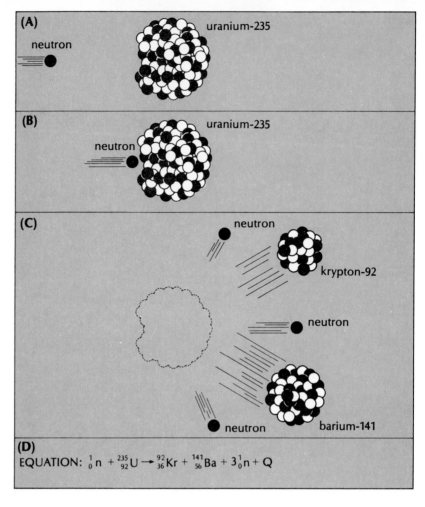

(A) neutron   uranium-235

(B) neutron   uranium-235

(C) neutron   krypton-92   neutron   neutron   barium-141

(D)
EQUATION: $^{1}_{0}n + {}^{235}_{92}U \rightarrow {}^{92}_{36}Kr + {}^{141}_{56}Ba + 3{}^{1}_{0}n + Q$

Figure 31-6

A chain reaction produced by the fission of uranium-235. The neutrons shown in Figure 31-5 (C) can collide with other uranium-235 nuclei, causing them to split and produce even more neutrons. If a large enough mass of uranium-235 is present (the critical mass), this chain reaction gets out of control. The enormous amount of heat that is produced results in the fireball that is observed when an atomic bomb explodes.

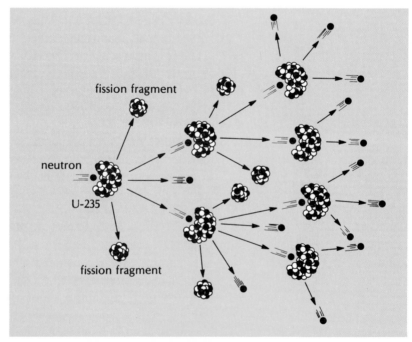

fission fragment

neutron

U-235

fission fragment

and krypton nuclei. At the same time, an excess of 2 or 3 neutrons are produced, plus an enormous amount of energy. The following equation describes the change:

$$_{92}^{235}U + _{0}^{1}n \longrightarrow _{56}^{141}Ba + _{36}^{92}Kr + 3\left(_{0}^{1}n\right) + \text{energy} \qquad \textbf{(Eq. 18)}$$

one neutron   three neutrons

It was suggested that such a nuclear reaction could be used as the basis for a chain reaction in which fission, started by a single neutron, released other neutrons. These, in turn, would produce fission in nearby atoms. See Figures 31-5 and 31-6.

Critical mass. The discoveries of slowed-down neutrons and U-235 fission were instrumental in making it possible to produce nuclear fission reactions on a practical scale. However, another problem had to be solved. In order for a chain reaction to take place, the neutrons released by fission must be captured by other U-235 nuclei and produce additional fissions. If the sample of uranium in which fission starts is too small, too many of the released neutrons will escape from the material without striking other nuclei. Then, no chain reaction will develop. As the size of the sample of U-235 is increased, a point is reached at which enough of the neutrons are captured to keep the reaction going. A very small additional increase in the amount of U-235 will lead to a rapid build-up in the rate of fission and to the generation of enough heat to result in an explosion. The amount of fissionable material that will support a self-sustaining chain reaction is called the **critical mass.** Atomic bombs have been made from U-235 and from other fissionable elements such as plutonium. To make an atomic bomb explode, neutron bombardment is initiated when two or more portions of fissionable material are rapidly brought together. Each portion is less than the critical mass, but their combined mass is slightly larger than the critical mass.

Questions for Sections 31-7 through 31-9

15. (a) Using the Einstein formula, calculate the joules produced when 1 kg of mass is converted entirely to energy. (The speed of light is 3 x 10^8 m/sec.) (b) If 1 kg of coal is burned, approximately 3 x 10^7 joules of energy are released. How many tons of coal, when burned, would produce approximately the energy obtained as the answer in part (a)? (c) Why is there no detectable change of mass in ordinary exothermic chemical reactions?

*16. (a) Why is it possible to use nuclear reactions to check the Einstein mass-energy formula? (b) If 1.0 g of energy is equivalent to 9.0×10^{13} joules, how many joules of energy are produced when 1.0 g of $_{3}^{7}Li$ is changed to helium by the nuclear reaction in Figure 31-4?

17. (a) What is *atomic fission?* (b) What is the purpose of a fission reactor? Mention briefly one contribution made to our knowledge of atomic fission by (c) Fermi, (d) Hahn and Strassmann, (e) Meitner.

(continued, next page)

31-10 Fission Reactors

A nuclear reactor is a device in which a nuclear chain reaction is carried out at a controlled rate. A fission reactor is one in which the controlled chain reaction is a fission reaction. Such a reactor is usually a nuclear furnace. Nuclear energy is converted to heat. A typical fission reactor uses blocks or cylinders of U-235 or Pu-239 (a plutonium isotope) as fuel. The reactor is also called an **atomic pile.**

The nature of the fuel in a reactor depends upon the purpose, design, and power requirements. The blocks of fuel are surrounded by graphite, which is used to slow down the neutrons produced by the fission. Such a substance is called a **moderator.** Slow neutrons not only have a greater chance of being captured by the nuclei of the atoms of fuel, but also give up energy in the form of heat when their velocity is reduced. As the products of fission scatter through the pile, their energy is also dissipated as heat. The action of the neutrons is controlled by means of **control rods** made of cadmium steel, which can absorb neutrons. The number of new neutrons available for fission is kept equal to the number used up by fission. In this manner, the reaction rate is modified and the reactor becomes a furnace in which heat is generated at a constant rate. See Figure 31-7.

Figure 31-7

The principle of the nuclear reactor. One of the U-235 nuclei in the uranium fuel, like that at (1), undergoes fission, releasing energy and several high-speed neutrons. (The first fission may be triggered by a neutron produced by cosmic rays.) Several things can happen to the high-speed neutrons. Most of them are slowed by colliding with the atoms of the moderator (2). Some of them are then absorbed by the atoms of the control rods (3). Still others, like that at (4), are captured by atoms of U-238, producing U-239, which decays by beta emission to Pu-239, a fissionable plutonium isotope also usable as a reactor fuel. Finally, in the most essential step for continuing the reaction, some neutrons, like that at (5), are captured by other atoms of U-235, resulting in fissions and a repetition of the steps described above.

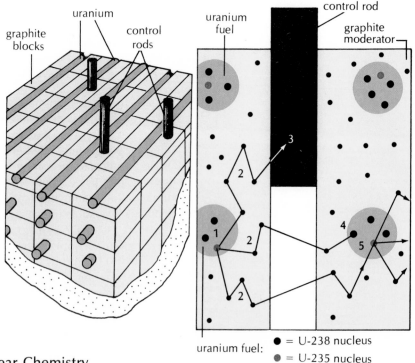

31-11 Nuclear Fuels

Uranium-235. Natural uranium consists chiefly of the isotope U-238. It contains less than 1% of the U-235 isotope, but only U-235 is fissionable. In order to make pure U-235, or enriched uranium (containing more than 1% U-235), the isotopes must be separated. The process of separation by chemical means is difficult because isotopes of an element are chemically alike. Separation can be accomplished by physical means, making use of the slight difference in atomic mass between U-235 and U-238. In one method, uranium ions are passed through a strong magnetic field. In the field, the lighter U-235 ions are deflected more than the U-238 ions. Another method was used in the preparation of the first atomic bomb. This method makes use of the fact that the gaseous hexafluorides of the two isotopes diffuse through a porous wall at different rates. Lars Onsager, a chemistry professor at Yale University, proposed this gaseous diffusion process. It is now the standard method for obtaining U-235.

The manufacture of U-235 is slow and expensive. Therefore, many fission reactors are not fueled with pure U-235, but with uranium that has been enriched with enough U-235 to sustain a chain reaction. Moreover, the presence of U-238 in the reactor leads to the production of plutonium, atomic number 94, in the form of a fissionable isotope. The plutonium can be removed and used as a nuclear fuel or explosive. Thus, the fission reactor using enriched uranium not only produces energy, but also manufactures another fuel. A reactor used in this manner is called a **breeder reactor.**

Manufacture of plutonium. The production of plutonium in the breeder reactor occurs as a result of three nuclear reactions. Neutron capture changes U-238 to the radioactive isotope U-239. The radioisotope undergoes beta decay, resulting in a new element, *neptunium,* atomic number 93. Like U-239, neptunium is radioactive, and through beta decay it forms plutonium, element 94. The equations for the nuclear reactions leading to the formation of plutonium are:

$$^{238}_{92}\text{U} + ^{1}_{0}\text{n} \longrightarrow ^{239}_{92}\text{U} \qquad \textbf{(Eq. 19)}$$

$$^{239}_{92}\text{U} \longrightarrow ^{239}_{93}\text{Np} + ^{0}_{-1}\text{e} \qquad \textbf{(Eq. 20)}$$

$$^{239}_{93}\text{Np} \longrightarrow ^{239}_{94}\text{Pu} + ^{0}_{-1}\text{e} \qquad \textbf{(Eq. 21)}$$

Plutonium-239, though radioactive, is relatively stable. Its half-life is 24 000 years. Its importance lies in the fact that it is fissionable by slow neutrons and can be used as a source of atomic energy. Being chemically different from uranium, it can be separated from that element with relative ease. This is done after the mixture of these elements is removed from the breeder reactor.

Uranium (at. no. 92) is the element of highest atomic number found naturally on the earth. Neptunium (no. 93) and plutonium (no. 94) were the first elements of higher atomic number than uranium to be synthesized. Elements whose atomic numbers are greater than the atomic number of uranium are called **transuranium** or **transuranic elements.** Additional transuranium elements have been synthesized in the laboratory. As of 1980, the list included elements 93 to 105 as definitely confirmed, and 106 and 107 reported.

31-12   Uses of Fission Reactors

The neutrons produced in fission reactors have been used to synthesize new elements and to make useful and important radioisotopes. The large amounts of heat released by the fission process have been used to make steam for the production of electricity. Nuclear electric power plants are in operation in a number of countries. In addition to stationary power plants, submarines and surface vessels are also powered by atomic energy. Nuclear reactors require heavy and costly shielding, making reactors impractical for powering trains and planes.

A number of pollution problems have been created by the use of nuclear reactors. Their fission products are highly radioactive and cannot be discarded as ordinary wastes. They must be stored for a long time or disposed of in special ways. In 1981, some scientists suggested storing nuclear wastes inside the extensive salt domes found around the Gulf of Mexico. Another problem is the heating of the water used as a coolant in some reactors. When this water enters streams and lakes, it may be hot enough to kill the marine life. Water rendered too hot for marine life is said to be thermally polluted.

Questions for Sections 31-10 through 31-12

20. Define the following terms: (a) nuclear reactor, (b) fission reactor, (c) atomic pile, (d) nuclear fuel.
21. (a) Explain the use of graphite as a moderator in a nuclear reactor. (b) Describe the function of the cadmium steel control rods in the reactor.
22. (a) A diffusion method is used to separate U-235 from U-238. Upon what principle is this based? (b) What is the composition of the uranium fuel used in many fission reactors? (c) What happens to the U-238 that is used in a reactor?
*23. (a) What is a breeder reactor? (b) What is the mass number and atomic number of the element formed when the $^{238}_{92}U$ atom captures a neutron? (c) What elements are formed in the successive beta decay reactions that follow?
*24. (a) What is the chief use of plutonium? (b) How else may it be used? (c) Why can it be easily separated from the uranium from which it is made? (d) What are *transuranic elements*?
25. (a) Mention three (3) products of fission reactors. (b) What pollution problems can arise because of fission reactor products and the water coolant?

31-13   Fusion Reactions

As illustrated in Figure 31-4, a lithium nucleus can combine with a proton (hydrogen nucleus) to form two helium nuclei. The combined mass of the two helium nuclei is slightly less than that of the original nuclei, and the difference in mass appears as energy. Similar exothermic reactions among the lighter nuclei are known to be possible. In all such reactions, two or more light nuclei combine to form a single nucleus of slightly less total mass. These reactions are called **fusion reactions** or **nuclear fusions.**

Of particular interest are the fusion reactions in which nuclei of hydrogen isotopes combine to form helium. Hydrogen nuclei are positively charged particles and will repel one another. The closer the nuclei come together, the greater the force of repulsion becomes. In order for fusion reactions to occur, the reacting nuclei must have very high kinetic energies. These energies must be great enough to overcome the forces of repulsion, thereby permitting the nuclei to interact, or fuse. Nuclei can attain such high kinetic energies only under conditions of extremely high temperatures, such as those found in the sun and other stars. Fusion reactions are often called thermonuclear reactions, referring to the high temperatures involved.

It has been suggested that the chief source of the radiant energy emitted by the sun is the conversion of hydrogen to helium. This conversion requires several steps, the net result of which is the fusion of four hydrogen nuclei into one helium nucleus. A temperature of about 20 million degrees Celsius is required to trigger the reaction:

$$4\left({}_{1}^{1}\text{H}\right) \longrightarrow {}_{2}^{4}\text{He} + 2\left({}_{1}^{0}\text{e}\right) + \underbrace{Q}_{\text{symbol for energy}} \qquad \textbf{(Eq. 22)}$$

In larger, more massive stars than the sun, the conditions are favorable for fusion reactions involving carbon and nitrogen nuclei. These reactions release even more energy than do hydrogen fusion reactions.

Thermonuclear devices. Bombs based on fusion reactions are called **thermonuclear devices.** The exact reactions are closely guarded secrets, but they probably include one or more of the three hydrogen isotopes (Chapter 4) as reactants. Helium is probably the end product. For example, two deuterium nuclei can be fused to form the helium nucleus:

$$2\left({}_{1}^{2}\text{H}\right) \longrightarrow {}_{2}^{4}\text{He} + Q \qquad \textbf{(Eq. 23)}$$

A deuteron (deuterium nucleus) can be made to react with a triton (tritium nucleus) with the liberation of tremendous amounts of energy:

$${}_{1}^{2}\text{H} + {}_{1}^{3}\text{H} \longrightarrow {}_{2}^{4}\text{He} + {}_{0}^{1}\text{n} + Q \qquad \textbf{(Eq. 24)}$$

The hydrogen-lithium reaction might also be used. Since very high temperatures are needed to start a fusion reaction, a fission bomb is probably used to trigger the reaction. Fusion bombs with explosive forces equivalent to millions of tons (megatons) of TNT have already been developed.

31-14 Fusion Reactors

A device in which fusion reactions can be carried out at a controlled rate is called a *fusion reactor*. Intensive research is now being conducted to develop fusion reactors to provide a practical method of using fusion reactions as a source of industrial power. Fusion power plants would produce relatively little radioactive waste and would not require scarce materials, such as uranium, for fuel. Water could be used as an inexhaustible source of hydrogen isotopes, the most commonly used fuel in fusion reactions. The chief problem is developing a practical method of producing the extremely high temperatures required in order for fusion reactions to occur. A second problem is the creation of a vessel for containing the fusion reaction. The high-energy reactants, if allowed to contact the vessel walls, will cause the vessel itself to melt. One approach being explored is the use of a strong magnetic field to act as a container or "bottle" within which the fusion reaction would take place.

Questions for Sections 31-13 and 31-14

26. (a) Define *nuclear fusion*. (b) State an example of such a reaction. (c) Why must the reacting nuclei in a fusion reaction possess very high kinetic energies?
*27. (a) What fusion reaction may be a source of the sun's energy? (b) Write the nuclear equation for this reaction. (c) What approximate temperature is needed to start it?
28. (a) What is a *thermonuclear device*? (b) Write the nuclear equation for the fusion of two deuterium nuclei. (c) What are two possible uses for fusion reactions?
29. (a) What is a *fusion reactor*? (b) What are two advantages of using a fusion reactor, instead of a fission reactor, as a source of energy?

CHAPTER SUMMARY

1. A nuclear reaction is one that brings about changes in the nuclei of atoms.
2. The nuclear equation shows atomic numbers and mass numbers; these quantities must be balanced.
3. Natural radioactivity involves nuclear reactions which emit alpha or beta particles in addition to gamma radiation. A radioactive element is either an alpha or beta emitter.
4. The U-238 decay series includes a number of natural radioactive changes. The final product is a stable isotope, Pb-206.
5. Two other radioactive series exist in nature, namely, the U-235 and Th-232 series. Each one begins with a radioactive element having a long half-life and ends with a stable lead isotope.
6. Artificial transmutation of elements can be attained by bombarding nuclei of elements with atomic or subatomic particles.
7. Elements that are made radioactive by nuclear reactions in the laboratory are said to possess induced radioactivity.

8. Neutrons can be used as "bullets" to produce radioactive isotopes of the element being bombarded. Such radioisotopes have important uses in medicine, biochemistry, research, and other fields.

9. Radioactive dating of the age of the earth can be accomplished by measuring the quantity of U-238, and of lead or helium, found in minerals.

10. The amounts of C-14 and C-12 found in dead organic remains can be used as a means of estimating the ages of these remains up to about 75 000 years.

11. Particle accelerators are used to bombard atomic nuclei with fast-moving charged particles. These particles may be protons, deuterons, or alpha particles.

12. The Einstein formula, $E = mc^2$, shows the quantitative relationship between mass and energy.

13. Nuclear fission refers to the splitting of atomic nuclei. It can be controlled by the use of a fission reactor.

14. The fission of U-235 was used in the first atomic bombs.

15. The critical mass is the amount of fissionable material that will support a self-sustaining chain reaction.

16. In a fission reactor, blocks of fuel are surrounded by graphite which acts as a moderator, slowing down neutrons so that they can be easily captured. Cadmium steel rods are used to absorb neutrons and so control their action.

17. The most common nuclear fuels are U-235, mixed with U-238, and plutonium.

18. A breeder reactor not only produces energy, but also manufactures another nuclear fuel.

19. The chief use of fission reactors is to supply energy that can be converted to electricity. The disposal of radioactive wastes and the high-temperature water coolant are problems that must be solved.

20. In fusion reactions, two or more nuclei are combined to form a single nucleus. Fusion reactions take place only at extremely high temperatures.

21. If successfully developed, fusion reactors will supply practically inexhaustible amounts of energy, produce little radioactive waste, and not require scarce elements for fuel.

TERMS YOU SHOULD KNOW

radioisotope	radioactive dating	nuclear fission	control rods
nuclear reaction	particle accelerator	fission reactor	breeder reactor
radioactive series	cyclotron	chain reaction	transuranic element
artificial radioactivity	synchrotron	critical mass	fusion reactor
positron	linear accelerator	atomic pile	nuclear fusion
tracer	mass-energy relation	moderator	thermonuclear device

REVIEW QUESTIONS

(The periodic chart should be used as a reference where needed.)

Section 31-1   **1.** Write the symbol, including the mass number and atomic number, for each of the nuclei of the following elements: (a) helium, (b) the most common hydrogen atom, (c) U-235, (d) Th-234, (e) H-2.

2. Write the nuclear equation for the change that occurs when the U-235 atom emits an alpha particle.

31-2 3. For the following nuclear equations, supply the symbol, mass number, and atomic number of the missing particle:

(a) $^{232}_{90}\text{Th} \rightarrow {}^{228}_{88}\text{Ra} + ?$ (d) $^{35}_{17}\text{Cl} + {}^{1}_{0}\text{n} \rightarrow {}^{35}_{16}\text{S} + ?$

(b) $^{234}_{91}\text{Pa} \rightarrow {}^{234}_{92}\text{U} + ?$ (e) $^{209}_{83}\text{Bi} + ? \rightarrow {}^{210}_{84}\text{Po} + {}^{1}_{0}\text{n}$

(c) $^{14}_{7}\text{N} + ? \rightarrow {}^{14}_{6}\text{C} + {}^{1}_{1}\text{H}$

4. For the following nuclear equations, supply the symbol, mass number, and atomic number of the missing element:

(a) $^{218}_{84}\text{Po} \rightarrow ? + {}^{0}_{-1}\text{e}$ (c) $^{7}_{3}\text{Li} + {}^{4}_{2}\text{He} \rightarrow ? + {}^{1}_{0}\text{n}$

(b) $^{14}_{7}\text{N} + {}^{4}_{2}\text{He} \rightarrow ? + {}^{1}_{1}\text{H}$ (d) $^{54}_{26}\text{Fe} + {}^{2}_{1}\text{H} \rightarrow {}^{4}_{2}\text{He} + ?$

5. A certain radioactive series starts with $^{241}_{94}\text{Pu}$ and proceeds through 13 steps. Five of the steps are beta emissions. Eight are alpha emissions. What is the end-product of the series?

31-3 6. (a) Write the nuclear equation for the first reaction used to produce a nuclear transmutation. (b) Write the nuclear equation for the production of $^{30}_{15}\text{P}$ and neutrons by the bombardment of aluminum by alpha particles. (c) Compare the stabilities of the elements produced in (a) and (b). (d) If a positron is produced in the decay of an atom of $^{30}_{15}\text{P}$, what must the other product be? (e) What type of radioactivity is shown by the phosphorus?

31-4 7. (a) What radioisotope was produced when the Joliot-Curies bombarded ordinary sodium atoms with neutrons? (b) Why are neutrons more effective, generally, for bombarding nuclei than protons or alpha particles?

8. (a) When an atom of $^{81}_{35}\text{Br}$ is subjected to gamma radiation, a neutron is set free. Write the symbol, atomic number and atomic mass of the radioisotope produced. (b) In the diagnosis and treatment of thyroid disorder, the patient is given water containing I-131, an iodine radioisotope. How can the iodine intake be measured?

31-5 9. The half-life of C-14 is about 5 700 years. An organic relic is found to contain C-14 and C-12 in a ratio that is one-sixteenth as great as the ratio in the atmosphere. What is the age of the relic?

10. (a) The half-life of U-238 is 4.5 billion years. The final product of its decay is Pb-206. If a sample of mineral shows an equal number of atoms of these isotopes to be present, what estimate can be made of the age of the mineral? (b) Ra-226 has a half-life of 1620 years. Why can't it be used to estimate the age of the earth?

31-6 11. (a) Why can't neutrons be accelerated by the cyclotron? (b) Compare the cyclotron and synchrotron, stating one similarity and one difference. (c) How does the linear accelerator differ from the accelerators mentioned in (b)?

31-7 12. (a) What are the units for the speed of light, in the Einstein mass-energy equation, if energy is measured in joules? (b) Using the units in (a), what is the mass unit?

31-8 13. In a nuclear reaction converting lithium to helium by bombarding the lithium with protons, the total mass of reactants is found to be 8.023 g. The mass of the product is 8.016 g. How many joules of energy are liberated?

31-9 14. (a) Explain why the fission of U-235 can be used as the basis for a chain reaction. (b) Explain the importance of the critical mass, stating what will happen if the fuel mass is greater than the critical mass or less than the critical mass.

15. When struck by a neutron, the U-235 nucleus may be split into Ce-144 and Sr-90 nuclei, emitting four electrons and two neutrons for each fission. Write the nuclear equation for the change.

31-10 16. (a) Why is a fission reactor often called an atomic pile? (b) How does the purpose of the moderator differ from that of the control rods? (c) Why are low-energy neutrons more effective than fast neutrons in producing nuclear reactions?

31-11 17. (a) Why are fission reactors generally fueled with a mixture of U-235 and U-238 instead of pure U-235? (b) How does this fuel create a breeder reactor?

18. Pu-239 is formed from U-238 by 3 successive nuclear reactions. In the first reaction, a neutron is captured. The second and third involve beta decay. Write the 3 equations.

19. When a plutonium atom captures a neutron, it may split into Ce-144 and Sr-90. Two beta particles and six neutrons are emitted for each atom that is split. (a) Write the nuclear equation. (b) Why can the fission act as the basis for a chain reaction? (c) Why does plutonium's long half-life (24 000 years) contribute to its importance?

31-12 20. (a) Name three (3) uses of fission reactors. (b) Why isn't nuclear power used in aircraft? (c) Suggest one means that might be safely used for the disposal of radioactive wastes.

31-13 21. It has been suggested that many common isotopes were formed by the fusion of alpha particles. (a) Which of the following elements might have been formed from alpha particles without the emission of any particles? $^{10}_{4}\text{Be}$, $^{12}_{6}\text{C}$, $^{16}_{8}\text{O}$, $^{32}_{16}\text{S}$, $^{40}_{18}\text{Ar}$. (b) Write the nuclear equations for the reactions forming these elements.

FOR FURTHER THOUGHT

31-2 1. For each step of a radioactive decay series, are the following statements true (1) always, (2) sometimes, or (3) never? If you answer "sometimes," give reasons or examples.
(a) The atomic number of the next element decreases.
(b) The mass number of the next element decreases.
(c) The atomic number of the next element increases.
(d) The mass number of the next element increases.
(e) Energy is released.
(f) The next element is radioactive.

31-5 2. The age of a rock (that is, the time since the rock was formed) may sometimes be calculated from the ratio of Pb-206 to U-238 in the rock. For the method to be reliable, which of the following assumptions or conditions must be true?
(a) The rock must contain a large amount of uranium.
(b) When the rock formed, it did not contain any Pb-206.
(c) All the Pb-206 in the rock today came from the decay of U-238.
(d) The rock has not moved since it was formed.
(e) The rate of decay of U-238 to Pb-206 has been constant.
(f) The decay of U-238 has now stopped.

APPENDICES

Appendix A Calculating with Numbers in Scientific Notation

Scientific notation is discussed in Section 2-4, page 17. The rules for calculating with numbers in scientific notation are the same rules as those that govern the addition, subtraction, multiplication, and division of expressions in algebra, as illustrated below.

ADDITION

Algebraic	Scientific notation		
$5a$	5×10	5×10^3	5×10^{-5}
$+ \, 2a$	$+ \, 2 \times 10$	$+ \, 2 \times 10^3$	$+ \, 2 \times 10^{-5}$
$7a$	7×10	7×10^3	7×10^{-5}

SUBTRACTION

Algebraic	Scientific notation		
$5a$	5×10	5×10^3	5×10^{-5}
$- \, 2a$	$- \, 2 \times 10$	$- \, 2 \times 10^3$	$- \, 2 \times 10^{-5}$
$3a$	3×10	3×10^3	3×10^{-5}

Note: In order to add or subtract quantities written in scientific notation, they must be expressed with the same power of 10. For example, to add 5.8×10^3 and 2.16×10^4, rewrite 5.8×10^3 as 0.58×10^4. (Both expressions have the same value, 5800.) Then add:

$$
\begin{array}{r}
0.58 \times 10^4 \\
+2.16 \times 10^4 \\
\hline
2.74 \times 10^4
\end{array}
$$

MULTIPLICATION

Algebraic	Scientific notation
$3a \times 2a^2 = 6a^3$	$(3 \times 10) \times (2 \times 10^2) = 6 \times 10^3$
$3a^{-5} \times 2a^2 = 6a^{-3}$	$(3 \times 10^{-5}) \times (2 \times 10^2) = 6 \times 10^{-3}$
$2a^{-3} \times 4a^{-2} = 8a^{-5}$	$(2 \times 10^{-3}) \times (4 \times 10^{-2}) = 8 \times 10^{-5}$

DIVISION

Algebraic	Scientific notation
$\dfrac{6a^5}{2a^2} = 3a^3$	$\dfrac{6 \times 10^5}{2 \times 10^2} = 3 \times 10^3$
$\dfrac{6a^{-5}}{2a^2} = 3a^{-7}$	$\dfrac{6 \times 10^{-5}}{2 \times 10^2} = 3 \times 10^{-7}$
$\dfrac{6a^5}{2a^{-2}} = 3a^7$	$\dfrac{6 \times 10^5}{2 \times 10^{-2}} = 3 \times 10^7$
$\dfrac{6a^{-5}}{2a^{-2}} = 3a^{-3}$	$\dfrac{6 \times 10^{-5}}{2 \times 10^{-2}} = 3 \times 10^{-3}$

Practice Problems

(Answers are given in Appendix I.)

1. Express the following in scientific notation.

   (a) 61   (d) 0.061
   (b) 0.61   (e) 6 100 000
   (c) 610   (f) 0.000 000 061

2. Add the following.

   (a) 7.5×10^4 (b) 8.75×10^{-6} (c) 8.10×10^4 (d) 2.35×10^{-4}
     $+ 6.2 \times 10^4$ $+ 9.25 \times 10^{-6}$ $+ 6.36 \times 10^5$ $+ 4.80 \times 10^{-5}$

3. Subtract the following.

   (a) 5.0×10^3 (b) 7.89×10^{-2} (c) 2.35×10^6 (d) 1.09×10^{-3}
     $- 2.9 \times 10^3$ $- 6.78 \times 10^{-2}$ $- 8.40 \times 10^5$ $- 7.80 \times 10^{-4}$

4. Multiply the following.

   (a) $(2.0 \times 10^3) \times (4.0 \times 10^4)$ (d) $(4.10 \times 10^{-2}) \times (1.80 \times 10^5)$
   (b) $(6.0 \times 10^6) \times (4.0 \times 10^4)$ (e) $(5.0 \times 10^2) \times (3.2 \times 10^{-4})$
   (c) $(3.0 \times 10^{-3}) \times (1.4 \times 10^{-3})$ (f) $(8.0 \times 10^{-3}) \times (6.0 \times 10^3)$

5. Divide the following.

   (a) $(6.0 \times 10^6) \div (2.0 \times 10^2)$ (d) $(7.2 \times 10^3) \div (2.4 \times 10^{-2})$
   (b) $(8.0 \times 10^2) \div (1.6 \times 10^5)$ (e) $(5.4 \times 10^{-6}) \div (1.8 \times 10^{-3})$
   (c) $(3.9 \times 10^{-3}) \div (1.3 \times 10^2)$ (f) $(9.1 \times 10^{-4}) \div (7.0 \times 10^{-6})$

Appendix B   Rules for Determining Significant Figures in a Calculated Result

Significant figures are discussed in Section 2-6, page 19.

MULTIPLICATION AND DIVISION   A simple rule that usually holds is that the number of significant figures in a product or a quotient obtained from measured quantities is the same as the number of significant figures in the quantity having the smaller number of significant figures. Several examples are given to illustrate this rule.

Example 1	**Unrounded answer**	**Answer rounded to the correct number of significant figures**
4.29 cm $\times$ 3.24 cm	13.8996 cm^2	13.9 cm^2

Explanation: Both measured quantities have 3 significant figures. Therefore, the answer should be rounded to 3 significant figures.

Example 2	**Unrounded answer**	**Answer rounded to the correct number of significant figures**
4.29 cm $\times$ 3.2 cm	13.728 cm^2	14 cm^2

Explanation: One of the measured quantities (3.2 cm) has only 2 significant figures. Therefore, the answer should be rounded to 2 significant figures.

Example 3	Unrounded answer	Answer rounded to the correct number of significant figures
$\dfrac{8.47 \text{ cm}^2}{4.26 \text{ cm}}$	1.988 262 9 cm	1.99 cm

Explanation: Both measured quantities have 3 significant figures. Therefore, the answer should be rounded to 3 significant figures.

Example 4	Unrounded answer	Answer rounded to the correct number of significant figures
$\dfrac{8.47 \text{ cm}^2}{4.2 \text{ cm}}$	2.016 666 6 cm	2.0 cm

Explanation: One measured quantity has only 2 significant figures. Therefore, the answer should be rounded to 2 significant figures.

ADDITION AND SUBTRACTION
When adding or subtracting measured quantities, round the sum or difference so that it has the same number of decimal places as the quantity having the least number of decimal places.

Example 5	Unrounded answer	Answer rounded to the correct number of significant figures
5.34 cm 9.3 cm + 6.12 cm	20.76 cm	20.8 cm

Explanation: The measurement 9.3 cm is significant to only one decimal place. The second decimal place could be as large as a 9 (9.39) or as small as a 0 (9.30). We have no idea what this digit should be. Therefore, we have no idea of what the second decimal place in the answer should be. The answer should be rounded to one decimal place.

Example 6	Unrounded answer	Answer rounded to the correct number of significant figures
9.309 cm 64.2 cm 98.235 cm + 6.72 cm	178.464 cm	178.5 cm

Explanation: The measurement 64.2 cm is significant to only 1 decimal place. Therefore, the answer should be rounded to 1 decimal place.

Example 7	Unrounded answer	Answer rounded to the correct number of significant figures
7.524 cm − 4.31 cm	3.214 cm	3.21 cm

Explanation: The measured quantity 4.31 is significant to only two decimal places. The answer should therefore be rounded to 2 decimal places.

Zeros as place holders. Zeros used as place holders are not significant figures. For example, in the measurement 0.015 meter, there are only two significant figures, the 1 and 5. The first zero merely calls attention to the presence of the decimal point. The second zero is a place holder. Neither zero is a significant figure. The same measurement in centimeters would be 1.5 cm, illustrating that a change from one unit to another has no effect on the number of significant figures in a measurement. In the measurement 0.0150 meter, there are three significant figures, the 1, 5, and the last 0. Here the first zero calls attention to the decimal point, and the second is a place holder. The third zero, a significant figure, is deliberately written to indicate that the measurement has been made to three-digit precision.

A problem arises in connection with zeros to the left of a decimal place. In the measurement 200 meters, are both zeros significant, only one, or neither? To avoid misunderstandings, it is always best to write such measurements in scientific notation. To show one-digit significance, we would write the measurement as 2×10^2. This means that the measurement is closer to 200 than to 100 or 300. To show two-digit significance, the measurement would be expressed as 2.0×10^2 meters. This means that the measurement is closer to 200 than to 210 or 190. For 3-digit significance, we would write 2.00×10^2. This means that the measurement is closer to 200 than to 201 or 199.

Practice Problems

(Answers are given in Appendix I.)

For questions 1 to 4 below, select the answer that has the correct number of significant figures.

1. 5.22 m × 82.7 m =
   (a) 431.694 m^2 (b) 431.69 m^2 (c) 431.7 m^2 (d) 432 m^2

2. 0.0322 cm × 6.5 cm =
   (a) 0.2 cm^2 (b) 0.21 cm^2 (c) 0.209 cm^2 (d) 0.2093 cm^2

3. $\dfrac{4.08 \text{ mL}}{0.061 \text{ mL}}$ =
   (a) 67   (b) 66.9   (c) 66.89   (d) 66.885

4. $\dfrac{9.475 \text{ g}}{12.05 \text{ cm}^3}$ =
   (a) 0.7863 g/cm^3 (b) 0.786 g/cm^3 (c) 0.79 g/cm^3 (d) 0.8 g/cm^3

For questions 5 to 8, round off each answer to the correct number of significant figures.

5.	6.
4.375 g	2.5725 mL
14.62 g	14.55 mL
+ 327.9 g	0.035 mL
346.895 g	+ 4.88 mL
	22.0375 mL

7.	8.
16.748 cm	6.0098 mL
− 1.512 cm	− 2.51 mL
15.236 cm	3.4998 mL

Appendix C A Sample pH Problem

The concept of pH is discussed in Section 24-5, page 478. Below is a sample problem that illustrates how a hydrogen ion concentration expressed in molarity is converted to a concentration expressed in pH.

SAMPLE PROBLEM

The concentration of the hydrogen ion in a solution is 5.21×10^{-2} molar. What is the pH of this solution?

Solution

The pH can be found by carefully applying the definition of pH. The pH is the negative logarithm to the base 10 of the hydrogen ion concentration.

$$pH = - \left(\log_{10}[H^+] \right)$$

In this problem, $[H^+] = 5.21 \times 10^{-2}$

$$pH = - \left(\log_{10} 5.21 \times 10^{-2} \right)$$

For the next step, recall that one of the laws of logarithms states that $\log ab = \log a + \log b$. Applying this law to the expression above, we get:

$$pH = - \left(\log_{10} 5.21 + \log_{10} 10^{-2} \right)$$

But the logarithm to base 10 of 10^{-2} equals -2. Therefore, the above expression can be written:

$$pH = - \left(\log_{10} 5.21 + -2 \right)$$
$$= -\log_{10} 5.21 + 2$$

The table of logarithms in Appendix D shows that $\log_{10} 5.21 = 0.7168$. Substituting this value into the above expression gives:

$$pH = -0.7168 + 2$$
$$= +1.283$$

Our result tells us that a solution whose hydrogen ion concentration is 5.21×10^{-2} has a pH of $+1.283$.

Practice Problems

(*Answers are given in Appendix I.*)

Find the pH of the solutions whose hydrogen ion concentrations are:

1. 0.0543 molar
2. 0.000 139 molar
3. 2.46×10^{-10} molar
4. 3.21×10^{-4} molar
5. 0.173 molar

Find the molar concentrations of the hydrogen ion in the solutions whose pH's are:

6. 9.609
7. 3.857
8. 3.494
9. 0.762
10. 1.265

Appendix D Logarithms of Numbers

N	0	1	2	3	4	5	6	7	8	9
10	0000	0043	0086	0128	0170	0212	0253	0294	0334	0374
11	0414	0453	0492	0531	0569	0607	0645	0682	0719	0755
12	0792	0828	0864	0899	0934	0969	1004	1038	1072	1106
13	1139	1173	1206	1239	1271	1303	1335	1367	1399	1430
14	1461	1492	1523	1553	1584	1614	1644	1673	1703	1732
15	1761	1790	1818	1847	1875	1903	1931	1959	1987	2014
16	2041	2068	2095	2122	2148	2175	2201	2227	2253	2279
17	2304	2330	2355	2380	2405	2430	2455	2480	2504	2529
18	2553	2577	2601	2625	2648	2672	2695	2718	2742	2765
19	2788	2810	2833	2856	2878	2900	2923	2945	2967	2989
20	3010	3032	3054	3075	3096	3118	3139	3160	3181	3201
21	3222	3243	3263	3284	3304	3324	3345	3365	3385	3404
22	3424	3444	3464	3483	3502	3522	3541	3560	3579	3598
23	3617	3636	3655	3674	3692	3711	3729	3747	3766	3784
24	3802	3820	3838	3856	3874	3892	3909	3927	3945	3962
25	3979	3997	4014	4031	4048	4065	4082	4099	4116	4133
26	4150	4166	4183	4200	4216	4232	4249	4265	4281	4298
27	4314	4330	4346	4362	4378	4393	4409	4425	4440	4456
28	4472	4487	4502	4518	4533	4548	4564	4579	4594	4609
29	4624	4639	4654	4669	4683	4698	4713	4728	4742	4757
30	4771	4786	4800	4814	4829	4843	4857	4871	4886	4900
31	4914	4928	4942	4955	4969	4983	4997	5011	5024	5038
32	5051	5065	5079	5092	5105	5119	5132	5145	5159	5172
33	5185	5198	5211	5224	5237	5250	5263	5276	5289	5302
34	5315	5328	5340	5353	5366	5378	5391	5403	5416	5428
35	5441	5453	5465	5478	5490	5502	5514	5527	5539	5551
36	5563	5575	5587	5599	5611	5623	5635	5647	5658	5670
37	5682	5694	5705	5717	5729	5740	5752	5763	5775	5786
38	5798	5809	5821	5832	5843	5855	5866	5877	5888	5899
39	5911	5922	5933	5944	5955	5966	5977	5988	5999	6010
40	6021	6031	6042	6053	6064	6075	6085	6096	6107	6117
41	6128	6138	6149	6160	6170	6180	6191	6201	6212	6222
42	6232	6243	6253	6263	6274	6284	6294	6304	6314	6325
43	6335	6345	6355	6365	6375	6385	6395	6405	6415	6425
44	6435	6444	6454	6464	6474	6484	6493	6503	6513	6522
45	6532	6542	6551	6561	6571	6580	6590	6599	6609	6618
46	6628	6637	6646	6656	6665	6675	6684	6693	6702	6712
47	6721	6730	6739	6749	6758	6767	6776	6785	6794	6803
48	6812	6821	6830	6839	6848	6857	6866	6875	6884	6893
49	6902	6911	6920	6928	6937	6946	6955	6964	6972	6981
50	6990	6998	7007	7016	7024	7033	7042	7050	7059	7067
51	7076	7084	7093	7101	7110	7118	7126	7135	7143	7152
52	7160	7168	7177	7185	7193	7202	7210	7218	7226	7235
53	7243	7251	7259	7267	7275	7284	7292	7300	7308	7316
54	7324	7332	7340	7348	7356	7364	7372	7380	7388	7396

N	0	1	2	3	4	5	6	7	8	9
55	7404	7412	7419	7427	7435	7443	7451	7459	7466	7474
56	7482	7490	7497	7505	7513	7520	7528	7536	7543	7551
57	7559	7566	7574	7582	7589	7597	7604	7612	7619	7627
58	7634	7642	7649	7657	7664	7672	7679	7686	7694	7701
59	7709	7716	7723	7731	7738	7745	7752	7760	7767	7774
60	7782	7789	7796	7803	7810	7818	7825	7832	7839	7846
61	7853	7860	7868	7875	7882	7889	7896	7903	7910	7917
62	7924	7931	7938	7945	7952	7959	7966	7973	7980	7987
63	7993	8000	8007	8014	8021	8028	8035	8041	8048	8055
64	8062	8069	8075	8082	8089	8096	8102	8109	8116	8122
65	8129	8136	8142	8149	8156	8162	8169	8176	8182	8189
66	8195	8202	8209	8215	8222	8228	8235	8241	8248	8254
67	8261	8267	8274	8280	8287	8293	8299	8306	8312	8319
68	8325	8331	8338	8344	8351	8357	8363	8370	8376	8382
69	8388	8395	8401	8407	8414	8420	8426	8432	8439	8445
70	8451	8457	8463	8470	8476	8482	8488	8494	8500	8506
71	8513	8519	8525	8531	8537	8543	8549	8555	8561	8567
72	8573	8579	8585	8591	8597	8603	8609	8615	8621	8627
73	8633	8639	8645	8651	8657	8663	8669	8675	8681	8686
74	8692	8698	8704	8710	8716	8722	8727	8733	8739	8745
75	8751	8756	8762	8768	8774	8779	8785	8791	8797	8802
76	8808	8814	8820	8825	8831	8837	8842	8848	8854	8859
77	8865	8871	8876	8882	8887	8893	8899	8904	8910	8915
78	8921	8927	8932	8938	8943	8949	8954	8960	8965	8971
79	8976	8982	8987	8993	8998	9004	9009	9015	9020	9025
80	9031	9036	9042	9047	9053	9058	9063	9069	9074	9079
81	9085	9090	9096	9101	9106	9112	9117	9122	9128	9133
82	9138	9143	9149	9154	9159	9165	9170	9175	9180	9186
83	9191	9196	9201	9206	9212	9217	9222	9227	9232	9238
84	9243	9248	9253	9258	9263	9269	9274	9279	9284	9289
85	9294	9299	9304	9309	9315	9320	9325	9330	9335	9340
86	9345	9350	9355	9360	9365	9370	9375	9380	9385	9390
87	9395	9400	9405	9410	9415	9420	9425	9430	9435	9440
88	9445	9450	9455	9460	9465	9469	9474	9479	9484	9489
89	9494	9499	9504	9509	9513	9518	9523	9528	9533	9538
90	9542	9547	9552	9557	9562	9566	9571	9576	9581	9586
91	9590	9595	9600	9605	9609	9614	9619	9624	9628	9633
92	9638	9643	9647	9652	9657	9661	9666	9671	9675	9680
93	9685	9689	9694	9699	9703	9708	9713	9717	9722	9727
94	9731	9736	9741	9745	9750	9754	9759	9763	9768	9773
95	9777	9782	9786	9791	9795	9800	9805	9809	9814	9818
96	9823	9827	9832	9836	9841	9845	9850	9854	9859	9863
97	9868	9872	9877	9881	9886	9890	9894	9899	9903	9908
98	9912	9917	9921	9926	9930	9934	9939	9943	9948	9952
99	9956	9961	9965	9969	9974	9978	9983	9987	9991	9996

Appendix E Table of Solubilities of Inorganic Compounds in Water

This table of solubilities is discussed in Section 17-10, pages 341 and 342.

TABLE OF SOLUBILITIES IN WATER										
i — nearly insoluble ss — slightly soluble s — soluble d — decomposes n —not isolated	acetate	bromide	carbonate	chloride	chromate	hydroxide	iodide	nitrate	phosphate	sulfate	sulfide
Aluminum	ss	s	n	s	n	i	s	s	i	s	d
Ammonium	s	s	s	s	s	s	s	s	s	s	s
Barium	s	s	i	s	i	s	s	s	i	i	d
Calcium	s	s	i	s	s	ss	s	s	i	ss	d
Copper II	s	s	i	s	i	i	n	s	i	s	i
Iron II	s	s	i	s	n	i	s	s	i	s	i
Iron III	s	s	n	s	i	i	n	s	i	ss	d
Lead	s	ss	i	ss	i	i	ss	s	i	i	i
Magnesium	s	s	i	s	s	i	s	s	i	s	d
Mercury I	ss	i	i	i	ss	n	i	s	i	ss	i
Mercury II	s	ss	i	s	ss	i	i	s	i	d	i
Potassium	s	s	s	s	s	s	s	s	s	s	s
Silver	ss	i	i	i	ss	n	i	s	i	ss	i
Sodium	s	s	s	s	s	s	s	s	s	s	s
Zinc	s	s	i	s	s	i	s	s	i	s	i

Appendix F Balancing Equations by the Half-Reaction (Ion-Electron) Method

Balancing redox equations by the half-reaction (ion-electron) method is discussed in Section 28-11, page 563. A sample problem illustrating the method is given below.

Redox equations can also be balanced by another method, a method that makes use of oxidation numbers. This method is discussed in Section 26-8, page 522, where a sample problem is given illustrating the method.

SAMPLE PROBLEM

Write a balanced equation for the reaction between a solution of iron (II) sulfate, $FeSO_4$, and potassium permanganate, $KMnO_4$, in dilute acid solution.

Solution

Step 1 *Identify the oxidizing and reducing agents that are taking part in the reaction.* Since half-reactions (table in Figure 28-12, page 559) always involve some ions, we need to write the reactants in terms of ions for those substances that are ionic substances. $FeSO_4$ is composed of Fe^{2+} ions and SO_4^{2-} ions. $KMnO_4$ is composed of K^+ ions and MnO_4^- ions.

Iron (II) ion, Fe^{2+} Checking Figure 28-12, note that Fe^{2+} occurs as both an oxidizing agent (27th entry down) and as a reducing agent (15th entry down).

Sulfate ion, SO_4^{2-} The polyatomic sulfate ion is stable. It does not appear among any of the oxidizing or reducing agents in Figure 28-12. Evidently, it is a spectator ion.

Potassium ion, K^+ The potassium ion is a very weak (inactive) oxidizing agent since it appears on the left almost at the very bottom of the table (3rd entry from the bottom). It reacts with only very strong reducing agents, such as Li and Rb, none of which are present in this reaction. It must be a spectator ion.

Permanganate ion, MnO_4^- The permanganate ion is a strong oxidizing agent (2nd entry in the table) in the presence of dilute acid (H^+ ions).

Our search for oxidizing and reducing agents has led us to the following:

MnO_4^- ———— a strong oxidizing agent in the presence of H^+ ions (2nd entry in Figure 28-12)

Fe^{2+} ———— a reducing agent (15th entry in Figure 28-12)

Fe^{2+} ———— an oxidizing agent (27th entry in Figure 28-12)

The reducing agent, Fe^{2+}, will react only with the oxidizing agent that is above it in the table, namely, with MnO_4^-.

Step 2 *Having identified the oxidizing and reducing agents, write the half-reactions of which they are a part:*

2nd entry, Figure 28-12:
$$MnO_4^- + 8H^+ + 5e^- \longrightarrow Mn^{2+} + 4H_2O \qquad \text{(Eq. 1)}$$

15th entry, Figure 28-12:
$$Fe^{3+} + e^- \longrightarrow Fe^{2+} \qquad \text{(Eq. 2)}$$

Since the oxidizing agent (MnO_4^-) reacts with the reducing agent Fe^{2+}, the last half-reaction should be reversed so that Fe^{2+} appears as a reactant:

$$Fe^{2+} \longrightarrow Fe^{3+} + e^- \qquad \text{(Eq. 3)}$$

Step 3 *Equalize the electrons in the two half-reactions.* Five electrons are gained in Equation 1 while only one is lost in Equation 3. To equalize the number of electrons, all terms in Equation 3 must be increased by a factor of 5.

$$5Fe^{2+} \longrightarrow 5Fe^{3+} + 5e^- \qquad \text{(Eq. 4)}$$

Adding Equations 1 and 4 gives the correctly balanced ionic equation:

$$MnO_4^- + 8H^+ + 5e^- \longrightarrow Mn^{2+} + 4H_2O$$
$$+ 5Fe^{2+} \longrightarrow 5Fe^{3+} + 5e^-$$
$$\overline{5Fe^{2+} + MnO_4^- + 8H^+ \longrightarrow 5Fe^{3+} + Mn^{2+} + 4H_2O} \qquad \text{(Eq. 5)}$$

You should now check Equation 5 to make certain that it balances with respect to both numbers of atoms and charge.

* * * * *

To convert Equation 5 to a molecular equation, the spectator ions, K^+ and SO_4^{2-}, need to be added to it. Everywhere there is a positively charged ion in Equation 5, a compound should be formed of the positive ion and the sulfate ion. Thus, Fe^{2+} becomes $FeSO_4$. H^+ becomes H_2SO_4. Fe^{3+} becomes $Fe_2(SO_4)_3$. Mn^{2+} becomes $MnSO_4$. Wherever there is a negatively charged ion, the potassium ion should be added to form a compound. Thus MnO_4^- becomes $KMnO_4$. When these molecular formulas are substituted for the ionic formulas in Equation 5, the result is:

$$5FeSO_4 + KMnO_4 + 4H_2SO_4 \rightarrow \tfrac{5}{2}Fe_2(SO_4)_3 + MnSO_4 + 4H_2O \textbf{ (Eq. 6)}$$

Notice that where the ionic equation had $8H^+$, the molecular equation has $4H_2SO_4$. The coefficient of 8 had to be halved because 4 molecules of H_2SO_4 contain 8 hydrogen atoms. Also, where the ionic equation had $5Fe^{3+}$, the molecular equation has $\tfrac{5}{2}Fe_2(SO_4)_3$ because $\tfrac{5}{2}$ formula units of $Fe_2(SO_4)_3$ contain 5 iron atoms.

A final check of Equation 6 shows that something is missing from it. There are too few SO_4 units on the right side of the equation and there are no potassium atoms there. The missing atoms are supplied by forming a compound of the spectator ions. That is, the compound potassium sulfate K_2SO_4 is added to the right. Its coefficient should be $\tfrac{1}{2}$:

$$5FeSO_4 + KMnO_4 + 4H_2SO_4 \longrightarrow \tfrac{5}{2}Fe_2(SO_4)_3 + MnSO_4 + 4H_2O$$
$$+ \tfrac{1}{2}K_2SO_4 \qquad \textbf{(Eq. 7)}$$

To rid the equation of the fractional coefficients $\tfrac{5}{2}$ and $\tfrac{1}{2}$, all terms in the equation may be doubled, giving:

$$10FeSO_4 + 2KMnO_4 + 8H_2SO_4 \longrightarrow$$
$$5Fe_2(SO_4)_3 + 2MnSO_4 + 8H_2O + K_2SO_4 \qquad \textbf{(Eq. 8)}$$

Practice Problems

(*The answers are given in Appendix I.*)

Balance the following problems by the ion-electron method. Consult the table of half-reactions in Fig. 28-12, page 559.

1. $KMnO_4(aq) + HCl(aq) \longrightarrow$
$$KCl(aq) + MnCl_2(aq) + H_2O(l) + Cl_2(g)$$
2. $Cu(s) + HNO_3(aq) \longrightarrow Cu(NO_3)_2(aq) + H_2O(l) + NO(g)$
3. $Zn(s) + HNO_3(aq) \longrightarrow Zn(NO_3)_2(aq) + NO_2(g) + H_2O(l)$
4. $Cu(s) + K_2Cr_2O_7(aq) + H_2SO_4(aq) \longrightarrow$
$$K_2SO_4(aq) + CuSO_4(aq) + Cr_2(SO_4)_3(aq) + H_2O(l)$$
5. $FeSO_4(aq) + KMnO_4(aq) + H_2SO_4(aq) \longrightarrow$
$$Fe_2(SO_4)_3(aq) + MnSO_4(aq) + H_2O(l) + K_2SO_4(aq)$$

Appendix G   Periodic Table

s orbitals filling

1**
GROUP
1A

Period 1

1.00794	+1
H	−1
1	
1s	

Key / legend:

Atomic Mass — 12.0111	−4
Symbol **C**	+2
	+4

Selected Oxidation States

Atomic Number — **6**

Electron Configuration — [He] $2s^2 2p^2$

s orbitals filling

1** GROUP 1A	2 GROUP 2A

d orbitals filling

Transition Elements

Period	Group 1A	Group 2A	3 GROUP 3B	4 GROUP 4B	5 GROUP 5B	6 GROUP 6B	7 GROUP 7B	8 GROUP ←	8 GROUP →	9 GROUP 8
2	6.941 +1 **Li** 3 [He] $2s^1$	9.01218 +2 **Be** 4 [He] $2s^2$								
3	22.98977 +1 **Na** 11 [Ne] $3s^1$	24.305 +2 **Mg** 12 [Ne] $3s^2$								
4	39.0983 +1 **K** 19 [Ar] $4s^1$	40.08 +2 **Ca** 20 [Ar] $4s^2$	44.9559 +3 **Sc** 21 [Ar] $3d^1 4s^2$	47.88 +2 +3 +4 **Ti** 22 [Ar] $3d^2 4s^2$	50.9415 +2 +3 +4 +5 **V** 23 [Ar] $3d^3 4s^2$	51.996 +2 +3 +6 **Cr** 24 [Ar] $3d^5 4s^1$	54.9380 +2 +4 +7 **Mn** 25 [Ar] $3d^5 4s^2$	55.847 +2 +3 **Fe** 26 [Ar] $3d^6 4s^2$		58.9332 +2 +3 **Co** 27 [Ar] $3d^7 4s^2$
5	85.4678 +1 **Rb** 37 [Kr] $5s^1$	87.62 +2 **Sr** 38 [Kr] $5s^2$	88.9059 +3 **Y** 39 [Kr] $4d^1 5s^2$	91.224 +4 **Zr** 40 [Kr] $4d^2 5s^2$	92.9064 +3 +5 **Nb** 41 [Kr] $4d^4 5s^1$	95.94 +3 +6 **Mo** 42 [Kr] $4d^5 5s^1$	(98) +4 +6 +7 **Tc** 43 [Kr] $4d^6 5s^1$	101.07 +3 **Ru** 44 [Kr] $4d^7 5s^1$		102.906 +3 **Rh** 45 [Kr] $4d^8 5s^1$
6	132.905 +1 **Cs** 55 [Xe] $6s^1$	137.33 +2 **Ba** 56 [Xe] $6s^2$	**La-Lu** 57 - 71	178.49 +4 **Hf** 72 [Xe] $4f^{14} 5d^2 6s^2$	180.948 +5 **Ta** 73 [Xe] $4f^{14} 5d^3 6s^2$	183.85 +6 **W** 74 [Xe] $4f^{14} 5d^4 6s^2$	186.207 +4 +6 +7 **Re** 75 [Xe] $4f^{14} 5d^5 6s^2$	190.2 +3 +4 **Os** 76 [Xe] $4f^{14} 5d^6 6s^2$		192.22 +3 +4 **Ir** 77 [Xe] $4f^{14} 5d^7 6s^2$
7	(223) +1 **Fr** 87 [Rn] $7s^1$	226.025 +2 **Ra** 88 [Rn] $7s^2$	**Ac-Lr** 89 - 103	(261) **Unq*** 104	(262) **Unp** 105	(263) **Unh** 106	(262) **Uns** 107	(265) **Uno** 108		(266?) **Une** 109

d orbitals filling

| 138.906 +3 **La** 57 [Xe] $5d^1 6s^2$ |
| 227.028 +3 **Ac** 89 [Rn] $6d^1 7s^2$ |

Lanthanoid Series

140.12 +3 +4 **Ce** 58	140.908 +3 **Pr** 59	144.24 +3 **Nd** 60	(145) +3 **Pm** 61	150.36 +2 +3 **Sm** 62

Actinoid Series

232.038 +4 **Th** 90	231.036 +4 +5 **Pa** 91	238.029 +3 +4 +5 +6 **U** 92	237.048 +3 +4 +5 +6 **Np** 93	(244) +3 +4 +5 +6 **Pu** 94

*The systematic names and symbols for elements of atomic number greater than 103 will be used until the approval of trivial names by IUPAC.

**Column numbers above the word GROUP are those assigned by IUPAC in 1984.

The arrangement of the elements in the periodic table is related to the electron configurations of the elements. The electron configuration of an element is usually the result of one electron being added to the configuration of the element that precedes it in the table. The table shows the orbitals that are being filled by that last electron.

Notice that a space appears below the first two elements in the table, hydrogen and helium. A space is left below hydrogen to show that hydrogen, although in group 1, is not a member of the alkali metals (Li, Na, K, Rb, Cs, Fr) because hydrogen's set of properties is unlike the set of properties common to the alkali metals.

The space below helium exists for a different reason. Helium is a noble gas and, as such,

of the Elements

s orbital filling

18 GROUP 0
4.00260 0
He
2
1s²

p orbitals filling

13 GROUP 3A	14 GROUP 4A	15 GROUP 5A	16 GROUP 6A	17 GROUP 7A	18 GROUP 0
10.81 +3	12.0111 −4 +2 +4	14.0067 −3 −2 −1 +1 +2 +3 +4 +5	15.9994 −2	18.998403 −1	20.179 0
B 5	**C** 6	**N** 7	**O** 8	**F** 9	**Ne** 10
[He] 2s²2p¹	[He] 2s²2p²	[He] 2s²2p³	[He] 2s²2p⁴	[He] 2s²2p⁵	[He] 2s²2p⁶
26.98154 +3	28.0855 −4 +2 +4	30.97376 −3 +3 +5	32.06 −2 +4 +6	35.453 −1 +1 +3 +5 +7	39.948 0
Al 13	**Si** 14	**P** 15	**S** 16	**Cl** 17	**Ar** 18
[Ne] 3s²3p¹	[Ne] 3s²3p²	[Ne] 3s²3p³	[Ne] 3s²3p⁴	[Ne] 3s²3p⁵	[Ne] 3s²3p⁶

10 GROUP →	11 GROUP 1B	12 GROUP 2B						
58.69 +2 +3	63.546 +1 +2	65.39 +2	69.72 +3	72.59 +2 +4	74.9216 −3 +3 +5	78.96 −2 +4 +6	79.904 −1 +5	83.80 0 +2
Ni 28	**Cu** 29	**Zn** 30	**Ga** 31	**Ge** 32	**As** 33	**Se** 34	**Br** 35	**Kr** 36
[Ar] 3d⁸4s²	[Ar] 3d¹⁰4s¹	[Ar] 3d¹⁰4s²	[Ar] 3d¹⁰4s²4p¹	[Ar] 3d¹⁰4s²4p²	[Ar] 3d¹⁰4s²4p³	[Ar] 3d¹⁰4s²4p⁴	[Ar] 3d¹⁰4s²4p⁵	[Ar] 3d¹⁰4s²4p⁶
106.42 +2 +4	107.868 +1	112.41 +2	114.82 +3	118.71 +2 +4	121.75 −3 +3 +5	127.60 −2 +4 +6	126.905 −1 +5 +7	131.29 0 +2 +4 +6
Pd 46	**Ag** 47	**Cd** 48	**In** 49	**Sn** 50	**Sb** 51	**Te** 52	**I** 53	**Xe** 54
[Kr] 4d¹⁰5s⁰	[Kr] 4d¹⁰5s¹	[Kr] 4d¹⁰5s²	[Kr] 4d¹⁰5s²5p¹	[Kr] 4d¹⁰5s²5p²	[Kr] 4d¹⁰5s²5p³	[Kr] 4d¹⁰5s²5p⁴	[Kr] 4d¹⁰5s²5p⁵	[Kr] 4d¹⁰5s²5p⁶
195.08 +2 +4	196.967 +1 +3	200.59 +1 +2	204.383 +1 +3	207.2 +2 +4	208.980 +3 +5	(209) +2 +4	(210) −1 +5	(222) 0
Pt 78	**Au** 79	**Hg** 80	**Tl** 81	**Pb** 82	**Bi** 83	**Po** 84	**At** 85	**Rn** 86
[Xe] 4f¹⁴5d⁹6s¹	[Xe] 4f¹⁴5d¹⁰6s¹	[Xe] 4f¹⁴5d¹⁰6s²	[Xe] 4f¹⁴5d¹⁰6s²6p¹	[Xe] 4f¹⁴5d¹⁰6s²6p²	[Xe] 4f¹⁴5d¹⁰6s²6p³	[Xe] 4f¹⁴5d¹⁰6s²6p⁴	[Xe] 4f¹⁴5d¹⁰6s²6p⁵	[Xe] 4f¹⁴5d¹⁰6s²6p⁶

Mass numbers in parentheses are those of the most stable or most common isotope.

f orbitals filling

151.96 +2 +3	157.25 +3	158.925 +3	162.50 +3	164.930 +3	167.26 +3	168.934 +3	173.04 +2 +3	174.967 +3
Eu 63	**Gd** 64	**Tb** 65	**Dy** 66	**Ho** 67	**Er** 68	**Tm** 69	**Yb** 70	**Lu** 71
(243) +3 +4 +5 +6	(247) +3	(247) +3 +4	(251) +3	(252)	(257)	(258)	(259)	(260)
Am 95	**Cm** 96	**Bk** 97	**Cf** 98	**Es** 99	**Fm** 100	**Md** 101	**No** 102	**Lr** 103

has the same set of properties as the other noble gases (Ne, Ar, Kr, Xe, Rn). However, there is an important difference between helium and the other noble gases. Helium is the only member of the family to have only two valence electrons. All the others have the stable octet. The space in the table highlights this difference.

Notice that the last few elements in the table (from atomic numbers 104 to 109) all have symbols made up of three letters, whereas all the other elements have one- or two-letter symbols. An unsettled dispute exists over who were the first people to discover elements 104 to 109. The International Union of Pure and Applied Chemistry (IUPAC) has temporarily assigned these three-letter symbols until the dispute is settled.

Appendix H   Supplementary Readings

Chapter 1

Compton, Charles. *Inside Chemistry*. McGraw-Hill, Inc., 1979.

Hampel, Clifford A., and Gessner G. Hawley. *Glossary of Chemical Terms*, 2nd ed. Van Nostrand-Reinhold Co., Inc., 1982.

Judson, Horace Freeland. "Century of the Sciences." *Science 84*, November 1984.

Lederman, Leon M. "The Value of Fundamental Science." *Scientific American*, November 1984.

Weart, Spencer. *Scientists in Power*. Harvard University Press, 1979.

Woodburn, John H. *Opportunities in Chemistry*, 2nd ed. National Textbook Company, 1978.

Chapter 2

Kempf, Albert F., and Thomas J. Richards. *Metric System Made Simple*. Doubleday and Company, 1977.

Parry, Robert W., et al. *Chemistry: Experimental Foundations*, 4th ed. (Uncertainty in measured and derived quantities). Prentice-Hall, Inc., 1987.

Taffel, Alexander. *Physics—Its Methods and Meanings*. (Measuring length, time, mass, and weight). Allyn and Bacon, Inc., 1986.

Chapter 3

Ambroggi, Robert P. "Water." *Scientific American*, September 1980.

Asimov, Isaac. *New Guide to Science* (The elements). Basic Books, 1984.

———. *A Short History of Chemistry* (Ancient science and alchemy). Greenwood Press, 1979.

Weast, Robert C., ed. *Handbook of Chemistry and Physics*, 66th ed. (The elements). Chemical Rubber Company, 1985-86.

Chapter 4

Mohs, Mayo. "Blowin' in the Wind" (Windpower). *Discover*, June 1985.

Peterson, Ivars. "Building for the Sun" (Solar energy). *Science News*, May 25, 1985.

Sassin, Wolfgang. "Energy." *Scientific American*, September 1980.

Chapter 5

Maranto, Gina. "Are We Close to the Road's End?" (Increase in atmospheric carbon dioxide). *Discover*, January 1986.

Revelle, Roger. "Carbon Dioxide and World Climate." *Scientific American*, August 1982.

Yulsman, Tom. "Greenhouse Earth" (Carbon dioxide and climate). *Science Digest*, February 1984.

Chapter 6

Asimov, Isaac. *A Short History of Chemistry* (Gases). Greenwood Press, 1979.

Conant, James B. *Science and Common Sense* (Work of Boyle and Lavoisier). Yale University Press, 1951.

Scott, Arthur F. "The Invention of the Balloon and the Birth of Chemistry." *Scientific American*, January 1984.

Chapter 7

Petit, Charles. "Neptune's Forge" (Ocean-floor minerals). *Science 83*, Jan/Feb 1983.

Rona, Peter A. "Mineral Deposits from Sea-Floor Hot Springs." *Scientific American*, January 1986.

Walker, Jearl. "The Amateur Scientist" (What happens when water boils?). *Scientific American*, December 1982.

Chapter 8

Holtzclaw, Henry F., Jr., et al. *College Chemistry*, 7th ed. (Symbols, formulas, and equations). D.C. Heath and Company, 1984.

Weast, Robert C., ed. *Handbook of Chemistry and Physics*, 66th ed. (Inorganic and organic compounds, formulas and physical constants). Chemical Rubber Company, 1985-86.

Chapter 9

Gabel, Dorothy. *Solving Chemistry Problems (A Student's Illustrated Guide to Applying the Mole Concept)*. Allyn and Bacon, Inc., 1983.

Sienko, Michell J., and Robert A. Plane. *Chemistry*, 5th ed. (Stoichiometry). McGraw-Hill, Inc., 1976.

Chapter 10

Holtzclaw, Henry F., Jr., et al. *College Chemistry*, 7th ed. (Symbols, formulas, and equations). D.C. Heath and Company, 1984.

McQuarrie, Donald A., and Peter A. Rock. *General Chemistry* (Chemical reactions). W.H. Freeman and Company, 1984.

Chapter 11

Gabel, Dorothy. *Solving Chemical Problems (A Student's Illustrated Guide to Applying the Mole Concept)*. Allyn and Bacon, Inc., 1983.

Sienko, Michell J., and Robert A. Plane. *Chemistry*, 5th ed. (Stoichiometry). McGraw-Hill, Inc., 1976.

Chapter 12
Asimov, Isaac. *New Guide to Science* (Atoms and atomic particles). Basic Books, 1984.
————. *A Short History of Chemistry* (Atoms). Greenwood Press, 1979.
Hänsch, Theodor W., et al. "The Spectrum of Atomic Hydrogen." *Scientific American*, March 1979.
Patterson, E. C. *John Dalton and Atomic Theory*. Doubleday and Company, 1978.
Quigg, Chris. "Elementary Particles and Forces." *Scientific American*, April 1985.
Walker, Jearl. "The Amateur Scientist" (How can you view the spectra of streetlights?) *Scientific American*, January 1984.

Chapter 13
Landa, Edward R. "The First Nuclear Industry." *Scientific American*, November 1982.
Mewaldt, Richard A., et al. "Samples of the Milky Way" (Variation in isotope ratios in the galaxy). *Scientific American*, December 1982.
Taffel, Alexander. *Physics—Its Methods and Meanings* (Quantum theory model of the atom). Allyn and Bacon, Inc., 1986.
Taubes, Gary. "Waiting for the Protons to Die" (Are protons stable?). *Discover*, April 1984.

Chapter 14
Cohen, Marvin L., et al. "The Quantum Mechanics of Materials." *Scientific American*, June 1982.
Hansen, James. "The Delicate Architecture of Cement." *Science 82*, December 1982.
Parry, Robert W., et al. *Chemistry: Experimental Foundations*, 3rd ed. (Covalent and ionic bonds). Prentice-Hall, Inc., 1982.

Chapter 15
Birchall, J.D., and Anthony Kelly. "New Inorganic Materials." *Scientific American*, May 1983.
Hazen, Robert M., and Larry W. Finger. "Crystals at High Pressure." *Scientific American*, May 1985.
Millot, Georges. "Clay." *Scientific American*, April 1979.
Walker, Jearl. "The Amateur Scientist" (What forces hold together sand castles and mud pies?) *Scientific American*, January 1982.

Chapter 16
Asimov, Isaac. *A Short History of Chemistry* (Periodic table). Greenwood Press, 1979.
Walker, Jearl. "The Amateur Scientist" (How can the amateur detect metals in air, liquids, or solids?) *Scientific American*, February 1981.

Chapter 17
Broecker, Wallace S. "The Ocean." *Scientific American*, September 1983.
Edmond, John M., and Karen Von Damm. "Hot Springs on the Ocean Floor." *Scientific American*, April 1983.

Chapter 18
Holtzclaw, Henry F., Jr., et al. *College Chemistry*, 7th ed. (Colligative properties of solutions). D.C. Heath and Company, 1984.
Sienko, Michell J., and Robert A. Plane. *Chemistry*, 5th ed. (Solutions). McGraw-Hill, Inc., 1976.

Chapter 19
Gardiner, William C., Jr. "The Chemistry of Flames." *Scientific American*, February 1982.
Kidder, Tracy. "A Perch in the Sky" (Measuring ozone in the atmosphere). *Science 83*, March 1983.
Ronn, Avigdor M. "Laser Chemistry." *Scientific American*, May 1979.
Sinfelt, John H. "Bimetallic Catalysts." *Scientific American*, September 1985.

Chapter 20
Barker, J.A., and Douglas Henderson. "The Fluid Phases of Matter." *Scientific American*, November 1981.
Lavenda, Bernard H. "Brownian Motion." *Scientific American*, February 1985.
Rifkin, Jeremy. *Entropy: A New World View*. Bantam Books, 1981.

Chapter 21
Epstein, Irving R., et al. "Oscillating Chemical Reactions." *Scientific American*, March 1983.
Parry, Robert W., et al. *Chemistry: Experiemental Foundations*, 3rd ed. (Equilibrium). Prentice-Hall, Inc., 1982.
Walker, Jearl. "The Amateur Scientist" (Oscillating chemical systems). *Scientific American*, July 1978.

Chapter 22
McQuarrie, Donald A., and Peter A. Rock. *General Chemistry* (Solubility and precipitation reactions). W.H. Freeman and Company, 1984.
Parry, Robert W., et al. *Chemistry: Experimental Foundations*, 3rd ed. (Solubility equilibria). Prentice-Hall, Inc., 1982.

Chapter 23
Angell, James B., et al. "Silicon Micromechanical Devices" (Involves etching with acids). *Scientific American*, April 1983.
Snyder, Solomon H. "Medicated Minds" (Lithium salts). *Science 84*, November 1984.

Chapter 24 Likens, Gene E., et al. "Acid Rain." *Scientific American*, October 1979.
McQuarrie, Donald A., and Peter A. Rock. *General Chemistry* (Acids and bases). W.H. Freeman and Company, 1984.
Peterson, Ivars. "A Material Loss" (Acid rain). *Science News*, September 7, 1985.
Sitwell, Nigel. "Our Trees Are Dying" (Acid rain). *Science Digest*, September 1984.

Chapter 25 McQuarrie, Donald A., and Peter A. Rock. *General Chemistry* (Titration). W.H. Freeman and Company, 1984.
Parry, Robert W., et al. *Chemistry: Experimental Foundations*, 3rd ed. (Acid-base titration). Prentice-Hall, Inc., 1982.

Chapter 26 Brill, Winston J. "Biological Nitrogen Fixation." *Scientific American*, March 1977.
Cloud, Preston, and Aharon Gibor. "The Oxygen Cycle." *Scientific American*, September 1970.
Delwiche, C.C. "The Nitrogen Cycle." *Scientific American*, September 1970.
Henahan, John F. "Fire." *Science 80*, Jan/Feb 1980.
Mann, Charles. "The New Fire Fighters." *Science Digest*, April 1984.
Ratloff, Janet. "Cleaner Cooking with Gas" (Kitchen-range combustion). *Science News*, January 14, 1984.

Chapter 27 Holtzclaw, Henry F., Jr., et al. *College Chemistry*, 7th ed. (Electrochemistry and oxidation-reduction). D.C. Heath and Company, 1984.
Sienko, Michell J., and Robert A. Plane. *Chemistry*, 5th ed. (Electrochemistry). McGraw-Hill, Inc., 1976.

Chapter 28 Fickett, Arnold P. "Fuel-Cell Power Plants." *Scientific American*, December 1978.
McQuarrie, Donald A., and Peter A. Rock. *General Chemistry* (Electrochemical cells). W.H. Freeman and Company, 1984.
Parry, Robert W., et al. *Chemistry: Experimental Foundations*, 3rd ed. (Electrochemical cells). Prentice-Hall, Inc., 1982.

Chapter 29 Morrison, Robert T., and Robert N. Boyd. *Organic Chemistry*, 4th ed. (Organic chemistry, in general, and hydrocarbons). Allyn and Bacon, Inc. 1983.
Rosenthal, Gerald A. "The Chemical Defenses of Higher Plants." *Scientific American*, January 1986.
Walker, Jearl. "The Amateur Scientist" (Candle flames). *Scientific American*, April 1978.

Chapter 30 Friedel, Robert. "The Plastics Man" (Leo Baekeland). *Science 84*, November 1984.
Miller, Julie Ann. "Redesigning Molecules Nature's Way" (Protein engineering). *Science News*, September 28, 1985.
"Molecules of Life, The." *Scientific American* (Entire issue), October 1985.
Morrison, Robert T., and Robert N. Boyd. *Organic Chemistry*, 4th ed. (Organic compounds). Allyn and Bacon, Inc., 1983.
Ratloff, Janet. "Dioxin: Is Everyone Contaminated?" *Science News*, July 13, 1985.
Taubes, Gary. "Electrifying Plastics" (Plastics that conduct electricity). *Discover*, June 1984.

Chapter 31 Chiles, James. "Learning to Live with Plutonium." *Science Digest*, July 1984.
Fritzsch, Harald. *Quarks: The Stuff of Matter*. Basic Books, 1983.
von Hippel, Frank, et al. "Stopping the Production of Fissile Materials for Weapons." *Scientific American*, September 1985.
Kidder, Tracy. "Taming a Star" (Fusion power). *Science 82*, March 1982.
Lewis, Harold W. "The Safety of Fission Reactors." *Scientific American*, March 1980.
Rosenthal, Elizabeth. "The Hazards of Everyday Radiation." *Science Digest*, March 1984.
Taubes, Gary. "Detecting Next to Nothing" (Use of accelerators to create fundamental particles). *Science 85*, May 1985.
Weinberg, Steven. *The Discovery of Subatomic Particles (Scientific American Library)*. W.H. Freeman and Company, 1983.

Appendix I
Answers to Questions Marked with an Asterisk

Page 17

12. (a) 1 m = 1000 mm
    (b) 1 m/1000 mm; 1000 mm/1 m
    (c) ? mm = 5.43 m × 1000 mm/1 m
    (d) 5430 mm

Page 18

17. (a) 4.0×10 (e) 4.004×10^3
    (b) 4.00×10^2 (f) 4.400×10^3
    (c) 4×10^{-1} (g) 4×10^{-3}
    (d) 4.04×10^2 (h) 4.04×10^{-2}
18. (a) 610   (d) 66
    (b) 6010   (e) 0.000 601
    (c) 0.060   (f) 60 100
21. (a) 1.2×10^{10} (c) 8.0×10^{-2}
    (f) 5.0×10^5

Page 23

29. −0.4%

Page 33

9. 19.3 g/cm^3

Page 53

20. (a) 283 K   (b) 253 K
21. (a) −248°C   (b) 27°C

Page 56

27.
(a) heat = $m_{H_2O} \times \Delta t_{H_2O} \times$ sp.ht.H_2O
(b) 3.0×10^5 cal

Page 70

3. 3 newtons/cm²

Page 72

11. (a) up   (b) 35 mm Hg

Page 89

7. (b) decreased
8. (a) decrease (b) 300 mL
   (c) $V_2 = 600 \text{ mL} \times \dfrac{200 \text{ mm Hg}}{400 \text{ mm Hg}}$
   (d) 300 mL

Page 96

18. (a) $A = KB$ (b) 140 K

Page 99

22. (a) increase
24. (a) increase   (b) 200 mL
    (c) $V_2 = 100 \text{ mL} \times \dfrac{400 \text{ K}}{200 \text{ K}}$

Page 100

28. It will increase.
29.
$$T_2 = 240 \text{ K} \times \frac{1000 \text{ mm Hg}}{400 \text{ mm Hg}}$$
$$= 600 \text{ K}$$

Page 104

34.
(a) less   (b) less
(c) $V_2 = 850 \text{ mL} \times \dfrac{730 \text{ mm Hg}}{760 \text{ mm Hg}}$
$$\times \frac{273 \text{ K}}{300 \text{ K}}$$
(d) 743 mL   (e) 1.11 g

Page 106

36. (a) 1 atm

Page 124

9. 760.4 mm Hg

Page 128

18. (a) ? cal = 539 cal/g
         × 250 g
    (b) 1.35×10^5 cal

Page 131

26. (a) ? cal = 80 cal/g
         × 440 g
    (b) 3.5×10^4 cal

Page 151

10. (a) 1 atom
11. (a) 2+
12. (a) 2 ions
13. (a) 2−
14. (a) equivalent (b) 6+
    (c) 6−
16. (a) $BaCl_2$ (b) Li_2S
    (c) $Sr_3(PO_4)_2$

Page 154

17. (a) sodium, Na^+; chloride, Cl^-
    (b) barium, Ba^{2+}; bromide, Br^-
    (c) calcium, Ca^{2+}; sulfate, SO_4^{2-}
20. (a) $(NH_4)_2CO_3$

Page 163

3. contains lithium & nitrogen, in ratio of 3 Li to 1 N

Page 165

6.

el.	at. mass		# atoms		
Mg	24 u	×	1	=	24 u
N	14 u	×	2	=	28 u
O	16 u	×	6	=	96 u
					148 u

Page 169

12. (a) 150 g   (b) 0.10 mole
13. 120 g

Page 173

15. 11.2 L   16. 14.0 g

Page 175

19. 70% iron, 30% oxygen
20. 70% iron, 30% oxygen

Page 179

24. CN
25. CN
26. C_2N_2

Page 185

7. (c) $2Na + Cl_2 \rightarrow 2NaCl$

Page 189

9. (a) $4Na + O_2 \longrightarrow 2Na_2O$
   (b) $2Cu + S \longrightarrow Cu_2S$
   (c) balanced
   (d) $2AgNO_3 + H_2SO_4 \longrightarrow$
   $$Ag_2SO_4 + 2HNO_3$$

   (e) balanced
10. (a) iron + oxygen $\longrightarrow$ iron(III)oxide
    (b) $Fe + O_2 \longrightarrow Fe_2O_3$
    (c) $4Fe + 3O_2 \longrightarrow 2Fe_2O_3$

Page 194

20. (a) H^+ (b) Zn^{2+} (c) Cl^-
22. (a) 2 moles (1.20×10^{24})
    (b) 2 moles (1.20×10^{24})
    (c) 2 moles (1.20×10^{24})
    (d) 4 moles (2.41×10^{24})

Page 196

25. (a) $2H_2 + O_2 \longrightarrow 2H_2O$
    (b) $2Na + Cl_2 \longrightarrow 2NaCl$
    (c) $N_2 + 2O_2 \longrightarrow 2NO_2$
    (d) $NH_3 + HCl \longrightarrow NH_4Cl$
    (e) $4Al + 3O_2 \longrightarrow 2Al_2O_3$

Page 201

34. (a) $2Na(aq) + 2H_2O(l) \longrightarrow$
    $\qquad 2Na^+(aq) + 2OH^-(aq) + H_2(g)$
    (b) $Ca(s) + Mg^{2+}(aq) \longrightarrow$
    $\qquad Ca(aq)^{2+} + Mg(s)$
    (c) $Ba^{2+}(aq) + SO_4^{2-}(aq) \longrightarrow BaSO_4(s)$
    (d) $CO_3^{2-}(aq) + Ca^{2+}(aq) \longrightarrow CaSO_3(s)$
    (e) $2Ag^+(aq) + Zn(s) \longrightarrow$
    $\qquad Zn^{2+}(aq) + 2Ag(s)$
    (f) $SO_4^{2-}(aq) + Ba^{2+}(aq) \longrightarrow BaSO_4(s)$

Page 203

1. (a) $2Al(OH)_3 \longrightarrow Al_2O_3 + 3H_2O$
   (b) $3Ti + 2N_2 \longrightarrow Ti_3N_4$
   (c) $2Al + 3ZnCl_2 \longrightarrow 2AlCl_3 + 3Zn$
2. (a) decomp.; $CaCO_3 \longrightarrow CaO + CO_2$
   (b) s.repl.; $2KBr + Cl_2 \longrightarrow 2KCl + Br_2$
3. (a) $Ca^{2+} + CO_3^{2-} \longrightarrow CaCO_3$
   (b) $Ag^+ + Cl^- \longrightarrow AgCl$

Page 209

2. (a) 1 mole (b) 1/2 mole (c) 1 g
3. 22.2 g
4. 7.18 g

Page 214

6. 28.2 u
7. C_2H_6
10. 54.6 L

Page 216

13. 6.69 g

Page 336

6. (a) benzene (b) acetone (c) water

Page 343

17. (a) (1) 130 g/100 g H_2O
       (2) 40 g/100 g H_2O
       (3) 70 g/100 g H_2O
    (b) NaCl
    (c) KNO_3
18. (a) soluble
    (b) nearly insoluble
    (c) slightly soluble

Page 349

4. 396 g

Page 351

30. (a) 0.0540 mole
    (b) 3.16 g
33. 2.5 M

Page 352

36. 0.0500 m

Page 364

14. $-0.45°C$

Page 366

18. 120 g

Page 367

22. (a) $5.03°C/molal$
    (b) 85g

Page 373

2. proper angle of approach
   of colliding particles;
   proper amount of energy

Page 377

7. (a) Decrease the volume
   of the gases. (b) Add more solute
   or evaporate some solvent.
8. Frequency of collisions
   between reacting particles is
   increased.

Page 380

12. (a) $Na + S \longrightarrow NaS$;
    $NaS + Na \longrightarrow Na_2S$

Page 384

15. (a) Molecules may approach at
    wrong angles or lack enough ener-
    gy. (b) short-lived particle
    formed when reacting molecules
    collide at proper angle & with
    enough energy (c) may form prod-
    ucts or break down to reactants
    (d) min. amt. energy needed to
    form activated complex

Page 392

4. (a) heat of formation at 25°C &
   1 atm pressure; $\Delta H_f°$
   (b) -68.3 kcal/mole
   (c) -57.8 kcal/mole
   (d) $H_2(g) + 1/2O_2(g) \longrightarrow$
   $\qquad H_2O(l) + 68.3$ kcal

Page 393-394

8. -135.4 kcal
9. -135.4 kcal
10. 56.8 kcal

Page 400

16. (a) measure of disorder of a sys-
    tem (b) Molecules in gas phase
    are less organized. (c) Mg, C, & O
    atoms are more ordered in $MgCO_3$;
    also, a gas is formed in the reac-
    tion. (d) Orderly arrangement of
    atoms in sugar crystals is dis-
    rupted by water solvent. (e) Higher
    temp. increases speed & random-
    ness of molecules.

Page 403

20. (a) $-\Delta H, +T\Delta S$ (b) $-\Delta H, -T\Delta S$
    (c) $+\Delta H, +T\Delta S$
22. (a) -0.0336 kcal/K (b) -5.2 kcal

Page 405

24. -177 kcal/mole

Page 412

3. (a) both forward & reverse reactions are occurring (b) equivalent
   (c) either A & B, or C & D

Page 417

7. 3.8×10^{-2}
9. CO_2 is formed at same rate it is used up.
10. 0.40

Page 421

13. (a) 1.8×10^{-11} is small, indicating the conc. of products is small (b) 1.0×10^{16} is large, indicating most of the mixture is in the form of products

Page 424

20. (a) no effect (b) shift to right (c) shift to left (d) shift to right

Page 426

23. 2.38×10^{-3}

Page 435

7. $[Ag^+][Cl^-] = (5.0 \times 10^{-5})(5.0 \times 10^{-3})$, which is greater than K_{sp} of AgCl
8. AgCl

Page 438

11. 1.8×10^{-18}
14. 7.6×10^{-7}
17. 1.3×10^{-4} molar

Page 447

3. (a) H_2O molecules surround the Na^+ & Cl^- ions, which are dispersed through the solution.
   (b) $CaCl_2 \longrightarrow Ca^{2+}(aq) + 2Cl^-(aq)$
   (c) $Na_3PO_4 \longrightarrow 3Na^+(aq) + PO_4^{3-}(aq)$
   (d) $AlCl_3 \rightarrow Al^{3+}(aq) + 3Cl^-(aq)$
   (e) $(NH_4)_2SO_4 \longrightarrow$
       $2NH_4^+(aq) + SO_4^{2-}(aq)$

Page 453

11. 5.00×10^{-2} M
13. 2.1×10^{-3} M

Page 457

17. (a) $Mg + 2H^+ \longrightarrow Mg^{2+} + H_2$
    (b) $Zn + 2H^+ \longrightarrow Zn^{2+} + H_2$

Page 461

26. (a) $Ca(OH)_2 \longrightarrow Ca^{2+} + 2OH^-$
    (b) $Ca(OH)_2 + 2HCl \longrightarrow$
        $CaCl_2 + 2H_2O$
    (c) $KOH + HC_2H_3O_2 \longrightarrow$
        $KC_2H_3O_2 + H_2O$

Page 463

28. 3.0×10^{-3} M

Page 473

3.
(a) Arrhenius: a hydroxide that releases OH^- in soln.; Brønsted-Lowry: accepts protons (b) Arrhenius: CO_3^{2-} is not a hydroxide; Brønsted-Lowry: accepts protons

Page 475

5. (a) SO_3^{2-}, S^{2-}, OH^-, $H_2PO_4^-$
   (b) HNO_3, HCl, HSO_4^-, H_3O^+

Page 478

9. 2.0×10^{-13} M

Page 480

13. (a) 4.00 (b) 5.00 (c) 1.00
15. 1.0×10^{-10} M

Page 490

3. (a) red, red, colorless
   (b) yellow, red-blue, colorless
   (c) yellow, blue, red

Page 492

6. (a) 0.0800 M (b) 0.0730 g
7. 4.50×10^{-4} M

Page 495

13. (a) acetate ion (b) sodium ion
    (c) $C_2H_3O_2^- + H_2O \longrightarrow$
        $HC_2H_3O_2 + OH^-$
    (d) $C_2H_3O_2^-$ reacts with H_2O to produce an excess of OH^-

Page 497

16. (a) phenolphthalein (b) methyl orange (c) any one of them

Page 500

20. 2.50 N
22. 12.0 g

Page 502

25. 0.300 N

Page 515

7. (a) Al: 0, 3+; O: 0, 2−
   (b) Fe: 0, 2+; Sn: 2+, 0; Cl: 1−, 1−
   (c) Na: 0, 1+; Br: 0, 1−

Page 518

9. (a) 6+ (b) 5+ (c) 2+

Page 520

12. (a) 2−, rule 3

Page 521

17. O_2: ox. agent; oxidation # dec.
    Cl: red. agent; oxidation # inc.

Page 523

19. (a) HNO_3: 1+, 5+, 2−; H_2S: 1+, 2−; NO: 2+, 2−; S: 0; H_2O: 1+, 2−
    (b) N dec. from 5+ to 2+; S inc. from 2− to 0.
    (c) $2HNO_3 + 3H_2S \longrightarrow$
        $2NO + 3S + 4H_2O$
20. (a) $2KMnO_4 + 16HCl \longrightarrow 2KCl + 2MnCl_2 + 8H_2O + 5Cl_2$
    (b) $3Cu + 8HNO_3 \longrightarrow 3Cu(NO_3)_2 + 4H_2O + 2NO$
    (c) $2K_2Cr_2O_7 + 2H_2O + 3S \longrightarrow$
        $3SO_2 + 4KOH + 2Cr_2O_3$

Page 525

22. (a) 31.6 g (b) 21.0 g (c) 8.00 g
24. 0.150 N

Page 530

3. (a) cations (b) gain electrons
   (c) reduction

Page 533

9. $2Na^+ + 2e^- \longrightarrow 2Na$;
   $2Cl^- \longrightarrow Cl_2 + 2e^-$;
   $2Na^+ + 2Cl^- \longrightarrow 2Na + Cl_2$

Page 536

10. (a) $2H_2O \longrightarrow O_2 + 4H^+ + 4e^-$
    (b) $2H_2O + 2e^- \longrightarrow H_2 + 2OH^-$
    (c) $6H_2O \longrightarrow 2H_2 + O_2 + 4H^+ + 4OH^-$
    (d) $2H_2O \longrightarrow 2H_2 + O_2$

17. (a) anode: silver strip or bar; cathode: metal spoon; electrolyte: soln. of ionic silver compound
    (b) $Ag^+ + e^- \longrightarrow Ag$
    (c) $Ag \longrightarrow Ag^+ + e^-$
    (d) Ratio is 1:1.

3. (a) A strip of Cu is placed inside a porous cup containing an aq. soln. of $CuSO_4$. The cup is then placed inside a beaker that contains a strip of Zn immersed in an aq. soln. of $ZnSO_4$.
    (b) $Zn \rightleftharpoons Zn^{2+} + 2e^-$
    (c) $Cu^{2+} + 2e^- \rightleftharpoons Cu$
    (d) Zn atoms have a greater tendency to lose electrons than Cu atoms; more electrons are driven from the Zn to the Cu electrode through the conductor.
    (e) $Zn + Cu^{2+} \longrightarrow Zn^{2+} + Cu$

7. (a) The positively charged zinc ions would flow from the beaker to the cup to replace the positively charged copper(II) ions that are removed from solution by their reduction. Negatively charged sulfate ions pass from the cup into the beaker to help neutralize the positively charged zinc ions that are formed by the oxidation of zinc metal.
    (b) The ions can diffuse through the wall of the cup in either direction to maintain electrical neutrality at the electrodes.

10. (a) the Cu electrode (b) the Ag electrode (c) the pos. Ag electrode (d) from the Cu strip to the Ag strip (e) The Cu strip becomes more neg. charged than the less active Ag strip; electrons flow to the more pos. Ag strip.

12. (a) 25°C, 1 M ion conc., 1 atm pressure of any gas (b) 0.00 volt
    (c) $Ag^+ + e^- \longrightarrow Ag$; $H_2 \longrightarrow 2H^+ + 2e$

15. (a) −0.34 volt (b) −0.76 volt
    (c) −1.10 volts (d) No. A net neg. voltage indicates the net reaction is not spontaneous.

20. (a) 2.43 volts (b) 3.05 volts
    (c) 0.59 volt
21. (a) −0.74 volt (b) $Cr \longrightarrow$
    $Cr^{3+} + 3e$

24. (a) anode: iron; cathode: tin; electrolyte: acid rain (b) Iron is a more active red. agent & loses electrons more readily than tin does; the less active tin must accept electrons.
26. (a) $Ag \longrightarrow Ag^+ + e$
    $NO_3 + 4H^+ + 3e^- \longrightarrow NO + 2H_2O$
    $3Ag + NO_3^- + 4H^+ \longrightarrow$
    $\qquad\qquad 3Ag + NO + 2H_2O$

3. generally nonelectrolytes & insoluble in polar solvents
5. (a)

(b) It makes the molecule look flat.
(c) H atoms are arranged symmetrically around the C atom; all bonds are covalent. (d) tetrahedral structure (e) C atom must have 4 covalent bonds.

9. (a) CH_3CH_2OH; CH_3OCH_3
    (b) have same mol. comp., C_2H_6O, but diff. struc. formulas

23. (a) 2,2,3-trimethylpentane
    (b) 3-ethyl-5-methylheptane
    (c) 3-methylhexane
24. (a)

28. (a) triple bond (b) C_nH_{2n-2}
    (c) C_2H_2, acetylene; C_3H_4, propyne; C_4H_6, butyne; C_5H_8, pentyne (d) $CH_3-C\equiv CH$; $CH\equiv CCH_2CH_3$

33. (a) a ring of 6 C atoms with alternating single and double bonds
    (b) C_nH_{2n-6} (c)
    (d) coal tar
    (e) drugs, dyes, explosives, plastics
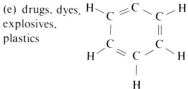

38. (a) 1,2-dichloroethane,

$$\begin{array}{c} H \quad H \\ | \quad\; | \\ H-C-C-H \\ | \quad\; | \\ Cl \quad Cl \end{array}$$

(b) iodoethane

$$\begin{array}{c} H \quad H \\ | \quad\; | \\ H-C-C-H \\ | \quad\; | \\ H \quad I \end{array}$$

(c) 1,2-dichloroethene,

$$\begin{array}{c} Cl \quad Cl \\ | \quad\; | \\ H-C=C-H \end{array}$$

(d) 1,1,2,2-tetrachloroethane,

$$\begin{array}{c} Cl \quad Cl \\ | \quad\; | \\ H-C-C-H \\ | \quad\; | \\ Cl \quad Cl \end{array}$$

3. (a) an alcohol in which the OH group is attached to a C atom bonded to 1, or no other, C atom; ethyl alcohol, CH_3CH_2OH (b) an alcohol in which the OH group is attached to a C atom bonded to 2 other C atoms; 2-propanol,

$$\begin{array}{c} OH \\ | \\ CH_3-CH-CH_3 \end{array}$$

(c) an alcohol in which the OH group is attached to a C atom bonded to 3 other C atoms; 2-methyl-2-propanol, CH_3

$$CH_3-\overset{\overset{\displaystyle CH_3}{|}}{\underset{\underset{\displaystyle CH_3}{|}}{C}}-OH$$

5. (a) methanol (b) ethanol (c) wood alcohol, methyl alcohol (d) grain alcohol, ethyl alcohol (or just alcohol)

Page 613

12. (a) copper(I)oxide plus metallic copper (b) silver (c) red. agent

13. (a)
$$CH_3-\overset{\overset{\displaystyle CH_3}{}}{\underset{\underset{\displaystyle O}{\|}}{C}}$$

(b)
$$CH_3-CH_2-\overset{\overset{\displaystyle}{}}{\underset{\underset{\displaystyle O}{\|}}{C}}-CH_3$$

(c) propanone (d) solvent for organic compounds

Page 617

15. (a) ROR′

(b) $CH_3-CH_2-O-CH_2-CH_3$

(c) It is flammable, irritating to the respiratory tract, & produces nausea as an aftereffect.

(d) solvent for gums, fats, & waxes, and as a lab anesthetic

Page 618

18. (a) produce hydronium ions in water soln. & neutralize bases
(b) esterification
(c) $CH_3COOH + C_2H_5OH \longrightarrow CH_3COOC_2H_5 + H_2O$
(d) a catalyst (conc. H_2SO_4) & warming the reacting mixture
(e) $CH_3COOCH_3 + H_2O \overset{H^+}{\underset{\Delta}{\longrightarrow}} CH_3OH + CH_3COOH$

Page 621

23. (a) a chemical reaction that is catalyzed by an enzyme
(b) $C_6H_{12}O_6 \longrightarrow 2C_2H_5OH + 2CO_2$
(c) zymase

Page 623

26. (a) An ester is split into its alcohol & carboxylic acid parts; the base changes the acid to a salt. (b) glycerine & sodium stearate (c) The addition of salt to the products of a saponification reaction causes the soap to rise to the top of the mixture.

Page 634

3. (a) change of a neutron to a proton (b) Mass # stays the same; at. # (nuclear charge) inc. by 1 unit.
(c) $^{234}_{90}Th \longrightarrow ^{234}_{91}Pa + ^{0}_{-1}e$

Page 637

6. (a) Nitrogen was changed to oxygen. (b) E. Rutherford (c) He bombarded nitrogen gas with alpha particles.
(d) $^{14}_{7}N + ^{4}_{2}He \longrightarrow ^{17}_{8}O + ^{1}_{1}H$

Page 639

12. (a) $^{14}_{6}C \longrightarrow ^{14}_{7}N + ^{0}_{-1}e$

(b) By comparing the ratio of C-14 to C-12 in the remains of an organism to the atmospheric ratio of C-14 to C-12, the age of the material can be determined.
(c) 75 000 years

Page 643

16. (a) The energies produced in such reactions can be measured & related to the loss of mass involved.
(b) 2.3×10^{11} joules

Page 646

23. (a) a reactor that produces energy and manufactures another nuclear fuel at the same time
(b) $^{239}_{92}U$ (c) neptunium & plutonium
24. (a) as a nuclear fuel in a reactor that generates electrical energy
(b) as an atomic explosive
(c) The elements are chemically different so they can be separated by chemical means. (d) synthetic elements with atomic #'s above 92

Page 648

27. (a) the conversion of hydrogen to helium
(b) $4(^{1}_{1}H) \longrightarrow ^{4}_{2}He + 2(^{0}_{1}e) + Q$
(c) 20 million degrees Celsius

Appendix A
Answers to Practice Problems

1. (a) 6.1×10 (d) 6.1×10^{-2}
   (b) 6.1×10^{-1} (e) 6.1×10^{6}
   (c) 6.1×10^{2} (f) 6.1×10^{-8}
2. (a) 13.7×10^{4} or 1.37×10^{5}
   (b) 18.00×10^{-6} or 1.800×10^{-5}
   (c) 71.7×10^{4} or 7.17×10^{5}
   (d) 28.3×10^{-5} or 2.83×10^{-4}
3. (a) 2.1×10^{3}
   (b) 1.11×10^{-2}
   (c) 15.1×10^{5} or 1.51×10^{6}
   (d) 0.31×10^{-3} or 3.1×10^{-4}
4. (a) 8.0×10^{7}
   (b) 24×10^{10} or 2.4×10^{11}
   (c) 4.2×10^{-6}
   (d) 7.38×10^{3}
   (e) 16×10^{-2} or 1.6×10^{-1}
   (f) 48×10^{0} or 4.8×10
5. (a) 3.0×10^{4} (d) 3.0×10^{5}
   (b) 5.0×10^{-3} (e) 3.0×10^{-3}
   (c) 3.0×10^{-5} (f) 1.3×10^{2}

Appendix B
Answers to Practice Problems

1. (d) 2. (b) 3. (a) 4. (a)
5. 346.9 g
6. 22.04 mL
7. 15.236 cm
8. 3.50 mL

Appendix C
Answers to Practice Problems

1. pH = 1.265
2. pH = 3.857
3. pH = 9.609
4. pH = 3.494
5. pH = 0.762
6. conc. $H^+ = 2.46 \times 10^{-10}$ M
7. conc. $H^+ = 1.39 \times 10^{-4}$ M
8. conc. $H^+ = 3.21 \times 10^{-4}$ M
9. conc. $H^+ = 1.73 \times 10^{-1}$ M
10. conc. $H^+ = 5.43 \times 10^{-2}$ M

Appendix F
Answers to Practice Problems

1. 2, 16 $\longrightarrow$ 2, 2, 8, 5
2. 3, 8 $\longrightarrow$ 3, 4, 2
3. 1, 4 $\longrightarrow$ 1, 2, 2
4. 3, 1, 7 $\longrightarrow$ 1, 3, 1, 7
5. 10, 2, 8 $\longrightarrow$ 5, 2, 8, 1

Glossary

absolute temperature scale: See *Kelvin scale*.

absolute zero: The temperature at which all molecular motion should cease. Theoretically, absolute zero is the lowest temperature possible. It is $-273.15°C$ or 0 K (zero kelvin).

accuracy: An indication of how close a measurement is to its accepted value.

acid: A substance that forms hydronium ions in water solution (Arrhenius); a proton donor (Brønsted).

acid anhydride: An oxide of a nonmetal that can react with water to form an acid.

acid-base neutralization: An acid-base reaction in which equivalent quantities react.

acid-base titration: The procedure used to determine the acidity or basicity of a solution. The reactant of known concentration used in this procedure is called the *standard solution*.

acid radical: The negative ion of an acid.

activated complex: The short-lived particle formed as the result of a collision of particles in a chemical reaction. In this complex, the electrons have the opportunity to shift positions and produce new combinations of atoms.

activation energy: The amount of energy required to initiate a chemical action.

activity: The tendency of a substance to react chemically with other substances.

activity series: An arrangement of elements in the order of their relative activities.

addition polymer: A polymer produced by addition reactions between molecules of unsaturated organic compounds.

addition reaction: An organic reaction in which one substance is added on to the structure of a second substance to produce a single compound.

adsorption: The process whereby molecules or ions are made to adhere to a solid surface.

alcohol: (1) A class of organic compounds which consist of a hydrocarbon group and one or more hydroxyl groups. (2) A common name for ethyl alcohol.

aldehyde: A class of organic compounds which consist of a hydrocarbon group and one or more $-CHO$ groups.

alicyclic hydrocarbons: Cyclic hydrocarbons that do not possess the typical aromatic ring structure.

aliphatic hydrocarbons: Hydrocarbons that have an open-chain structure—either straight or branched.

alkadiene: An unsaturated hydrocarbon in which two pairs of carbon atoms possess double bonds.

alkali: A strongly basic hydroxide of a Group 1A metal.

alkali metal: An element in Group 1A of the periodic table.

alkaline earth metal: Any of the elements in Group 2A of the periodic table.

alkane: A member of the saturated series of hydrocarbons. Its type formula is C_nH_{2n+2}.

alkane derivative: A compound obtained by substituting an atom or group of atoms for one or more hydrogen atoms in a normal alkane.

alkene: A member of the unsaturated olefin series of hydrocarbons. Its type formula is C_nH_{2n}.

alkyl group: A hydrocarbon group with the general formula C_nH_{2n+1}.

alkyne: A member of the acetylene series of hydrocarbons characterized by a triple carbon-carbon bond in the molecule. The type formula is C_nH_{2n-2}.

alloy: A substance composed of two or more metals.

alpha particle: A helium nucleus.

alternating current: An electric current that surges back and forth through a conductor at a definite rate.

amalgam: An alloy of mercury.

amphiprotic: The term applied to substances that can function as acids in some reactions and as bases in others.

amphoteric: A term with the same meaning as amphiprotic, except that this term is usually applied specifically to hydroxides that can function as acids or bases.

analysis: Decomposing a substance into two or more simpler substances.

angstrom: A unit of length equal to 1×10^{-8} cm.

anhydride: An oxide that can combine with water to form an acid (acid anhydride) or a base (basic anhydride).

anhydrous: Without water. Usually applied to the product obtained by removing the water from a hydrate.

anion: An ion carrying a negative charge.

anode: An electrode at which oxidation (loss of electrons) occurs.

aqueous: Made of, with, or by water.

aromatic: A class of organic compounds characterized by the benzene ring structure.

artificial radioactivity: See *induced radioactivity*.

atmosphere: The layer of air surrounding the earth. Also, a unit of pressure: 1 atmosphere = 760 mm Hg.

atom: The smallest particle of an element that can enter into chemical change. It consists of a central nucleus and electron clouds outside the nucleus.

atomic mass: The exact mass of an atom in atomic mass units.

atomic mass unit: A unit of mass equal to exactly $\frac{1}{12}$ the mass of a carbon-12 atom. Abbreviated u.

atomic number: The number of protons in the nucleus of an atom.

atomic pile: A nuclear reactor. It consists of blocks of fuel surrounded by graphite acting as a moderator. Control rods are inserted at various points to regulate the number of neutrons being absorbed.

atomic radius: One-half the measured distance from the

nucleus of one atom to that of the next atom in the solid phase of the element.

atomic weight: The mass assigned to an element, in atomic mass units, based upon the weighted average of its naturally occurring isotopes.

Avogadro's number: The number of particles in a mole; this number is approximately 6.023×10^{23}.

barometer: An instrument used to measure atmospheric pressure.

base: A hydroxide that produces hydroxide ions in aqueous solution (Arrhenius); a proton acceptor (Brønsted).

basic anhydride: An oxide of a metal that can react with water to produce a base.

benzene series: A family of aromatic hydrocarbons with the type formula C_nH_{2n-6}.

beta particle: An electron.

binary compound: A compound consisting of only two elements.

biochemical: Related to the chemistry of living organisms and processes.

boiling: Turbulence in a liquid caused by the rapid formation of bubbles of vapor at the boiling point.

boiling point: The temperature at which the vapor pressure of a liquid is equal to the external pressure. At a pressure of 1 atm, the boiling point of water is 100°C.

boiling point elevation: The increase in the boiling point of water caused by the presence of a solute (see *molal boiling point constant*).

bond: See *chemical bond.*

bond angle: The angle formed by the bonds that connect a given atom to two other atoms.

bond energy: The amount of energy required to break a chemical bond.

branch-chain: An organic group attached as a side-chain to a carbon atom in the longest continuous straight chain of carbon atoms.

breeder reactor: A nuclear reactor that not only produces energy, but also produces another nuclear fuel.

bright-line spectrum: A spectrum that shows separate bright lines, each with its own definite wavelength.

buffer: A solution that will resist the change in pH that would ordinarily be produced by the addition of small amounts of acid or base.

burning: See *combustion.*

calorie: The quantity of heat required to raise the temperature of one gram of water by one degree Celsius.

calorimeter: An apparatus used to measure the heat change in a chemical reaction.

carbohydrate: An organic compound of carbon, hydrogen, and oxygen, in which the ratio of hydrogen atoms to oxygen atoms usually is 2 to 1.

carboxylic acid: A group of organic compounds that contain the carboxyl group, $-COOH$.

catalyst: A substance that changes the speed of a chemical reaction without being permanently altered itself.

cathode: The electrode at which reduction (gain of electrons) occurs.

cathode rays: Streams of electrons that emanate from the cathode of a discharge tube.

cation: An ion carrying a positive charge.

Celsius scale: The temperature scale on which the boiling point of water is 100°, and the freezing point, 0°.

chain reaction: A series of reactions in which each reaction is initiated by the energy produced in the preceding one.

chemical bond: The force holding atoms together in a combined state. This force may be due to the attraction of opposite charges (ionic bond), to the magnetic and electrical attractions of shared electrons (covalent bond), or a combination of these attractions.

chemical change: A change in the composition and properties of a substance, or substances, as the result of a chemical reaction.

chemical equation: A condensed statement that uses formulas to show the reactants and products in a chemical change.

chemical equilibrium: A condition in which two chemical changes exactly oppose one another. Equilibrium is a dynamic condition in which concentrations do not change and the rates of opposing reactions are equal.

chemical property: A characteristic of a substance that is observed when it undergoes chemical changes.

chemical reaction: An action that produces a chemical change.

chemistry: The study of matter, its structure, properties, and composition, and the changes that matter undergoes.

classical mechanics: The branch of physics based on the laws of motion stated by Isaac Newton (17th century).

coefficients: A number preceding formula units (atoms, ions, molecules) in balanced chemical equations, indicating the relative number of units involved in the reaction.

colligative properties: (1) Properties that are bound together under the same rule, law, or hypothesis. (2) Properties of solutions that depend only on the *number* of particles present.

combination: See *direct combination.*

combustion: A chemical reaction producing noticeable light and heat.

complex ion: See *polyatomic ion.*

compound: A substance of definite composition which may be decomposed into two or more simpler substances by chemical change.

concentrated solution: One that contains a relatively large amount of solute.

concentration: The quantity of substance contained in a given volume of medium (solid, solution, etc.) It may be expressed as percentage, molarity, etc.

conceptual definition: One that is based upon the interpretation of observed facts.

condensation: The process whereby a gas or vapor is changed to a liquid. Also, any process in which a substance is made more compact or dense.

condensation polymer: A polymer that is formed by a condensation reaction.

condensation reaction: A chemical reaction in which a small molecule, such as water, is split off while large molecular units are being combined.

conductivity: The property whereby a substance can transmit particles, a fluid, etc. Usually applied to the conduction of heat and electricity.

conductor: A substance, such as a metal, that can transmit heat or electricity.

conjugate pair: An acid and a base that may be formed reversibly from one another in a protolysis reaction. The conjugates differ in composition by only a hydrogen atom.

continuous spectrum: A spectrum in which the colors blend into one another.

control rods: Rods used in a reactor to absorb neutrons and thereby regulate the nuclear reaction. Generally made of cadmium steel.

coordinate covalent bond: A chemical bond between two atoms in which one of the atoms furnishes all of the shared electrons.

copolymer: A polymer that is made from two or more different monomers.

covalence: The number of pairs of electrons shared by an element or group involved in covalent bonding.

covalent bond: (1) A bond consisting of one pair of shared electrons. (2) The force of attraction between elements sharing electrons.

covalent molecule: One in which the atoms are held together by shared electrons.

cracking: The process of breaking down large organic molecules in crude oil to smaller ones in order to increase the supply of gasoline.

critical mass: The quantity of fissionable material that will support a self-sustaining chain reaction.

critical pressure: The pressure required to liquefy a gas at its critical temperature.

critical temperature: The maximum temperature at which it is possible to liquefy a gas by increasing the pressure.

crystal: A solid consisting of plane faces and having a definite shape. The particles are arranged in a repeated pattern characteristic of the crystal.

cubic centimeter: The volume defined by a cube, each side of which is one centimeter long. It is equal in volume to one milliliter.

cyclic compound: A compound in which the atoms are arranged in the form of a ring.

cycloalkane: A cyclic, saturated hydrocarbon. It has the general formula C_nH_{2n}.

cycloalkene: A hydrocarbon that has one double bond between two of the carbon atoms in the ring structure. Its type formula is C_nH_{2n-2}.

cycloalkadiene: A cyclic hydrocarbon that has two double bonds between two different pairs of carbon atoms. Its type formula is C_nH_{2n-4}.

cyclotron: A particle accelerator in which electromagnetic forces are used to accelerate charged particles (protons, deuterons, etc.) in a spiral path for the pur-

pose of bombarding atomic nuclei.

data: See *scientific data*.

decomposition: A chemical change in which a substance is broken down to form two or more simpler substances.

decrepitation: The change of water to steam that occurs when crystals containing mechanically enclosed water are heated.

dehydrating agent: A substance that combines readily with water and can remove it from compounds in which it is held in chemical combination.

dehydration: The process of removing hydrogen and oxygen, as water, from a compound.

deliquescence: The process whereby a substance absorbs moisture from the air and eventually dissolves in it.

denatured alcohol: Commercial alcohol that is rendered unfit for drinking by the addition of poisonous or ill-smelling substances.

density: Mass per unit volume.

derivative: A compound obtained (derived) from a hydrocarbon by a substitution or addition reaction.

destructive distillation: The process whereby substances are decomposed by heating them in the absence of air and then the resulting gases condensed into liquids by cooling.

detergent: A cleansing agent that is not a soap. Detergents, such as sodium lauryl sulfate, do not form precipitates in hard water.

deuterium: An isotope of hydrogen with a mass number of 2. It is commonly called heavy hydrogen.

deuteron: The nucleus of a deuterium atom. It contains one proton and one neutron.

diffusion: The spontaneous spreading of a solid, liquid, or gas.

dihydroxy alcohol: An alcohol with two hydroxyl groups to the molecule. Also called a glycol.

dilute solution: A solution that contains a relatively small concentration of solute.

dipole: A molecule in which the centers of positive and negative charge do not coincide. One end of a dipole is somewhat positive and the other end somewhat negative. Also called a polar molecule.

direct combination: A chemical reaction in which two or more substances combine to form a single product. Also called synthesis.

direct current: An electric current moving in one direction only.

discharge tube: A glass tube containing air at very low pressure and two electrodes sealed in, one at each end. A high voltage passed through the tube produces rays of light which appear to travel from the cathode to the anode.

dissociation: The separation of the ions of an ionic compound, usually brought about by dissolving an ionic compound in water.

distillate: The liquid obtained by condensing the vapor produced during distillation.

distillation: The process in which a liquid is evaporated and the vapors condensed.

double replacement: See *ion-exchange reaction*.

ductility: The property of a substance that allows it to be drawn into a wire.

effective collision: One in which reactants collide at the correct angle and with sufficient energy to form an activated complex from which the products are formed.

effervescence: The rapid escape of gas from a liquid in which it had been dissolved or in which it is being formed by chemical action.

efflorescence: The process by which a hydrate at room temperature loses its water of hydration and changes to a powder.

electric current: A flow of charged particles. The ordinary electric current is a flow of electrons.

electrical conductivity: The ability of a substance to transmit an electric current.

electrochemical cell: An arrangement of electrodes and electrolyte in which a spontaneous redox reaction is used to produce a flow of electrons to an external circuit.

electrolysis: A chemical reaction brought about by an electric current.

electrolyte: A substance whose water solution conducts an electric current.

electrolytic conduction. See *ionic conduction*.

electromagnetic spectrum: The spectrum of all radiation resulting from fluctuations of electric currents and vibrations of charged particles. Electromagnetic radiation travels at the speed of light and includes visible light, X rays, ultraviolet light, infrared light, radio waves, etc.

electromotive force: The potential difference between two points in an electric current. It is this difference that causes electrons to move in an electric current.

electron: The fundamental negative particle in matter. Its mass is 0.00055 u.

electron configuration: A shorthand notation describing the distribution of electrons among the sublevels of an atom.

electron-dot symbol: A device consisting of the symbol of an element surrounded by dots representing valence electrons. The dots are arranged in positions representing the orbitals of the valence electrons.

electronegativity: The attraction of an atom for electrons in the covalent bond. The most electronegative element, fluorine, is assigned the arbitrary value of 4.0 on the electronegativity scale.

electroplating: A process in which electrolysis is used as a means of coating an object with a layer (plate) of metal.

electrostatic force: The force of attraction or repulsion that exists between two electrically charged bodies.

electrovalence: The number of electrons an atom loses or gains in forming an ionic bond.

electrovalent bonding: See *ionic bonding*.

element: A substance that cannot be decomposed into simpler substances by ordinary chemical means.

empirical formula: The formula showing the simplest ratio in which the atoms combine to form a compound.

emulsion: Two or more liquids intimately dispersed in one another, resulting in a product that is usually milky in appearance.

endothermic reaction: A chemical change in which heat energy is absorbed.

endpoint: The point in a titration at which an indicator shows that, within the desired range of accuracy, equivalent quantities have reacted.

energy: The ability to do work. It can be transferred or transformed. It remains constant in amount during a chemical or physical change.

energy level: One of the regions in an atom to which electrons are restricted. Also called orbit or shell.

enthalpy: A measure of the internal energy of a system.

entropy: The degree of randomness or a measure of the probability of existence of a system.

enzyme: An organic substance produced by living cells and capable of acting as a catalyst in biochemical reactions.

equation: See *chemical equation*.

equilibrium: See *physical equilibrium* and *chemical equilibrium*.

equilibrium constant: An expression of the ratio between reaction product concentrations and reaction reactant concentrations. It expresses the extent to which the equilibrium has proceeded in either direction.

equilibrium displacement: Shifting the point of equilibrium and, therefore, changing the concentrations of substances involved.

equivalent masses: The masses of interacting substances that are equal in chemical reacting value.

ester: The product, other than water, of the reaction between an alcohol and an acid.

esterification: The alcohol-acid reaction that produces an ester.

ether: A class of organic compounds having the general formula $R\text{-}O\text{-}R'$, in which each R indicates a hydrocarbon group. Also used to indicate the most common ether, diethyl ether.

evaporation: The escape of molecules from a liquid into the gaseous phase.

excited state: The condition of an atom whose electrons are at higher energy levels than the ones they normally occupy.

exothermic reaction: A chemical change in which heat is released.

experiment: A carefully devised plan and procedure for making observations and gathering facts.

external circuit: A term used when discussing galvanic cells. It consists of the electrodes and the attached conductors through which electrons travel from one electrode to the other.

family: Elements with similar properties that fall into the same vertical column of the periodic table.

fat: An ester of glycerine and a higher fatty acid.

fatty acid: Long-chain carboxylic acids that occur as esters in fats and oils. The most common fatty acids are palmitic, stearic, and oleic acids.

fermentation: A chemical change in an organic compound that is catalyzed by an enzyme and does not involve reaction with oxygen.

filtrate: The liquid that has been passed through a filter.

filtration: The process by which suspended matter is separated from a liquid by passing the mixture through paper or other material that will hold the suspended matter and allow the liquid to pass through.

fission: The splitting of an atomic nucleus into two smaller nuclei that are approximately equal in mass.

fission reactor: A nuclear reactor used to control fission reactions.

formula: The representation of the composition of a substance using symbols and subscripts.

formula mass: The sum of all the atomic masses in a formula.

fractional distillation: The separation of a mixture of two or more liquids by utilizing differences in their boiling points.

free energy: A measure of the tendency of a change to occur spontaneously.

freezing: The change of phase from a liquid to a solid.

freezing point: The temperature at which a liquid changes to a solid. Normal freezing points are measured at a pressure of 760 mm Hg.

freezing point depression: The lowering of the freezing point of a liquid that occurs when substances are dissolved in the liquid.

frequency: The number of wave vibrations per unit time.

functional group: The atom or group of atoms that characterizes the structure of a family of organic compounds and determines many of their properties.

fusion: (1) The change of a solid to a liquid. (2) A nuclear reaction in which two or more light nuclei combine to form a single nucleus.

fusion reactor: A nuclear reactor in which fusion reactions are carried out at a controlled rate.

galvanic cell: See *electrochemical cell.*

gamma rays: High-frequency electromagnetic waves similar to X rays, but of greater frequency.

gas: The phase of matter in which molecules are widely separated. A gas does not have a definite volume or shape.

glycol: See *dihydroxy alcohol.*

gram: A basic unit of mass, equal to one-thousandth the mass of the standard kilogram.

gram atomic mass: The quantity of an element that has a mass in grams numerically equal to its atomic mass in atomic mass units. Also called gram-atom.

gram equivalent mass: The mass of an element or compound that will react with, or replace, 1.008 g of hydrogen or a gram equivalent mass of any other substance.

gram formula mass: The sum of the gram-atoms represented in a formula.

gram molecular mass: The quantity of a substance that has a mass in grams numerically equal to its molecular mass in atomic mass units.

gram molecular volume: See *molar volume.*

gravitation: Force of attraction between bodies of matter. The magnitude of this force depends essentially on the masses of the bodies.

group: (1) See *family.* (2) A combination of two or more elements that persists as a unit in many of its chemical reactions.

half-life: The time required for the nuclear disintegration of half the atoms in a radioactive sample.

half-reaction: The reduction or oxidation portion of a redox reaction.

halogens: The family of elements in Group 7A of the periodic table. All members of this family are active nonmetals.

hard water: Water that contains calcium, magnesium, or ferrous ions in solution. Soap reacts with these ions to form a precipitate.

heat: The form of energy produced by molecular motion.

heat of condensation: The quantity of heat released when a unit mass of a vapor condenses to liquid at a constant temperature.

heat of crystallization: The quantity of heat released when a unit mass of a liquid is changed to solid at constant temperature.

heat of formation: The heat absorbed or given off when a mole of a compound is formed from its elements.

heat of fusion: The quantity of heat required to change a unit mass of a solid to liquid at a constant temperature.

heat of reaction: The quantity of heat liberated or absorbed during a chemical change.

heat of vaporization: The quantity of heat required to vaporize a unit mass of liquid at a constant temperature.

heavy hydrogen: See *deuterium.*

heavy water: Water in which the hydrogen atoms are deuterium isotopes.

hertz: A unit of frequency expressing the number of waves passing a given point each second.

heterogeneous mixture: A mixture in which the ingredients are not uniformly dispersed.

heterogeneous reaction: A reaction that involves reactants in more than one phase.

homogeneous mixture: A uniform intermixture of particles. Samples from different parts of this mixture show the same composition.

homogeneous reaction: A reaction in which all the reactants are in the same phase.

homologous series: A series of hydrocarbons that have the same general formula. The formula of each member differs from the preceding one by a $-CH_2$ group.

Hund's rule: The principle that states that no electrons are paired in a given orbital until all the orbitals of the same sublevel have received at least one electron.

hybridization: The process whereby bonding tendencies of electrons in different sublevels are modified and become alike.

hydrate: Crystal consisting of a solid substance combined chemically with water in a definite ratio.

hydration: The chemical addition of water to an ion or to a compound.

hydride: A compound in which hydrogen is combined with an element of lower electronegativity than itself.

hydrocarbon: An organic compound consisting solely of the elements hydrogen and carbon.

hydrogen bond: The bond formed between a hydrogen atom in one molecule and a highly electronegative atom (N, O, F) in another molecule. The attraction is chiefly electrostatic.

hydrogen half-cell: The combination of electrode and solution that is used as a standard for redox potentials. It is assigned a potential of 0.00 volt.

hydrogenation: A chemical change in which hydrogen is combined with some other substance.

hydrolysis: Any chemical reaction in which water is one of the reactants.

hydrolysis constant: The equilibrium constant for a hydrolysis reaction that is in equilibrium.

hydronium ion: The H_3O^+ ion, which is formed by the combination of a proton with a water molecule. Its presence accounts for the properties of acids.

hygroscopic: A substance that absorbs moisture from the air.

hypothesis: A proposed explanation of observed facts or events. It is subjected to confirmation by further observation and experimentation.

ideal gas: Any gas that obeys the gas laws perfectly. Actually, no such gas exists.

ideal gas law: The relationship represented by the equation $PV = nRT$.

immiscible: Liquids that are insoluble in one another.

increment: The formula difference between consecutive members of a homologous series.

indicators: Organic substances that change color at certain pH values. The colors and pH values vary with the indicator.

induced radioactivity: Artificial radioactivity produced by bombarding the nuclei of stable atoms with high energy particles, thereby producing radioactive atoms.

inert: Unable to enter into chemical reaction.

inertia: The property of all matter which allows it to resist change in its state of rest or motion.

interionic attraction: Attraction between ions of opposite charge. For ions in solution, this attractions decreases their velocities and their ability to conduct the electronic current.

internal circuit: The pathway travelled by ions inside a galvanic cell.

ion: An atom or a group of atoms with an excess positive or negative charge.

ion-exchange reaction: A reaction in which two ionic compounds exchange ions to form two different ionic compounds. Also known as a double replacement reaction.

ion-product: The product of the molar concentrations of the ions in an ionic solution raised to powers equal to their coefficients in the equation showing their dissociation.

ion-product constant of water: The product of the concentrations of the hydronium and hydroxide ions in aqueous solution or pure water. At 25°C, its value is 1.0×10^{-14}.

ionic bonding: Bonding between ions resulting from the transfer of electrons from one of the bonding atoms to the other.

ionic conduction: The transmission of electric current by ions.

ionization: Any process that results in the formation of ions.

ionization constant: The equilibrium constant for the reaction involving the ionization of a weak electrolyte.

ionization energy: The energy required to remove the most loosely held electron from a neutral atom. The energy required to remove a second electron is called the second ionization energy.

ionization potential: The ionization energy given in units of volts.

isomers: Compounds with the same molecular formula but different structural formulas.

isotopes: Atoms of the same element having different mass numbers due to the different number of neutrons in their nuclei.

IUPAC system: The most widely accepted system for naming organic compounds, approved by the International Union of Pure and Applied Chemistry.

joule: A basic unit of energy in the international system (SI system). It is equal to one newton-meter.

Kelvin scale: A temperature scale on which zero (0 K) is the lowest temperature that is theoretically attainable. It is called absolute zero and the scale is often called the absolute scale. The units (degrees) on the Kelvin scale are the same size as those on the Celsius scale.

kernel: The part of the atom exclusive of its valence electrons.

ketone: A family of organic compounds characterized by the functional carbonyl group.

kilogram: The standard unit of mass in the metric system. It is equal to 1000 grams.

kinetic energy: Energy of motion.

kinetic theory: The theory that explains the properties of matter in terms of molecular motion.

lattice: A repeating structure consisting mostly of open space. It is used to refer to the pattern of points that describes the arrangement of atoms or molecules in a crystal.

linear accelerator: A particle accelerator in which positive ions are accelerated by means of synchronized fields of electric force.

liquefaction: The process in which a gas is converted to a liquid.

liquid: The phase of matter in which the molecules are held closer together and more tightly than in the gaseous phase. Has a definite volume but indefinite shape.

liter: A volume equal to 1000 milliliters or 1000 cubic centimeters.

lye: A common name used for sodium hydroxide or potassium hydroxide, both very strong bases. The word is derived from *alkali,* the term used to describe any strong base.

malleable: Capable of being rolled or hammered into sheets.

manometer: A U-tube containing mercury or some other liquid, used to measure the pressure of confined gases.

mass: A measure of the quantity of matter in a body.

mass-action expression: A fraction formed from the concentrations of the reactants and products of a reaction, each concentration raised to a power indicated by its coefficient in a balanced equation.

mass-energy relation: The Einstein formula, $E = mc^2$, relates mass and energy, showing that mass can be converted into energy and energy into mass.

mass number: The total number of protons and neutrons in the nucleus of an atom.

matter: Anything that occupies space and has mass.

mechanics: The branch of physics that deals with the motions of bodies under the influence of forces.

melting: The change of phase from solid to liquid.

melting point: The temperature of a mixture in which a solid is changing to a liquid. Same as the freezing point of the same substance.

metal: An element characterized by high luster, good heat and electrical conductivity, and the ability to lose electrons easily in chemical change.

metallic bond: The attractive force that binds metal atoms together. It is due to the attractive force that the mobile electrons exert on the positive ions.

metallic conduction: Electrical or heat conduction by the mobile valence electrons.

metalloid: An element that has significant metallic and nonmetallic properties.

meter: The basic unit of length in the metric system. It is equal to 39.37 inches.

milliliter: One-thousandth of a liter.

miscible: Liquids that are soluble in one another.

mixture: An association of two or more substances that are not chemically combined.

model: See *scientific model.*

moderator: The substance used in a nuclear reactor to slow down the velocity of the neutrons.

molal boiling point constant: The number of degrees by which the boiling point of a solvent is raised in a l-molal solution of a nonelectrolyte.

molal freezing point constant: The number of degrees by which the freezing point of a solvent is depressed in a l-molal solution of a nonelectrolyte.

molality: The concentration of a solution expressed in the number of moles of solute per 1000 g of solvent.

molar volume: The volume occupied by a gram molecular mass of a gas or vapor. This volume is 22.4 liters at standard conditions.

molarity: The concentration of a solution expressed in moles of solute per liter of solution.

mole: The Avogadro number of any particle of definite composition. The term *mole* is also used to indicate the quantity of a substance that has a mass in grams numerically equal to its molecular mass. This mass contains the Avogadro number of molecules.

molecular formula: A formula that indicates the actual number of atoms of each element in one molecule of a substance.

molecular mass: The mass of a molecule in atomic mass units.

molecule: The smallest particle of a covalent substance that can exist free and still have the composition and properties of that substance. See *formula.*

monohydroxy alcohol: An alcohol with only one hydroxyl group in its molecular formula.

monomer: The simple repeating unit in a polymer.

natural radioactivity: The nuclear decay in naturally occurring elements that have been radioactive since their creation.

net potential: The voltage obtained from a galvanic cell. It is mathematically equal to the sum of the oxidation and reduction potentials.

network solid: A structure with strong covalent bonds extending from atom to atom in a continuous three-dimensional pattern. It has a high melting point and is very hard.

neutral solution: A solution that is neither acid nor basic. A water solution with an equal concentration of hydronium and hydroxide ions.

neutralization: A reaction between a base and acid in which all the hydronium ions of the acid combine with all the hydroxide ions of the base.

neutron: The neutral particle found in the nucleus of an atom. Its mass is 1.00867 u.

noble gas: A member of the family of extremely inactive gases found in Group O of the periodic table.

nonelectrolyte: A substance whose water solution does not conduct an electric current.

nonmetal: An element that gains electrons in chemical reactions and whose properties (such as brittleness and poor electrical conductivity) contrast with those of metals.

nonpolar molecule: A covalent molecule that is electrically symmetrical.

normal alkane: Straight-chain or unbranched alkane.

normal solution: A solution that contains one gram equivalent mass of solute per liter of solution.

normality: The concentration of a solution expressed in gram equivalent masses of solute per liter of solution.

nuclear energy: Energy produced as a result of nuclear change.

nuclear fission: See *fission.*

nuclear fuel: An element in which nuclear change is used as a source of energy.

nuclear fusion: See *fusion.*

nuclear reaction: Reaction involving a change in the nuclear contents of one or more atoms. In nuclear reactions, mass is converted to energy.

nuclear reactor: A device in which a nuclear reaction is carried out at a controlled rate.

nucleons: The collective name for the particles (neutrons and protons) present in the nucleus of an atom.

nucleus: The small, extremely dense, positively charged central part of an atom.

octet: A stable outer shell of eight electrons, arranged as four orbital pairs.

oil: (1) An ester of glycerine and an unsaturated higher fatty acid. (2) A viscous hydrocarbon product of petroleum distillation.

olefin: A name used for alkenes because their halides are usually oily liquids. Olefin means oil former.

open-chain: A term used to describe straight-chain or branched-chain organic structures to distinguish them from ring structures.

operational definition: A definition based upon directly observable properties or effects.

orbit: See *energy level.*

orbital: That part of the atom where electrons are most likely to be found. An orbital may hold one, two, or no electrons.

orbital pair: Two electrons of opposite spin in an atomic orbital.

organic chemistry: That branch of chemistry devoted to the study of carbon and its compounds.

organic compound: A compound of carbon.

ore: A mineral that is used as a commercial source of a metal.

oxidation: (1) A chemical combination with oxygen (old definition). (2) A loss of electrons in an atom or an algebraic increase in its oxidation number (modern definition).

oxidation potential: The value, in volts, which measures the tendency for a given oxidation half-reaction to occur.

oxidation state (number): In ionic compounds, it is equal to the ionic charge. In covalent compounds, it is the charge assigned to the atom in accordance with rules involving electronegativities. The algebraic sum of the oxidation numbers in a molecule is zero.

oxide: A compound of oxygen and another element or group of elements.

oxidizing agent: A substance that gains electrons in chemical action or undergoes an algebraic decrease in its oxidation state.

paraffin series: The alkane family of organic compounds. This name emphasizes the inactivity of the alkanes.

particle accelerator: A device that accelerates charged particles to desired speeds by means of electric and magnetic fields. The particles are used to bombard atomic nuclei.

pascal: The unit of pressure in the metric system. It is the pressure of 1 newton per square meter. The newton is a force that equals about one-tenth the mass of a kilogram.

percentage by mass (percentage composition): A measurement of the concentration of a given substance in a larger mass of matter. It is obtained by dividing the mass of the given substance by the mass of the entire sample and multiplying by 100.

period: A horizontal sequence of the periodic table. Following the first period of H and He, the others range from an alkali metal on the left to a noble gas on the right.

periodic law: The properties of the elements are a periodic function of their atomic numbers.

peroxide: A compound containing the O_2^{2-} anion. The term is also used to refer to the most common peroxide, hydrogen peroxide.

petroleum: An oily, liquid mixture made up chiefly of saturated hycrocarbons. Depending upon the source, petroleum also contains unsaturated hydrocarbons, aromatics, and some nitrogen and sulfur derivatives.

pH: A convenient method of expressing the acidity or basicity of a solution in terms of values related inversely to the hydrogen ion concentration. A neutral solution has a pH of 7. Acid solutions have values below 7, basic solutions, above 7.

pH meter: An electronic device for measuring pH of a solution.

phase: The physical state of matter, e.g., solid, liquid, or gas.

phase equilibrium: A physical equilibrium involving different phases of a substance, such as the equilibrium in an ice-water mixture at 0°C.

physical change: A change in which the composition and chemical properties of a substance are not altered.

physical equilibrium: A system in which two physical changes oppose each other at the same rate.

physical property: A characteristic of a material that can be observed without a chemical change taking place.

Planck's constant: In developing his quantum theory, Planck used the equation, $E = hf$, where E is the energy of a quantum of radiation of frequency f. Planck's constant is the proportionality constant h. It is equal to 6.6×10^{-34} joule/hertz.

plastic: A substance, usually a polymer, that can be molded into shape while soft and then hardened by heat, cooling, or air.

pOH: The negative of the logarithm of the concentration of hydroxide ions in a solution. The sum of the pH and the pOH for any aqueous solution is 14.

polar bond: A covalent bond in which the electron pair is not shared equally by the bonded atoms.

polar molecule: See *dipole*.

polyatomic ion: A particle made up of two or more elements that carries a net electrical charge and acts as a unit in chemical change. The bonds between the atoms of the ion are covalent. Sometimes called an ionic radical.

polymer: A compound made up of molecules of high molecular mass. Each molecule consists of smaller units, monomers, united in a repeating pattern.

polymerization: The process by which a polymer is formed.

positron: A positive subatomic particle with the same mass as the electron. Its charge is equal in quantity but opposite in sign to that of the electron.

potential energy: Energy that an object possesses due to its position, condition, or composition.

precipitate: A solid that makes a sudden appearance in a liquid or gaseous phase.

precision: A measure of the agreement between the numerical values of two or more measurements that have been made using the same methods.

pressure: Caused by molecular impacts and is measured in terms of force per unit area.

primary alcohol: A monohydroxy alcohol in which the carbon atom holding the −OH group is bonded to only one other carbon atom. Methyl alcohol is the one primary alcohol that is an exception to the rule.

proof: Indicates the proportion of alcohol in a beverage. It is twice the percentage of alcohol by volume.

property: A quality or characteristic that can be used to describe a substance.

protolysis reaction: A chemical reaction in which protons are donated and accepted.

proton: The fundamental positive particle found in the nucleus of an atom. Its mass is 1.00720 u.

proton acceptor: A substance that combines with a proton in chemical reaction. In terms of the Brønsted-Lowry theory, it is a base.

proton donor: A substance that loses a proton in chemical action. An acid in terms of the Brønsted-Lowry theory.

quanta: The units in which energy is absorbed or radiated. The amount of energy in a quantum is proportional to the frequency of the radiated energy.

quantum mechanics: Also called wave mechanics. Highly mathematical theories of atomic structure based on the belief that energy is absorbed and radiated in definite units (quanta). One conclusion of quantum mechanics is that the energy of an electron is restricted to certain definite values.

quantum numbers: Values used to express the energy of an electron. Each electron in an atom is assigned four quantum numbers which describe its energy due to position, shape, spin, and magnetic moment.

radiation: Emission of waves of energy, such as light waves, X rays, alpha rays, etc.

radical: An atom (or group of atoms) which acts as a unit in chemical change. The simple radical consists of one element; the complex radical, to which the term radical is usually applied, contains more than one element.

radioactive dating: The use of half-lives of radioisotopes in determining the age of the earth, ancient relics, and similar objects.

radioactive decay: See *radioactivity*.

radioactive series: A chain of radioisotopes in which radioactive decay leads from a heavy element with a long half-life to a final product which is a stable isotope.

radioactivity: The spontaneous breakdown of atomic nuclei, accompanied by the release of some form of radiation.

radioisotope: A radioactive isotope of an element.

rate-determining step: The slowest step of a reaction mechanism.

reactant: One of the starting substances involved in a chemical reaction.

reaction: See *chemical reaction*.

reaction mechanism: The series of steps by which reacting particles rearrange themselves to form the products of a chemical reaction.

reaction rate: The rate at which a reactant is used up or a product is formed. Usually expressed in terms of moles per unit volume per unit of time.

reactions that go to completion: Reactions that are not reversible to any practical extent.

redox reaction: An oxidation-reduction reaction.

reducing agent: The substance in a redox reaction that loses electrons, or increases its oxidation state.

reduction: The algebraic decrease in oxidation state or the gain of electrons in a chemical action.

reduction potential: The value, in volts, which measures the tendency for a given reduction half-reaction to occur.

reversible reaction: One in which the products can react, under suitable conditions, to produce the original reactants.

ring structure: A closed arrangement of bonded atoms, such as those found in cyclic organic compounds.

salt: An ionic solid consisting of a positive ion and a negative ion other than the hydroxide ion. Also, the term used for the most common salt, sodium chloride.

salting out: The addition of a concentrated NaCl solution in soap manufacture to precipitate the soap.

saponification: The hydrolysis of an ester in basic solution. The term means *soap making,* and is commonly applied to the reaction used to make soap.

saturated compound: An organic compound in which the carbon atoms are joined by single bonds.

saturated solution: One that has dissolved as much solute as it can under the existing conditions.

science: A branch of study which attempts to find logical explanations for all that is observable. For pure science, discovery and explanation are ends in themselves. Applied science, or technology, is the practical application of scientific discoveries.

scientific data: The results of the observations made during a scientific experiment.

scientific law: Statement of a relationship between observed facts. It may be a qualitative statement or a mathematical formula.

scientific method: The manner in which scientists proceed to solve a problem. They state the problem, collect observations, search for scientific laws, form hypotheses and theories, and modify these theories when necessary.

scientific model: A mental picture that helps to explain something that cannot be seen or experienced directly.

scientific notation: A number expressed as a product of two factors. The first is a number falling between 1 and 10; the second is a power of 10.

secondary alcohol: A monohydroxy alcohol in which the carbon atom holding the −OH group is bonded to two other carbon atoms.

shell: See *energy level.*

significant figures: The digits in a measurement that are certain, plus one digit that is uncertain.

single replacement: A reaction in which an element replaces a less active element in a compound, setting the replaced element free.

slow oxidation: Oxidation in which no noticeable heat or light is evolved.

soap: A metallic salt of a higher fatty acid.

solid: That phase of matter which has a definite crystalline form and melting point.

solid solution: A solution of solid in solid, in which one of the components takes up positions in the crystal lattice of the other. Often found in alloys.

solubility: The amount of solute that can dissolve in a given amount of solvent at given conditions.

solubility curve: A graph of the relationship between solubility and temperature.

solubility product constant: The equilibrium constant for the solution of a slightly soluble ionic compound. It is equal to the product of the concentrations of the ions raised to powers equal to their subscripts in the formula.

solubility product expression: The mathematical statement showing the products of the ionic concentrations that result in a solubility product constant.

solute: The dissolved substance in a solution.

solution: A uniform mixture of particles of molecular size.

solvent: That part of the solution in which the solute is dissolved.

specific gravity: The ratio of the mass of a given volume of a substance to that of an equal volume of a standard. Water is the standard for liquids and solids; hydrogen, oxygen, or air may be used for gases.

specific heat: The number of calories required to raise the temperature of one gram of a substance by 1°C.

spectral lines: Lines of definite wavelengths found in a bright-line spectrum.

spectrum: A series of colored bands of bright lines, arranged in the order of their wavelengths, produced by the passage of radiation through a prism, diffraction grating, or similar device.

spontaneous chemical change: A chemical change that, having been initiated, will continue under the existing conditions.

stable compound: One that is not easily decomposed by the application of energy.

standard conditions: The temperature and pressure at which many scientific measurements are made and compared. Usually, 0°C and 760 mm of mercury.

standard heat of formation: The heat of reaction when one mole of a compound is formed from its elements at standard conditions (25°C and 1 atm).

standard solution: A solution of known concentration.

standing wave: A wave that can meet itself without any overlap. This is true of the electron's probability wave.

standard electrode potential: The voltage obtained at standard conditions when a given half-cell is operated in combination with the standard hydrogen electrode. Standard electrode potentials are represented by the symbol $E°$.

steam distillation: A process in which steam is used to vaporize a volatile component of a liquid mixture. The vapor is then condensed by cooling.

Stock system: A system of formula nomenclature that is used to name the ions of an element that has variable valence. It states the name (or symbol) of the element followed by a Roman numeral that expresses the charge on the ion.

stoichiometry: The name given to the study of the quantitative relationships that can be derived from formulas and equations.

straight-chain compound: Compounds, generally hydrocarbons, that do not have a ring structure. Such hydrocarbons are also called open-chain or aliphatic hydrocarbons.

stress: A change in condition that affects the speed of a chemical reaction.

strong acid: An acid that is highly ionized in water solution and, therefore, has a high concentration of hydronium ions in the solution.

strong base: A base that is highly ionized in water solution, where it forms a high concentration of hydroxide ions.

strong electrolyte: A substance whose water solution is an excellent conductor of electricity due to its high degree of ionization.

structural formula: A chemical formula that indicates the arrangement of the atoms in a molecule by use of connecting lines between symbols for the atoms.

subatomic particles: Particles that are constituent parts of atoms (protons, electrons, neutrons, etc.).

sublevels: Divisions of the principal energy levels of an atom. For example, the third principal level can be divided into the *s*, *p*, and *d* sublevels.

sublimation: The change of a solid to a vapor (or the reverse) without passing through the liquid phase.

subscript: A number written at the lower right side of a symbol to indicate the number of atoms present in the molecule.

subshells: See *sublevels*.

substance: A sample of matter, all parts of which have one set of identifying properties.

substituent: The substituted element or group in a substitution reaction.

substitution reaction: Any organic reaction in which an element or group replaces another element or group in a molecule.

supersaturated solution: A solution containing more solute than a saturated solution at the same conditions. Such solutions are unstable and can easily be changed to a saturated solution by causing the excess solute to precipitate out of solution.

symbol: One or two letters used to designate an atom of an element.

synchrotron: A type of cyclotron that focuses the beams of the accelerated particles by means of a series of electromagnets.

synthesis: The chemical combination of simple substances to form a more complex substance.

temperature: The property or condition of a body that determines the direction of heat flow between it and another body. It is a measure of the average kinetic energy of the molecules.

ternary acid: An acid whose molecule consists of three elements.

ternary compound: A compound consisting of three elements.

tertiary alcohol: An monohydroxy alcohol in which the carbon atom holding the hydroxyl group is bonded to three other carbon atoms.

tetrahedral configuration: A molecular structure in which the relative positions of the atoms, or groups of atoms, are the corners of a tetrahedron.

theory: (1) An explanation of observed relationships that has been verified to some extent. (2) An intellectual scheme that unifies a great many observed facts, such as the *cell theory, atomic theory, theory of continental drift*.

thermometer: An instrument used for measuring temperature.

thermonuclear device: A bomb based upon a nuclear fusion reaction.

tincture: A solution in which the solvent is ethyl alcohol.

titrant: A solution of known concentration (standard solution) used in a titration to determine the concentration of another solution.

titration: The process by which the concentration of a solution is determined by reaction with a standard solution.

torr: A unit of pressure equivalent to 1 mm of mercury.

tracer: A radioisotope that can be followed through its chemical reactions because of its radioactivity. Also called a *tagged atom*.

transition element: One of the elements in a transition series. An element with an incomplete subshell located in one of its inner shells.

transition series: A group of metals, all of which have an incomplete inner shell of electrons. Found in periods 4 to 7 of the periodic table.

transmutation: The conversion of one element to another by means of a nuclear change.

transuranic element: The elements with atomic numbers greater than that of uranium.

triad: A group of three elements of the same chemical family. Attention was called to their properties by Dobereiner in 1828.

trihydroxy alcohol: An alcohol, such as glycerol, that has three hydroxyl groups in the molecule.

tritium: The isotope of hydrogen with the mass number of 3. Its nucleus, the triton, contains one proton and two neutrons.

ultraviolet radiation: Electromagnetic radiation of wavelengths shorter than those of visible light. They are found in the range of the spectrum just beyond the violet.

unsaturated compound: An organic compound in which some of the carbon atoms are joined by double or triple valence bonds.

unstable compound: One that is easily decomposed by the application of energy.

valence: The combining power of an element, equal to the number of atoms of a univalent element with which one of its atoms can combine.

valence electrons: The electrons in the outermost shell (valence shell) of an atom.

van der Waals forces: Electrostatic attractions of molecules for nearby molecules caused by the constant motion of the electron clouds. The unsymmetrical distribution of electron charge creates a dipole in the molecule and induces opposite charges in nearby molecules.

vapor: The gaseous phase of a substance that, under ordinary conditions, exists as a liquid or solid.

vapor pressure: The pressure that is exerted, at a given temperature, by the vapor of a solid or liquid.

vapor pressure depression: The decrease in the vapor pressure of a liquid that occurs when substances are dissolved in the liquid.

velocity of light: The rate of motion of light waves. This is equal to 3×10^8 meters per second, or 186,000 miles per second.

viscosity: The resistance of a fluid to flow. Viscosity is caused by intermolecular attractions.

viscous liquid: A liquid of high viscosity.

volatile: Describes a substance which can be easily evaporated.

volt: The unit of electrical potential.

voltaic cell: See *electrochemical cell*.

voltage: See *electromotive force*.

volume: The amount of space occupied in three dimensions.

water of hydration: The water held in chemical combination in a hydrate. Also known as *water of crystallization*.

wave: A means of energy transfer.

wavelength: The distance between a point in a wave and the corresponding point in the next wave.

wave mechanics: See *quantum mechanics*.

wave velocity: The distance a given peak of the wave moves in a unit of time. It is equal to the frequency of the wave multiplied by its wavelength.

weak acid: An acid that is only slightly ionized in water solution.

weak base: A base that is only slightly ionized in water solution.

weak electrolyte: A substance whose water solution is a poor conductor of electricity due to the fact that it is only slightly ionized in solution.

weight: A measure of the force of gravitational attraction between the earth and a given object.

work: The result of a force acting on a body and producing motion. Quantitatively, it is equal to the product of the force and the distance through which it acts.

X ray: Electromagnetic radiation of very short wavelength.

Index

Absolute error, 23
Absolute zero, 51-52
Accelerators, particle, 638-639; linear, 639
Accuracy in measurement, 19
Acid, Arrhenius's definition of, 447-449; Brønsted-Lowry definition of, 472-473
Acid anhydrides, 458
Acid-base indicators, 455-456, 486-489; choice of, 497
Acid-base neutralization, 488
Acid-base pairs, conjugate, 474-475
Acid-base titration, 490-492
Acids, binary, 157; ternary, 158; in paper, 415; ionization constants for, 450; properties of, 453-456; importance of, 456; preparation of, 457-458; naming, 458; carboxylic, 614-617
Actinide series, 316-317
Activated complex, 381
Activation energy, 46-47, 381; and temperature, 383; and catalysts, 384
Addition reactions in hydrocarbons, 595-597
Air pressure, 68-69; measurement of, 70
Alcohols, 604-609; denatured, 608; properties of, 609
Aldehydes, 610-612
Alicyclic hydrocarbons, 589-590
Aliphatic hydrocarbons, 596
Alkadienes, 578, 588-589
Alkali metals, 317-318
Alkaline earth metals, 317-318
Alkanes, 578, 580-582; derivatives, IUPAC system for naming, 583-586
Alkenes, 578, 587-588
Alkyl groups (radicals), 581
Alkynes, 578, 588
Alloys, 336
Alpha particle, 232-234, 267-268
Alvarez, Luis, 422
Alvarez, Walter, 422
Amalgams, 336
Amphiprotic substances, 482-483
Amphoteric substances, 482-483
Analysis, modern instruments of, 76; quantitative, 145; qualitative, 145
Analysis reactions, 194, 195-196
Angstrom (Å) unit, 319
Anhydride, acid, 458; basic, 464
Anions, 148, 238
Anode, 533
Aqueous solutions, 334
Applied science, 2-3
Aromatic hydrocarbons, 578, 590-592
Arrhenius, Svante, 443

Arrhenius's definition, of acids, 447-449; of bases, 459
Artificial radioactivity, 634-636
Atmosphere, as unit of pressure, 70
Atom, Bohr model of, 242-244; electron configuration of, 256; energy levels in, 242-244; ground state of, 256; kernel of, 261; nucleus of, 227; orbital model of, 255; Rutherford model of, 232-233; wave-mechanical model of, 252-253; evolution of, 263
Atomic mass, 163; defined, 230-232
Atomic mass unit, 163; defined, 231
Atomic number, 227
Atomic pile, 644
Atomic radius, 318-319
Atomic theory, Dalton's, 223-224; 263; 272; modern, 223, 224
Atomic weight, 229
Avogadro, Amedeo, 111
Avogadro's law, 111, 210
Avogadro's number, 112; as in the mole, 112, 165, 167, 170-173, 207-208, 210

Bakelite, 607
Balance, for measurement of mass, 26
Balancing chemical equations, 185-186
Balancing redox equations, 522; using half-reactions, 563
Barometers, mercury, 69-70
Barometric pressure, 68-69
Base, Arrhenius's definition of, 459; Brønsted-Lowry definition of, 472
Bases, common, 463; properties of, 460-461, ionization constants for, 462; preparation of, 463-464
Basic anhydrides, 464
Becquerel, Henri, 265-266
Benzene series, 590-592
Benzene compounds, naming, 592-593
Beta particles, 267-268
Binary acids, 157
Binary compounds, 156-157
Biochemical reactions, 620
Blood, analysis of, 258
Bohr, Niels, 236, 249; and classical mechanics, 248-249
Bohr model of the atom, 242-244
Boiling, 73-74, 122-124
Boiling point, 73, 122-124; elevation of, 361-362

Bond, defined, 272; ionic, 274-276; covalent, 280-282; triple covalent, 282; metallic, 285; polarity of, 291; hydrogen, 295-299
Bond angle, 300
Bond energy, defined, 285; and chemical change, 286-287
Bond strength, 285-287
Bonding, defined, 272; coordinate covalent, 284; directional, 300-301; in organic compounds, 572
Born, Max, 557
Boyle, Robert, 81, 86
Boyle's law, 86-89; and the kinetic theory, 108
Branched-chain hydrocarbons, 577
Breeder reactors, 645
Bright-line spectra, 239-240
Brønsted, J.H., 472
Brønsted-Lowry, theory, 472-475
Buffers, 480-482
Burning, theories of, 7-8
Butyl rubber, 597

Calorie, 53-54
Calorimetry, 54
Carbohydrates, 618-621
Carboxylic acids, 614-617
Carr, Emma Perry, 560
Carver, George Washington, 188
Catalysis, 376
Catalysts, defined, 195, 376; and activation energy, 384; and equilibria, 424
Cathode, 533
Cathode rays, 225-226
Cations, 148, 275
Cell, electrochemical, 542-547; galvanic, 542-547; voltaic, 542-547; Daniell, 546
Celsius, Anders, 51
Celsius temperature scale, 51-52
Chadwick, James, 227-228, 234
Changes of phase, 33-34
Charge, electric, 58; conservation of, 58-59
Charge/mass ratio of the electron, 226
Charles, Jacques, 97
Charles's law, 97-99; formation of, 5; and the kinetic theory, 108
Chemical bonds; see bonds
Chemical bonding, see bonding
Chemical change, 35; and bond energy, 286-287; direction of, 394-395; and the Gibbs free energy equation, 400-403; see also Reaction
Chemical defense, in insects, 8

Chemical energy, defined, 45, 286
Chemical equations, 182-183; coefficients in, 184, 193; balancing, 185-186; showing phases in, 189-190; showing energy changes in, 190-191; ionic, 191
Chemical equilibrium, 410-412; law of, 416-417
Chemical formulas, 144-145
Chemical kinetics, as a science, 372
Chemical properties, 31
Chemical reactions, 147; types of, 194; defined, 272
Chemical symbols, 39
Chemistry, as a science, 8; as a study of matter, 27
Chemistry, organic, see organic chemistry
Classical mechanics, 248-249
Coal gasification, 50
Coefficients, 184-193
Colligative properties, 366
Collision theory, 373
Combined gas laws, 102-104
Combustion, 46-47; of hydrocarbons, 595
Compounds, defined, 40; stability of, 390-391
Concentrated solutions, 345
Conceptual definitions, 471
Condensation, defined, 75; 119-120; heat of, 126
Conductor, electrical, 61
Conduction, ionic, 528; metallic, 528
Conjugate acid-base pairs, 474-475
Conservation, of matter, 36, 220-221, 223; of energy, 48-49; of charge, 58-59
Constant heat summation, law of, 392-393
Continuous spectrum, 328-329
Control rods, 644
Conversion factors, 14-16
Conversion of energy, 47-48
Cooking, use of chemistry in, 385
Coordinate covalent bonding, 284
Covalent atomic radii, 318-319
Covalent bonding, 280-283
Covalent bonds, 280-281; triple, 282
Cracking, 598
Critical mass, 643
Critical pressures, 125
Critical temperatures, 125
Crookes, William, 226
Crystal formation, 133
Crystal lattice, 132, 294-295
Crystallization, heat of, 129-130
Crystals, 132-134; covalent, 293-294; ionic, 294-295
Curie, Marie, 266-267
Curie, Pierre, 266
Current, electric, 61, 528-529; direct, 528

MATTER HAS 3 BASIC FORMS
* SOLID
* LIQUID
* GAS

ENERGY COMES IN 3 FORMS
+ HEAT
+ LIGHT
+ MOTION

Experiment p 4

A burning substance removes oxygen from the air

Photo Credits

Photographs on the following pages by Edward M. Steele: 27, 29, 34, (lower) 35, 41, 42, 49, 73, 74, 78, 118, 126, 129, 132, 133, 135, 136, (top) 146, 164, 166, 175, 178, 184, 187, 198, 199, 232, 258, 275, 303, 334, 338, 350, 352, 353, 372, 374, 378, 385, 393, 395, 404, 412, 426, 446, 447, 451, 456, 460, 462, 466, 467, 487, 489, 490, 495, 496, 502, 543, 564, 572, 573, 575, 619, 621, 624. 3-(upper) The Granger Collection; (lower left) Union Carbide Corporation; (lower right) Du Pont. 4-(left) Du Pont; (right) Du Pont. 6-The Granger Collection. 8-Thomas Eisner. 23-Dave Schaefer. 27-Dave Schaefer. 32-NASA. 33-NASA. 35-(upper) U.S. Steel. 44-Factory Mutual Engineering Company. 46-Philip Jon Bailey/ Taurus Photos. 47-Factory Mutual Engineering Corporation. 50-Billings Energy Corporation. 54-U.S. Borax. 76-Dave Schaefer. 81-The Bettmann Archive. 87-Monsanto. 88-Du Pont. 95-Dave Schaefer. 103-Wide World. 127-Paul Conklin. 130-Du Pont. 131-Ken Karp. 146-(bottom) Foto Werner H. Müller/Peter Arnold Inc. 149-USDA Photo by Bob Bjork. 152-Ken Karp. 170-Richard Pasley/Stock Boston. 168-E.R. Degginger. 169-E.R. Degginger. 186-Mike Malyszko/Stock Boston. 188-The Bettmann Archive. 197-Martin Rogers/Uniphoto. 205-Dave Schaefer. 215-Dave Schaefer. 223-The Bettmann Archive. 226-Solarex Corporation. 233-The Bettmann Archive. 245-Dave Schaefer. 249-(top left) Culver Pictures; (top right) The Bettmann Archive; (bottom) Danish Ministry of Foreign Affairs. 266-French Cultural Services. 273-The Bettmann Archive. 274-Courtesy Bell Laboratories. 279-(top) Sam Sweezy/Stock Boston; (bottom) Ron Ruhoff/Colorado Dept. of Public Relations. 308-Sovfoto. 310-Sovfoto. 335-David Conklin. 365-Paul Conklin. 373-Dominique Roger/UNESCO. 376-Monsanto. 377-Union Carbide Corporation, Linde Division. 380-Monsanto. 391-Wide World Photos. 413-Courtesy Columbia University. 415-Dave Schaefer. 416-Du Pont. 420-Paul Conklin. 422-UPI/Bettmann Newsphotos. 444-Dave Schaefer. 452-Courtesy Allegheny County Crime Lab, Pittsburgh, PA. 474-Peter Vadnai, Editorial Photocolor Archives. 481-Du Pont. 490-Courtesy IBM. 498-Les Todd/Duke Photographic Dept. 501-Martin Rogers/Stock Boston. 510-Elizabeth Crews/Stock Boston. 514-Peter Arnold, Inc. 522-Lisa Fouree/Metropolitan State University. 523-NASA. 524-Michal Heron. 532-Joe McNulty/Discover Magazine. 557-UPI/Bettmann Newsphotos. 560-Mt. Holyoke College Library/ Archives. 589-Joshua Tree Productions/Editorial Photocolor Archives. 594-Du Pont. 597-Paul Conklin. 616-Lee Klopfenstein, Courtesy Joan Bowman, Diamond Shamrock Corporation. 631-Courtesy Chemistry Department, Lawrence Berkeley Laboratory, University of California, Berkeley. 637-Ivan Masser/American Cancer Society. 638-Wide World Photos.

Index of Reference Tables

Commonly Used Tables

Other Tables

THE CHEMICAL ELEMENTS

(Atomic masses in this table are based on the atomic mass of carbon-12 being exactly 12.)

NAME	SYMBOL	ATOMIC NUMBER	ATOMIC MASS†	NAME	SYMBOL	ATOMIC NUMBER	ATOMIC MASS†
Actinium	Ac	89	(227)	Neon	Ne	10	20.2
Aluminum	Al	13	27.0	Neptunium	Np	93	(237)
Americium	Am	95	(243)	Nickel	Ni	28	58.7
Antimony	Sb	51	121.8	Niobium	Nb	41	92.9
Argon	Ar	18	39.9	Nitrogen	N	7	14.01
Arsenic	As	33	74.9	Nobelium	No	102	(255)
Astatine	At	85	(210)	Osmium	Os	76	190.2
Barium	Ba	56	137.3	Oxygen	O	8	16.00
Berkelium	Bk	97	(247)	Palladium	Pd	46	106.4
Beryllium	Be	4	9.01	Phosphorus	P	15	31.0
Bismuth	Bi	83	209.0	Platinum	Pt	78	195.1
Boron	B	5	10.8	Plutonium	Pu	94	(244)
Bromine	Br	35	79.9	Polonium	Po	84	(210)
Cadmium	Cd	48	112.4	Potassium	K	19	39.1
Calcium	Ca	20	40.1	Praseodymium	Pr	59	140.9
Californium	Cf	98	(251)	Promethium	Pm	61	(145)
Carbon	C	6	12.01	Protactinium	Pa	91	(231)
Cerium	Ce	58	140.1	Radium	Ra	88	(226)
Cesium	Cs	55	132.9	Radon	Rn	86	(222)
Chlorine	Cl	17	35.5	Rhenium	Re	75	186.2
Chromium	Cr	24	52.0	Rhodium	Rh	45	102.9
Cobalt	Co	27	58.9	Rubidium	Rb	37	85.5
Copper	Cu	29	63.5	Ruthenium	Ru	44	101.1
Curium	Cm	96	(247)	Samarium	Sm	62	150.4
Dysprosium	Dy	66	162.5	Scandium	Sc	21	45.0
Einsteinium	Es	99	(254)	Selenium	Se	34	79.0
Erbium	Er	68	167.3	Silicon	Si	14	28.1
Europium	Eu	63	152.0	Silver	Ag	47	107.9
Fermium	Fm	100	(257)	Sodium	Na	11	23.0
Fluorine	F	9	19.0	Strontium	Sr	38	87.6
Francium	Fr	87	(223)	Sulfur	S	16	32.1
Gadolinium	Gd	64	157.2	Tantalum	Ta	73	180.9
Gallium	Ga	31	69.7	Technetium	Tc	43	(97)
Germanium	Ge	32	72.6	Tellurium	Te	52	127.6
Gold	Au	79	197.0	Terbium	Tb	65	158.9
Hafnium	Hf	72	178.5	Thallium	Tl	81	204.4
Helium	He	2	4.00	Thorium	Th	90	232.0
Holmium	Ho	67	164.9	Thulium	Tm	69	168.9
Hydrogen	H	1	1.008	Tin	Sn	50	118.7
Indium	In	49	114.8	Titanium	Ti	22	47.9
Iodine	I	53	126.9	Tungsten	W	74	183.9
Iridium	Ir	77	192.2	Unnilennium	Une	109	(266?)
Iron	Fe	26	55.8	Unnilhexium	Unh	106	(263)
Krypton	Kr	36	83.8	Unniloctium	Uno	108	(265)
Lanthanum	La	57	138.9	Unnilpentium	Unp	105	(262)
Lawrencium	Lr	103	(256)	Unnilquadium	Unq	104	(261)
Lead	Pb	82	207.2	Unnilseptium	Uns	107	(262)
Lithium	Li	3	6.94	Uranium	U	92	238.0
Lutetium	Lu	71	175.0	Vanadium	V	23	50.9
Magnesium	Mg	12	24.3	Xenon	Xe	54	131.3
Manganese	Mn	25	54.9	Ytterbium	Yb	70	173.0
Mendelevium	Md	101	(258)	Yttrium	Y	39	88.9
Mercury	Hg	80	200.6	Zinc	Zn	30	65.4
Molybdenum	Mo	42	95.9	Zirconium	Zr	40	91.2
Neodymium	Nd	60	144.2				

†Numbers in parentheses give the mass number of the most stable isotope.

Periodic Table

(handwritten notes at top) lose electron or outer shell!! Neither lose or gain electron; gains electron normally +1

s orbitals filling

1**
GROUP
1A ⊕ **+1**

Period 1

1.00794	+1
H	−1
1	
1s	

Legend

Atomic Mass — 12.0111	−4
Symbol — **C**	+2 — Selected Oxidation States
Atomic Number — 6	+4
Electron Configuration — [He] $2s^2 2p^2$	

s orbitals filling

| 1** GROUP 1A | 2 GROUP 2A ⊕ **+2** |

---- **d orbitals filling** ----

---- **Transition Elements** ----

Period	Group 1A	Group 2A	Group 3 / 3B	Group 4 / 4B	Group 5 / 5B	Group 6 / 6B	Group 7 / 7B	Group 8	Group 9
2	6.941 +1 **Li** 3 [He] $2s^1$	9.01218 +2 **Be** 4 [He] $2s^2$							
3	22.98977 +1 **Na** 11 [Ne] $3s^1$	24.305 +2 **Mg** 12 [Ne] $3s^2$							
4	39.0983 +1 **K** 19 [Ar] $4s^1$	40.08 +2 **Ca** 20 [Ar] $4s^2$	44.9559 +3 **Sc** 21 [Ar] $3d^1 4s^2$	47.88 +2 +3 +4 **Ti** 22 [Ar] $3d^2 4s^2$	50.9415 +2 +3 +4 +5 **V** 23 [Ar] $3d^3 4s^2$	51.996 +2 +3 +6 **Cr** 24 [Ar] $3d^5 4s^1$	54.9380 +2 +3 +4 +7 **Mn** 25 [Ar] $3d^5 4s^2$	55.847 +2 +3 **Fe** 26 [Ar] $3d^6 4s^2$	58.9332 +2 +3 **Co** 27 [Ar] $3d^7 4s^2$
5	85.4678 +1 **Rb** 37 [Kr] $5s^1$	87.62 +2 **Sr** 38 [Kr] $5s^2$	88.9059 +3 **Y** 39 [Kr] $4d^1 5s^2$	91.224 +4 **Zr** 40 [Kr] $4d^2 5s^2$	92.9064 +3 +5 **Nb** 41 [Kr] $4d^4 5s^1$	95.94 +3 +6 **Mo** 42 [Kr] $4d^5 5s^1$	(98) +4 +6 +7 **Tc** 43 [Kr] $4d^6 5s^1$	101.07 +3 **Ru** 44 [Kr] $4d^7 5s^1$	102.906 +3 **Rh** 45 [Kr] $4d^8 5s^1$
6	132.905 +1 **Cs** 55 [Xe] $6s^1$	137.33 +2 **Ba** 56 [Xe] $6s^2$	**La-Lu** 57 - 71	178.49 +4 **Hf** 72 [Xe] $4f^{14} 5d^2 6s^2$	180.948 +5 **Ta** 73 [Xe] $4f^{14} 5d^3 6s^2$	183.85 +6 **W** 74 [Xe] $4f^{14} 5d^4 6s^2$	186.207 +4 +6 +7 **Re** 75 [Xe] $4f^{14} 5d^5 6s^2$	190.2 +3 +4 **Os** 76 [Xe] $4f^{14} 5d^6 6s^2$	192.22 +3 +4 **Ir** 77 [Xe] $4f^{14} 5d^7 6s^2$
7	(223) +1 **Fr** 87 [Rn] $7s^1$	226.025 +2 **Ra** 88 [Rn] $7s^2$	**Ac-Lr** 89 - 103	(261) **Unq*** 104	(262) **Unp** 105	(263) **Unh** 106	(262) **Uns** 107	(265) **Uno** 108	(266?) **Une** 109

→ GROUP 8 —

---- **d orbitals filling** ----

| 138.906 +3 **La** 57 [Xe] $5d^1 6s^2$ |
| 227.028 +3 **Ac** 89 [Rn] $6d^1 7s^2$ |

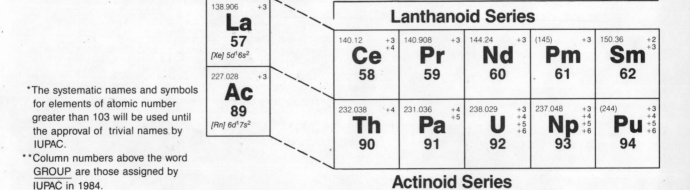

Lanthanoid Series

| 140.12 +3 +4 **Ce** 58 | 140.908 +3 **Pr** 59 | 144.24 +3 **Nd** 60 | (145) +3 **Pm** 61 | 150.36 +2 +3 **Sm** 62 |

| 232.038 +4 **Th** 90 | 231.036 +4 +5 **Pa** 91 | 238.029 +3 +4 +5 +6 **U** 92 | 237.048 +3 +4 +5 +6 **Np** 93 | (244) +3 +4 +5 +6 **Pu** 94 |

Actinoid Series

*The systematic names and symbols for elements of atomic number greater than 103 will be used until the approval of trivial names by IUPAC.

**Column numbers above the word GROUP are those assigned by IUPAC in 1984.